Human Physiology

Edited by
R. F. Schmidt and G. Thews

Translated by Marguerite A. Biederman-Thorson

With 569 Figures, Most in Color

Springer-Verlag
Berlin Heidelberg New York 1983

Professor Dr. med. Robert F. Schmidt, Ph. D.
Physiologisches Institut der Universität
Röntgenring 9
D-8700 Würzburg, Fed. Rep. Germany

Professor Dr. Dr. Gerhard Thews
Physiologisches Institut der Universität
Saarstraße 21
D-6500 Mainz, Fed. Rep. Germany

Translation of "Physiologie des Menschen", 20. Auflage, 1980
ISBN 3-540-09446-6 Springer-Verlag Berlin Heidelberg New York
ISBN 0-387-09446-6 Springer-Verlag New York Heidelberg Berlin

ISBN 3-540-11669-9 Springer-Verlag Berlin Heidelberg New York
ISBN 0-387-11669-9 Springer-Verlag New York Heidelberg Berlin

Library of Congress Cataloging in Publication Data
Physiologie des Menschen. English. Human physiology. Bibliography: p. Includes index. 1. Human physiology.
I. Schmidt, Robert F. II. Thews, Gerhard, 1926–. III. Title. [DNLM: 1. Physiology. QT 104 P55]
QP 34.5.P48513 1983   612   82-7333
ISBN 0-387-11669-9 (U.S.)   AACR2

© by Springer-Verlag Berlin · Heidelberg 1983
Printed in Germany

Typesetting and binding: G. Appl, Wemding, printing: aprinta, Wemding

2124/3140-543210

Preface

Human Physiology is the English version of a time-honored German textbook first published by HERMANN REIN in 1936. We undertook the preparation of a completely revised 20th edition with the intention of making the book accessible to a wide range of English-speaking readers. The subject-matter was therefore organized so as to correspond to the structuring of physiology courses in most countries of the world.

The book is directed primarily at students of medicine. Its aim is to enable them to understand living processes in the human organism, providing the basis for the scientific understanding of pathological changes. The material was chosen to give the reader not only the knowledge required for passing examinations, but also information necessary for a subsequent professional career. For this reason special attention was devoted to pathophysiological aspects.

We hope that the book will prove a useful reference on the present status of physiology for physicians in private and hospital practice as well as for its primary readership. The book should also serve biologists, biochemists, pharmacologists, pharmacists, and psychologist as a source of information on the physiological principles underlying their disciplines.

In order to facilitate quick reference, we have striven for clear organization, lucid presentation, the accentuation of key ideas, and instructive illustrations. For the sake of compactness we have dispensed with historical introductions, accounts of unproven hypotheses, and descriptions of specialized measuring techniques. The references provided at the end of each chapter are of two sorts: textbooks and handbooks providing interested readers with guidelines for further study, and selected original papers describing recent or little-known findings.

We would like to express our gratitude here to all those who assisted in the preparation and production of this textbook. Most of all we want to thank our coauthors for their willingness to take the ideas and wishes of the editors into consideration, thereby enhancing the book's clarity and balance. We are especially grateful to the staff of the Gay & Benz studios in Stuttgart for their excellent renderings of the illustrative material. We are particularly indebted to Dr. Marguerite Biederman-Thorson, Oxford, for her outstanding translation. Finally we would like to thank the publisher and his staff for their generous support in the preparation of this book.

August 1982

R. F. SCHMIDT
G. THEWS

List of Authors

Professor Dr. H. Altner
Fachbereich Biologie der Universität,
Universitätsstraße 31
D-8400 Regensburg

Professor Dr. H. Antoni
Physiologisches Institut der Universität,
Hermann-Herder-Straße 7
D-7800 Freiburg i. Br.

Professor Dr. J. Boeckh
Fachbereich Biologie der Universität,
Universitätsstraße 31
D-8400 Regensburg

Professor Dr. K. Brück
Physiologisches Institut am Klinikum der
Justus-Liebig-Universität, Aulweg 129
D-6300 Gießen

Professor Dr. J. Dudel
Physiologisches Institut der Technischen
Universität, Biedersteiner Straße 29
D-8000 München 40

Professor Dr. Dr. J. Grote
Physiologisches Institut I
der Universität,
Nußallee 11
D-5300 Bonn

Professor Dr. O.-J. Grüsser
Physiologisches Institut der Freien
Universität, Arnimallee 22
D-1000 Berlin 33

Professor Dr. O. Harth
Abteilung für Biophysik am
Physiologischen Institut der Universität,
Saarstraße 21
D-6500 Mainz

Professor Dr. W. Jänig
Physiologisches Institut der Universität,
Olshausenstraße 40–60
D-2300 Kiel

Professor Dr. R. Klinke
Zentrum der Physiologie
Theodor-Stern-Kai 7
D-6000 Frankfurt 70

Professor Dr. J. C. Rüegg
II. Physiologisches Institut der Universität,
Im Neuenheimer Feld 236
D-6900 Heidelberg

Professor Dr. R. F. Schmidt
Physiologisches Institut der Universität,
Röntgenring 9
D-8700 Würzburg

Professor Dr. Dr. G. Thews
Physiologisches Institut der Universität,
Saarstraße 21
D-6500 Mainz

Professor Dr. H.-V. Ulmer
Sportphysiologische Abteilung am
Fachbereich 26 der Universität,
Saarstraße 21
D-6500 Mainz

Professor Dr. F. Waldeck
Fa. C. H. Boehringer Sohn,
Geschäftsleitung
D-6507 Ingelheim

Professor Dr. Ch. Weiss
Physiologisches Institut der Medizinischen
Hochschule,
Ratzeburger Allee 160
D-2400 Lübeck

Professor Dr. E. Witzleb
Institut für Angewandte Physiologie und
medizinische Klimatologie der Universität,
Olshausenstraße 40/60
D-2300 Kiel

Professor Dr. M. Zimmermann
II. Physiologisches Institut der Universität,
Im Neuenheimer Feld 236
D-6900 Heidelberg

Table of Contents

Part I. Nervous System

Part III. Blood, Circulation and Respiration

Part IV. Metabolism, Digestion and Excretion. Endocrine Regulation

Part I
Nervous System

1 Function of Nerve Cells

J. DUDEL

The nervous system – the subject of the first part of this book – is composed of **nerve cells** or **neurons.** The human brain contains about 25 billion such nerve cells; it, together with the spinal cord, constitutes the central nervous system (CNS). Only about 25 million nerve cells lie in the periphery or connect the periphery to the central nervous system. The nerve cells communicate with one another in a variety of ways by **synapses,** which far outnumber (by about a thousand-fold) the nerve cells. Synaptic contacts are also made with other types of cell, in particular receptors (information-receiving cells – e. g., in the sense organs) and effectors (e. g., the muscle cells). Because receptors and muscle cells have many functional features in common with the nerve cells, they will also be discussed in this part of the book.

In the following section (1.1) the general aspects of nerve cells and their function are outlined. Most of the points mentioned here will be taken up again in later chapters, and discussed in greater detail and depth.

1.1 Nerve Cells: General Structure and Function

Nerve cells. A nerve cell consists of a soma (the cell body with its nucleus) and projections from it, typically of different kinds – the dendrites and the axon (Fig. 1-1). The dendrites frequently branch at several points, spreading through the space near the soma. Usually they make many synaptic contacts with other nerve cells. The axon arises from the soma at the axon hillock. Whereas the diameter of the soma is 5–100 μm, the axon tapers down to 1–16 μm and is usually long in comparison with its diameter; axons in the periphery can be over a meter in length.

Glial cells. The nerve cells are usually surrounded by accessory cells called glial cells. The glial cells, more numerous than the neurons, take up at least half of the volume of the central nervous system. The peripheral axons are also ensheathed in glial cells, the Schwann cells. Neurons and glial cells are separated by an intercellular cleft 15–20 nm wide. These clefts communicate with one another, forming the extracellular fluid space of the neurons and glia. Substances are exchanged between nerve cells and glial cells by way of this interstitial space (the terms interstitial space and extracellular volume are defined on p. 646).

The volume of the interstitial space in the brain is 12–14% of the total volume. This is quite sufficient to ensure that the nerve cells are adequately supplied with oxygen and nutrients by diffusion. It is unnecessary (and unlikely in the case of glucose, for example) for nutrients to be transported through the glial cells [4, 43].

Evidently the glia functions more to support and protect the neurons than as a source of supply. Further details about glial function are presented in Section 1.4.

Solute exchange. Dissolved substances can move into the interstitial space from the blood capillaries and, in the CNS, from the cerebrospinal fluid in the ventricles of the brain. The capillary network in the brain is very dense, so that most neurons are less than 50 μm away from a capillary [4]; the diffusion paths for oxygen, CO_2 and metabolites are short. The human cen-

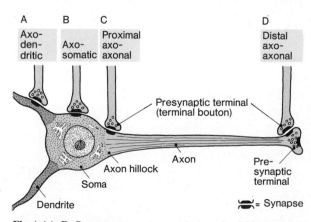

Fig. 1-1 A–D. Synapses on a neuron. **A** Axo-dendritic synapse. **B** Axo-somatic synapse. **C** Proximal axo-axonal synapse, usually inhibitory. **D** Distal axo-axonal synapse, always inhibitory (presynaptic inhibition)

tral nervous system consumes about 20% (50 ml/min) of the total resting oxygen uptake. Interruption of the blood supply for about 10 s causes pronounced disruption of cerebral function and unconsciousness, and after 8–12 minutes the brain is usually irreversibly damaged. The circulatory system is regulated in such a way as to guarantee top priority to the brain (cf. Chapter 18).

Blood-brain barrier. Some substances in the plasma can reach the intercellular clefts in the brain only slowly or not at all; that is, there is effectively a blood-brain barrier. The mechanisms constituting this barrier are not known in any detail. It probably derives in part from a special structure of the walls of the capillaries in the brain and in their relation to the neuroglia. In addition to structural obstacles to diffusion, selective exchange processes between the glial cells and the interstitial spaces are likely to be involved. For a more extensive treatment of the morphology and micromorphology of the nerve cells and the accessory tissue, the reader is referred to textbooks of anatomy and histology.

General functions of nerve cells. The nerve cells are specialized for the processing of **information.** Apart from this special function the nerve cells, like other cells, must *maintain* their own structure and function, *adjust* to changing demands, and often exert an *organizing* influence on neighboring cells – e. g., by initiating the formation of synaptic structures in cells with which they make synapses (cf. Section 1.3). The mechanisms permitting neuronal *plasticity* (the functional adaptation of neurons and groups of neurons; cf. e. g. Chapter 4, p. 79), and the processes of *transcellular organization* are still mostly unknown, but they are crucial to the development of normal function in the nervous system and the organs it innervates, and are intimately involved in learning and memory.

In the special task of *information processing* by a single nerve cell, information is received, conducted over a more or less long distance, and passed on to one or more other cells. Information is usually received by way of synapses on the dendrites or the soma (Fig. 1-1), and comes from other nerve cells. But a neuron can also receive information via synapses with cells specialized for information uptake – the *receptors* of the sense organs – or even receive information directly from the outside world by way of specialized dendrites. The conduction of information occurs by way of the axon (Fig. 1-1), a slender structure extending for a relatively long distance. Finally, the information is passed on to other cells – neurons or effectors (e. g., muscle or gland cells) – by way of synapses between these cells and the information-carrying neuron.

The information we speak of here is an abstract concept (cf. Chapter 15). It is encoded in the neuron as an electrical or chemical signal. In this chapter we are concerned primarily with the nature of the electrical signals and their propagation along the axon, though mention is also made of chemical signals and their propagation. The special mechanisms of signal reception and transmission at synapses are treated in Chapter 3.

1.2   The Resting Potential

Nerve and muscle cells, like other cells in the body, are bounded by a lipoid-protein membrane which acts as a good electrical insulator. It is identical to the neuro- or sarcolemma (respectively) visible in the electron microscope. Across this membrane, between the interior of the cell and the extracellular fluid, there is usually an electrical potential difference, the **membrane potential.** This potential influences the processes of exchange through the membrane and in this respect is important, for example, for the function of the epithelium of the renal tubules (cf. Chapter 27). In nerve and muscle cells changes in the membrane potential are the basis of the function of these cells – information processing and contraction. Thus this potential and its alteration must be examined here in detail.

Measurement of the Membrane Potential

An arrangement for measuring the membrane potential is shown in Fig. 1-2. The sensor that detects the potential within the cell is a microelectrode, a glass capillary pulled out to a very fine tip (less than 1 µm diameter) and filled with a conducting solution. The reference electrode in the extracellular space is a chlorided silver plate [2, p. 242]. When the measurement is begun both electrodes are in the extracellular space, and there is no potential difference between them; the graph in Fig. 1-2 B shows the value zero for the "extracellular potential." When the measurement electrode is advanced through the cell membrane into the cell (Fig. 1-2, right), the voltmeter shows a stepwise change in potential to around -80 mV. This voltage is the **membrane potential.**

In nerve and muscle cells the membrane potential remains constant for long periods, if the cells are not activated by some external influence. The membrane potential of such resting cells is called the **resting potential.** The resting potential of nerve and muscle cells is always negative; its magnitude is constant and characteristic of each cell type. In warm-blooded animals it ranges from -55 to -100 mV except for smooth muscle cells, which have resting potentials as small as -30 mV.

Charge Distribution at the Membrane

When the interior of the cell is *more negative* than the external medium, there must be a surplus of *negative electrical charges* within the cell. In aqueous saline solutions like those in the cell and the extracellular space electrical charges are carried by ions – the salt molecules, dissociated into *anions* and *cations*. Within the cell, therefore, there are surplus negative ions (anions). They can move freely in the aqueous solution, so that within the intracellular or extracellutar space the charges are uniformly distributed, and local accumulations or deficits cannot exist for long. Therefore the charge imbalance that produces the resting potential must be located at the "solid phase" bounding the cell, the cell membrane. Anions are present in excess on the inside of the membrane, and cations in equal numbers on the outside.

To assist quantitative consideration of the electrical situation at the membrane, let us view it as a *capacitor.* It consists of two conducting media, the intra- and extracellular saline solutions, separated by a thin insulating layer, the membrane. The insulating membrane is about 6 nm (60 Å) thick. If a capacitor with this "plate separation" is charged to a resting potential of -75 mV, it must bear about 5000 pairs of negative and positive ions per μm^2 cell surface [5].

To illustrate the numerical relations between the ions involved, a very small region of membrane is shown in Fig. 1-3, an area of 1 μm $\times$ .001 μm, with the adjacent intra- and extracellular spaces only 1 μm deep. Given a resting potential of -90 mV, this membrane area would be occupied by 6 anions and 6 cations. But each of the adjacent volumes of saline solution contains 220,000 ions. Quantitatively, then, the charge imbalance across the cell membrane is *very slight.* Nevertheless, it is the basis of the resting potential and thus of the function of the nervous system.

Concentration distribution of the ions. It is notable in Fig. 1-3 that there is not only a charge imbalance at the membrane, but also a nonuniform distribution of *ion species* inside and outside the cell. The greatest difference is found in the K^+ ions: with 100,000 K^+ intracellularly, there are only 2000 K^+ outside. The difference is reversed in the case of Na^+, with

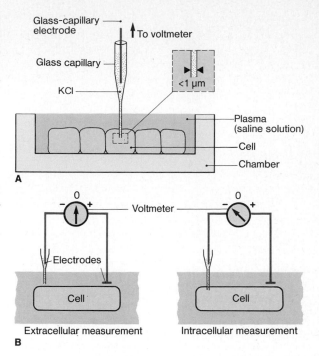

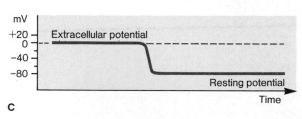

Fig. 1-2 A–C. Intracellular measurement of membrane potential. **A** The cell is placed in a chamber and the space around it filled with plasma (or saline solution). **B** *Left:* with recording and reference electrode both extracellular the voltmeter between the two registers zero. *Right:* with the recording electrode in the cell and the reference electrode outside, the voltmeter shows the resting potential. **C** The potential before and after the electrode penetrates the cell

108,000 Na^+ outside and only 10,000 Na^+ inside. The distribution of chloride ions is the opposite of the K^+ distribution. Most of the intracellular anions are large protein ions, designated A^-. In Table 1-1 the *ion concentrations* in a *muscle cell* and in the extracellular space are given for a mammal in mmol/l [5]. In general, the intracellular K^+ concentration of nerve and muscle cells is 20 to 100 times higher than the extracellular concentration, the intracellular Na^+ concentration 5 to 15 times lower than the extracellular, and the intracellular Cl^- concentration 20 to 100 times lower than the extracellular. Thus the concentration distribution of chloride is about the reciprocal of the potassium-ion distribution.

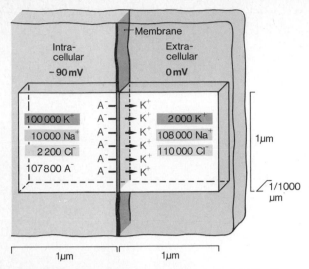

Fig. 1-3. Membrane charge at the resting potential. The charge on a small part of the membrane with an area of 1 μm × .001 μm, 6 K⁺ and 6 anions (A⁻), is compared with the number of ions in the volumes 1 μm × 1 μm × .001 μm on either side of the membrane. The arrows indicate the diffusion of K⁺ out of the cell through the membrane. The membrane capacitance is taken as 1 μF/cm²

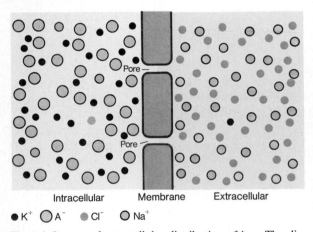

● K⁺   ◯ A⁻   ● Cl⁻   ○ Na⁺

Fig. 1-4. Intra- and extracellular distribution of ions. The diameters of the circles symbolizing the ions are proportional to the diameters of the (hydrated) ions. A⁻ denotes the large intracellular protein anions. The "pores" through the membrane are just wide enough to allow the passage of K⁺

Table 1-1. Intra- and extracellular ion concentrations: muscle cell of a warm-blooded animal

Intracellular		Extracellular	
Na⁺	12 mmol/l	Na⁺	145 mmol/l
K⁺	155 mmol/l	K⁺	4 mmol/l
Cl⁻	4 mmol/l	Other cations	5 mmol/l
HCO₃⁻	8 mmol/l	Cl⁻	120 mmol/l
A⁻	155 mmol/l	HCO₃⁻	27 mmol/l
Resting potential	−90 mV	Other anions	7 mmol/l

K⁺ Distribution and Resting Potential

The uneven distribution of the various ions in the extra- and intracellular space is required for the existence of the resting potential. This potential between the intra- and extracellular spaces comes into being because the membrane is not a perfect insulator, but is to some extent **permeable** to certain ion species. K⁺ ions in particular can diffuse fairly readily through the membrane. One can think of the membrane as interrupted by **pores,** channels with lumen so narrow that only the relatively small K⁺ ions can pass through. The relative sizes of the pores and the different ions, and the relative abundance of the latter, are illustrated in Fig. 1-4. The species of chief interest here, K⁺, is shown in red. These K⁺ ions diffuse through the membrane whenever they encounter a pore opening. Because there are far more K⁺ ions on the inside of the membrane, such encounters will occur much more often there, and there will be more passages from inside to outside than in the reverse direction. There is a *net outflow of K⁺* from the cell, driven by the higher intracellular concentration or osmotic pressure of K⁺. This K⁺ outflow would soon equalize the osmotic pressures or concentrations of this ion, if it were not counteracted by an equivalent force in the opposite direction.

This *opposing force* is brought about by the electrical charge of the K⁺ ions. When a K⁺, driven by the osmotic pressure difference, leaves the cell it takes a positive charge with it; that is, it adds a positive charge to the outer side of the membrane capacitor, matched by an equal negative charging of the inner side. Thus, as shown in Fig. 1-3, a membrane potential is created. The polarity of this potential is such as to counteract the outflow of other cations; a positive potential repels positive ions. The outflow of positive charges in itself builds up an electrical potential that impedes the outflow of more positive charges. The membrane potential continues to increase until the force counteracting K⁺ outflow is equal to the osmotic pressure of the K⁺ ions. At this potential inflow and outflow of K⁺ are in equilibrium; it is therefore called the **K⁺ equilibrium potential,** abbreviated E_K.

The K⁺ equilibrium potential is thus determined by the concentration ratio K_i/K_o, between the potassium ions inside and outside the cell, and by the fact that diffusion through the membrane is limited to K⁺. Such diffusion potentials are described in general by the *Nernst equation:*

$$E_{ion} = \frac{R \cdot T}{z \cdot F} \cdot \ln \frac{\text{extracell. conc. of the ion}}{\text{intracell. conc. of the ion}}$$

Here R is the universal gas constant, T the absolute temperature, z the valence of the ion (negative for anions) and F the Faraday constant [1, 4]. Reducing all the constants to a single number, we find for potassium

$$E_K = -61\,\text{mV} \cdot \log(K_i^+/K_o^+)$$

For $K_i^+/K_o^+ = 39$, as in Table 1-1,

$$E_K = -61\,\text{mV} \cdot \log 39 = -61\,\text{mV} \cdot 1.59$$
$$= -97\,\text{mV}.$$

The resting potential given in Table 1-1 is -90 mV, which corresponds to a first approximation with the potassium equilibrium potential.

Dependence of the resting potential on the extracellular K^+ concentration. The postulated agreement between resting potential and E_K can be checked experimentally. The extracellular K^+ concentration can be changed over a wide range *in vitro* while the resting potential is measured. The Nernst equation demands that the resting potential change in proportion to the logarithm of the external K^+ concentration. The measured change in the resting potential is shown in Fig. 1-5 (circles); as K_o^+ is lowered the resting potential rises to -120 mV, and when K_o^+ is increased to 50 mM the potential is reduced to -25 mV. The relation predicted by the Nernst equation is shown by the line in Fig. 1-5. The measured data agree fairly well with this line; that is, to first approximation the experiment corroborates the interpretation of the resting potential as a K^+ equilibrium potential. It is notable, however, that for K_o^+ less than ca. 7 mmol/l the resting potential is always less negative than E_K. The reason for this systematic departure is discussed in the next section.

Fig. 1-5 makes it clear that relatively small changes in the extracellular K^+ concentration can have a marked effect on the resting potential and thus on cellular function. Such changes in the concentration of K^+ in the blood plasma do occur under pathological conditions (e. g., renal malfunction), and it is important that the physician then check the K^+ concentration and correct it therapeutically when necessary.

Contribution of Cl^- to the Resting Potential

The description of the resting potential as a K^+ equilibrium potential must be modified to take account of the fact that K^+ is not actually the only ion that can cross the membrane. Cell membranes are also permeable, for example, to chloride ions. In nerve cells the permeability to Cl^- is usually far lower than that to K^+, but in muscle fibers the permeability to Cl^- predominates [8, 19]. As we have seen (Table 1-1), the dis-

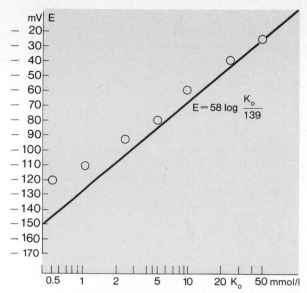

Fig. 1-5. Dependence of the resting membrane potential (ordinate) on the extracellular K^+ concentration K_o^+ (abscissa, logarithmic scale). The circles denote the membrane potentials measured intracellularly at various K_o^+, and the straight line is the relationship between potassium equilibrium potential and K_o^+ calculated from the Nernst equation. After [7]

tribution of Cl^- across the membrane is the reverse of the K^+ distribution. The potential given by the Nernst equation for this reciprocal distribution of Cl^- (z negative!) is the same as that for the K^+ distribution. As a rule, then, the Cl^- equilibrium potential is about equal to the resting potential, and in cells with high Cl^--permeability K^+ and Cl^- contribute about equally to the resting potential.

The reciprocal distribution of K^+ and Cl^- is not a matter of chance. The relatively small intracellular Cl^- concentration, 5 mmol/l, can easily be altered by inflow and outflow of Cl^-. It is automatically adjusted to the membrane potential, because when the potential departs from E_{Cl} chloride flows in or out. Thus if the resting potential is close to E_K, Cl^- becomes distributed in a *concentration ratio reciprocal to that of K^+*.

In contrast to chloride, it is not possible for the K^+ to adjust the intra/extracellular concentration ratio according to the membrane potential. There can be no appreciable change in the high intracellular K^+ concentration, because the K^+ in the cell must balance out the charge of the anions. Most of the intracellular anions are large protein molecules of constant concentration. Their negative charge must be compensated by the intracellular K^+ or Na^+ ions. The Na^+ concentration in the cell is kept low (near 10 mmol/l) by mechanisms to be discussed later, so that the K^+ concentration, like that of the large anions within the cell, can hardly change. The high intracellular K^+ concentration is thus enforced indirectly by the concentration of the impermeant intracellular protein anions, and the negative E_K results from the high intracellular K^+ concentration. The negative resting potential of the cell, then, can be regarded as a consequence of the high concentration of intracellular anions to which the membrane is impermeable.

The Passive Na^+ Inflow

As Fig. 1-5 shows, when the extracellular K^+ concentration is at or below normal, the resting potential is as much as 30 mV less negative than E_K. The reason for this discrepancy is that the membrane is not completely impermeable to Na^+. There is a steep Na^+ concentration gradient from outside to inside, ca. 10:1 (Table 1-1), and sodium inflow is further enhanced by the inside-negative membrane potential, which attracts positive ions. Even with a membrane very slightly permeable to Na^+ these ions will flow into the cell and reduce the amplitude of the negative membrane potential. That such Na^+ inflow is responsible for the departure of the resting potential from E_K in Fig. 1-5 is demonstrated by a simple experiment. If Na^+ inflow is prevented by replacing the extracellular Na^+ with a large impermeant cation (e.g., choline), the resting potential is equal to E_K even at low K^+ concentrations. The sodium inflow occurring at rest is called **passive** because it follows the existing concentration and potential gradients.

Ion conductance and permeability of the membrane. In order to quantify statements such as "the membrane permeability to Na^+ is low" we shall introduce the concept of **membrane conductance g.** Electrical *conductance* is the *reciprocal of resistance;* it is the ratio of the flowing current to the driving voltage. The conductance of ions through the membrane is thus the ratio of the net flow of the ion species through the membrane to the voltage driving this flow. The driving voltage is zero at the equilibrium potential of the ion species in question, and increases as the membrane potential E departs from the equilibrium potential. For example, the potassium conductance g_K is given by [4, 21]

$$g_K = I_K/(E\text{-}E_K)$$

where I_K is the net flow of potassium (the potassium current) through the membrane when the membrane potential equals E. The net ion currents I_K and I_{Na} can be measured experimentally (cf. p. 14), and it is found that at the resting potential g_K *is 10–25 times as high as* g_{Na}.

Even though the sodium conductance g_{Na} is relatively small, there is a considerable passive inward sodium

current I_{Na}, because the flow of sodium into the cell is driven by a large potential difference (E-E_{Na}). E_{Na}, according to the Nernst equation (p. 6), with a concentration ratio Na_i^+/Na_o^+ of 1:12 (cf. Table 1-1) is +65 mV, so that its difference from the resting potential (E-E_{Na}) is −155 mV. The passive inward sodium current is thus $I_{Na} = g_{Na} \cdot (E\text{-}E_{Na}) = g_{Na} \cdot (-155\text{ mV})$. For maintenance of a stable resting potential, this inward Na^+ current must be compensated by an equally large outward K^+ current. The quantity (E-E_K), the departure of the resting potential from the potassium equilibrium potential, must be made ca. +8 mV for $I_K = g_K \cdot (E\text{-}E_K) = g_K \cdot (+8\text{ mV})$ to be equal to I_{Na}, given the ratio $g_K/g_{Na} = 20$. That is, because of the passive Na^+ inflow the resting potential must become somewhat more positive than the potassium equilibrium potential, so that the electrical charge carried in by the sodium is compensated by passive K^+ outflow.

Permeability. Another important measure of the degree to which diffusing substances can pass through the membrane is *permeability*. The permeability p of a dissolved substance is defined by the diffusion equation, which describes the dependence of velocity of flow dS/dt of the substance S on the membrane area A and the difference in concentration of the substance across the membrane (C_o–C_i) [1, 5]:

$$dS/dt = p \cdot A(C_o\text{–}C_i)$$

The permeability constant p has units of velocity; for simple diffusion of an uncharged particle $p = D \cdot \beta/l$, where D is the diffusion constant of the particle in the membrane, β is the distribution coefficient of the substance in the membrane, and l is the thickness of the membrane. Because the diffusing particles of special interest in neurophysiology (the ions) are charged, the definition of permeability becomes more complicated, for the velocity of diffusion depends on the potential. In this case a permeability P can be defined by assuming that the electrical field strength within the membrane is constant. This permeability P for ions is

$$P = \beta \cdot u/l \cdot R \cdot T/F$$

where u is the mobility of the ion in the membrane, and $R \cdot T/F$ is the constant we encountered in the Nernst equation (p. 6). The velocity of flow of an ion is proportional to P, but depends in a complicated way upon the concentration difference and the membrane potential. Because the derivation of P for ions is relatively complex, the electrical conductance g is usually preferred for quantitative analysis in neurophysiology. g can be calculated from P and the membrane potential [1].

The permeabilities P_K, P_{Na} and P_{Cl} for the K^+, Na^+ and Cl^- ions can be used to calculate the potential of a membrane permeable to all these ions, by an expansion of the Nernst equation (p. 6). According to this "constant-field equation" the membrane potential E is given by [1, 5]

$$E = \frac{R \cdot T}{F} \cdot \ln \frac{P_K \cdot [K^+]_o + P_{Na} \cdot [Na^+]_o + P_{Cl} \cdot [Cl^-]_i}{P_K \cdot [K^+]_i + P_{Na} \cdot [Na^+]_i + P_{Cl} \cdot [Cl^-]_o}$$

Instability of the resting potential with purely passive ion currents. The continual passive Na^+ inflow and

K$^+$ outflow under resting conditions has far-reaching consequences. Such a system is not in equilibrium; the cell is steadily losing K$^+$ and acquiring Na$^+$, and the intracellular concentrations of these ions must fall and rise, respectively. The K$^+$ loss causes a decrease in the resting potential, which of course as a predominantly K$^+$ potential must diminish when the intra/extracellular concentration difference becomes smaller. As discussed on p. 7, when the membrane potential is reduced the intracellular Cl$^-$ concentration, and thus the total anion concentration, decreases. The associated increase in osmotic pressure causes an influx of water, and the cell begins to swell. The water uptake further reduces the intracellular K$^+$ concentration, and the resting potential continues to fall. The vicious circle proceeds until the swelling of the cell and the progressive equilibration of the ion concentrations on the two sides of the membrane abolish cellular function.

This decline in resting potential and elimination of concentration differences, a necessary consequence of purely passive transmembrane ion flow, does not occur in normal tissue. Therefore there must be ion flow across the membrane other than the passive currents considered so far. Evidence as to the nature of these inferred processes is provided by the pathological syndrome associated with extreme *oxygen or energy deficiency* in a tissue. Under these conditions one observes precisely the changes in ion distribution and the water influx described above. Evidently the maintenance of normal intracellular ion concentrations, and thus of the resting potential, requires metabolic energy.

The Sodium Pump

Demonstration of active transport of Na$^+$ out of the cell. Na$^+$ ions that have entered a cell passively, down the concentration and potential gradients, can diffuse back up these gradients only in vanishingly small proportions. Because the intracellular Na$^+$ concentration must not be allowed to rise, the inflowing Na$^+$ ions must be removed from the cell **actively,** by a membrane process that consumes metabolic energy. The active transport of ions against electrical and concentration gradients is also called an *ion pump* [1]. The existence of a Na$^+$ pump can best be demonstrated with *radioactive Na$^+$ ions*. Fig. 1-6 illustrates two such experiments on a nerve cell. Before the experiment the radioactive sodium isotope ^{24}Na$^+$ was injected into the cell. As the experiment proceeds, intracellular ^{24}Na$^+$ flows out into the bathing medium, where it can be identified by its radioactive decay. The rate of decay in the external solution is

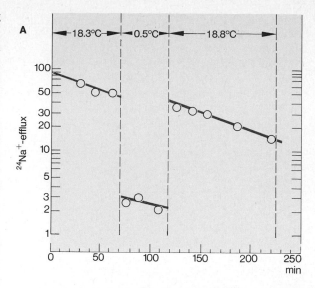

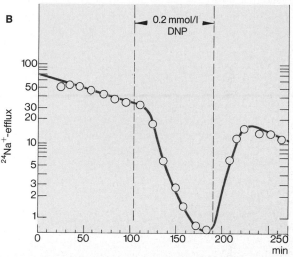

Fig. 1-6 A, B. Demonstration of active Na$^+$ transport. Ordinates: outflow of radioactive ^{24}Na$^+$ from the cell (in counts per minute). Abscissa: time since the beginning of the experiment. A The cell is cooled from 18.3° C to 0.5° C and warmed again; during the cold period Na$^+$ outflow is inhibited. B Inhibition of Na$^+$ outflow by 0.2 mmol/l dinitrophenol (DNP). After [24]

proportional to the outflow of ^{24}Na$^+$, indicated on the ordinate in Fig. 1-6 A and B. The ^{24}Na$^+$ outflow falls off exponentially in time, because as the isotope leaves the cell it accounts for a progressively smaller fraction of the total intracellular Na$^+$ concentration. When the nerve of Fig. 1-6 A is rapidly cooled to 0.5 °C, the Na$^+$ outflow is reduced by a factor of 10. After rewarming the outflow returns to that just prior to cooling. This marked *temperature dependence* of Na$^+$ outflow shows that it cannot be a matter of diffusion, for diffusion is only slightly slowed by cooling. The temperature dependence proves that a complicated chemical reaction is involved – an active transport.

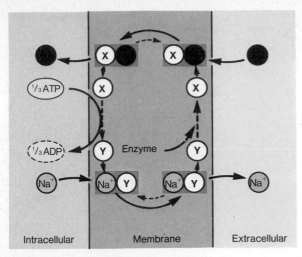

Fig. 1-7. Coupled Na^+-K^+ pump. Diagram of the transport of Na^+ and K^+ through the membrane by the carriers X and Y. Energy is provided by the breakdown of adenosine triphosphate (ATP) into adenosine diphosphate (ADP). After [27]

Fig. 1-6 B shows further that the Na^+ outflow depends on the availability of *metabolic energy*. The application of dinitrophenol (DNP) reduces outflow by a factor of ca. 100 within an hour. DNP penetrates the cells and there blocks energy-supplying metabolic processes, so that the reduction of the Na^+ outflow by DNP must be due to a lack of metabolic energy. Again, the demonstration that Na^+ outflow depends on the provision of energy shows that Na^+ is being removed from the cell by **active transport.**

The sodium pump is not only a feature of nerve- and muscle-cell membranes; it is probably present in all cells. It has been most often studied in the erythrocyte membrane. It is most active in the epithelium of the renal tubules, where it brings about the reabsorption of Na^+ from the primary urine and indirectly regulates the rate of water loss from the body (cf. Chapter 27).

The coupled Na^+-K^+ pump. The active transport of Na^+ out of the cell has a component coupled to the flow of K^+ into the cell [24]. This coupled Na^+-K^+ pump is advantageous in that it saves energy – a property of real importance to the energy balance of the cell. In muscle cells, for example, it has been estimated that 10–20% of the resting metabolism supports active transport. To assist in understanding the mode of operation of the coupled pump the model in Fig. 1-7 has been developed. At the inside of the membrane Na^+ becomes bound to a carrier Y, forming the molecule NaY. NaY diffuses through the membrane and splits apart spontaneously at the outside of the membrane. The concentration of NaY is therefore small at the outer side, and the outflow of NaY predominates

over the inflow. This temporary binding to the carrier molecule Y thus enables Na^+ to diffuse outward, against its concentration and potential gradients. At the outer side of the membrane the carrier molecule Y is converted to a carrier molecule X, which binds to K^+ in the external solution. The resulting compound KX diffuses through the membrane, splitting into K^+ and X at the inner side. On the inside metabolic energy is used – adenosine triphosphate (ATP) is split – to reconvert the carrier molecule X to the molecule Y. This is the only endothermic reaction in the cycle; the coupling of X to K^+ saves about half of the energy that would be required for uncoupled Na^+ transport. The existence of such a coupled Na^+-K^+ pump can be demonstrated by the removal of K^+ ions from the external solution. When no K^+ is available to form the complex KX at the outer side of the membrane, the coupled pump is blocked and the outflow of Na^+ from the cell falls to about 30% of normal.

Electroneutral and electrogenic sodium pumps. The complex NaY of sodium and the carrier molecule is usually electroneutral. Therefore during the transport process there is no flow of electric charge through the membrane; such an *electroneutral Na^+ pump* has no direct effect on the membrane potential. There are also, however, **electrogenic Na^+ pumps** [4, 11, 37]. These transport Na^+ through the membrane as a positively charged complex, and the charge displacement produces an increased negativity of the cell interior, a so-called hyperpolarization. Electrogenic pumps have been demonstrated by experiments like that of Fig. 1-6, in which activity of the Na^+ pump is severely impeded by cooling or poisoning. In the case of an electrogenic pump, the immediate result is reduced negativity of the membrane potential. Among the cells in which electrogenic pumps make a major contribution to the membrane potential are thin nerve fibers (cf. Fig. 1-10, hyperpolarizing afterpotential of Group IV fibers) and cardiac muscle cells.

Survey of the Ion Currents through the Membrane

The diagram in Fig. 1-8 summarizes the ion currents through the membrane that contribute to the resting potential. Here Cl^- currents and electrogenic pumping processes are neglected. In this diagram the K^+ and Na^+ ions flow through channels of width corresponding to the magnitude of the associated ion current, and slope corresponding to the electrochemical potential. The resting potential is taken to be -80 mV.

The flow of K^+ ions is predominantly passive from inside to outside, down the small electrochemical gradient of − 11 mV, but there is also a considerable passive K^+ inflow against the gradient. The relatively great width of the two passive K^+ channels reflects the high K^+ conductance of the membrane. The difference between the two passive K^+ currents is made up by the active inward transport of K^+, here (like all the active-transport processes) drawn in red. The slope of the Na^+ channels is very steep, because the sodium equilibrium potential is so far from the resting potential. Therefore passive diffusion of Na^+ can occur only "downhill" – a channel representing the passive outward diffusion of Na^+ would not be visible on the scale of this diagram. The passive Na^+ inflow must be compensated entirely by active outward transport of Na^+, accomplished by the Na^+-K^+ pump shown in red. The Na^+ channels through the membrane are all far narrower than the K^+ channels, so that even though the driving potential is large the Na^+ currents are smaller than the K^+ currents. This difference reflects the fact that the membrane conductance for Na^+ is far smaller than that for K^+.

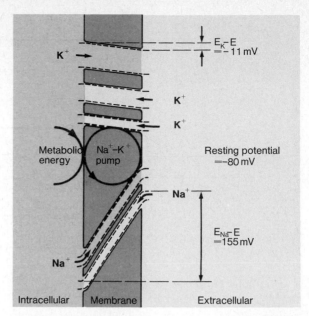

Fig. 1-8. Passive and active movements of ions through the membrane. The width of the channels indicates the magnitude of the associated ion currents, and the channel slope indicates the driving force for ion flow. The Na^+-K^+ pump generates transport *(red)* in a direction opposed to the driving force. After [13]

1.3   The Action Potential

The function of nerve cells in the body is to receive information, to carry it to other parts of the system, to compare it with other information and finally to control the function of other cells. Muscle cells, under the control of nerves, contract. When these two types of cell are "active" in their respective ways, brief positive-going changes in the membrane potential appear – the **action potentials.**

Time Courses of Action Potentials

Action potentials can be recorded from nerve and muscle cells by means of intracellular electrodes (cf. Fig. 1-2). Typical examples of action potentials in various tissues of mammals are shown in Fig. 1-9. In all these action potentials there is an abrupt rise from the negative resting potential to a positive peak near + 30 mV. The potential then returns at different rates to the resting level; the action potential lasts ca. 1 ms in nerves, ca. 10 ms in skeletal muscle and more than 200 ms in cardiac muscle.

Several phases of the action potential can be distinguished, as shown in Fig. 1-10. The action potential begins with a very rapid positive-going change in potential, the **upstroke,** which lasts only 0.2–0.5 ms. During the upstroke the cell membrane loses its normal charge or "polarization"; the upstroke is therefore al-

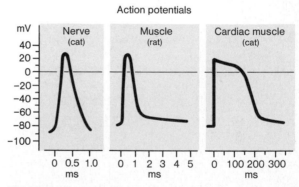

Fig. 1-9. Action potentials of various mammalian tissues. *Ordinate:* intracellular membrane potential; *abscissa:* time since the beginning of the action potential. The time scales of the different action potentials vary widely

so called the *depolarization phase.* As a rule, the depolarization crosses the zero line and the membrane potential becomes positive. This positive part of the action potential is called the **overshoot.** The phase following the peak, during which the original resting membrane voltage is restored, is called **repolarization.**

Afterpotentials. The last part of the repolarization phase is slowed in some types of action potential; the muscle action potential in Fig. 1-9 is a good example. About 1 ms after onset of the action potential there is

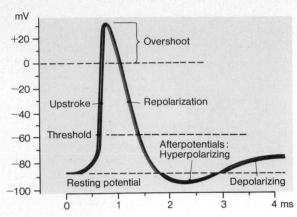

Fig. 1-10. Phases of the action potential; the time course of a nerve action potential as shown in Fig. 1-8. The phases labelled here are described in the text

a distinct inflection of the repolarization curve; the following slowly changing potential is called the *depolarizing afterpotential*. In other tissues, such as nerve cells of the spinal cord, the repolarization curve rapidly crosses the resting potential, so that for some time the potential is more negative than the resting potential; this is called a *hyperpolarizing afterpotential* (cf. Fig. 1-10).

The Origin of the Action Potential

Threshold and excitability. How is the resting potential – otherwise kept so constant by the mechanisms just discussed – disturbed as much as to produce an action potential? Action potentials are always elicited when the membrane is *depolarized* from the resting potential to ca. − 50 mV. The mechanisms that bring about this initial depolarization will be treated later (p. 23). The potential at which depolarization gives rise to an action potential is called the **threshold** (Fig. 1-10). At this threshold potential the membrane charge becomes unstable; it dissipates by an intrinsic mechanism which leads to a reversal of polarity – the rapid upstroke to the peak of the action potential. This state of automatic, progressive breakdown of the membrane charge is called **excitation.** Excitation usually lasts less than 1 ms. It is like an explosion, forceful but soon over. The depolarizing phase of the action potential in turn sets in motion processes that restore the resting membrane charge.

All-or-none law. The action potential, then, is a sequence of membrane depolarization and repolarization that is constant for each cell, an *autoregenerative process* triggered whenever membrane depolarization passes the threshold potential. Cells in which action potentials can be elicited are called *excitable*. Excitability is a typical property of nerve and muscle cells. The time course of the action potential is constant and characteristic of each cell type. It is very little affected by the way or the frequency with which excitation is elicited. The fact that action potentials are so constant in shape has been called the *"all-or-none" law of excitation*.

Ion currents during the action potential. The resting potential, as shown in the previous section, is very close to the equilibrium potential of the K^+ ions, to which the membrane is most permeable at rest. If the interior of the cell becomes positive with respect to the extracellular space during the action potential, the membrane conductance for Na^+ (g_{Na}) must have increased, for only Na^+ has a positive equilibrium potential, at + 60 mV, more positive than the peak of the action potential. This inference is confirmed by the experimental finding that action potentials can be triggered only when the extracellular Na^+ concentration is high. Should these extracellular sodium ions be lacking, there cannot be an increased inward sodium current no matter how much g_{Na} increases, and thus there can be no depolarization phase of the action potential. The basis of excitation, then, is an increase in the *membrane conductance for Na^+*, brought about by depolarization to threshold. However, the K^+ conductance of the membrane is also involved. If an increase in K^+ conductance is prevented by certain chemicals, such as tetraethylammonium, the action potential repolarizes much more slowly. This effect indicates that an increase in K^+ *conductance* is an important factor in repolarization of the membrane. The action potential is thus based on a cycle of Na^+ inflow into the cell and subsequent K^+ outflow. The quantitative relationship among the ion currents flowing during the action potential and their time courses can be found only with the help of the "voltage-clamp" method discussed below.

It should again be pointed out here that the ion displacements occurring during the action potential are negligible in comparison with the high concentrations of the ions in the intra- and extracellular spaces. As for the resting potential discussed with reference to Fig. 1-3, to charge the inside of a small area of membrane (1 μm × .001 μm) to − 90 mV only 6 K^+ ions were required. The change of membrane charge to + 30 mV during the action potential requires an influx of 9 Na^+ ions. Of course, during the action potential the inward sodium current serves not only to alter the charge on the membrane capacitor but also to depolarize still unexcited regions of the membrane and to compensate for outward K^+ currents (cf. Fig. 1-26), so that the total Na^+ inflow is many times that necessary to recharge the membrane capacitor. But even this total ion redistribution is quantitatively insignificant in view of the hundreds of thousands of ions in the adjacent volumes. A single action potential has essentially no effect on the intra- or extracellular ion con-

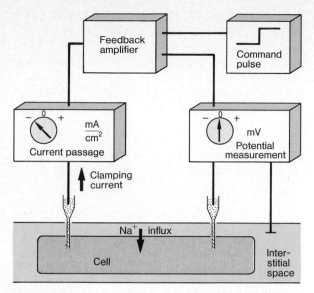

Fig. 1-11. Voltage clamp. The measured potential is compared with the command voltage, and any difference is eliminated by the automatic injection of an appropriate compensatory current

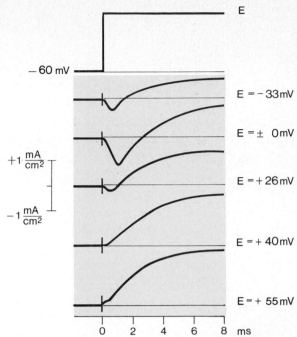

Fig. 1-12. Clamp currents following voltage changes. At the top is the time course of a step of depolarization that shifts the membrane potential of a squid giant axon from the resting potential, -60 mV, to a clamp potential E. The resulting clamp currents are shown below; the calibration given for E $=$ $+26$ mV also applies to the other curves. Positive clamp currents are associated with an outflow of positive ions from the cell, and negative currents with the inflow of positive ions. After [21]

centrations. It would take a large number of action potentials to increase the intracellular Na^+ concentration appreciably, and such an increase is prevented by the Na^+ pump (p.9).

Kinetics of Ion Currents during Excitation

Voltage clamp. During excitation the depolarization changes the membrane conductance for various ions, and these conductance changes in turn bring about potential changes. This complex process can be understood only by measuring the relationships of the different membrane conductances to the membrane potential. In such measurements one parameter, the potential, is kept constant and the membrane currents associated with each set potential are observed. The *"voltage-clamp"* arrangement used for this purpose (Fig. 1-11) employs two intracellular electrodes, one of which is used (as in Fig. 1-2) to measure the membrane potential. The second serves to inject current into the cell. The current is provided by an electronically controlled amplifier that compares the measured membrane potential with a command voltage set by the experimenter and continually matches the two by adjusting the amount of current that enters the cell. In the example in Fig. 1-11, a sodium inflow that would tend to depolarize the membrane is compensated by an equal but opposite **clamp current.** The clamp currents in a voltage clamp are thus the mirror image of the currents flowing through the membrane at a given potential.

Membrane currents following depolarization. The result of the first voltage-clamp experiments carried out by Hodgkin and Huxley on the squid giant axon to clarify the ion fluxes during the action potential [20–23] is shown in Fig. 1-12. With a fiber diameter as great as 1 mm, the squid giant axon is ideally suited to such experiments; it has become the standard preparation for the study of the action potential. This analysis has provided insights that also apply in large part to other preparations, such as the nerves of vertebrates [10, 15, 38, 42]. In Fig. 1-12, the line at the top shows the programmed depolarization of the membrane from -60 mV, the resting potential of this preparation, to the desired clamp potential E. With the smallest potential step, to E $=$ -33 mV, a small negative current flows for ca. 1 ms following depolarization and then gives way to a maintained positive current. Both of these current components are amplified following a step to E $=$ 0 mV. Greater depolarization, to E $=$ $+26$ mV, reduces the initial negative current component, and with E $=$ $+40$ mV it vanishes entirely. With depolarization to $+55$ mV a positive component appears in place of the early negative component. Whereas the initial negative current changes its

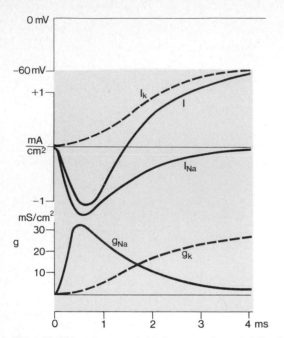

Fig. 1-13. Ion currents and conductance changes following a change of membrane potential in the squid giant axon. At the top is the time course of the depolarization from −60 mV to 0 mV, induced by voltage clamp. Below it are curves representing the total clamp current I and its components I_{Na} and I_K *(red)*, and the time courses of the membrane conductances g_{Na} and g_K calculated from the clamp currents. After [21]

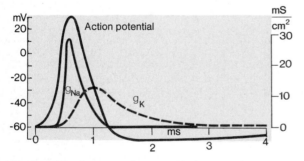

Fig. 1-14. Membrane conductances during an action potential in the squid giant axon. g_{Na} and g_K are calculated from series of depolarizing steps like those of Figs. 1-12 and 1-13. After [23]

direction for depolarization beyond +40 mV, the subsequent positive current component increases steadily with depolarization.

The reversal of current direction at +40 mV identifies the initial current as a **Na⁺ current.** In the squid axon E_{Na} is +40 mV; at potentials negative to +40 mV Na⁺ must flow into the cell (negative clamp current) and at more positive potentials there is an outward flow (positive clamp current). A reversal potential identical to E_{Na} thus demonstrates that the initial current component is carried by Na⁺. This conclusion is confirmed by a further finding. If Na⁺ in the extracel-

lular solution is replaced by an impermeant ion (p.8) so as to prevent Na⁺ inflow, the initial negative current component disappears. Suprathreshold depolarization is thus accompanied by a *sodium current* lasting for 1–2 ms.

K⁺ can flow through the membrane as well as Na⁺, and the component of the clamp current that appears after the Na⁺ current must be primarily a K⁺ current. This component is visible in isolation in Fig. 1-12 at E = +40 mV, for at E_{Na} there is by definition no net sodium current. At this potential the clamp current develops with some delay, after 8 ms reaching a maximum at which it remains constant for a long time. By using sodium-free solutions as the extracellular medium the sodium current can be eliminated at potentials other than E_{Na}, so that the clamp current corresponds to the pure K⁺ current. Such experiments have shown (i) that the **K⁺ current** (I_K) rises with a delay at all depolarizations and reaches a maximum in 5–10 ms, (ii) that I_K increases with the magnitude of depolarization, and (iii) that after reaching the maximum I_K does not decline as depolarization is maintained.

Time courses of the Na⁺ and K⁺ currents and conductances. The clamp current I following a depolarizing step is thus a potential-dependent composite of a Na⁺ and a K⁺ current (I_{Na} and I_K). The two components are shown separately in Fig. 1-13, for a depolarization to 0 mV. I_{Na} rises rapidly after depolarization and begins to fall again after only 0.5 ms. By contrast, I_K rises slowly and is still submaximal by the time that I_{Na} has returned nearly to zero. The conductances g_{Na} and g_K can be calculated from the associated ionic currents (p.8). These are plotted in the lower half of Fig. 1-13. g_{Na} and g_K can be described exactly by a system of equations [23] that takes into account their dependence on the membrane potential and on the time since the potential was changed. If allowance is made for the resistance and capacitance of the cell membrane, this system of equations can be used to reconstruct the time course of voltage change following a suprathreshold depolarization; the resulting curve matches precisely the time course of the action potential (Fig. 1-14). This procedure demonstrates that the action potential is fundamentally determined by the potential- and time-dependence of g_{Na} and g_K. Moreover, Fig. 1-14 shows that depolarization to threshold elicits a rapid rise of g_{Na}, which autoregeneratively brings about the depolarization phase of the action potential. At the peak of the action potential g_{Na} has begun to fall, while g_K continues to rise slowly and makes possible the rapid repolarization phase.

The Inactivation of the Na⁺ System

In the squid axon under maintained depolarization illustrated in Fig. 1-13, g_{Na} begins to decline after ca. 0.5 ms; in vertebrate nerve cells and at higher temperatures this decline can begin in less than 0.1 ms. The rapid decrease in g_{Na} is called *inactivation*. The rate and extent of the decrease are markedly *potential-dependent* [22]. One can measure the potential-dependence of inactivation by keeping the membrane potential at the level E for a few ms, until inactivation of g_{Na} has reached a steady state at this potential. Then the inward sodium current brought about by excitation starting at E (e.g., depolarization to 0 mV) is measured. The result of such an experiment is shown in Fig. 1-15. I_{Na} is plotted on the ordinate as a fraction of the maximal possible I_{Na}, while the abscissa indicates the membrane potential E *before* excitation was triggered. It is evident that the maximal I_{Na} can be reached only from potentials ca. 30–40 mV more negative than the resting potential, and that from potentials 20–30 mV more positive than the resting potential no I_{Na} can be elicited at all. At these potentials the Na⁺ system is fully **inactivated,** and cannot be activated by any depolarization. In the range of potentials between 30 mV more negative and 20 mV more positive than the resting potential, g_{Na} can be activated to varying degrees by depolarization; depolarization from the resting potential itself elicits only ca. 60% of the maximal possible sodium inflow. That is, at the resting potential the sodium system is about 40% inactivated. The degree of inactivation of the Na⁺ system is related to the membrane potential in the same way in mammalian nerve and muscle cells [12].

Influences on inactivation. The potential-dependent inactivation of the Na⁺ system crucially affects the excitability of the cells under various conditions. For example, if the resting potential of a mammalian cell becomes more positive than −50 mV (e.g., due to lack of oxygen or to the action of a muscle relaxant of the succinyl-choline type; cf. p.58), the sodium system is completely inactivated and the cell is inexcitable. Subtler influences on excitability are exerted by substances that affect the potential-dependence of inactivation itself. The most important example of such a substance is **Ca⁺⁺.** When the calcium-ion concentration increases the potential-dependence of inactivation is shifted to the right, and a decrease has the opposite effect. Therefore an increase in Ca⁺⁺ concentration makes the Na⁺ system more activatable. At the same time, however, the range of potentials in which depolarization elicits a rapid rise in g_{Na} is shifted in the positive direction; that is, the threshold potential becomes more positive. Similarly, at lower Ca⁺⁺ concentrations the threshold becomes more

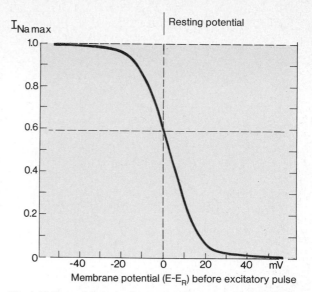

Fig. 1-15. Potential-dependence of sodium-system inactivation. Abscissa ($E-E_R$): departure of the membrane potential from the resting potential (−60 mV). From each of these initial potentials the membrane was depolarized to −16 mV, and the resulting maximal Na⁺ current (I_{Namax}) is plotted as a fraction of the I_{Namax} corresponding to full activation of the sodium system (ordinate). After [22]

negative, approaching the resting potential [14]. It follows that when the *Ca⁺⁺ concentration increases* the cells become *less excitable,* and when the *Ca⁺⁺ concentration is lowered excitability increases.* The latter is the basis of the syndromes of *tetany* and other calcium-deficiency states of the blood; when inadequate Ca⁺⁺ is present, uncontrolled muscular excitation and cramps develop. Effects like those of altered Ca⁺⁺ concentration are produced by local anesthetics such as Novocain, and digitalis glycosides [10, 12, 44] and some anti-arrhythmic drugs act similarly on cardiac muscle; the great therapeutic value of all of these derives from a reduction of excitability, by shifting the potential-dependence of Na⁺-system inactivation or the threshold potential.

In contrast to g_{Na}, g_K *is not inactivated.* Fig. 1-13 showed that after the depolarizing step g_K rises slowly and remains constant at the maximum level. The increase in g_K is responsible for the repolarization phase of the action potential; the fact that g_K can remain high indefinitely during depolarization ensures that the potential will return to the resting level under all circumstances.

Refractory periods. As a further important consequence of Na⁺-system inactivation, the membrane can become **refractory.** This phenomenon is illustrated in Fig. 1-16. If the membrane is depolarized immediately following an action potential, no excitation is

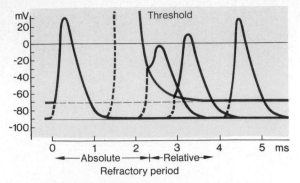

Fig. 1-16. Refractoriness following excitation. An action potential is elicited in a nerve of a mammal *(left),* and further stimuli are applied at various times thereafter. The solid red line denotes the threshold potential and the dashed black lines, the depolarization of the fiber up to the threshold. In the absolute refractory period the fiber is inexcitable, and in the relative refractory period it is excited at a threshold higher than normal

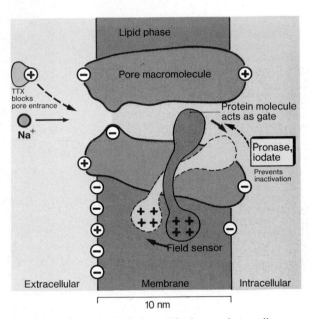

Fig. 1-17. Model of a Na$^+$ channel in the membrane, diagrammatic. The membrane components and the ions are drawn approximately to scale. The Na$^+$ ions can pass through the pore; the *dashed arrows* indicate the inhibitors tetrodotoxin (TTX, which blocks the pore entrance) and pronase or iodate (which prevent inactivation). After[10, 18]

induced at the threshold for the previous action potential or by any greater depolarization. This state of complete inexcitability, which in nerve cells lasts for ca. 1 ms, is called the **absolute refractory period.** It is followed by a **relative refractory period,** in which action potentials can be elicited by large depolarizations, though these potentials are of smaller than normal amplitude. Not until several ms have elapsed following an action potential does it become possible to elicit an action potential of normal amplitude by the

normal threshold depolarization; the return to this condition marks the end of the *relative refractory period.* As mentioned above, refractoriness results from the inactivation of the Na$^+$ system during the preceding action potential. Although the membrane recovers from inactivation due to repolarization, this recovery is a gradual process requiring a few ms, and during this time the Na$^+$ system is not yet activatable, or activatable to only a limited extent. The **absolute refractory period limits the maximal frequency** with which action potentials can be triggered. If, as in Fig. 1-16, the absolute refractory period ends 2 ms after the onset of the action potential, the cell can be excited at a rate of at most 500/s. There are cells with still shorter refractory periods, so that in the extreme case excitation can be repeated at a rate as high as 1000/s. In most cells, however, the maximal action-potential frequency is less than 500/s.

Membrane structure and excitation. The capacity of the cell to become excited is based on the sodium system – that is, the ability of the cell membrane to increase its Na$^+$ conductance rapidly and strongly for a few ms during depolarization. In recent years much research has concentrated on the question of the molecular mechanism of this fast sodium system. Study was facilitated by the discovery of a substance, **tetrodotoxin,** that in concentrations of 10^{-10} to 10^{-7} mol/l specifically inhibits or blocks the *fast sodium system.* Inhibition by tetrodotoxin changes neither the potential-dependence nor the inactivation of the Na$^+$ system – a situation best explained by the hypothesis that a tetrodotoxin molecule acts only to block the entrance to a Na$^+$ channel through the membrane, the unblocked channels remaining unaffected [34, 42]. On this assumption, by finding the tetrodotoxin concentration that blocks half the channels one can estimate the *number of channels per unit area of membrane.* Such calculations indicate that there are about 50 sodium channels per μm^2 of membrane, giving a mean channel separation of 140 nm [33]. This distance between the Na$^+$ channels is quite large compared with their diameter, ca. 0.5 nm (Fig. 1-17). Of the metal ions, only Li$^+$ can pass through a Na$^+$ channel as readily as sodium; the permeability to K$^+$ and Ca^{++} is very much lower, and anions are entirely excluded. Therefore the wall of the Na$^+$ channel is thought to bear a fixed negative charge, which repels anions and facilitates the passage of Na$^+$ (cf. Fig. 1-17). The channel is so narrow that the cations within it can only be partially hydrated, and form hydrogen bonds with oxygen atoms in the pore wall in transit. Such a model [7] can explain the observed permeabilities of metal ions as well as those of organic cations such as hydroxylamine, which can traverse the Na$^+$ channel almost as readily as Na$^+$ itself. The entrance to the Na$^+$ channel constitutes the selectivity filter that practically restricts entry to Na$^+$ ions. At rest the Na$^+$ channels are closed; they open only during depolarization. Within the Na$^+$ channel, then, there is a *potential-controlled gate*. This is a component of the pore that is affected by the membrane potential by way of a charged "sensor" in the lipid phase of the membrane. In a state of depolarization these charges shift and bring about a change in molecular conformation that opens the passage (Fig. 1-17). The charge displacement is measurable as a gating current immediately prior to the Na$^+$ inflow at the onset of excitation [4, 10, 18, 42]. The pore opens for only a short time, for inactivation occurs within 1 ms. Whether this inactivation mechanism is also a property of the "gate" in Fig. 1-17, or whether a second "inactivation plug" closes the pore, is not yet clear. Measurements of the gating current indicate that the opening and inactivation of the gate are interlinked. On the other hand, inactivation can be selectively eliminated by injecting into the cell either iodine or the protein-splitting enzyme pronase. If there is a separate inactivation mechanism, then, it must be located at the inner end of the pore.

The K$^+$ channels can be described similarly. The selective blocking agent in this case is tetraethylammonium (TEA), which can block on either side of the membrane. The density of the K$^+$ channels in the membrane is somewhat less than that of the Na$^+$ channels. The sizes of the molecules that can pass through the K$^+$ channel indicate an ion-selective entrance ca. 0.3 × 0.3 nm in cross section. The K$^+$ channel also has a potential-controlled gate, which opens the channel after depolarization. In contrast to the Na$^+$ channel, however, the K$^+$ channel has no inactivation mechanism [10, 18, 42].

Ion Currents during the Afterpotentials

In many cells, the rapid depolarization of the action potential is followed by depolarizing or hyperpolarizing afterpotentials (Figs. 1-9 and 1-10). These afterpotentials have various causes; two of the more important types will be described briefly here.

A **brief hyperpolarizing afterpotential** immediately after repolarization is exhibited by many nerve cells and some cardiac-muscle cells (cf. Fig. 1-10). This afterpotential is an overshooting repolarization; when the repolarization phase reaches the resting potential g_K has not yet returned to its resting level (Fig. 1-14) and is thus higher with respect to g_{Na} than in resting conditions. Therefore the membrane potential approaches E_K more closely than when at rest. The resulting hyperpolarization fades away along with the

increased g_K [19]. This mechanism of brief hyperpolarization following an action potential participates in the development of repetitive excitation, and will be discussed again in that context (p. 27).

Prolonged **hyperpolarizing afterpotentials,** which summate when excitation is repeated at a high rate, are especially pronounced in the very thin nerve fibers of vertebrates, the Group IV fibers. These prolonged hyperpolarizing afterpotentials are produced by an **electrogenic Na$^+$ pump** (p. 10), which removes from the cell the Na$^+$ that entered during excitation [37]. They disappear when pump activity is prevented by metabolic blocking agents such as DNP (cf. Fig. 1-6).

1.4 Extracellular Space and Neuroglia

So far we have concentrated on the cells and the cell membranes, on the assumption that they are surrounded by a large volume of extracellular fluid with a constant concentration of ions. In fact, this is only a rough approximation. As discussed in Section 1.1, the nerve cells in the CNS are packed in among glial cells, so that the extracellular space is limited to the intercellular cleft, only about 15 nm wide (Fig. 1-18). Similarly, the peripheral axons are closely enveloped by Schwann cells. These intercellular clefts are quite adequate for the long-term provision and removal of substances by diffusion, but intense neural activity can cause the ion concentrations in the extracellular space to change considerably for short periods. During the action potential Na$^+$ ions flow into the cell and K$^+$ ions flow out of it, and similar movements occur during the excitatory synaptic potentials (p. 61). The high extracellular Na$^+$ concentration is not appreciably changed in the process, but the *K$^+$ concentration can increase* considerably. The extracellular K$^+$ concentration can be measured by means of microelectrodes filled with selective K$^+$-ion exchangers. When the nerve cells are very active the extracellular K$^+$ concentration has been found to rise from the normal 3–4 mmol/l to as much as 10 mmol/l [4, 31]. Such elevated extracellular K$^+$ concentrations, as stated by the Nernst equation (cf. Fig. 1-5), cause considerable depolarization of the nerve cells. It may be that depolarization due to increased extracellular K$^+$ concentration is one causative factor in the development of convulsive discharge in the brain, such as occurs in epileptic seizures [4, 31, 41]. After intense activity the active transport of K$^+$ can bring its extracellular concentration below normal, causing hyperpolarization of the nerve cells. *Shifts of the Ca^{++} concentration* in the extracellular space associated with

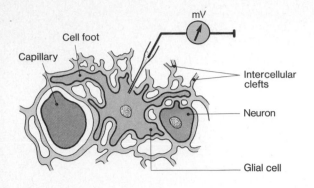

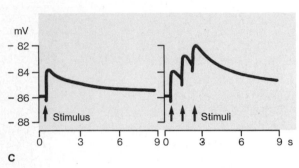

Fig. 1-18 A–D. Properties of the glial cells. **A** Schematic drawing of the relations among neurons, glia and capillaries at the electron-microscopic level. An astrocyte *(light red)*, penetrated by a microelectrode for the measurement of membrane potential, lies between a capillary and a neuron. All the cellular elements are separated from one another by intercellular clefts ca. 15 nm wide *(width exaggerated* in the diagram). **B** Dependence of the glial membrane potential (ordinate) on the extracellular K^+ concentration, K_o^+. The mean resting potential (RP) is -89 mV. The data depart from the potential calculated by the Nernst equation only at $K_o^+ = 0.3$ mmol/l. **C** Depolarization of glial cells by activity of nearby neurons in the optic nerve of a salamander *(Necturus)*, elicited by 1 stimulus or 3 at intervals of 1 s (↑). **D** Depolarization of glial cells in the same preparation during series of stimuli lasting 20 s, within which the stimuli are repeated at rates of 1/s, 2/s and 5/s; the latter causes depolarization by almost 20 mV. Note in C and D that the time course of depolarization is much slower (seconds!) than that of the action potential. After [4]

activity have also been found, with Ca^{++}-sensitive electrodes.

How do the *glial cells* react to changes in the *intercellular* ion concentrations? Fig. 1-18 A illustrates the measurement of the membrane potential of a glial cell, and in B the membrane potentials found for various extracellular K^+ concentrations are plotted. The data correspond to the curve for a K^+ electrode calculated from the Nernst equation more closely than was the case in the muscle cell (Fig. 1-5). The predominance of K^+ *permeability* is thus even more pronounced in the *glial-cell membrane*. Accordingly, the glial cell also becomes depolarized when activity of the adjacent neurons causes the extracellular K^+ concentration to rise (Fig. 1-18 C and D). When the K^+ concentration subsequently falls, glial-cell depolarization decreases with a time constant of several seconds. This decrease in the extracellular K^+ concentration is caused in part by the glia. The glial cells make electrical connections with one another by way of *tight junctions,* as do epithelial and smooth muscle

cells. When glial cells in a small region are depolarized owing to local increase in extracellular K^+ concentration, current flows between the depolarized and the non-depolarized cells. This electrical current causes K^+ to flow into the depolarized glial cells, decreasing its extracellular concentration. Because of the high K^+ permeability and the electrical connections of the glial cells, these cells act as a *buffer* with respect to increases in the extracellular K^+ concentration. There is no evidence of active uptake of K^+ into glial cells by means of an ion pump, although the glial cells probably take up transmitter substance actively at some synapses and thus limit the duration of its action.

Unlike nerve cells, glial cells are not excitable; when they are depolarized, the Na^+ conductance of their membranes does not increase. Their membrane conductance also does not change in the presence of synaptic transmitter substances.

1.5   Electrotonus and Stimulus

Excitation occurs when the membrane is depolarized to or beyond the threshold – a process also called **stimulation.** The stimulus as a rule is an imposed electric current that depolarizes the membrane as it flows through. Before considering the way in which stimuli elicit excitation, therefore, we shall first treat the depolarization of the membrane by electric current, beginning with voltage changes so small that they do not alter membrane conductance.

Electrotonus in the Case of Homogeneous Current Distribution

The simplest arrangement for the study of membrane responses to current flow is achieved with a spherical cell with intracellular electrodes for the application of current and recording of membrane potential (Fig. 1-19 A). When a constant positive current is switched on (Fig. 1-19 B), the inflowing positive charges progressively discharge the membrane capacitor and thus depolarize the membrane. Accordingly, the potential electrode records a rapid depolarization at the beginning of the current pulse. But the rate of depolarization very soon slows, for when the membrane potential shifts away from the resting potential the equilibrium of the ion fluxes is disturbed, and during depolarization more K^+ ions flow out of the cell. This countercurrent of positive ions through the membrane removes some of the charge introduced by the electric current, and discharge of the membrane capacitor is necessarily slowed. Eventually, at an increasingly slower rate, the depolarization reaches a final level at which the ion current through the membrane is equal to the electric current applied by the electrode; there is then no further discharge of the membrane capacitor (Fig. 1-19). The potential change caused by the current pulse is called an **electrotonic potential** or *electrotonus*. The final level, or the amplitude, of the electrotonic potential is proportional to the *membrane resistance* (the reciprocal of the membrane conductance) to the ion currents. The rate of rise of the electrotonic potential at the very beginning is determined only by the membrane capacitance; only *capacitive current* is flowing. When the countercurrent of ions begins to flow through the membrane, the potential begins to change exponentially, with the exponent $-t/\tau$. t is time, and the *membrane time constant* τ is the product of membrane resistance and membrane capacitance. τ ranges from 5 to 50 ms in different cells.

An exponential curve like that of electrotonus (or, for example, the decay in activity of a radioactive substance) is described by $e^{-t/\tau}$. τ is called the time constant because at time $t = \tau$ the exponent is -1. In such a curve, then, τ can be found by locating on the abscissa the time at which the amplitude has fallen to $e^{-1} = 1/e = 37\%$ of the starting value.

Electrotonus in Elongated Cells

Almost all nerve and muscle cells are very long as compared with their diameter; a nerve fiber, for example, with a diameter of only 1 μm can be a meter long. Current applied within such a cell will be very inhomogeneously distributed as it flows out, a marked departure from the situation illustrated in Fig. 1-19. Electrotonic potentials in an elongated muscle fiber are shown in Fig. 1-20, as they appear at the site of current injection (E_0) and at distances of 2.5 mm and 5 mm ($E_{2.5}$ and E_5). These curves differ in shape from that of Fig. 1-19; they are not simply exponential and they vary with distance. E_0, at the site of current injection, rises very rapidly, so that at a time corresponding to the membrane time constant τ it is within 16% of its final value (rather than the 37% in Fig. 1-19). This steeper slope is caused by the inhomogeneous current distribution; at first the membrane capacitor is discharged in a small region near the current source, and only then does current begin to flow through the interior of the cell, which has considerable longitudinal resistance, to more distant parts of the membrane. There, again, the membrane capacitor must be discharged before further current flow occurs, so that as distance from the current source increases the time course of the electrotonic potential becomes progressively slower. In Fig. 1-20 there is a distinct delay before the onset of the electrotonic potential 5 mm away from the current electrode (E_5), and even after 120 ms the final value E_{max} has not been reached [25].

Even when the injected current has been flowing so long that a new charge distribution has been established, more current flows through the membrane near the point of injection than through areas further away, for at more distant points the current must overcome not only the membrane resistance but also the longitudinal resistance within the cell. The final value E_{max} of the electrotonic potential is plotted as a function of distance from the current electrode in the bottom graph of Fig. 1-20. E_{max} falls off exponentially with distance x, the exponent being $-x/\lambda$. The quantity λ is called the **membrane length constant**; in Fig. 1-20 it is 2.5 mm, and in other cells it ranges from 0.1 to 5 mm [25]. The length constant λ is a measure of the distance over which electrotonic potentials can spread in elongated cells. At the distance 4 λ, for

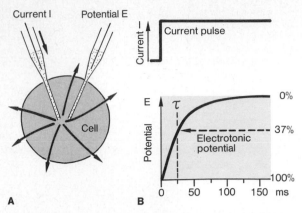

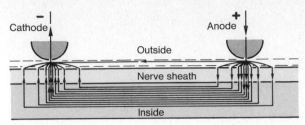

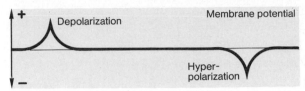

Fig. 1-19 A, B. Electrotonic potential of a spherical cell. **A** Intracellular electrodes measure the membrane potential E and inject a current I, which is distributed as shown by the red arrows. **B** Time course of a current pulse and the electrotonic potential measured simultaneously in the cell. The time constant τ of the electrotonic potential is established by the time at which the potential has approached to within 37% (1/e) of its final value

Fig. 1-21. Arrangement for extracellular application of current. Current flows from the anode to the cathode, both outside the nerve; part flows through the film of fluid on the surface of the nerve, and part flows through the nerve sheath and along the interior of the nerve fibers. The *curve below* shows the changes produced by the current in the membrane potential of a nerve fiber. After [28]

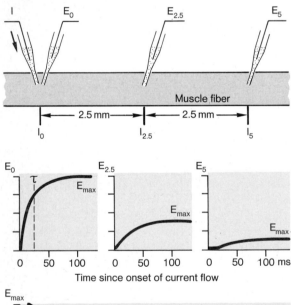

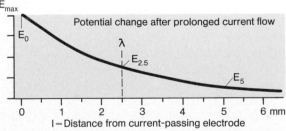

Fig. 1-20. Electrotonic potentials in an elongated cell. *Top:* Injection of current I into a muscle cell; the electrotonic potential is measured at distances of 0, 2.5 and 5 mm. *Middle:* Time courses of the electrotonic potentials at the three distances; each reaches a different final value E_{max}. *Bottom:* Relationship between E_{max} and distance from the site of current injection. The membrane length constant λ is equal to the distance at which E_{max} has fallen to 37% (1/e) of the amplitude at the site of current injection

example, the amplitude of the electrotonic potential is only 2% of that near the current-injection site; thus in nerves electrotonic potentials are measurable some centimeters, at most, from the site of origin.

It should be emphasized once again that this discussion of the effects of injected current applies only to potential changes so small that they do not change the ion conductance of the membrane. Electrotonic potential implies *passive* behavior of the membrane. Therefore if the polarity of the injected current is reversed, mirror-image electrotonic potentials result. When depolarization reaches the threshold region the behavior of the membrane is no longer passive, for g_{Na} begins to rise. This transition from electrotonus to stimulation is discussed below.

Membrane polarization by way of extracellular electrodes. The injection of current through an intracellular electrode, as illustrated in Figs. 1-19 and 1-20, creates a simple current-flow situation that assists the understanding of electrotonus. In medical research and in neurology, however, cells are usually polarized by extracellular electrodes. The preferred method is to place a nerve fiber over two metal electrodes connected to a voltage source. Current flow in this situation is diagrammed in Fig. 1-21. The positive electrode is called the *anode,* and the negative one is the *cathode.* Current flows from one to the other through the film of fluid adhering to the fiber, but because the interior of the fiber also presents a relatively low resistance, part of the current crosses the membrane at the anode, flows through the cell to the cathode, and there crosses the membrane again. These currents through the membrane are accompanied by changes in the membrane potential; at the anode the positive charges delivered to the outside of the membrane increase the charge on the membrane capacitor and thus increase the membrane potential. As a result, K^+ ions flow into the cell, carrying the current through the membrane. At the anode, then, the membrane becomes hyperpolarized. A mirror-image change, a depolarization, occurs at the cathode. The voltage profile along the nerve fiber is shown in the lower part of Fig. 1-21. The voltage change is greatest at the site of the greatest current density, directly at the electrodes.

Usually when current is applied to nerve or muscle the intent is to depolarize and thus to stimulate the cell; the hyperpolarization at the anode is not particularly desired. In this case it is better to use an anode of large surface area or position it far from the nerve, so that the current density at the anode is less and the hyperpolarization of the cell, although more extensive, is of lower amplitude. The small-area electrode at which the lines of current and the polarization are concentrated is called the *different electrode,* and the large-area electrode of opposite polarity is called the *indifferent electrode.*

Stimulus and Threshold

When a depolarizing electrotonic potential passes the threshold it elicits excitation. The current pulse that brings about this potential change is called the *stimulus.* Because of the membrane capacitance, the potential change induced by a current pulse occurs with some delay (Fig. 1-20). Therefore the threshold is usually reached a few ms after the stimulus current has been switched on. The stimulus must last long enough for the threshold to be reached; that is, the current pulse must be of adequate duration as well as adequate amplitude. Within limits, a very high stimulus amplitude can compensate for short duration.

Near-threshold stimuli. It often happens that the dendrites and somata of nerve cells are depolarized just barely to the threshold, so that very slight differences in intensity determine whether the information is passed on in the form of an action potential or not. The action potential is triggered at the threshold because the depolarization has caused an increase in sodium conductance g_{Na}, and the resulting sodium influx becomes so great that the membrane automatically continues to depolarize. However, the Na^+ inflow elicited by depolarization does not begin abruptly at the *threshold potential,* but at potentials a few mV lower. This can be seen in the set of electrotonic potentials shown in Fig. 1-22, elicited by a uniformly incremented series of hyperpolarizing and depolarizing current pulses. Only the two smallest depolarizing

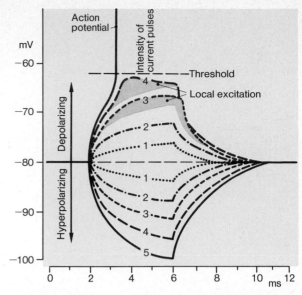

Fig. 1-22. Electrotonic potentials and local responses. Current pulses (4 ms in duration) of relative amplitudes 1, 2, 3, 4 and 5 in the hyperpolarizing direction produce proportional electrotonic potentials. With depolarizing currents of amplitudes 1 and 2, the potentials are mirror images of those with hyperpolarizing currents. The depolarizations produced by current amplitudes 3 and 4 exceed those of electrotonic potentials at levels beyond -70 mV, by amounts indicated by the red areas below the curves. The active or nonlinear depolarization, in excess of electrotonus, is called local excitation. The depolarizing current of amplitude 5 produces a depolarization that passes the threshold and triggers an action potential

electrotonic potentials are mirror images of the hyperpolarizing potentials. The third and fourth depolarizations rise more rapidly and are larger than the corresponding hyperpolarizations, and the fifth depolarization is suprathreshold. The extra depolarization in the curves only slightly below threshold is shown by the red-shaded areas; it is called the **local response** and is caused by the increase in Na^+ conductance in this potential range. During such local responses the Na^+ inflow may very well exceed the K^+ outflow, but the Na^+ current is still not strong enough to depolarize the membrane as rapidly as necessary to trigger an action potential (see below), or to excite adjacent regions. The state of excitation is not fully developed, so that it remains a local phenomenon and is not propagated. A local response of this sort, of course, can easily be converted to full excitation by a small additonal stimulus such as a synaptic potential (cf. p. 59).

Threshold Shifts; Accommodation

So far we have regarded the threshold, the minimal degree of depolarization necessary to trigger an action potential, as a fixed potential. But we have also

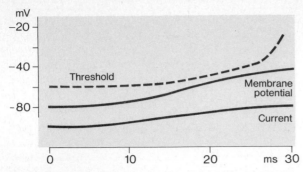

Fig. 1-23. If depolarization is produced slowly enough, by a gradually rising current, the threshold potential also slowly becomes more positive. When this accommodation process brings the threshold into the region of −50 mV the cell becomes inexcitable

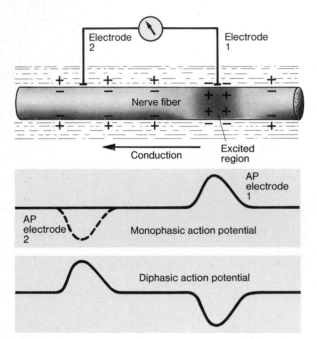

Fig. 1-24. The action potential as seen by extracellular electrodes. The potential is conducted from right to left *(above)*, and the excited region of the fiber has just reached Electrode 1; the recorded potential follows the solid *red* curve *(middle line)*. When the action potential reaches Electrode 2, the potential change shown by the dashed red line is recorded. Each deflection in this red curve is a monophasic action potential. The two together constitute a diphasic action potential, plotted in the *lower* graph as a function of time

learned about various influences that can change the activatability of the Na$^+$ system (cf. p. 15) and thus shift the threshold. The most important of these is the potential at which the stimulus is initiated. Prolonged depolarization inactivates the Na$^+$ system, and hyperpolarization makes it more readily activatable (Fig. 1-15). One consequence is that when, starting at the resting potential, the membrane is depolarized relatively slowly (Fig. 1-23), the Na$^+$ system is exten-

sively or completely inactivated before the threshold potential is reached. This slow depolarization then either elicits an abnormally small action potential at a potential positive to the normal threshold, or it fails to excite altogether (Fig. 1-23). The increase in threshold caused by slow depolarization is called **accommodation.** Accommodation occurs, for example, in cells of the central nervous system when they are depolarized by the summation of slowly rising synaptic potentials (cf. p. 59).

The reverse of accommodation can also occur, in that hyperpolarization can shift the threshold in the negative direction.

Electrical currents are of significance in neurophysiology apart from their use as stimuli to nerves; they can be applied to the skin for therapeutic purposes, and they are sometimes involved in accidents. Direct current acts as a stimulus chiefly when it is turned on and off, although strong currents can warm the tissue so much as to damage it, and if the voltage is too high sparks can be generated that cause deep skin wounds. Low-frequency alternating current (e.g., 50 Hz) has the same effects, with somewhat less tendency to generate sparks. It also stimulates excitable tissue at the frequency of the current alternation; such stimuli, especially if they arrive in the relative refractory period (vulnerable phase) of the myocardial action potential, can easily induce lethal fibrillation of the heart. For this reason, low-frequency a. c. is particularly dangerous. Alternating current at high frequencies (over 10 kHz) cannot depolarize a membrane to threshold during a half cycle, and the next half cycle eliminates the depolarization; as a result, such currents do not act as stimuli, but only warm the tissue. Therefore frequencies between 0.5 and 1 MHz can be used therapeutically in **diathermy,** for controlled local warming of tissue.

1.6 Propagation of the Action Potential

The role of the nerve fiber, and of the muscle-fiber membrane, is to disseminate information (or controlling signals) – to conduct excitation. To understand the mechanism underlying the conduction of excitation, we must consider the physiology of excitation discussed in Section 1.3 in the light of the laws governing longitudinal spread of currents and potentials (Sec. 1.5). We shall begin by describing the propagation of excitation in a nerve.

Measurement of Conduction Velocity

When a nerve is excited (e. g., by an electrical current pulse) the action potentials can be recorded with extracellular electrodes (Fig. 1-24). These action potentials appear not only at the site of stimulation, but also at considerable distances – a meter away, for example. The potentials have the *same amplitude* everywhere, but they appear with a *delay* proportional to the distance from the stimulus site. In a motor nerve, for instance, an action potential arrives at a point 1 m away from the site of stimulation in 10 ms, from which it follows that it is *conducted* along the nerve at a velocity of 100 m/s.

Fig. 1-24 illustrates the procedure of recording with extracellular electrodes. Two electrodes are placed in contact with the nerve fiber, which has been dissected free from the surrounding tissue over a certain distance and in this region is surrounded by an electrically insulating medium such as mineral oil or air. If a wave of excitation passes along the fiber from right to left, as it reaches Electrode 1 the surface of the fiber under this electrode loses its positive charge; this region becomes negative with respect to the region under Electrode 2, and the meter shows a positive voltage change corresponding approximately to the time course of the intracellular action potential. When the excitation reaches Electrode 2 the meter records a voltage change of reversed polarity, a negative action potential. Because the overall voltage change recorded with two electrodes has a positive and a negative component, it is called a *diphasic* action potential. From the time separating the positive and negative peaks and the distance between the recording electrodes the conduction velocity can be calculated. Usually the two phases of the action potential are not as distinctly separated as in Fig. 1-24. With a conduction velocity of 100 m/s and an action-potential duration of 1 ms, for example, the action potential occupies 100 mm of the nerve fiber (100 m/s · 1 ms), so that for complete separation of the phases of the diphasic action potential an exposed nerve 20 cm long would be required. This is usually impracticable, and therefore the two phases of the diphasic potential usually overlap.

It is also possible to record *monophasically* with extracellular electrodes. If the nerve is damaged, or depolarized by raising the K^+ concentration, in such a way as to prevent conduction of the action potential in Fig. 1-24 from Electrode 1 to Electrode 2, only the potential change shown in red is recorded – a monophasic action potential. Essentially monophasic potentials, though very small ones, can also be recorded by a single microelectrode next to the excited nerve or nerve cell; in this case the reference electrode must be far from the excited region, in the surrounding bath or in the animal. Such *"monopolar recording"* measures the voltage difference between the nearby extracellular solution and the "distant ground" produced by the local currents in the nerve fiber. The measured potential changes thus correspond to the time course of the membrane current during excitation (Fig. 1-26). For monopolar extracellular recording it is unnecessary to insulate the excited structure; this method is therefore particularly useful for studying the physiology of the CNS.

The compound action potential of a mixed nerve. A nerve in the leg, for example, contains fibers widely varying in function and diameter, and their conduction velocities also vary. When an electrode is placed in contact with the whole nerve, the first action potentials it records are those of the most rapidly conducting fibers, followed by various groups of potentials of other, slower fibers. That is, the action potential of such a nerve is compounded of a spectrum of fiber groups and conduction velocities (Fig. 1-25). The individual notches in this compound potential are associated with particular groups of fibers, listed in Table 1-2a together with their functions. This classification, by ERLANGER and GASSER [16], includes both motor and sensory fibers; the Lloyd/Hunt classification [30] shown in Table 1-2b, for sensory nerves, is also widely used.

Mechanism of Conduction

It is characteristic of the conducted action potential that excitation is complete at each point on the nerve fiber, so that the amplitude of the action potential is always the same. These all-or-none excitatory processes at different places in the membrane are coupled with one another by the mechanism of electrotonic spread of stimulus currents along the fiber. The Na^+ ions flowing inward at an excited membrane site act as a current source for a depolarizing electrotonic potential at a nearby, not yet excited site. When this depolarization reaches threshold it elicits excitation there. Thus the state of excitation propagates, by electrotonic coupling, from excited to not yet excited membrane areas.

Note that there is a fundamental difference between the conduction of an action potential and the conduction of voltage pulses along a telegraph wire. In the wire current flows from one pole of a voltage source at one end of the wire to the other pole of a voltage source at the other end. The amplitude of the voltage pulse decreases with distance. In electrophysiological terms, the conduction in the telegraph wire is purely electrotonic. When an action potential is conducted the poles of the voltage sources in each region of the membrane are on the inside and the outside of the fiber, and the current is essentially a membrane current, perpendicular to the direction of propagation.

Membrane currents during the conducted action potential. Fig. 1-26 represents a "stop-action photo" of the voltage and current conditions along a nerve fiber as an action potential is conducted from right to left. The length of fiber occupied by the action potential depends on the conduction velocity; with a conduction velocity of 100 m/s and an action-potential dura-

Table 1-2a. The Erlanger/Gasser classification of nerve fibers

Fiber type	Function (examples)	Avg. fiber diameter (μm)	Avg. cond. velocity (m/s)
Aα	primary muscle-spindle afferents, motor to skeletal muscles	15	100 (70–120)
Aβ	cutaneous touch and pressure afferents	8	50 (30–70)
Aγ	motor to muscle spindles	5	20 (15–30)
Aδ	cutaneous temperature and pain afferents	< 3	15 (12–30)
B	sympathetic preganglionic	3	7 (3–15)
C	cutaneous pain afferents, sympathetic postganglionic	1 (unmyelinated)	1 (0.5–2)

Table 1-2b. The Lloyd/Hunt classification of nerve fibers

Group	Function (examples)	Avg. fiber diameter (μm)	Avg. cond. velocity (m/s)
I	primary muscle-spindle afferents and afferents from tendon organs	13	75 (70–120)
II	cutaneous mechanoreceptors	9	55 (25–70)
III	deep pressure sensors in muscle	3	11 (10–25)
IV	unmyelinated pain fibers	1	1

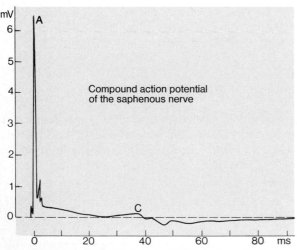

Fig. 1-25. Compound action potential of a mammalian nerve, measured with an extracellular electrode. All the fibers in the nerve were stimulated simultaneously at some distance from the recording site. The first action potentials to arrive are those of the most rapidly conducting fibers, the A-fibers; those of the slow C fibers appear about 38 ms later. The C-fiber deflection is followed by a prolonged hyperpolarizing afterpotential. The separate "humps" in the A-fiber deflection correspond to the α-, β-, γ- and δ-fiber subgroups. After [5]

the peak the increased g_K and the resulting K^+ outflow initiate repolarization. Between A and C the inflow of positive charges predominates in the membrane current i_m; the excess positive charges flow away, as shown at the top of Fig. 1-26, through the interior of the fiber on both sides. This excess current is characteristic of the *conducted* action potential. In a non-conducted action potential at an isolated spot on the membrane, there is no net inward current at the peak of the action potentials, for the Na^+ inflow equals the K^+ outflow. At the time of the peak of a conducted action potential the net inward ion flux is still about 80% of maximal; this current is required for the **electrotonic spread** along the fiber.

The part of the action potential critical for propagation is to the left of Line A in Fig. 1-26. In this region of the membrane the membrane current i_m flows outward and depolarizes the membrane **electrotonically.** The current source for the electrotonic depolarization is in the excited part of the membrane around B. The electrotonic depolarization at the beginning of the action potential reaches the threshold region just before Line A: g_{Na} increases, more Na^+ enters the cell and excitation results. The initial phase of the action potential is an electrotonic event, and the velocity of potential conduction thus depends on the fiber constants τ and λ, which describe the spread of electrotonic potentials.

At the end of the action potential, to the right of C in Fig. 1-26, there is also an outward current i_m that tends

tion of 1 ms, the length of the abscissa in Fig. 1-26 would correspond to 10 cm. The piece of fiber between the marker lines A and C is fully excited; the Na^+ inflow caused by the sharp increase in g_{Na} rapidly discharges the membrane capacitance, and after

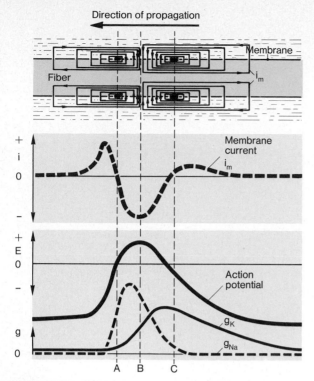

Fig. 1-26. Propagation of the action potential. The black curves show the time course of the action potential and of the associated membrane conductances g_{Na} and g_K. The red curve shows the membrane current i_m. The lines of current flow in and around the fiber are diagrammed at the top. The vertical dashed lines mark the times of maximal rate of rise (A), peak potential (B), and maximal rate of repolarization (C). After[35]

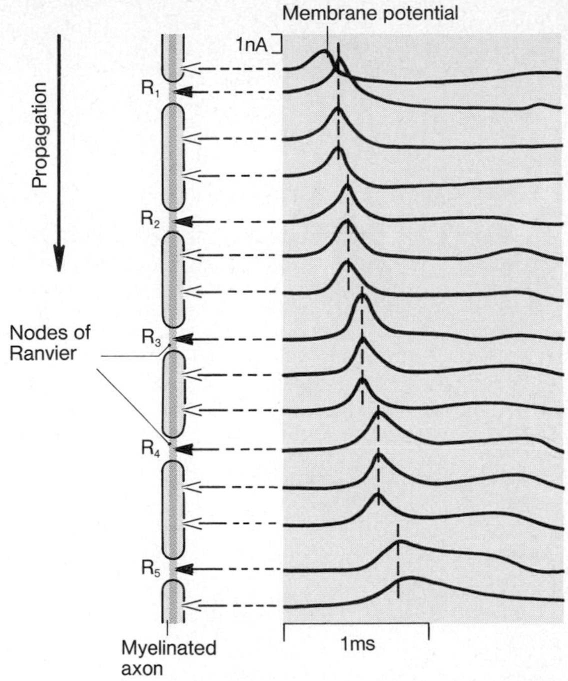

Fig. 1-27. Saltatory conduction. *Right:* time course of the membrane potential recorded at the points along the myelinated axon indicated by the arrows. $R_1, R_2, R_3 \ldots$ are nodes of Ranvier. Propagation of the action potential *(from top to bottom)* is delayed only at the nodes. After[26]

to depolarize the membrane. In the case of a conducted action potential this depolarization is prevented by the high g_K in this part of the membrane. But if g_K is relatively low or the effects of other depolarizing influences are added, the electrotonic membrane currents at the end of the action potential can cause new, so-called **repetitive excitation** (cf. Fig. 1-28).

It is because of the membrane current i_m that action potentials can be recorded with extracellular electrodes, for such electrodes measure the current density in the extracellular solution. Extracellular microelectrodes in the CNS record, from nerve cells and fibers, triphasic "spikes" proportional to the membrane current i_m in Fig. 1-26. i_m in turn, during a conducted action potential, is proportional to the second derivative of the intracellular potential with respect to time [23].

Factors determining conduction velocity. The conduction velocity of a nerve fiber can be found, by elaborate calculations, from the potential- and time-dependences of the ion currents and the conditions determining electrotonic spread – fiber diameter, membrane resistance and membrane capacitance. The result of such calculations closely matches the measured data [5, 23], which confirms the applicability of the ionic theory of excitation and of electrotonus. Here we shall discuss only the qualitative factors affecting conduction velocity.

One of these is the *amplitude of the inward Na^+ current,* for the more current is available after excitatory discharging of the membrane, the more current can flow into adjacent, not yet excited regions and accelerate depolarization there. The inward Na^+ current can be reduced by decreasing the Na^+ concentration and by enhanced inactivation of the Na^+ system when the resting potential is depressed or under the influence of local anesthetics (cf. p. 15). Under all these conditions the conduction velocity of the action potential is *lowered,* and in the extreme case conduction is blocked.

The electrotonic spread of the membrane currents also has a fundamental effect on conduction velocity. Because the resistance and the capacitance of a unit area of membrane are nearly the same in all excitable cells, electrotonic spread is determined chiefly by the **fiber diameter.** The membrane area of a nerve fiber is proportional to its diameter, whereas the cross-sec-

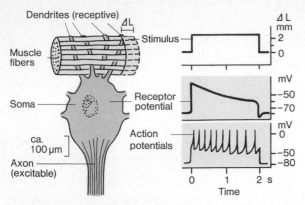

Fig. 1-28. Receptor potential and action potentials in a stretch receptor. *Left:* schematic drawing of a crustacean stretch receptor. The stimulus ΔL depolarizes the dendrites so as to produce the receptor potential recorded from the soma. *Right:* the repetitive action potentials triggered by the receptor potential at the base of the axon

tional area of the fiber increases as the square of the diameter. Thus when the fiber diameter increases the longitudinal resistance inside the fiber, determined by cross-sectional area, decreases with respect to the membrane resistance. The consequence is more extensive spread of the electrotonic currents (increase in length constant λ) and accelerated conduction. Although the membrane capacitance also rises, in proportion to the membrane area, as diameter increases – which tends to reduce conduction velocity – the effect of the lower longitudinal resistance predominates. The net result is that the conduction velocity increases about as the square root of fiber diameter. This relationship is also evident in Table 1-2.

Conduction in myelinated nerves. Because of their special structure, myelinated nerve fibers conduct action potentials especially rapidly. These fibers display a normal cell membrane only in very short segments, the nodes of Ranvier. In the internodal regions membranes are wound around the cell many layers thick, which greatly increases the membrane resistance. Therefore when the potential is changed practically no current flows through the membrane of the internodes, and an action potential at one node of Ranvier spreads to the adjacent nodes electrotonically and almost without decrement, through the internodes. The conduction time through the internodes is practically zero; the excitation leaps from one node to the next. This **saltatory conduction,** with no loss of time in the internodes, is well illustrated by the recordings shown in Fig. 1-27. Delays occur only at the nodes, where the electrotonic potential must reach the threshold and elicit excitation. The membrane of the node is specialized for excitation; the density of the Na^+ channels here is about 100 times greater than in unmyeli-

nated nerve fibers [10]. The acceleration of conduction by the myelinated parts of the fibers is considerable, and makes possible the many parallel rapidly-conducting nerve pathways in vertebrates. In these nerves all the fibers with conduction velocities above 3 m/s are myelinated; only the very slow C fibers (Group IV fibers) are unmyelinated. Invertebrates can achieve high conduction velocities, up to 10 m/s, only by developing a few unmyelinated "giant axons" almost 1 mm in diameter.

1.7 The Generation of Excitation in Receptors

So far we have considered only the excitation elicited by electrical stimuli. In the organism such electrical stimulation hardly ever occurs, even though action potentials are usually elicited indirectly by electrotonic depolarization. The natural stimulus site of the organism is the sense organs with stimuli such as light, sound, pressure, or acidity. The cells that detect these natural stimuli and send information about them to the nervous system are called **receptors;** the general aspects of receptor function are the subject of this section.

The Receptor Potential

Fig. 1-28 is a schematic drawing of a stretch receptor in a crustacean muscle, one of the best-studied receptor preparations [29]. It consists of a nerve cell with a relatively large soma, having dendrites in contact with muscle fibers and an axon that can conduct action potentials centrally. When the receptor is stimulated by stretching the muscle fibers there is a measurable *depolarization* of the soma, which vanishes at the end of the stimulus. This is called the **receptor potential** (or *generator potential*). The receptor potential must arise in the dendrites, for these are the only part of the cell in contact with the stretch stimulus. The receptor potential lasts as long as the stimulus, and its amplitude increases with stimulus intensity; it is a *representation of the stimulus* rather than an all-or-none response like the action potential. It is brought about by an increase in the Na^+ conductance of the stretched dendrite membrane, which depends on the degree of stretch. The resulting inflow of Na^+ ions produces the depolarizing receptor potential, which spreads electrotonically to the soma. This primary transformation of the stimulus into a receptor potential is called **transduction,** and the receptor is thus a transducer.

Other receptor cells in which the generation of activity is accessible to study have also been found to have depolarizing receptor potentials caused by an increase in membrane conductance, for sodium in particular. The receptor potentials of the primary visual cells (rods and cones) of the retina are a special case, in that they become *hyperpolarized* (cf. p. 245).

The energetic aspect of stimulus-to-receptor-potential transduction is also of interest. The stimulus is not the source of energy for the receptor potential. It only controls – by interaction with membrane processes still incompletely understood – the flow of ions through the membrane that results from transmembrane concentration differences. Thus a single light quantum can trigger membrane currents so large that the resulting receptor potential has a measurable effect on the activity of the visual cell. Transduction is therefore associated with an *amplification process*.

Transformation of the Receptor Potential into Excitation

In the axon of the stretch receptor a series of action potentials appears during the stimulus (Fig. 1-28). These action potentials are elicited by the receptor potential, which by spreading electrotonically from the dendrites over the soma depolarizes the base of the axon, where it can exceed the threshold for excitation. The first action potential generated repolarizes the membrane beyond the level of the receptor potential, with a hyperpolarizing afterpotential (for mechanism see p. 17), and during this relative hyperpolarization the Na$^+$ system can recover from inactivation sufficiently that the depolarization phase following the afterpotential again reaches the threshold for an action potential. Therefore the maintained depolarization caused by the stimulus generates a rhythmic series of action potentials, the frequency of which depends on the amplitude of the receptor potential. The action potentials are conducted to the CNS, carrying in **frequency-coded** form all the information the center receives about the magnitude and duration of the stimulus. The **transformation** of the receptor potential into a series of action potentials in many receptors occurs near the point where the axon leaves the receptor cell. In addition to these *primary receptors* there are *secondary receptors,* in which the receptor potential is not transformed into action potentials. Here the transformation occurs in the terminals of an afferent nerve cell, which make synaptic contact with the receptor cell. Important examples of secondary receptors include the human visual and auditory receptor cells.

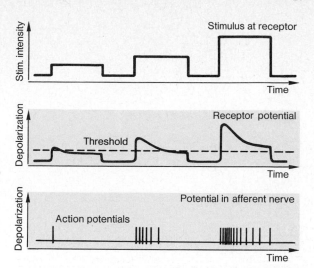

Fig. 1-29. Adaptation of the receptor potential and the coding of stimulus intensity. *Top:* three stimuli of increasing amplitude; *middle:* the associated receptor potentials, which adapt at an intermediate rate, exceeding the action-potential threshold *(dashed red line)* for various fractions of their duration. The frequency of the action potentials elicited by the suprathreshold receptor potentials is shown in the *lower* record

Adaptation

The receptor potential of the stretch receptor in Fig. 1-28 stays at a relatively constant amplitude as long as a constant stimulus is maintained. This form of stimulus-dependence is unusual; in most receptors, as in Fig. 1-29, the receptor potential decays during a constant stimulus. The receptor "adjusts itself" to the stimulus: **adaptation** occurs. The rate of adaptation varies widely among different receptor types, and these differences are largely characteristic of the receptor function. There are *extremely slowly adapting* receptors like that of Fig. 1-28, which monitor the state of stretch of a muscle; others, such as thermoreceptors in the skin and light receptors, adapt with *intermediate speed* (Fig. 1-29), and there are *very rapidly adapting* receptors such as the vibration sensors called Pacinian corpuscles (p. 215) in which a receptor potential lasting only a few ms appears whenever the stimulus changes. Receptors in the last category are especially well suited to record *alteration* of a stimulus with high sensitivity and temporal resolution, whereas slowly adapting receptors in most cases serve to detect long-term conditions important to the body, such as state of stretch or hydrogen-ion concentration. The adaptation of the receptor potential of course is reflected in a decrease in the frequency of the action potentials it elicits (Fig. 1-29, bottom) during the maintained stimulus. However, the action-potential frequency need not always be proportional to the receptor potential, for during the receptor

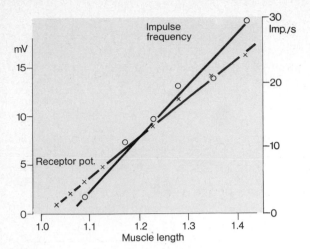

Fig. 1-30. Linear response characteristic of a stretch receptor in crustacean muscle. The amplitude of the receptor potential (*black,* left ordinate) and the frequency of the elicited action potentials (*red,* right ordinate) are plotted as a function of the length of the stretched muscle. After [39]

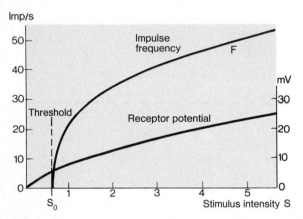

Fig. 1-31. Amplitude of the receptor potential and frequency of the action potentials in a receptor, as a function of stimulus intensity. Abscissa: stimulus intensity S; ordinate *red:* amplitude of the receptor potential; ordinate *black:* frequency F of the action potentials. The response of this receptor is described by power functions. S_0 is the threshold intensity for action potentials

potential the threshold can rise slowly so that the action-potential frequency is reduced even though the receptor potential stays constant. Moreover, a new adaptation can occur at the stage of action-potential generation, as at other stages of information transfer in the sensory nervous system.

Coding of Stimulus Amplitude as Impulse Frequency

In addition to illustrating adaptation, Fig. 1-29 shows responses to stimuli differing in amplitude; as stimulus amplitude increases, so does the amplitude of the

receptor potential and the frequency of the action potentials. The transformation of the amplitude of an electrical potential into an impulse frequency, which serves to carry information in the sensory system, is also widely used in information technology – for example, in the frequency modulation of a radio signal. Here we shall consider briefly the quantitative relationships between stimulus amplitude and impulse frequency. This "transfer function" is not the same in all receptors. A slow stretch receptor like that of Fig. 1-28 can have a *linear transfer function* over a wide range; that is, the frequency of the receptor action potentials is proportional to stimulus amplitude.

Fig. 1-30 shows the result of an experiment on this receptor. Many receptors have transfer functions like that shown in Fig. 1-31; the receptor potential (and the action-potential frequency, with suprathreshold stimuli) rises rapidly at low stimulus amplitude, but the sensitivity of the receptor decreases progressively as stimulus amplitude increases; stimulus increments in this upper range change the action-potential frequency relatively little. Transfer functions of this sort are found in sense organs responsive to stimuli varying widely in amplitude – for example, the strongest light to which a photoreceptor must respond can be 10^6 times as bright as the weakest light stimulus. Transfer functions with curvature oppposite to that of Fig. 1-31 are rare; pain receptors typically behave in this way, with progressively greater increases in action-potential frequency as stimulus intensity increases.

The various forms of transfer functions, relating a suprathreshold stimulus $(S-S_0)$ to impulse frequency F, can best be expressed by a *power function:*

$$F = k \cdot (S-S_0)^n$$

where k is a constant and the exponent n, always positive, is characteristic of the receptor type. With $n = 1$, the power function is a straight line with slope k; values of n smaller than 1 give curves of the form shown in Fig. 1-31, and those greater than 1 give upward-concave curves like those of a pain receptor.

Further aspects of receptor physiology will be treated in the chapters on general sensory physiology and on the individual sense organs.

1.8 Axonal Transport

In addition to its specific function as a conductor of action potentials, the axon is a channel along which materials are transported. Proteins synthesized in

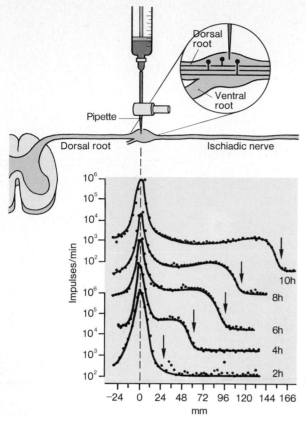

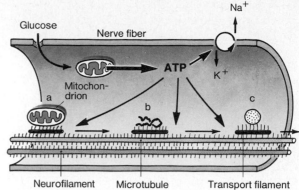

Fig. 1-33. Hypothetical transport mechanism in a nerve fiber. Microtubules and neurofilaments bear fine projections over which, in a reaction involving ATP dephosphorylation, the transport filaments *(red)* slide at a velocity of 410 mm/d. The transported material shown here, bound to the transport filaments, includes a mitochondrion *(a)*, a protein molecule *(b)* and a vesicle *(c)*. ATP is made available by the oxidation of glucose in mitochondria; it is used both for transport and for the K^+-Na^+ pump in the membrane. After [36]

Fig. 1-32. Experiment to demonstrate rapid axonal transport in sensory fibers of the cat ischiadic nerve. Tritium-labelled leucine is injected into a dorsal-root ganglion, and the radioactivity in the ganglion and the sensory fibers is measured 2, 4, 6, 8 and 10 h later *(graph)*. The abscissa indicates the distance from the ganglion of the measurement sites on the ischiadic nerve. The radioactivity is indicated on a logarithmic scale in counts per minute; the scale, shown only for the top and bottom curves, is the same for all. The "wave" of increased radioactivity *(arrows)* moves with a constant velocity of 410 mm/d. After [36]

the cell body, synaptic transmitter substances (cf. Chapter 3) and small molecules move down the axon to the nerve terminal, together with cell organelles such as mitochondria. Retrograde transport has also been found for most of these, and viruses or bacterial toxins can enter in the periphery and travel along the axon.

Rapid Axonal Transport

In most cases the axon does not simply act as a passive conductor, like a hose; axonal transport is an active process, as shown by the experiment illustrated in Fig. 1-32. Radioactively labelled leucine was injected into a dorsal-root ganglion, and 2, 4, 6, 8 and 10 h thereafter the radioactivity of the ischiadic nerve was

measured over a length of 166 mm from the cell bodies. The peak of radioactivity at the site of injection hardly changes during the 10 hours. But there is a wave of activity that moves toward the periphery at a uniform rate of ca. 34 mm per 2 h, or 410 mm/d. This velocity of *rapid axonal transport* has been found in all neurons of warm-blooded animals. There are no measurable differences between thin, unmyelinated nerve fibers and the thickest axons, nor between motor and sensory fibers. Transport velocity also does not depend appreciably on the kind of radioactive molecule injected. Various radioactive molecules – e.g., a number of amino acids which are incorporated into proteins in the soma – can be used as markers, with the same result. Analysis of the radioactive substances at the periphery shows that though the radioactivity is principally in protein fractions, some is found in transmitter substances and in free amino acids. In view of the differing properties of these substances and particularly the great differences in molecule size, the uniformity of the rate of transport in all cases can be explained only by a *carrier mechanism* common to all.

In addition to this rapid transport there are *slower transport processes* in the axon by which, for example, large proteins are carried. In these cases it appears that the transport mechanism itself is no slower; rather, the substances are intermittently shunted into a cell compartment not involved in transport. For instance, mitochondria move for a time at the speed of rapid transport and then come to rest, or their direction of transport reverses. The result is slow transport.

Even at this rate, about 1000 mitochondria per day move toward the periphery through the cross section of a medium-sized axon [9].

Retrograde Transport

Some substances have been found to move in the retrograde direction, from the periphery to the cell body. For example, *acetylcholinesterase* undergoes retrograde transport, at about half the velocity of rapid axonal transport. A substance widely used as a marker in neuroanatomy, *horseradish peroxidase,* is also transported toward the soma.

Retrograde transport appears to be a central factor in the *regulation of protein synthesis* in the cell body. A few days after transection of an axon chromatolysis begins in the soma, indicating disturbed protein synthesis. The time until the appearance of *chromatolysis* is correlated with the duration of retrograde transport from the point of transection to the soma. Thus the disturbance of protein synthesis can be interpreted as a consequence of the absence of a "signal substance" that normally arrives from the periphery to regulate the rate of protein synthesis.

Mechanism of Transport

Energetics of transport. Rapid axonal transport is dependent on a sufficient supply of *metabolic energy*. When oxygen deficiency or toxins that interfere with energy metabolism (e. g., dinitrophenol; cf. Fig. 1-6 B) have reduced the ATP level in the axon to about half, rapid axonal transport is blocked. This blockade is soon reversed when the energy supply is restored. Evidently, then, rapid axonal transport is an energy-consuming active process like the ion pump (cf. p.9).

Microtubules. In addition to neurofibrils and reticular structures, the axons contain microtubules. These hollow tubules, with a diameter of ca. 25 nm, can extend the entire length of the axon and often seem to bear fine projections at regular intervals. The walls of the microtubules consist of the protein tubulin, associated with an ATPase.

Mitotic poisons such as colchicine or *Vinca* alkaloids also block axonal transport. In high concentrations they cause disruption of the microtubules. It is therefore thought that the inhibition of axonal transport by these toxins is mediated by their action on the microtubules. The possibility of a similar mode of action on mitosis is currently under discussion.

Transport-filament hypothesis. Some of the neurofibrils consist of actin, the protein that brings about muscular contraction by sliding along the specific muscle protein myosin (cf. Fig. 2-2, p. 33). *Actin* [9] accounts for 10–15% of the protein content of nerve fibers, and 25% in muscle fibers. The current view is that in the axon the *microtubules,* perhaps acting jointly with parts of the *neurofibrils,* play the role of the myosin in muscle, and that *transport filaments,* probably composed of actin, *slide* along the microtubules (Fig. 1-33 [36]). In so doing, they would react with the projections on the microtubules in such a way that ATP is broken down, providing the energy for transport. This hypothesis is largely drawn from the mechanism of muscle contraction, which is understood in detail (cf. p.32). The transport filaments slide along the microtubules at a constant speed, and therefore the transported substances or organelles, bound to the transport filaments, also move at constant velocity regardless of their individual properties. It is characteristic of muscle contraction that the reaction of myosin, actin and ATP can occur only in the presence of an adequate concentration of calcium ions (p.35). Similarly, calcium ions are required for axonal transport.

Axonal Transport and Pathological Conditions

There are two ways in which axonal transport is known to be involved in pathological conditions of the nervous system: disease pathogens or toxins can be transported along the axons, and transport itself can be impaired [36].

Transport of viruses and toxins. It has been shown that viruses injurious to the nervous system, the poliomyelitis and herpes viruses, are transported along the axon to the cell body. Similarly, retrograde transport brings the tetanus toxin elaborated by bacteria in skin wounds through the axons to the CNS, where it gives rise to potentially lethal muscle spasms [36].

Disturbance of transport. In a number of neuropathies (diseases of the nerves) the distal axon becomes unfunctional before any pathological signs are detectable in the cell body. Such injury can be caused by various industrial toxins, such as acrylamide. It is likely that they derive at least in part from a disturbance of axonal transport. Conditions that hamper energy metabolism in the axons can also disturb axonal transport; such mechanisms have been proposed for the pathogenesis of beriberi and alcohol polyneuropathy. Axonal transport is also under consideration as the target of other toxins and factors too numerous to mention here. Development is very rapid in this new area of research, and promises important insight into the mechanisms underlying diseases of the nervous system.

1.9 References

Textbooks and Handbooks

1. DAVSON, H.: A Textbook of General Physiology, 4th Ed. London: Churchill 1970
2. Handbook of Physiology. I The Nervous System. Vol. 1 Cellular Biology of Neurons. KANDEL, E. R. (Ed.) Baltimore: Williams & Wilkins 1977
3. KATZ, B.: Nerve, Muscle and Synapse. New York: McGraw-Hill 1966
4. KUFFLER, S. W., NICHOLLS, J. G.: From Neuron to Brain. Sunderland, Mass.: Sinauer Associates, Inc. 1976
5. RUCH, T. C., PATTON, H. D.: Physiology and Biophysics. Philadelphia: Saunders 1966
6. COOKE, I., LIPKIN, M.: Cellular Neurophysiology, a Source Book. New York: Holt, Rinehart and Winston 1972 (Collection of important original publications)

Research Reports and Reviews

7. ADRIAN, R. H.: The effect of internal and external potassium concentration on the membrane potential of frog muscle. J. Physiol. (Lond.) 133, 631 (1956)
8. ADRIAN, R. H., FREYGANG, W. H.: The potassium and chloride conductance of frog muscle membrane. J. Physiol. (Lond.) 163, 61 (1962)
9. BERTHOLD, C. H.: Morphology of normal peripheral axons. In: Physiology and Pathobiology of Axons. WAXMAN, S. G. (Ed.) New York: Raven Press 1978
10. CAHALAN, M.: Voltage clamp studies on the node of Ranvier. In: Physiology and Pathobiology of Axons. WAXMAN, S. G. (Ed.) New York: Raven Press 1978
11. CARPENTER, D. O., ALVING, B. O.: A contribution of an electrogenic Na^+ pump to membrane potential in Aplysia neurons. J. gen. Physiol. 52, 1 (1968)
12. DUDEL, J., TRAUTWEIN, W.: Elektrophysiologische Messungen zur Strophantinwirkung am Herzmuskel. Arch. exper. Path. Pharmakol. 232, 393 (1958)
13. ECCLES, J. C.: The Physiology of Nerve Cells. Baltimore: Johns Hopkins Press 1957
14. FRANKENHAEUSER, B., HODGKIN, A. L.: The action of calcium on the electrical properties of squid axons. J. Physiol. (Lond.) 137, 218 (1957)
15. FRANKENHAEUSER, B., HUXLEY, A. F.: Action potential in myelinated nerve fibre of Xenopus laevis as computed on basis of voltage clamp data. J. Physiol. (Lond.) 171, 302 (1964)
16. GASSER, H. S., GRUNDFEST, H.: Axon diameters in relation to the spike dimensions and the conduction velocity in mammalian A-fibers. Amer. J. Physiol. 127, 393 (1939)
17. HILLE, B.: The permeability of the sodium channel to metal cations in myelinated nerve. J. gen. Physiol. 59, 637 (1972)
18. HILLE, B.: Ionic channels in excitable membranes. Biophys. J. 22, 283–294 (1978)
19. HODGKIN, A. L., HOROWICZ, P.: The effect of sudden changes in ionic concentrations on the membrane potential of single muscle fibres. J. Physiol. (Lond.) 153, 370 (1960)
20. HODGKIN, A. L., HUXLEY, A. F.: Currents carried by sodium and potassium ions through the membrane of the giant axon of Loligo. J. Physiol. (Lond.) 116, 449 (1952)
21. HODGKIN, A. L., HUXLEY, A. F.: The components of membrane conductance in the giant axon of Loligo. J. Physiol. (Lond.) 116, 473 (1952)
22. HODGKIN, A. L., HUXLEY, A. F.: The dual effect of membrane potential on sodium conductance in the giant axon of Loligo. J. Physiol. (Lond.) 116, 497 (1952)
23. HODGKIN, A. L., HUXLEY, A. F.: Quantitative description of membrane current and its application to conduction and excitation in nerve. J. Physiol. (Lond.) 117, 500 (1952)
24. HODGKIN, A. L., KEYNES, R. D.: Active transport of cations in giant axons from Sepia and Loligo. J. Physiol. (Lond.) 128, 28 (1955)
25. HODGKIN, A. L., RUSHTON, W. A. H.: The electrical constants of a crustacean nerve fibre. Proc. roy. Soc. B 133, 444 (1946)
26. HUXLEY, A. F., STÄMPFLI, R.: Evidence for saltatory conduction in peripheral myelinated nerve fibres. J. Physiol. (Lond.) 108, 315 (1949)
27. HOFFMAN, J. F.: Molecular mechanism of active cation transport. In: Biophysics of Physiological and Pharmacological Actions (SHANES, Ed.) Washington: Amer. Ass. Adv. Sci. 1961
28. KATZ, B.: Electrical properties of the muscle fibre membrane. Proc. roy. Soc. B 135, 506 (1948)
29. KUFFLER, S. W.: Mechanism of activation and motor control of stretch receptors in lobster and crayfish. J. Neurophysiol. 17, 558 (1954)
30. LLOYD, D. P. C., CHANG, H. T.: Afferent fibers in muscle nerves. J. Neurophysiol. 11, 199 (1948)
31. LUX, H. D.: Simultaneous measurement of extracellular potassium-ion activity and membrane currents in snail neurons. In: Ion and Enzyme Electrodes in Biology and Medicine. KESSLER, R. (Ed.) Munich: Urban and Schwarzenberg 1976
32. MULLINS, L. J., AWAD, M. Z.: The control of the membrane potential of muscle fibers by the sodium pump. J. gen Physiol. 48, 761 (1965)
33. NARAHASHI, T.: Mechanism of action of tetrodotoxin and saxitoxin on excitable membranes. Fed. Proc. 31, 1124 (1972)
34. NARAHASHI, T., MOORE, J. W.: Neuroactive agents and nerve membrane conductances. J. gen. Physiol. 51, 93 (1968)
35. NOBLE, D.: Applications of Hodgkin-Huxley equations to excitable tissues. Physiol. Rev. 46, 1 (1966)
36. OCHS, S., WORTH, R. M.: Axoplasmic transport in normal and pathological systems. In: Physiology and Pathology of Axons. WAXMAN, S. G. (Ed.) New York: Raven Press 1978
37. RANG, H. P., RITCHIE, J. M.: Electrogenic sodium pump in mammalian non-myelinated nerve fibres and its activation by various external cations. J. Physiol. (Lond.) 196, 183 (1968)
38. STÄMPFLI, R., HILLE, B.: Electrophysiology of frog peripheral myelinated nerve. In: Neurobiology of the Frog. LLINAS, R., PRECHT, W. (Eds.) New York: Springer 1977
39. TERZUOLO, C. A., WASHIZU, Y.: Relation between stimulus strength, generator potential and impulse frequency in stretch receptor of crustacea. J. Neurophysiol. 25, 56 (1962)
40. THOMAS, R. C.: Electrogenic sodium pump in nerve and muscle cells. Physiol. Rev. 52, 563–594 (1972)
41. TRACHTENBERG, N. C., POLLEN, D. A.: Neuroglia biophysical properties in physiologic function. Science 67, 1248 (1970)
42. ULBRICHT, W.: Ionic channels and gating currents in excitable membranes. Ann. Rev. Biophys. Bioeng. 6, 7–31 (1977)
43. WATSON, W. E.: Physiology of neuroglia. Physiol. Rev. 54, 245 (1974)
44. WEIDMANN, S.: Effects of calcium ions and local anaesthetics on electrical properties of Purkinje fibres. J. Physiol. (Lond.) 129, 568 (1955)

2 Muscle

J.C. RÜEGG

Muscles are "machines" for converting chemical energy **directly** into mechanical energy (work) and heat. Muscular work can easily be measured. When an isolated muscle of a cold-blooded animal – for example, the frog sartorius – is loaded with a light weight and then stimulated electrically with a brief current pulse, it twitches; in lifting the weight, it performs mechanical work (load times distance). A contraction of this sort, in which the muscle shortens under constant load, is called **isotonic**. By contrast, in an **isometric** contraction the tendons at the ends of the muscle are held so firmly that although the muscle exerts force it cannot shorten, and thus cannot do external work (it does do work in a physiological sense). The results of long research have made it possible to explain in considerable detail the way this muscle machine operates, at a molecular level and on the basis of physical and chemical laws.

2.1 The Molecular Mechanism of Contraction

A gram of skeletal muscle contains about 100 mg of "contractile proteins." The way in which these proteins – **actin** (molecular weight 42,000) and **myosin** (molecular weight 500,000) – interact during the elementary event in muscle contraction is described by the sliding-filament theory of HUXLEY and HANSON [9–13].

Sliding-Filament Theory

The contractile proteins actin and myosin form the thin and thick myofilaments in the myofibrils. They are arranged in parallel within the muscle cell, as shown in Fig. 2-1, a schematic drawing of a tiny part of a human muscle fiber. The drawing also shows one of the mitochondria (or sarcosomes) lying between the myofibrils, and part of the system of transverse and longitudinal tubules (the function of which is treated in Section 2.2).

Myofibrils are contractile bundles of filaments about 1 μm in diameter; partitions called Z disks subdivide them into many compartments ca. 2.5 μm long, the sarcomeres.

The structure of the sarcomeres is illustrated, highly schematically, in Fig. 2-1. In the light microscope one sees a regular sequence of light and dark bands across the sarcomeres; according to HUXLEY and HANSON [10], this **cross-striation** of the myofibrils results from a particularly regular arrangement of the actin and myosin filaments. In the middle of each sarcomere lie some thousand *"thick" filaments* of myosin, each with a diameter of ca. 10 nm. At either end of the sarcomere are about 2000 *"thin" (5 nm thick) filaments* of actin, attached to the Z disks like the bristles of a brush. The bundle of regularly arrayed, 1.6-μm-long myosin filaments in the middle of the sarcomere appears in the light microscope as a dark stripe 1.6 μm wide; because it is birefringent in polarized light (i.e., anisotropic) it is called the A band. On either side of the *A bands* are regions containing only thin fila-

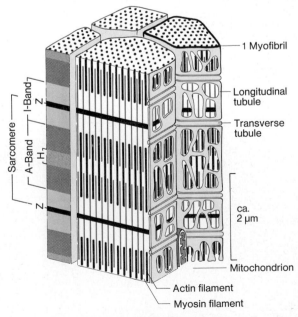

Fig. 2-1. Part of a human skeletal-muscle fiber, schematized from GARAMVÖLGYI

ments, which therefore appear light; these isotropic *I bands* extend to the Z lines. It is this periodically repeated alternation of light and dark bands in countless sarcomeres that gives the myofibrils of cardiac and skeletal muscle fibers their striated appearance.

In the resting muscle the ends of the thick and thin filaments usually overlap only slightly at the boundary between the A and I bands. The zone of overlap in the A band appears distinctly darker in the light microscope than the central zone, the *H zone,* in which there are no actin filaments. Many electron micrographs of this zone reveal a very narrow, dark *M line* in the middle of the sarcomere, a meshwork of supporting proteins that evidently holds the bundle of thick filaments together in the middle.

Shortening of the sarcomeres. The muscle shortens as a result of the shortening of countless sarcomeres connected "in series" in the myofibrils. By comparing the schematic structure of a sarcomere in two different functional states (Fig. 2-2), one can see how the striation and the myofilament arrangement change during contraction. During shortening the thin filaments of actin slide over the thick filaments of myosin, moving between them toward the middle of the bundle and of the sarcomere.

Fig. 2-2 illustrates a basic feature of the *sliding-filament theory* – that during the sliding process neither the myosin nor the actin filaments themselves shorten. This property gives rise to the light-microscope observation that the width of the A bands (1.6 μm) remains constant during contraction, whereas the I and H bands become narrower.

Nor does the filament length change when the muscle is stretched. Rather, the bundle of thin filaments is pulled further out of the array of thick filaments, so that the amount of overlap decreases.

Now, how is the "opposed sliding" of the actin filaments in adjacent half sarcomeres brought about?

Operation of the cross bridges. The myosin filament sends out transverse processes, the ca. 20-nm-long heads of about 150 myosin molecules; these form a bipolar array along the filament as shown in Fig. 2-3 A. During the contraction process each myosin head, or **cross bridge,** can link the myosin filament to an adjacent actin filament (Fig. 2-3 A). By a tilting movement of the heads they join forces to "row" the actin filaments toward the middle of the sarcomere. The bipolar arrangement of the myosin molecules in the two halves of a sarcomere in itself makes possible the opposite direction (arrows) of sliding of the actin filaments in the left and right halves of the sarcomere.

A single rotational movement of the cross bridges on an actin filament would shorten an individual sarcomere by only 2 × 10 nm, ca. 1% of its length. The sarcomeres of frog muscle fibrils during *isotonic contraction* shorten by as much as 1 μm, or 50% of their length, in a tenth of a second. To achieve this, the cross bridges would have to perform the rowing motion just described not once in this time span, but fifty times. Only the repeated release and reattachement of the myosin heads would eventually row or pull the actin filament to the middle of the sarcomere – rather as a long piece of rope is pulled in, hand over hand, by a team of men. Because the minimal shortenings of

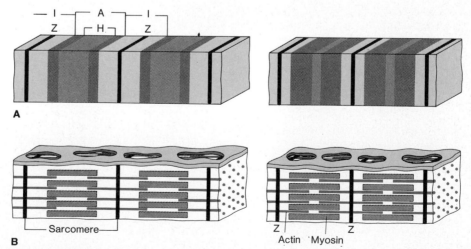

Fig. 2-2. A Banded structure of the myofibrils. *Left,* relaxed; *right,* contracted. **B** Arrangement of the myosin and actin filaments in the relaxed and contracted sarcomere. Note the additive shortening actions of the serially arranged sarcomeres. After [10]

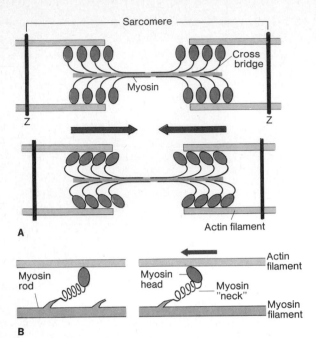

Fig. 2-3 A, B. Cross-bridge function. **A** Model of the way motion is produced: myosin filament with cross bridges on adjacent actin filaments; above before, below after the (actually asynchronous) "rowing strokes" of the bridges [11]. **B** Model [9] of force production by a cross bridge; left before, right after a bridge "stroke". The cross bridge corresponds chemically to the myosin subfragment "heavy meromyosin", which consists of subfragment I (myosin head) and subfragment II (myosin neck)

the myofibrils in a series of sarcomeres add up, in the above example of isotonic contraction a 2-cm-long frog muscle could lift a very light weight just 1 cm in 0.1 s. We can see that when the *rope-pulling principle* takes the form of countless sarcomeres connected in series, the repeated molecular movements of the cross bridges result in a macroscopic movement. When a *muscle relaxes* the myosin heads detach from the actin filaments. Because the actin and myosin filaments can then easily be moved past one another, the resistance of relaxed muscles to stretch is very low. A shortened muscle can be stretched back to its resting length by even a very light weight. During relaxation, then, lengthening is passive.

Recently, the molecular cross-bridge movements just described have been detected by means of an X-ray diffraction method (roentgen small-angle scattering from contracted muscle at ms time resolution [13]), thus verifying the proposed model of cross-bridge operation.

The production of muscular force. Thanks to the elasticity of the cross bridges, a sarcomere can develop force even if the filaments do not slide past one another – that is, under strictly isometric experimental conditions [9]. Fig. 2-3 B illustrates *isometric force production* by a cross bridge. First the head of the myosin molecule (cross bridge) attaches to the actin filament at right angles. Then it rotates about an angle of ca. 45°, perhaps be-

cause of the attraction of nearby attachment points on the myosin head and the actin filament. In so doing it acts like a miniature lever, to put the internal elastic structure of the cross bridge (possibly the "neck" part between the myosin head and the myosin filament) under tension. The resulting elastic stretching amounts to only about 10 nm. The elastic pull exerted by a single cross bridge is so slight that at least a billion cross bridges connected "in parallel" would have to combine their spring forces to develop 1 mN of muscular force. Here the cross bridges of the myosin filaments pull on the neighboring actin filaments with (additively) combined forces, like a team of men on a rope.

Even in isometric contraction the cross bridges should not be regarded as being in an uninterrupted state of tension (this happens only in rigor mortis; see below). Rather, a single myosin head releases the actin filament after only a hundredth or tenth of a second; but the recovery pause is equally short, and is followed by renewed attachment to the actin filament. Despite the rhythmic alternation between cross-bridge attachment and detachment, at a frequency of something like 5–50 Hz, the force exerted by the muscle does not oscillate in physiological conditions (with the exception of oscillating insect muscles), because from a statistical viewpoint about the same number of cross bridges are in the attached, tension-producing state at each moment.

Maintenance heat. A muscle maintaining a certain contractile tension under isometric conditions differs from a muscle shortening isotonically in that the former does no external work (for the product of force times distance is zero). But in each attach/detach cycle of the cross bridges internal work is done to stretch the elastic cross-bridge structures, and this is degraded to heat upon detachment. The maintenance heat (or "maintenance work") during a given period of time is greater, the greater the number and the higher the stroke frequency of the rowing cross bridges, as ATP is steadily consumed.

The Chemomechanical Energy Transformations

How can the muscle machine efficiently convert chemical energy directly to mechanical energy? This is probably the most burning question in current molecular muscle research.

ATP, direct source of energy for contraction. The correctness of this claim is no longer in doubt, since the hydrolytic splitting of ATP into adenosine diphosphate and phosphate during muscular contraction was demonstrated directly [14]. All the other energy-providing reactions in the muscle – for example, the aerobic and anaerobic breakdown of carbohydrates and the decomposition of creatine phosphate – cannot be considered as direct sources of energy for the muscle machine; it is clear that they serve only to regenerate continually the real fuel of the machine, ATP. These metabolic processes are treated extensively in biochemical textbooks, so that a brief summary (Table 2-1) will suffice here. Only if the reconstitution of ATP is prevented by appropriate metabolic poisons can the rate of ATP consumption during a contraction be monitored directly [14]. Isolated frog

Table 2-1. The direct and indirect energy sources in a muscle (frog sartorius)

Energy source	Content (μmol/g muscle)	Energy-providing reaction	Supplies:
Adenosine triphosphate (ATP)	ca. 3	$ATP \rightarrow ADP + P_i$	Mechanical energy[a] (and heat)
Creatine phosphate (PC)	ca. 20	$PC + ADP \rightarrow ATP + C$[b]	20 μmol ATP
Glucose units in glycogen	ca. 100	Anaerobic: broken down via pyruvate to lactate (glycolysis)	300 μmol ATP
		Aerobic: broken down via pyruvate to CO_2 and H_2O	3900 μmol ATP

ADP = adenosine diphosphate, C = creatine, P_i = inorganic phosphate

[a] Enough for ca. 8 single twitches

[b] Lohmann's reaction

muscles frozen very rapidly with liquid nitrogen at the peak of a stimulus-induced isotonic twitch contain on the average only 2.6 μM ATP per gram wet weight, whereas unstimulated control muscles contain 2.9 μM. Taking the place of the ATP that has been consumed is an equivalent amount (0.3 μM) of the reaction products adenosine diphosphate and phosphate. Thus the 0.3 μM ATP split during a twitch has provided the energy for the isotonic contraction and the heat produced in the process.

ATP is split hydrolytically and thus utilized energetically in the muscle by an *ATPase,* the enzyme *myosin* – a process activated by *actin.* Actin and myosin, of course, are the protein structures directly involved in the mechanical process of contraction, and ATP, with a single exception (rare nucleoside triphosphates), is the only substance in the muscle that can be utilized directly by the contractile proteins. Weber and Portzehl succeeded in spinning gel-like contractile threads of actin and myosin *(actomyosin threads),* which contract like living muscles with ATP and only ATP as the energy source [18]. This too is evidence that ATP is the direct source of energy for muscle contraction.

ATP consumption during contraction. Today we know that the myosin heads, which react with actin, themselves contain the catalytically active centers for the splitting of ATP. The ATPase of myosin is activated by actin in the presence of magnesium ions. Therefore under physiological ionic conditions – that is, in the presence of **magnesium ions** – ATP is always split to *liberate* ADP and phosphate only when the myosin head attaches to its activator actin. (Without actin the ADP that is formed is not liberated but rather blocks, for a matter of seconds, the catalytic center of the myosin and thus the continued splitting of ATP.) In each attach/detach cycle of a cross bridge ATP is split once and only once (probably one molecule ATP per cross bridge). This means that the more cross bridges are active, the greater the rate of ATP splitting and the force of the muscle; therefore the ATP-splitting rate (or metabolic rate) and the force produced by the muscle are usually proportional to one another.

Muscles can contract more rapidly, the more rapidly their cross bridges move – that is, the more rowing strokes they make per unit time. As a result, fast muscles consume more ATP (or energy) per unit time than slow muscles, and are less conservative of energy during tonic load-bearing. For "maintenance work" we therefore use chiefly the slow (tonic) **"red" muscles,** rich in myoglobin, whereas the myoglobin-poor **"white" muscles** are used for rapid movements.

Mode of action of ATP. The mechanism by which the energy donor ATP drives the rowing cross bridges is the subject of intensive research [9, 11, 12, 16]. Probably a molecule of ATP is bound to the cross bridge when its "rowing stroke" is completed, and thus provides energy for the separation of the reaction partners actin and myosin. Almost immediately thereafter the myosin heads detach from the actin; the ATP is then split into the products ADP and phosphate, with the intermediate formation of an enzyme-product complex. This splitting is the prerequisite for the next reattachment of the cross bridge to the actin, whereupon the ADP and phosphate are liberated and the rowing stroke occurs. When this stroke is completed a new molecule of ATP binds to the cross bridge, and a new cycle is begun. Only as long as ATP continues to be hydrolyzed – that is, as long as ATPase is activated – is cyclic cross-bridge activity possible, the repeated attachment and release of the bridges that produce muscle contraction. If the splitting of ATP is inhibited, the bridges cannot reattach, the resistance to stretch and the force of the muscle fibers fall to zero, and the muscle **relaxes.** After death the ATP level in the muscle cells falls; when it becomes lower than a critical limit the cross bridges become permanently (until autolysis) attached to the actin filament. In this state the actin and myosin filaments are rigidly connected to one another; the muscle is in **rigor mortis.** The analysis of the conditions for the states of contraction, rigor and relaxation

Table 2-2. Action of ATP on the contractile structures in muscle fibers and the *actin-myosin interaction*

ATP:	absent	present but not split	present, split by ATPase
State of muscle fiber:	rigid	relaxed	contracted
Myosin cross bridges:	attached to actin	detached from actin	alternately attached and detached
ATPase:	–	inhibited[a]	active[b]

[a] Ca^{++} less than 10^{-8} molar
[b] Ca^{++} ca. $10^{-6} - 10^{-5}$ molar

Table 2-3. Sequence of events in production of a twitch

1. Stimulation of muscle fiber
2. Action potential (membrane excitation)
3. Excitation-contraction coupling
   a. Conduction of excitation in T system
   b. Release of calcium from the longitudinal system (Fig. 2-5)
   c. Action of calcium on myofibrils (Fig. 2-4)
4. Contraction of the myofibrils

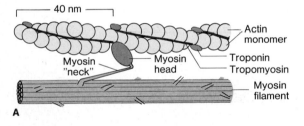

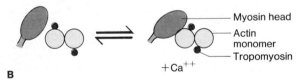

Fig. 2-4 A, B. Mode of action of the calcium ions during activation. **A** Actin filament and myosin filament in longitudinal section of fiber, **B** in cross section. When calcium ions are bound by the troponin, tropomyosin slides into the groove between the two actin strands of the filament, exposing the site of cross-bridge attachment. After [2]

(Table 2-2) is based on studies of "isolated contractile systems" [18].

In order to analyze the role of ATP in contraction and relaxation, WEBER et al. [18] first removed all the intrinsic ATP from single muscle fibers (for example, by extraction with aqueous glycerol solutions, which make the cell membrane permeable to ATP). Such glycerol-extracted ATP-free fibers are in rigor, but when they are immersed in an ATP-containing solution they become soft and stretchable again. When ATPase activity is inhibited, however, extracted ATP-containing muscle fibers are

always relaxed; they, like the abovementioned artificial actomyosin threads, contract only when the ATPase is activated. Renewed ATPase inhibition again causes relaxation of the "fiber model."

2.2 The Regulation of Muscle Contraction

Muscles are ordinarily excited by the action potentials of the innervating motoneurons, which – via neuromuscular transmission at the end plates (cf. p. 51) – elicit muscle action potentials (indirect muscle stimulation). Muscle fibers can also be *stimulated directly*, but only under experimental conditions. For example, when an isolated frog muscle is stimulated by a single electrical stimulus lasting ca. 1 ms, after ca. 1–2 ms a (conducted) *action potential* passes from the site of stimulation over the muscle fiber with a velocity of ca. 2 m/s; a few ms later the muscle fiber *twitches* (cf. Fig. 2-8). It is thus the action potential, or the excitation of the fiber membrane, that triggers contraction.

Excitation-Contraction Coupling

The transmission of the signal to contract, from the excited cell membrane to the myofibrils in the depths of the cell (excitation-contraction coupling), requires several sequential processes (Table 2-3) in which calcium ions play a key role.

Site and mode of Ca^{++} action. Intracellular injection of calcium ions causes contraction of the muscle fibers. Intact, living muscle fibers are less well suited for demonstration of this direct calcium effect on the myofibrils than fibers with the external cell membrane removed or destroyed. This can be done mechanically by "skinning" them, by means of detergents, or by the glycerol-extraction procedure mentioned above. *Skinned or extracted fibers* contract only when immersed in an ATP-containing bath that also contains at least *10^{-6} molar ionized calcium* to activate the ATPase. Under these conditions the cross bridges of the myosin filaments, by continually splitting ATP, can react cyclically with the actin filaments. If the activating agent, the ionized calcium, is withdrawn (for example, by adding calcium-chelating substances) the myofibrils **relax,** because the interaction between cross bridges and actin is prevented and therefore ATPase activity is inhibited (cf. Table 2-2). This relaxation effect is also completely reversible in experiments with extracted fibers. When the Ca^{++}

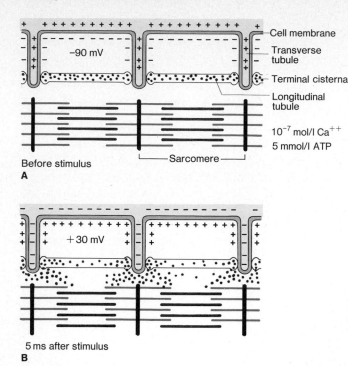

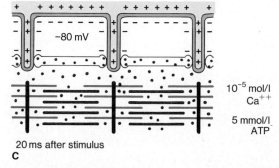

Fig. 2-5 A–C. Diagram of excitation-contraction coupling. **A** Relaxed muscle fiber with polarized cell membrane. The intracellular Ca^{++} concentration is below 10^{-7} molar. **B** During the action potential the polarization of the cell membrane and the transverse-tubule membrane is reversed; Ca^{++} ions begin to flow out of the terminal cisternae. **C** The intracellular Ca^{++} concentration has reached ca. 10^{-5} molar at the end of the action potential; the sarcomeres of the myofibrils contract. Inset: The temporal sequence of events in excitation-contraction coupling during the "latency" and at the beginning of contraction, in the frog sartorius (0° C)

concentration is raised in steps from 10^{-7} molar to 10^{-5} molar, the extracted fibers respond with a graded increase in contractile force and ATPase activity, both becoming maximal at concentrations of 10^{-6} to 10^{-5} molar.

The **mechanism** by which calcium ions activate the fiber can be better understood by considering the structure of the actin filaments (Fig. 2-4). About 1 μm long and 5–7 nm thick, the actin filament consists of two chains of beadlike 5-nm-thick actin monomeres twisted together. This structure is well illustrated by taking two strings of beads and winding them together into a "spiral" with 14 beads in each turn (Fig. 2-4 A). At regular intervals of ca. 40 nm the actin chains bear spherical *troponin molecules,* and threads of *tropomyosin* run along the grooves between the two chains. Studies using the X-ray diffraction method (röntgen small-angle scattering) [12] have shown that in the absence of calcium ions – that is, in the relaxed state of the myofibrils – the tropomyosin threads are positioned such as to block the attachment of myosin cross bridges to the actin strands. Under the influence of the activating calcium ions the tropomyosin threads slip deeper into the grooves between the actin strands, exposing the sites of attachment of the myosin cross bridges. As a result, the myosin bridges at-

tach to the actin filament (Fig. 2-4 B), split ATP and develop muscular force.

These activation effects are elicited by an action of calcium on troponin, such that the latter functions as a sort of *"calcium switch"*. That is, by binding with calcium ions the troponin molecule is deformed in such a way that it pushes the tropomyosin into the groove in the double strand of actin – into the "activated position."

Storage and release of calcium ions. Relaxed muscles contain over 1 μmol of calcium per gram wet weight. If the calcium salts were not locked away in special intracellular storage regions, the calcium-rich muscle fibers would be permanently contracted.

The structure of the intracellular systems for calcium storage varies somewhat in different muscles (for human skeletal muscle see Fig. 2-1; for frog muscle, Fig. 2-5). At many positions on the muscle cell the outer membrane is invaginated into the fiber along a line perpendicular to the long axis of the fiber, forming a tube; this *system of transverse tubules (T system)* communicates with the extracellular space. The tubules (diameter 50 nm) usually surround the single myofibrils at the level of the Z disks (frog muscle) or in the region of the I bands (muscles of higher vertebrates).

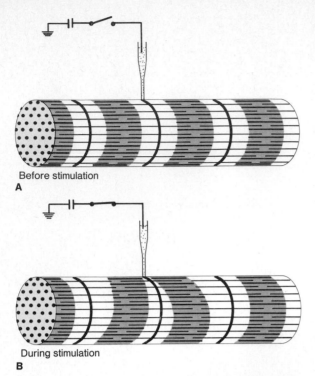

A Before stimulation

B During stimulation

Fig. 2-6 A, B. Demonstration that the T system can be activated locally. From [8]. Weak local stimulation of striated muscle fiber of a frog (in the Z-disk region, immediately over a T tubule) causes shortening of the adjacent I bands under the micro-cathode. **A** Before, **B** during stimulation

Perpendicular to the transverse system – that is, parallel to the myofibrils – there is a *longitudinal system* of tubules (the actual *sarcoplasmic reticulum)*. The vesicles at the ends of these tubules, the *terminal cisternae,* are closely apposed to the membranes of the transverse system, forming a *triad structure.* It is in these vesicles that the intracellular calcium is stored. In contrast to the transverse system, the longitudinal system does not communicate with the extracellular space.

Excitation-contraction coupling is brought about by the spread of the action potential along the membranes of the transverse system, to the interior of the cell. In this way the excitation rapidly invades the depths of the fiber, jumps across to the longitudinal system and ultimately causes the calcium ions stored in the terminal cisternae to be released into the intracellular fluid around the myofibrils, initiating a contraction (Fig. 2-5).

In a single twitch, contraction soon ceases (Fig. 2-8): **muscle relaxation** occurs when the activating Ca^{++} ions are returned by the calcium pump to the channel system of the sarcoplasmic reticulum. This process involves an active, ATP-consuming transport [7]. The Ca^{++} ions are removed until the Ca^{++}-ion concentration is reduced to less than 10^{-8} M. This reduction

inhibits the actomyosin ATPase and the interaction of actin and myosin cross bridges, which then detach (see Table 2).

Spread of excitation to the interior of the fiber. This process is the first step in excitation-contraction coupling, as Huxley and Taylor [8] have shown (Fig. 2-6). By applying weak current pulses to a frog muscle fiber through a microelectrode they produced local depolarization of an area of the membrane so small that only one transverse tubule (at the level of the Z disks) was stimulated. The resulting local contraction (contracture) was limited to the superficial myofibrils in the two half sarcomeres adjacent to the tubule. As stimulus intensity was increased, the deeper myofibrils in the fiber were brought into action. Evidently the membranes of the transverse tubule system are particularly excitable by electric current, can conduct excitation, and constitute an important link in the process of signal transmission between the cell membrane and the calcium stores.

Only by the electrical transmission of signals along the transverse system can the rapid mobilization of the calcium stores deep in the fiber be ensured, and only in this way can the very brief *latency* between stimulus and contraction be explained. Diffusion of calcium ions from the external membrane to the centrally located fibrils in a muscle fiber 100 μm thick would take far longer than the observed stimulus-to-contraction latency, so that for *skeletal muscle fibers* such a mechanism can be ruled out on temporal grounds alone.

Calcium release in a single twitch. What is the evidence that calcium is released? Rüdel and his co-workers [3] isolated from certain luminous jellyfish the protein *aequorin,* which when reacting with calcium ions emits light, and injected it into an isolated muscle fiber. The fiber was then mounted in an "isometric" arrangement and stimulated electrically at intervals of 100 or 200 ms. A highly sensitive photometer (photomultiplier) recorded directly the luminescence (light emission) of aequorin that accompanied the intracellular release of calcium ions (Fig. 2-7). With a stimulus frequency of 5 Hz the luminescence is transient, because the released calcium is soon pumped back into the sarcoplasmic reticulum; the muscle twitches. But when the stimuli are repeated at 10 Hz the second stimulus arrives only 100 ms after the first, when the fiber is not yet completely relaxed. The second twitch is superimposed on the residual contraction from the first, the third twitch is superimposed on the preceding ones, and so on. **Summation** of individual twitches results in an increase in both the maximal tension of a contraction cycle and the amount of contraction remaining after each twitch in the series – even though (as the light emission indicates) the intracellular calcium level returns almost to the resting level after each twitch. The experiment of Fig. 1-7 makes it clear that the increase in total tension by the superposition of single twitches at intervals as short as 100 ms **cannot** be ascribed to an increase in the intracellular calcium-ion level.

Calcium release in tetanus. If the stimuli are repeated at a high rate, 20 Hz or more, the calcium-ion level remains high during the intervals because there is not enough time for the calcium pump to return all the calcium ions to the longitudinal system of the sarcoplasmic reticulum. In these conditions, as Fig. 2-7 shows, the individual twitches fuse (almost) completely. This state of maintained contraction, or **tetanus,** occurs whenever the interval between the stimuli (or action potentials in the cell membrane) is less than ca. ⅓ of the time required for a single twitch. Thus the fusion frequency is lower, the longer the duration of the single twitch; for this reason, it is temperature-dependent. The minimal time interval between successive effective stimuli in tetanus cannot be smaller than the **refractory period,** which corresponds roughly to the duration of an action potential.

All-or-none law. Single fast twitch fibers in skeletal muscle obey this law. That is, subthreshold stimuli trigger no action potential, and no calcium is released. But as soon as a particular *threshold* intensity is exceeded, a fully developed action potential is triggered and maximal calcium release ensues; the calcium ions give rise to a maximally strong twitch, which cannot be increased by raising the stimulus intensity (Fig. 2-8).

On the other hand, the contractile force of electrically stimulated whole muscles does depend on stimulus intensity. For example, a just-suprathreshold stimulus elicits an all-or-none response only in the fibers close to the electrode, where the current density is greatest; for excitation of all the fibers a considerably greater (maximal) stimulus is required. Therefore only supramaximal stimulation suffices to activate an isolated whole muscle uniformly and reliably.

The "all-or-none" law does **not** imply that the "all-or-none" response of a stimulated muscle fiber will be the same size at all times. For example, a single stimulus delivered shortly after relaxation from a tetanus often elicits a far stronger single twitch than it did before "conditioning" by the tetanus. The cause of this **"posttetanic potentiation"** is as little understood as the mechanism underlying **muscular fatigue,** a decrease in the strength of contraction when stimulation is repeated. In both cases the action potentials are of normal size. During oxygen deficiency, and even more after metabolic poisoning with iodine acetate, repeated stimulation results not only in reduced

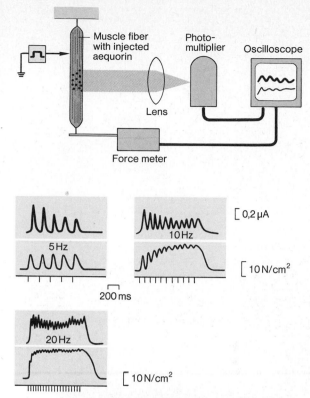

Fig. 2-7. Demonstration of intracellular calcium release in muscle fibers. Light emission *(red curves)* and isometric force development in an isolated muscle fiber of the clawed frog stimulated directly with 0.5-ms current pulses at frequencies of 5, 10 and 20 Hz (stimulus marks below graphs). Note the summation and fusion of the *single twitches* to (incomplete) *tetanus* as stimulus frequency is raised. Isometric force development calibrated in N/cm² muscle cross section, light emission due to action of calcium calibrated in units of photomultiplier anodal current intensity. *Above:* experimental setup used by RÜDEL [3]

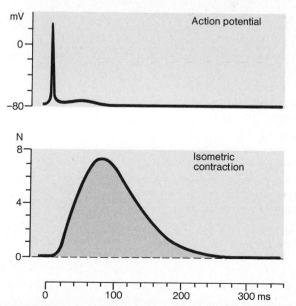

Fig. 2-8. Time course of action potential and isometric twitch in striated muscle (adductor pollicis)

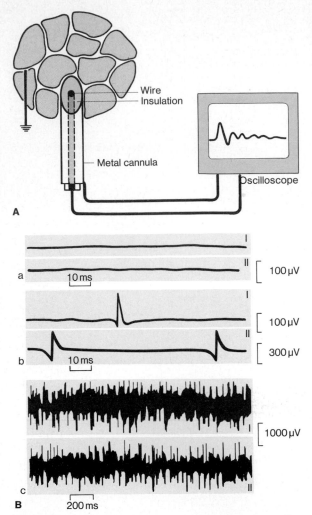

guished from tetanus by the absence of a conducted action potential. The membrane potential may be *locally depolarized* to some extent for a prolonged period, as in potassium contracture, or it may be near the resting potential as in *caffeine contracture*. In unphysiologically high concentration (in the millimolar range) caffeine penetrates the muscle fibers and, without exciting the membrane, acts intracellularly to release calcium ions from the sarcoplasmic reticulum and thus cause contracture. In *potassium contracture* the degree of maintained depolarization and of contractile tension in a muscle fiber depends on the concentration of potassium ions in the bath, as long as the solution also contains calcium ions. Removal of the extracellular calcium would deplete the intracellular calcium and eventually cause *excitation-contraction decoupling*. A decoupled muscle does not contract even if the membrane is depolarized.

The *contraction of the "tonus fibers"* is always a contracture. Direct or indirect electrical stimulation of tonic striated muscle fibers (slow fibers in the eye muscles, some of the intrafusal fibers) does not trigger a conducted action potential, but rather causes local depolarization of the membrane. As the intensity or frequency of a suprathreshold stimulus is increased, the tonic depolarization of the membrane becomes more pronounced and both the amount of calcium released intracellularly and the strength of contraction increase. Unlike twitch fibers, the tonic fibers do not obey the all-or-none law; the force they develop is regulated by varying the intracellular calcium-ion concentration. This property was first demonstrated by Ashley, who used the aequorin method described above to study the tonic muscle fibers of the barnacle *Balanus*.

Fig. 2-9 A, B. Electromyography. **A** Extracellular recording technique, with concentric needle electrode inserted between the fibers of a motor unit in a muscle (extracellular). **B** Extracellular action potentials are recorded simultaneously from two different motor units (I and II) in a muscle, with two electrodes. a, relaxed muscle; b, weak voluntary contraction (note the asynchronous activity of the two motor units); c, maximal voluntary contraction. After [2]

Table 2-4. Large and small motor units

Muscle:	Lateral rectus of eye	Biceps of arm
Motor units/muscle	1740	774
Muscle fibers/unit	13	750
Maximal force/unit (N)	0.001	0.5

contractile strength but also in slower relaxation; eventually, when the ATP supply is exhausted, the poisoned muscle cannot relax at all – it becomes **rigid.** The states of **irreversible rigidity** *(rigor)* and *tetanus* should be strictly distinguished from the different kind of prolonged tension now to be discussed.

Contracture. Contracture is a reversible, non-propagated state of maintained contraction. It is distin-

Regulation of Muscle Force in the Human Body

A motor unit consists of **one** motor neuron **and** the group of muscle fibers it innervates. Motor units vary widely in size. In the extrinsic eye muscles, for instance, a motoneuron supplies only ca. half a dozen muscle fibers. In other muscles the group of fibers supplied by one neuron is a great deal larger; the motor unit can often comprise between 500 and 1000 fibers (Table 2-4). Because the all-or-none law applies to the individual fibers, the force produced by a motor unit in a single twitch varies only slightly; within the unit all the fibers are either stimulated and contracted or relaxed. But a change in *stimulus frequency* affects the force exerted. Because of the superposition and summation effects mentioned above, the force in complete tetanus (with a high rate of α-motoneuron discharge) is about twice that in an incompletely fused tetanus, at a lower rate of stimulation. Even with a very low impulse rate – for example, 5 to 10 per second – the low total tension *(tonus)* of the muscle does not undulate, because in the various asynchronously active motor units the maxima of the twitches or incomplete tetani occur at different times.

Correlation between contractile force and action-potential frequency. When the rate of motoneuron discharge rises from 5 to 50 per second, the twitching or incompletely fused tetanus of the motor units is converted to a smooth, fused tetanus; as a result, the force of contraction is at least doubled. By inserting needle electrodes into motor units [2] one can record extracellularly the frequency of the muscle action potentials (Fig. 2-9). Such **electromyographic studies** have shown that the amount of muscle force voluntarily exerted is correlated with the frequency of the action potentials in the motor units, proving that force can be increased by raising the frequency of stimulation [2].

Recruitment of motor units. The force and contraction velocity (cf. p. 45) of a muscle can also be increased by the activation of more and more motor units (recruitment). Here the force can be more finely regulated, the smaller the size (and thus the force) of each motor unit. During a slight voluntary increase in muscle tension electromyographic recordings (with extracellular needle electrodes) show action potentials in only a few motor units; when the muscle is strongly tensed – after recruitment – very many units are firing. Accordingly, the integrated electrical activity of the muscle recorded by *surface electrodes* on the skin also increases progressively, the more powerfully the parts of the muscle beneath the skin contract.

Reflex tonus. Even when apparently at rest, some muscles exhibit a low level of electromyographically recordable activity. Because of the low-frequency reflexogenic periodic tensing of only a few motor units some (but not all) postural muscles are often in a state of involuntary tension, at a constant level owing to the asynchronous operation of the functional units. This *neurogenic "tonus"* can be modulated by the γ-fiber system of the muscle spindles (p. 85); during mental effort or excitement it is often involuntarily enhanced, and it vanishes completely only in a state of deep relaxation.

Clinical electromyography. In certain disorders involving muscle innervation (p. 107) passive movement or stretch of the muscles causes reflexly increased tone, and thus resistance to stretch. Accordingly, the electromyographically recorded muscle activity is increased during passive movement *(spasticity* or *rigidity).* In diseases of the *myotonia* type the cell membranes of the musculature are so excitable that even the introduction of the needle electrode for

electromyography triggers bursts of muscle impulses. Spontaneous action potentials *(fibrillation potentials)* are also recorded during the first stage following denervation, before the onset of *atrophy* owing to inactivity of the denervated muscle.

2.3 Muscle Mechanics

The *force* produced by a muscle or muscle-fiber bundle is the sum of the forces exerted by the individual fibers. The thicker a muscle, and the greater its "physiological" cross-sectional area (the sum of the individual fiber areas), the stronger the muscle is. For example, in cases of muscular *hypertrophy* the muscle force and fiber thickness increase by equivalent amounts.

Per unit cross-sectional area (cm^2), mammalian striated muscles usually develop maximal forces of more than 4 kgf (40 N), whereas those of poikilotherms are capable of only ca. 30 N.

Muscular force does not only depend on activation under central nervous control (see above), but is also crucially affected by the external mechanical conditions under which the muscle is working.

Auxotonic and isometric contractions. In the human body the skeletal muscles transmit force to the skeleton by way of elastic, somewhat stretchable structures, the tendons. Therefore the muscle *tends to shorten during force development* and thereby to stretch and develop tension in the elastic structures connecting the muscle to the skeleton. This kind of muscle contraction, in which the length of the muscle decreases at the same time as its force increases, is called **auxotonic contraction.** The maximal muscle force measured under auxotonic experimental conditions (with a stretchable elastic connection between muscle and force transducer) is called the *auxotonic contraction maximum.* It is considerably smaller than the contractile force developed by a muscle kept at a constant length – i. e., in **isometric contraction.** Experimentally, isometric contractions are studied by clamping the relaxed, resting muscle at its two ends so that the tension developed by the activated muscle is measured without allowing the muscle to shorten.

Even then, however, the contractile elements of the muscle fibers (myosin heads) can transmit force to the tendons or measuring device only by intramuscular structures which themselves are elastic. Some of these are within the cross bridges [9] (cf. Fig. 2-3), and some in the actin filaments, the Z disks and the attachment sites of the tendons. In a simplified model of this situation the muscle is a system of contractile elements

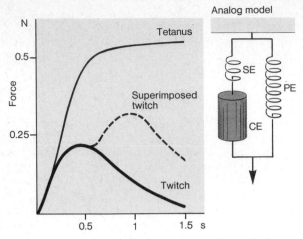

Fig. 2-10. Summation and fusion of single twitches during repeated stimulation (stimulus interval 500 ms for twitch superposition, 50 ms for smooth tetanus; frog muscle, 0° C). From [2]. Analog model of the muscle: CE contractile element; SE series elastic element; PE parallel elastic element

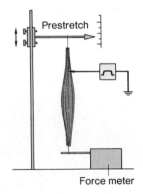

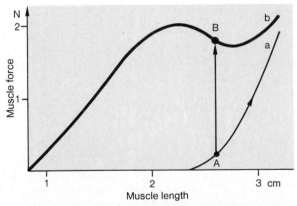

Fig. 2-11. Relation between force and muscle length. *a,* passive tension curve; *b,* curve of isometric maxima. The total force generated with a given prestretching (e. g., at B) is composed of the passive tension A and the active contractile force (B–A). *Above:* Arrangement for isometric experiment. Frog muscle at resting length (1_0 ca. 2.3 cm) is held between a force transducer (below) and a fixed point that can be moved up to stretch the muscle or down to release the stretch (below 1_0). (A muscle hanging loosely contracts to the preset short length, $< 1_0$, before the isometric tension buildup begins.)

(CE) and elastic elements (SE) in series with one another, represented by a mechanical analog in Fig. 2-10. During activation the contractile elements (auxotonically) shorten by ca. 1% and thus stretch the *series elastic elements;* it is this stretching that produces the measurable force.

Single twitch, superposition of twitches, tetanus. Under isometric conditions a single stimulus results in a rapid increase in contractile tension, which soon falls off again (isometric single twitch, Fig. 2-10; cf. p. 38). If the muscle is stimulated a second time before the twitch is over, the second twitch is superimposed on the first, so that the total tension is greater than that during the first twitch *(mechanical summation).* When the stimuli recur at brief intervals the twitches fuse into tetanus (Fig. 2-10; cf. p. 39). There is as yet no generally accepted explanation of the fact that the tension achieved during tetanus or superposition of single twitches is much greater than the force of a single twitch. During the brief activation of the muscle at the beginning of a single twitch elastic tension develops in the cross bridges between the actin and myosin filaments. But according to recent research the activation time does not suffice for all the cross bridges to attach. During the longer period of activation permitted by repeated stimulation (e. g., in tetanus) additional attachments are possible. The number of cross bridges attaching the actin to the myosin – and thus the force of the muscle – should, according to the sliding-filament theory, depend on the amount of overlap of thick and thin fibers, and therefore of course on the length of the sarcomere or muscle.

Isometric Contractile Force and Muscle Length

In the relaxed state a muscle held at the "resting length" by clamps at both ends does not exert any force on the holder. But if one end of the muscle is pulled out (Fig. 2-11) so as to stretch the fibers, passive tension develops in the muscle. That is, the resting muscle is elastic; but unlike a rubber band, its tension does not increase linearly with stretch. By plotting the measured force against imposed length in a rectangular coordinate system, one obtains a length-tension diagram of the resting muscle, the **resting tension curve.** It rises more steeply, the more the muscle is stretched (Curve *a* in Fig. 2-11). The modulus of elasticity of the resting muscle thus increases with stretch. This elasticity resides largely in stretchable structures in parallel with the contractile fibrils (hence the term *parallel elasticity),* such as the sarcolemma around the muscle fiber, the longitudinal system of the sarcoplasmic reticulum, and connective-tissue structures

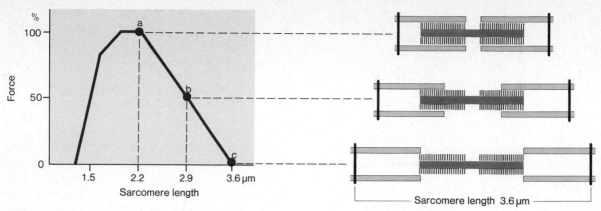

Fig. 2-12. Relation between contractile force, sarcomere length and filament overlap. *Left:* the maximal isometric force developed in tetanus with the muscle fiber at different lengths (indicated as sarcomere length on the abscissa); ordinate, force in percent of maximal force with muscle at resting length (sarcomere length 2.2 μm). *Right:* Overlap of myosin and actin filaments of a sarcomere at the lengths 2.2, 2.9 and 3.6 μm. After [6]

between the fibers. The myofibrils, by contrast, in the relaxed state offer practically no resistance to stretch; the actin and myosin filaments are not linked by cross bridges and can be readily moved past one another.

Prestretching determines not only the amount of passive elastic tension in the resting muscle, but also the amount of additional force the muscle can develop at the given length when it is activated. The isometric increase in force during contraction is (additively) superimposed on the passive tension of the resting muscle; the peak contraction under these conditions is the *isometric contraction maximum*. The passive elastic forces of the stretched longitudinal tubules and the sarcolemma are additively combined with the active contractile forces in the myofibrils because these structures are arranged in parallel, as illustrated by a mechanical analog model (Fig. 2-10, inset). The force-vs.-length diagram obtained by plotting the isometric contraction maxima measured at different muscle or sarcomere lengths against the length gives the *curve of isometric maxima* (Curve *b* in Fig. 2-11. To find the relationship between active contractile force and muscle or sarcomere length, we must subtract from this curve the passive tension curve. The curve so obtained (Fig. 2-12) has a characteristic maximum at about the resting length of the muscle, at which the sarcomere length is between 2.0 and 2.2 μm. At smaller muscle or sarcomere lengths the force is less because the actin and myosin filaments impede one another, and because in shortened muscles excitation-contraction coupling is impaired. These disturbing factors prevent most muscles from shortening to less than 50–70% of their resting length (cf. points where the curve of isometric maxima in Fig. 2-11 intersects the abscissa). When muscle fibers are stretched to more than the resting length contractile force de-

creases because the actin filaments are pulled out of the bundle of myosin filaments. With a sarcomere length of 2.9 μm, for example, the myofibrils can exert only ca. 50% of the maximal force, because each myosin filament overlaps the actin filaments by only half the normal distance, and only half of the myosin heads can attach to the actin. The dynamic resistance to stretch brought about by cross-bridge elasticity (Huxley's "immediate stiffness" [91]) is then also halved. With sarcomere lengths of more than 3.6 μm the resting tension curve and the curve of isometric maxima coincide (Fig. 2-11); at this length the myofibrils can no longer develop active force because the actin and myosin filaments no longer overlap at all. These mechanical experiments verify the prediction, at first entirely theoretical, that muscular force can be produced only by the interaction of actin and myosin filaments (in the sense of cross-bridge formation) [6].

Relation between Load and Shortening of the Muscle

Isotonic contraction is the shortening of a muscle under constant tension, or load. To record this shortening, an isolated resting muscle is suspended from a holder by one end. The other end is connected to a loaded lever (Fig. 2-13, inset), the tip of which moves by an amount proportional to the shortening of the muscle. The weight on the lever stretches the resting muscle passively. The relationship between the force pulling on the muscle (load) and the degree of muscle stretch can be represented in a length-tension diagram by the *resting tension curve* (*a* in Fig. 2-13; cf. also p. 42 and Fig. 2-11). When "tetanic" stimulation is applied to a loaded, prestretched muscle in the experimental arrangement of Fig. 2-13 (inset), it contracts **isotonically**; it maintains constant tension as it short-

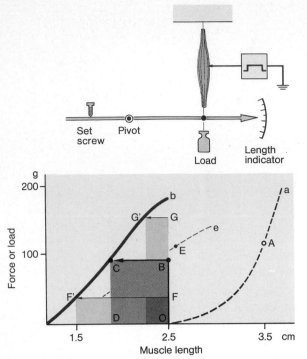

Fig. 2-13. Relation between load and shortening. Abscissa: muscle length; ordinate: muscle force or load (100 g load corresponds to a force of 1 N). Passive elongation of a resting frog muscle (starting length $l_0 = 2.5$ cm) as load is increased (resting tension curve a). OA: stretch caused by 120-g load. Isotonic contraction during tetanic stimulation of the muscle loaded with 120 g brings it to the length indicated by the curve of isotonic maxima e (AE). OBC: isotonic afterloaded contraction in tetanus with 90-g load is composed of isometric tension buildup (OB) followed by an isotonic shortening phase, in which the load is lifted 0.6 cm (BC); the work done corresponds to the area OBCD. The gray shaded rectangles (OGG' and OFF') correspond to the muscle work done with loads of 160 and 30 g. 30-g load lifted the distance F–F'; 160-g load, G–G'. b, curve of isotonic afterloaded maxima. *Above:* Arrangement for measuring afterloaded contraction or (without set screw) isotonic contraction

Table 2-5. The effect of load on shortening distance and work performed

Load (g)	3	5	9
Shortening (cm)	0.5	0.36	0.12
Work (g · cm)	1.5	1.8	1.1
Duration of twitch (s)	0.55	0.48	0.4

Isotonic afterloaded twitches of a 3-cm-long frog sartorius at 0° C. Force of isometric twitch: 0.12 N (cf. [15])

ens, lifting the load and thereby doing mechanical work (load times distance). The amount of shortening (distance) is less, the greater the load. Thus the muscle length when contraction is maximal depends in a characteristic way on the previously applied load, as described by the curve of isotonic maxima (e in

Fig. 2-13). To study the influence of the load on the distance it is lifted while eliminating the effect of differential prestretching, we use another form of contraction, as follows.

Afterloaded contraction. Prestretching of the muscle by its load can be prevented if the load is supported or the position of the lever fixed (set-screw in Fig. 2-13) prior to contraction. Then the tetanically stimulated muscle at first contracts isometrically, maintaining the initial length while developing enough tension to bear the load. Thereafter isotonic contraction lifts the load up from its support, with a force equivalent to the force of gravity on the load. In an afterloaded contraction the distance the load is raised is greater, the smaller the load. Therefore a muscle is shorter at the time of peak contraction when lightly loaded than when the load is heavier. The "length-tension diagram" obtained by plotting these final lengths on the abscissa of a rectangular coordinate system, with the load (or muscle tension or force) on the ordinate, gives the curve of afterloaded maxima (Curve b in Fig. 2-13, which is distinctly above Curve e for the isotonic maxima, and nearly coincides with the curve of isometric maxima, b in Fig. 2-11). The approximate agreement between the isometric maxima and the afterloaded maxima is not accidental; during an afterloaded contraction the sarcomeres of a loaded muscle can of course shorten only to the length at which the (isometrically possible) maximal muscle force is at least equal to the opposing force of the load.

The muscular work done in a tetanic afterloaded contraction is the product of distance (muscle shortening) and load; it is given by the area of a rectangle in the length-tension diagram of Fig. 2-13 that has sides corresponding to the force component and the amount of shortening. It is evident in Fig. 2-13 that the work done with a moderate load (area OBCD) is greater than that with very large or small loads (gray areas); it is zero when the load equals the maximal isometric force and when the muscle shortens without a load.

The relationship between load and work during a single twitch is very similar (Table 2-5). In afterloaded twitches, however, the distance and work are less than in afterloaded tetani, because the period of activation in a twitch is too brief to allow as much muscle shortening as during tetanus.

Relation between Contraction Velocity and Force (Load)

In isotonic tetanic activation of a muscle not only the amount of shortening but also the rate of shortening depends on the load; the smaller the load, the greater the amount of shortening per unit time (Fig. 2-14, inset). An unloaded muscle shortens with the maximal velocity.

The **maximal (unloaded) shortening velocity** of a sarcomere is the maximal rate at which the actin and myosin filaments can slide past one another. The more rapidly the cross bridges split ATP and interact with actin, the higher the velocity of the elementary sliding process. Slow tonic fibers, like those in our postural muscles, contain a myosin with low ATPase activity and a different composition from the myosin with high ATPase activity in the fast fibers of muscles chiefly used for movement. Recent studies have shown that the fast fiber type can be transformed into the slow type; BULLER and ECCLES transected the motor nerve fibers of a slow and a fast muscle and exchanged the two nerve endings when reimplanting them in the muscles. After a few weeks, when this cross-innervation had become established, the originally fast muscle contracted slowly and the originally slow muscle rapidly. Because the shortenings of the sarcomeres in series in a myofibril add, for a given speed of sarcomere shortening a long muscle will contract more rapidly than a short muscle. For example, the sartorius of a frog contracts at a rate of 0.2 m/s (ca. 10 muscle lengths per second), each of the ca. 2-μm-long sarcomeres shortening to 1 μm in 50 ms. The much longer human arm muscles, by contrast, shorten at a rate of 8 m/s.

As shown in Fig. 2-14, contraction velocity decreases hyperbolically with increasing load (HILL's **force-velocity relation**), reaching ca. ⅕ of the maximal rate (achieved during unloaded shortening) when the relative muscle load is equivalent to half the maximal force that can be exerted under isometric conditions. If the load is just equal to the isometrically achievable force, the muscle does not shorten. With even greater loads it is stretched (braking action of muscles when walking downhill!).

Because the contractile force a muscle must exert during shortening is equivalent to the load, the load-velocity relation described by Hill implies a corresponding relation between contractile force and shortening speed. During rapid shortening the muscle develops less contractile force than during slow shortening or when it is stretched. This property explains the everyday experience that we can make very rapid "light" movements only if little force is required, when the muscles are not loaded (free to move); conversely, the greatest muscle force is achieved during slow movements, as when pushing a large object. Heavy weights can be lifted or shifted, if at all, only very slowly. This is not inconsistent with our ability to vary the rate of muscular contraction voluntarily. For example, when *all* the fibers of a muscle participate in lifting a given load, the *relative* load on the *individual* active muscle fiber is smaller, and therefore its contraction velocity is greater than when only a *fraction* of the fibers are active. We can thus increase the rate of muscle shortening under a given load by the recruitment of additional motor units.

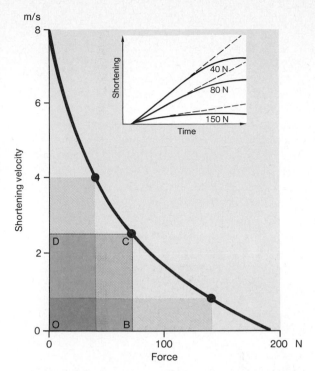

Fig. 2-14. Relation between force and contraction velocity. Ordinate: speed of shortening of a human arm muscle, in m/s. Abscissa: muscle load, expressed as the muscle force (in N) required to hold it. The area OBCD indicates the optimal mechanical power, at a contraction velocity 2.5 m/s. Light gray rectangles: power with loads of 4 and 14 kg. Modified from [19]. Inset: time course of the isotonic afterloaded contraction with loads of 4, 8 or 15 kg. Dashed lines indicate curve slope (= shortening velocity)

Muscle power is the product of muscle force and shortening velocity. In the example of a human arm muscle illustrated in Fig. 2-14, the maximal power (200 W) is reached at a contraction velocity of 2.5 m/s. In this diagram power is represented by the area of a rectangle with sides corresponding to the force and velocity components. It is "graphically" demonstrated there that power is greater with moderate loads (area OBCD) or contraction rates than under extreme conditions (light gray rectangles). We apply this principle when we use appropriate gears while bicycling, or follow a zig-zag path up a montain.

2.4 Muscle Energetics

Muscle heat and energy turnover. When a muscle is activated the elevated intracellular concentration of free calcium ions initiates contraction and the increased splitting of ATP; in the process, the metabolic rate of the muscle increases by a factor of 100 to

1000. According to the first principle of thermodynamics (conservation of energy) the chemical energy converted in the muscle must equal the sum of mechanical energy (muscular work) and heat production. Even if no physically measurable muscle work is done – as during a maintained isometric tetanic contraction – there is a continual transformation of chemical energy to heat within the muscle **(maintenance heat)**, at a rate proportional to the duration and tension of the contraction. Even when contraction is isometric the myosin cross bridges are in continual cyclic activity, and the "internal" work associated with this ATP splitting and heat production is considerable. It is for this reason that "inactive activities" such as standing at attention are tiring. An additional amount of ATP is converted when a muscle lifts a load and thus does external work. The extra metabolism is then proportional to the work done (Fenn effect).

Efficiency. Hydrolysis of one mole of ATP supplies ca. 48 kJ of energy. But only ca. 40–50% of this energy is converted to mechanical energy or work. The remaining 50–60% is dissipated as heat **(initial heat)** at the onset of and during the contraction of a muscle, which becomes somewhat warmer in the process. The elementary transformation in the myofibrils thus occurs with an efficiency of about 40–50%. During natural muscular activity, however, the mechanical efficiency is usually only ca. 20–30%, because during and after contraction "energy-recapturing" recovery processes are occurring outside the myofibrils. These – for example, the activity of ion pumps and the oxidative regeneration of ATP – are associated with considerable heat production **(recovery heat).** The more work is done, the more heat is produced, with a higher consumption of energy sources (carbohydrate and fat) and of oxygen. This relationship, by the way, is the reason we become tired, sweaty and breathless when climbing a hill but not when coming down.

Energy metabolism. During steady, prolonged muscular activity ATP is regenerated **aerobically,** chiefly by way of **oxidative phosphorylation.** The energy required for synthesis derives from the oxidation of carbohydrates or fat. The system is stable, in a dynamic equilibrium, when the rate of ATP formation is just equal to the rate of ATP breakdown, so that the intracellular ATP level (ca. 5 mmol/l) and that of phosphocreatine (ca. 30 mmol/l) are constant. In the performance of endurance sports the rate of ATP splitting, which of course is coupled to the power output, is often 100 or even 1000 times greater in the working muscles than when the muscles are at rest. A

steady state, and thus long-term performance, can be achieved only if the rate of ATP resynthesis by oxidative phosphorylation can be increased to match the increased ATP consumption. Such an increase has the following consequences for metabolism: The O_2 consumption of the muscle tissue is up to 50–100 times as high as at rest, because to form one mole of ATP ca. 3 mole of O_2 is required. The rate of glycogen breakdown in the muscle is correspondingly elevated, because each glucose unit in the glycogen provides only 39 mole ATP.

This increase in the activity-supporting metabolism of the muscle of course makes it essential that oxygen and glucose be more rapidly supplied. Local dilation of the blood vessels (nutritive reflex) in the muscle can increase the rate of blood flow by a factor of 20; cardiac output and pulse rate double or triple, and the respiratory minute volume rises accordingly. There is no general rule as to which of these factors critically limits performance. It may be the circulation or the mitochondrial enzyme capacity, which determines the rate of oxidative breakdown of glucose; the latter is fully exploited, for example, when a well-trained long-distance runner is running at a speed of 6 m/s [2].

The limit for long-term performance can be exceeded in the short term – for example, in the final spurt of a race – if *additional* glycogen is broken down **anaerobically,** in **glycolysis** (Table 2-1). In this reaction ATP formation occurs 2–3 times as rapidly, and the mechanical power produced by the muscle is 2–3 times as great as during (aerobically supported) long-term performance. The sprinter running only a short distance can go almost twice as fast (ca. 10 m/s) as the long-distance runner. 30 seconds is about the limit for this high performance, because the anaerobic energy reserves required to support the high rate of ATP formation are limited, and because glycolysis results in an accumulation of lactic acid in the cell fluid and in the blood; the end result is metabolic acidosis, which restricts performance capacity and causes **fatigue** (cf. p. 39).

Anaerobic processes are necessary for the short-term provision of energy, not only for brief peak physical exertion but also at the beginning of long-term muscular activity, because some time is required for oxidative metabolism (as well as glycolysis) to adjust to the increased demand. Therefore a steady state, in which just as much ATP is formed by oxidative phosphorylation per unit time as is split by ATPase, is reached only after 0.5–2 minutes. It is after this time of metabolic adjustment that an initially exhausted runner may get "second wind."

However, until this dynamic equilibrium is reached, ATP is regenerated from ADP and creatine phosphate by the Lohmann reaction (Table 2-1) so rapidly that its intracellular level stays practically constant:

$$ADP + creatine\ phosphate = ATP + creatine$$

While this reaction is proceeding the intracellular *phosphocreatine* level falls until the aerobic formation of ATP has reached a rate high enough to meet the current requirement for ATP. The pool of creatine phosphate is usually not replenished until the contraction is over, when the Lohmann reaction proceeds in the opposite direction; the ATP required is supplied by oxidative phosphorylation – that is, an oxygen-consuming reaction – during the first minutes of recovery. In a sense (according to Hill) this oxygen consumption amounts to repayment of an **oxygen debt**; according to Wilkie it corresponds approximately to the amount of energy the muscle has converted anaerobically at the beginning of or during its activity and has not yet repaid by aerobic energy-supplying processes [2]. The oxygen debt resulting entirely from (anaerobic) hydrolysis of creatine phosphate can be as great as 4 l; the glycolytic energy yield during extreme physical exertion (see above) increases the debt to as much as 20 l, for the lactate so formed and released into the bloodstream (up to 1.5 g/l) can be eliminated only by using up oxygen. Some of the lactate is oxidized in the myocardium and some (predominantly in the liver) is used for the neosynthesis of glycogen (cf. textbooks of biochemistry).

2.5   Smooth Muscle

Smooth muscle cells are spindle-shaped, ca. 50–400 µm long and 2–10 µm thick. Joined by special intercellular contacts (desmosomes), they form a network with intermeshed collagen fibers. Because the myosin and actin filaments are not regularly arranged, smooth muscle cells lack the striation typical of cardiac and skeletal muscle. Smooth muscle cells shorten by sliding of the myofilaments toward and over one another, but the rate of sliding and of ATP splitting is 100 to 1000 times slower than in striated muscles. For this reason smooth muscles are especially well suited for prolonged maintained contraction, without fatigue and with little energy consumption. Their contractile tension per unit cross-sectional area of muscle is as great as that of skeletal muscle (30–40 N/cm²), and in the long term they can support as great a load. The energy consumed in the process, however, as measured by oxygen consumption, is smaller by a factor of 100–500 [17].

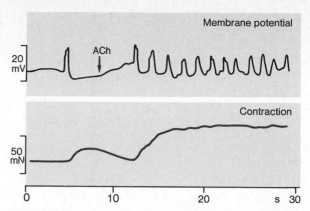

Fig. 2-15. A spontaneous action potential *(upper trace)* triggers a single twitch in the isolated tenia coli. Acetylcholine administration *(arrow)* raises the frequency of the action potentials; the single twitches fuse to a tetanus. *Lower trace (red):* time course of muscle tension

Myogenic activity of spontaneously active muscles. In many intestinal smooth muscles (e. g., the taenia coli) the single twitch elicited by an action potential lasts several seconds (Fig. 2-15). Therefore when two twitches occur at an interval of less than 2 **s** they are superimposed, and at frequencies below 1 Hz they fuse to a more or less complete tetanus (tetaniform "tonus") differing from that of striated muscle only in the low fusion frequency and the low frequency of the accompanying action potentials. The "tonus" is myogenic; unlike skeletal muscle, the smooth muscle of the intestine, ureter, stomach and uterus exhibits spontaneous tetaniform contractions after isolation and denervation, and even after the intramural ganglion cells are blocked.

The action potentials, then, are not triggered by nerve impulses. In other words, they are not neurogenic but – as in the heart – myogenic in origin.

Myogenic excitation originates in pacemaker cells identical to the other muscle cells in structure but differing in their electrophysiological properties, as follows. Prepotentials or pacemaker potentials depolarize the membrane to threshold and thus elicit action potentials. Owing to the inflow of positive ions (mainly Ca^{++}), the membrane is depolarized to the zero level and, for a few milliseconds, beyond it – to + 20 mV. Repolarization is followed by another prepotential, which elicits a new action potential. The size of the interval between the pacemaker action potentials depends both on the rate of depolarization of the prepotentials and on the difference between the initial membrane potential and the threshold potential. In the experiment of Fig. 2-15 the pacemaker membrane potential is high (ca. − 50 to − 70 mV) and the "firing" rate is low. When *acetylcholine* is administered to this tenia coli preparation (large-intestine

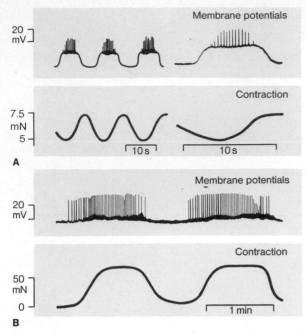

20 mV

Membrane potentials

7.5 mN
5

Contraction

10 s   10 s

A

20 mV

Membrane potentials

50 mN
0

Contraction

1 min

B

Fig. 2-16 A, B. Phasic rhythmic activity in smooth muscle. **A** Gastric-antrum musculature. Rhythmic depolarizations of the membrane potential with superimposed "spike bursts" *(upper trace)* cause fluctuations in tone (lower trace). **B** Tenia coli; electrical activity *(above)* and rhythmic contractions (below). After GOLENHOFEN

musculature; cf. p. 118) the pacemaker cells are depolarized to a near-threshold level and the action-potential frequency rises. The twitches they trigger fuse to an almost complete tetanus. The more frequent the action potentials, the more complete the tetanus and the stronger the contraction resulting from summation of the single twitches. Conversely, application of *noradrenalin* to the tenia coli hyperpolarizes the membrane, and thus lowers the action-potential frequency and the tonus. These are the mechanisms underlying the modulation of the spontaneous activity of the pacemakers by the autonomic nervous system and its transmitters (cf. p. 114), and by the intestinal nervous system, which is involved in the regulation of peristalsis (cf. p. 119).

The excitation spreads through the muscle by way of special "tight" junctions (nexuses) between the cell membranes of adjacent muscle cells. These low-resistance contact regions allow the depolarization of an excited cell to be electrotonically transmitted to neighboring cells. As soon as the local current flowing through a nexus depolarizes the membrane to threshold an action potential results, which in turn excites other electrotonically coupled cells. In this way the activity spreads through the whole muscle at a rate of ca. 5–10 cm/s; the muscle behaves like a single functional unit, following almost synchronously the activity of its pacemaker.

Myogenic rhythms. Fluctuations of myogenic tonus with periods of seconds or minutes – think, for example, of the pendular and segmentation movements of the small intestine (cf. p. 596) – are brought about by spontaneous changes in the activity of the pacemakers cells. When the membrane of a pacemaker cell is depolarized for seconds or minutes at a time, it triggers a volley of action potentials that produces a tetanic contraction.

GOLENHOFEN distinguishes between relatively brief, organ-specific rhythms and the longer *minute rhythms* ("slow waves"). In the smooth muscles of the gastric antrum (Fig. 2-16 A) the slow wave is shorter and more conspicuous than in the tenia of the colon (Fig. 2-16 B). It is still unclear whether the slow oscillations of the membrane potential (depolarization waves) are caused by rhythmic activity of an electrogenic sodium pump.

Responses of smooth muscle to stretch. In contrast to the skeletal muscles, most smooth muscles in the stretch experiment often behave not like more or less elastic structures but like distinctly plastic or viscoelastic bodies. After an initial elastic rise in tension the smooth muscle exhibits plastic compliance; in this poststretching phase tension declines, rapidly at first and then ever more slowly (Fig. 2-17). Because of its *plasticity* the smooth muscle can be completely relaxed in both the shortened and the stretched state. Think, for example, of the urinary bladder, which by yielding plastically as it fills prevents an excessive rise in internal pressure.

In many cases strong stretching produces a *stretch-activated contraction* (Fig. 2-17), superimposed on the passive behavior just described. This contraction results from the increasing depolarization of the pacemaker cells as the muscle is stretched, which raises the frequency of the action potentials. As described above, the increased discharge rate causes a stronger contraction. The stretch-activated contraction is significant with regard to *autoregulation* of the blood vessels (p. 423) and the automatic emptying of the filled urinary bladder, when neural regulation is eliminated by destruction of the spinal cord.

Non-spontaneous smooth muscles. The smooth muscles of the arterioles and arteries, like the muscles in the seminal ducts and iris and the ciliary muscles, usually exhibit little (cf. p. 423) or no spontaneous activity. In contrast to the muscles of the intestine, their activity is often not myogenic but neurogenic in origin, elicited by the impulses in the autonomic nerve fibers that supply them. The differences are explained by structural properties. The nexuses providing electrotonic coupling of these muscle cells are

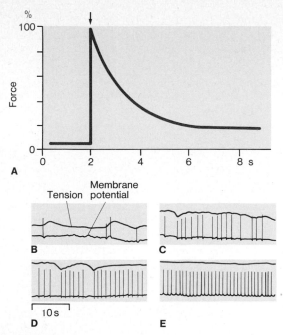

%
100

Force

0

0   2   4   6   8 s

A

Tension   Membrane
            potential

B   **C**

D   **E**

10 s

Fig. 2-17. A Viscoelastic behavior of a smooth muscle. When the muscle is stretched *(arrow)* its tension rises suddenly. As a result of plastic or viscoelastic compliance of the musculature, in the subsequent "poststretching" phase the muscle tension falls off quasi-exponentially. **B–E** Stretch-activated contraction of a smooth muscle. Recordings of membrane potential in a single cell *(black* traces) and force developed by a strip of tenia coli *(red* traces) before **(B)** and after **(C–E)** increasing passive stretch [4]. **B** Unstretched preparation; low-frequency action potentials followed by single twitches. **C–E** Stretching causes bursts of action potentials; the single twitches fuse to an incomplete tetanus **(C,D)** or complete tetanus **(E)**

more sparsely distributed, whereas many muscle cells make direct neuromuscular contact with the innervating nerve fibers (cf. p. 118). Thus the transmitter substances released when a nerve impulse arrives reach these effector cells by diffusion and activate them. In the muscle cells of seminal ducts or arterioles, for instance, they give rise to neurogenic prepotentials followed by action potentials, which elicit a tetaniform contraction. When directly applied to an isolated vessel muscle, noradrenalin produces a maintained contraction *(contracture):* the membrane of the cell – with the exception of the smooth muscles of the pulmonary and ear arteries – is depolarized throughout the time that noradrenalin acts.

Excitation-contraction coupling. Excitation of the smooth muscle cells causes either an *increased calcium-ion inflow* through the cell membrane or a *release of calcium ions* from intracellular stores. In both cases the result is an increase in the sarcoplasmic Ca^{++} concentration, which activates the contractile structures [5]. Like cardiac and skeletal muscle,

smooth muscles always relax when the intracellular calcium-ion concentration falls below about 10^{-8} mol/l. But they relax much more slowly, for the processes of uptake of calcium ions into the poorly developed *sarcoplasmic reticulum* or removal through the cell membrane are slower. Removal of the Ca^{++} results in splitting, by a phosphatase, of a functionally important phosphate group from a peptide chain of the myosin. The dephosphorylated myosin heads are incapable of forming cross bridges to the actin. At the beginning of a contraction the calcium ions released from the sarcoplasmic reticulum activate, in conjunction with the calcium-binding protein *calmodulin,* a special enzyme (myosin light chain kinase) that transfers a phosphate group from ATP to the myosin, thus setting off the actin-myosin interaction and the contraction. It is still unclear whether, in addition to this mechanism, control of smooth-muscle contractility involves a troponin-like calcium switch, nor is it certain how intracellularly formed cyclic adenosine monophosphate (c-AMP) lowers the tonus of the smooth muscle cell. Possibly, c-AMP may cause an inhibition of the enzyme myosin light chain kinase or an enhancement of calcium uptake into the sarcoplasmic reticulum.

2.6   References

Textbooks and Handbooks

1. CARLSON, F.D., WILKIE, D.R.: Muscle Physiology. Englewood CLIFF, N.J.: Prentice Hall (1974)
2. WILKIE, D.R.: Muscle. London: Edward Arnold 1976

Research Reports and Reviews

3. BLINKS, J.R., RÜDEL, R., TAYLOR, S.R.: Calcium transients in isolated amphibian skeletal muscle fibres: Detection with aequorin. J. Physiol. *277*, 291–323 (1978)
4. BÜLBRING, E., BRADING, A.F., JONES, A.W., TOMITA, T.: Smooth Muscle. London: Edward Arnold 1970
5. CASTEELS, R., GODFRAIND, T., RÜEGG, J.C.: Excitation-Contraction Coupling in Smooth Muscle. Amsterdam: Elsevier North Holland 1977
6. GORDON, A.M., HUXLEY, A.F., JULIAN, F.J.: The variation in isometric tension with sarcomere length in vertebrate muscle fibres. J. Physiol. (Lond.) *184,* 170 (1966)
7. HASSELBACH, W.: Relaxing factor and the relaxation of muscle. Progr. Biophys. mol. Biol. *14,* 167–222 (1964)
8. HUXLEY, A.F., TAYLOR, R.E.: Local activation of striated muscle fibres. J. Physiol. (Lond.) *144,* 426 (1958)
9. HUXLEY, A.F.: Muscular contraction. J. Physiol. (Lond.) *243,* 1–43 (1974)
10. HUXLEY, H.E., HANSON, J.: Changes in the cross-striation of muscle during contraction and stretch and their structural interpretation. Nature *173,* 973 (1954)
11. HUXLEY, H.E.: The mechanism of muscular contraction. Science *164,* 1356 (1969)
12. HUXLEY, H.E.: Structural changes in the actin and myosin contain-

ing filaments during contraction. Cold Spr. Harb. Symp. quant. Biol. *37*, 361 (1973)

13. Huxley, H. E., Simmons, R. M., Faruki, A. R., Kress, M., Bordas, J., Koch, M. H. J.: Msec time resolved change in X-ray reflections from contracting muscle during rapid mechanical transients, recorded using synchrotron radiation. Proc. Natl. Acad. Sci., USA *78*, 2297 (1981)

14. Infante, A. A., Davies, R. E.: Adenosine triphosphate breakdown during a single isotonic twitch of frog sartorius muscle. Biochem. biophys. Res. Commun. *9*, 410 (1962)

15. Jewell, B. R., Wilkie, D. R.: An analysis of the mechanical components in frog striated muscle. J. Physiol. (Lond.) *143*, 515 (1958)

16. Mannherz, H. G., Schirmer, R. H.: Die Molekularbiologie der Bewegung. Chemie in unserer Zeit *6*, 165–202 (1970)

17. Rüegg, J. C.: Smooth muscle tone. Physiol. Rev. *51*, 201 (1971)

18. Weber, H. H., Portzehl, H.: The transference of the muscle energy in the contraction cycle. Progr. Biophys. mol. Biol. *4*, 61 (1954)

19. Wilkie, D. R.: The relation between force and velocity in human muscle. J. Physiol. *110*, 249–280 (1950)

3 The Transmission of Excitation from Cell to Cell

R. F. SCHMIDT

The junction of an axonal ending with a nerve cell, a muscle cell, or a gland cell was given the name **synapse,** around the turn of the century, by SHERRINGTON. In mammals – and thus in humans – the **chemical synapse** is most common. In this type, when an action potential reaches the end of the axon, a chemical substance is released there, and causes *excitation* or *inhibition* at the membrane of the adjacent cell. Electrical synapses are relatively rare; here the axonal action potential elicits *excitation* or *inhibition* in the next cell without the intervention of a chemical transmission process. At both chemical and electrical synapses, signals are almost always transmitted only from the presynaptic (axonal) side to the postsynaptic region of the next cell. That is, the function of a synapse is analogous to that of a **valve.**

Normally the membranes of the pre- and postsynaptic sides of a synapse are separated from one another by a *synaptic cleft* 10–50 nm (100–500 Å) wide. Quantitative analysis shows that with such a gap so much current would be lost in the extracellular medium as to make the electrical transmission of excitation practically impossible [10]. Viewed in this light, chemical transmission is a necessary **amplifying mechanism.**

Synapses are of crucial significance in the brain for several reasons. *First,* without their **valve action** orderly activity of the central nervous system would hardly be conceivable. *Second,* the efficacy of synapses can be modified; for example, they transmit better when frequently used than when they are used rarely or not at all (cf. p. 74). Thus synapses have a degree of **plasticity** and hence have a function in **learning** and **memory.** *Third,* synapses are the **sites of action** of many **drugs,** ranging from neuromuscular blocking agents to psychomimetics (see, e.g., pp. 57 and 142).

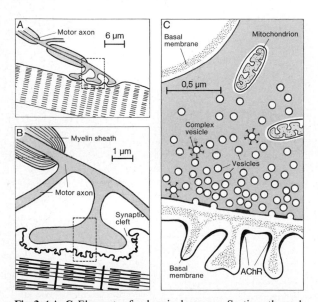

Fig. 3-1 A–C. Elements of a chemical synapse. Sections through the end-plate region of a skeletal muscle fiber; **B** and **C** are enlarged sections of **A** and **B,** respectively. Schematized from electron micrographs of many authors. The synaptic cleft is disproportionately wide in each drawing; in warm-blooded animals it averages 10–20 nm in width, and in the frog, 50 nm. AChR, subsynaptic localization of the ACh receptors; the basal membrane may be the site of the cholinesterase. For histological details see [1, 9, 10, 13, 23]

3.1 The Neuromuscular Junction: A Chemical Synapse

Structural Elements of the End Plate

The axons of the motoneurons in the ventral horn of the spinal cord (motor axons) make synapses with skeletal muscle fibers. Because of their shape these synapses are called **neuromuscular end plates.** They have all the typical morphological characteristics of *chemical synapses* (Fig. 3-1). The *presynaptic ending* is separated from the *subsynaptic membrane* on the postsynaptic side by the **synaptic cleft.** In the electron microscope, the *subsynaptic* (postsynaptic) membrane of a chemical synapse usually looks somewhat thicker than the remainder of the postsynaptic membrane outside the synaptic region. Moreover, at the neuromuscular end plate it exhibits regular **subsynaptic infoldings,** which considerably increase the surface area of the subsynaptic membrane as compared with the presynaptic ending (for details see [1, 9, 10, 13, 23]).

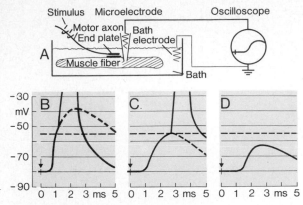

Fig. 3-2 A–D. Demonstration of the end-plate potential. **A** Diagram of the experimental arrangement. Only one muscle fiber is shown, with its motor axon. The motor axon is stimulated electrically. To avoid a short circuit between the stimulating electrodes, the nerve is lifted into the air or into a layer of mineral oil during stimulation. **B** Intracellularly recorded changes in the potential of the muscle-fiber membrane, with the preparation in normal Tyrode solution. Only the bottom part of the conducted action potential is shown. **C, D** Potential shapes after addition of d-tubocurarine. The threshold for a conducted action potential (*dashed red* line at −55 mV) is barely (**C**) or not (**D**) reached. What remains in **D** is the end-plate potential, which had been obscured by the action potential in B and C. The amplitude of the end-plate potential decreases with increasing concentration of curare and duration of exposure. *Arrows* in **B–D** mark stimulus times

The presynaptic ending contains *mitochondria,* as well as many submicroscopic spherical structures called **synaptic vesicles.** These vesicles, ca. 50 nm in diameter, are particularly numerous in the vicinity of the synaptic cleft, at places where the axoplasmic membrane is thickened. These presynaptic membrane thickenings are opposite the openings of the subsynaptic invaginations. This electron microscopic picture in itself suggests that the vesicles contain the **transmitter substance** that is released into the synaptic cleft during excitation; it may be that the release occurs chiefly at the subsynaptic infoldings. (There are also small numbers of **complex vesicles,** the significance of which is discussed on p. 55; see also Fig. 3-7 E.)

The End-Plate Potential

Demonstration of the end-plate potential. Fig. 3-2 A shows the experimental procedure used to study synaptic transmission in a nerve-muscle preparation *in vitro.* With an intact preparation in normal physiological saline solution (Tyrode's solution), stimulation of the motor axon to the muscle cell triggers a conducted action potential (Fig. 3-2 B), which in turn triggers a contraction of the muscle fiber. If a small amount (of

the order of 10^{-7} to 10^{-6} g/ml) of the Indian arrow poison *curare* is added to the solution, the initial membrane depolarization barely reaches the threshold (Fig. 3-2 C) or fails to reach it (Fig. 3-2 D), returning to the resting potential after a few milliseconds (in this case no twitch occurs). This local depolarization is called the **end-plate potential.** The dashed black lines in Fig. 3-2 B, C indicate that end-plate potentials were also produced here, but were largely obscured by the action potentials. *Depending on their amplitude, then, end-plate potentials can be supra-or subthreshold.*

End-plate potentials in situ. The end-plate potentials of a healthy muscle *in situ* are always well above threshold, so that each presynaptic action potential triggers a twitch of the associated muscle fiber. Poisoning with curare reduces the amplitude of the end-plate potential, to a subthreshold level if the curare concentration is high enough; since subthreshold potentials can elicit no muscle-fiber action potential and thus no contraction, the neuromuscular transmission is *blocked.* A person poisoned with curare suffocates, because of the blockade of neuromuscular transmission in the skeletal musculature – including the respiratory muscles (for mechanism of curare action see p. 58).

The nature of the end-plate potential. The **time course of the end-plate potential** is represented by a simple curve, with a rise time of 1–2 ms and a fall time of 5 to at most 20 ms. When the end-plate potential is recorded at increasing distances from the end-plate, as in Fig. 3-3, its amplitude appears smaller and the rise and fall times longer. This finding is an unequivocal sign (cf. p. 19) that the end-plate potential **spreads electrotonically** from its site of origin, the *subsynaptic membrane.*

Time course of the end-plate current. The end-plate potential is produced by a *current through the subsynaptic membrane,* elicited by the action of the presynaptically released transmitter acetylcholine (see below) on the subsynaptic membrane. In voltage-clamp experiments, the time course of the end-plate current has been measured directly (refs. in [9]). As Fig. 3-4 shows, the **end-plate current** reaches a maximum in less than 1 ms and dies away in another 1–2 ms. The end-plate potential rises at about the same rate; its considerably longer fall time results from the passive electrical properties of the muscle-fiber membrane, particularly the membrane capacitance and membrane resistance [3, 10].

A reduction in temperature prolongs the *time course* of the end-plate current and diminishes its *amplitude,* both with a Q_{10} of about 3. Drugs that extend the duration of transmitter action on the subsynaptic membrane (examples on p. 58) also prolong the end-plate current, but in this case the amplitude increases [28]. Note also that for a given end-plate current the *amplitude of the end-plate potential* depends on the overall resistance of the muscle-fiber membrane. Therefore thin muscle fibers as a rule, other conditions being equal, have distinctly larger end-plate potentials than thick fibers.

Subsynaptic conductance changes during the end-plate current. The nature of the conductance changes during the initial phase of the end-plate potential was first studied by measuring the equilibrium potential of the end-plate potential, and then further clarified by measuring the equilibrium potential of the end-plate current in voltage-clamp experiments [3]. As shown diagrammatically in Fig. 3-5, the *equilibrium potential of the end-plate potential* – the membrane potential at which transmitter action produces no net flow of current and thus no potential change – is ca. -5 to -15 mV in normal physiological saline solution, about midway between the equilibrium potentials for potassium ($E_K = -90$ mV) and sodium ($E_{Na} = +55$ mV).

When the concentrations of Na^+ and K^+ in the external solution are changed, the equilibrium potential of the end-plate potential is shifted, but when the extracellular Cl^- is replaced by other anions there is no such change. This result, together with those previously mentioned and others, has led to the conclusion that during the time in which the transmitter is acting on the subsynaptic membrane (ca. 1–2 ms) the **membrane conductance for small cations** (Na^+, K^+) is greatly increased [3, 10, 19]. Under normal conditions, therefore, because of the initial distribution of the ions (cf. Table 1-1, p. 6) the main result will be a flow of Na^+ ions into the muscle fiber and hence a reduction in membrane potential, for at a membrane potential of -80 mV the driving force for Na^+ flow is greater than that for K^+ flow. There is thus a net inward current, carried by Na^+ ions. If the conductance change is large enough, the muscle-fiber membrane at the end plate is depolarized to threshold and the resulting conducted action potential (cf. Fig. 3-2) spreads over the entire muscle cell.

The Release of Transmitter Substance

Miniature end-plate potentials and the quantum hypothesis. An intracellular electrode in a resting muscle fiber records small brief membrane depolarizations at irregular intervals (Fig. 3-6). Their time course resembles that of the normal end-plate potential, but they are many times smaller in amplitude (compare ordinate scale in Fig. 3-6 with that in 3-3). Therefore

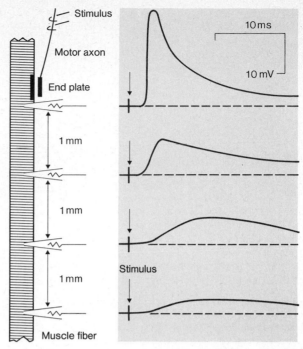

Fig. 3-3. Electrotonic nature of the end-plate potentials. Stimulation and recording as in Fig. 3-2 A. Enough curare has been added to the bath to prevent the end-plate potentials from reaching suprathreshold amplitude. Potentials are recorded at progressively further distances (1 mm intervals) from the end plate along the muscle fiber. (Modified from Fatt and Katz, 1951)

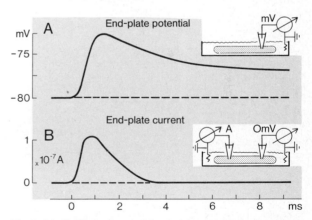

Fig. 3-4 A, B. Time course of the end-plate potential **A** and the associated end-plate current **B**. As the insets show, in **A** the change in potential following activation of the end plate was measured, and in **B** the current required to keep the membrane potential constant during end-plate activation was measured (voltage-clamp method). After [28]

they are called **miniature end-plate potentials** [10]. These, like the end-plate potentials, arise only at the subsynaptic membrane and spread electrotonically into the surrounding membrane. As Fig. 3-6 shows, their amplitude is so small that they can be recorded only in the immediate vicinity of the end plate. The

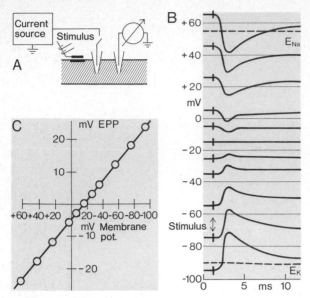

Fig. 3-5 A–C. Measurement of the equilibrium potential of the end-plate potential. **A** shows the experimental set-up. In **B** end-plate potentials were elicited with the initial membrane potential set between -95 mV and $+65$ mV. The equilibrium potentials for potassium (E_K) and sodium (E_{Na}) are indicated by dashed red lines. In **C** the relation between starting potential (abscissa) and amplitude and polarity of the end-plate potential (ordinate) is plotted. The equilibrium potential is ca. -15 mV. (From data of Fatt and Katz, 1951; del Castillo and Katz, 1954; Burke and Ginsburg, 1965)

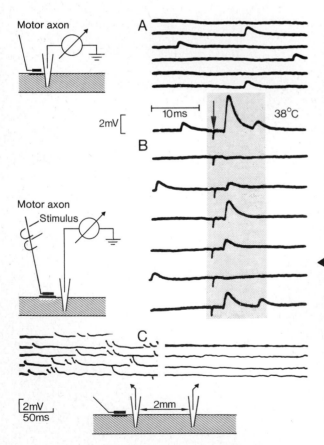

pharmacology of the end-plate potentials and the miniature end-plate potentials is also identical. It can be concluded that the latter are produced by the spontaneous release of small amounts of transmitter.

Miniature end-plate potentials all have about the same amplitude (Fig. 3-6). Apparently, then, they are produced by approximately equal amounts of acetylcholine. These "packets" of acetylcholine (ACh) have been called **quanta.** It has been shown that the normal end-plate potential is also caused by the release of quanta. When the amount of transmitter released per action potential is reduced by removing Ca^{++} from the bathing solution (or adding Mg^{++}; for mechanism see p. 55), it becomes evident (Fig. 3-6 B) that the end-plate potential is probably always composed of *integral multiples of the miniature end-plate potentials* – that is, it is brought about by the practically simultaneous release of a large number of quanta.

In summary, the following picture has developed. The resting end plate, at statistically distributed intervals (on average ca. once per second), releases a quantum of transmitter, which triggers a miniature end-plate potential at the subsynaptic membrane. In other words, there is a certain *statistical probability* at each point in time that a quantum of transmitter will be released. This probability is considerably increased for a short time by the *presynaptic action potential,* so that within a millisecond some hundreds of quanta are released – enough to produce an end-plate potential. For example, it has been estimated that the end plate of the frog releases ca. 200 quanta per presynaptic action potential. The estimates for other synapses are as high as 2000 quanta. The total amount of acetylcholine released at an end plate by an action potential has been found to be 1.5×10^{-15} g (refs. in [17, 23]).

As was mentioned above, the presynaptic vesicles have long been regarded as the places where the transmitter is stored. The **"quantum hypothesis"** is thus essentially based on two findings: 1. the *electron microscopic* observation of synaptic vesicles, and 2.

Fig. 3-6 A–C. Miniature end-plate potentials. **A** Recording from a resting muscle fiber. As the inset shows, the microelectrode is inserted directly adjacent to the end plate. **B** End-plate potentials produced by electrical stimulation of the associated motor neuron (red arrow and shading) with fiber in a saline solution containing 1 mM Ca^{++} and 6 mM Mg^{++}. Some spontaneous miniature end-plate potentials also occur in these records. Two stimuli fail to elicit an end-plate potential; in the other cases the amplitude of the response corresponds to that of a miniature end-plate potential or an integral multiple thereof. **C** Recording of miniature end-plate potentials near the end plate and 2 mm away from it (see inset). (**A, B** after Liley, 1956; **C** after Fatt and Katz, 1952)

the *physiological* finding that transmitter release is quantal in nature. Since their discovery at the end plate, vesicles and miniature potentials have been found in many other chemical synapses; in fact, it has been possible to isolate synaptic vesicles by ultracentrifugation. They have been found to contain ACh (acetylcholine) or other substances thought to have a transmitter function [39, 40]. It may be, then, that at all synapses with presynaptic vesicles the transmitter is released in quanta – even those with unknown transmitters. Such a *quantum* (not to be confused with the physical concept of the energy quantum) probably contains some thousands of transmitter molecules, which are poured out into the very narrow (ca. 0.1 μm) synaptic cleft within 1–2 ms, and thus can act almost simultaneously at the subsynaptic membrane. At the frog end plate, one quantum contains about 10^3 to 10^4 acetylcholine molecules and in the rat there are between 4000 and 20000 molecules [17, 32]; for other synapses there are as yet no sufficiently well-founded estimates. At the moment we cannot say whether the miniature potentials have a physiological significance, as no relevant data are available.

Life cycle of synaptic vesicles. Fig. 3-7 E shows schematically how synaptic vesicles arise from **complex vesicles.** The latter are formed from infoldings of the cell membrane; they consist of a smooth-walled inner vesicle, apparently identical with the synaptic vesicle, and an outer envelope of hexagonally arranged material. The complex vesicles form **cisternae,** from which the synaptic vesicles are constricted off (refs. in [17]). The hypothesis of vesicle production presented here postulates further that the vesicle membrane fuses with the presynaptic membrane when the transmitter it contains is released, and that the site of vesicle formation is not the same as the release zone. The latter can also be distinguished from the rest of the membrane by electron microscopic criteria (Figs. 3-1 and 3-7 E, F).

The release of transmitter by the action potential; synaptic latency. An increase in the extracellular K^+ concentration lowers the membrane potential (cf. p. 7). At the same time, in a preparation such as that of Fig. 3-6, one can see that increase in the extracellular K^+ concentration raises the frequency of the miniature end-plate potentials. Their frequency also increases when the presynaptic membrane potential is lowered by externally applied current. The probability of quantal release thus depends at least in part on the membrane potential of the presynaptic ending, the frequency of the miniature end-plate potentials increasing as the membrane potential depolarizes and decreasing as it hyperpolarizes.

The *action potential* is a marked but very brief depolarization of the membrane. Despite its brevity, the action potential causes the probability of transmitter release to increase many thousandfold above its resting value. This increase lasts less than 1 ms, so that some hundreds of quanta are suddenly released. The hypothesis requires further experimental support. In any case, a number of experiments – in particular the variation of action-potential amplitude by changing the resting potential and the imitation of the action potential by externally imposed membrane-potential changes – have shown fairly clearly that the size of the end-plate potential (that is, the number of quanta released per action potential) depends on the amplitude and duration of membrane depolarization (cf. [9–12, 23]).

The time that elapses from the arrival of the action potential at the presynaptic ending to the onset of the subsynaptic charge displacement is called the **synaptic latency.** At the end plate in the rat it is ca. 0.2 ms [18]. Comparable values are found at most excitatory and inhibitory synapses in the central nervous system.

The role of calcium. If Ca^{++} is removed from the solution bathing an *in vitro* preparation, the presynaptic action potential releases not hundreds of quanta, but fewer; the number released per impulse varies about a mean that depends on the prevailing Ca^{++} concentration. When the Ca^{++} concentration is low, as shown in Fig. 3-6 B, the amplitudes of the elicited end-plate potentials are low multiples of the amplitude of the miniature end-plate potentials. Occasionally not even one quantum is released. The size of the quanta themselves is unchanged. These experiments leave no doubt that the presence of Ca^{++} is absolutely essential for the quantum release triggered by a presynaptic action potential to proceed normally. It seems that four Ca^{++} ions are required for the release of one quantum. The addition of Mg^{++} has an effect similar to that of Ca^{++} removal. Apparently the Mg^{++} ions compete with the Ca^{++} ions, crowding them away from the binding sites at the presynaptic membrane.

Studies of a cephalopod synapse have given rise to the following hypothesis for the role of Ca^{++} in synaptic transmission [10, 11]. Depolarization of the presynaptic membrane, either by an action potential or by a current pulse, opens not only Na^+ but also Ca^{++} pores (channels) in the presynaptic membrane, so that Ca^{++} ions, following their concentration gradient, can enter the presynaptic membrane. This process has a threshold of 30–40 mV depolarization, and the degree to which Ca^{++} permeability is changed depends on the amount of depolarization. Accordingly, transmitter release increases with the magnitude and duration of depolarization. As at the end plate, Mg^{++} and also Mn^{++} prevent the flow of Ca^{++} into the presynaptic end-

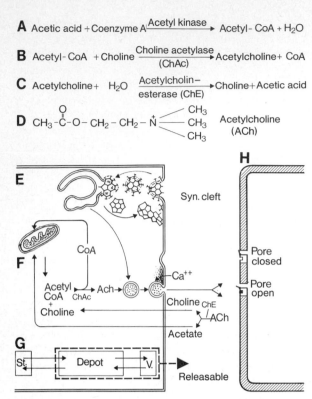

A Acetic acid + Coenzyme A $\xrightarrow{\text{Acetyl kinase}}$ Acetyl- CoA + H$_2$O

B Acetyl- CoA + Choline $\xrightarrow[\text{(ChAc)}]{\text{Choline acetylase}}$ Acetylcholine+ CoA

C Acetylcholine+ H$_2$O $\xrightarrow[\text{esterase (ChE)}]{\text{Acetylcholin–}}$ Choline+Acetic acid

D $CH_3-\overset{\overset{O}{\|}}{C}-O-CH_2-CH_2-\overset{+}{N}\Big\langle\begin{matrix}CH_3\\CH_3\\CH_3\end{matrix}$ Acetylcholine (ACh)

Fig. 3-7 A–H. Acetylcholine as transmitter substance. **A, B** Biosynthesis and **C** breakdown of acetylcholine (structure in **D**). In **E** the formation of new vesicles is shown schematically [23]. See explanation in text. **F** summarizes the processes of synthesis, storage and release of ACh and the re-uptake from the synaptic cleft of the products of ACh splitting. **G** shows that in addition to the fraction A immediately available for release there is a larger depot fraction to be drawn upon, whereas a third, smaller stationary fraction St cannot be released from the ending. In **H** two subsynaptic ACh receptors are diagrammed; when a receptor binds to ACh *(red)* the membrane pore becomes open to small cations

ing and thus prevent transmitter release. At other peripheral synapses, too, Ca^{++} is necessary for normal release of transmitter, so that it can be inferred that Ca^{++} plays the same role at all chemical synapses.

As to the **mechanism** by which Ca^{++} acts at the presynaptic ending, no details are yet known. It is possible that in the resting state the negative charges of vesicles and presynaptic membrane cause the two to repel one another electrostatically. When excitation causes the Ca^{++} ions, with their double positive charge, to flow into the presynaptic ending, they could **shield the fixed negative charge** of the membrane, allowing the vesicles to approach it.

Pathophysiology of transmitter release. The toxin produced by the bacterium *Clostridium botulinum* (in spoiled meat, fish or canned goods) acts on the end plate like the removal of Ca^{++}; even minute quantitatives (nanograms) of **botulinum toxin** block the release of ACh, thus causing muscular paralysis, which is often fatal because it stops respiration. *Botulinum toxin* is heat-sensitive; therefore an effective means of protection against this toxin is to thoroughly boil or roast the food in question.

The Transmitter Acetylcholine; Its Subsynaptic Receptors

Synthesis of acetylcholine. There is no doubt that **acetylcholine** (ACh), the acetic-acid ester of choline, is the transmitter substance at the vertebrate neuromuscular junction (for other transmitter functions of ACh see p.65). Synthesis in the presynaptic ending occurs as summarized in Fig. 3–7 A, B, F. **Choline** must first be taken into the ending by a *transport mechanism*. About half of the choline so obtained is derived from the previously released and then hydrolyzed ACh (cf. Fig. 3-6 C, F), and the rest probably comes from the blood plasma. Repetitive activation of the ending considerably increases the activity of the transport mechanism, so that even when stimulated at 20 Hz for 5 min ACh synthesis can keep pace with the release of ACh [9]. The transport mechanism can be blocked by **hemicholinium,** which soon leads to the interruption of ACh synthesis and thus to neuromuscular blockade (cf. p.58).

The enzyme choline acetylase (ChAc) is formed in the soma of the motoneuron, and in about 10 days time is transported in the axon to the presynaptic endings [23]. The mechanism by which the ACh it synthesizes is taken into the vesicle is not yet known.

Forms of storage. Only a small part (15–20%) of the ACh stored in the vesicles seems to be an **immediately available fraction,** which can be released directly either spontaneously or under the influence of an action potential; the greater **depot fraction** can be mobilized only with a certain delay (Fig. 3-7 G). This hypothesis is supported, first, by the finding that newly formed ACh is released about twice as rapidly as ACh that has been present for some time; second, at nonphysiologically high stimulus frequencies the amount of ACh released per impulse falls to a level such that the amount released per minute remains constant. If the uptake of choline is blocked by hemicholinium, it is not possible for all the ACh in the ending to be released. Thus there must be a third, **stationary fraction** (Fig. 3-7 G), perhaps not present in vesicular form. An exchange among these three fractions appears to be possible (arrows in Fig. 3-7 G). The *histological correlates of these three fractions* are not yet clear, though it is plausible that the vesicles in the vicinity of the synaptic cleft represent the immediately available fraction, whereas the remaining vesicles account for all or most of the depot fraction (refs. in [23]).

The subsynaptic receptors. Having reached the subsynaptic (postsynaptic) membrane, ACh binds with specific macromolecules called (pharmacological)

receptors. This binding causes the opening of the sub-synaptic pores for Na^+ and K^+ (Fig. 3-7 H, cf. also p. 53). The receptors can be irreversibly blocked by the snake poison *α-bungarotoxin*. (Tetrodotoxin does not block these subsynaptic receptors, or the membrane pores or channels they control.) By applying radioactively labelled bungarotoxin and then ultracentrifugeing and filtering the membrane extract, it can be shown that bungarotoxin is bound to a *lipoprotein* with a molecular weight of ca. 300 000. This lipoprotein is therefore probably the ACh receptor. Other experimental results are consistent with this hypothesis [8–12, 13, 19, 23]. For example, inhibition of protein synthesis reduces the rate of replacement of ACh receptors; in adult animals the half-time of this reconstruction process is normally days, whereas it is apparently only a few hours in juveniles.

Distribution and density of ACh receptors. Microelectrophoretically applied ACh normally elicits depolarization only at the end plate, and not at the other parts of the muscle-fiber membrane. The ACh receptors are thus situated only in the subsynaptic membrane, and not in the adjacent postsynaptic regions. Similarly, injection of ACh into the muscle fiber does not cause membrane depolarization; like all other transmitters, ACh acts only at the *outer surface* of the subsynaptic membrane. In rats and frogs bungarotoxin binds to $2–4 \times 10^7$ sites per end plate, so that assuming one receptor per binding site and taking account of the end-plate surface area, one arrives at a receptor density of ca. 10^4 receptors per μm^2 [12, 19].

A **denervated** muscle fiber (e. g., by transection of the motor axon) becomes sensitive to ACh over its entire surface; that is, the muscle-fiber membrane is **hypersensitive** to ACh. (At the same time the muscle begins to atrophy and *fibrillations* appear, frequent spontaneous asynchronous twitches of the individual muscle fibers.) A similar *hypersensitization* is observed in cases of "functional denervation" by botulinum toxin, of nerve blockade with diphtheria toxin or local anesthetics, and of congenital disturbances of ACh release [9, 12, 13]. This hypersensitization is partly due to the absence of muscular activity, but it also results in part from the elimination of unknown presynaptic factors that affect muscle-fiber metabolism rather than directly influencing synaptic transmission; together, the latter are called **trophic factors.** Hypersensitivity can be prevented by inhibiting protein synthesis, which again indicates the lipoprotein character of the ACh receptors [9, 19]. When reinnervation has occurred or the block is removed, the ACh receptors outside the end-plate region disappear.

Inactivation of ACh receptors. If an endplate is exposed to the action of ACh for several hundred ms, the initially depolarized membrane gradually repolarizes even though ACh is still present; the subsynaptic receptors become refractory to ACh – that is, they are **inactivated** or **desensitized.** The reasons for receptor inactivation are still unclear (refs. in [9, 19]).

Termination of the ACh action. ACh normally acts on the subsynaptic membrane for only a very short time (1–2 ms; cf. p. 53), because some of it diffuses away and some is hydrolyzed by the enzyme **acetylcholinesterase** (that is, it is split into the ineffective components *choline* and *acetic acid;* cf. Fig. 3-7 C, F). Special staining methods have shown that *acetylcholinesterase* is present at the end plate in large amounts (so-called specific or true cholinesterase). But cholinesterases can also be found in the blood – in the erythrocytes (also specific) and in the plasma (so-called unspecific or pseudo-cholinesterases, which also split other choline esters). Thus the ACh that diffuses from an end plate into the surrounding extracellular space and into the bloodstream is also broken down into choline and acetic acid. Most of the products of ACh splitting are taken back into the presynaptic ending, where they are resynthesized to ACh. Fig. 3-7 F gives a summary of the main events in the ACh cycle. Other transmitter substances have also been shown to have, or to be likely to have, comparable cycles (cf. pp. 66–69).

Myasthenia gravis. This chronic disturbance of neuromuscular transmission is characterized by weakness and abnormal fatigability of the skeletal musculature. It is caused by a *decrease in the number of subsynaptic acetylcholine receptors.* Thus even though sufficient ACh is released presynaptically the end-plate potentials are smaller than normal, and some fail to reach threshold. Therefore when ACh release is slightly reduced in the course of the day's muscular work, the neuromuscular blockade of many end plates results. The disappearance of the receptors is brought about by an *autoimmune response directed specifically against the ACh receptors.* Most patients have developed antibodies against ACh receptors, which either increase the rate of receptor breakdown or block the receptors. Although it does not act on the cause of the disorder, an effective treatment has proved to be the administration of *cholinesterase inhibitors* (ambenonium, neostigmine, pyridostigmine), which prolong the time during which ACh can act on the receptors that are available. Thymus removal and the administration of prednisone can have an additional favorable effect on the disease; the mechanism of their action is not yet known. Immunosuppressive medications can also be used, but their potential side effects (bone-marrow dysplasia, increased danger of infection, production of tumors) must be kept in mind [8].

Neuromuscular Blockade

Mechanisms of neuromuscular blockade. The preceding discussion of neuromuscular transmission has surely made clear that there are a number of possible means of affecting neuromuscular transmission. A drug or a toxic substance, for example, can inhibit transmission in the following ways:

- it can block the **conduction of excitation** in the presynaptic ending (example: local anesthetics);
- it can block the **release of transmitter** (examples: *in vivo* botulinum toxin, *in vitro* withdrawal of Ca^{++} or competitive displacement by Mg^{++} or Mn^{++});
- it can interfere with the **production of transmitter** (example: hemicholinium, which inhibits the uptake of choline into the presynaptic ending);
- it can act at the **subsynaptic ACh receptor.** It can *block* the receptor by *irreversibly binding* to it (example: α-bungarotoxin), or it can *competitively* – that is, reversibly and to a degree depending on the concentrations of the two partners – *displace* ACh from its site of action (examples: curare, pancuronium), or it can induce a *prolonged subsynaptic depolarization and receptor inactivation* (examples: succinylcholine, decamethonium);
- it can inhibit **cholinesterase** and thus the splitting of ACh, so that the transmitter acts long enough to cause subsynaptic depolarization and receptor inactivation and thus, as in the example of succinylcholine, produce neuromuscular blockade (examples: organophosphates, but only in toxic doses).

Clinical applications. Blocking of neuromuscular transmission is used extensively during *anesthesia*. The patient, who must receive artifical respiration during this time, then requires only the relatively shallow anesthesia necessary to eliminate consciousness and pain sensations, which without neuromuscular blockade would permit undesirable motor reflexes and high muscle tone. The advantage of the light anesthesia lies in the fact that it is less toxic, more readily controlled and more rapidly reversible. In general, substances used to relax the muscles during anesthesia or in other therapeutic situations are called **relaxants** [13].

Depolarizing muscle relaxants. Substances that imitate the action of ACh at the subsynaptic receptor for *relatively long times* (because they are not broken down by cholinesterase, or not rapidly enough) block the transmission of excitation because of the depolarization of the subsynaptic membrane (and the subsequent receptor inactivation). Such substances are categorized as **depolarizing muscle relaxants.** *Succinylcholine* is the most important example of this group. In accordance with the mechanism of action just described, after i. v. injection of succinylcholine a brief period of disorganized (fascicular) muscle twitches precedes complete relaxation.

Non-depolarizing muscle relaxants. Substances that compete with ACh for subsynaptic receptor sites, without changing the membrane conductance, are called **non-depolarizing muscle relaxants.** Curare (d-tubocurarine) and pancuronium can be taken as prototypes of this group. Curare induces muscular relaxation more slowly than succinylcholine, but its effects persist considerably longer. As expected from its mechanism of action, the relaxation is not preceded by muscle twitches.

Cholinesterase inhibitors. Cholinesterase inhibitors could also be used to produce neuromuscular blockade, because delayed splitting of ACh prolongs the depolarization of the subsynaptic membrane. But because of the severe side effects on other cholinergic synapses, they are not employed clinically in this way. On the other hand, there are non-therapeutic applications of various organophosphates (insecticides and some nerve gases) as *irreversible* cholinesterase inhibitors. And in cases of curare-type blockade or reduction of ACh receptors (myasthenia gravis, see above) neuromuscular transmission can be restored or returned to normal by the administration of *reversible* cholinesterase inhibitors (examples: ambenonium, neostigmine, pyridostigmine).

3.2 Central Excitatory Chemical Synapses

The basic events in the generation of excitation at chemical synapses are those just described for the neuromuscular end plate. Thus we can now turn directly to the more complex features of the transmission of excitation in central neurons. That is, whereas each muscle fiber as a rule has only one end plate and each end-plate potential is normally far above threshold, central neurons usually have many dozen to several thousand synapses [1, 3], and the excitatory postsynaptic potentials of the *individual* synapses are almost always below threshold, so that the *simultaneous* activity of many synapses is required to generate conducted excitation. Moreover, the soma and dendrites of a central neuron bear not only *excitatory* but also *inhibitory* synapses, which when activated oppose the production of conducted excitation.

The Excitation of the Motoneuron

Because of its size (soma diameter up to 100 μm), its relative accessibility and its well-known excitatory and inhibitory connections, the motoneuron has proved especially well suited to the study of neuronal synaptic potentials. Moreover, the results obtained with motoneurons can be applied to the majority of

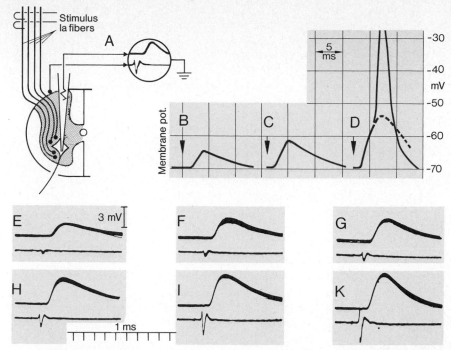

Fig. 3-8 A–K. Excitatory postsynaptic potentials (EPSPs). **A** Diagram of the experimental arrangement. The EPSPs are recorded intracellularly from a motoneuron after stimulation of the homonymous (associated) muscle-spindle afferents (Ia fibers). **B–D** Schematic drawing of the effect of increasing stimulus intensity. The EPSP elicits a conducted action potential when it reaches the threshold (− 60 mV). **E–K** EPSP of a motoneuron in the quadriceps muscle of the cat. The unipolar extracellular recording of the afferent volley in the zone of entry of the dorsal root (cf. **A**) serves as a measure of the number of afferent fibers excited and as a marker for the measurement of spinal latency; it appears as a triphasic deflection of the lower trace. **E–K** from [4]

central neurons without major restrictions; they will thus be used as the basis of the present discussion.

Excitatory postsynaptic potentials, EPSPs. The surface of a motoneuron, except for the axon hillock and the axon, is covered with a large number of synapses. It has been estimated that each motoneuron has ca. 6000 axo-somatic and axo-dendritic synapses. Some of them are excitatory and some inhibitory, and the axons leading to them are in most cases those of central neurons. But some of the axons that make excitatory synapses are afferent nerve fibers from stretch receptors of the muscle spindles in the skeletal musculature, which enter the spinal cord by way of the dorsal roots. These synapses can be activated by electrical stimulation of the muscle nerves, and the postsynaptic processes can be recorded by an intracellular microelectrode.

An experiment of this sort is illustrated in Fig. 3-8 A. When the afferents are stimulated electrically (arrows in B, C, D), after a brief latency the membrane potential exhibits a depolarization with a time course, in B and C, similar to that of the end-plate potential. The amplitude of depolarization depends on the number of afferents excited, and thus on the intensity of the electrical stimulus (B < C < D). As a measure of the number of afferents excited in an experiment, one can record extracellularly the afferent volley in the region where the dorsal root enters the cord (Fig. 3-8 A and lower record in E-K). This record can be used to measure the *spinal latency,* the time until appearance of the intracellular depolarization. Because (as shown in D) the depolarization can excite the neuron so as to produce a conducted action potential, it is called an **excitatory postsynaptic potential** (EPSP). EPSPs are thus analogous to the end-plate potentials at the neuromuscular junction. But whereas the end-plate potential is produced by the activation of a single synapse, the end plate, the EPSPs are usually caused by the simultaneous activation of several synapses. The rising phase of an EPSP lasts about 2 ms, and the falling phase lasts 10–15 ms. This time course is independent of the amplitude of the EPSP (Fig. 3-8 E-K), which implies that the EPSPs elicited simultaneously at different synapses add in amplitude – and, moreover, that they do not influence one another. (The mutual independence of the "unitary" EPSPs holds only in certain limits, but these can be disregarded here.)

Ionic mechanism of the EPSP. All results indicate that the EPSP arises from a *brief conductance increase for small cations,* in direct analogy to the ionic mechanism of the end-plate potential. In addition, the conductance for Cl^- ions seems to be increased. The equilibrium potential of the EPSP is ca. -15 mV. The duration of the conductance change, as computed from the time course of the EPSP and the membrane time constant of the motoneuron, is 1–2 ms [3, 17]. The unknown transmitter, then, acts on the subsynaptic membrane of the motoneuron about as long as ACh acts at the end plate. That the transmitter for the EPSP is not ACh has been established beyond doubt by many pharmacological tests. Candidates are Substance P (p.68) and glutamate [12, 20].

The triggering of the action potential. The membrane of the **axon hillock,** the region where the axon leaves the soma, has a distinctly lower threshold for triggering an action potential than that of the soma and dendrites. In motoneurons, therefore, and probably in other (if not all) nerve cells, conducted action potentials originate at the axon hillock, which is thus the common site at which the activity of all somatic and dendritic synapses becomes effective. Because the axon arises directly from the axon hillock, once an action potential has been generated there its propagation into the periphery is ensured.

Effectiveness of somatic and dendritic synapses. Because EPSPs spread passively (electrotonically) over the cell membrane, somatic synapses near the axon hillock would be expected to influence the excitability of a neuron more than the more distant dendritic synapses. This may be partially correct, but the disadvantage of distance seems to be compensated to some extent by the occurrence of particularly large EPSPs in the dendrites. The cause of this difference probably lies in the cable properties of the dendrites – that is, on the postsynaptic side [9]. The relative importance of the somatic and dendritic synapses, however, is not yet entirely clear.

Cell size and excitability. Other things being equal, the *excitability of a motoneuron is greater, the smaller the neuron.* Conversely, a motoneuron is *more readily inhibited, the larger it is* [21, 22]. Small motoneurons are thus easier to excite and harder to inhibit than large motoneurons, and the same relationship probably applies to other neurons. The excitability of a neuron is probably a function of its input resistance. Because this is higher in a small cell, a given current through the subsynaptic membrane gives rise to a larger EPSP than it would in a large cell. Because this relationship has not been found for inhibitability, it

may be inferred that during inhibition the conductance changes are a more decisive factor than the membrane-potential shifts they induce (cf. p.62).

The size of a motoneuron seems to be of considerable functional significance in several respects. For example, **large motoneurons** also have axons with large diameter and correspondingly high conduction velocity. These axons supply many (often around 1000) muscle fibers (that is, they form large *motor units;* cf. p.40). The muscle fibers innervated by the thick motor axons are of the large "white" rapidly contracting type, which can develop large tension but soon fatigue. They enter complete tetanus (cf. Fig.2-7, p.39) only when the excitation frequency is high (ca. 50 Hz). When the large motoneurons are strongly depolarized, by an intracellularly applied current or by equivalent transsynaptic activity, the initial high discharge rate declines sharply; there is *rapid adaptation.* These are thus called **phasic motoneurons.**

The thin axons of the small motoneurons supply considerably fewer muscle fibers, forming smaller motor units. These muscle fibers are also thinner than those supplied by the large motoneurons; they contract more slowly and develop less maximal tension, but do not fatigue as rapidly and achieve complete tetanus at lower excitation frequencies (ca. 20 Hz). These muscle fibers tend to be of the "red" muscle type. When the small motoneurons are depolarized the result is a prolonged discharge with only slight adaptation. Therefore, they are called **tonic motoneurons.**

In addition to neurons that are clearly of the large, phasic or small, tonic types, there are intermediate forms. The skeletal muscles are innervated by varying proportions of large and small motoneurons, depending on their function. Muscles that participate often in rapid movements tend to be innervated more by phasic motoneurons, whereas muscles specialized for sustained work have a predominantly tonic innervation. But each motor unit, as was evident in the above comments, consists of a single type of muscle fiber. This *uniformity* within a motor unit arises during development as a consequence of a "trophic" influence, not yet understood in detail, of the motoneuron on the muscle fibers it supplies. Thus when ontogeny is completed, the motoneurons innervating each muscle, and thus its proportions of small and large motor units, are fixed.

The relationships between cell size and excitability, and those between size of a motoneuron and the properties of the muscle fibers it supplies (the motor unit), have a surprising consequence. As a muscle does progressively harder work, the *first* motor units brought into play are always the *small* ones, with their slowly contracting red fibers, which develop slight but finely graded force. Only when great to extreme strength is required do the large motor units come into action, their thick pale fibers developing large but less accurately controllable force. It is therefore by no means the case that all motor units are put to work equally often during a lifetime. The "work load" is very unevenly distributed; *small motoneurons and the associated muscle fibers are active much more frequently than large motor units.*

Gamma motoneurons. The motoneurons described so far innervate the working musculature. Their axons are of the $A\alpha$ type (cf. Table 1-2, p.24). Together, they are called the **α motoneurons** (alpha motoneurons). But there is another group of particularly small motoneurons, with thin axons of the $A\gamma$ type. These **γ motoneurons** (gamma motoneurons) constitute about a third of all motoneurons. They innervate the muscle fibers of the muscle spindles (cf. p.83). Most γ motoneurons exhibit a resting discharge; their discharge rate is usually higher than that of the α motoneurons, and they often give repetitive responses. These properties appear to be a direct consequence of their small size.

EPSPs in Other Nerve Cells

The observations so far made of other neurons, though in part very incomplete, indicate that EPSPs of the type just described also occur in other neurons of the CNS. Somewhat shorter and longer time courses, with regard to both the rising and falling phases of the EPSP, have been observed; on the whole, the currently prevailing view is that the EPSPs of motoneurons tend to have shorter time courses than most other EPSPs. But this statement can be made only with the qualification that the *majority* of central synapses have not yet been studied, and most of those that have been are of necessity in *large* neurons [3, 4, 9, 11, 12, 18].

Finally, peripheral sympathetic ganglion cells have been found to have remarkably slow EPSPs (lasting many seconds to minutes; p.119). Such potentials may be highly significant in the *long-term transmission of information* from neuron to neuron, for they offer the simplest means of adjusting the level of excitability for long periods.

3.3 Central Inhibitory Chemical Synapses

Two types of inhibition are known to exist: in **postsynaptic inhibition** the excitability of the soma and dendrite membrane of the neuron is decreased, whereas in **presynaptic inhibition** the release of transmitter at presynaptic endings is reduced or prevented entirely. In the vertebrate CNS postsynaptic inhibition appears to play the larger role; presynaptic inhibition is found chiefly at the presynaptic endings of somatic and visceral afferents, and is less common in the remainder of the nervous system.

Postsynaptic Inhibition

Inhibitory postsynaptic potentials in the motoneuron. From measurements of reflex contractions it has long been known that stimulation of muscle-spindle afferents not only excites the homonymous motoneurons but simultaneously inhibits the antagonistic moto-

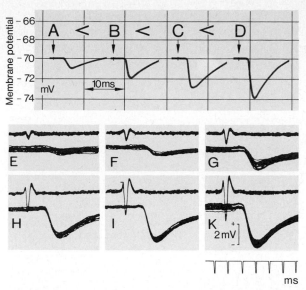

Fig.3-9 A–K. Inhibitory postsynaptic potentials (IPSPs). Experimental set-up as in Fig.3-8 A, except that a nerve antagonistic to the motoneuron is stimulated. **A–D** Schematic representation of inhibitory postsynaptic potentials as the afferent stimulus intensity is increased. **E–K** Inhibitory postsynaptic potentials in a motoneuron of the semitendinosus muscle of the cat; stimulation of quadriceps nerve. The afferent volleys recorded from the zone of entry of the dorsal root (extracellular, unipolar recording; cf. Fig.3-8 A) appear as triphasic deflections of the upper trace. Note that the spinal latency is distinctly longer than that in Fig.3-8, which indicates that there is an interneuron in the spinal reflex path. **E–K** from [3]

neurons (for details see p.86). The potentials thus generated in such an antagonistic motoneuron are shown in Fig.3-9. Each stimulus elicits a *hyperpolarizing* potential shift, with a time course, independent of amplitude, that closely resembles the time course of the EPSP. The hyperpolarization drives the membrane potential away from the threshold for conducted excitation, inhibiting the motoneuron. Therefore the hyperpolarizations in Fig.3-9 are called **inhibitory postsynaptic potentials (IPSPs).**

Ionic mechanism of the IPSP. The time course of the IPSP is practically the mirror image of that of the EPSP, with a rise time of 1–2 ms and a fall time of 10–12 ms. Here, too, the subsynaptic conductance change lasts about 1–2 ms [3]. Measurement of the **equilibrium potential** of the IPSP with the arrangement diagrammed in Fig.3-10 A (cf. Fig.3-5) gave a value of $E_{IPSP} = -80$ mV. Because the equilibrium potential of the K^+ ions is ca. -90 mV, and that of the Cl^- ions is equal to the resting potential, E_{IPSP} is about halfway between E_K and E_{Cl}. This finding suggested that during the time that the inhibitory transmitter is acting on the subsynaptic membrane there is a marked increase in the conductance for K^+ and

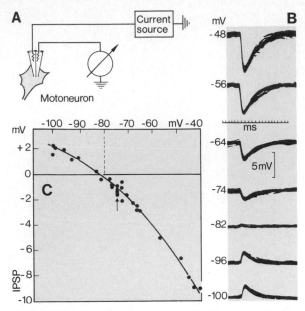

Fig. 3-10 A–C. Measurement of the equilibrium potential of the inhibitory postsynaptic potential. **A** One barrel of a double-barreled intracellular microelectrode is used to change the membrane potential of the motoneuron by means of an adjustable current source. **B** Inhibitory postsynaptic potentials in a motoneuron to the semitendinosus muscle, elicited by constant-intensity stimulation of the quadriceps nerve. Amplitude and polarity of the resulting IPSPs depend on the membrane potential. **C** Graphic representation of the complete series of measurements, some of which were shown in **B**. Abscissa: Membrane potential; ordinate: maximal amplitude of the IPSP. Hyperpolarizing IPSPs are plotted below the zero line, and depolarizing above. The equilibrium potential is ca. −80 mV. The resting potential of the cell was −74 mV (*arrow* in **C**). From [3]

Cl^- [3, 17]. This hypothesis is supported by the finding that intracellularly (electrophoretically) injected small cations or small anions can pass through the activated subsynaptic membrane of inhibitory synapses, whereas ions with a diameter greater than that of the hydrated K^+ ion (e.g., Na^+) cannot.

Pore hypothesis. The general impression derived, in particular by ECCLES [3, 4, 17, 18], from these findings and similar results of experiments on other synapses is that the transmitters act on subsynaptic membranes to open **pores** or **channels** of a certain diameter, through which all ions with a smaller diameter can pass. If the wall of the pore is electrically charged, this charge obstructs the passage of ions with a charge of the same polarity. That is, a negatively charged pore would pass only cations, and not anions.

Inhibitory effects of the IPSP. The inhibition exerted by the IPSP is based on both the **hyperpolarization of the membrane potential** and the **initial increase in membrane conductance**. The differential action of

these two inhibitory mechanisms can be seen in Fig. 3-11 B. An EPSP produced late in the IPSP is simply shifted by an amount corresponding to the hyperpolarization at the time (middle and right recordings in B), whereas one produced during the initial phase of the IPSP is smaller than the control EPSP (in A). The sketches in C show the reason for this difference between the active and the subsequent phase. On the left, excitatory and inhibitory synapses are activated at about the same time; the influx of Na^+ ions through the subsynaptic membrane of the excitatory synapse is partially compensated by the outflow of K^+ ions at the inhibitory synapse. The resulting potential change in the depolarizing direction is therefore smaller than that at the time illustrated on the right, when the inhibitory synapse is not activated.

According to the description given so far, the **role of the Cl^- ions in production of the IPSP** is small. This is true as long as the IPSP is initiated at the normal resting potential, for E_{Cl} is at the resting potential. But if the IPSP is initiated when the membrane potential is depolarized (temporarily, by an EPSP), the increased Cl^- permeability enhances the inflow of Cl^- ions and thus contributes to the increase in IPSP amplitude that is evident, for example, in Fig. 3-10.

If the membrane potential is at the equilibrium potential of the IPSP, by definition the activation of inhibitory synapses does not cause a potential shift. Nevertheless, during the active phase of the IPSP the cell is inhibited by the increased K^+ and Cl^- conductance of the membrane. During this time whatever charge displacement occurs is at least partially compensated by the charge displacement that then ensues at the inhibitory subsynaptic membrane (cf. Fig. 3-11 C). During repetitive asynchronous activation of many inhibitory synapses the conductance can increase so greatly that even large excitatory currents produce only slight depolarization.

Transmitter release at inhibitory synapses. The mechanism of transmitter release at inhibitory synapses probably closely resembles that at excitatory synapses. *Synaptic vesicles* are present at both types of synapse, and excitatory and inhibitory synapses are indistinguishable by any other morphological criterion. The inhibitory transmitter at motoneurons and many other – but not all – inhibitory synapses is the amino acid **glycine** (cf. p. 68).

The blocking of inhibitory synapses. Two poisons are known to block synaptic transmission at inhibitory synapses on motoneurons, and probably other central neurons, thus causing **convulsions. Strychnine** competes with the inhibitory transmitter at the subsynaptic membrane (cf. the action of curare at the end plate), while **tetanus toxin** probably prevents the release of the transmitter from the inhibitory presynaptic ending (cf. the effects of Mg^{++} and botulinum toxin at the end plate). Because a tetanus infection, once manifest, is usually lethal, active protection by innoculation (with tetanus toxoid) is to be generally recommended.

IPSPs at other neurons. As far as is yet known, the results of studies on motoneurons apply to other neurons as well. Certainly in a number of central (including cortical) neurons IPSPs essentially analogous to those of motoneurons have been observed. With regard to details of the time course, however, there can be considerable differences. The excitatory and inhibitory synaptic events occurring at the membranes of central neurons can be summarized as in Fig. 3-12. Activation of the excitatory subsynaptic membrane causes depolarization, which may reach the threshold (EPSP on the left) and elicit a conducted action potential at the axon hillock. At the activated inhibitory subsynaptic membrane the permeability to K^+ and Cl^- ions is increased, causing hyperpolarization (red tracing on the right). Because of the IPSP, the EPSP fails to reach threshold and the cell is inhibited.

In sympathetic ganglia slow synaptically elicited hyperpolarizations have been observed, analogous to the slow EPSPs; these **slow inhibitory postsynaptic potentials** (cf. p. 119) have synaptic latencies of 30–100 ms and a duration of several hundred milliseconds.

Presynaptic Inhibition

Demonstration and definition of presynaptic inhibition. When monosynaptic EPSPs are elicited in a motoneuron by the stimulation of homonymous musclespindle afferents, the amplitude of these EPSPs can be reduced (Fig. 3-13 A, B) by the prior stimulation of certain other afferents (for functional organization see p. 91), even though no IPSP is generated in the motoneuron. Moreover, an intracellular electrode reveals no other changes in the properties of the postsynaptic membrane (threshold, antidromic excitability, resistance). Therefore it is very likely that the reduction of the EPSP has a *presynaptic* cause – that is, a reduced release of transmitter at the presynaptic endings of the excitatory synapses. This form of inhibition is called **presynaptic inhibition** [3]. The objections so far raised against this hypothesis have been, for the most part, refuted [9, 26, 27]. The advantage of presynaptic inhibition lies in its selectivity; single inputs to a nerve cell can be inhibited, whereas postsynaptic inhibition reduces the excitability of the neuron as a whole.

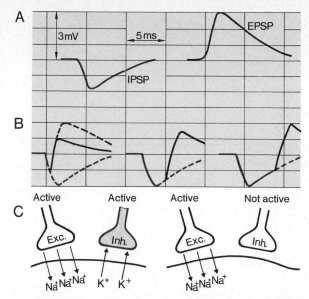

Fig. 3-11 A–C. Effect of IPSP on EPSP. Experimental arrangement as in Figs. 3-8 and 3-9. Stimulation of the antagonistic nerve gives the IPSP in **A**, and stimulation of the homonymous nerve gives the EPSP. In **B** the EPSP was triggered about 1, 3 and 5 ms after the onset of the IPSP. **C** is a diagram of the subsynaptic permeability changes occurring when excitatory and inhibitory synapses are activated simultaneously *(left)* and when only the excitatory synapses are activated. After ECCLES et al.

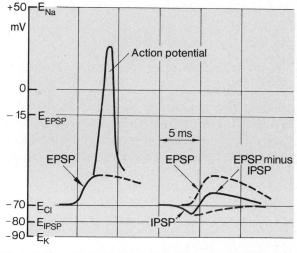

Fig. 3-12. The effect of an IPSP on the action potential. Experimental arrangement as in Fig. 3-11. The homonymous nerve is stimulated strongly enough to produce a suprathreshold EPSP *(left)*. *On the right,* the antagonistic nerve is stimulated about 3 ms before the homonymous nerve. The equilibrium potentials of Na^+, K^+, Cl^-, EPSP and IPSP are shown. After Eccles

Axo-axonal synapses: histological substrate of presynaptic inhibition. The activation of axo-axonal synapses appears to be responsible for the diminished release of transmitter in presynaptic inhibition. Such axo-axonal synapses have been found by electron

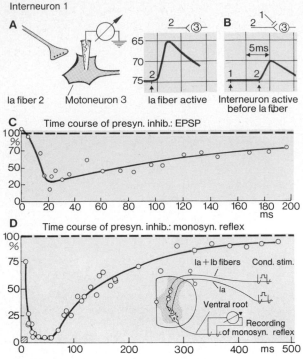

Fig. 3-13 A–D. Presynaptic inhibition. **A** Experimental arrangement to demonstrate presynaptic inhibition of a monosynaptic EPSP in a motoneuron (cf. inset in **D** and Fig. 3-8). **B** EPSP after stimulation of the homonymous Ia fibers without *(left)* and with prior activation of presynaptic inhibitory interneurons. **C** Time course of the presynaptic inhibition of the monosynaptic EPSP of a plantar motoneuron by prior (conditioning) afferent volleys in the Group-I fibers of the nerves to the knee flexors of the cat. **D** Time course of presynaptic inhibition of a monosynaptic reflex. The inset shows the experimental arrangement and the reflex path for presynaptic inhibition, which includes at least 2 interneurons. (Experiments of ECCLES et al., cited in [3] and [26])

microscopy at many places where physiological findings suggest the existence of presynaptic inhibition (refs. in [26, 27]). In particular, the presynaptic endings of those *afferent fibers* that end in the *spinal cord* and in the *dorsal-column* and *trigeminal nuclei* seem to be under strong presynaptic control (cf. p. 91). The **axo-axonal synapses** have all the characteristics of **chemical** synapses – for example, presynaptic vesicles, synaptic cleft and thickening of the postsynaptic membrane. Examples of axo-axonal synapses are shown schematically in Fig. 3-13 A and in Fig. 1-1, p. 3.

Time course of presynaptic inhibition. Fig. 3-13 illustrates in C the time course of the presynaptic inhibition of a motoneuronal EPSP, and in D the time course of the depression of a monosynaptic reflex induced by presynaptic inhibition. Inhibition becomes maximal ca. 15–20 ms after its onset, and the return to the control level takes 100–150 ms, or often even long-

er. The time course of *presynaptic inhibition* is thus *considerably longer* than that of *postsynaptic inhibition* of motoneurons.

Mechanism of presynaptic inhibition; the significance of primary afferent depolarization, PAD. Activation of the axo-axonal synapse induces depolarization on the postsynaptic side. This depolarization can be recorded intracellularly in primary afferent fibers in the spinal cord (Fig. 3-14 A, C), in which case it is called **primary afferent depolarization (PAD).** Because the PAD spreads electrotonically along the afferent fibers into the dorsal root, it can also be recorded extracellularly there. This potential is called the **dorsal root potential (DRP;** Fig. 3-14 B, D). The *time course of the PAD,* and thus of the DRP, corresponds to that of presynaptic inhibition (compare Fig. 3-13 with Fig. 3-14). The PAD is thus a postsynaptic potential in a primary afferent fiber, which appears during presynaptic inhibition of this fiber at the subsynaptic membrane of the axo-axonal synapse and spreads passively (electrotonically) in the antidromic direction along the afferent. The PAD is probably caused chiefly by an increase in Na^+ permeability of the subsynaptic membrane [9]. With intense activation of the axo-axonal synapse the sharply rising PAD can elicit antidromic potentials in the primary afferent fiber (so-called **dorsal-root reflexes,** DRR). These seem to have no physiological significance, but they have been used in the experimental analysis of presynaptic inhibition as a sign of a large PAD [26].

The reduction of transmitter release during presynaptic inhibition probably occurs by way of a *decrease in amplitude of the presynaptic action potential,* by inactivation (cf. p. 15). In the extreme case, apparently, the conducted excitation in the presynaptic endings becomes completely blocked, so that the action potential can enter the ending only by passive electrotonic spread, releasing very little or no transmitter.

Pharmacological influences on presynaptic inhibition. Certain **convulsant poisons** (bicuculline, picrotoxin, but not strychnine) inhibit presynaptic inhibition – an effect that must certainly be involved in the initiation of convulsions by these poisons. The most selective action seems to be that of *bicuculline,* for *picrotoxin* apparently also acts at other sites in the CNS. Because these substances are competitive antagonists of the transmitter GABA at other synapses (cf. p. 68), it seems likely that GABA is also the transmitter at the axo-axonal synapse [15, 26].

3.4 The Transmitters at Chemical Synapses

On page 56 the "life cycle" of a transmitter molecule was described, with ACh as the example. For all other transmitter substances as well, it has been demonstrated or can be inferred that systems for their synthesis, storage, release, and inactivation and for the return of their breakdown products into the presynaptic ending exist, and that after release the substance reacts with subsynaptic receptors. The abundance of data assembled to date cannot be discussed in detail here. Therefore in the following paragraphs, after a basic introduction, commentary will be largely restricted to those findings that are either of relatively broad significance or of great clinical interest.

Absence of Transmitter Specificity

Dale's principle. Dale and his co-workers in the 1930's showed that ACh is the transmitter at the neuromuscular junction and in sympathetic ganglia. His findings led him to the view that each neuron constitutes a unit with regard to its metabolism, and thus releases the same transmitter at all its presynaptic endings. This interpretation became known as **Dale's principle.** In mature neurons no exceptions to this rule have yet been discovered. However, in the course of their development some neurons temporarily synthesize and release more than one transmitter substance. Moreover, in the terminals of some unusual neurons two potential transmitter substances seem to coexist.

Concept of functional and ionic specificity. The discovery of an inhibitory interneuron in the reflex path of direct inhibition (cf. p. 78) implied to Eccles that a given transmitter in the CNS should always have only excitatory or only inhibitory actions. In this view, each central neuron can be classified as an excitatory or an inhibitory neuron; this is the **concept of functional specificity.** This concept was expanded by the suggestion that each central transmitter should always produce the same changes in ion permeability, which then would lead either to EPSPs or to IPSPs: the *concept of ionic specificity.* In the vertebrate nervous systems, so far, no striking exceptions to the concept of functional specificity are known. By contrast, the concept of ionic specificity has been found not to hold in several cases, at least in the peripheral nervous system. For example, ACh has an excitatory action on the neuromuscular end plate, at the Renshaw cell and at certain autonomic synapses (p. 114), but it is inhibitory at the synapses between vagus and car-

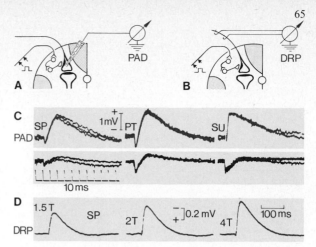

Fig. 3-14 A–D. Demonstration of primary afferent depolarization by presynaptic inhibition. **A, C** Intracellular recording from a dorsal root fiber of the sural nerve. Stimulation of the sup. peroneal *(SP)*, post. tibial *(PT)* and sural *(SU)* nerves generates the intracellular potential fluctuations labelled *PAD*. The records shown just below these were obtained directly outside the fiber (field potentials) during identical stimulation. Subtraction of the field potentials from the intracellular potentials above them gives the primary afferent depolarization induced by activation of the axo-axonal synapse. **B, D** Extracellular recording of primary afferent depolarization from a lumbar dorsal-root filament (dorsal-root potential, DRP). The sup. peroneal nerve *(SP)* was stimulated with the multiples of the threshold intensity T indicated in **D.** (Experiments of ECCLES et al., cited in [26])

diac muscle fibers. It is to be concluded that the **properties of the subsynaptic membrane,** rather than those of the transmitter, determine whether the action of the transmitter is excitatory or inhibitory. Viewed in this light, it seems conceivable in principle that there could be a nervous system with only one transmitter, which by binding with the appropriate subsynaptic receptors causes a wide variety of conductance changes. The fact that this is not the general case may indicate that transmitters have other functions apart from their actions at synapses – for example, as chemotactic or trophic factors.

Acetylcholine as a Transmitter Substance in the Nervous System

ACh at Renshaw cells. In accordance with Dale's principle, ACh is the transmitter substance released by motoneurons not only at the end plate, but also at their presynaptic endings on the *Renshaw cells.* Subsynaptic ACh receptors with an excitatory action can be assigned to two classes, clearly distinguishable pharmacologically. Receptors of the *nicotinic* type are blocked by curare and mediate a brief EPSP; receptors of the *muscarinic* type bring about a longer EPSP and are insensitive to curare (for the full definition of nicotinic and muscarinic properties see p. 114; for physiology of the Renshaw cell see p. 91). The two kinds of EPSP appear to be produced by different changes in conductance.

ACh in the autonomic nervous system. In the *sympathetic part* of the autonomic nervous system ACh acts as the transmitter at all ganglionic synapses, at the synapses in the adrenal medulla, and at the postganglionic synapses in the sweat glands. In the *parasympathetic* part it is also the transmitter in all the ganglia as well as at postganglionic effector synapses. The clinically important physiology and pharmacology of all these synapses is discussed in Chapter 6 (pp. 111–121). Both the normal EPSP and the slow EPSP in sympathetic ganglia (p. 119) are brought about by ACh. Feldberg pointed out that ACh is the transmitter of all axons that leave the central nervous system (motoneurons and preganglionic autonomic nerve fibers).

ACh as transmitter in the central nervous system. ACh and acetylcholine esterase have been demonstrated in many brain fractions, sometimes in considerable amounts; but apart from the cholinergic synapses at the Renshaw cell it has not yet been possible to provide convincing identification of other central *cholinergic* synapses. Nevertheless, it is very likely that ACh functions as a transmitter in the central nervous system as well [20].

Adrenergic Transmitter Substances

Distribution, nomenclature, evidence. The category adrenergic transmitters includes **adrenalin** and **noradrenalin** and their precursor **dopamine.** *Noradrenalin* is the transmitter at all postganglionic sympathetic endings, with the exception of the sweat glands (cf. p. 114). *Adrenalin* is secreted along with noradrenalin in the adrenal medulla (cf. p. 116). In the cases of *noradrenalin* and *dopamine* it is practically certain that they also act as transmitters in the CNS – in the hypothalamus and the nuclear regions of the motor brainstem ganglia, for instance, as well as in the spinal cord and other places. Details are given in the sections concerned with these regions.

Adrenalin, noradrenalin and *dopamine* together are called **catecholamines**; together with serotonin (5-hydroxytryptamine), they are also called **monoamines.** A method developed by Falk et al. can be used to make the monoamines visible in the **fluorescence microscope.** Comparisons of animals pharmacologically pretreated in such a way that one or another monoamine is selectively abolished allow each individual

monoamine to be identified [14, 16]. The catecholamines are found not only in neurons but also in certain other types of cells, called *chromaffin cells* or *pheochrome cells* because of the characteristic histochemical reaction of their granules [1]. In this category are cells of the adrenal medulla, the epididymis, and the sympathetic paraganglia (e.g., the corpora paraaortica, or Zuckerkandl's organ).

Biosynthesis of the catecholamines. Noradrenalin and adrenalin are derived from tyrosine in a series of enzyme-catalyzed steps of synthesis. The main synthesis pathway, beginning with phenylalanine and arriving at the catecholamines dopamine, noradrenalin and adrenalin by way of tyrosine and dopa, is illustrated in Fig. 3-15. The step that limits the rate of synthesis is the hydroxylation of tyrosine to dopa by **tyrosine hydroxylase.** Little is known as yet about the subcellular distribution of this enzyme or of **dopa decarboxylase,** but neither seems to be (or to be only) bound to particles. By contrast, it appears certain that dopamine-β-hydroxylase is localized in the storage granules (vesicles). In addition to the chief pathway shown in Fig. 3-15, there are various other metabolic side paths by which *noradrenalin* is synthesized. The physiological significance of these synthetic pathways, however, is apparently very slight [2].

Storage. In the **granules** of the cells in the *adrenal medulla* the presence of adrenalin and noradrenalin has been demonstrated directly (refs. in [9]). Their concentration there is twice the osmolarity of the body fluid, so that they cannot be in free solution. Because they are stored in a constant stoichiometric proportion to ATP, calcium and magnesium, it is plausible that they are bound to these in the form of complexes. In the *sympathetic nerve endings,* too, the greater part of the noradrenalin appears to be stored in the **vesicles,** so that the situation here can be regarded as analogous to that in the adrenal medulla.

Release of catecholamines by action potentials. On the whole, the processes underlying release of noradrenalin at sympathetic nerve endings seem to be analogous to those underlying the release of acetylcholine at the motor end plate. The presence of calcium ions is necessary, and an excess of magnesium ions has an inhibitory effect. The transmitter is released in quanta, single elementary quanta being released occasionally in resting conditions. The vesicles visible in the electron microscope are very probably the morphological substrate of the electrophysiologically demonstrable transmitter quanta. Analogous relationships can be inferred for transmission by the other catecholamines [2].

Termination of transmitter action. Unlike cholinergic transmission, in adrenergic transmission enzymatic breakdown plays no appreciable role. The catecholamines are converted to biologically inactive metabolites by **monoamine oxidase** (MAO) and **catechol-O-methyl-transferase** (COMT), but even the simultaneous blocking of both paths of enzymatic breakdown causes no appreciable enhancement or prolongation of the effect on the target organ produced by either sympathetic stimulation or intravenous injection of noradrenalin.

A more important factor in the termination of catecholamine action appears to be the nearly complete **uptake** or *re-uptake* of the transmitter into the presynaptic nerve endings. Noradrenalin uptake into the sympathetic neurons has been characterized as *active transport* across the membrane, independent of calcium but dependent on the sodium concentration and on intact aerobic and anaerobic energy metabolism. It must be assumed that the situation at the other catecholaminergic nerve endings is analogous. The *re-uptake of transmitter* is thus not only significant with regard to the rapid termination of the action on the target organ; it also prevents emptying of the presynaptic stores when they are drawn upon repeatedly [2].

Serotonin *(5-hydroxytryptamine, 5-HT).* 5-HT is a monoamine, but it is not counted as one of the adrenergic transmitters in the strict sense. 5-HT is formed in the body by hydroxylation and decarboxylation of the essential amino acid *tryptophan* (Fig. 3-16). It is inactivated primarily by monoamine oxidases, by conversion to 5-hydroxyacetaldehyde and then to 5-hydroxy-indoleacetic acid. The role of 5-HT as a transmitter substance is not yet clear. In the CNS it is found chiefly in the raphe nuclei of the brainstem and in the hypothalamus, where it seems to participate especially in regulation of the sleeping/waking state (cf. p. 160). The chemical relationship or antagonism between 5-HT and various hallucinogens such as LSD (lysergic acid diethylamide) indicates that the 5-HT level in the brain also influences other aspects of behavior (p. 143).

Pharmacology. The opportunities for influencing adrenergic transmission pharmacologically are extraordinarily numerous. In recent years drugs have been developed that act on the different steps in synthesis and enzymatic breakdown of the monoamines (especially the catecholamines), that interfere with their storage or release by action potentials, and that inhibit the action on the receptors in the target organ or the return of the transmitter into the nerve ending. Because the enzyme systems of the catecholamines,

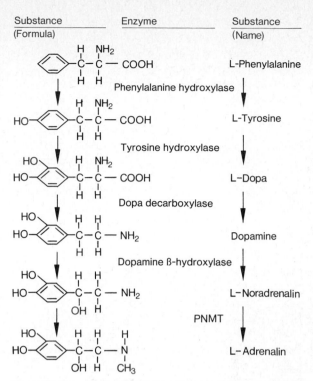

Fig. 3-15. Biosynthesis of noradrenalin and adrenalin, showing the enzymes involved. PNMT, phenylethanolamine-N-methyl-transferase. The part of the molecule changed at each step of the synthesis is shown in *red*

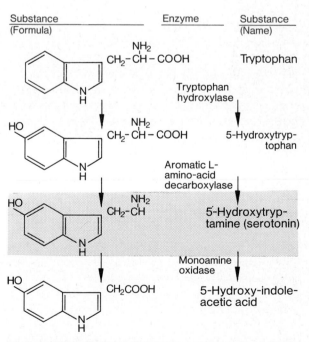

Fig. 3-16. Biosynthesis and breakdown of serotonin *(red background),* showing the enzymes involved. Serotonin is first deaminated to 5-hydroxyacetaldehyde by monoamine oxidase (MAO) and then oxidized to 5-hydroxy-indoleacetic acid

like their storage and transport mechanisms, often exhibit no strict chemical specificity, there is the further possibility that the physiological transmitter substances may be replaced by so-called **false transmitters** or *substitute transmitters*. This possibility is particularly interesting because it not only allows for the general attenuation or enhancement of physiological effect achievable with other methods, but in addition offers a chance to establish novel action patterns – modified qualitatively as well as quantitatively – which in future may be of great therapeutic importance. The necessary details with regard to the autonomic nervous system are covered on p. 115. To the extent that important pharmacological aspects of adrenergic transmission in other parts of the CNS are known, they are discussed in the relevant sections.

Amino Acids

Some amino acids are found in the CNS in relatively high concentrations. As a result, they have long been suspected of functioning as transmitters. Many pharmacological and, in particular, microelectrophoretic studies have given support to this idea. The picture that seems to emerge is that ACh and the monoamines, in addition to their roles in the peripheral and autonomic nervous systems, are important mainly for the function of the higher and highest parts of the CNS, whereas the large afferent and efferent excitatory and inhibitory tract systems tend rather to employ the amino acids as transmitters [2, 9, 11, 12, 15, 20, 25].

Gamma-aminobutyric acid **(GABA)** is synthesized exclusively in the nervous system, being derived from *glutamic acid* with the help of *glutamine decarboxylase*. It is found everywhere in the CNS, in widely varying concentrations. When applied electrophoretically, GABA (like a number of other *neutral amino acids*) as a rule has an inhibitory action. There is some evidence that GABA is involved in **presynaptic inhibition** in vertebrates, as the *transmitter at the axo-axonal synapses* (cf. p. 64 [15, 26]). GABA has been unequivocally shown to be an inhibitory transmitter in crustaceans. Certain convulsant poisons – in particular the alkaloid *bicucullin, picrotoxin,* and *penicillin* – appear to be more or less specific antagonists of GABA.

The ubiquitous amino acid **glycine** also seems to serve as a transmitter; at least, it is probably responsible for certain forms of **postsynaptic inhibition** in the spinal cord. *Strychnine* seems to be a specific antagonist of *glycine*. Because it abolishes the postsynaptic inhibition, strychnine administration causes convulsions [15].

Glutamic acid and other *acidic amino acids* usually have an **excitatory** action when applied microelectrophoretically. Because glutamic acid is found throughout the CNS, it is entirely likely that it not only serves as a precursor of GABA (see above) but in addition functions as a transmitter itself [9, 15].

Other Possible Transmitters

Histamine. Histamine is produced by the decarboxylation of the amino acid histidine. Fairly large concentrations are found in the hypophysis and the adjacent median eminence of the hypothalamus. In the remaining parts of the CNS the histamine content is very low. Otherwise, there are only a few pharmacological findings that might indicate a transmitter function of histamine.

Neuroactive peptides. The number of recognized neuroactive peptides, consisting of more or less long chains of amino acids, is steadily increasing. Some of them are **neurohormones,** substances released from nerve cells to be carried by the bloodstream to their (non-neuronal) target sites. Among these are the *releasing hormones,* which act on the adenohypophysis (survey on p. 664), and *antidiuretic hormone* (vasopressin) and *oxytocin* (p. 661), which are synthesized in the hypothalamus and stored in the neurohypophysis.

Other peptides may be **transmitters** in the strict sense. Substance P, for example, which is composed of eleven amino acids, has been proposed as the transmitter of primary afferent fibers in the spinal cord [5].

Still other peptides "modulate" the activity of neurons not by synapses, but by their general presence as hormones. It is likely that the *endorphins* are examples of such **neuromodulators.** The term "endorphin" is derived from the fact that these substances bind to the same central nervous membrane receptors as do morphine and other opiates, and thus amount to "endogenous" morphine (strictly speaking, it is more correct to say that the opiates bind to the endorphin receptors). This relationship makes it plausible that the endorphins play a role in modulating the conduction and processing of pain. However, this is probably not their only function [2, 6, 7].

At present it must remain an open question whether a peptide synthesized and subsequently released by a nerve cell always performs only one of the tasks outlined above – neurohormone, neurotransmitter or neuromodulator. It is entirely possible that when one or another peptide is released it acts both locally, as a transmitter, and elsewhere as a hormone and/or modulator.

Prostaglandins. The biological significance of this special group of polyunsaturated fatty acids is only now being discovered. In the sympathetic nervous system they appear to have a neuromodulator action (p. 116). Cerebral tissue and cerebrospinal fluid also contain prostaglandins, the role of which is still unknown. It is thought that increased amounts of prostaglandins are synthesized in inflamed tissue, where they may sensitize the pain receptors. The analgesic effect of acetylsalicylic acid (aspirin) is ascribed in part to inhibition of prostaglandin synthesis.

3.5   Electrical Synapses

On the assumption that the electrical properties (resistance, capacitance) of the synaptic regions correspond roughly to those found in other parts of excitable membranes, it can be calculated – as KATZ [10] has clearly demonstrated – that the presynaptic action potential as a rule provides so little current that the postsynaptic membrane of a typical **chemical synapse** (noncontiguous pre- and postsynaptic membranes separated by a synaptic cleft) is depolarized by far less than 0.1 mV. Chemical transmission is thus an indispensable amplification mechanism at these synapses.

But in some populations of cells the morphological contacts are considerably more intimate than those at chemical synapses; this is the case, for example, in most smooth muscles and in myocardial cells. These cell populations represent **functional syncytia**. The junctions between them (e.g., the intercalated disks of the myocardial cells) have electrical properties barely or not at all distinguishable from those of the remaining cytoplasm, so that action potentials are conducted away from them in both directions, over the cell boundaries. The cell junctions in the functional syncytia are not called synapses.

In the CNS, in addition to chemical synapses, there are regions of intimate contact between nerve cells where the synaptic cleft is not the usual 20 nm wide, but only 2 nm, with no fusion of the membranes (unlike the tight junctions, p. 18). Since *electrical synapses* have been found in crustaceans and goldfish, there is a tendency to regard these **gap junctions** between nerve cells as the morphological substrate of *electrical synapses*.

To all appearances, **electrical synapses** are far less common in the mammalian nervous system than chemical synapses. Most electrical synapses are excitatory. A few of them have a pronounced rectifying effect – that is, they conduct electrical currents distinctly better from the pre- to the postsynaptic side than in the other direction. Although electrical synapses are apparently mostly of the **excitatory** type, they can also be inhibitory, under certain morphological conditions [9].

Ephaptic transmission. Every excitable cell is surrounded by a conducting medium, the extracellular space (cf. p. 3). The extracellular currents associated with the action potentials of excited cells are carried by the ions in this medium (cf. p. 5). But these extracellular currents also flow through cells in the vicinity of the excited cell, to an extent that corresponds to the ratio of the membrane resistance to that of the extracellular fluid. Because this ratio is very large, the transmembrane currents are very small. However slight the effect may be, though, the currents do make some change in the membrane potential of the cells through which they flow, and thus have some influence on their excitability. This form of *intercellular communication* is called **ephaptic interaction.**

In *peripheral nerves* ephatic interaction is negligible, and the same is true of central tracts. But in exceptional cases of *injury and disease* suprathreshold ephatic transmission between nerve fibers can apparently occur. The (pathological) contact site is called an **ephapse.** It may be that certain inappropriate sensations experienced by people with nerve damage are caused in part by such ephapses.

The degree to which ephaptic influences are significant in the densely packed neuron populations of the CNS is uncertain. It is conceivable, for example, that they play a role in synchronizing the discharges of such populations, but as yet this possibility is not supported by experimental evidence.

3.6   References

Textbooks and Handbooks

1. AKERT, K., WASER, P.G. (Eds.): Mechanisms of Synaptic Transmission. Progress in Brain Research Vol. 31. Amsterdam: Elsevier 1969
2. COOPER, J.R., BLOOM, F.E., ROTH, R.H.: The Biochemical Basis of Neuropharmacology. 3rd Edition. New York: Oxford University Press 1978
3. ECCLES, J.C.: The Physiology of Synapses. Berlin-Göttingen-Heidelberg-New York: Springer 1964
4. ECCLES, J.C.: The Inhibitory Pathways of the Central Nervous System. The Sherrington Lectures IX. Springfield/Ill.: Ch.C. Thomas 1969
5. VON EULER, U.S., PERNOW, B. (Eds.): Substance P. Nobel Symposium 37. New York: Raven Press 1977
6. GAINER, H. (Ed.): Peptides in Neurobiology. New York-London: Plenum Press 1977
7. GANONG, W.F., MARTINI, L. (Eds.): Frontiers in Neuroendocrinology, Vol. 5. New York: Raven Press 1978

8. Grob, D. (Ed.): Myasthenia gravis. Ann. N. Y. Acad. Sci. *274*, 1–682 (1976)

9. Kandel, E. R. (Vol. Ed.): Handbook of Physiology: Section 1: The Nervous System. Vol. I. Cellular Biology of Neurons, Parts 1 and 2, pp. 1–1182. American Physiological Society, Bethesda, Maryland 1977

10. Katz, B.: Nerve, Muscle, and Synapse. New York: McGraw-Hill 1966

11. Kuffler, S. W., Nicholls, J. G.: From Neuron to Brain. A Cellular Approach to the Function of the Nervous System. Sunderland, Mass.: Sinauer Associates, Inc. 1976

12. The Synapse. Cold Spring Harbor Symp. Quant. Biol. *40*, 1–694 (1976)

13. Zaimis, E. (Ed.): Neuromuscular Junction. Berlin-Heidelberg-New York: Springer 1976

Research Reports and Reviews

14. Corrodi, H., Jonsson, G.: The formaldehyde fluorescence method for the histochemical demonstration of biogenic amines. J. Histochem. Cytochem. *15*, 65 (1967)

15. Curtis, D. R., Johnston, G. A. R.: Amino acid transmitters in the mammalian central nervous system. Ergebn. Physiol. *69*, 97 (1973)

16. Dahlström, A.: Fluorescence histochemistry of monoamines in the CNS. In: Jasper, H. H., Ward, A. A., Pope, A. (Eds.): Basic Mechanisms of the Epilepsies, p. 212. Boston: Little Brown and Co. 1969

17. Eccles, J. C.: The ionic mechanisms of excitatory and inhibitory synaptic action. Ann. N. Y. Acad. Sci. *137*, 473 (1966)

18. Eccles, J. C.: Excitatory and inhibitory mechanisms in brain. In: Jasper, H. H., Ward, A. A., Pope, A. (Eds.): Basic Mechanisms of the Epilepsies, p. 229. Boston: Little, Brown and Co. 1969

19. Gage, P. W.: Generation of end-plate potentials. Physiol. Rev. *56*, 177–247 (1976)

20. Krnjević, K.: Chemical nature of synaptic transmission in vertebrates. Physiol. Rev. *54*, 418 (1974)

21. Henneman, E., Somjen, G., Carpenter, D. O.: Functional significance of cell size in spinal motoneurons. J. Neurophysiol. *28*, 560 (1965)

22. Henneman, E., Somjen, G., Carpenter, D. O.: Excitability and inhibitability of motoneurons of different sizes. J. Neurophysiol. *28*, 599 (1965)

23. Hubbard, J. I.: Microphysiology of vertebrate neuromuscular transmission. Physiol. Rev. *53*, 674 (1973)

24. Hubbard, J. I., Schmidt, R. F.: An electrophysiological investigation of mammalian motor nerve terminal. J. Physiol. (Lond.) *166*, 145 (1963)

25. Iiversen, L. L.: Neurotransmitters, neurohormones, and other small molecules in neurons. In: Schmitt, F. O. (Ed.): The Neurosciences, 2nd Study Program, p. 768. 1970

26. Schmidt, R. F.: Presynaptic inhibition in the vertebrate central nervous system. Ergebn. Physiol. *63*, 20 (1971)

27. Schmidt, R. F.: Control of the access of afferent activity to somatosensory pathways. In: Iggo, A. (Ed.): Handbook of Sensory Physiology, Vol. II, p. 151. Berlin-Heidelberg-New York: Springer 1973

28. Takeuchi, A., Takeuchi, N.: Active phase of frog's endplate potential. J. Neurophysiol. *22*, 395 (1959)

29. Whittaker, V.:aP.: The vesicle hypothesis. In: Andersen, P., Jansen, J. K. S. (Eds.): Excitatory Synaptic Mechanisms, p. 66. Oslo: Universitetsforlaget 1970

30. Whittaker, V. P.: Origin and function of synaptic vesicles. Ann. N. Y. Acad. Sci. *183*, 21 (1971)

4 Physiology of Small Groups of Neurons; Reflexes

R. F. Schmidt

4.1 Typical Neuronal Circuits

This section describes simple **neuron networks** of the kind commonly found in various parts of the brain. These *basic neural circuits* serve, for example, to amplify weak signals, attenuate too intense activity, emphasize contrasts, maintain rhythms or keep a group of neurons in its optimal working range by an adjustment of gain. These *neuron networks* are like integrated circuits in electronics, prefabricated elements that perform frequently needed functions and can be built into a great variety of electronic apparatus.

Divergence and Convergence

Divergence. The afferent fibers of peripheral receptors, which enter the spinal cord in the dorsal roots, there *split up into many collaterals* that run to the spinal nerves. This **divergence** is shown schematically in Fig. 4-1 A. It serves to make afferent information accessible simultaneously to various sections of the CNS. The splitting of the dorsal-root fibers into numerous collaterals is but one example of the divergence found in *practically all parts* of the central nervous system. It is so prevalent that we may speak of a *divergence principle of neuronal connectivity*.

Quantitative estimates of divergence are extraordinarily difficult, because in almost no case are either histological or physiological methods adequate to follow all the collaterals of a neuron. An exception worth mentioning is the *motor axons*, which split up into more or less numerous collaterals within the muscle. Because each muscle fiber is supplied by only one collateral, the **average divergence of each motor axon** can be calculated from the number of motor axons entering the muscle. In man values ranging from 1:15 (extrinsic eye muscles) to 1:1900 (limb musculature) to even more have been found [14]. In addition, before leaving the spinal cord motor axons send out collaterals to the Renshaw cells, but the number of these is not precisely known.

Convergence. Fig. 4-1 A shows two afferent fibers, each with an axon that diverges to 4 neurons, in such a way that 3 of the total of 5 neurons make connections with both afferent fibers. From the viewpoint of the neurons, then, two afferent fibers **converge** onto

each of these neurons. Most neurons of the central nervous system receive inputs from many dozen to thousands of axons, so that we can speak of a *convergence principle of neuronal connectivity*. For example, on the average about 6 000 axon collaterals terminate on a *motoneuron;* they come from the periphery and from very diverse regions in the central nervous system, forming both inhibitory and excitatory synapses (Fig. 4-1 B).

Function of convergence. Because some thousands of axon collaterals converge onto a single motoneuron, it depends on the *sum* and *direction* of the *synaptic processes* acting at each moment whether a motoneu-

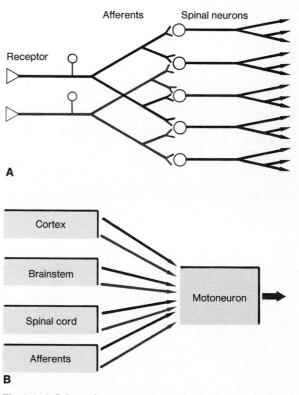

Fig. 4-1. A Schematic representation of the divergence of two dorsal-root fibers (afferents) onto spinal neurons. The axons of these neurons in turn branch into many collaterals. **B** Diagram of the excitatory *(black arrows)* and inhibitory *(red arrows)* influences converging onto a motoneuron. The motoneuron is the "final common path"

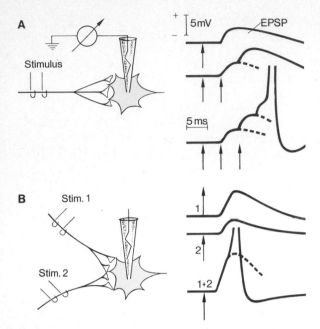

Fig. 4-2 A, B. Facilitation in the nervous system. **A** Temporal facilitation: single stimulus *(one arrow)* and double stimulus (two arrows, interstimulus interval ca. 4 ms) produce a subthreshold EPSP; the third stimulus *(three arrows)* evokes an action potential. **B** Spatial facilitation: Stimuli 1 and 2 each elicit a subthreshold EPSP, but simultaneous stimulation of both axons evokes an action potential

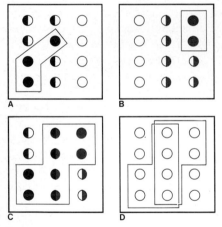

Fig. 4-3 A–D. Facilitation and occlusion. **A–C** Spatial facilitation. The population comprises 12 neurons, 4 of which can be excited by two different afferent inputs (middle row of neurons in **A–C**). With input **A** excitation is subthreshold in three of these neurons (**A,** half-filled circles) and suprathreshold in one (filled circle). Input **B** gives subthreshold excitation in all 4 neurons. Simultaneous activation of inputs **A** and **B** (**C**) produces suprathreshold excitation of all the neurons common to **A** and **B.** As a result, the total number of neurons with suprathreshold excitation is greater than the sum of those excited by the single stimuli (8 > 3 + 2). **D** Occlusion. If excitation is already suprathreshold in the neurons common to the two inputs when only one input is activated (neurons enclosed in both the black and the red outlines in (**D**)), simultaneous activation of both inputs produces suprathreshold excitation in a total number of neurons smaller than the sum of those excited by each stimulus alone (8 < 6 + 6)

ron sends out a conducted action potential or not. In this sense, the motoneuron (like most other neurons) *processes* or **integrates** the excitatory and inhibitory events occurring at its membrane. Long before the discovery of excitatory and inhibitory postsynaptic potentials, this integrative function of the motoneurons was known from studies of muscle contractions elicited by peripheral and central electrical stimulation. Around the turn of the century, the English physiologist Sherrington had already described the motoneuron as the **final common pathway of the motor system** – that is, the cell that weighs all the excitatory and inhibitory influences, one against the other. Action potentials are discharged only when the excitatory influences predominate, or in modern terms, when suprathreshold excitatory postsynaptic potentials are produced.

Temporal and Spatial Facilitation; Occlusion

Temporal facilitation. On the left in Fig. 4-2 A is shown an experimental arrangement for testing the effect produced in a neuron by repetitive stimulation of an axon. The records on the right reveal that because of their relatively long time course (ca. 15 ms) excitatory postsynaptic potentials (EPSPs) triggered in rapid succession are additive, eventually becoming suprathreshold. This type of increase in excitability of a neuron, by *successive EPSPs,* is called **temporal facilitation.** Temporal facilitation of the response to activity in an axon is possible because the duration of the EPSPs is longer than the axonal refractory time. Temporal facilitation is of great physiological importance because many neural processes (for example, receptor discharge) occur repetitively and thus can summate to produce suprathreshold excitation at synapses.

Spatial facilitation. The experimental arrangement in Fig. 4-2 B demonstrates **spatial facilitation:** stimulation of either of the two axons alone produces subthreshold EPSPs, whereas simultaneous stimulation of both gives rise to a conducted action potential – a process that could not be brought about by the individual EPSPs. *In general terms* **facilitation,** whether *spatial* or *temporal,* is occurring when more conducted impulses appear than correspond to the sum of the effects of the individual inputs. This general definition of facilitation is illustrated in Fig. 4-3 A–C; in C the number of neurons exhibiting suprathreshold excitation is greater (8) than the sum of the neurons with suprathreshold excitation in A (3) and B (2).

Occlusion. But it can also happen (Fig. 4-3 D) that when each of two inputs to a neuron population is

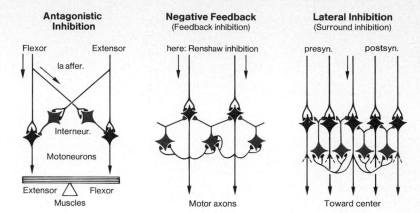

Antagonistic Inhibition

Flexor · Extensor

Ia affer.

Interneur.

Motoneurons

Extensor △ Flexor
Muscles

Negative Feedback
(Feedback inhibition)

here: Renshaw inhibition

Motor axons

Lateral Inhibition
(Surround inhibition)

presyn. · postsyn.

Toward center

Fig. 4-4. Typical inhibitory circuits. In all three neuronal circuits the inhibitory interneurons are shown in *red*

stimulated alone the excitation of all or nearly all the neurons is *suprathreshold*. In this case simultaneous stimulation of both inputs will produce suprathreshold excitation in a very few more neurons than were excited by the single stimuli, so that the total does not even reach the algebraic sum of the single stimuli. This phenomenon is called **occlusion.** The process of facilitation illustrated in Fig. 4-3 A–C has thus been converted to *occlusion* by an increase in the excitability of the neurons involved (e.g., as a result of additional excitatory inputs). The general point is this: if the effect of several stimuli occurring simultaneously or in rapid succession is greater than the sum of the effects of the individual stimuli, we term this *facilitation;* if the response to a combined stimulus is less than the sum of the responses to the individual stimuli, the term *occlusion* applies.

Simple Inhibitory Circuits

Preliminary comments on nomenclature. The term **homonymous** is applied to all motoneurons that send their axons to the same muscle, or that innervate the muscle from which a corresponding afferent comes. **Agonistic** or **synergistic** muscles act to move a joint in the same direction, and **antagonistic** muscles act to move it in opposite directions.

Antagonist inhibition. The Ia afferents of the muscle spindles make excitatory synapses with their homonymous motoneurons and, by way of an interneuron, inhibitory synapses with antagonistic motoneurons (for details see pp. 76 and 87). This situation is diagrammed in Fig. 4-4 A. For example, if the Ia afferents from the muscle spindle of a flexor muscle are activated (arrows), they excite the motoneurons of the homonymous flexor muscle and inhibit the motoneurons to the extensor muscles that act on the same joint. This inhibition is called **antagonist inhibition** or **reciprocal inhibition** [4]. Physiologically, this antagonist inhibition is extremely useful, for it facili-

tates movement of the joint "automatically," without any additional voluntary or involuntary control.

Forward inhibition. In the case of antagonist inhibition shown in Fig. 4-4 A the antagonistic motoneurons are inhibited without having previously been excited. This type of inhibition is called **forward inhibition** or *feed-forward inhibition.* Forward inhibition occurs at many places in the central nervous system.

Feedback inhibition. If the inhibiting interneurons act on the cells by which they themselves were activated, this form of inhibition is **backward inhibition.** In this case the inhibition exerted is greater, the greater the original excitation. In electronics such circuits have come to be known as *negative feedback,* and this has given rise to the widespread use of the term **feedback inhibition** in biology.

Renshaw inhibition. An especially clear example of *feedback inhibition* is provided by the motoneurons. As shown in Fig. 4-4 B, these (even within the spinal cord) send collaterals to interneurons, the axons of which in turn make inhibitory synapses with motoneurons. This inhibitory circuit is called **Renshaw inhibition** in honor of its discoverer, and the inhibitory interneurons are called **Renshaw cells** [3] (for function see p. 91).

Lateral inhibition. A similar form of *feedback inhibition* found in the nervous system is illustrated in Fig. 4-4 C. The inhibitory interneurons are connected in such a way that they act not only on the excited cell itself (arrow), but also on neighboring cells with the same function that are not or are less excited. The result is that these cells are particularly strongly inhibited. Inhibition of this sort is called **lateral inhibition,** because it ensures the production of an inhibitory zone lateral to the excitation. Because the excitation is surrounded by inhibition on all sides, the situation is also called **surround inhibition.** Lateral inhibition plays a particularly large role in afferent systems,

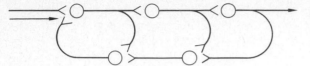

Fig. 4-5. Neuronal circuit giving positive feedback. If suitably dimensioned, this hypothetical circuit could generate reverberating excitation

where it takes the form of postsynaptic inhibition in some cases (right in Fig. 4-4C) and presynaptic inhibition in others (left in Fig. 4-4C). Its advantages are described on p. 181.

Activity-Enhancing Circuits and Mechanisms

Positive feedback. The great significance of inhibitory circuits in the normal function of the central nervous system is generally acknowledged, for it has been demonstrated in a variety of experiments. On the other hand, although the suggestion has repeatedly been put forward it remains debatable whether the central nervous system also comprises circuits for positive feedback – circuits in which excitation of a cell increases its own excitation, so that the *excitation reverberates*. An example of such **excitatory feedback** is illustrated in Fig. 4-5. It could serve to ensure that activity, once induced, is maintained for a long time. Various lines of thought have led to the proposal that *short-term memory* is due to the reverberation of excitation in positive-feedback circuits, but there is essentially no experimental corroboration of this proposal (cf. p. 169). For the present, then, we cannot say whether excitatory feedback occurs to an appreciable extent in the central nervous system, or what physiological significance it may have.

Synaptic potentiation. Repeated use of a synapse often causes a considerable enlargement of the synaptic potentials. This **synaptic potentiation** often occurs *during* the tetanic stimulation, in which case it is called **tetanic potentiation** (Fig. 4-6). If tetanic potentiation outlasts the series of stimuli, or begins only after the stimulus is terminated, the term **posttetanic potentiation** is used (Fig. 4-6 C–F).

The *extent and duration of posttetanic potentiation* depend very much on the synapse concerned and on the duration and frequency of the repetitive stimulation. Single stimuli or brief tetani leave only a slight, brief potentiation (Fig. 4-6C), but as stimulation is prolonged a degree of potentiation many times the original level can be induced (Fig. 4-6 E, F), lasting for minutes to hours (Fig. 4-6 D–F). From a **functional** point of view, posttetanic potentiation amounts to the

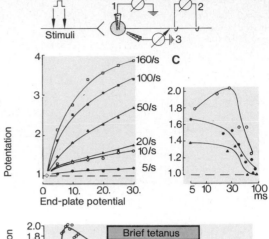

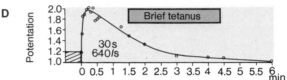

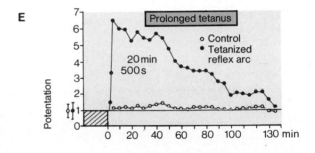

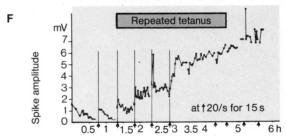

Fig. 4-6 A–F. Tetanic (**B**) and posttetanic potentiation (**C–F**) at peripheral (**B, C**) and central (**D–F**) synapses. **A** Diagram of the experimental arrangements. Potentiation is recorded either (i) as an intracellular synaptic potential (**B–D**), (ii) as an extracellular mass reflex from the ventral root (**E**), or (iii) with an extracellular microelectrode in the neuropil itself (**F**). **B** Tetanic potentiation of an end-plate potential by repetitive stimulation at the frequencies indicated. The degree of potentiation is proportional to the stimulus frequency. Frog, with neuromuscular transmission blocked by replacement of Ca^{++} by Mg^{++}. **C** Brief posttetanic potentiation in the same preparation following one, two and five conditioning stimuli. **D, E** Posttetanic potentiation of the reflex arc of the monosynaptic stretch reflex of the cat. Degree and duration of potentiation are dependent on the duration of the tetanus. (After CURTIS, ECCLES and SPENCER.) **F** Posttetanic potentiation of the discharge of granule cells in the hippocampus, in the course of repeated brief tetani (arrows, 10 Hz for 15 s). (From measurements by Bliss and Lømo.) (**B, C**) from [13], (**D–F**) from [5]

facilitation of a central nervous process by *practice,* and is thus a **learning process.** It seems significant in this context that particularly long posttetanic potentiation has been found in the *hippocampus* (Fig. 4-6 F), for this structure is thought to play a special role in memory and learning (cf. p. 167).

Mechanism of posttetanic potentiation. Of the various presynaptic factors that might give rise to posttetanic potentiation, three seem to bear chief responsibility. First, the repetitive activation of the presynaptic axon membrane leads to an increase (hyperpolarization) of the resting potential and thus to an increase in the **amplitude of the action potential.** The enlarged action potential releases more transmitter into the synaptic cleft (cf. p. 55). This process is approximately the reverse of what happens during presynaptic inhibition, in which reduction of the amplitude of the presynaptic action potential results in the release of less transmitter substance (p. 64). Second, repetitive activation makes more transmitter available for release. This **mobilization** also improves synaptic transmission, because for each action potential a larger fraction of the transmitter stored in the presynaptic ending is released. Third, the presynaptic calcium concentration rises during tetanic stimulation, because the calcium ions flowing into the nerve ending during the action potential are slow to leave it. Accordingly, the rate of transmitter release increases (p. 55). This may be the most important factor in both tetanic and posttetanic potentiation [1, 8, 9, 11].

Synaptic Depression

A situation in which the postsynaptic potentials during or following a tetanic stimulation are smaller than the controls is called **synaptic depression;** in analogy with potentiation, *tetanic and posttetanic depression* may be distinguished. It is possible that synaptic depression occurs at many places in the nervous system, as a neuronal correlate of habituation (p. 79). In invertebrates it has been shown that the habituation of simple behavioral responses is directly ascribable to depression of the synapses involved, and the same is true of the cat flexor reflex [8]. Synaptic depression is thus entirely comparable to synaptic potentiation as an elementary learning process.

4.2   Reflexes

The *receptors* are the sensors of the organism, which permit it to detect changes in itself or in the environment and subsequently react to them. In many cases the afferents from the receptors make connections such that whenever they are activated the result is a particular stereotyped behavior, which in the course of *phylogenetic* or *individual* development has proved to be an especially appropriate response. Such *stereotyped reactions of the organism to sensory stimuli* are called **reflexes.**

The term **reflex** was introduced to the physiological nomenclature more than 200 years ago by UNZER (1771), to denote the observation by HALES (1730) and WHYTT (1775) that painful stimulation of the hind leg of a decapitated frog causes the leg to be pulled away, as long as the spinal cord is not destroyed. HALL (1833), and above all SHERRINGTON (ca. 1900), in their analyses of the segmental reflexes, laid the foundations of the reflex concept as it is now understood and widely applied [6, 7, 10].

Many **examples** are familiar from everyday life. Grasping a hot object causes us to pull the hand away even before we become conscious of the heat pain, and thus before we could have reacted voluntarily. Touching the cornea of the eye causes an immediate blink (corneal reflex); foreign bodies in the trachea cause coughing; when food contacts the posterior wall of the throat swallowing is initiated. But most reflexes take place without our consciously noticing them – for example, the reflexes that ensure the passage of food through stomach and intestines and its mechanical breakdown there, and those that continuously adjust circulation and respiration to the momentary needs of the body. And we are normally just as little aware of all the motor reflexes that, day in and day out, keep the body upright in space, maintain balance, and by an appropriate combination of co-directional and opposed forces enable us to carry out voluntary movements with ease and accuracy.

The classification of reflexes (the polysynaptic reflexes in particular) into *groups* and *types,* necessary here on didactic grounds, should not be allowed to obscure the fact that there are many kinds of intermediate forms, and that every established **category** is arbitrary in one way or another. Another aspect easily lost sight of when single reflexes are considered in isolation is that most *moto- and interneurons are involved in many reflex arcs.* A motor axon to the throat musculature, for example, participates in swallowing, sucking, coughing, sneezing and breathing reflexes – that is, it forms the *final common path* for a large number of reflex arcs.

Components of a Reflex Arc; Reflex Time

The term **reflex arc** denotes a complete neuronal circuit extending from the peripheral receptor through the central nervous system to the peripheral effector. The elements of a reflex arc, as shown in Fig. 4-7 (top), are the peripheral *receptor,* an *afferent pathway,* one or more *central neurons,* an *efferent pathway* and an *effector.*

All *receptors* participate in reflexes of some kind, so that their afferent fibers serve as the *afferent pathway* in the reflex arc concerned. The number of *central*

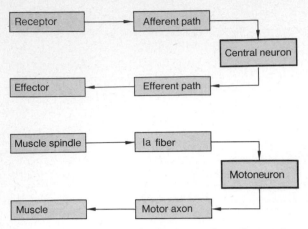

Fig. 4-7. *Top:* General terms for the elements in a reflex arc. *Bottom:* Reflex-arc elements in the monosynaptic stretch reflex

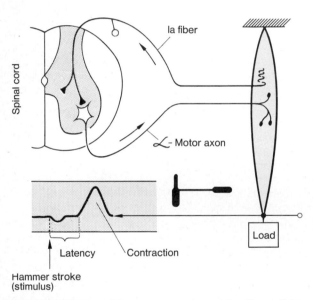

Fig. 4-8. Reflex arc of the monosynaptic stretch reflex. A light tap with a hammer on the recording level of the measuring instrument connected to the muscle (downward deflection in the record) after a brief latency produces contraction of the muscle. The reflex arc underlying this reflex is diagrammed, from the muscle spindles via the Ia fibers to the motoneurons and back to the muscle

neurons in a reflex arc is always greater than one, with the exception of the monosynaptic stretch reflex. The *efferent pathway* is represented by either the motor axons or the postganglionic fibers of the autonomic nervous system, and the *effectors* are the skeletal musculature or smooth musculature, the heart, and the glands.

The time between onset of a stimulus and action of the effector is called the **reflex time.** In most cases it is determined chiefly by the *conduction time* in the afferent and efferent pathways and in the central parts of the reflex arc (the conduction velocities of human

nerve fibers are all somewhat smaller than those given in Table 1-2, p. 24, for the cat [2]). To this are added the times required for (i) the transformation of a stimulus into a conducted impulse at the receptor, (ii) transmission across synapses at central neurons (synapse time), (iii) transmission from the efferent pathway to the effector (e. g., end-plate potential) and (iv) activation of the effector by excitation of the membrane (e. g., excitation-contraction coupling).

The Monosynaptic Reflex Arc

The reflex arc described in this section has a receptor of relatively complex structure, the muscle spindle. It is recommended that the reader first become acquainted with the physiology of this organ (pp. 83–86), before continuing here.

Stretch reflex elicited by muscle stretch. In the discussion of central excitatory synapses and in Fig. 4-4 A it has been stated and shown that the *Ia fibers* make excitatory synapses with homonymous motoneurons. Activation of the *primary muscle-spindle endings* by stretching the muscle must therefore cause *excitation of the homonymous motoneurons.* An experiment to illustrate this is diagrammed in Fig. 4-8. Brief stretching of the muscle by tapping the recording lever lightly with a hammer results, as the recorded curve in the lower left of the picture shows, in a contraction of the muscle after a brief latency. The volley of action potentials entering the spinal cord thus (among other actions) elicited *monosynaptic EPSPs* in homonymous motoneurons, of which some were suprathreshold and caused a slight twitch of the muscle. This reflex, with only one central synapse – that between the Ia fibers and the homonymous motoneuron – is called the **monosynaptic stretch reflex** of the musculature. As shown in Fig. 4-7 (bottom), it is the simplest example of a complete reflex arc. In addition to the expression *stretch reflex* the term **myotatic reflex** is also commonly used.

The best-known example of a monosynaptic stretch reflex is the **patellar tendon** ("knee-jerk") **reflex:** the quadriceps muscle is stretched briefly by striking its tendon lightly below the patella. After a short latency there is a slight twitch of the muscle which causes the freely hanging lower leg to be raised slightly. The expression "tendon reflex" is thus misleading; here, as in the other "tendon reflexes," a monosynaptic muscle-stretch reflex is involved. Clinically important examples of such reflex tests include the following: stretching the muscle that closes the mouth by tapping the chin (masseter reflex), stretching the biceps muscle by tapping its tendon at the elbow or by striking the radius, stretching the triceps by tapping its tendon just over the olecranon, and stretching the triceps

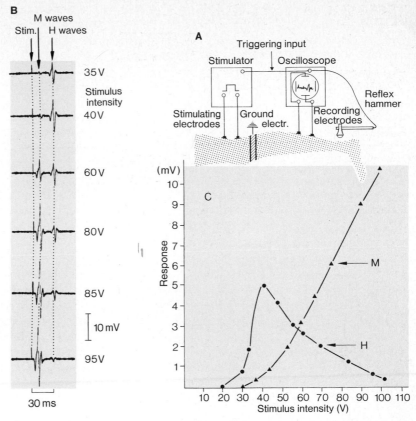

Fig. 4-9 A–C. Production and recording of H- and T-reflexes in humans. **A** Experimental arrangement. A reflex hammer with contact switch is used to elicit a T-reflex of the triceps surae. Closure of the switch when the tendon is tapped triggers the oscilloscope beam, which displays the electromyographically recorded response. To elicit the H-reflexes the tibial nerve is stimulated through the skin with 1 ms square-wave stimuli. Stimulus and deflection of the oscilloscope beam are synchronized with one another. **B** H and M responses as stimulus intensity is increased. **C** Amplitudes of the H and M responses *(ordinate)* plotted as a function of stimulus intensity *(abscissa).* Healthy subject. **B, C** from HOPF, H. C., STRUPPLER, A.: Elektromyographie. Stuttgart: Thieme 1974

surea in the lower leg by tapping the calcaneal tendon (Achilles-tendon reflex). Monosynaptic stretch reflexes elicited by tapping a tendon are also given the clinical designation **T-reflexes.**

Systematic testing of the stretch reflexes is of special significance in that the reflex arcs pass through different spinal segments, so that disturbances in individual reflexes can provide evidence as to the level of a pathological process in the spinal cord. On the whole, there is great variation in the normal vigor of a stretch reflex, which depends heavily on the activity in other (facilitatory or opposed) inputs to the neurons involved (see below). Except in extreme cases, therefore, the feature of clinical significance is less the vigor of the reflex than the question whether there is a difference between the reflexes on the two sides, or whether certain reflexes stand out as abnormal when compared with the overall reflex behavior. Disturbances in reflexes can lie within the elements of the reflex arc itself (Fig. 4-7), but there can also be changes in the other inputs to the motoneurons, of

spinal or supraspinal origin (cf. Figs. 4-1 B and 5-1, p. 82), that cause under- or overexcitability of these neurons. Altogether, then, the production of T-reflexes is a simple test for intactness of the motor reflexes, which in the case of an unsatisfactory outcome must be supplemented by additional diagnostic procedures [2, 12].

Facilitation of T-reflexes. Weak patellar-tendon and other T-reflexes of the lower limbs can often be elicited more readily when the patient is told to hook his hands together in front of his chest and try to pull them apart, or to press the hand of a third person (Jendrassik's maneuver). The exertions required by these actions cause a *facilitatory activation* of the motoneurons in the lumbar cord.

H-reflex. In both the laboratory and neurological practice the human monosynaptic stretch reflex can also be induced by electrical stimulation of the Ia afferents of a muscle nerve. This form of the monosynaptic stretch reflex is called the **H-reflex** (after Paul

Hoffmann). Usually the H-reflex is elicited by electrical stimulation of the tibial nerve at the back of the knee, and the response is recorded electromyographically from the surface (cutaneous electrodes) or the interior (needle electrodes) of the triceps surae muscle, in particular the soleus component (Fig. 4-9). Because the Ia fibers have the lowest threshold of all nerve fibers, with weak stimuli (20–30 V in Fig. 4-9 C) at first only the reflex response (H wave) appears, with a latency of 30–35 ms. With stronger stimuli (from 35 V on in Fig. 4-9 B, C) there is progressively greater excitation of α-motoneurons as well, which activate the muscle with a latency of 5–10 ms (M waves in Fig. 4-9 B, C). As the stimulus intensity continues to increase, both responses at first become progressively larger; then, while the M response proceeds to increase to the maximum, the H response becomes steadily smaller. When the M response is maximal the H response is almost completely suppressed (stimulus intensity $\geqq$ 95 V in Fig. 4-9 B, C).

The *decrease in the H response as stimulus intensity increases* is brought about by the antidromic action potentials in the α-motoneurons. These invade the soma and dendrites of the motoneurons, and come into collision with the excitatory events triggered by the Ia fibers. It can happen either that a motoneuronal impulse triggered by way of the (more rapidly conducting) Ia fibers encounters an antidromic impulse and the two extinguish one another, or that the antidromic impulse makes the motoneuron refractory just at the time that the Ia excitation occurs.

Silent period. After a T- or H-reflex the muscle tone falls off sharply for a brief period (100–500 ms). At least four factors combine to produce this **post-reflex silent period:** 1. The synchronous reflex contraction relieves the tension on the muscle spindles and thus reduces or stops the tonic, excitatory afferent input from the primary muscle-spindle endings (cf. Figs. 5-5, p. 85 and 5-6, p. 86). 2. The reflex contraction activates Golgi tendon organs, which have an inhibitory action on the associated motoneurons (cf. Fig. 4-4 B). 3. The synchronous excitation of the motoneurons causes a transitory enhancement of Renshaw inhibition (cf. Fig. 4-4 B). 4. The hyperpolarizing afterpotentials following the action potentials in the motoneurons participating in the reflex reduce their excitability temporarily.

Stretch reflex by intrafusal contraction. The *physiological significance of the monosynaptic reflex arc* goes far beyond its usefulness in diagnosis. It will be described in detail elsewhere (p. 86). Here we mention only that there is a second way to excite the primary muscle-spindle ending, in addition to stretching the muscle – by *contraction of the intrafusal muscle fibers*. Their contraction makes no change in the length or tension of the muscle as a whole; too little force is exerted, even if all the intrafusal muscles contract at the same time. But the intrafusal contraction does suffice

to stretch the central parts of the intrafusal fibers and thus induce excitation in the primary sensory endings, which initiates the monosynaptic stretch reflex.

Polysynaptic Reflexes

Except for the monosynaptic stretch reflex, all reflex arcs comprise several central neurons in series. These reflexes are thus **polysynaptic.** Polysynaptic reflexes may be initiated by muscular, cutaneous or visceral receptors. They are classified as **autonomic** if their reflex arcs terminate in the effectors of the autonomic nervous system (cf. p. 112), or as **polysynaptic motor reflexes** if their effectors are the skeletal muscles.

Polysynaptic motor reflexes. Polysynaptic motor reflexes play a large role in the entire motor performance of an organism – in movement *(locomotor reflexes),* food intake *(nutritional reflexes),* and avoiding dangerous environmental influences *(protective reflexes),* for example. The simplest example of such a reflex was shown in Fig. 4-4 A: in addition to their monosynaptic connection to homonymous motoneurons, the Ia fibers exert an *inhibitory* influence on *antagonistic* motoneurons, by way of an interneuron (drawn in red in Fig. 4-4 A). This reflex arc thus has two central synapses – it is **disynaptic.** This **reciprocal inhibition** (p. 87) is the shortest inhibitory reflex arc known. Therefore this inhibition is also called *direct inhibition* [3, 4].

Most of the other excitatory and inhibitory inputs to the motoneurons from peripheral receptors have more than one – often very many – *interneurons* in their reflex arc; they are not di- but rather *polysynaptic.* Consider two examples. (i) When the lips of the newborn touch the mother's breast, suckling movements are initiated. The same movements can be elicited by a fingertip or a pacifier, which demonstrates clearly the reflex character of the response. The **suckling reflex** is a *nutritive reflex.* The receptors in its polysynaptic reflex arc are touch-sensitive structures in the skin of the lips (mechanoreceptors; cf. p. 213); the effectors are the muscles of the lips, cheeks, tongue, throat, thoracic cage and diaphragm. The suckling reflex is thus a very complicated polysynaptic reflex, particularly in view of the fact that the sucking movements must be coordinated with the normal respiration. (ii) If a piece of filter paper soaked with acid is laid on the back of a decerebrate frog, after a short latency the animal will wipe it away with whichever hindleg is closest. This is an example of a **protective reflex.** The nociceptors (cf. p. 228) for this **wiping reflex** are within the skin of the back, whereas the musculature in the hindleg is the effector.

Properties of polysynaptic reflexes. In characterizing the properties of polysynaptic reflexes it is important to keep in mind that even in the monosynaptic stretch reflex the response is not a fixed (automaton-like) result of the stimulus, but rather can be modified by other facilitatory and inhibitory influences that may be acting on the motoneuron at the same time. The polysynaptic reflex arcs, with their greater number of central neurons, offer a still better opportunity to adjust the outcome of the reflex to the momentary demands of the organism.

The cough reflex is highly suitable for examination of the **properties of polysynaptic reflexes,** for stimulation of the receptors in the mucosa of trachea and bronchi elicits not only coughing but also conscious sensations. Hence it is possible to compare stimulus intensity with the reflex response. A slight "tickling" or "scratching" in the throat causes coughing, not immediately, but after a little while. Thus in polysynaptic reflexes *subthreshold* stimuli can *summate* to a *suprathreshold* stimulus. This **summation** is a central phenomenon – that is, it takes place at the interneurons and motoneurons of the reflex arc; the subjective sensations (tickling, scratching) experienced prior to triggering of the reflex are a clear sign that the receptors responsible for the reflex are already excited at that time. As stimulus intensity increases the time between the onset of the stimulus and the completion of the reflex, the **reflex time,** becomes shorter even in the suprathreshold range; that is, the *reflex time is strongly dependent on stimulus intensity.* (By contrast, the reflex time in the monosynaptic stretch reflex is practically constant.) The reduction in reflex time of the polysynaptic reflex as stimulus intensity rises is chiefly a consequence of the temporal and spatial facilitation of the central neurons in the reflex arc, owing to the increased repetitive discharge by the receptors. Finally, in polysynaptic reflexes the **form of the response** depends very much on stimulus intensity, such that strong stimuli cause the reflex to be extended to groups of muscles previously not involved – a phenomenon called **irradiation.** Evidently strong stimuli bring the originally subthreshold excitation of some neurons into the suprathreshold range. *Irradiation* is well demonstrated by the cough reflex; a gentle clearing of the throat involves chiefly the muscles of the throat itself, whereas violent choking coughing brings the muscles of chest, shoulders, abdomen and diaphragm into play.

A number of other properties of polysynaptic motor reflexes, such as *local sign, habituation, sensitization* and *conditioning,* bring into sharp relief the **plasticity of the polysynaptic reflex response.** The term **local sign** refers to the fact that the location of the stimulus can affect the response; for example, following painful stimulation of a leg the flexor muscles of the hip, knee and foot joints contract by different amounts, depending on the stimulus site. **Habituation** is observed with non-painful, non-injurious cutaneous stimuli; for instance, when the abdomen is stroked repeatedly at the *same place* and with the *same intensity* the reflex

becomes *attenuated* even though the excitability of the receptors, motoneurons and skeletal muscles involved remains unchanged [8, 10, 16]. A change in stimulus site or stimulus parameters (especially an increase in intensity) restores the normal reflex response. This restoration is called **dishabituation.** The original response also returns after stimulation has been interrupted for some time. Habituation probably results from synaptic depression (p. 75) [8].

Repeated *painful* stimuli lead to **sensitization.** The reflex threshold is reduced, the reflex time shortened, the receptive field enlarged and the reflex irradiated [8, 16]. The term **conditioning** denotes the *long-term changes in the reflex response* produced by the capacity of polysynaptic reflexes to adapt in a learning process. For example, in an experiment designed so that to end a painful stimulus the subject had to *move toward the stimulus,* it was possible to produce a reversal of the movements constituting the flexor reflex [15]. The expressions *to condition* and *conditioning* are also used to designate the procedure by which such changes are brought about (cf. Fig. 3-13 B, p. 64).

Congenital and acquired reflexes. The discussion so far has been restricted to reflexes that are observed in almost the same form in all individuals of a given species, with no special conditions required (cf. preceding paragraph). These stereotyped reactions are largely predetermined in the structural design of the nervous system; the *preformed* reflex arcs are usually located in the phylogenetically older parts of the central nervous system – the spinal cord and brainstem – even when the reflexes are very complex (e. g., wiping reflex of decerebrate frog). In addition, each organism has the ability to learn reflex reactions, which help it to respond better and with less effort to the constantly changing situations in the environment. The reflex arcs for these acquired reflexes (which can also be forgotten) usually lie in the higher levels of the central nervous system. Familiar examples of acquired reflexes, which have been thoroughly studied in experiments, are the **conditioned reflexes** and the behavioral changes produced by **operant conditioning,** described in Chapter 8, p. 185.

4.3 References

Textbooks and Handbooks

1. COTTRELL, G. A., USHERWOOD, P. N. R. (Eds.): Synapses. Glasgow and London: Blackie 1977
2. DESMEDT, J. E.: New Developments in Electromyography and Clinical Neurophysiology, Vols. 1–3. Basel: Karger 1973
3. ECCLES, J. C.: The Physiology of Nerve Cells. Baltimore: Johns Hopkins Press 1957

4. ECCLES, J.C.: The Inhibitory Pathways of the Central Nervous System. The Sherrington Lectures IX. Springfield/Ill.: Ch.C.Thomas 1969
5. ECCLES, J.C.: The Understanding of the Brain. New York: McGraw-Hill 1973
6. FEARING, F.: Reflex Action. A Study in the History of Physiological Psychology. Baltimore: Williams and Wilkins 1930
7. FULTON, J.F.: Physiology of the Nervous System. London-New York-Toronto: Oxford University Press 1943
8. KANDEL, E.R.: Cellular Basis of Behavior. San Francisco: W.H.Freeman and Co. 1976
9. KANDEL, E.R. (Vol. Ed.): Handbook of Physiology, Section 1: The Nervous System. Vol. I.Cellular Biology of Neurons, Parts 1 and 2, pp.1–1182. American Physiological Society, Bethesda, Maryland 1977
10. SHERRINGTON, C.S.: The Integrative Action of the Nervous System. New Haven: Yale University Press. 2nd Ed. 1947, reprinted 1961 (1906)
11. THESLEFF, S. (Ed.): Motor Innervation of Muscle. London-New York-San Francisco: Academic Press 1976

12. WALTON, J.N.: Brain's Diseases of the Nervous System, 8th Edition. Oxford: Oxford University Press 1977

Research Reports and Reviews

13. BRAUN, M., SCHMIDT, R.F., ZIMMERMANN, M.: Facilitation at the frog neuromuscular junction during and after repetitive stimulation. Pflügers Arch. ges. Physiol. *287*, 41–55 (1966)
14. FEINSTEIN, B., LINDEGAARD, B., NYMAN, E., WOHLFART, G.: Morphologic studies of motor units in normal human muscles. Acta anat. (Basel) *23*, 127 (1955)
15. HAGBARTH, K.E., FINER, B.L.: The plasticity of human withdrawal reflexes to noxious stimuli in lower limbs. Prog. Brain Res. *1*, 65–78 (1963)
16. HAGBARTH, K.E., KUGELBERG, E.: Plasticity of the human abdominal skin reflex. Brain *81*, 305–319 (1958)

5 Motor Systems

R. F. SCHMIDT

5.1 Survey of the Neural Control of Posture and Movement

Only by using our skeletal muscles can we interact with and influence our environment. The musculature makes possible a broad spectrum of movements – from simple walking and running to the precise movements of the fingers during writing or the finely adjusted movements of speaking and the facial expressions and gestures that serve to convey subtle thoughts and emotions.

Two kinds of motor function can be distinguished: **maintenance of position** (posture) and **movement.** In practice, the two functions are inextricably conjoined. For example, goal-directed hand or foot movements can perform the desired actions only if the body and the arm or leg are first put into an appropriate position. On the other hand, for a position to be maintained it is necessary that any force tending to disturb this position be counteracted by appropriate compensatory movements. Movement without postural control is as impossible as postural control without movement. In analyzing motor activity, however, the distinction between **postural functions** – the holding functions, which support the body in a certain attitude and in particular keep it upright despite the force of gravity – and **goal-directed movements** is a useful one.

The structures responsible for the neural control of posture and movement *("motor centers")* are distributed throughout the central nervous system, from the cerebral cortex to the spinal cord. They are arranged in a well-defined hierarchy, which must be interpreted in the light of the progressive adaptation of motor function during evolution. This process was not so much a reconstruction of existing motor systems as a superposition of additional control systems to achieve particular kinds of performance.

The left column in Fig. 5-1 gives a rough outline of the organization of the motor centers, for preliminary orientation. With certain reservations, particular motor functions can be ascribed to these centers; they are listed in the middle column of Fig. 5-1. The right column gives key words that summarize the central nervous processes accompanying a planned movement.

Spinal motor systems. At the level of the spinal cord, as a rule, between the sensory afferents and the motoneurons (the output to the effectors) there are a varying number of interneurons, which make a large number of connections; the pattern of activation of these interneurons determines whether the generation of a movement will be promoted or inhibited. The interneuronal circuitry (reflex arcs), the basis of the **spinal reflexes,** is fixed anatomically but its mode of operation governed to a great extent by other spinal or higher centers, in that the course followed by signals through the various reflex arcs can be differentially altered. The original definition of **reflex,** from which the name was derived, was based on the notion that every reflex movement was a stereotyped output following a particular sensory input, as though *reflected* by a mirror; now it is clear that this is not the case. A much broader definition is required to include the inhibitory reflexes as well. In this sense, a spinal motor reflex would be a change in neuronal activity, elicited by sensory afferents at the spinal level, that promotes or inhibits movements. The spinal reflexes amount to a *library of elementary postural and movement programs* upon which the organism can draw as required, with no need for the higher levels of the central nervous system to become involved with the details of execution of the programs.

Higher motor systems. As a category distinct from the spinal systems, the *higher motor systems* are those supraspinal centers involved in motor control. Whereas postural functions and their coordination with goal-directed movement are controlled chiefly by structures in the brainstem, the performance of the directed movements requires the participation of still higher centers. As Fig. 5-1 shows, the **drives to act** and the **movement designs** produced in the subcortical motivation areas and in the association cortex are subsequently converted to *movement programs*. The formation of these involves the basal ganglia and the cerebellum, both of which act on the motor cortex by way of thalamic nuclei. The cortex, together with the deeper motor structures in brainstem and spinal

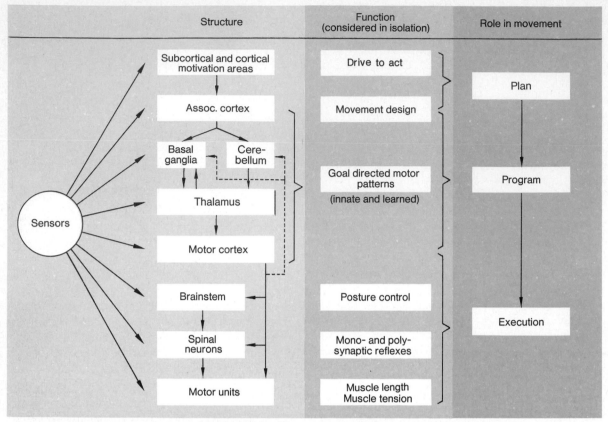

	Structure	Function (considered in isolation)	Role in movement

Subcortical and cortical motivation areas

Assoc. cortex

Basal ganglia   Cerebellum

Thalamus

Sensors

Motor cortex

Brainstem

Spinal neurons

Motor units

Drive to act

Movement design

Goal directed motor patterns
(innate and learned)

Posture control

Mono- and poly-synaptic reflexes

Muscle length
Muscle tension

Plan

Program

Execution

Fig. 5-1. Survey of the motor system. The most important structures and their main connections are listed in the left-hand column. For simplicity, all the sensory inputs are classified together at the far left. The middle column emphasizes the most conspicuous function of each structure when studied in isolation, and the right-hand column shows how these are associated with the initiation and execution of a movement. Note the parallel position of the basal ganglia and the cerebellum, and the involvement of the motor cortex at the transition between program and execution

cord, is responsible for the execution of the movement.

Accompanying movements such as the swinging of the arms during walking or the expressions and gestures associated with speaking in many cases are controlled by deeper brain structures, so that involvement of the motor cortex is not absolutely required. Disappearance of such accompanying movements is characteristic of certain pathological states – for example, the Parkinson syndrome (cf. p. 108). (The system controlling **ocular movements** is discussed separately, beginning on p. 268).

The distinctions between *conscious* and *unconscious* and between **voluntary** and **involuntary** motor acts are intentionally ignored in this chapter, for all such acts are produced by way of the same motor centers (cf. Fig. 5-1).

In the clinic, on the other hand, the terms *voluntary* (volitional) and *involuntary* (automatic) movement are often used. What is meant is that in the opinion of the observer and/or according to the patient's report the movement has been *willed* or *not willed*. The observer bases his opinion on behavioral characteristics (p. 184), and the patient bases his on his subjective experience. As long as one keeps in mind the limits of these viewpoints, it is justified on practical grounds to retain these terms in everyday usage.

To avoid the difficulty of arbitrarily dividing movement into "automatic" and "volitional," the English neurologist Hughlings Jackson, around the turn of the century, proposed that all motor performance (movements or movement complexes) be arranged in a hierarchy of levels, from "most automatic" to "least automatic." This categorization still appears to be useful. For example, breathing is a very automatic movement complex involving the chest and shoulder musculature, which continues even during the deepest sleep and under anesthesia, when all other movement complexes have long since been suspended. The participation of the same muscles in coughing or in a movement of the trunk is "less automatic," and their participation in singing or speaking is a "least automatic" movement. This example also makes clear that on the whole the "more automatic" movements are based largely on inborn central behavior patterns (programs), whereas the "less" or "least" automatic movements tend to be learned in the course of a lifetime. The more or less automatic movements of a given muscle group – and herein lies the clinical usefulness of this categorization – are often impaired in a characteristic manner by damage to different parts of the brain, so that from the nature of the movement impairment one can infer the site and nature of the central disturbance.

Coupling of sensory and motor systems. Sensory information and motor action are intimately intermeshed. For movements to be carried out in a functionally appropriate way, all the structures involved in their production require and receive information from the periphery as to the momentary position of the body and the progress of the desired movement (Fig. 5-1 left). Moreover, certain kinds of sensory information – for example, from the senses of sight and touch – can be acquired only with the assistance of differentiated motor acts. When one is aware of this close coupling, introduction of the occasionally used expression "sensorimotor" becomes superfluous. In the following text, afferent sensory information is always treated under the heading "motor" when the emphasis is on its transmission to effector-motor structures, and under "sensory" when its perceptive-sensory function is being considered.

5.2   Spinal Motor Systems

The great significance of afferent inputs to the motor systems is particularly clear at the spinal level. Two sense organs in the muscle – the *muscle spindles* and the *tendon organs* – are in the foreground on the afferent side; on the efferent side, the *motoneurons* form the *final common path for all motor reflexes* (SHERRINGTON).

Receptors for the Spinal Sensory and Motor Systems

Structure of the muscle spindles. Every muscle contains a number of muscle fibers that are *thinner* and *shorter* than the ordinary fibers. They are arranged in small groups, each group surrounded by a *connective-tissue capsule*. Because of its shape this structure is called a **muscle spindle** (Fig. 5-2). The muscle fibers inside the capsule are called **intrafusal** (Latin *fusus* = spindle) muscle fibers, while the ordinary fibers that make up most of the muscle are called *extrafusal muscle fibers* or working musculature.

Two types of intrafusal fibers can be distinguished, on the basis of the arrangement of the nuclei. The nuclei of the **nuclear-chain**

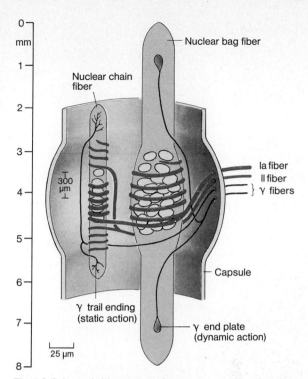

Fig. 5-2. Schematic illustration of the structure of a muscle spindle, a composite of many histological and physiological data, especially those of BARKER, BOYD, MATTHEWS and their coworkers. To obtain a rough idea of the dimensions of the spindle, note the different longitudinal and transverse scales

fibers form a chain-like array in the middle part of the fiber, whereas those of the **nuclear-bag fibers** form a densely packed mass that fills up the entire cross section of the fiber over a short distance (Fig. 5-2). The *nuclear-bag fibers* are about twice as long as the *nuclear-chain fibers,* and their diameter is twice as large. The two types of muscle fiber appear to serve different functions (cf. p. 85). The muscle spindles are attached at either end to the perimysium of extrafusal fascicles, by way of tendon-like strands of connective tissue 0.5–1 mm in length (for further details see [11, 12, 15].

Afferent innervation (Fig. 5-2). Every muscle spindle is entered, at the level of the nuclear region, by a thick myelinated nerve fiber (diameter ca. 10–20 μm), together with other nerve fibers (see below) and blood vessels. The single large fiber divides within the spindle, sending a branch to each muscle fiber that winds around the fiber over about 300 μm in the middle section – an **annulospiral ending**. The afferent nerve fibers with these endings are designated by the name of the group to which they belong, the **Ia fibers,** or as primary muscle-spindle afferents (cf. Table 1-2, p. 24). Accordingly, the annulospiral endings are also called **primary sensory endings.** Each Ia fiber appears to supply only one muscle spindle.

Many, but not all, muscle spindles are innervated in addition by one or more *afferent fibers of Group II* (diameter ca. 4–12 μm; cf. Table 1-2, p. 24). These sensory fibers terminate peripheral to the primary sensory endings, *almost exclusively on the nuclear-chain fibers* (Fig. 5-2). These receptor structures are called the **secondary sensory endings.** In addition to their spiral parts these endings also exhibit multiply branched structures, the "flower-spray" endings. In contrast to the Ia fibers, the Group II fibers often branch to supply two or more spindles.

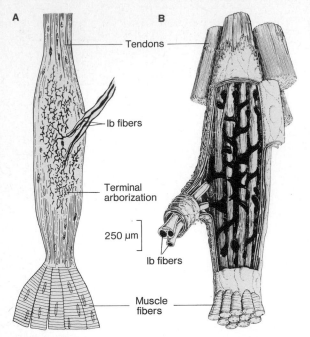

Fig. 5-3. A Drawing of a Golgi tendon organ as seen in the light microscope, by Ramon y Cajal (1906). **B** Reconstruction of the terminal arborization (red) of a Ib fiber within a tendon organ. From R. V. Krstić: Die Gewebe des Menschen und der Säugetiere. Berlin–Heidelberg–New York: Springer 1978

Efferent innervation (Fig. 5-2). The intrafusal muscle fibers are innervated by motoneurons, as are the extrafusal fibers. But the efferent **fusimotor nerve fibers** to the spindles originate in somata considerably smaller than those of the α motoneurons (cf. p. 60), and the axons too are smaller in diameter (2–8 μm) than the α motor nerve fibers (diameter 12–21 μm) to the extrafusal musculature. Because the fusimotor nerve fibers are in the Aγ category, they are called γ **fibers,** and the motoneuron as a whole is called a γ **motoneuron.** Within the muscle the γ fibers branch to several muscle spindles and within these, to several intrafusal muscle fibers. The γ fibers have two types of endings on the polar (peripheral) parts of the intrafusal muscle fibers, γ **end plates** (mainly on nuclear-bag fibers) and γ **trail endings** (mainly on nuclear-chain fibers; cf. Fig. 5-2). The γ end plates are like the end plates on extrafusal muscle fibers (cf. Fig. 3-1), whereas the γ trail endings are long, thin structures, diffusely reticular in places (for details see [11, 12, 15]). A γ fiber always has only one kind of terminal structure, either plate or trail, at all its endings.

Structure of the tendon organs. In the tendons of all homeotherm muscles, near the junction with the muscle, are receptors called **tendon organs** (or *Golgi tendon organs;* Fig. 5-3). These consist of the tendon fascicles of about 10 extrafusal muscle fibers enclosed in a connective-tissue capsule and supplied by one or two thick myelinated nerve fibers (diameter 10–20 μm). The afferent nerve fibers are called **Ib fibers.** After entering the capsule they divide into thinner branches, eventually becoming unmyelinated, and form highly ramified endings among the tendon fascicles (Fig. 5-3; for details see [11, 12, 15]).

Distribution of muscle spindles and tendon organs. Practically all mammalian striated muscles contain **muscle spindles.** Exceptions are the extraocular muscles of some animals, such as the rabbit, cat and dog. But humans and many other mammals have numerous typical muscle spindles in these muscles as well. The number of muscle spindles per muscle depends on the muscle's size and function. In humans it varies from about 40 spindles in the small hand muscles to 500 spindles in the triceps muscle of the arm. The density of spindles – that is, the number of muscle spindles per gram of muscle tissue – is particularly high in small muscles that participate in fine movements, such as the eye muscles and the small muscles of neck and hands. In humans, for example, the inferior rectus muscle of the eye has 47 spindles and a total weight of 0.37 g, or ca. 130 spindles/g. The superior oblique muscle of the head (140 spindles, 3.3 g) and the short abductor muscle of the thumb (80 spindles, 2.7 g) have 43 and 29 spindles/g, respectively, whereas the spindle density is much lower in the large muscles near the trunk – for example, 1.4 spindles/g in the triceps of the arm (520 spindles, 364 g) and 0.36 spindles/g in the teres major (44 spindles, 123 g). These data alone imply that the muscle spindles probably play an important role in the regulation of posture and movement. But some peculiarities in their distribution have yet to be explained in terms of function; for example, the density of spindles in the eye muscles of the cow is very high, whereas those of the horse have no spindles at all. The number of **tendon organs** per muscle has not been extensively investigated. As far as is known, they are usually somewhat less numerous than the muscle spindles. A general rule of thumb is that there are 50–80 tendon organs for every 100 muscle spindles [1, 15].

Position and discharge pattern of the muscle spindles and tendon organs. In terms of their *adequate stimulus,* muscle spindles and tendon organs are both **stretch receptors.** However, their arrangement in the muscle differs (Fig. 5-4); the muscle spindles lie in **parallel** with the extrafusal fibers, and the tendon organs are **in series** with them. As a result, there are characteristic differences in the discharge pattern, especially during contraction of the muscle, which can be understood by comparing the diagrams of the two receptors in Fig. 5-4.

When a muscle is stretched to about its resting length (Fig. 5-4 A) most of the primary muscle-spindle endings (those of Ia fibers) discharge, whereas the tendon organs (supplied by Ib fibers) as a rule are silent. During **stretching** (Fig. 5-4 B) the discharge rate of the Ia fibers increases, and the tendon organs also begin to discharge. **Isotonic contraction** of the extrafusal musculature (Fig. 5-4 C) decreases the tension in the muscle spindle, so that the discharge of the receptor ceases. The tendon organ, however, remains stretched and its discharge rate actually increases transiently during the contraction, because the acceleration of the load briefly stretches the tendon organ still more.

Dynamic and static sensitivity of the muscle spindles and tendon organs. The discharge rate of the Ia fibers depends not only on the final amount by which the muscle is stretched, but also, during the stretching process, on the rate at which it is stretched (cf. Fig. 5-5). The *primary muscle-spindle endings* thus have both **dynamic** and **static sensitivity.** In control-systems terminology, they are *proportional-differential sensors,* abbreviated **PD receptors.** At the end of a stepwise stretch to a new length the dis-

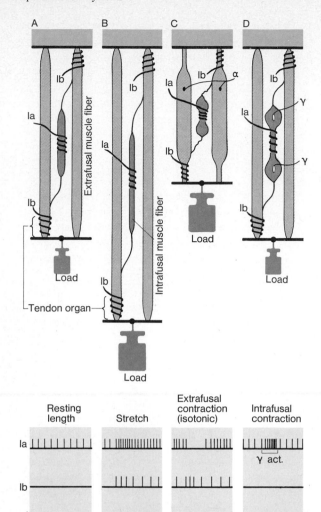

Fig. 5-4 A–D. Schematic drawing of the positions and the discharge patterns of the muscle spindles and the Golgi tendon organs in the muscle at rest (**A**) and their changes in shape under passive stretch (**B**), during isotonic contraction of the extrafusal muscle fibers (**C**) and during contraction of the intrafusal muscle fibers alone (**D**, γ act.). The combination of (**B**) and (**D**) causes especially strong activation of the muscle-spindle afferents. Ia, discharge patterns of the primary muscle-spindle afferents in their Ia fibers. Ib, discharge patterns of the tendon organs, in Ib fibers. M. L., muscle length

charge rate at first decreases rapidly and then more slowly (rapid and slow **adaptation**), until finally, within about a minute, a steady impulse frequency is reached that is about proportional to the muscle length, in an intermediate range of stretch [15]. The dynamic sensitivity of the **secondary spindle endings** (Fig. 5-5) and the **tendon organs** is distinctly lower than that of the primary muscle-spindle endings. The secondary spindle endings and the tendon organs are thus *proportional sensors or* **P receptors** [29].

These findings imply that the **muscle spindles** measure **primarily the length** of the muscle, whereas the **tendon organs** measure **primarily the tension**. It would there-

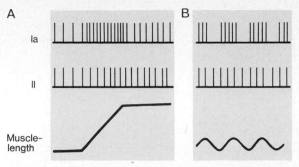

Fig. 5-5 A, B. Discharge pattern of a primary (Ia) and a secondary (II) spindle afferent during ramp (**A**) and sinusoidal (**B**) stretching of the muscle. Upward deflection of the lower curves signifies increase in muscle length. Measurements by P. B. C. Matthews [15]

fore be expected that during *isometric contraction* the discharge rate of the tendon organs would greatly increase, whereas that of the muscle spindles would remain about the same. (In fact, the discharge rate of the muscle spindles actually decreases, because even though the external length of the muscle remains constant, within it there is a shortening of the contractile elements and corresponding lengthening of the elastic elements, which reduces the load on the muscle spindles.)

Action of the fusimotor nerve fibers. There is a second way to excite the primary muscle-spindle ending, apart from stretching the muscle – by *contraction of the intrafusal muscle fibers* owing to activation of the fusimotor γ motor axons. Contraction of the intrafusal fibers alone does not change the length or tension of the muscle as a whole, but it does stretch the central parts of the intrafusal fibers themselves and thus excites the sensory endings (Fig. 5-4 D). These two means of spindle activation, (i) *stretching the muscle* and (ii) *intrafusal contraction,* can have additive effects (Fig. 5-6). On the other hand, intrafusal contraction can more or less compensate the action of extrafusal contraction, so that even during extrafusal contraction the muscle spindles can continue to function as length sensors. In other words, *intrafusal prestretching* of the stretch receptor can serve to adjust its **threshold** and its **range of sensitivity**.

Dynamic and static γ fibers. Two types of motor γ fibers can be distinguished. The **dynamic fusimotor fibers** increase the velocity sensitivity of the muscle spindles, while raising the static sensitivity only slightly (Fig. 5-6 C, F); the **static fusimotor fibers** reduce the velocity sensitivity but cause a great increase in the maintained discharge associated with a given amount of stretch (Fig. 5-6 B, E). The differential actions of the dynamic and static γ fibers presumably derive from the different structures they innervate, the dynamic γ fibers supplying the intrafusal nuclear-bag muscle fibers (Fig. 5-2), while the static γ fibers innervate the nuclear-chain fibers [1, 3, 15, 23].

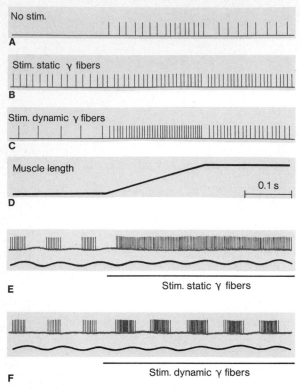

No stim.

A

Stim. static γ fibers

B

Stim. dynamic γ fibers

C

Muscle length

0.1 s

D

Stim. static γ fibers

E

Stim. dynamic γ fibers

F

Fig. 5-6 A–F. The action of static (**B, E**) and dynamic (**C, F**) γ motoneurons on the background discharge and response to stretch of a primary spindle afferent during ramp (**A–D**) and sinusoidal (**E, F**) stretching of the muscle. In each case single γ fibers innervating the muscle spindle were stimulated. In **B** and **C** the stimulation was continued for the entire duration of the recording; in **F** and **E** stimulation was begun during the recording (as indicated). The static γ motoneurons bring about a distinct increase in the background frequency and a reduction in dynamic sensitivity (**B, E**), whereas the dynamic γ motoneurons change the background frequency only slightly but induce a distinct increase in dynamic sensitivity (**C, F**). Measurements by Crowe and Matthews, 1964, cited by P. B. C. Matthews [15]

Properties of secondary sensory spindle endings. The secondary sensory endings, those of the Group II afferent fibers from the muscle spindles (cf. Fig. 5-2), are also **stretch receptors.** However, they have a *higher threshold* and a *lower dynamic sensitivity* than the primary sensory endings. In accordance with the distribution of innervation described in the preceding paragraph, both threshold and sensitivity can be adjusted by the activation of *static fusimotor fibers,* whereas dynamic fusimotor fibers are without effect [15].

Functions of the Muscle Spindles and Tendon Organs

In the discussion of the monosynaptic stretch reflex (p. 76) it was mentioned that the Ia fibers make monosynaptic *excitatory* connections to the *homonymous* motoneurons, and that activation of the muscle spin-

dles by stretch or intrafusal contraction leads to contraction of the muscle. In addition there was a brief mention, in connection with Fig. 4-4 A (p. 73), of the fact that the Ia fibers make disynaptic *inhibitory* connections with antagonistic motoneurons. In this section we shall proceed from this information, first considering the central connections of the Ia afferents and the significance of this reflex path to motor performance, and then turning to the central connections and functions of the tendon organs.

Stretch reflex for the control of muscle length. As will be described in greater detail in Chapter 15 from the viewpoint of control theory, the stretch reflex can be regarded as a control mechanism for the regulation of muscle length. That is, stretching the muscle causes activation of the muscle spindles, monosynaptic excitation of the motoneurons, and contraction – a shortening of the muscle that counteracts the stretching. This *reflex maintenance of muscle length* is particularly important with regard to the preservation of **maintained tone** in the postural muscles. For example, while standing upright, whenever the knee joint bends even so slightly that the bending is neither seen nor felt, the associated stretching of the quadriceps muscle enhances the activity in the primary muscle-spindle endings (cf. patellar tendon reflex, Fig. 4-8). As a result, the α motoneurons to the quadriceps are additionally activated (Fig. 5-7) and the tone of the muscle is increased, instantly counteracting the incipient bending. Conversely, excessive contraction of the muscle reduces the stimulus to its stretch receptors. Their discharge rate, the excitatory input to the motoneurons, is diminished, and the muscle tone decreases. By means of this control circuit, then, the *length of the muscle* is kept constant. The monosynaptic stretch reflex serves as a **length servomechanism,** to maintain constant muscle length on the basis of the feedback from the muscle spindles. Changes in the load on the muscle are automatically compensated by this mechanism. Adequate sensitivity of the muscle spindles is ensured by the contraction of the intrafusal fibers. Increase in the dynamic sensor function of the spindles (by way of the dynamic γ fibers), in particular, brings about a stronger response to changes in muscle length and thus an improvement in postural control.

Stretch reflexes and reciprocal antagonist inhibition as a length-control system. The Ia fibers make not only *monosynaptic* excitatory connections with homonymous motoneurons (reflex arcs of the stretch reflex), but also *disynaptic* inhibitory connections with the *antagonistic* motoneurons (Fig. 5-7, cf. Fig. 4-4 A). This inhibition is called **reciprocal antagonist inhibi-**

tion. It supports the contraction of homonymous and antagonistic muscles produced or promoted by Ia-fiber activity, by simultaneous inhibition of the antagonists acting at the same joint. Because the Ia fibers of the antagonist muscle make corresponding connections (Fig. 5-7), passive (externally imposed) changes in joint position activate *four reflex arcs,* which together oppose the change in joint position, thus trying to keep the *initial muscle length constant.* For instance, if the influence of gravity causes the knee joint in Fig. 5-7 to begin to bend, stretching of the muscle spindles of the extensor *(first)* increases the excitation of the extensor motoneurons and *(second)* increases the inhibition of the flexor motoneurons. Moreover, the lessening of muscle-spindle stretch in the flexor reduces both *(third)* the homonymous excitation of the flexor motoneurons and *(fourth)* the reciprocal inhibition of the extensor motoneurons (this kind of "removal of inhibition" is called *disinhibition*). The net result is that the excitation of the extensor motoneurons increases and that of the flexor motoneurons decreases. Together, the reflex arcs constitute a **length-control system** for the muscle.

Phasic and tonic stretch reflexes. When a muscle is stretched to a constant length a frequent result – especially in decerebrate animals and in patients with certain central motor disturbances – is an increase in muscle tone, in which a **phasic component,** observable while the stretch is increasing, can be distinguished from a **tonic component,** which persists while the final length is being held constant. The transition between the two components is not well defined. The monosynaptic reflex pathway previously discussed is a major factor in both components, but not the only one. For example, it is likely that the Ia afferents participate in the tonic stretch reflex, in particular, not only by way of the monosynaptic arc but also by polysynaptic routes. Moreover, the Group II afferents from the secondary muscle-spindle endings can probably also contribute to the tonic component, again predominantly by polysynaptic spinal reflex paths. In addition to the monosynaptic stretch reflex, then, there exist polysynaptic stretch reflexes as well [11, 15]. – The significance of descending influences is discussed on pp. 93 ff.

Functions of the γ-spindle loop. It is evident from the discussion so far that there are two ways to elicit contraction of the extrafusal musculature: *first* by **direct** excitation of the α motoneurons, and *second* by excitation of the γ motoneurons, which initiate the stretch reflex by causing intrafusal contraction and thus activate the extrafusal musculature. The latter possibility

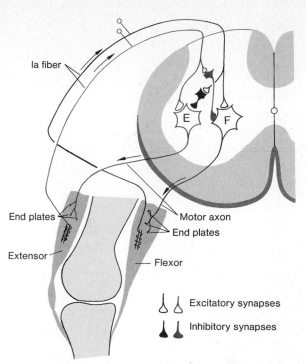

Fig. 5-7. Reflex paths for the stretch reflex and reciprocal antagonist inhibition. F, flexor motoneurons; E, extensor motoneurons of the knee joint. The flexor and extensor muscles of this joint and the actions of the synapses are indicated in the drawing

is called the γ-spindle loop (Fig. 5-8 A). A change in the activity of static fusimotoneurons, in particular, changes muscle length by way of the resulting change in the basic discharge rate of the spindle afferents (Fig. 5-6 B, E), and thus permits or promotes a movement.

When muscle contraction is initiated by way of the γ-spindle loop, then, contraction of the intrafusal musculature is followed by enhanced contraction of the extrafusal musculature, until the original discharge rate of the primary spindle afferents is reached once again. The γ-spindle loop, incorporating a stretch-reflex arc, in this case is a **servomechanism** in which the controlled variable *muscle length* **follows** the controlling variable *muscle-spindle length.*

Fig. 5-8 B is a graph of the relation between muscle length (abscissa) and discharge rate of a primary spindle afferent (ordinate) for different stimulus frequencies (0, 30, 50, 90 Hz) of the associated γ fiber. For example, if the frequency of the γ discharge rises from 30 to 50 Hz, the afferent discharge is represented by the shift from Point 1 to Point 2. The original afferent discharge rate is restored by shortening the muscle to Point 3. Thus the γ efferents allow the muscle length to change **without** continual changing of the discharge rate of the muscle-spindle receptors. (Because the altered joint position has stretched the antagonists, if Point 3 is to be at the same level on the ordinate as Point 1 the tension in the antagonistic intrafusal muscle fibers must be diminished somewhat.)

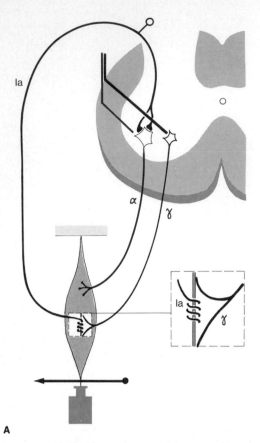

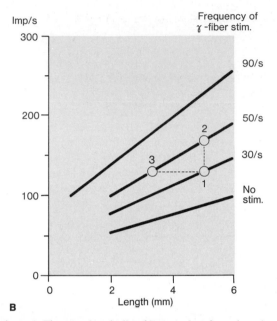

Fig. 5-8 A, B. Reflex path of the γ-spindle loop (*red* in **A**) and the influence of fusimotor activity on the discharge rate of a primary muscle-spindle ending (ordinate in **B**). With supraspinal activation of the γ loop there is usually a simultaneous descending activation of the associated (homonymous) α motoneurons (α-γ coactivation, indicated by the red and black descending pathways). The muscle spindle of **B** was taken from the soleus muscle of the cat; its resting length was varied as shown on the abscissa and the frequency of fusimotor stimulation was changed as shown at the right. **B** after A. CROWE and P. B. C. MATTHEWS, J. Physiol. (Lond.) *174*, 109 (1964)

Alpha-gamma coactivation during movements. Originally it was thought that during goal-directed movements **direct excitation of the α motoneurons** (Fig. 5-8 A) was used chiefly when speed was of greatest importance, while **activation of the γ-spindle loop** was used for particularly smooth and finely graded movements [9]. Study of various movements (cat: breathing, chewing, walking; man: finger movements) has since shown that although as a rule extrafusal contraction is associated with an increase in spindle discharge (and thus intrafusal contraction), this increase *does not precede* the movement, as would be required if the movement were elicited by the γ motoneurons, but rather *follows it with a slight latency* (Fig. 5-9). Under these conditions the α and γ motoneurons are evidently activated simultaneously; the activity in the spindle afferents, however, because of the lower conduction velocity of the γ fibers and the time required for intrafusal contraction, is delayed with respect to the electromyographically recorded activity (EMG) [42]. This α-γ coactivation is also termed *α-γ coupling.* The main *role of the γ innervation* is therefore probably to prevent relaxation of the muscle spindle during extrafusal contraction, in order to ensure that the accuracy of the muscle spindle as a sensor – and thus the stabilizing action of the stretch reflex – is preserved even during movement. In addition, the increased spindle activity produced by activity of the γ motoneurons serves to support the movement in progress [3, 4, 11, 15, 42].

Secondary muscle-spindle afferents. The central connections of the Group-II afferents from muscle spindles are considerably different from those of the Ia afferents. Apart from the now well-established monosynaptic excitation of homonymous motoneurons – the extent and functional significance of which, however, cannot yet be evaluated – the segmental reflex circuitry of the secondary spindle afferents to a great extent resembles that of the afferents that can elicit the flexor reflex (p. 90). The implication is that regardless of their muscle of origin, under certain con-

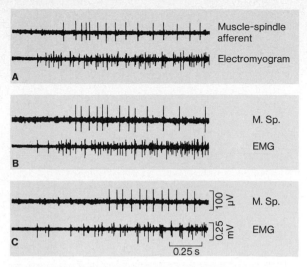

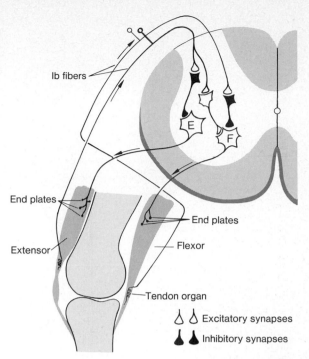

Fig. 5-9 A–C. α-γ coactivation during active finger movement by a human subject. The finger was bent three times (**A, B, C**). The upper oscilloscope trace in each pair shows the activity of a muscle-spindle afferent (M. Sp.) from the flexor digitorum longus muscle, and the lower shows the electromyogram (EMG) of the same muscle, recorded with needle electrodes, as a reflection of its α motor activity. From [42]

Fig. 5-10. Segmental connectivity of the Ib fibers from the tendon organs in a muscle. Representation analogous to Fig. 5-7. The excitatory connection of the flexor Ib fibers to the extensor motoneuron E has been omitted, because a corresponding reflex action is not routinely observed

ditions they exert an excitatory influence on all the flexors of the limb involved, and an inhibitory influence on all the extensors. Thus their action is not limited, as is that of the Ia afferents in most cases, to the synergists and antagonists acting at the same joint; rather, it extends to the control of movement of the entire limb [33].

Segmental connections of the Ib fibers; role of the tendon organs. To a first approximation, the segmental connections of the Ib fibers are the mirror image of those of the Ia fibers (Fig. 5-10). The tendon organs have *di- or trisynaptic inhibitory* connections with their *homonymous* and synergistic agonistic motoneurons (this inhibition is called **autogenic inhibition** = self-inhibition), and *disynaptic excitatory* connections with *antagonistic* motoneurons [6, 7, 29]. Note, however, that this connectivity has not been observed in all cases. In particular, the excitatory actions of the *flexor* Ib fibers on extensor motoneurons has often failed to appear, or appeared only under certain conditions; evidently supraspinal control plays a major role here. Moreover, the expression *autogenic inhibition* encompasses only part of the function of Ib afferents, for they influence not only the motoneurons of synergistic and antagonistic muscles, but also motoneurons to muscles that act at other joints [29].

Tendon organs as sensors in a tension-control system. Because the tendon organs measure the tension in the muscle (p. 84), an increase in muscle tension owing to extrafusal contraction causes an inhibition of the

homonymous motoneurons, by way of the activation of Ib afferents. Conversely, a decrease in muscle tone causes *disinhibition* (reduction of inhibition) and thus an activation of homonymous motoneurons. In other words: the *reflex arc of the tendon organs* is organized in such a way that it can serve to keep the **tension of the muscle constant.** Every muscle, then, has two feedback systems (control circuits): a *length-control system* with the muscle spindles as sensors, and a *tension-control system* with the tendon organs as sensors. The action of the length-control system is essentially restricted to a single muscle and its antagonist, whereas the tension-control system of the Ib afferents contributes to the control of muscle tone in the whole limb.

When the external load on a muscle is changed, it is physically impossible to keep both the length and the tension of the muscle constant. If the load increases (cf. Fig. 5-4 A, B) the muscle either becomes longer or must increase its tension in order to keep its length constant. In this (common) situation, then, the length-control and tension-control systems work against one another rather than together. According to Houk [30], this conflict could be resolved if neither the length nor the tension of the muscle is kept constant as an individual variable, but rather the **muscle stiffness,** de-

Cutan. afferent (group III fiber from nociceptor)

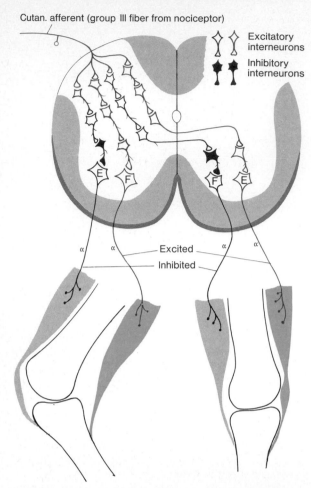

◇ ◇ Excitatory
interneurons

◆ ◆ Inhibitory
interneurons

Fig. 5-11. Intrasegmental connectivity of an afferent fiber from a nociceptor ("pain receptor") in the skin of the foot. The Group-III afferent fiber and the reflex paths for the ipsilateral flexor reflex and the contralateral extensor reflex are shown in *red*. E, extensor motoneurons; F, flexor motoneurons

fined as the ratio of tension change to length change. The experimental analysis of this suggestion is currently underway.

In decerebrate animals and in patients with spastically increased muscle tone, passive stretching of the muscle causes (by way of the stretch reflex) increasing muscle tension, until a state of extreme stretch is reached in which the muscle tone suddenly falls off. This abrupt drop in muscle tension, called the *"clasp-knife phenomenon,"* has been ascribed to the inhibitory action of the Golgi tendon organs [15]. It had been concluded that the role of the autogenic inhibition consisted in protecting the muscle from an increase in tension so great that it might cause tearing of the muscle or tendon. But because the Golgi tendon organs discharge and exert their influence in response to even a minimal rise in tension due to muscle contraction, it is doubtful that this "protective reflex" represents an important function of the tendon organs.

Polysynaptic Motor Reflexes

In addition to the muscle spindles and tendon organs, all the other somatosensory receptors make contributions to the complex of spinal reflexes. These are the **cutaneous receptors,** the **joint receptors,** and the **"free" nerve endings** of Group-III and -IV afferent fibers in the musculature. A feature common to all these afferents is that they reach the motoneurons by way of *polysynaptic reflex paths* (Fig. 5-11). The consequence is that the reflex responses, as discussed on p. 78, can be readily adjusted to the momentary situation.

Flexor reflex. If a hindpaw of a spinalized animal is painfully stimulated (by pinching, strong electrical stimuli, heat), the stimulated leg is pulled away by flexion of the ankle, knee and hip joints. Painful stimulation of the forepaw causes an equivalent *flexor reflex* of the foreleg. The receptors responsible for this reflex are in the skin. The reflex evidently serves to remove the limb from the vicinity of the painful (i.e., harmful) stimulus, and is thus a typical *protective reflex*. By palpating the musculature during a flexor reflex one can feel that the *extensor musculature* relaxes during flexion. The inference is that the extensor motoneurons of the flexed limb are inhibited during this time.

Very diverse flexor reflexes can be elicited by electrical stimulation of practically all somatosensory nerves, especially if the stimulus intensity is chosen such that Group-III and -IV afferents are excited. For this reason these afferents have been designated **flexor-reflex afferents** [27]. This concept has been widely adopted. However, the receptor afferents named above also make reciprocal connections with the same motoneurons in the same limb – that is, excitatory connections with extensor motoneurons, and inhibitory with flexor motoneurons. Thus each of these afferents has an excitatory and an inhibitory reflex route to each group of motoneurons. Which of the two paths is used depends on the controlling inputs from higher motor centers, and probably also on the momentary position and state of movement of the limb [10, 28].

Crossed extensor reflex. The reflex flexion of a hind or fore limb, as a rule, is accompanied by an increase in extensor tone of the contralateral limb, which helps to support the additional load that is shifted to this limb. This *contralateral* extensor reflex is also called the **crossed extensor reflex,** because the afferent activity crosses to the contralateral side of the spinal cord in the anterior commissure to induce the extension there (Fig. 5-11). During the excitation of the contralateral extensor motoneurons the contralateral flexor motoneurons are inhibited. Altogether, then, as Fig. 5-11 shows, painful stimulation of a limb evidently activates four types of motor reflex arcs, embracing all of the flexor and extensor motoneurons of the ipsi- and contralateral limbs. – Because the flexor reflexes and the crossed extensor reflex are progressively brought under supraspinal control as the central nervous system matures, and become obscured by complex reflex patterns, these reflexes can best be observed in an infant or in newborn domestic animals.

Role of the Group-III and -IV afferents from the muscles. Unlike the Group-I and -II muscle afferents, the chief functions of which are in the realm of motor control, the Group-III and -IV muscle afferents (which account for well over half of all afferent fibers) have important additional functions. Some of them are responsible for muscular pain [12, 15]. Others act on the autonomic nervous system in such a way as to participate in the control of blood flow through the muscle [37].

Recurrent inhibition and presynaptic inhibition in spinal motor systems. Recurrent and presynaptic inhibition are inhibitory mechanisms of widespread occurrence in the central nervous system. Their functional significance in spinal motor systems has not yet been entirely clarified.

The inhibition of motoneurons mediated by the action of recurrent collaterals of α motor axons on interneurons (**Renshaw inhibition;** cf. p. 73) evidently serves to prevent uncontrolled oscillation of motoneuron activity. In particular, Renshaw inhibition seems to **limit the discharge** rate of static motoneurons (those with a postural function) [29]. It has been proposed that deterioration of this frequency-limiting function of the Renshaw cells may be the cause of pathologically elevated muscle tone *(spasticity)*.

The significance of presynaptic inhibition (Fig. 3-13), p. 64; Fig. 3-14, p. 65) in motor systems, especially at the spinal level, remains an open question, although many details of the central circuitry are known [39, 40]. Fig. 5-12 summarizes the presynaptic-inhibitory reflex connections between the most important spinal afferents, illustrating the **general negative-feedback character** of this inhibition (like that of Renshaw inhibition on the efferent side). Some fiber groups are less effective (Ia in particular), and others more so (Ib, cutaneous afferents). The details of the role of presynaptic inhibition in spinal reflex activity, however, cannot as yet be specified.

Connections among segmental reflexes. Although the above description distinguishes a number of reflex circuits of which the various afferents form a part, they are not strictly separated from one another. At the segmental level alone there is *extensive convergence* of signals from other sources onto the interneurons of the reflex pathways. For example, the interneurons for reciprocal antagonist inhibition (Ia inhibitory interneurons in Fig. 5-7, p. 87) are themselves inhibited by Renshaw cells and by the Ia inhibitory interneurons of the antagonist. In addition, they receive excitatory input by polysynaptic routes from cutaneous and other ipsi- and contralateral flexor-reflex afferents. To these are added diverse influences from higher motor centers. The full functional significance of this convergence remains to be discovered, but certain possibilities come readily to

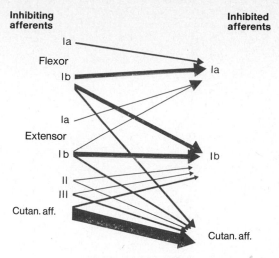

Fig. 5-12. The presynaptic inhibitory action of primary afferent fibers on Ia, Ib and cutaneous afferents in the spinal cord. The width of the arrows is roughly proportional to the strength of inhibition. After ECCLES et al. [39]

mind. For example, suppression of antagonist inhibition would seem to be useful when a joint is to be stabilized by simultaneous contraction of agonist and antagonist.

Intersegmental reflex connections. In addition to the reflex arcs discussed so far, limited to one or a few segments, the spinal cord comprises ascending or descending *intersegmental reflex pathways.* The interneurons of the intersegmental reflex pathways are **propriospinal neurons,** with their cell bodies in the gray matter of the spinal cord. Their axons run for various distances up and down in the white matter as **propriospinal tracts,** never leaving the spinal cord. Degeneration experiments (in which parts of the cord were completely isolated) have shown that the majority of spinal nerve cells are propriospinal neurons.

The intersegmental reflexes assist in the coordination of movements initiated at various levels in the spinal cord – in particular, the coordination between fore and hind limbs and that of neck and limb movements [10, 28, 41]. The afferent impulses for these intersegmental reflexes seem to come from the secondary muscle-spindle endings, the cutaneous receptors, and other flexor-reflex afferents; impulses in Ia and Ib fibers as a rule are without effect.

By way of the segmental and intersegmental reflexes, the spinal cord is capable of *executing complex movements and adjusting them to one another,* when an appropriate signal is received from the periphery or from higher parts of the central nervous system. We refer to this as the **integrative function** of the spinal cord, keeping in mind that in the higher vertebrates – mammals in particular – the higher levels of the central nervous system have increasingly taken control of the spinal functions (Fig. 5-1).

Functions That Persist in the Isolated Spinal Cord

Spinal locomotion. The basic pattern of locomotion – that is, the progression of a person or animal through the surroundings by means of coordinated limb movements – is programmed at the level of the spinal cord [10, 28, 41]. Painful stimulation of one limb of a spinal animal leads to reflex movements of all four limbs, and if the stimulation is prolonged these can develop into a rhythmic flexion and extension of the three unstimulated limbs. If such an animal is held with its feet on a treadmill, under certain conditions it can carry out coordinated walking movements that closely resemble those of a freely walking animal. These walking movements can be maintained by the spinal cord alone, with no feedback of information from the receptors activated by the movement. In a spinal animal paralyzed with curare, under certain conditions rhythmically alternating volleys of impulses can be recorded from extensor and flexor motoneurons, which correspond roughly to those discharged in freely walking animals. Because they occur without actual movement, they are called *fictive locomotion*. Fictive locomotion is generated by – hypothetical – **locomotor centers** in the spinal cord. There appears to be one such center associated with each limb. The coordination of the centers with one another is achieved by the propriospinal systems and by tracts that cross the cord within individual segments.

Humans are also thought to have spinal locomotor centers. For example, the stepping reflex of the newborn is regarded as a manifestation of the locomotor centers activated by stimuli to the skin. As the central nervous system matures, however, these centers are evidently brought under such strong supraspinal control that in an older person they cannot become independently active. It is probably because of this development that it has not yet been possible to elicit coordinated locomotion in human *paraplegics*.

Even at the spinal level, then, there are sequences of movement that are not triggered by external stimuli – that is, **reflex-controlled** – but rather are **program-controlled** and thus can be sustained in the absence of external influences. The higher motor centers comprise far more of these *stimulus-independent movement programs*. Some of them are innate, such as breathing, and others are acquired in the course of a lifetime. Think, for example, of sporting and professional skills such as gymnastics and typewriting, which after sufficient practice become nearly automatic. The central spinal and supraspinal movement programs are not only stimulus-independent, they can also be carried out *without any sensory feedback* (cf. p. 100).

Paraplegia. The question of what can be achieved by reflexes in the isolated human spinal cord is of great practical significance, in view of the facts that accidental *spinal transection* (especially in automobile accidents) is becoming increasingly common, and that modern methods of intensive care make it increasingly likely that these patients can be brought through the acute stage and rehabilitated to live a useful and tolerable life.

In cases of complete **paraplegia** (usually with the cord severed in the thoracic region, T_2 to T_{12}) there is (i) an immediate and permanent *paralysis of all voluntary movement* in the muscles supplied by spinal segments caudal to the injury; (ii) *conscious sensations* associated with the region supplied by the separated spinal segments are also *lost* forever; and (iii) all reflexes in the affected parts of the body are initially extinguished (areflexia).

The motor reflexes recover in the subsequent weeks and months. Given correct care, recovery follows a fundamental pattern discernible despite many individual differences. There are four stages: (i) **Complete areflexia** usually lasts 4–6 weeks. It is followed by a period lasting 2 weeks to several months, in which (ii) **small reflex movements** of the toes, especially the great toe, can be observed. In the next stage (iii) **flexor reflexes** become steadily more pronounced – first those of the toe (Babinski's sign) and ankle joints, whereas later flexor movements of the knee and hip joints appear. *Mass flexor reflexes* are in some cases accompanied by *crossed extensor reflexes*. The foot, especially its sole, is by far the most sensitive *reflexogenic zone* for these complex responses; even non-painful tactile stimuli suffice to trigger widespread flexor reflexes. In the *chronic stage* (iv), which is reached after 6 months or more, the flexor reflexes also predominate as a rule. Now, however, stronger **extensor reflexes** can also occur, and may give rise to prolonged *extensor spasms*. The latter can be so intense that the patient can actually stand briefly without support ("spinal standing"). The extensor reflexes are best elicited by stretching the flexor muscles (especially the hip flexors) suddenly by a small amount. In this stage, then, the excitability of all reflex pathways is evidently increased. Departures from this clinical picture – especially marked extensor reflexes and elevated muscle tone shortly after the injury – are usually a sign that the spinal cord has not been completely transected, and thus that the prospect of motor and sensory improvement is correspondingly better [32, 36]. The changes in *autonomic reflexes* following spinal transection are discussed on p. 126.

Spinal shock. The reversible motor and autonomic areflexia following spinal-cord transection is called **spinal shock.** In experiments on animals *functional transection,* by local cooling or anesthesia, also brings on spinal shock. Once the reflexes have returned following an initial transection, a second transection below the first does not produce spinal shock. Therefore the decisive factor in spinal-shock induction is the loss of the connection to the rest of the central nervous system.

As to the **causes of spinal shock** and the mechanisms by which the reflexes are restored, our knowledge is very incomplete and unsatisfactory. It is striking that the depth and duration of spinal shock increase markedly with increasing cerebral dominance (encephalization). In *frogs* spinal shock lasts only a few minutes, whereas it persists for hours in *carnivores,* days or weeks in *monkeys,* and as long as several months in *anthropoid apes* and *humans.* It may be inferred that cutting the descending pathways eliminates many excitatory inputs to α or γ motoneurons and other spinal neurons, and perhaps in addition disinhibits inhibitory spinal neurons, the net result being a marked suppression of reflexes. But there is as yet no answer to the questions of which mechanisms are responsible for the return of certain spinal functions, and why the human recovery period lasts many months.

5.3 Motor Functions of the Brainstem

Ordinarily equilibrium is maintained and the body is kept in the normal upright position in the earth's field of gravity by reflexes, with no need for conscious intervention. These **postural motor functions** are largely the responsibility of the brainstem (cf. Fig. 5-1), which performs them on the basis of information from the corresponding receptor systems – especially the equilibrium organ and the neck region (cf. p. 95). The chief experimental procedure for study of these functions is to interrupt the connections between the brainstem and the higher motor centers, in some cases eliminating the cerebellum as well [14, 20]. By ablating or destroying selected small regions of tissue, by stimulation experiments and by recording with microelectrodes, the *motor centers* in the brainstem can be localized more precisely [2, 9].

Functional Anatomy of the Brainstem Motor Centers

The **brainstem** in the *physiological* sense comprises the **medulla oblongata, pons** and **mesencephalon** (midbrain) (Fig. 5-13). At its caudal end the brainstem is continuous with the *spinal medulla* (spinal cord), and its rostral end is bounded by the *diencephalon*. Of the many structures in the brainstem, only those involved in motor function will be considered here.

Motor centers of the brainstem. If the motor centers of the brainstem are defined as those structures with efferent fibers that directly influence the motor reflex pathways in the spinal cord (and the cranial motor nerves) and themselves form part of the efferent pathways from higher motor centers, three such centers can be demarcated (Fig. 5-13): (i) the **red nucleus** *(nucleus ruber),* (ii) the nuclear regions of the vestibular nerve, especially the **lateral vestibular nucleus** or *Deiters' nucleus,* and (iii) certain parts of the reticular formation.

The **red nucleus** lies in the mesencephalon (Fig. 5-13) at the level of the corpora quadrigemina. Its most important efferent projection is the rubrospinal tract, which *crosses* immediately after leaving the nuclear region and runs through the spinal cord ventral and somewhat lateral to the *lateral corticospinal tract.* The

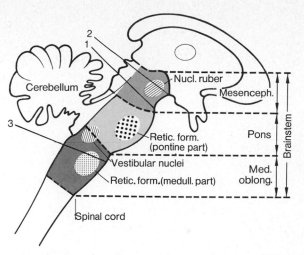

Fig. 5-13. Schematic survey of the positions of the motor centers in the brainstem – medulla oblongata, pons and mesencephalon (midbrain). When communication with the parts of the brain above the indicated three levels of section is interrupted the result is a decerebrate animal (1), a midbrain animal (2) and a high spinal animal (3). Further discussion in text

fibers end in the gray matter of the spinal cord, dorsal to the nuclear regions of the motoneurons (open circles in Fig. 5-14 A) in Rexed's laminae V to VII. The *rubrospinal tract,* when stimulated alone electrically, predominantly **excites α and γ flexor motoneurons,** by way of interneurons (Fig. 5-15). The extensors are inhibited by the rubrospinal tract. (With regard to the corticospinal tract, which exerts similar effects, cf. p. 104).

The **lateral vestibular (Deiters') nucleus** (Fig. 5-13) gives rise to the uncrossed **vestibulospinal tract,** which projects ventromedially into the spinal cord and there terminates in the medial parts of the ventral horn (squares in Fig. 5-14 A), but largely outside the motoneuron nuclei. The *vestibulospinal tract* has an **excitatory action on α and γ extensor motoneurons** (Fig. 5-15) and inhibits the flexors. The excitatory action is in part *monosynaptic.*

In the **reticular formation** of the brainstem a region can be distinguished in the pons and another in the medulla oblongata (Fig. 5-13) that give rise to the two **reticulospinal tracts** [35]. The uncrossed medial reticulospinal tract contains fibers from the pontine region; the lateral reticulospinal tract, arising in the medullary nuclear region, contains both crossed and uncrossed fibers. Both tracts end in the gray matter, again largely outside the motoneuron nuclei (Fig. 5-14 B); the regions of termination of the *pontine fibers are like those of the vestibular* pathway, and those of the *medullary fibers are like those of the rubrospinal and corticospinal tracts* (cf. Fig. 5-15). This correspondence extends to their function: the medullary fibers **excite α and γ flexor motoneurons** (and in-

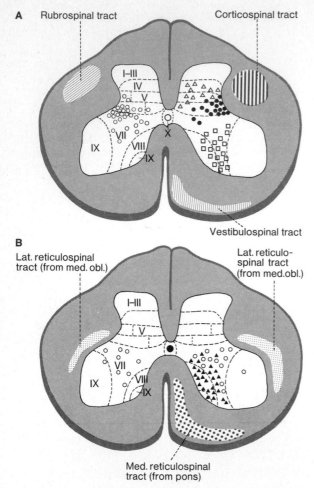

A
Rubrospinal tract   Corticospinal tract

Vestibulospinal tract

B
Lat. reticulospinal   Lat. reticulo-
tract (from med. obl.)   spinal tract
                                                           (from med.obl.)

Med. reticulospinal
tract (from pons)

Fig. 5-14 A, B. Position of the most important descending motor pathways in the spinal cord *(red;* each type of shading indicates the same tract in Figs. 5-13 to 5-15), showing the regions where they terminate. The subdivision of the nuclear regions in the gray matter *(Roman numerals)* is that of Rexed. **A** In the left part of the drawing are the position and terminations *(open circles)* of the rubrospinal tract, and on the right are those of the vestibulospinal tract *(endings: squares)* and of the corticospinal tract. The endings of the corticospinal fibers from MI *(filled circles;* cf. pp. 103, 104) are distinctly ventral to those of the fibers from SI *(triangles).* **B** Position and terminations of the medullary *(endings: open circles)* and pontine *(endings: triangles)* reticulospinal tracts. (Modified from BRODAL [2], incorporating data of NYBERG-HANSEN and BRODAL)

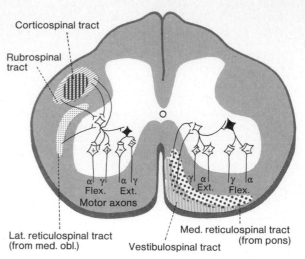

Corticospinal tract

Rubrospinal
tract

Lat. reticulospinal tract   Med. reticulospinal tract
(from med. obl.)   (from pons)
                    Vestibulospinal tract

Fig. 5-15. Schematic representation of the main actions of the motor tracts in the spinal cord on flexor and extensor motoneurons. The tracts situated dorsally and laterally (corticospinal, rubrospinal and lat. reticulospinal) excite α and γ flexor motoneurons and inhibit the extensor motoneurons. The tracts lying medially and ventrally (vestibulospinal and med. reticulospinal) have mirror-image actions

dent in the different distribution of their endings (Fig. 5-14) and other findings [2, 3].

The present anatomical and functional categorization of the descending pathways, though well supported by experiments, in future will have to be expanded in many respects. It emphasizes the postural functions of these pathways and their role in simple locomotor movements. But it takes no account of the fact that the same pathways are also employed to carry out goal-directed movements, which in the case of the arms and hands in particular are not limited to flexion and extension.

Motor Function in Decerebrate Animals

Decerebrate rigidity. When in an animal such as a cat the brainstem is transected at the level of the tentorium of the cerebellum (along Line 1 in Fig. 5-13), so that the spinal cord is isolated from the red nucleus and more rostral motor elements, there soon develops a marked increase in the tone of the entire extensor musculature. All four limbs are held in the maximally extended position, and head and tail are pulled toward the back. This posture is called **decerebrate rigidity.** If a decerebrate animal is set upright it remains on its feet, for the tone of the extensor muscles is so high that the joints cannot bend. The unnaturally outstretched posture of the animal appears like a caricature of normal standing.

hibit the extensors), whereas the pontine fibers **excite** α **and** γ extensors (and inhibit flexors) (Fig. 5-15).

Thus the **supraspinal descending pathways** can be roughly subdivided into *two classes with opposite actions* on the flexor and extensor motoneurons. As Fig. 5-15 shows, the *pathways in each class are close to one another in the* spinal cord, arranged in such a way that those with an excitatory action on flexors are dorsolateral to those that excite extensors. The two classes employ *separate interneuron systems,* as is evi-

The decisive **cause of decerebrate rigidity** is the predominant influence of *Deiters' nucleus* on the extensor motoneurons, in the absence of the red nucleus and still higher motor centers (cf. p. 93 and Fig. 5-15). This effect is clearly demonstrated by the fact that a cut through the cord caudal to this nucleus (Line 3 in Fig. 5-13) abolishes the decerebrate rigidity. Moreover, unilateral coagulation of this nuclear region causes most of the symptoms to disappear on the ipsilateral side.

Gamma and alpha rigidity. The decerebrate rigidity just described is eliminated by transection of the dorsal roots (Sherrington). This result indicates that it is basically maintained by the γ loop. For this reason the term γ **rigidity** is also used [9]. In *ischemic decerebration* (by ligation of the carotid and basilar arteries), in which large parts of the cerebellum and the pons are also inactivated, the rigidity persists after the dorsal roots are transected to interrupt the γ loop. In this α **rigidity,** then, the direct excitatory influence on the α extensor motoneurons predominates. (The cerebellum has an inhibitory action on Deiters' nucleus. Therefore removal of the cerebellum intensifies the decerebrate rigidity, whereas stimulation of the cerebellum reduces or abolishes it.)

Tonic reflexes. The distribution of tonus in the musculature of a decerebrate animal can be changed by passive movement of the head. Because moving the head changes both its position in space and its position with respect to the body, this change in tone could be produced by signals from the equilibrium organ and/or the receptors in the neck. To examine the change more closely, then, it is necessary to eliminate one or the other source of information. For example, if both labyrinths are removed the position of the head in space is no longer signalled, but the neck receptors continue to signal each change in head position with respect to the body. In the *motor centers of the brainstem* these signals cause appropriate *corrections of the distribution of tone in the body musculature* (Fig. 5-16), together called the **tonic neck reflexes.** Similarly, the changes in tone distribution initiated by the equilibrium organs are called **tonic labyrinthine reflexes.** All such reflexes fall in the category of **tonic reflexes** *(postural or stance reflexes),* because they determine the posture of a quietly standing animal.

Examples of tonic neck reflexes. If the head of a standing decerebrate animal from which the labyrinths have been removed is bent upward (red arrow in Fig. 5-16 A), the tone of the limb musculature changes as indicated: the extensor tone in the hindlimbs is reduced and that in the forelimbs is increased. When the head is bent downward (red arrow in Fig. 5-16 B) the opposite changes in tone distribution occur: The extensor tone in the forelimbs is reduced and that in the hindlimbs is increased. A third example: if the head is turned to the side, so that the equilibrium of the body's posture is disturbed, the disturbance is compensated by an appropriate increase in tone of the limb musculature. When the head is turned to the right (shifting the weight of the body toward the right side) the extensor tone in both right limbs increases. In all three cases the new posture is maintained as long as the head remains in the changed position.

Tonic labyrinthine reflexes. When neck reflexes are excluded by fixing the position of the head with respect to the body of a de-

Decerebrate animal, labyrinths removed

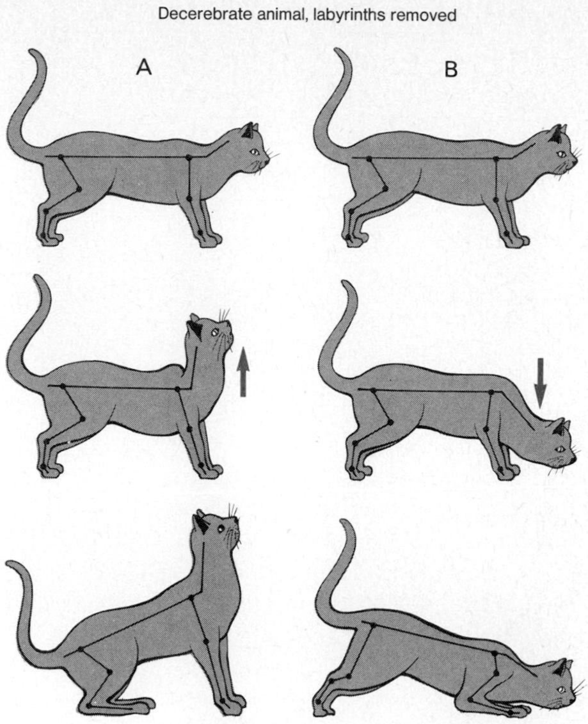

Fig. 5-16 A, B. The elicitation of postural reflexes in a decerebrate animal from which the organs of equilibrium (labyrinths) have been removed. Passive upward bending of the head (*red arrow* in **A**) causes a reduction of extensor tone in the hindlimbs and an increase in extensor tone in the forelimbs. Passive downward bending of the head (*red arrow* in **B**) has the opposite effect

cerebrate animal, the labyrinths being intact, change in the spatial orientation of the head plus the body elicits very distinct changes in extensor tone of all four limbs [14, 20]. The extensor muscles in the four limbs always respond in the *same way,* either contracting or relaxing.

Compensatory eye positioning. An interesting *special case of postural reflexes* is the **compensatory positioning of the eyeball** such that the visual field tends to be retained despite alternation of head position – that is, to keep the image on the retina the same. In man and in animals with frontal eyes, this compensation occurs chiefly by way of the optic signals from the overlapping visual fields. But in animals with eyes on the side and little or no overlap of the two visual fields, the distribution of tension in the eye musculature is governed largely by the interaction of labyrinth and neck reflexes. For example, if the head of a rabbit is turned so that the right half of the face is downward, the right eye is rotated upward and the left eye (now on top) is rotated downward. It is because of this **counterrotation of the eyes** that the eyes do not entirely follow the position of the head, but rather tend to retain their position with respect to the horizon.

Motor Functions of the Midbrain Animal

Performance of a midbrain animal. If not only the medulla oblongata and pons, but also the mesencephalon, are largely left in communication with the spinal

Table 5-1. Reflexes for body posture and position

Static reflexes		Statokinetic reflexes
Postural reflexes	Righting reflexes	
e.g.	e.g.	e.g.
Tonic neck reflexes	Labyrinthine righting reflexes	Head-turning reactions
Tonic labyrinthine reflexes	Neck righting reflexes	Eye-rotation reactions
Compensatory eye positioning		Elevator reaction
		Orientation in free fall

cord (midbrain animal; cut along Line 2 in Fig. 5-13), the motor abilities of the organism are considerably improved and extended. The two most notable differences from a decerebrate animal are (i) that the midbrain animal exhibits *no* pronounced decerebrate rigidity, and (ii) that the midbrain animal can *right itself* independently. Because the brainstem inputs relating to motor activity are the same in both preparations, these improvements must be brought about chiefly by the motor centers of the midbrain. The decisive factor in the **improvement of tone distribution,** for example, is that the influence of the **red nucleus** eliminates the bias toward the extensors (cf. p. 93 and Fig. 5-15).

Righting reflexes. Still more important than the absence of decerebrate rigidity is the ability of the midbrain animal to *right itself;* that is, whenever the body is put in an abnormal position the standard attitude is resumed readily and accurately. The return to the normal position is brought about by reflexes called **righting reflexes** (cf. Table 5-1).

It has been shown that to restore the normal position the righting reflexes occur in a particular sequence – in concatenation, as it were. The first event is always that signals from the labyrinth bring the head into the normal position. These reflexes are called **labyrinthine righting reflexes.** This movement – raising the head from the reclining position, for example – changes its position with regard to the rest of the body, and this change is signalled by the receptors in the neck. The result is that the trunk follows the head into the normal position. In analogy with the labyrinthine righting reflexes, these reflexes are called **neck righting reflexes.**

Function of the tonic and righting reflexes. Because of the righting reflexes, the normal posture and equilibrium of the body are maintained involuntarily. In addition to the *labyrinthine* and *neck righting reflexes,* there are a number of other righting reflexes; for ex-

ample, the *receptors on the body surface* can initiate movement to adjust the position of head and body. Considering that *optical righting reflexes* also exist – though they are eliminated in midbrain animals they can be demonstrated under other experimental conditions – it becomes clear that righting the body into the normal position under the influence of these manifold inputs is one of the best-ensured functions of the central nervous system. The tonic and righting reflexes guarantee *assumption of the basic position* and the *adoption and maintenance of a particular posture.* An important feature of these reactions is that the head, in which the eyes, ears and olfactory organ are situated, plays a dominant role. Thus even stimuli originating at a distance can cause the body to assume an appropriate posture, often a defensive posture.

Static and statokinetic reflexes. The supporting, tonic and righting reflexes together are often called **static reflexes,** because they determine and maintain the position and equilibrium of the body during quiet reclining, standing and sitting in a wide variety of postures. In addition to these, the midbrain animal exhibits a number of reflexes that are elicited by movement and themselves consist of movements. They are called the **statokinetic reflexes** (Table 5-1).

Examples of statokinetic reflexes. Many of these reflexes are initiated by the labyrinths. The best known are the head- and eye-turning reactions. For example, if an animal is rotated clockwise, the head turns counterclockwise. Such reactions are *compensatory* – that is, eyes and head are moved in such a way that the visual images are retained as nearly as possible during the movement. When the movement is stopped they are then kept in position by static reflexes (compensatory eye positioning; see above). Other important statokinetic reflexes ensure balance and correct positioning of the body during jumping and running. Among these are the "elevator reaction" (increased extensor tone with linear acceleration downward, increased flexor tone with upward acceleration) and the complex of reflexes that helps a cat always to land on its feet. (In regard to vestibular nystagmus see p. 278.) That the midbrain functions go beyond the statokinetic reflexes is demonstrated by the fact that coordinated walking movements can be elicited in a midbrain animal by electrical stimulation of circumscribed mesencephalic areas.

Role of the brainstem in postural motor function. As an overall simplification, we may say that the midbrain animal differs little from the intact animal with regard to posture, righting and stepping responses. From experiments on decerebrate and midbrain animals it is evident that the motor centers of the brainstem coordinate the action sequences in the righting and postural reflexes, enlisting the musculature of the entire body to achieve a specific result.

Role in goal-directed movement. The contribution of the brainstem to postural function just described is only part of its significance in motor performance as a whole (cf. [28, 41]). The motor centers in the brainstem receive inputs from the motor cortex and in turn send signals to the cerebrum, particularly by way of their connections to the cerebellum (cf. Figs. 5-19 to 5-21). These connections apparently serve chiefly to coordinate postural and goal-directed movements (cf. p. 100).

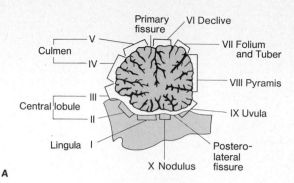

A

5.4 The Cerebellum

There is no doubt that the *cerebellum* plays a crucial role in the *nervous control of posture and movement*. It is likely that a number of activities can be carried out optimally only with the participation of the cerebellum. However, the cerebellum is not necessary for life; people congenitally lacking a cerebellum exhibit no fundamental motor deficits in their everyday routine.

Despite great experimental efforts and considerable advances in the last two decades, the *mechanisms of cerebellar activity* are only beginning to be explained [2, 5, 8, 13, 17]. But since there is no other central nervous structure about which we know more than we do about the cerebellum, there is reason to hope that the study of the cerebellum will soon provide new and decisive breakthroughs in our understanding of central nervous activity.

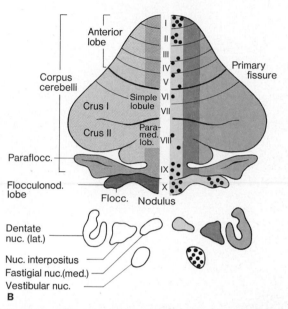

B

Functional Anatomy of the Cerebellum

The structural aspects of the cerebellum crucial to an understanding of the functional relationships are summarized in Fig. 5-17. The sagittal section in A shows the characteristic *folding of the cerebellar cortex*, the individual lobules of which are designated both by the classical names and the Roman numerals later assigned by Larsell, which have been widely adopted [2].

The left half of the diagram of the cerebellar surface in Fig. 5-17 B shows the **phylogenetic relationships.** It is immediately clear that in the higher mammals the *neocerebellum* (hemispheres, vermis caudal to the primary fissure) is far more extensive than the *paleocerebellum* (vermis of the anterior lobe, pyramis, uvula, paraflocculus) and the small *archicerebellum* (flocculonodular lobe). This phylogenetic subdivision corresponds roughly to a **subdivision in terms of the afferent inputs** (cf. p. 99). Accordingly, the archicerebellum is often also referred to as the *vestibulocerebellum*, the paleocerebellum as the *spinocerebellum*, and the neocerebellum as the *pontocerebellum*.

Fig. 5-17 A, B. Survey of the functional anatomy of the cerebellum. **A** Sagittal section (monkey) with lobules numbered according to Larsell. **B** shows on the left the subdivision on phylogenetic grounds, into archicerebellum (flocculonodular lobe, *red*), paleocerebellum *(gray-red)* and neocerebellum *(light red)*. On the right in **B** is the subdivision into longitudinal zones obtained by projecting the cerebellar cortex onto the cerebellar nuclei. Corresponding cortical and nuclear regions are identically marked. The vestibular nucleus (DEITERS') receives direct inputs from the vermis (red dots; cf. Fig. 5-19). After JANSEN and BRODAL in [2]

A classification of *greater functional significance* than those just described is the subdivision into three longitudinal zones derived primarily by *projection of the outputs from the cerebellar cortex* (the Purkinje-cell axons) onto the cerebellar nuclei (on the right in Fig. 5-17 B). The *vermian part* of the cerebellar cortex projects to the **fastigial nucleus;** the *pars intermedia*, just lateral to the vermis, projects to the **nucleus interpositus**, which in man consists of the globose and emboliform nuclei. The *hemisphere* projects to the **dentate nucleus.** Of all the cerebellar nuclei, each of which is represented bilaterally in the white matter of the cerebellum, the dentate is the largest in primates,

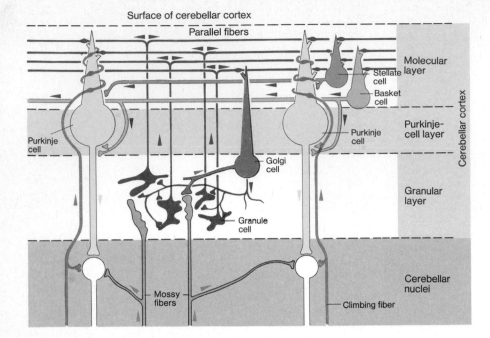

Surface of cerebellar cortex

Parallel fibers

Molecular layer

Stellate cell

Basket cell

Purkinje cell

Purkinje cell

Purkinje-cell layer

Cerebellar cortex

Golgi cell

Granular layer

Granule cell

Cerebellar nuclei

Mossy fibers

Climbing fiber

Fig. 5-18. The most important neuronal connections in the cerebellar cortex, according to studies by ECCLES et al. Inhibitory cells are shown in *red*. Detailed discussion in text

in accordance with the great increase in volume of the hemispheres.

Although the various structural subdivisions just discussed have been derived mainly from experiments on animals, they can be applied to the **human cerebellum** as well if the phylogenetic developments and the somewhat different nomenclature are taken into account [2, 13].

The Cerebellar Cortex

Structure [13, 17]. The cerebellar cortex has a large surface. Unfolded, it would cover an area of $17 \times 20 \text{ cm}^2$ (width $\times$ length). Despite its great extent the **cerebellar cortex,** apart from regional variations, is largely uniform in structure (Fig. 5-18). The most superficial of the three layers, the **molecular layer,** is separated from the lowermost, the **granular layer,** by the **Purkinje-cell layer.** The names of the molecular and granular layers are derived from their appearance in fresh cross sections of the cortex, the one being finely dotted and the other grainy.

Neurons of six different types, with their processes, occupy the various layers of the cerebellar cortex (Fig. 5-18). The small (1) **granule cells** (numbering 10^{10} to 10^{11} in man) of the granular layer send their axons into the molecular layer. There the axons divide in a T pattern, sending a branch (a **parallel fiber**) 1–2 mm in each direction along the folium. On the way these branches pass through the *dendritic arborizations* of cells of *all the other five types,* forming *synapses* with them. The granular layer also includes the larger (2) **Golgi cells,** the dendrites of which extend far into the molecular layer while their axons pass to the granule cells.

Between the two other layers lie the (3) **Purkinje cells** (15 million in humans), large neurons with a *dendritic tree* that branches extensively within the molecular layer. The *axons* of the Purkinje cells run to the cerebellar nuclei, and a smaller fraction terminate in the vestibular nuclei. These are the only "output" of the cerebellar cortex.

The remaining three cell types, (4) **basket cells,** (5) **stellate cells** and (6) **Lugaro cells,** lie in the *molecular layer.* Whereas the course of the Lugaro-cell axons is unknown (therefore they are not shown in Fig. 5-18), the axons of the other two cell types run to the Purkinje cells, those of the *basket cells to the soma* and those of the *stellate cells to the dendrites.*

Two types of axons (fibers) enter the cerebellar cortex. In Fig. 5-18 one of them is labelled **climbing fiber.** This type passes through the granular layer and ends in the molecular layer, on the dendrites of the Purkinje cells. The branches of the climbing fibers "climb" up those of the dendritic tree, clinging like ivy to its twigs. Each Purkinje cell is reached by only one climbing fiber, but each climbing fiber supplies 10–15 Purkinje cells. The cell bodies of the climbing fibers all lie in the *inferior olive* (cf. p. 99). All the other – considerably more numerous – cerebellar afferents end as **mossy fibers** (about 50 million in man) on the granule cells, each mossy fiber first dividing into many collaterals. Because of this *divergence* each mossy fiber reaches many cells in the cerebellar cortex. Conversely, each cerebellar-cortex cell is reached by many parallel fibers, so that by way of the granule cells many hundred mossy fibers *converge* onto each cortical cell.

Synaptic connectivity. We owe our knowledge of the connections of the cells in the cerebellar cortex chiefly to Eccles and his coworkers [8, 26]. They are summarized in simplified form in Fig. 5-18, which shows the excitatory (black) or inhibitory (red) actions of the individual neuronal elements. The **climbing fibers** make numerous *excitatory* synapses on the dendritic tree of the Purkinje cells, so that a single impulse in a climbing fiber causes multiple discharge of the Purkinje cell. The **mossy fibers** excite the granule cells and these, by way of the **parallel fibers,** excite *all the other* neuronal elements. The actions of the latter, however, are *all inhibitory;* the **Golgi cells** inhibit the granule cells (feedback inhibition; cf. p. 73), and discharge of the **Purkinje cells** (induced by mossy or climbing fibers) causes inhibition of the cells in the cerebellar nuclei. Except for the granule cells, then, *all the neurons* with cell bodies in the cerebellar cortex are inhibitory. Nowhere else in the central nervous system has such a predominance of inhibition been found.

Purkinje cells exhibit a *resting discharge,* which brings about a tonic **inhibition of the cerebellar nuclei** (Fig. 5-18). When the Purkinje-cell activity is increased, owing to excitation by mossy or climbing fibers, the nuclei are **more strongly inhibited;** on the other hand, inhibition of the Purkinje cells (directly by stellate or basket cells, or indirectly by Golgi cells) disinhibits the cerebellar nuclei. Because all the excitatory inputs to the cerebellum are *converted to inhibition* after at most two synapses, after 100 ms the effect of each input is extinguished and the region involved is again ready to process a new input. It is plausible that this automatic "erasing" is especially important with regard to the participation of the cerebellum in rapid movements.

(Fig. 5-17 B) was discussed on p. 97. The further projections of these nuclei, each to different structures in the brainstem and cerebrum, will be described below in the context of function (Figs. 5-19 to 5-21). Here we mention only a feature that will not be returned to later, the efferent connections of the cortex of the *vestibulo- (archi-) cerebellum.* Some of these are *direct* (bypassing the cerebellar nuclei) projections to the vestibular nuclei, and some go to *all* the cerebellar nuclei. Thus *participation of the vestibular system in all operations* of the cerebellum is ensured.

Various feedback circuits provide the cerebellum with a regular supply of information about the substrate on which it has acted. This feedback can occur by a relatively direct route (for example, via the reticular formation; cf. Fig. 5-19) or by way of a few relay stations, as in the rubro-olivo-cerebellar pathway (cf. Figs. 5-20 and 5-21); but it can also be very complex, with relay stations at various levels of the motor system. Examples of the latter case are paths involving the brainstem nuclei, the peripheral motor system and the spinal relay nuclei (Figs. 5-19 and 5-20) or the thalamus, the motor cortex and the pontine relay nuclei (Fig. 5-20). This continual flow of information enables the cerebellum to correct departures from the desired constellation of excitation relatively quickly.

Afferent and Efferent Connections of the Cerebellum

Afferents, somatotopy. As noted briefly on p. 97, the inputs to the cerebellum can be divided into three groups: 1. inputs from the vestibular nerve and its nuclei, 2. somatosensory inputs, primarily from the spinal cord, and 3. descending inputs, primarily from the cerebral cortex.

The (1) **vestibular inputs** are almost all to the nodulus and flocculus – that is, to the **archi-** or **vestibulocerebellum** (Fig. 5-17 B). Of the (2) **somatosensory inputs** from the spinal cord, the ventral (Gower) and dorsal (Clarke) spinocerebellar tracts from the hindlimbs have been known for the longest time, but there are at least 10 other tracts, the courses and transmission properties of which have been well elucidated [34]. About half of these tracts, including the two named above, terminate as *mossy fibers;* the other pathways consist of *spino-olivary tracts,* which in the olive transmit excitation to neurons that send the *climbing fibers* to the cerebellar cortex. The endings of these pathways, chiefly in the **paleo-** or **spinocerebellum** (Fig. 5-17 B), are **organized somatotopically** to some extent. Other inputs to these regions include somatosensory afferents from the head region, and visual and auditory afferents.

The *entire cerebral cortex,* in addition to other regions of the brain, contributes to the (3) **descending inputs** to the cerebellum [2, 13]. Most of them synapse in the *pontine nuclei* with fibers that run to the **neo-** or **pontocerebellum.** Inputs from the *motor areas of the cortex* (defined on p. 102) end chiefly in the pars intermedia, and those from the rest of the cortex end in the hemispheres (cf. Figs. 5-20 and 5-21).

Efferents. The subdivision of the cerebellum into **three longitudinal zones** derived from the *projection of the cerebellar cortex onto the cerebellar nuclei*

Functions of the Cerebellum

On the basis of what has been learned from the pathological or experimental destruction of the cerebellum or parts thereof, as well as from stimulating and recording experiments, the **functions of the cerebellum** can be summarized as follows. Its primary role is to supplement the activity of the other motor centers and to correlate them. In particular, it is responsible for (i) the control of posture and muscle tone, (ii) course correction during *slow* goal-directed movements (if necessary) and coordination of these movements with the postural system, and (iii) the unimpeded performance of the *rapid* goal-directed movements "designed" by the cerebrum. Simplifying the situation somewhat, we can say that each of these **three tasks** is the responsibility of one of the **three longitudinal zones** of the cerebellum. This allocation will now be discussed.

Vermis and postural functions. As summarized in Fig. 5-19, the **vermis** receives afferent input chiefly from the *somatosensory system,* and in turn influences *Deiters' nucleus,* both directly and indirectly, along with the medullary and pontine *reticular formation,* by way of the **fastigial nucleus** (cf. Fig. 5-17 B). Thus the vermis has direct access to the brainstem centers for postural control and to their descending pathways (cf. Figs. 5-13 to 5-15). As the simplest example of this action note that removal of the vermian parts of the cerebellum *disinhibits* Deiters' nucleus

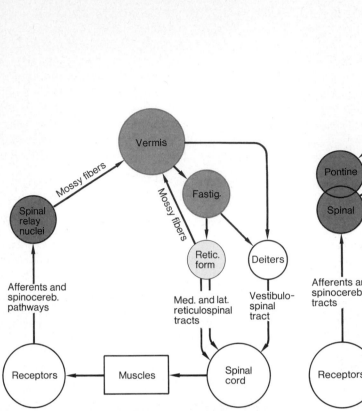

Fig. 5-19. Participation of the vermis in the control and regulation of posture by way of the fastigial and DEITERS' nuclei. For simplicity, the climbing-fiber input to the vermis, which parallels the mossy fibers, has been omitted

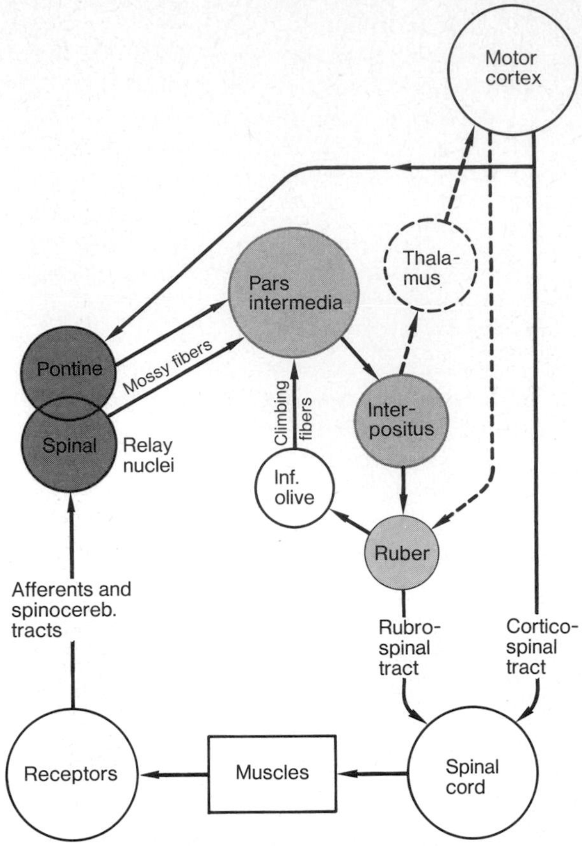

Fig. 5-20. Pars intermedia and nucleus interpositus as elements of the motor system. The afferent inputs from the periphery correspond to those of the vermis (cf. Fig. 5-19). In addition, the pars intermedia receives afferent inputs from collaterals of the corticospinal tract, which enable it to participate in the course correction of goal-directed movements and in the coordination of goal-directed and postural movements. The climbing fibers paralleling the spinal and pontine mossy fibers have been omitted

and thus intensifies the extensor rigidity of a decerebrate animal; conversely, stimulation of the vermis reduces extensor tone (cf. p. 95). The vermis is thus capable of ensuring that the afferent information continually being fed back to signal the momentary state of posture and movement is immediately made available for the maintenance or alteration of body position. In this way the *vermis controls posture, tone, supporting movements and the balance of the body,* an activity in which it is assisted by the vestibulocerebellum (see above).

Pars intermedia: course correction and coordination (Fig. 5-20). The **pars intermedia** receives afferent input from the *somatosensory system* and also, by way of collaterals of the corticospinal tract, from the *motor cortex.* Its efferent activity is carried by way of the **nucleus interpositus** (or globose and emboliform nuclei) to the motor centers in the brainstem, especially

the *red nucleus.* A lesser efferent projection passes through the thalamus back to the *motor cortex.* The *advance notice* of intended directed movement it receives by way of the collaterals of the corticospinal tract, together with the feedback from the somatosensory system, enables the pars intermedia (i) to *coordinate the postural and goal-directed motor systems with one another* – for example, to shift the center of gravity at an appropriate time, and (ii) to *carry out course corrections* by signals sent to the red nucleus as well as those fed back directly to the motor cortex. Corrections of this sort are presumably most important for movement sequences that have not (or not yet) been sufficiently well learned or often enough practiced.

Hemispheres: rapid goal-directed movements (Fig. 5-21). The afferent inputs to the **hemispheres** are derived from the *entire cerebral cortex* (frontal, parietal, temporal and occipital lobes). These *cerebro-cerebel-*

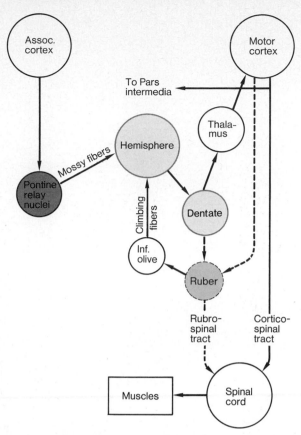

Fig. 5-21. Cerebellar hemispheres and dentate nucleus as elements of the motor system. The afferent inputs come from association areas of the cortex, not directly from the periphery (by contrast, cf. Figs. 5-19 and 5-20). The movement designs coming from the cerebral cortex are converted to movement programs by the hemispheres and their nuclei. In parallel to the path from the cerebral cortex shown here is another by way of the basal ganglia (cf. Figs. 5-1 and 5-25)

cuit involving corticospinal-tract collaterals shown in Fig. 5-21 is also an integral part of the circuit responsible for course correction and coordination with postural systems. As will be discussed on p. 105, the circuit shown in Fig. 5-21 is supplemented by a comparable circuit running in parallel from the *association cortex* through the *basal ganglia* and the *thalamus* to the motor cortex (Fig. 5-1 and 5-25).

Function of the mossy and climbing fibers. In Figs. 5-19 to 5-21 some of the climbing-fiber inputs (all of which arrive by way of the inferior olive) are omitted for simplification. They are largely derived from the same peripheral and central structures as the input by way of mossy fibers. The respective roles of the two fiber types, however, are very little understood and will therefore not be treated here.

Crossed and uncrossed tracts. Another important aspect of the way the cerebellum is incorporated into the motor system has also been omitted from Figs. 5-19 to 5-21 – that is, the question whether the individual tracts cross to the opposite side or not. It is answered, in some cases, in the preceding or following sections; in other cases the answer can be found in the literature [2, 5, 34]. For the present it suffices to note that *each half of the cerebellum* acts primarily on the *ipsilateral side of the body.*

Pathophysiological Aspects

The functions of the cerebellum just described suggest that *disturbances of cerebellar activity* will be manifest chiefly as disturbances of muscular coordination during movement and of *muscle tone.* Accordingly, the following symptoms are most characteristic of cerebellar deficits [5]:

1. **Asynergia** or *dyssynergia,* defined as the inability to supply the correct amounts of neural activity to the various muscles involved in a movement. The individual components in a movement program are carried out not simultaneously but rather in succession *(decomposition of movement),* the movements go too far or not far enough and are subsequently overcompensated *(dysmetria),* so that the patient walks with feet wide apart in an uncertain and overshooting gait *(cerebellar ataxia),* and it is no longer possible to carry out a rapid sequence of movements *(adiadochokinesia* or *dysdiadochokinesis).*

2. **Tremor,** not at rest but during movement *(intention tremor).* During goal-directed movements this trembling can develop into such a sweeping oscillation that the goal is missed (disturbance of course correction, particularly associated with damage to the cerebellar nuclei).

3. **Hypotonus** of the musculature – that is, *too-low muscle tone,* often accompanied by *muscular weakness* and *rapid fatiguing* of the musculature. This is primarily a symptom of lesions in the hemispheres, whereas lesions of the vermis alone (anterior lobe) tend more to produce hypertonus (see above).

lar tracts, by way of the pontine nuclei, comprise about 20 million fibers – twenty times as many as the corticospinal tract! The *movement designs* they convey to the motor system (cf. p. 107) are converted to *movement programs* in the hemispheres and the **dentate nucleus,** which are sent to the *motor cortex,* chiefly by way of the *ventrolateral nucleus of the thalamus,* for the *execution of the movement.* In addition, the dentate nucleus has access to the motor centers of the brainstem by way of the *red nucleus.*

The pathways shown in Fig. 5-21 are used chiefly for the *elicitation and execution of rapid ballistic goal-directed movements,* movements either so rapid that control or regulation by somatosensory feedback is *impossible on temporal grounds,* or so well controlled that such feedback is *not required* (for example: rapid movements in high-performance sport, in playing music and in speaking, as well as saccadic eye movements). As was evident in Fig. 5-20, however, the cir-

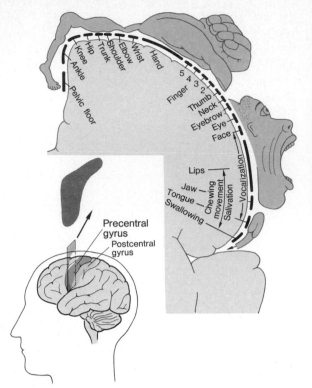

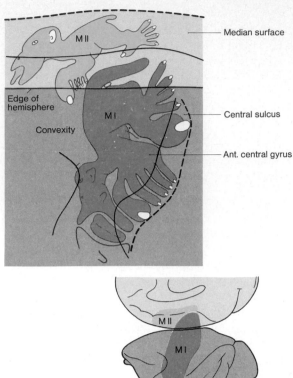

Fig. 5-22. Motor representation of the body in the human precentral gyrus. Schematic somatotopic projection onto a plane in the precentral gyrus, the orientation of which in the human skull is shown in the inset at lower left. The drawing illustrates the relative magnitude of representation of individual regions (motor homunculus). The corresponding somatotopic subdivision of the postcentral gyrus (sensory homunculus) is shown in Fig. 9-11, p. 203. (After PENFIELD and RASMUSSEN [18])

Fig. 5-23. Primary (MI) and secondary (supplementary, MII) motor areas in the cerebral cortex of the monkey. The lower drawing shows the location of these areas on the cerebral cortex, and the upper shows the somatotopic representation, which corresponds roughly to that in man (cf. Fig. 5-22). With regard to the primary and secondary somatosensory fields cf. Figs. 9-2 and 9-9. (After WOOLSEY et al.)

4. **Nystagmus** (cf. pp. 267 and 278), 5. **vertigo** and 6. **speech defects** are other symptoms of cerebellar lesions. A classical summary of the cerebellar syndrome is Charcot's triad: *nystagmus, intention tremor* and *staccato* ("scanning") *speech*.

For further *details of clinical symptomatology* and of the methods of examination the reader is referred to the literature [2, 5]. The nature and extent of the symptoms depend fundamentally on the site and degree of damage – for example, on whether the cerebellar cortex, cerebellar nuclei or afferent and efferent pathways are involved. But many interpretations in this area remain highly controversial. The situation is made more difficult by the fact that **cerebellar defects** as a rule can be extremely **well compensated** by the central nervous system, so that the patient is quite inconspicuous in his everyday activities. In such cases an appropriately *refined examination technique* is necessary to reveal the defect.

5.5 Functions of the Motor Cortex and the Basal Ganglia

Centers of particular importance for *goal-directed movements* are the **motor cortex** and the **basal ganglia.** Therefore their functions are treated together here. Because the two are extensively linked to one another by way of thalamic structures (cf. Fig. 5-1), the *motor role* of the **thalamus** is also considered in this section (for its other functions see p. 201). In conclusion we shall turn – though only briefly, because so little is known – to the *drive to act* and the *movement design*.

Which Are the Motor Areas of the Cortex?

More than a hundred years ago, FRITSCH and HITZIG (1870) and FERRIER (1873) showed that *electrical stimulation* of circumscribed areas in the cerebral cortex of a number of mammals could elicit movements of the contralateral limbs. These areas were and are called the **motor cortex.** Not only in an anesthetized animal, but in the waking *human* as well, electrical stimulation of the exposed brain surface, especially by Penfield and his coworkers, has demarcated *motor areas of the cortex* [18]. Two aspects of the motor cortex have been recognized: (i) first, its **somatotopic organization** (Fig. 5-22), the orderly spatial mapping of the periphery of the body onto the motor cortex, and later (ii) a **multiple representation** of the periphery in several motor areas (Fig. 5-23).

Somatotopy. The most important motor area in the human cortex is the **precentral gyrus** (Areas 4 and 6 of Brodmann; cf. Fig. 7-2, p. 146). Its somatotopic organization is diagrammed in Fig. 5-22. It is immediately apparent that those parts of the body with especially good motor abilities, such as the fingers, lips and tongue, are represented in a region of the precentral gyrus far out of proportion to their sizes, whereas the trunk and proximal limbs occupy relatively small regions (cf. also Fig. 5-23). The motor area extends not only over the visible surface of the precentral gyrus but also into the depths of the central sulcus, over the medial edge of the hemisphere and somewhat beyond the precentral gyrus in the rostral direction (Figs. 5-22 and 5-23).

Multiple representation. In addition to the **primary motor cortex** (abbreviated **MI**) just described, there is a **secondary motor cortex (MII),** also somatotopically arranged, in the depths of the interhemispheric fissure, adjacent to the primary motor cortex and somewhat rostral to it (Fig. 5-23). Both areas also comprise a *sensory* projection of the periphery of the body, so that, following Woolsey, we can also speak of a primary and secondary **motosensory cortex,** abbreviated **MsI** and **MsII.** Accordingly, the primary and secondary *somatosensory fields SI* and *SII* (p. 203), because of their motor projection, are also referred to as the sensorimotor cortex SmI and SmII. Altogether, then, we may speak of **four motor fields** – in order of importance, MI, MII, SI, and SII – or of **four sensory fields** in the order SI, SII, MI, MII, depending on the particular aspect under consideration. In the following, if not expressly stated otherwise, the motor cortex will be understood to be MI only. (The field MII is frequently also called the supplementary motor area.)

Functional Organization of the Motor Cortex

Structure of the motor cortex. The general structure of the cerebral cortex is described in detail beginning on p. 145, and is illustrated in Fig. 7-1, p. 145. The *precentral gyrus* and the areas immediately ventral to it are of the type called *heterotypical agranular cortex* (Fig. 7-3, p. 146). In man the precentral gyrus is characterized chiefly by its remarkable thickness, 3.5–4.5 mm, and by the **giant pyramidal cells** (Betz's cells, diameter 50–100 μm) in Layer V (counting from the surface). The axons of these and other, less large pyramidal cells in Layer III are the output of the motor cortex, passing toward the internal capsule, whereas their dendrites are mostly oriented toward the cortical surface.

Cortical columns [16, 19, 22]. The arrangement of the pyramidal cells, perpendicular to the surface, corresponds to that of many interneurons in the motor cortex, so that here (as in the remainder of the neocortex) there is a *histologically* discernible *columnar arrangement* of the cortical neurons. Moreover, *stimulation experiments on the surface of the cortex* (see above) have suggested that pyramidal cells of comparable function are close to one another, for otherwise the precise cortical representation of the periphery of the body would be difficult to explain. The existence of **functional cortical columns** has been confirmed by experiments in which a microelectrode was used for intracortical stimulation and the response was measured either as the facilitation or inhibition of monosynaptic reflex discharges or electromyographically in the muscle. This sort of **motor column,** by which a group of related motoneurons can be excited or inhibited, has a diameter of about a millimeter and contains many hundred pyramidal cells. Adjacent motor columns frequently overlap – even if they elicit opposed movements when stimulated. Histologically, columns of ca. 80 μm diameter are distinguishable, so that a *functional* motor column consists of several of these. Unfortunately, the terms ordinarily used in speaking of cortical columns do not always distinguish the two clearly enough.

Cortical neurons and movement. So far little is known about the functional organization of motor columns. The most informative experiments have involved recording with implanted microelectrodes of the activity of single pyramidal cells in animals performing motor tasks (Fig. 5-24). *Large pyramidal cells* with axons that conduct at high velocity tend to discharge only *during* movement, whereas *small pyramidal cells* with low conduction velocity discharge *continually* though their discharge rate changes during movement. Neighboring pyramidal cells within a motor column can change their activity level in the same direction, in opposite directions, or with no correlation, depending on the movement performed. The **common denominator** for this behavior is the **movement of the associated joint,** which depending on the situation is moved in one or another direction or kept fixed.

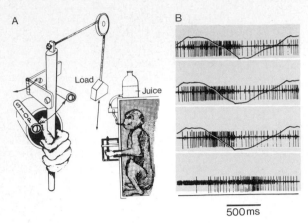

500ms

Fig. 5-24 A, B. Discharge of two pyramidal cells in the precentral motor cortex of a monkey *(Macaca mulatta)* during flexion (upwards in B) and extension of the wrist. **A** shows the experimental arrangement. By operant conditioning (with fruit juice as the reward) the monkey is trained to perform certain sequences of movement in response to a light signal. A microelectrode holder is chronically implanted in the top of the skull. **B** Recordings from two pyramidal cells differing distinctly in action-potential amplitude. During movement (upper three records) the impulses in both cells are correlated with the extension of the wrist. Both cells are spontaneously active in the absence of motion (lower record). (Measurements of EVARTS, from [21])

These results show that those cortical neurons that affect a particular muscle are not restricted to a single motor column, as the stimulation experiments might have implied. Rather, a **motor column** is a **functional neuron population** that influences a number of muscles acting on a particular joint. This conclusion supports the old thesis that not muscles but rather **movements are represented in the cortex.** This does not mean that muscles have no cortical representation, rather that they are multiply represented. The experimental finding that motoneurons of a muscle can often be excited over large regions of the motor cortex (many mm² in area) is consistent with this interpretation [19].

The cause and significance of the different discharge patterns of large and small pyramidal cells are not known. Perhaps these two types correspond to the large (phasic) and small (tonic) α motoneurons of the spinal cord, but it is also possible that they separately control the α and γ motoneurons.

Efferent Connections of the Motor Cortex

Many histological procedures (e.g., anterograde and retrograde degeneration) and physiological methods (e.g., measurement of evoked potentials after orthodromic or antidromic stimulation) as well as many clinical-pathological findings have been applied in recent decades to the study of the efferent connections of the motor cortex. It has turned out that the motor areas, MI and SI in particular, act on the lower motor systems in three ways: (i) directly on the motoneurons, either monosynaptically or by way of a few interneurons, (ii) indirectly by way of connections with other motor centers such as the pars intermedia of the cerebellum (Fig. 5-20), and (iii) still more indirectly by influencing the transmission and processing of information in the sensory projection nuclei, such as the cuneate nucleus or the thalamus. In this section we shall be concerned chiefly with (i).

Corticospinal tract. Leaving the motor areas in each half of the brain, about a million efferent fibers form the *corticospinal tract* to the spinal cord by way of the internal capsule, cerebral peduncle, pons, pyramids and pyramidal decussation (for details of its course see [2, 19]). In the pyramidal decussation 75–90% of the fibers cross to the opposite side, where they run in the dorsolateral quadrant of the spinal cord as the *lateral corticospinal tract* (Figs. 5-14, 5-15). The other, smaller part continues caudally uncrossed, in the anteromedial regions. This part as a rule goes no further than the cervical and thoracic cord, some of the axons crossing to the contralateral side at the segmental level, so that the percentage of crossed axons increases still further.

Because of its passage through the pyramids, the *corticospinal tract* is also called the **pyramidal tract.** The pyramidal tract is ordinarily considered to include the corticofugal fibers that leave the tract within the pyramids or even above it, passing to the motoneurons of the cephalic nerves as the *corticobulbar tract.* **Phylogenetically** the pyramidal tract is the youngest of the descending tracts; it is considerably better developed in primates and in humans than in other mammals.

The *corticospinal and corticobulbar tracts originate* in all the areas of the motosensory cortex. About 30% of the fibers come from Area 4 (precentral gyrus), 30% from the area just rostral to it, Area 6, and 40% from the parietal lobe (SI and SII, Areas 3, 1, 2; cf. Fig. 7-2). On their way to the spinal cord the axons give off **numerous collaterals** to other important motor-system structures, including the thalamus, the red nucleus, the pontine nuclei (which send the mossy fibers to the cerebellum; cf. Fig. 5-20), the inferior olive (which sends the climbing fibers to the cerebellum), the dorsal-column nuclei and probably also the reticular formation. The **axonal endings in the spinal cord** are mainly on *interneurons,* though in primates and man at least some make *monosynaptic* connections with α motoneurons. The axons arising from MI end in a part of the gray matter distinctly ventral to the endings of the axons from SI (Fig. 5-14). As mentioned on p. 93, the influence of the *corticospinal tract* (together with the rubrospinal and lateral reticulospinal tracts) is predominantly **excitatory on flexors** and inhibitory on extensors (Fig. 5-15).

The **conduction velocity** of the great majority of fibers in the *corticospinal tract* is **low.** Only about 30 000 of the million fibers on each side are thick myelinated fibers with high conduction velocity (60–120 m/s). These arise from Betz's giant pyramidal cells in the precentral gyrus. All the other fibers are thin myelinated or unmyelinated fibers with conduction velocities of 1 m/s to 25 m/s. Their actions have as yet been little studied.

Cortical efferents to the brainstem. About the *same motosensory areas* that give rise to the pyramidal tract also send efferents to the motor centers of the brainstem (cf. p. 93). These are primarily **corticorubral connections,** which synapse in the red nucleus with fibers that form the *rubrospinal tract* (cf. Figs. 5-14, 5-15, 5-20), and **corticoreticular connections** to the pontine and medullary motor structures (Fig. 5-13) that give rise to the medial and lateral reticulospinal tracts (Figs. 5-14, 5-15). These tracts are distinguished from the pyramidal tracts by the anatomical term "extrapyramidal tracts." Functionally, however, the two "systems" are so intimately linked that it does not seem reasonable to separate them. One of the main tasks of the cortical efferents that synapse in the brainstem nuclei is probably to initiate or reinforce the postural and supporting movements of trunk and limbs that enable well-adjusted goal-directed movements to be carried out. Among other things, then, they serve to couple goal-directed and postural functions. It has been shown, for example, that after the corticospinal tract alone has been transected in the monkey, refined movements of the fingers are no longer possible, though arm movements with rough grasping motions are fairly well preserved. The additional interruption of the rubrospinal connection made controlled grasping practically impossible.

The Basal Ganglia

The **basal ganglia** are an important **subcortical link** between the "associative" cerebral cortex (cf. Fig. 7-25) and the motor cortex (Figs. 5-1, 5-25). Their significance is particularly apparent in the severe disturbances of muscle tone, posture and movement that follow disorders of these nuclei – for example, in Parkinson's syndrome (cf. p. 108). But there are still many gaps in our knowledge about these structures, largely because they are so difficult to reach for experimental purposes [21, 31].

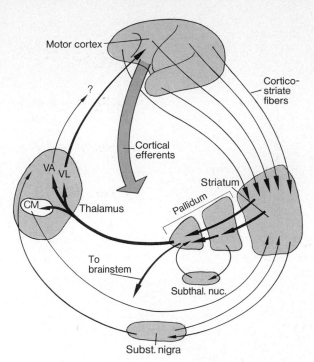

Fig. 5-25. Summary of the most important afferent, efferent and intrinsic connections of the basal ganglia. CM, centrum medianum; VA, ventral anterior nucleus; VL, ventral lateral nucleus; Nuc. subth., subthalamic nucleus. Detailed description in text. (After DELONG in [21])

Components of the basal ganglia. The term *basal ganglia* encompasses the **striatum** (consisting of the *caudate nucleus* and *putamen*), the **pallidum** (also called globus pallidus, with an outer and an inner part), the **substantia nigra** and the **subthalamic nucleus** (Fig. 5-15). Often the claustrum is also included, and less often, the amygdala [2].

Afferent and efferent connections. Fig. 5-25 summarizes the most important afferent, efferent and internal connections of the basal ganglia. The **striatum** receives the **majority of all afferents** to the basal ganglia, which come almost entirely from three sources: (i) the entire cerebral cortex, (ii) the intralaminar nuclei of the thalamus, and (iii) the substantia nigra (dopaminergic pathway!). The **efferents from the striatum** go to the *pallidum* and the *substantia nigra*. The latter, in addition to the dopaminergic pathway to the striatum, sends another to the thalamus. The **inner part of the pallidum** sends out the most important **efferents** from the basal ganglia, to end chiefly in the *thalamus* and to a lesser extent in the *tegmentum* of the midbrain. Essentially, then, as noted at the outset, the basal ganglia constitute an intermediate link in the chain of connections between the entire **non-motor cerebral cortex** and the **motor cortex.** In this respect they are comparable to the hemispheres of the cere-

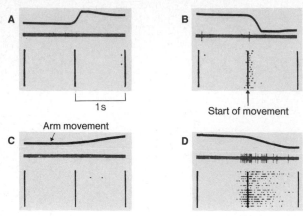

Fig. 5-26 A–D. Impulse activity (*red* dots in lower parts of **A** to **D**) of a neuron in the putamen that fired preferentially during ramp (slow) movements in one direction (**D**). During slow movements in the opposite direction (**C**) or rapid movements (**A, B**) the neuron remained silent (**A, C**) or discharged only a few impulses (**B**). Twelve tests of each movement are plotted in a vertical array, each impulse being represented by a dot. Above each plot the original record of one of the twelve responses is shown. Note in **D** that the neuron begins to discharge before the onset of movement (vertical line). Experimental arrangement as in Fig. 5-24 A. (Measurements in *Macaca mulatta* by DE-LONG, from [21])

bellum (cf. Figs. 5-1 and 5-21). *Cerebellar hemispheres* with dentate nucleus and *basal ganglia* are thus **afferent** to the *precentral motor cortex* (Figs. 5-1, 5-21, 5-25).

Basal-ganglion neurons and movement. Clinical (discussed on p. 108) and experimental evidence indicates that the **basal ganglia** may be particularly important in the execution of uniform, slow **"ramp"** **movements** (cf. Kornhuber in [21]). A graphic example of the behavior of neurons in the putamen during arm movements by a waking monkey is shown in Fig. 5-26. This neuron exhibited distinct, prolonged impulse discharge only when the movement was slow and in a particular direction. During slow movement in the opposite direction (C) or rapid movements (A, B) the neuron remained silent (A, C) or discharged only a few impulses (B). The onset of discharge in D (dots) clearly preceded the onset of movement (middle vertical line). This observation supports the inference that putamen neurons of this type are involved in the initiation and maintenance of ramp movements.

Motor Cortex, Thalamus, Basal Ganglia and Movement

Motor cortex and movement. It is possible, as described above, to elicit contractions of single muscles and even movements of joints by electrical stimulation of the precentral gyrus in man and animals, but purposeful complex sequences of movement can never be produced in this way. Moreover, stimulation experiments on small children and adults, on a skilled pianist and a manual laborer have given entirely identical results [16, 18]. These and other findings indicate that the motor cortex is not responsible for the *design* of inborn or acquired goal-directed movements. Rather it is one, in fact the **last supraspinal station** for the conversion of *cortically* induced movement designs into **movement programs.** At the same time, as a glance at Fig. 5-1 shows, it is the beginning of the chain of structures that serve primarily for the **execution of movements.** (Remember, however, that many complex movement sequences involve exclusively subcortical structures.)

The exact role of the motor cortex in the execution of movement is unknown. Experiments of the kind shown in Fig. 5-24 have so far given no clear indication as to which of the many aspects of muscular activity (for example, the force, speed, duration and direction of a movement) are under the special control of cortical neurons. The only definite finding is that there are large numbers of cortical neurons in which the discharge rate can be correlated with certain movements (see, e. g., Fig. 5-24) and, as would be expected, that the increase in discharge often precedes the movement. It also seems to be the case that at least when a certain position is to be maintained the chief function of the cortex is to *select the muscles to be used* and not, as was previously thought, to control the muscular force exerted [38].

Cooperation among basal ganglia, thalamus and motor cortex. In the process by which a movement program is elaborated, the motor cortex receives its input from the *thalamus* and the *basal ganglia* (cf. Fig. 5-25). The latter, as described above, receive afferents mainly from the entire cerebral cortex and may be responsible in particular for the **performance of slow movements.** On the other hand, the special tasks of the thalamic nuclei involved in movement, the anterior ventral and lateral ventral nuclei, are not yet known. In any case, within these nuclei the total **somatosensory information** is available for incorporation into whatever sequence of actions is planned. Moreover, these nuclei also receive information from the cerebellum by way of the dentate nucleus (Fig. 5-21).

Comparison between cerebellum and basal ganglia. The cerebellum and basal ganglia project to the motor cortex by way of the thalamus (Figs. 5-1, 5-21, 5-25). In terms of hierarchy, then, they are **centers of equal rank** that participate in the **programming of cortically induced movements.** But there are striking differences in the motor disturbances caused by diseases or destruction of these structures. Whereas **cerebellar** deficits are associated chiefly with hypotonus, asynergy and intention tremor (cf. p. 101), as will be explained on p. 108 the **basal ganglia** are associated with rigidity, akinesia and tremor at rest, and under certain conditions with uncontrolled involuntary movements. Evidently the cerebellum and basal ganglia perform **different tasks** at a *functionally comparable* level – tasks of which, as shown in pp. 99 and 105, only certain aspects have as yet become apparent.

The Drive to Act and the Movement Design

The generation of neuronal impulse patterns leading from the initial drive to perform some act to the conception and design of the required movement – whether these drives arise in (subcortical) **innate releasing mechanisms** (cf. pp. 135 and 307) or in our **free will** – is a complete mystery. If thoughts can lead to actions, the neurophysiologist is forced to assume that it is possible for **thinking to change the neuronal activity of the brain** so that the efferent outflow from the motor cortex produces the desired movement. This conversion of thinking and willing into cortical impulse patterns, however, is far beyond the limits of our present understanding.

Readiness potential. The first steps in exploring the neurophysiological events that precede a movement have already been taken. For example, when an experimental subject is required to perform a movement in response to the second of two successive signals, an electrode over the cerebral cortex records a slow negative wave preceding the movement. This is called the **expectancy potential,** for it is the consequence of the expectation of the second stimulus elicited by the first stimulus [43].

On the other hand, if the subject is told to make a voluntary movement such as bending a finger repeatedly at irregular intervals, with no sensory stimuli to act as a signal, another potential called the **readiness potential** is observed. It is a slowly rising surface-negative potential beginning about 800 ms before the movement, which can be recorded over the entire convexity of the skull (Fig. 5-27). The readiness potential is thought to be related to the processes that precede the sending out of a movement program from the motor cortex [25]. Near the time of the movement it gives way to more rapid and more spatially delimited potentials, especially pronounced over the contralateral motor areas, which reflect the activity of these areas before and after onset of the movement.

The readiness potential can thus be regarded as the neuronal correlate of a movement design. It is astonishing that it is so widespread and develops so long before the movement. Evidently in this stage of the conception of a willed act large parts of the cerebral cortex interact, and their participation in the preparation of the program requires considerable time.

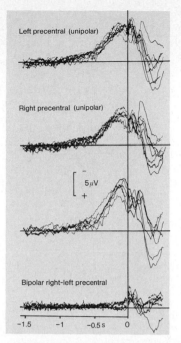

Fig. 5-27. Cerebral potentials recorded from the human scalp prior to voluntary rapid bending of the right index finger. The potentials were obtained by the method of reverse analysis of many single responses recorded on magnetic tape. Eight experiments with the same subject on different days, 1000 movements in each experiment. The upper three rows represent monopolar recording with both ears as reference; the lower curve was obtained by bipolar recording between the left and right precentral hand regions of the motor cortex. The readiness potential begins ca. 0.8 s before the onset of movement. It is bilateral and widespread over the precentral and parietal regions. The premotion positivity, also bilateral and extensive, begins about 90 ms before onset of movement. The motor potential appears only in the bipolar record. It is unilateral over the left precentral hand area, and begins 50 ms before the movement is first evident in the electromyogram. The potentials to the right of the zero point (i.e., after movement has begun) are largely reafferent signals elicited by sensory stimuli. (Measurements by KORNHUBER et al., in [21])

5.6 Pathophysiology of Motor Systems

Up to this point, disturbances and deficits of the motor system have been treated only to the extent that they contribute to an understanding of the function in question. For example, the abilities of the isolated spinal cord were considered with reference to paraplegia (p. 92), the role of the brainstem motor centers with reference to decerebrate and midbrain animals (pp. 94, 95), and cerebellar functions with reference to the consequences of cerebellar lesions (p. 101). In the following we will turn to some symptoms or syndromes commonly encountered in neurology for which a pathophysiological basis can be given – though sometimes only in outline (for details see, e.g., [2, 3]).

Peripheral Paralysis

The transection of motor axons (for instance, in an accident) or the degeneration of motoneurons (for instance, in poliomyelitis) causes a **flaccid paralysis** characterized by reduced muscle tone (hypotonia), atrophy (degeneration of the muscles; p. 57), diminution (paresis) or abolition (paralysis) of the force of gross movements and corresponding impairment of fine movements. The monosynaptic stretch reflexes are weakened or extinguished. All these symptoms are obvious consequences of the damage.

Pathophysiology of the Basal Ganglia

Lesions in the basal ganglia lead to various forms of movement disturbance, of which the best known is **Parkinson's syndrome** (shaking palsy). The patients are conspicuous because of their mask-like facial expression, the absence or severe restriction of communicative gesture, their hesitant gait with small steps, and the trembling of their hands. Examination reveals the symptoms *akinesia, rigidity* and *resting* or *alternating tremor,* to varying degrees. **Akinesia** is a form of motor constraint in which the patient has great, often insurmountable, difficulty in starting a movement and in bringing it to an end. **Rigidity** is a maintained increase in muscle tone independent of joint position or movement; it can be described as plastic or *waxy resistance.* During passive movement the muscles give way not gradually but in jerks – the *cogwheel phenomenon.* The **resting tremor** (4–7 Hz, most marked at the ends of the extremities) is suppressed during goal-directed movements and resumes when they have been completed.

Pathophysiologically *akinesia* can be interpreted as a defect of programming of movement. Whether this is a primary failure of a generator function in the basal ganglia (cf. Kornhuber in [21]) or the result of changes in areas of the cerebral cortex connected with the basal ganglia is uncertain. *Rigidity* and *tremor* are to be regarded as due to a disinhibition of the motor functions of the basal ganglia resulting in overactivity. The latter term also applies to other diseases of the basal ganglia distinguished chiefly by overshooting movements of one sort or another (for example, chorea, athetosis, hemiballismus).

The probable **cause of Parkinson's syndrome** is the destruction of the (inhibitory?) pathway from the substantia nigra to the striatum (Fig. 5-25), which releases dopamine as the transmitter in the striatum. Parkinson's syndrome, the akinesia in particular, can therefore be successfully **treated by administration of L-dopa,** the precursor of dopamine (dopamine itself is in-

effective because it cannot pass the blood-brain barrier). By contrast, stereotactic lesions in the pallidum and thalamus (VL), which interrupt the projection to the motor cortex (Fig. 5-25), can ameliorate the overshooting symptoms but not the akinesia.

Pathophysiology of the Motor Cortex and Its Efferents

Capsular hemiplegia. Lesions in the region of the motor cortex that cause overexcitation (e.g., epileptic attacks) or deficiency symptoms, as well as interruptions of the cortical motor efferents, are rare in the everyday experience of the physician. An exception is the complete or partial blocking of the cortical efferents in the region of the internal capsule by bleeding, or thrombosis in the medial cerebral artery at the point where it leaves the lenticulostriate artery (stroke, apoplexy). The consequence, following an initial shock stage with flaccid paralysis of the contralateral side of the body (flaccid hemiplegia), is a *paralysis with distinct hypertonia of the musculature,* manifest chiefly in an increased resistance to passive movements **(spastic hemiplegia).** The predominant spasticity is in the antigravity muscles – the extensors of the legs and the flexors of the arms (in a four-legged animal it would be the extensors of all limbs). Goal-directed movement is to some extent restored after a while, but it usually amounts to no more than gross mass movements of the flexors and extensors *(flexor or extensor synergy).*

The pathophysiological process underlying spastic hemiplegia is the interruption of cortical motor efferents, **always both** the *corticospinal tract* **and** the pathways to the brainstem.

Spasticity resembles the decerebrate rigidity observed in animal experiments (p. 94). Like decerebrate rigidity, it can be abolished by transection of the dorsal roots, which indicates involvement of the γ loop. Apparently elimination of the cortical efferents causes the influence of Deiters' nucleus (which itself is not reached directly by the cortex) to predominate, resulting in an increase (disinhibition) of antigravity-muscle activity (cf. Fig. 5-15), partly by enhancement of the stretch reflexes, their *phasic* components in particular. (By contrast, *rigidity* appears to involve an increase in the *tonic* component of the stretch reflex. It may be that in the former case increased activity of the dynamic fusimotor fibers dominates, and in the latter an increase in static-fiber activity; cf. p. 85.)

Originally, **capsular paralysis** was predominantly ascribed to interruption of the corticospinal tract (see next paragraph). But experimental transections of this pathway alone in primates (in the pyramid or cerebral peduncle) and corresponding clinical-path-

ological observations in humans have shown that the only consequence, after the recovery phase, is that the dexterity of the fingers is restricted to some extent, with very little or no increase in muscle tone and stretch reflexes. By contrast, in animal experiments a condition resembling capsular hemiplegia can be induced by ablation of the motor cortex in the broad sense – MI, MII and in some circumstances SI and SII as well [24]. Thus *capsular hemiplegia* results from the **elimination of various descending tracts** from the motor cortex **in combination** [2]; it is likely that the abolition of fine movements is due chiefly to the interruption of the corticospinal tract and the projection to the red nucleus (cf. Figs. 5-20, 5-21).

Unfortunately, because the importance of the corticospinal tract in goal-directed movement was once overestimated, the paralytic symptoms associated with the motor cortex and its efferents came to be known as *pyramidal-tract symptoms* or the *pyramidal-tract syndrome*. Spasticity has been ascribed to the additional involvement of the *extrapyramidal motor system*. Moreover, the motor disturbances following lesions of the basal ganglia (p. 108) are still referred to as *extrapyramidal movement disturbances* [19]. As this chapter shows, the distinction between pyramidal and extrapyramidal tracts, however correct anatomically, makes no sense **functionally** – indeed, it is **misleading.** It is to be hoped that this insight will bring about an appropriate change in the clinical nomenclature.

Similarly, it is no longer justified to regard **Babinski's sign** (tonic dorsiflexion of the great toe with or without tonic plantar flexion and fanning out of the other toes) as a reliable symptom of pyramidal-tract damage. Many clinical-pathological and human-experimental findings also contradict this one-sided interpretation, for they show that Babinski's sign can also occur under a number of other conditions [2].

5.7 References

Textbooks and Handbooks

1. BOYD, J. A., DAVEY, M. R.: Composition of Peripheral Nerves. Edinburgh–London: Livingstone 1968
2. BRODAL, A.: Neurological Anatomy in Relation to Clinical Medicine, 2nd Edition. New York–London–Toronto: Oxford University Press 1969
3. DESMEDT, J. E. (Ed.): Human Reflexes, Pathophysiology of Motor Systems, Methodology of Human Reflexes. Basel–München–Paris–London–New York–Sydney: Karger 1973
4. DESMEDT, J. E. (Ed.): Cerebral Motor Control in Man: Long Loop Mechanisms. Basel–München–Paris–London–New York–Sydney: Karger 1978
5. DOW, R. S., MORUZZI, G.: The Physiology and Pathology of the Cerebellum. Minneapolis: University of Minnesota Press 1958
6. ECCLES, J. C.: The Physiology of Nerve Cells. Baltimore: Johns Hopkins Press 1957
7. ECCLES, J. C.: The Inhibitory Pathways of the Central Nervous System. The Sherrington Lectures IX. Springfield/Ill.: Ch. C. Thomas 1969
8. ECCLES, J. C., ITO, M., SZENTÁGOTHAI, J.: The Cerebellum as a Neuronal Machine. Berlin–Heidelberg–New York: Springer 1967
9. GRANIT, R.: The Basis of Motor Control. London–New York: Academic Press 1970
10. HERMAN, R. M., GRILLNER, S., STEIN, P. S. G., STUART, D. G. (Eds.): Neural Control of Locomotion. New York–London: Plenum Press 1970
11. HOMMA, S. (Ed.): Understanding the Stretch Reflex. Progress in Brain Research 44, Amsterdam–Oxford–New York: Elsevier 1976
12. HUNT, C. C. (Ed.): Muscle Receptors. Handbook of Sensory Physiology III/2. Berlin–Heidelberg–New York: Springer 1974
13. LARSELL, O., JANSEN, J.: The Comparative Anatomy and Histology of the Cerebellum. The Human Cerebellum, Cerebellar Connections and Cerebellar Cortex. Minneapolis: University of Minnesota Press 1972
14. MAGNUS, R.: Körperstellung. Berlin: Springer 1924
15. MATTHEWS, P. B. C.: Mammalian Muscle Receptors and Their Central Actions. London: Arnold 1972
16. MOUNTCASTLE, V. B.: Medical Physiology, Vol. I. 13th Edition. Saint Louis: Mosby 1974
17. PALAY, S. L., CHAN-PALAY, V.: Cerebellar Cortex, Cytology and Organization. Berlin–Heidelberg–New York: Springer 1974
18. PENFIELD, W., RASMUSSEN, T.: The Cerebral Cortex of Man. New York: Macmillan 1950
19. PHILLIPS, C. G., PORTER, R.: Corticospinal Neurones. London–New York–San Francisco: Academic Press 1977
20. RADEMAKER, G. G. J.: Das Stehen. Berlin: Springer 1931
21. SCHMITT, F. O., WORDEN, F. G. (Eds.): The Neurosciences, Third Study Program. Cambridge/Mass–London: MIT Press 1974

Research Reports and Reviews

22. ASANUMA, H.: Recent developments in the study of the columnar arrangement of neurons within the motor cortex. Physiol. Rev. *55*, 143 (1975)
23. BARKER, D., EMONET-DÉNAND, F., LAPORTE, Y., PROSKE, U., STACEY, M. J.: Morphological identification and intrafusal distribution of the endings of static fusimotor axons in the cat. J. Physiol. (Lond.) *230*, 405 (1973)
24. BRODAL, A.: Self-observations and neuroanatomical considerations after a stroke. Brain *96*, 675 (1973)
25. DEECKE, L., SCHEID, P., KORNHUBER, H.: Distribution of readiness potential, pre-motion positivity, and motor potential of the human cerebral cortex preceding voluntary finger movements. Exp. Brain Res. *7*, 158 (1969)
26. ECCLES, J. C.: The cerebellum as computer. J. Physiol. (Lond.) *229*, 1 (1973)
27. ECCLES, R. M., LUNDBERG, A.: Synaptic actions in motoneurones by afferents which may evoke the flexion reflex. Arch. ital. Biol. *97*, 199 (1959)
28. GRILLNER, S.: Locomotion in vertebrates: central mechanisms and reflex interaction. Physiol. Rev. *55*, 247 (1975)
29. HAASE, J., CLEVELAND, S., ROSS, H.-G.: Problems of postsynaptic autogenous and recurrent inhibition in the mammalian spinal cord. Rev. Physiol. Biochem. Pharmacol. *73*, 73 (1975)
30. HOUK, J. C.: Regulation of stiffness by skeletomotor reflexes. Ann. Rev. Physiol. *41*, 99 (1979)
31. KEMP, J. M., POWELL, T. P. S.: The connexions of the striatum and globus pallidus: synthesis and speculation. Phil. Trans. B *262*, 441 (1971)
32. KUHN, R. A.: Functional capacity of the isolated human spinal cord. Brain *73*, 1 (1950)
33. LUNDBERG, A., MALMGREN, K., SCHOMBURG, E. D.: Comments on reflex actions evoked by electrical stimulation of Group II muscle afferents. Brain Res. *122*, 551 (1977)
34. OSCARSSON, O.: Functional organization of spinocerebellar paths. In: IGGO, A. (Ed.): Handbook of Sensory Physiology, Vol. II, Somatosensory System, p. 340. Berlin–Heidelberg–New York: Springer 1973

35. PETERSON, B. W.: Reticulospinal projections to spinal motor nuclei. Ann. Rev. Physiol. *41*, 127 (1979)
36. PUCHALA, E., WINDLE, W. F.: The possibility of structural and functional restitution after spinal cord injury. A review. Exp. Neurol. *55*, 1 (1977)
37. SATO, A., SCHMIDT, R. F.: Somatosympathetic reflexes: afferent fibers, central pathways, discharge characteristics. Physiol. Rev. *53*, 916 (1973)
38. SCHMIDT, E. M., JOST, R. G., DAVIS, K. K.: Reexamination of the force relationship of cortical cell discharge patterns with conditioned wrist movements. Brain Res. *83*, 213 (1975)
39. SCHMIDT, R. F.: Presynaptic inhibition in the vertebrate central nervous system. Ergebn. Physiol. *63*, 20 (1971)
40. SCHMIDT, R. F.: Control of the access of afferent activity to somatosensory pathways. In: IGGO, A. (Ed.): Handbook of Sensory Physiology, Vol. II, Somatosensory System, p. 151. Berlin–Heidelberg–New York: Springer 1973
41. SHIK, M. L., ORLOVSKY, G. N.: Neurophysiology of locomotor automatism. Physiol. Rev. *56*, 465 (1976)
42. VALLBO, A. B.: Muscle spindle response at the onset of isometric voluntary contractions in man. Time difference between fusimotor and skeletomotor effects. J. Physiol. (Lond.) *218*, 405 (1971)
43. WALTER, W. G.: Slow potential waves in the human brain associated with expectancy, attention and decision. Arch. Psychiat. Nervenkr. *206*, 309 (1964)

6 The Autonomic Nervous System

W. Jänig

The *autonomic nervous system*, innervating the smooth musculature of all organs, the heart and the glands, mediates the neuronal regulation of the *internal milieu*. The actions of this system, as its name implies, are in general not under direct voluntary control. These characteristics distinguish the autonomic nervous system from the somatic nervous system, which mediates afferent and efferent communication with the environment and, for the most part, is subject to voluntary control and accessible to consciousness.

The autonomic and somatic systems operate hand in hand. At the central level, particularly in the brainstem and cerebrum, their neuronal morphological substrates are indistinguishable. In the periphery, however, the two are quite distinct.

Although a major function of the autonomic nervous system is to help keep the internal milieu of the body constant despite changes in load (homeostasis; cf. Cannon [4]), it also controls organs and organ systems that are only indirectly related to the homeostatic functions (e. g., neuronal control of the sexual organs and the intraocular muscles).

6.1 The Peripheral Autonomic Nervous System

Anatomical Subdivisions

The peripheral autonomic nervous system is entirely efferent, and consists of two populations of neurons in series. The terminal neurons, corresponding to the motoneurons in the somatic system, are outside the central nervous system, with their cell bodies in the autonomic ganglia. Because their axons leave the ganglia to reach the effector organs, they are called postganglionic neurons. The neurons that send axons into the ganglia to synapse with the somata of the postganglionic neurons, by the same convention, are called preganglionic neurons. Their somata lie within the central nervous system.

The peripheral autonomic nervous system has two parts, the sympathetic and the parasympathetic systems. The two originate at different levels in the neuraxis. The sympathetic fibers emerge from the thoracic part of the spinal cord and the upper two or three lumbar segments **(thoracolumbar system),** and the parasympathetic fibers originate in the brainstem and the sacral segments **(craniosacral system).**

The term *"sympathetic"* originally embraced the entire peripheral autonomic nervous system. GASKELL [2] subdivided this system into cranial, thoracolumbar and sacral elements. LANGLEY [2] restricted the term "sympathetic" to the thoracolumbar system, and on the basis of pharmacological and functional criteria combined the cranial and sacral subdivisions as the *parasympathetic* system [2]. This classification proved appropriate and useful, and has been retained.

Sympathetic system. The cell bodies of the preganglionic sympathetic neurons are in the lateral horn of the thoracic and lumbar spinal cord. The axons of these neurons are thin, but many are myelinated; their conduction velocities range from 1 to 20 m/s. They leave the spinal cord in the ventral roots and the white rami communicantes (Fig. 6-10, p. 122), and terminate in the paired paravertebral ganglia or the unpaired prevertebral ganglia. The paravertebral ganglia are connected by nerve strands to form a chain on either side of the vertebral column, extending from the base of the brain to the sacrum. From these *sympathetic trunks* the even thinner, unmyelinated postganglionic axons either pass in the gray rami (Fig. 6-10) to the effectors in the periphery of the body, or form special nerves that supply organs in the head region or in the thorax, abdomen and pelvis (Fig. 6-1). From the prevertebral ganglia (celiac, superior mesenteric and inferior mesenteric) the postganglionic fibers pass through plexuses or special nerves to the organs in the abdomen and pelvis.

Most sympathetic ganglia are *remote* from the organ supplied; correspondingly, their postganglionic axons are long. Only a few, relatively small sympathetic ganglia are situated near the reproductive organs, and send out short postganglionic axons. The effectors supplied by the sympathetic system are the smooth muscles in all organs (vessels, viscera, excretory organs, lungs, hairs, pupils), the heart and some

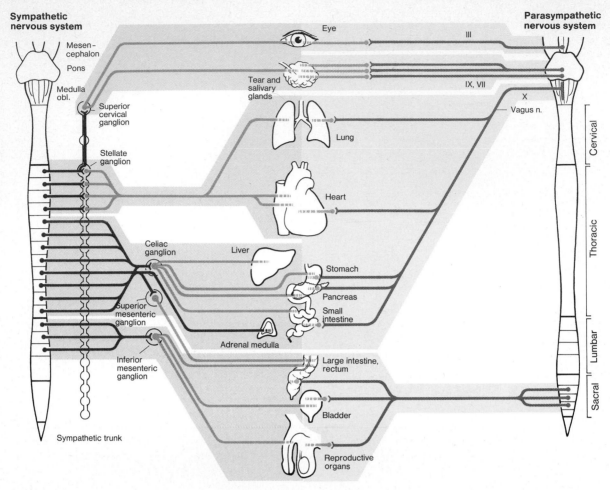

Fig. 6-1. Arrangement of the peripheral autonomic nervous system. Solid lines: preganglionic axons. Shaded lines: postganglionic axons. The sympathetic innervation of vessels, sweat glands and piloerector muscles is not shown

of the glands (sweat, salivary and digestive glands). In addition, sympathetic postganglionic fibers innervate adipose cells, liver cells and perhaps the renal tubules.

Parasympathetic system. The cell bodies of the preganglionic parasympathetic neurons are in the sacral cord and the brainstem (Fig. 6-1). Some of the axons are myelinated and others unmyelinated; all are very long as compared with those of the sympathetic preganglionic neurons. They form special nerves to the parasympathetic postganglionic neurons, which are *near or in* the effector organs. The preganglionic parasympathetic fibers for the muscles within the eye and for the glands in the head leave the brainstem in cranial nerves III (oculomotor), VII (facial) and IX (glossopharyngeal). The preganglionic parasympathetic fibers to the organs in the thorax and abdomen run in the *vagus nerve* (cranial nerve X). The sacral parasympathetic fibers to the pelvic organs run in the pelvic nerve.

Parasympathetic ganglia are found only in the head region and near the effector organs in the pelvis; the other postganglionic cells are scattered in or on the walls of the gastrointestinal tract *(intramural ganglia),* the heart and the lungs. The parasympathetic system innervates the *smooth musculature* and glands of the gastrointestinal tract, the excretory organs, the genitalia and the lungs; it also innervates the atria of the heart, the tear and salivary glands, and the muscles within the eye. Except for the arteries of the genitalia (especially the penis, the clitoris and the labia minora) and possibly those in the brain, it does *not* innervate the smooth muscles in blood vessels.

Visceral afferents. Afferents from receptors in the internal organs usually run in autonomic nerves and are therefore called visceral afferents. This group includes afferents from the organs in the thoracic, abdominal and pelvic cavities – for example, the gastrointestinal tract, heart, aorta, bladder and so on. Some of these receptors signal the *intraluminal* pressure (e. g., in the arterial system) or the degree of fullness of the hollow organs (e. g., the bladder; cf. p. 125) by measuring the stretch of the walls; they usually respond most strongly to change in the wall ten-

Table 6-1. Effects of sympathetic and parasympathetic activation on various organs

Organ or organ system	Parasympathetic stimulation	Sympathetic stimulation	Adrenergic receptors
Cardiac muscle	Decreased heart rate	Increased heart rate	β
	Decreased contractile force (atria only)	Increased contractile force	β
Blood vessels:			
Arteries in skin and mucosa	–	Vasoconstriction	α
Arteries in abdomen	–	Vasoconstriction	α
Arteries in skeletal muscle	–	Vasoconstriction	α
		Vasodilation (by circulating adrenalin only)	β
		Vasodilation (cholinergic)	
Arteries in heart (coronaries)	–	Vasoconstriction	α
		? Vasodilation	β
Arteries in penis (clitoris and labia minora?)	Vasodilation	?	
Veins	–	Vasoconstriction	α
Brain	Vasodilation (?)	Vasoconstriction	α
Gastrointestinal tract:			
Longitudinal and circular muscle	Increased motility	Decreased motility	α and β
Sphincters	Relaxation	Contraction	α
Capsule of spleen	–	Contraction	α
Urinary bladder:			
Detrusor muscle	Contraction	Relaxation	β
Trigone (internal sphincter)	–	Contraction	α
Genital organs:			
Seminal vesicle	–	Contraction	α
Vas deferens	–	Contraction	α
Uterus	–	Contraction	α
		Relaxation (depends on species and hormonal status)	β
Eye:			
Dilator muscle of pupil	–	Contraction (mydriasis)	α
Sphincter muscle of pupil	Contraction (miosis)	–	
Ciliary muscle	Contraction (accommodation)	Slight relaxation (insignificant)	β
Tracheal-bronchial musculature	Contraction	Relaxation	β
Piloerector muscles	–	Contraction	α
Exocrine glands:			
Salivary glands	Copious serous secretion	Slight mucous secretion (submaxillary gland)	α
Tear glands	Secretion	–	
Digestive glands	Secretion	Decreased secretion or –	α
Nasopharyngeal glands	Secretion	–	
Bronchial glands	Secretion	?	
Sweat glands	–	Secretion (cholinergic)	
Metabolism:			
Liver	–	Glycogenolysis Gluconeogenesis	β
Adipose cells	–	Lipolysis (free fatty acids in blood increased)	β
Insulin secretion (from cells in islets of Langerhans)	–	Reduction	α

sion. Other receptors monitor the pH and electrolyte concentration in the organs (e.g., the stomach) and still others are excited by painful stimuli in the visceral region. Part of the visceral afferents enter the spinal cord along with somatic afferents, and like them have cell bodies in the spinal ganglia. Many of the visceral afferents from thoracic and abdominal organs run in the vagus nerve and are called *vagal afferents.* The functions of visceral afferents are treated in the chapters dealing with the associated organs.

The Actions of Sympathetic and Parasympathetic Fibers on Effector Organs

The actions of the peripheral autonomic nervous system on the various organs it innervates can be studied by the electrical stimulation of autonomic nerves. The study of these actions is necessary (i) to understand the operation of the organs in the body with autonomic regulation under physiological conditions, and the interplay between the sympathetic and parasympathetic systems in vivo, (ii) to evaluate the responses of autonomically innervated organs under pathological conditions and (iii) to judge the effect of therapeutic drugs that simulate or block the sympathetic and parasympathetic actions.

Many internal organs receive both sympathetic and parasympathetic innervation (cf. Table 6-1). The influences exerted by the two are largely **antagonistic.** For example, stimulation of the associated sympathetic nerves causes increase in beat frequency and stroke volume of the heart, decrease in intestinal motility, relaxation of the gallbladder and bronchi and contraction of the sphincters of the gastrointestinal tract. Excitation of parasympathetic fibers to these organs (electrical stimulation of the vagus nerve; cf. Fig. 6-1) has the opposite effects: decrease in heart rate and the contractile force of the atria, increase in intestinal motility, contraction of gallbladder and bronchi and relaxation of the sphincters of the gastrointestinal tract. Under physiological conditions it is always the sum of these opposed effects that regulates the activity of these organs.

In most situations the two systems act "synergistically". This **functional synergy** is particularly evident in the reflex effects exerted on the heart by the baroreceptors (cf. Fig. 18-28, p. 427). Excitation of the baroreceptors when the arterial blood pressure rises decreases the beat frequency and contractility of the heart. This decrease is brought about by an *increase* in the activity of parasympathetic fibers to the heart, accompanied by a *decrease* in sympathetic activity (compare the data in Table 6-1 with Fig. 18-28).

In many organs receiving both sympathetic and parasympathetic innervation the parasympathetic regulation predominates under physiological conditions; these organs include the urinary bladder and some

exocrine glands (cf. Table 6-1). There are also organs with only sympathetic or only parasympathetic innervation – almost all blood vessels, the spleen, the smooth eye muscles, some exocrine glands and the smooth musculature of the hair follicles (cf. Table 6-1).

Glycogenolysis in the liver and lipolysis in fat cells, which cause an increase in the blood concentrations of glucose and free fatty acids, respectively, can be elicited by sympathetic stimulation but are unaffected by parasympathetic activity. This influence of the sympathetic system on *metabolism* is discussed on pp. 116 f. The actions of the autonomic nervous system on the individual organs are described in detail in the relevant chapters.

Neurohumoral Transmission in the Peripheral Autonomic Nervous System

Excitation is transmitted chemically from the preganglionic to the postganglionic neuron and from the postganglionic neuron to the effector. As far as is known, neurohumoral transmission in the peripheral autonomic nervous system in principle occurs by the same mechanisms as that at the neuromuscular end plate and at central synapses (cf. pp. 58 f.). In contrast to the end plate, however, the pre- and postsynaptic structures in the autonomic nervous system are extremely variable (myocardial cells, smooth muscle cells, gland cells, neurons). Moreover, the density and pattern of innervation varies greatly among the different smooth muscles (cf. pp. 118 f.).

Acetylcholine. Acetylcholine is probably released at all preganglionic autonomic nerve endings and by most postganglionic parasympathetic neurons (Fig. 6-2). Some sympathetic postganglionic neurons are also cholinergic – those to the sweat glands and perhaps the vasodilator neurons to the resistance vessels in the skeletal musculature.

The actions of acetylcholine on the postsynaptic membranes of the postganglionic neurons can be simulated by *nicotine,* and its action on the effector cells, by *muscarine* (a toxin from the mushroom *Amanita muscaria*). This finding led to the hypothesis that there are two kinds of macromolecular (pharmacological) receptors with which acetylcholine reacts; the actions produced at the two are called nicotinic and muscarinic (Fig. 6-2). There are drugs that *selectively* block one or the other action. The nicotinic action of acetylcholine on the postganglionic neurons can be blocked by quaternary ammonium bases, which are thus called ganglion-blocking agents. The muscarinic action of acetylcholine can be selectively blocked by *atropine*.

In pharmacology drugs that have the same action on effector cells as (cholinergic) postganglionic parasympathetic neurons are called **parasympathomimetics.** Drugs that block or weaken the action of acetylcholine on autonomic effector cells are called **parasympatholytics.** The latter substances are "antimuscarinic" drugs; a typical example is atropine.

Noradrenalin, adrenalin: α/β receptor concept. Because the transmitter substance in sympathetic postganglionic nerve endings is **noradrenalin,** these neurons are called **adrenergic neurons** (Fig. 6-2). The cells in the adrenal medulla, a homolog of the postganglionic neurons, release mainly adrenalin into the bloodstream (cf. p. 116). Noradrenalin and adrenalin are catecholamines (cf. p. 66).

As in the case of the parasympathetic system, there are **sympathomimetic** (adrenomimetic) drugs that imitate the action of sympathetic adrenergic neurons and **sympatholytic** (antiadrenergic) drugs that block it.

The responses of organs to noradrenalin and adrenalin, like those to acetylcholine and the other transmitters, are mediated by interaction of the catecholamines with specific structures in the cell membranes of the organs. These hypothetical membrane structures are called **adrenergic receptors.** On the basis of two purely pharmacological criteria, α and β adrenergic receptors (usually simply called α and β receptors) are distinguished. The criteria are (i) the relative effectiveness of equimolar doses of different catecholamines (usually adrenalin, noradrenalin and isoproterenol; cf. Fig. 6-3 A) in eliciting α and β adrenergic actions, and (ii) the effectiveness of sympatholytic drugs in blocking these α and β actions. The molecular structures of the α and β receptors are still essentially unknown, so that we cannot describe them either morphologically or biochemically.

An α *adrenergic* action is defined by (i) a progressive decrease in effectiveness in the sequence noradrenalin, adrenalin, isoproterenol (NA ≥ A ≫ I), and (ii) selective blocking of these effects by specific drugs (**α blocking agents;** Fig. 6-3 B) in low concentrations.

The β adrenergic actions are characterized pharmacologically as follows. (i) Equimolar doses of isoproterenol, adrenalin and noradrenalin are of decreasing potency in that order (I > A ≥ NA); the artificially synthesized catecholamine isoproterenol is therefore more effective than the natural ones. (ii) The β adrenergic actions can be eliminated by specific **β blocking agents** (Fig. 6-3 B), such as *dichlorisoproterenol,* a derivative of isoproterenol (cf. Fig. 6-3 A).

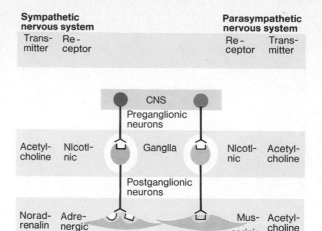

Fig. 6-2. Transmitter substances in the peripheral autonomic nervous system

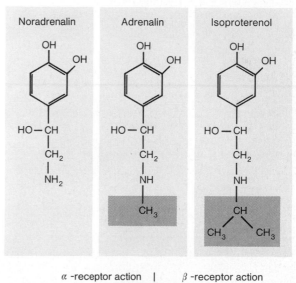

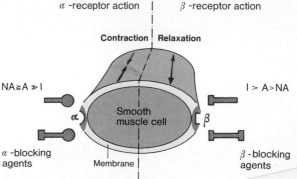

Fig. 6-3. A Molecular structure of nor~~ ~~ isoproterenol. **B** Action of ~~ ~~ (NA), adrenalin (A) and isop~~ ~~ tors. ">" and "=" signify st~~ ~~ respectively

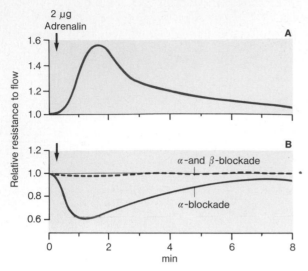

Fig. 6-4. Action of α and β blocking agents on the change in resistance to flow (ordinates) through an isolated, perfused skeletal muscle after intraarterial injection of adrenalin. [From SCHMIDT-VANDERHEYEN and KOEPCHEN: Pflügers Arch. *298,* 1–11 (1967)]

In Fig. 6-4 the α/β receptor concept is illustrated by the action of adrenalin on the arteries in the vascular bed of a skeletal muscle. The smooth musculature of these vessels contains both α and β receptors (Table 6-1). Excitation of the α receptors causes vasoconstriction, and excitation of the β receptors causes vasodilation (cf. Fig. 6-3 B). When the adrenalin level in the blood is high the vessels in the muscle constrict, because the α action predominates (Fig. 6-4 A). After blockade of the α receptors by a specific blocking agent the administration of adrenalin is followed by vasodilation (decrease in the peripheral resistance to flow) in the muscle (Fig. 6-4 B), because now only the β receptors are excited. After additional blockade of the β receptors by a β blocking agent adrenalin has practically no more effect on the vascular bed in the muscle (Fig. 6-4 B). Under physiological conditions low adrenalin levels in the blood are thought to have a dilating influence on the arteries of the muscle vessels, because the β receptor action predominates.

Most of the organs and tissues affected by catecholamines contain both α and β receptors in their cell membranes, and in most organs the two mediate opposite (antagonistic) effects. Under physiological conditions the response of an organ to the adrenalin and noradrenalin in the bloodstream or to excitation of its sympathetic innervation depends on whether the α or the β adrenergic action predominates.

Table 6-1 shows which receptors mediate these **physiological actions** of the two catecholamines at the important organs. Because noradrenalin very activates the β receptors of the myocardium

but reacts only weakly with the β receptors of the smooth musculature of the vessels and of the bronchi and trachea, the β receptors of the heart are designated $β_1$ and those of the vessels and bronchi, $β_2$. It is not yet possible reliably to separate the entire population of β receptors into the categories $β_1$ and $β_2$ [10, 34, 44].

Probably noradrenalin and acetylcholine are not the only transmitter substances in the peripheral autonomic nervous system. Experimental studies have shown that the effects elicited in many organs by stimulation of the autonomic nerves cannot be eliminated by blockade of either adrenergic or cholinergic transmission. For example, the cutaneous vessels of mammals are probably innervated by postganglionic vasodilator neurons that may release *histamine* as the transmitter. The smooth musculature of the gastrointestinal tract is inhibited by postganglionic parasympathetic neurons, the transmitter of which may be *ATP* (cf. p. 119). Other substances that have been considered as transmitters to autonomic effector cells and preganglionic neurons, or that have a neuromodulatory influence on synaptic transmission in the peripheral autonomic nervous system (cf. p. 68), are *substance P* and other *polypeptides, prostaglandin E* and *serotonin.* However, the role as transmitter in the peripheral autonomic nervous system has not been adequately documented for any of these substances [2].

The Adrenal Medulla. The Systemic Actions of Adrenalin and Noradrenalin

The adrenal medulla (AM) is a modified sympathetic ganglion. Its cells are ontogenetically *homologous* to the postganglionic neurons. These cells are activated by way of cholinergic synapses with preganglionic axons (cf. Fig. 6-1). The release of the catecholamines from the AM cells is entirely under neuronal control. Excitation of the preganglionic axons in man normally causes the release into the bloodstream of a mixture of a little over **80% adrenalin** and just under **20% noradrenalin.** The ratio of adrenalin to noradrenalin in the AM varies considerably among different species. For example, the whale's AM contains 70–80% noradrenalin, and that of the rabbit contains almost exclusively adrenalin. Adrenalin and noradrenalin are produced by different AM cells. The release of the two catecholamines can probably also be regulated relatively independently [12].

The catecholamines released by the AM act on the same effector organs as the postganglionic sympathetic neurons. Normally, however, it is likely that this action is important only in the case of organs or parts of organs with little or no postganglionic innervation (e.g., the media of arteries; cf. Fig. 6-6 A, C). Organs with extensive innervation (e.g., the vas deferens; cf. Fig. 6-6 B, C) are probably not appreciably affected by the blood-borne catecholamines. The catecholamines from the AM appear to serve chiefly in the regulation of **metabolic processes.** They act as catalysts to mobilize *free fatty acids* from adipose tis-

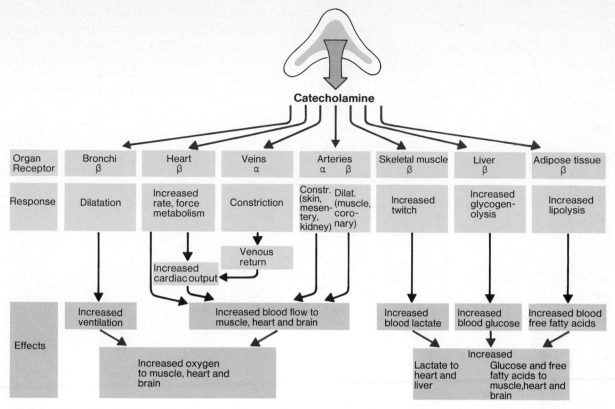

Fig. 6-5. Action of adrenalin from the adrenal medulla on various organs

sue, and *glucose* and *lactate* from glycogen (cf. Table 6-1). Adrenalin and noradrenalin from the AM should thus be regarded primarily as **metabolic hormones** (cf. pp.678 f.). These metabolic actions of the catecholamines are mediated predominantly by β receptors (cf. Table 6-1).

In a person **at rest** the adrenal medulla releases ca. 8–10 ng of catecholamines per kg body weight per minute. This rate of release depends on the resting activity in the preganglionic fibers – that is, it is determined by the CNS. In **emergency situations** such as loss of blood, hypothermia, hypoglycemia, hypoxia, burning or extreme physical loads the rate of release increases. During hard physical work, for example, the sympathetic nervous system brings about an increased transport of oxygen and oxidizable substrates to the skeletal musculature, the heart and the brain, by way of the catecholamines from the adrenal medulla. The AM catecholamines increase, by β adrenergic action, the levels of free fatty acids, glucose and lactate in the blood. Moreover, adrenalin acts on β receptors to produce vasodilation of the arteries of the skeletal muscles and myocardium (Fig. 6-5). Simultaneously, chiefly by the excitation of postganglionic neurons, the cardiac output increases, there is general venoconstriction and constriction of the arteries in skin and viscera, and the bronchi dilate.

These actions are mediated either by α or by β receptors (Fig. 6-5) [12].

Apart from emergency situations, the chief factor influencing the adrenal medulla is the **emotional state** of the organism. Under emotional stress the rate of catecholamine release can rise transiently to more than 10 times the resting rate. This release of AM hormones is controlled by the hypothalamus and the limbic system. The central-nervous mechanisms underlying this activation are largely unknown. It is conceivable that when stress situations are repeated indefinitely – a common feature of modern urban life and many types of work – the elevated blood catecholamine concentration can promote the occurrence of various illnesses.

The reactions of the effector organs in emergencies and severe emotional stress, brought about by the activation of the postganglionic sympathetic neurons and the adrenal medulla, can be called **emergency reactions.** They involve *uniform* responses of almost all outputs of the sympathetic nervous system, so that in this connection one can speak of a **sympathicoadrenal system** [4]. This uniform reaction of the sympathetic nervous system under internal and external extreme conditions is elicited chiefly by the hypothalamus.

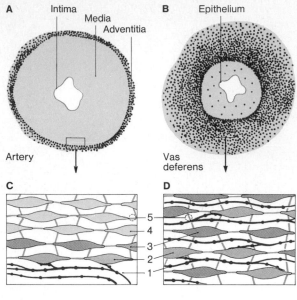

1 Nerve fibers with varicosities
2 Directly innervated muscle cells
3 Coupled muscle cells with electrotonically
   transmitted synaptic potentials
4 Indirectly coupled muscle cells,
   only action potentials
5 Nexus (low-resistance contact sites)

Fig. 6-6 A–D. Neuroeffector transmission in the peripheral autonomic nervous system. Distribution of the adrenergic innervation *(red)* in the smooth muscle of the artery in a rabbit ear (**A, C**; resistance vessel) and the vas deferens (**B, D**). From [3]

Surgical removal of the peripheral sympathetic nervous system in an animal (e.g., cat or dog) causes no serious deficits, no symptoms that interfere with the normal vital functions at rest. But the animal can no longer adapt to extreme loads, for the brain, heart and skeletal musculature are no longer provided with an adequately copious and rapid supply of oxygen, glucose and free fatty acids (cf. Fig. 6-5). Furthermore, the animal can no longer adapt adequately to thermal load [4].

Synaptic Organization of the Peripheral Autonomic Nervous System

The adrenergic neuron. Neuroeffector transmission.
Most adrenergic neurons have long, thin axons (Fig. 6-1) that branch repeatedly in the effector organs to form a so-called adrenergic plexus. The total length of the terminal branches of a neuron has been estimated to be as great as 10–30 cm. These branches exhibit **varicosities** (250–300 per mm) within which noradrenalin is synthesized, stored and inactivated. Excitation of the adrenergic neurons causes the release of noradrenalin from the varicosities into the extracellular space. The process occurs simultaneously in a large number of varicosities, and thus tends to affect the **smooth muscle tissue** as a whole rather than single smooth muscle cells. The individual muscle cells are joined by contacts having low electrical resistance (cf. Fig. 6-6). By way of these "tight junc-

tions" or *nexuses* postsynaptic potentials and action potentials are transmitted *electrotonically* to neighboring cells (coupled muscle cells in Fig. 6-6 C, D). More distant muscle cells are reached only by action potentials, which are generated in the directly innervated muscle cells when the postsynaptic potentials exceed threshold, and spread as a conducted wave of excitation through the entire mass of muscle (indirectly coupled muscle cells in Fig. 6-6 C, D). In this way there is a *synchronized contraction* of all the smooth muscle cells in a muscle following direct depolarization of only a few cells by the transmitter.

The **density of innervation** of smooth muscles varies greatly from organ to organ. Smooth muscles with very dense innervation contain many cells having direct neuromuscular contacts. The distance between the varicosities and the membranes of these smooth muscle cells is ca. 20 nm (Fig. 6-6 B, D; e.g., spermatic duct and ciliary muscle). This smooth musculature is entirely under neuronal control; circulating catecholamines have essentially no influence on it. Most blood vessels, by contrast, are innervated almost entirely by way of the adventitia; only the outer cells of the media are directly innervated (the neuromuscular separation, between the varicosities and the smooth muscle cells, is ca. 80 nm or more). Most of the smooth musculature of the media is influenced indirectly, by electrotonic transmission (Fig. 6-6 A, C). As a result of this nonuniform neuronal action, this musculature is exposed to the influence of catecholamines diffusing from the blood in the lumen of the vessel, for here they are not inactivated by being taken up into the varicosities (cf. p. 67).

Smooth musculature with little or no direct innervation by postganglionic axons, because the neuromuscular separation is too large, is more strongly affected by the circulating catecholamines. Examples of such smooth muscles are the large (elastic) arteries, the circular and longitudinal musculature of the intestine, and the uterine musculature [3].

Supersensitivity of autonomic effectors after denervation. Autonomic effector organs may exhibit atrophy to a certain degree due to inactivity, but do not degenerate when their innervation is destroyed. Within 2 to 30 days following denervation (varying from one organ to another) they become **supersensitive** to the transmitter substances of the peripheral autonomic nervous system and to chemically similar drugs. For example, if the pupil of an animal is deprived of sympathetic innervation by removal of the superior cervical ganglion, the first result is constriction of the pupil owing to predominance of the parasympathetic action (Table 6-1). After several weeks the pupil dilates again. The dilation increases when the animal is exposed to emotional stimuli. This expansion of the pupil is ascribable to *sensitization* of the denervated dilator muscle to the adrenalin and noradrenalin released into the blood by the adrenal medulla (cf. p. 116).

During emotional stimuli and in frightening situations the concentrations of these substances in the blood increase.

The mechanism by which autonomic effector organs become sensitized following denervation is not well understood. It will probably prove to involve changes in the electrophysiological properties, calcium binding and calcium permeability of the effector membranes. These changes are brought about by the elimination of the transmitters ordinarily produced by the postganglionic neurons. Denervation supersensitivity can be regarded as an *adaptation of the sensitivity of autonomic effector organs to the activity* of the postganglionic neurons innervating them. A chronic decrease in neuronal activity is accompanied by an elevated sensitivity of the effector, and a chronic increase reduces effector sensitivity [33].

Neurons in the central nervous system also become supersensitive to the associated transmitter substances and their mimetics following denervation. For example, after degeneration of the dopaminergic nigro-striatal system in Parkinson's disease, the neurons in the corpus striatum become sensitized to dopamine and drugs with a similar action (e.g., apomorphine; cf. Fig. 6-30). Accordingly, certain symptoms of this disease can be successfully treated with L-dopa, a precursor of dopamine – probably because this substance excites the sensitized striatal neurons in relatively low concentrations [58].

Sympathetic ganglia. As has been mentioned, transmission from pre- to postganglionic neurons in the autonomic sympathetic ganglia is *cholinergic* (Fig. 6-2). Many preganglionic axons converge on each postganglionic neuron; on the other hand, the collaterals of each preganglionic axon diverge onto many postganglionic neurons. There is an extraordinary variability among species and among ganglia in the quantitative degree of **convergence** and **divergence**. The number of postganglionic neurons in a ganglion is usually considerably higher than the number of preganglionic axons innervating them. In humans, for example, a million postganglionic neurons in the superior cervical ganglion are innervated by ten thousand preganglionic axons; that is, one preganglionic axon diverges to at least 100 postganglionic neurons. The divergent and convergent synaptic connections guarantee a high safety factor for the transmission of excitation in the ganglia. Here spatial and temporal summation of postsynaptic potentials plays a crucial role, for single impulses in preganglionic axons usually cannot elicit suprathreshold postsynaptic potentials.

In addition to the *nicotinic* synaptic transmission in the sympathetic ganglia, acetylcholine acts postsynaptically to elicit slowly rising, prolonged depolarizations or hyperpolarizations. These *slow synaptic potentials* are brought about largely by the *muscarinic action* of acetylcholine (cf. p. 114). The hyperpolariz-

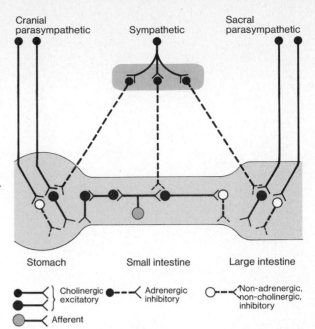

Fig. 6-7. Organization of the innervation of the intestinal musculature. Modified from [32]

ing potentials may be produced by way of catecholaminergic interneurons. The functional significance of these slow postsynaptic potentials is still unclear. They are thought to control the excitability of the postganglionic neurons and thus the threshold for the generation of conducted action potentials. In this case the sympathetic ganglia would be simple *integrative centers* [9, 52].

Intramural ganglia. Enteric nervous system. The gastrointestinal tract functions adequately even when its parasympathetic and sympathetic innervation is transected. Under these conditions reflex pathways in the walls of the digestive tract *(myenteric and submucosal plexuses)* take over the task of coordinating the various movements of digestion (peristalsis, rhythmic segmentation, pendular movements, etc.; cf. p. 596). These plexuses have long been regarded as a third category of autonomic nerves, the **enteric nervous system** [2]. Excitation of afferent neurons in the intestinal wall by the presence of a bolus initiates reflexes in which the bolus is shifted analward by contraction of the intestinal musculature on the oral side and simultaneous relaxation on the anal (aboral) side. These two reflexes, the basic elements in peristalsis (p. 596), occur within the wall of the intestine (Fig. 6-7, middle). The inhibitory neurons are neither cholinergic nor adrenergic; it may be that they release ATP as a transmitter (nonadrenergic, noncholinergic neurons; cf. Fig. 6-7). The excitatory neurons are cholinergic, but probably other transmitter substances such as **serotonin** also play a role.

The parasympathetic and sympathetic nervous systems *modulate* the activity of the digestive tract, each

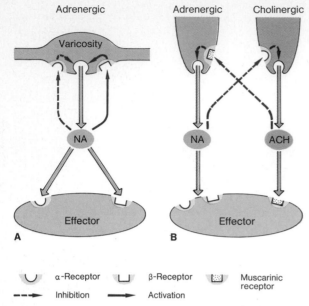

U α-Receptor   L β-Receptor   ▦ Muscarinic
                                        receptor
- - → Inhibition   ──→ Activation

Fig. 6-8. Presynaptic control of transmitter release by the transmitters. NA noradrenalin, ACH acetylcholine

acting on the enteric nervous system (Fig. 6-7). The preganglionic parasympathetic neurons appear not only to influence the postganglionic neurons that excite the intestinal musculature, but very probably also those with an inhibitory action (Fig. 6-7). Sympathetic postganglionic neurons have only weak direct actions on the smooth nonsphincteral muscle of the intestine. They *inhibit* the cholinergic (parasympathetic) postganglionic neurons and/or may inhibit the release of transmitter from the presynaptic endings of preganglionic parasympathetic neurons (discussed further below). In this way they modulate the parasympathetic flow of impulses from the CNS to the enteric nervous system; and thus adjust the activity of the intestinal musculature (Fig. 6-7). (Inhibition of postganglionic parasympathetic neurons by postganglionic sympathetic neurons also occurs in the bladder ganglia [32].)

Presynaptic control of transmitter release. The transmitter substances in the peripheral autonomic nervous system do not only act postsynaptically on the effector membranes and – in the autonomic ganglia – on the postganglionic neurons; they also influence the release of transmitter from the presynaptic structures themselves. These *presynaptic actions* of transmitter substances are mediated by **adrenergic** and **cholinergic receptors** in the presynaptic membranes.

The reaction between noradrenalin and presynaptic α adrenergic receptors decreases the rate of transmitter release, whereas the reaction with presynaptic β

adrenergic receptors increases it (Fig. 6-8 A). Under physiological conditions a high concentration of noradrenalin in the synaptic cleft, during intense excitation of the postganglionic neurons, may limit the release of noradrenalin by way of the presynaptic α receptors *(negative-feedback mechanism)*. A low noradrenalin concentration, with little excitation of the postganglionic neurons, appears to enhance noradrenalin release by way of the presynaptic β receptors *(positive-feedback mechanism)*. It is questionable whether this positive feedback is of physiological significance.

In organs with both sympathetic and parasympathetic innervation (e. g., the heart, bronchial musculature, gastrointestinal tract) the adrenergic and cholinergic presynaptic endings may interact with one another, producing reciprocal inhibition of transmitter release (Fig. 6-8 B). It can be demonstrated that in the heart less acetylcholine is released from excited parasympathetic neurons when the sympathetic neurons to the heart are stimulated at the same time. This action is mediated by α adrenergic receptors in the presynaptic cholinergic endings (Fig. 6-8 B). Conversely, excitation of parasympathetic neurons to the heart lowers the rate of noradrenalin release from postganglionic sympathetic neurons to the heart. This inhibitory action is mediated by muscarinic cholinergic receptors (cf. p. 114 and Fig. 6-8 B). The inhibitory interaction between cholinergic and adrenergic presynaptic endings shows that the *antagonism* between the sympathetic and parasympathetic systems may also exist at the presynaptic level [43, 57].

Pharmacologists have demonstrated the existence of pre- and postsynaptic receptor types other than the cholinergic and adrenergic receptors, in the peripheral autonomic nervous system; these include dopamine, opiate, angiotensin, other peptide and prostaglandin-E receptors. These pharmacological receptors probably have no physiological significance, although they are of potential use in *therapeutic medicine*. All the pharmacological receptors identified in the peripheral autonomic nervous system have also been found in the central nervous system, at pre- and postsynaptic sites. These central receptors are of great significance, under physiological conditions, for the regulation of central neuronal processes, and they are the sites of action of many centrally effective drugs.

Axon reflex. Antidromic excitation of thin cutaneous nociceptive afferents, by electrical stimulation of a dorsal root peripheral to a point of transection, or orthodromic excitation of these afferents by noxious stimulation of the skin with the dorsal roots transected, causes *vasodilation (reddening)* in the skin region innervated by the nociceptive afferents. This vasodilation can also be elicited following degeneration of the sympathetic innervation of the cutaneous vessels and after removal of the spinal cord. It cannot be elicited after the thin cutaneous afferents have degenerated. From these observations it has been concluded that efferent collaterals of the nociceptive cutaneous afferents innervate vessels in the skin, and that the vessels are dilated by activation of the collaterals. This reflex is therefore called an *axon reflex*. So far the inference is supported only by the indirect evidence given above; there is no histological confirmation of their existence. Another plausible explanation is that the excitation of cutaneous nociceptive afferents causes the release of vasodilator substances (e.g., ATP or substance P) from the receptive membranes. Such substances are present in the terminals of the thin cutaneous afferents, and their concentration decreases after the receptors have been stimulated. This mechanism would suffice without the assumption that the afferent fibers have efferent collaterals [28].

6.2 Central Organization of the Autonomic Nervous System in Spinal Cord and Brainstem

Resting Activity in the Autonomic Nervous System

The significance of resting activity in the regulation of autonomic organs. Many pre- and postganglionic neurons – especially to the blood vessels and the heart – are spontaneously active. This **neurogenic resting activity** is a fundamental factor in the autonomic control of organ function. For example, in vasoconstrictor fibers it keeps the smooth musculature of the vessels in a state of relative contraction. The degree of contraction determines the cross-sectional area of the blood vessels and thus the peripheral resistance to flow. With a resting state of intermediate contraction, blood flow through an organ can be either increased or decreased by changes in vasoconstrictor-fiber activity. Thus a single set of postganglionic neurons can produce both vasoconstriction and vasodilation.

The situation is illustrated in Fig. 6-9. The diagram shows the increase in resistance to flow in the arterial bed of a cat leg, when the lumbar sympathetic trunk is stimulated at increasing frequencies. The peripheral resistance prevailing at rest in vivo can be produced by ca. *two stimuli per second*. Decrease in stimulus frequency results in vasodilation and thus reduction of the peripheral resistance, whereas an increase causes vasoconstriction and greater peripheral resistance. When the resting activity of the vasoconstrictor fibers is abolished surgically or pharmacologically, the peripheral resistance is determined only by the spontaneous activity of the smooth musculature of the vessels **(basal myogenic activity)** and by the catecholamines adrenalin and noradrenalin circulating in the blood (cf. p. 116). The range within which blood flow can be regulated *physiologically* by change in vasoconstrictor activity is shaded red in Fig. 6-9 (cf. Fig. 18-26, p. 424).

The activity of many autonomically innervated organs is regulated as shown in Fig. 6-9. The level of resting activity in peripheral autonomic neurons can

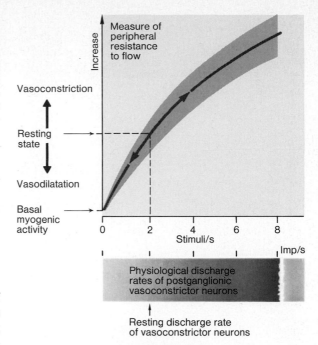

Fig. 6-9. Relation between resistance to blood flow in the skeletal muscle of a cat hindlimb (ordinate) and the frequency of suprathreshold electrical stimulation of the preganglionic axons in the lumbar sympathetic trunk. The *red area* indicates the range of measured data. [Modified from MELLANDER: Acta physiol. scand. *50*, Suppl. *176*, 1–86 (1960)]

be estimated by indirect methods (e.g., measuring the response of an effector organ during electrical stimulation of autonomic nerves) and by direct recording from pre- and postganglionic neurons. It varies from ca. 0.1 Hz to 5 Hz, and is likely to be about 2 Hz in vasoconstrictor neurons to the vessels in skin and muscle. Evidently the level of tonic activity in the autonomic neurons is adjusted to the properties of the smooth musculature. Because of the prolonged, relatively slowly rising and falling contractions of this musculature, low-frequency neurogenic resting activity produces a smooth contraction **(tonus)** [8].

The origin of the resting activity. So far we know little about the origin of the tonic activity in autonomic pre- and postganglionic neurons. It depends in part on the continuous influx of afferent activity from visceral and somatic receptors to the CNS; the activity in vagal efferents to the heart is reduced after transection of the baroafferents from the aortic arch and the carotid sinus. On the other hand, resting activity is based on the inherent ability of some central neurons to depolarize "spontaneously"; even in totally deafferented preparations autonomic nerves exhibit resting activity. The CNS structures that give rise to the resting activity are not definitely known, but the medulla oblongata is thought to be the chief site of origin.

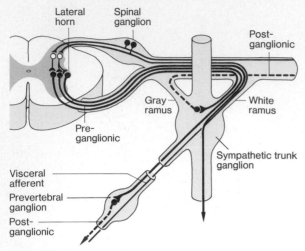

Fig. 6-10. Arrangement of the autonomic spinal reflex arc. [From RANSON and CLARK: The Anatomy of the Nervous System, Saunders, 1959]

Autonomic Reflexes of the Spinal Cord

Segmental organization of autonomic reflexes. By analogy with the sensorimotor system, in which the motoneuron is the final common path (p. 83), the preganglionic sympathetic and parasympathetic neurons (with some qualification; cf. p. 119) can be regarded as the final common path of the autonomic motor system. They integrate spinal excitatory and inhibitory influences and those descending from higher levels. The cell bodies of the preganglionic neurons in the sympathetic and sacral parasympathetic regions lie in the spinal cord at the level of the lateral horn, extending mediolaterally into the white matter, and are especially concentrated in the *intermediolateral nucleus.* These somata are oval in shape and are smaller and more numerous than somatic motoneurons. The synaptic connection between afferents and autonomic efferents at the spinal segmental level is called the **autonomic reflex arc.** Unlike the monosynaptic stretch reflex, even the simplest autonomic spinal reflex arcs probably have no direct connections between the (visceral and somatic) afferents and the preganglionic neurons; the shortest pathway is disynaptic. The autonomic reflex arc thus has a total of at least **three synapses** between the afferent and postganglionic neurons (Fig. 6-10) – two in the spinal gray matter and one in the autonomic ganglion.

The spinal organization of the sympathetic nervous system tends to be segmental or metameric. The preganglionic neurons of a segment receive spinal afferent input predominantly from the afferents entering the cord in the same segment. Segmental reflexes in preganglionic axons elicited by electrical stimulation of dorsal roots are most pronounced when the dorsal

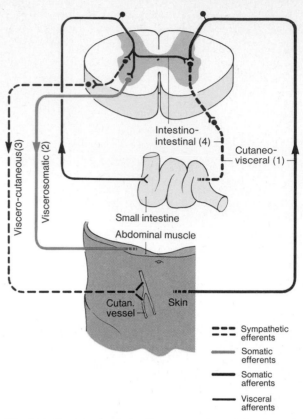

Fig. 6-11. Segmental spinal reflexes. Interneurons between afferents and the efferent neurons in the spinal cord are not shown

root of the same segment is stimulated, and become smaller when the stimulus is applied to those of adjacent segments. In contrast to the segmental reflexes, the reflexes involving supraspinal pathways do not change in magnitude when various adjacent or more distant dorsal roots are stimulated [40, 54].

A very specific segmental organization characterizes the afferent and autonomic innervation of certain organs. Afferents from the heart and from the excretory organs make synaptic contacts, at a segmental level, with preganglionic sympathetic and parasympathetic neurons innervating the same organs (intestino-intestinal reflexes, Fig. 6-11; cardio-cardial reflexes; evacuation reflexes, cf. pp. 125 ff.). It is likely that similar specific spinal-segmental reflexes are also associated with other organs.

The segmental organization of the autonomic innervation of organs can also be observed in the **clinic.** In pathological conditions of the viscera (e. g., gallbladder or appendix inflammation) the musculature over the site of the disorder is taut and the area of skin *(dermatome)* innervated by afferents and efferents of the same spinal-cord segment that serves the affected organ is reddened. This situation is explained by an inhibitory action of the visceral afferents from the affected viscus on the sympathetic cutaneous vasoconstrictor efferents from the same segment (*skin reddening:* reflex path 3 in Fig. 6-11) and an excitatory action on motoneurons (*protective tension* of the abdominal musculature: reflex path 2 in Fig. 6-11). Conversely, stimulation of thermoreceptors in the skin causes reflex inhibition of the viscera innervated by the same spinal segment, by way of sympathetic neurons (reflex path 1 in Fig. 6-11).

An important clue to the physician is the enhanced sensitivity to touch (**hyperesthesia**) and excessive pain sensitivity (**hyperalgesia**) in circumscribed skin areas that accompany internal disorders. It is likely that cutaneous nociceptive and non-nociceptive afferents and visceral afferents of a given spinal segment converge onto the same neurons of the spinothalamic tract (p. 230). Thus some of the information about the origin of the excitation from the internal organs is lost, and the cortex ascribes the excitation to the corresponding skin areas as well. Visceral pain ascribed to the skin is called **referred pain** (cf. p. 230), and the areas to which it is referred are called **Head's zones** (cf. Fig. 10-21, p. 230).

The typical Head's zones for heart, liver, gallbladder, stomach and large intestine are shown in Fig. 6-12 (the spinal segments receiving the visceral afferents from the organs are indicated in parentheses). Many patients with disorders of these organs (e.g., angina pectoris resulting from inadequate perfusion of the coronary vessels, gallbladder inflammation, gastric ulcers) report pains in the corresponding skin regions. This data assists the clinician in diagnosis.

Hyperpathia and the sympathetic system. Some conditions of chronic pain are distinguished by the peculiar unpleasant, burning or stinging sensations elicited by a number of normally painless skin stimuli. These painful sensations appear only after a considerable latency, require some time to disappear, and spread into adjacent regions (frequently over an entire limb). Such pain conditions are called **hyperpathia.** They are often accompanied by hyperesthesia, disturbances of vasomotion and sweat secretion, and in particular trophic disturbances of the affected tissue. For example, one observes cold or warm damp thin skin with trophic changes in the subcutaneous adipose tissue and demineralization of the bones. Such symptoms can appear when nerves are damaged by bullet wounds, or posttraumatically in the distal parts of the extremities. Clinical neurologists call the various combinations of these symptoms *causalgia, Sudeck's syndrome, posttraumatic pain syndrome, reflex sympathetic dystrophy* etc. Blockade of the sympathetic innervation of the affected limbs (by interrupting conduction in the sympathetic trunk, by administering drugs that empty the peripheral noradrenalin stores in the sympathetic nerve fibers, or by surgical sympathectomy) often relieves the chronic intolerable pain and improves the autonomic and trophic condition of the tissue. Therefore the efferent adrenergic sympathetic neurons are thought to be involved in producing the chronic pains (hyperpathia). But we can only guess at the processes leading to hyperpathia, with its accompanying autonomic and trophic disturbances. It may be that when injury alters the afferent in-

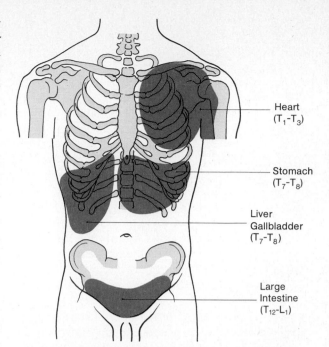

Fig. 6-12. Superficial hyperalgesic zones for heart, stomach, large intestine and liver and gallbladder. The spinal segments receiving the visceral afferents from the organs are indicated in parentheses. These zones correspond approximately to those in Fig. 9-5 which habe been described by other observers. [From WHITE, C. and SWEET, W. H.: Pain, Its Mechanism and Neurosurgical Control. Thomas, Springfield, Ill., 1955 and MONNIER, M. (ed.): Physiologie und Pathophysiologie des vegetativen Nervensystems. II. Band: Pathophysiologie. Hippokrates-Verlag, Stuttgart, 1963]

put, sympathetic activity excites or changes the excitability of the receptors of thick and thin afferent fibers, producing abnormal patterns of excitation in response to normally painless stimuli. These pathological excitation patterns may give rise to abnormal information processing in the spinal cord, resulting in pathological pain perception and impaired autonomic regulation [1, 18, 21, 46].

Autonomic reflexes following spinal-cord transection. Transection of the spinal cord causes **paralysis** in the parts of the body below the cut (cf. p. 92). The autonomic reflexes involving segments below the interruption are extinguished for 1–6 months in man. During the first one to two months the skin is dry and rosy, because the resting activity in the sympathetic fibers to sweat glands and vessels is very low. The somatosympathetic reflex activity of sudomotor and vasoconstrictor fibers elicited by painful or painless skin stimuli increases slowly in the course of months, eventually reaching a stage of **hyperreflexia**. In this stage skin stimulation (e.g., by sheets) frequently causes heavy sweating in the parts of the skin innervated by the isolated part of the spinal cord. Contractions of the urinary-bladder musculature or of the flexor muscles (flexor spasms) and rectal stretching can trigger reflexes that cause general vasoconstriction with dangerously elevated blood pressure, the release of catecholamines from the adrenal medulla, piloerection and sweat secretion. The bladder and colonic evacuation reflexes (p. 126) require similarly long times for recovery following spinal transection [1, 41]. The disappearance of the spinal autonomic reflexes after spinal transection is one aspect of **spinal shock** (p. 92). It is very probably due to the *interruption of the descending pathways* from the brainstem that control the autonomic spinal-reflex motor output. This descending control is much more pronounced in *primates* than in the lower vertebrates (e.g., frog). Therefore the duration and extent of the suppression of spinal reflexes after spinal transection are much greater in primates than in the lower vertebrates. Another factor that probably plays a role in spinal shock is the new growth of synapses in the spinal cord.

Regulatory performance of the isolated human spinal cord. The spinal cord isolated from the brain by transection in the cervical region below C_3 is capable of a number of regulatory functions after recovery from spinal shock. For example, painless thermal stimulation of the skin or the spinal cord causes the reflex loss of heat by sweat secretion and cutaneous vasodilation. When the body is moved from the horizontal to the erect position, or when blood is lost, there is a reflex increase in activity of the vasoconstrictors, by way of the spinal cord. The result is general vasoconstriction, especially of the venous system, which to a certain extent prevents a dangerous drop in arterial blood pressure (spinal regulation of bladder evacuation is discussed on p. 116). The isolated human spinal cord is thus in principle capable of the same autonomic performance as the spinal cord of lower mammals. This is of theoretical interest, because these observations imply that the human spinal cord comprises the same neuronal mechanisms for this control as does that of the lower mammals. But the findings are also of practical significance, because these spinal mechanisms can still be used for autonomic control in para- and quadriplegics, given correct care and appropriate training [1, 18].

Autonomic Capabilities of the Brainstem

The sites of the neuronal **autonomic "centers"** in the brainstem (medulla oblongata, pons, mesencephalon; cf. Fig. 5-13, p. 93), which affect the operation of the internal organs and organ systems (cardiovascular system, digestive tract, evacuation mechanisms; cf. the relevant chapters) by way of the peripheral autonomic nervous system, have been only approxi-

mately established. Such information has been obtained from experiments in which the performance of the organ systems was studied before and after transection of the brainstem, after the ablation of certain nuclear regions or tracts, and during the electrical stimulation of groups of neurons. At the cellular level, essentially nothing is known about the organization of the autonomic nervous system in the brainstem.

This lack of knowledge on one hand is due to technical difficulties, for the neurons and groups of neurons in the brainstem that are responsible for autonomic regulation are usually very small and thus hard to identify either neurophysiologically or neuroanatomically. On the other hand, there are conceptual difficulties; the notion that autonomic neuronal regulation of certain organs is based on discrete functional groups of neurons that can be readily located histologically ("centers") is only partially correct. Rather, single neurons and small groups of neurons appear to participate in the autonomic control of various organs that are functionally related to one another (e.g., reflex regulation of swallowing and vomiting, control of the salivary glands and the gastrointestinal tract). This implies that one cannot expect to find all the neurons that influence a particular organ in direct proximity to one another. Therefore the term "center" should be used only with reservations.

Medulla oblongata and circulation. The spinal sympathetic and parasympathetic reflex arcs are subject to descending inhibitory and excitatory influences from the brainstem. The participation of the lower brainstem in the control of circulation is especially obvious. The regions indispensable for this control, called the **circulatory center** (cf. Fig. 18-36, p. 435), lie in the caudal medulla oblongata. This is thought to be the site of the *generator of resting activity* in the peripheral sympathetic fibers to the vessels and heart, for two reasons. First, isolation from all parts of the brain cranial to the caudal medulla (decerebration; cf. p. 94) has almost no effect on level and regulation of the arterial blood pressure. Second, blood pressure remains unchanged even when practically all the afferent inputs to the circulatory center from the baro- and chemoreceptors and from the viscera, skin and musculature are eliminated.

The role of the medulla in blood-pressure regulation is impressively revealed by comparing high-spinal animals (transection of the cord in the upper cervical region) with decerebrate animals, in which only the medulla oblongata is intact. In **decerebrate animals** the regulation is nearly perfect; the vascular beds respond in a coordinated manner to changes in the spatial orientation of the body, so that the perfusion pressure remains the same in the different regions. In **spinal animals** the resting sympathetic activity is low and the diameters of the arteries and veins can no longer be adjusted; only the heart, which still communicates with the medulla by way of the vagus nerves, continues to be regulated. The sympathetic system still responds to painful stimuli and blood loss, and change of body orientation elicits weak compensatory vasoconstriction in the peripheral vascular beds, mediated by the spinal cord, which prevents excessive hypotension.

6.3 Micturition and Defecation

Neuronal Control of Bladder Evacuation

The urinary bladder stores and periodically evacuates completely the urine being continually produced by the kidneys. This function, so important for our social life, is based on myogenic mechanisms in the smooth muscle of the bladder and neuronal (autonomic and somatic) mechanisms. In the neural control of the bladder long collecting phases alternate with brief emptying phases. During the **collecting phases** emptying is prevented or made difficult by neural activity. The bladder fills at a rate of ca. 50 ml urine per hour. The plasticity of its smooth musculature (cf. p. 48) ensures that the pressure inside the bladder increases only slightly during the filling phase (Fig. 6-13). When the bladder has collected ca. 150–250 ml urine, the first signs of a brief *urge to urinate* appear. This urge is triggered by brief increases in the intravesical pressure. When the bladder contains ca. 250–500 ml, the **evacuation phase** normally begins. The ability of the bladder to retain the urine is called **continence,** and the act of emptying is called **micturition** (Fig. 6-13).

Structure and innervation of the urinary bladder (Fig. 6-14). The urinary bladder is a hollow muscle *(detrusor vesicae)*. Its wall consists of a network of long **smooth muscle cells.** At the base of the bladder is a triangular area of fine smooth muscle fibers (the *trigonum vesicae*), at the upper corners of which are the openings of the ureters. These ducts enter *obliquely,* so that when the intravesical pressure rises no urine can be forced back into the ureters. At the lower tip of the trigone the bladder opens into the urethra. A special arrangement of the muscle cells in this region provides a functional sphincter (the *internal sphincter*). The internal sphincter cannot be relaxed for micturition without the assistance of the detrusor muscle; when the bladder musculature contracts the fibers radiating into the urethra shorten it, producing an automatic passive opening of the internal sphincter. The urethra is also closed by an *external sphincter* formed by the striated musculature of the pelvic floor. This outer sphincter muscle is poorly developed in women.

The innervation of the bladder and the sphincters is illustrated in Fig. 6-14. The bladder musculature is excited by **parasympathetic fibers** in the pelvic nerve that arise in the 2nd to 4th sacral segments. This innervation is required for the normal control of bladder emptying. The sympathetic innervation inhibits the detrusor muscle and excites the musculature of the trigone. It arises in the upper lumbar cord. Its function is not clear. The external sphincter receives somatic innervation by way of

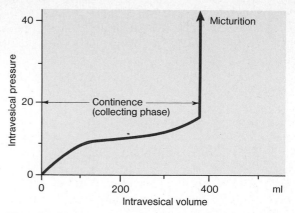

Fig. 6-13. Pressure-volume diagram (cystometrogram) of the human urinary bladder. The phase of urinary continence is defined by the flat part of the curve. The sudden rise in intravesical pressure coincides with the onset of micturition

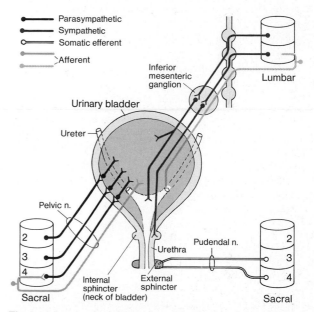

Fig. 6-14. Innervation of the urinary bladder

motor axons in the pudendal nerve, the somata of which are in the middle segments of the sacral region. The degree of bladder filling is signalled to the central nervous system by stretch receptors in the wall of the bladder, by way of afferent axons in the pelvic nerve. Afferents running together with the sympathetic axons probably signal noxious stimuli in the region of the trigone (e. g., those associated with bladder inflammation, cystitis) to the thoracolumbar spinal cord.

The voiding reflex. Urine is propelled from the renal pelvis into the bladder by peristaltic waves in the ureters. The more the bladder wall is stretched, the stronger is the stimulus to the stretch receptors within it. The activation of these receptors excites the parasympathetic neurons to the detrusor muscle, by way of reflex arc 1 in Fig. 6-15. The end result is evacuation of the bladder. As Fig. 6-15 shows, the reflex arc

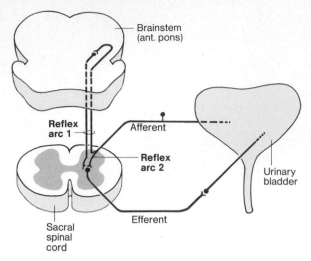

Fig. 6-15. Bladder-emptying reflex arc in a cat with brain intact (reflex arc 1) and a chronic spinal cat (reflex arc 2). Reflex path 2 does not function in the intact animal. Interneurons in spinal cord and brainstem are not shown. From [37]

is complete only if the **anterior pontine region** of the brainstem is intact. Electrical stimulation of this brainstem region can also elicit bladder emptying.

Once the bladder has begun to empty the process accelerates explosively until emptying is completed. This self-intensifying – that is, *positive-feedback* – process is probably based chiefly on the following reflexes: (i) increased activation of the bladder afferents by contractions of the detrusor, (ii) reflex activation of parasympathetic bladder efferents by afferents from the urethra excited by *urine flow,* and (iii) reflex blocking of central inhibitory processes at spinal and supraspinal levels. There is also a reflex **relaxation of the external sphincter** owing to inhibition of the motoneurons in the sacral cord.

After transection of the spinal cord above the sacral level, neither animals nor humans at first exhibit reflex emptying of the filled bladder. Not until the chronic stage has been reached, 1 to 5 weeks after the transection, does the voiding reflex again begin to operate **(automatic bladder).** This reflex arc is entirely spinal (pathway 2 in Fig. 6-15). It is very likely that micturition in infants is controlled by the same spinal reflex arc, which later is probably suppressed by inhibitory influences exerted at the spinal level by bladder afferents or elicited supraspinally.

During the first stages of **paraplegia** the bladder is *flaccid* and *atonic* for days to weeks. If the patient is properly cared for and urinary-tract infections are avoided, there is a gradual transition to the automatic-bladder phase, in which slight bladder filling causes reflex contractions of the detrusor and frequent urination. With adequate training paraplegics can learn to control their bladder evacuation. They can initiate reflex detrusor contractions themselves by tapping the lower abdomen (cf. segmental reflexes, p. 122), choosing a suitable time by observing

their own autonomic rhythms and aiding the evacuation process by pressing on the abdomen.

Suprapontine control of bladder function. The regulation of micturition and continence is a largely automatic, reflex process, but it is subject to modulation by the upper *brainstem,* the *hypothalamus* and the *cerebrum.* Neuronal control chiefly takes the form of *inhibition,* though some outputs are excitatory. The ascending and descending spinal pathways that conduct signals from and to the bladder and urethra, and the positions of the associated neuron populations in brainstem, hypothalamus and cortex, are largely unknown. The tasks of the "higher centers" are (i) to maintain continence even when the bladder is very full (to prevent emptying at unsuitable times) and (ii) to trigger and enhance evacuation at will, whenever it is desirable and possible [7, 37, 42].

Disturbances of micturition are very common and diverse. Involuntary **urine retention** follows paralysis or damage of the detrusor muscle (e. g., by inflammation or traumatic nerve injury), displacement of the urethra (e. g., by prostate tumor) or sphincter-muscle cramp. Urinary **incontinence** is the inability to retain urine voluntarily. It is especially common in women after giving birth (e. g., due to prolapse of the uterus because of pelvic-floor weakness) and in cases of organic brain disease (e. g., multiple sclerosis or arteriosclerosis of the cerebral vessels in the aged), and can also be purely psychogenic [1, 18].

Neuronal Control of Bowel Evacuation

Evacuation of the bowel **(defecation)** and maintenance of **fecal continence** are the most important tasks of the rectum and anus. These two functions are controlled by the intrinsic enteric nervous system, by parasympathetic sacral innervation and by somatomotor mechanisms. The role of the sympathetic innervation of the lower intestine has been little studied.

Continence. The distal end of the rectum is closed by two sphincters. The *internal anal sphincter* consists of smooth muscle and is not under voluntary control. The *external anal sphincter* is a striated muscle, innervated by motoneurons from the sacral cord (S_2–S_4) with axons running in the pudendal nerve. Normally both sphincters are closed. *Tonic contraction* of the external sphincter is maintained by a spinal reflex involving afferent impulses from the muscle and the surrounding tissue, especially the anal skin.

When the rectum is filled with intestinal contents, by peristaltic contractions of the descending colon, its wall is stretched and as a result there is simultaneous relaxation of the internal anal sphincter and enhanced contraction of the external sphincter. The relaxation of the internal sphincter is basically a *reflex by way of the enteric nervous system*. The contraction of the external sphincter is also a reflex, elicited by afferents running in the pelvic nerve to the sacral cord (Fig. 6-16). These events are accompanied by an urge to defecate – that is, conscious sensations triggered by the afferent impulses from receptors in the walls of colon and rectum. After some tens of seconds the relaxation of the internal sphincter fades away, and because of the plastic properties of the rectal musculature the rectum adjusts to the increase in its contents. Its wall tension decreases and as a result so does the urge to empty it. These neuronally controlled events permit a healthy person to maintain continence of the feces until the rectal content amounts to about 2 liters. Supraspinal, especially *cortical, mechanisms* make a large contribution to continence by exciting the motoneurons to the external sphincter and probably by inhibition of the parasympathetic spinal reflexes.

Defecation. Evacuation of the rectum is normally initiated by a *voluntary effort*. Supraspinal facilitation of the spinal parasympathetic reflex pathways to the lower intestine causes reflex contraction of the descending colon, sigmoid and rectum (the longitudinal musculature in particular). At the same time both sphincters relax. A prerequisite for defecation is a *rise in intraabdominal pressure* owing to increased tension in the muscles of the abdominal wall and to lowering of the diaphragm by contraction of the thoracic musculature, in the expanded position with glottis closed. By interaction of these mechanisms the floor of the pelvis is depressed and the entire column of feces in descending colon, sigmoid and rectum is expelled. *Destruction of the sacral cord* completely eliminates the defecation reflexes. After *transection of the spinal cord* above the sacral level the spinally organized defecation reflexes persist, but the voluntary motor patterns that assist defecation are abolished. They can be replaced by other actions (e. g., manual expansion of the external anal sphincter), so that paraplegics can achieve a *regular* daily control of fecal evacuation [7, 55].

6.4 Genital Reflexes

The genital reflexes in mammals – humans in particular – are very complex temporal and spatial sequences of reflex elements, involving *parasympathetic, sympathetic* and *motor efferents* as well as *visceral* and *somatic afferents*. Our knowledge of these reflexes in men is still very incomplete, and those of

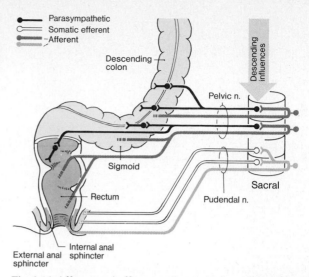

Fig. 6-16. Afferent and efferent pathways in the spinal defecation reflex. Interneurons between afferents and efferent neurons in the spinal cord are not shown

women are even less well understood. What we do know has been learned from experiments on animals, from studies of healthy people, and from clinical examination of patients with damaged spinal cord, sacral parasympathetic system or thoracolumbar sympathetic system [22, 29–31].

Genital Reflexes in the Man

The sexual response cycle of the man consists of several successive phases – **erection** of the penis, **emission** of semen (sperm and glandular secretions) into the posterior urethra, and the actual **ejaculation** of semen from the anterior urethra. **Orgasm** begins with or before emission, and ends with the end of ejaculation.

Erection. *Dilatation of the arteries* in the two corpora cavernosa of the penis and the corpus cavernosum of the urethra causes erection of the penis. The venous sinuses in the erectile tissue fill and expand maximally as the pressure rises. Restriction of the venous outflow from the erectile tissue is chiefly passive, by compression of the veins as they pass through the tunica albuginea. Dilation of the arteries is brought about by activation of *sacral parasympathetic neurons* with axons in the pelvic nerve (Fig. 6-17). These neurons are activated both *reflexly,* by afferents from the external genitalia and surrounding tissues, and *psychogenically* by supraspinal, probably cortical, structures. At the same time the afferent impulses from the genital organs give rise to sexual sensations. The **glans penis** bears the greatest concentration of mechanoreceptors; their afferents run in the dorsal nerve of the penis. The adequate stimulus to these receptors is provided by the sliding and massaging shear motion that accompanies copulation. An important factor in maintaining a state of excitation of the receptors in the glans penis during copulation is slipperiness of the surfaces of vagina and penis, which is produced reflexly by vaginal transudation (cf. p.130) and the activation of the bulbourethral glands in the man.

The erection reflex involves only the sacral cord (S_2-S_4), so that it functions in men with spinal transec-

tions as long as the cut is above this level. About a quarter of men with destroyed sacral cords can accomplish psychogenic penis erection. This erection is elicited by *sympathetic neurons in the lower thoracic and upper lumbar regions* (cf. Fig.6-17). Their axons synapse with the postganglionic sympathetic neurons in the inferior mesenteric ganglion or in the vicinity of the genitalia. It is not known whether these postganglionic neurons to the arteries in the erectile tissue are also cholinergic, nor whether (or to what extent) the sympathetic system contributes to the erection of a healthy man (Table 6-2).

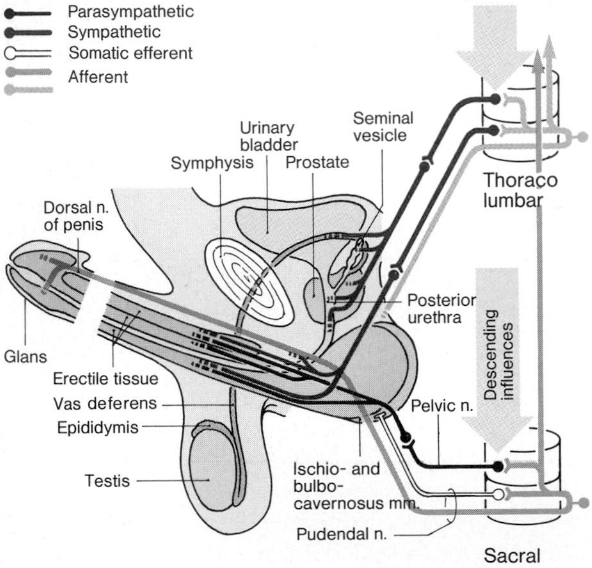

Emission and ejaculation. Emission and ejaculation are the high point of the male sexual act. As the afferents become highly excited during copulation, sympathetic efferents in the lower thoracic and upper lumbar segments become activated. The afferents that trigger emission run in the pudendal and pelvic nerves to the sacral cord, and with the sympathetic fibers to the thoracolumbar cord (Fig.6-17). Excitation of the sympathetic neurons causes contractions of the epididymis, vas deferens, seminal vesicle and prostate, which propel the semen into the posterior urethra. At the same time a reflex involving excitation of sympathetic fibers closes the internal sphincter of the bladder (cf. Fig.6-14) to prevent reflux of the secretions into the bladder.

After emission **ejaculation** begins. It is triggered by excitation of the afferents from the prostate and from the posterior urethra, which run in the pelvic nerves, as well as by afferents to the thoracolumbar cord from the epididymis, vas deferens and seminal vesi-

Fig. 6-17. Innervation of the male genitalia. Interneurons between afferents and efferent neurons in the spinal cord are not shown

Table 6-2. Summary of the neuronal control of the male genital reflexes. From [31]

	Erection	Emission and ejaculation	Orgasm
Afferents	From glans penis and surrounding tissue to sacral cord (in pudendal nerve)	From external and internal genitalia to sacral cord (pudendal and pelvic nerves) and to thoracolumbar cord (hypogastric plexus), afferents from skeletal musculature	Present if at least one afferent input intact (from genitalia to sacral or thoracolumbar cord, from skeletal muscle to sacral cord)
Autonomic efferents	1. Parasympathetic sacral (reflex and psychogenic) 2. Sympathetic thoracolumbar (psychogenic)	Sympathetic thoracolumbar	
Somatic efferents	–	To bulbo- and ischiocavernous muscles and muscles of pelvic floor	
Sacral cord destroyed	Present in 25% of patients (psychogenic), thoracolumbar	Present if erection can be elicited	Present
Spinal cord destroyed in upper thoracic or cervical region	Almost always present (reflex)	Almost never present	Always absent

---

cle. Stimulation of these afferents during emission initiates a reflex, through the sacral cord, that produces *tonic-clonic contractions* of the bulbocavernous and ischiocavernous muscles, which enclose the proximal erectile tissue (Fig. 6-17), and of the musculature of the pelvic floor. These rhythmic contractions expel the secretions, from the posterior through the anterior urethra, with simultaneous *rhythmic contractions* of the muscles of trunk and pelvic girdle. The latter contractions cause jerky movements of the pelvis, and serve chiefly to transport the semen into the proximal vagina and the cervix of the uterus. During the ejaculation phase the excitation of the parasympathetic and sympathetic innervation of the genitalia becomes maximal. This maximal excitation is partly due to the continuous afferent feedback from the skeletal musculature during the rhythmic contractions. After ejaculation the activity in the parasympathetic vasodilator neurons declines and the blood flows out of the erectile tissue through the veins, so that the erection gradually subsides.

Men with **sacral-cord disorders** often remain capable of emission and ejaculation, if these have been preceded by an erection, and they may experience orgasm. Efferent and afferent information to and from the genitalia in this case is conveyed by sympathetic fibers and afferents to the thoracolumbar cord (Fig. 6-17, Table 6-2). Paraplegics or quadriplegics with *transection above the mid-thoracic region* have lost essentially all capacity for emission, ejaculation and orgasm (Table 6-2). It is thought that in this case the sympathetic neurons in the lower thoracic and upper lumbar segments are permanently inhibited by sacral elements [18, 31].

Genital Reflexes in the Woman

The responses of female genitalia during the sexual response cycle have been studied quite thoroughly in recent years [22]. But the roles of the parasympathetic and sympathetic innervation are in part still a matter for speculation [31].

External genitalia. *Sexual stimulation* causes reflex and/or psychogenic changes in the external reproductive organs of the woman. The **labia majora,** which normally touch one another in the midline to protect the labia minora and the openings of vagina and urethra, spread apart, become thinner, and move in an anterolateral direction. If the excitation is continued they become congested with venous blood. The labia minora become so filled with blood that they double or triple in thickness, pushing out between the labia majora and lengthening the vaginal

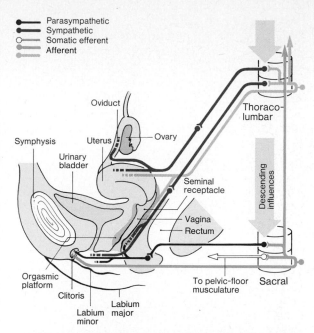

Fig. 6-18. Innervation of the female genitalia. Interneurons between afferents and efferent neurons in the spinal cord are not shown

cylinder. The swollen labia minora change color from pink to bright red. The color changes are so typical of a sexually excited woman that the labia minora have been called the "sex skin". **Glans** and **clitoris** also swell, increasing in both length and thickness. As excitation increases the clitoris is drawn against the margin of the symphysis.

Two mechanisms bring about these changes of the external genitalia during sexual excitation. The receptors in the genital organs, with axons running in the pudendal nerve to the sacral cord (S_2–S_4), initiate **reflexes** (Fig. 6-18); on the other hand, the responses can be entirely **psychogenic,** produced by the brain. Because of its dense afferent innervation, the *clitoris* plays a special role. Its mechanoreceptors are excited both by direct touch and indirectly – especially after retraction of the clitoris to the edge of the symphysis – by pull on the prepuce, by manipulation of the other external genitalia or by the thrusting of the penis. Excitation of the afferents from the mons pubis, the vestibule of the vagina, the perineal region and especially the labia minora can have just as marked effects during sexual excitation as excitation of the clitoral afferents. Excitation is enhanced by the swelling of the organs. It is not known whether afferents running with the sympathetic fibers also participate in these reflex events, but it appears likely.

The enlargement of the external genitalia results from a general **vasocongestion,** probably produced by vasodilator parasympathetic neurons in the sacral

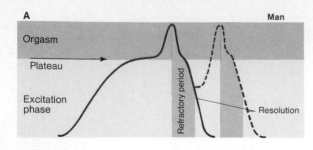

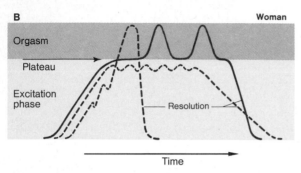

Fig. 6-19. Sexual response cycles of man and woman. Duration (abscissa) and intensity (ordinate) of the various phases vary widely among individuals. Modified from [22]

cord that send out axons in the pelvic nerves (Fig. 6-18). The erection of the clitoris, like that of the male penis, is produced by the engorgement of erectile tissue by blood. It is plausible that in analogy with the findings in the man (cf. Table 6-2), sympathetic innervation from the thoracolumbar cord also participates in the production of vasocongestion.

Internal genitalia. The internal reproductive organs of the woman undergo remarkable changes in the sexual response cycle. Within 10 to 30 s after afferent or psychogenic stimulation the *transudation* of a mucoid fluid through the squamous epithelium of the **vagina** begins. This transudate lubricates the vagina and is a prerequisite for the adequate stimulation of the penis during intercourse. The large vestibular glands (Bartholini's glands) play hardly any role in lubrication. Transudation results from a general venous congestion in the vaginal wall, probably under the influence of parasympathetic neurons from the sacral cord and sympathetic neurons from the thoracolumbar cord. The details of the transudation mechanism are as yet unknown.

Transudation is accompanied by a reflex expansion and elongation of the vagina. As excitation builds up local vasocongestion in the outer third of the vagina forms the **orgasmic platform** (Fig. 6-18). This thickening, together with the swollen labia minora, provides a long channel with the optimal anatomical characteristics for production of an orgasm in man and woman. During the orgasm the orgasmic platform

contracts 3 to 15 times, depending on the intensity of the orgasm. These contractions are probably neuronally mediated, by the sympathetic system, and are comparable to the emission and ejaculation of the man.

The **uterus** changes its position during sexual excitation, rising in the pelvis from its anteverted and anteflexed position so that at the height of excitation the cervix has moved away from the posterior wall of the vagina, leaving room in the inner third of the vagina for the reception of semen *(seminal receptacle)*. At the same time the uterus enlarges by as much as 50%. The *erection, elevation* and *enlargement* of the uterus are brought about by vasocongestion in the true pelvis, probably assisted by the neuronally produced contractions of the smooth musculature in the ligaments supporting the uterus. During orgasm the uterus contracts regularly. These contractions begin at the fundus and pass over the body of the uterus to its lower segment. The contractions of the uterus are probably mediated neuronally, by the sympathetic system.

After orgasm the changes in the external and internal genitalia usually disappear. The outer cervix remains open for ca. 20–30 min, extending into the seminal receptacle. Should *orgasm fail* to occur after intense excitation, the resolution phase proceeds more slowly (Fig. 6-19 B).

Extragenital Reactions during the Sexual Response Cycle

MASTERS and JOHNSON [22], on practical grounds, subdivided the **sexual response cycle** into four phases (Fig. 6-19) – the *excitation, plateau, orgasm* and *resolution phases*. The time course of this cycle varies widely among individuals. The excitation and resolution phases are the longest, with the plateau phase shorter and orgasm usually the shortest of all. In the **man** the overall cycle tends to be *stereotyped,* with little interindividual variation (Fig. 6-19 A). A *refractory period* follows the peak of orgasm and extends into the resolution phase; during this time a second orgasm cannot be produced by sexual stimulation. In the **woman** the sexual response cycle is considerably *more variable* in both duration and intensity (Fig. 6-19 B). Women are capable of multiple orgasms. If orgasm is not reached, the resolution phase lasts longer.

Orgasm is a response of the entire body. It consists of the reactions of the genitalia produced by the autonomic nervous system (particularly ejaculation in the man and the contraction of orgasmic platform and uterus in the woman), general autonomic reactions and excitation of the CNS, usually intense, which enhances sexual sensations and – in women, especially – tends to exclude other sensory perceptions.

During the sexual response cycle a variety of extragenital reactions can be observed [22]. *Heart rate* and *blood pressure* increase with the degree of excitation. Heart rate reaches a maximum around 100–180 per min, and blood pressure rises by ca. 20–40 mm Hg diastolic, 30–100 mm Hg systolic. The *respiratory rate* increases to as much as 40 per min. The external anal sphincter contracts rhythmically in the orgasm phase. Because of vasocongestion the **breast** of the woman becomes larger, and its pattern of superficial veins more pronounced. These reactions of the breast can also occur in the man, but are far less conspicuous. In many women and some men a **sexflush** of the skin can be observed. It typically begins over the epigastrium in the late excitation phase, and as excitation increases it spreads over the breasts, shoulders, abdomen and under some circumstances the entire body. The *skeletal musculature* contracts both voluntarily and involuntarily. Eventually there are nearly spastic contractions of the facial, abdominal and intercostal musculature. A common feature of orgasm is extensive loss of voluntary control of the skeletal musculature.

6.5 Functions of the Hypothalamus

In the vertebrates the **hypothalamus** is the part of the brain most important in regulating the internal milieu. It is a *phylogenetically old part of the brain,* and among the terrestrial vertebrates its *structure* has remained relatively constant, in contrast to that of the more recent parts of the brain such as neocortex and limbic system [13]. It is the center governing all the essential homeostatic processes in the body. A decerebrate animal can be kept alive with no particular difficulty, whereas an animal without the hypothalamus requires extreme care if it is to survive, for many of the homeostatic regulatory mechanisms have been eliminated. The *integrative functions* of the hypothalamus include *autonomic, somatic and hormonal* pathways. They are treated in the parts of the book related to the specific functions – for example, thermoregulation (p. 540), regulation of electrolyte balance (p. 668), endocrine regulating mechanisms (p. 663), regulation of sexual maturation (p. 676) and regulation of the sleeping/waking rhythm (p. 158).

The fundamental feature of **homeostasis** is that the internal milieu is kept constant within narrow limits, despite the severe perturbations that occur within the body as it adjusts to changing external conditions (e. g., exposure to heat and cold, perform-

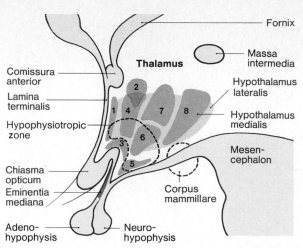

Fig. 6-20. Nuclear regions in the hypothalamus; sagittal section through the third ventricle, diagrammatic. 1. preoptic nucleus (preoptic area), 2. paraventricular nucleus, 3. supraoptic nucleus, 4. anterior nucleus (anterior area), 5. infundibular nucleus, 6. ventromedial nucleus, 7. dorsomedial nucleus, 8. posterior nucleus (posterior area). [From BENNINGHOFF-GOERTLER, Lehrbuch der Anatomie des Menschen, Vol. III, Urban und Schwarzenberg (1977)]

ance of hard work). The existence and efficacy of these homeostatic mechanisms in mammals, humans in particular, are a prerequisite for their ability to function in a large range of environments. Animals lacking some of the homeostatic mechanisms have limited ranges, and can survive only if they restrict themselves to certain climatic surroundings. This dependence on their environment makes them less free than organisms with effective homeostatic mechanisms. For example, the thermoregulatory ability of frogs is so limited that to survive the winter cold they must retreat to the depths of a lake, where the water does not freeze. By contrast, many mammals are as free to move about in winter as in summer, despite the wide variation in ambient temperature.

Functional Anatomy of the Hypothalamus

Topographic position and subdivisions. The hypothalamus is a small part of the brain, weighing only ca. 5 g, with rather diffuse boundaries. It is more a part of a *neuronal continuum* extending from the midbrain through the hypothalamus to the basal regions of the telencephalon, which are closely associated with the phylogenetically old olfactory system. As the ventral part of the *diencephalon,* the hypothalamus bounds the ventral half of the third ventricle, lying below (ventral to) the thalamus. It is bounded caudally by the mesencephalon and rostrally by the lamina terminalis, the anterior commissure and the optic chiasm (Fig. 6-20). Lateral to it lie the optic tract, the internal capsule and subthalamic structures.

Within the hypothalamus are three mediolaterally arranged zones [24], a periventricular, a medial and a lateral zone. The periventricular zone is a thin sheet adjacent to the third ventricle. Passing from front to back through the medial hypothalamus one can distinguish several nuclear regions (cf. red shading in Fig. 6-20). The preoptic region is phylogenetically part of the telencephalon, but is usually considered a hypothalamic structure. The ventromedial part of the hypothalamus gives rise to the hypophyseal stalk (infundibulum), with the adeno- and neurohypophyses. The anterior part of the hypophyseal stalk is called the **median eminence.** Many neurons in the preoptic and anterior hypothalamic regions and in the ventromedial and infundibular nuclei (nuclei 1, 4, 5 and 6 in Fig. 6-20) project into the median eminence and there release hormones from their axons into the portal circulation to the adenohypophysis (anterior pituitary gland). The nuclear regions containing hormone-producing neurons are together called the *hypophysiotropic zone* (dashed outline in Fig. 6-20). Neurons in the supraoptic and paraventricular nuclei (nuclei 2 and 3 in Fig. 6-20) project into the neurohypophysis (posterior pituitary gland) and control the production and release of oxytocin and ADH (vasopressin; cf. p. 661). With few exceptions (the supraoptic and paraventricular nuclei; cf. pp. 662 f.), it is impossible to assign particular functions to the individual nuclei.

In the **lateral hypothalamus** (Fig. 6-20) no nuclear regions can be distinguished. The neurons dispersed through the lateral hypothalamus surround the *medial forebrain bundle,* which rostrally continues into the basolateral structures of the limbic system and caudally passes to rostral structures of the midbrain. It consists of long and short ascending and descending axons (cf. Fig. 6-27 B).

Afferent and efferent connections of the hypothalamus [24]. The afferent and efferent connections of the hypothalamus indicate that this part of the brain is an important integration center for somatic, autonomic and endocrine functions (Fig. 6-21). The **lateral hypothalamus** is reciprocally connected with the upper brainstem, the paramedian mesencephalic region (limbic midbrain area of Nauta [51]), and the superordinate limbic system. It receives afferent inputs from the surface and interior of the body by way of ascending spinobulboreticular pathways. These pathways project into the hypothalamus by way of either the thalamus or the limbic midbrain area. Other afferent inputs from the remaining sensory systems reach the hypothalamus by way of multisynaptic pathways, some of which have not yet been identified. The efferent connections to the autonomic and somatic nuclei in brainstem and spinal cord are made by multisynaptic pathways in the reticular formation.

The **medial hypothalamus** makes reciprocal connections with the lateral hypothalamus and receives few direct afferent inputs from non-hypothalamic parts of the brain. Special neurons within the medial hypothalamus measure important parameters of the blood or cerebrospinal fluid (red arrows in Fig. 6-21) and thus monitor the **internal milieu.** Such receptors, for example, signal the temperature of the blood (warm neurons; cf. p. 540), the salt concentration in the plasma (p. 308) or the concentration of endocrine hormones in the blood. The efferent connections from the medial hypothalamus to the hypophysis are neuronal to the neurohypophysis and hormonal to the adenohypophysis. Thus the medial hypothalamus constitutes a boundary region between the endocrine and neuronal systems; it serves as a **neuroendocrine interface.**

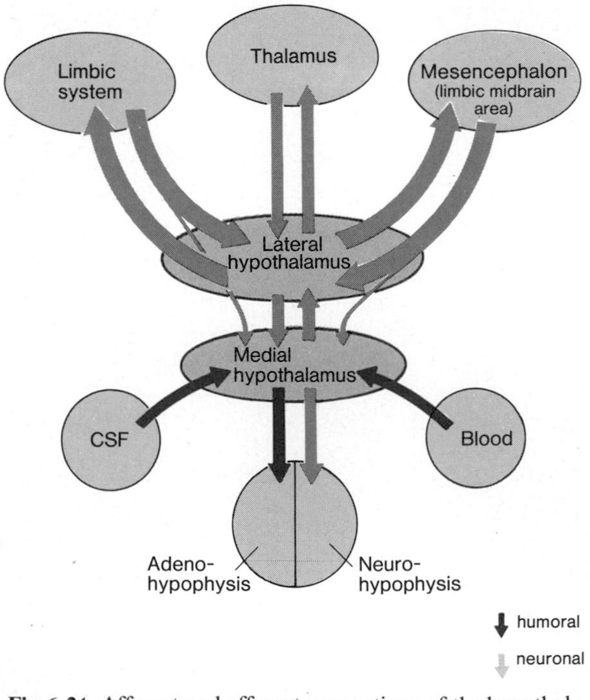

The Hypothalamo-Hypophyseal System

The activity of most endocrine glands is regulated by hormones from the adenohypohysis (anterior pituitary gland). These hormones in turn are released under the control of hormones produced by neurons in the hypophysiotrophic zone of the medial hypothalamus (cf. Fig. 6-20). We call these hypothalamic hormones *stimulating* and *inhibitory* **releasing hormones** (RH, IH in Fig. 6-22; cf. p. 659). The releasing hormones are liberated from the axons of neurons in the median eminence and are carried to the adenohypophysis by the blood in the hypothalamo-hypophyseal portal system.

Secretion of the hypothalamic hormones into the portal system by the neurons in the hypophysiotropic zone is controlled by the plasma concentrations of the hormones of the peripheral endocrine glands (long red arrows in Fig. 6-22). For example, when the cortisol level in the plasma rises, less CRH (corticotropic-hormone releasing hormone) is released in the median eminence, and thus the amount of ACTH released from the adenohypophysis is reduced (cf. Fig. 29-2,

Fig. 6-21. Afferent and efferent connections of the hypothalamus. Simplified schematic drawing

p.662). In general, an increase in the plasma concentration of the hormones of peripheral endocrine glands reduces the amount of the corresponding releasing hormone that enters the bloodstream in the medial hypothalamus. The hypothalamic hormones and the hormones of the adenohypophysis themselves may also participate in this regulation (dashed red arrows in Fig.6-22).

The *negative-feedback system* (Fig.6-22) involving medial hypothalamus, hypophysis and endocrine glands functions even without the controlling influence of the CNS – for example, in animals in which the medial hypothalamus has been surgically isolated from the rest of the CNS in situ. The CNS serves to adjust the system to the internal and external needs of the organism. Cortisol secretion by the adrenal cortex, for instance, increases when severe demands are made on the organism (*stress;* cf. p.558). The elevated cortisol secretion is brought about by an increase in activity of the CRH-producing neurons in the medial hypothalamus and thus an increase in the release of CRH in the median eminence. This central nervous control of the endocrine hypothalamo-hypophyseal system is mediated chiefly by the lateral hypothalamus and is initiated primarily by the preoptic region, structures of the limbic system (e.g., hippocampus and amygdala) and structures of the mesencephalon. The signals are thought to be conveyed by *aminergic neurons* (noradrenergic, dopaminergic or serotonergic). It is likely that these parts of the CNS also receive feedback information about the concentrations of the endocrine hormones in the plasma (Fig.6-22). The neurons involved can be shown to respond very specifically to endocrine hormones and to store these hormones intracellularly. As examples of the biological significance of CNS modulation of endocrine activity consider the circadian rhythmicity of ACTH release, the control of ovarian-hormone release during the menstrual cycle (p.676), control of cortisol release under stress (p.558) and the increase in metabolic rate due to increased thyroxin release during prolonged exposure to cold (p.672).

The extensive intermeshing of neuronal and endocrine structures in the hypothalamus can be illustrated by the connectivity of the neurons in the *hypophysiotropic zone*. A neuron that produces releasing hormone can be influenced by afferent neurons from structures in the limbic system (amygdala and hippocampus; cf. p.138) and from the preoptic area and anterior hypothalamus (Fig.6-23, upper part). The axon collaterals of this neuron project into a wide variety of brain structures (Fig.6-23, right). It is also subject to autoregulation by recurrent inhibition (Fig.6-23, left). The transmitter elaborated by the various axon collaterals is probably the releasing hor-

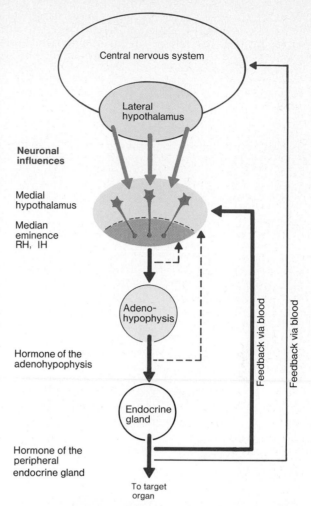

Fig.6-22. Neuroendocrine coupling by the hypothalamo-hypophyseal system. RH stimulatory releasing hormone; IH inhibitory releasing hormone

mone. These cells of the hypophysiotropic zone are thus **terminal integrating neurons** on one hand, and on the other, hormone-producing *endocrine cells* [26].

Hypothalamus and Cardiovascular System

Electrical stimulation of nearly all parts of the hypothalamus can elicit responses of the cardiovascular system. These effects are mediated primarily by the sympathetic system and by way of the vagus nerve to the heart. They indicate the prominent position of the hypothalamus in the *superordinate control of the circulation*. Stimulation of a given region can produce opposite effects in different organs (e.g., increased blood flow through the skeletal musculature and simultaneous decrease in skin perfusion). On the other hand, opposite vascular responses of an organ can be induced by stimulation of different regions in the hy-

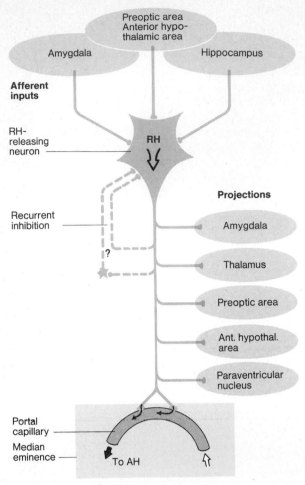

Fig. 6-23. Releasing-hormone-producing neuron in the hypophysiotropic zone, the basic element of neuroendocrine coupling in the hypothalamus. From RENAUD [26]

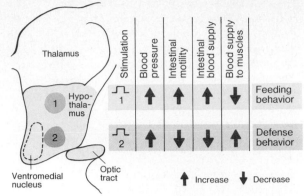

Fig. 6-24. Autonomic reactions in the induction of nutritive and defense behavior in the cat by electrical stimulation of the medial hypothalamus. Modified from FOLKOW and RUBINSTEIN: Acta physiol. scand. 65, 292–299 (1966)]

pothalamus. The biological significance of these circulatory effects with respect to the whole organism is revealed only when they are considered in relation to other responses of the organism to the same hypothalamic stimuli. That is, these cardiovascular effects are among the behavioral patterns or *homeostatic processes* that are integrated in the hypothalamus.

Examples are the production of nutritive behavior and of defensive behavior by topical electrical stimulation of the hypothalamus (Fig. 6-24; cf. also pp. 135 f.). During defensive behavior blood pressure and blood flow through the muscles increase, while less blood flows through the intestines. During electrically elicited nutritive behavior blood pressure and intestinal blood flow increase, and muscle blood flow decreases. Corresponding changes in cardiovascular parameters can be observed in other behavior patterns elicited by the hypothalamus – for example, thermoregulatory or sexual behavior.

The *simple servocontrol* of the cardiovascular system

(arterial systemic blood pressure, cardiac output, distribution of blood) resides in the lower brainstem (circulatory center; cf. p. 435). The efferents are sympathetic and parasympathetic axons to the various cardiovascular effectors, and the afferents come from arterial baro- and chemoreceptors and mechanoreceptors in the atria and ventricles of the heart (p. 426 ff.). This *medullary autoregulation* of the cardiovascular system in turn is under the control of the upper brainstem, and especially of the hypothalamus. This control involves neuronal connections between hypothalamus and medullary circulatory center, as well as direct neuronal connections from the hypothalamus to the preganglionic neurons. The cardiovascular system is under *higher-level neuronal control* by the hypothalamus during all of the more complex autonomic functions that go beyond simple servocontrol – for example, thermoregulation, the regulation of food intake, defensive behavior, physical work (see below), and so on.

Adjustment of the cardiovascular system during work. A mechanism of very special practical and theoretical significance is the matching of cardiovascular performance to the demands of physical work. During muscular effort the cardiac output rises (mainly by increase in heart rate) and at the same time more blood flows through the musculature, while less is channelled through skin and viscera (cf. Fig. 6-24). This circulatory adjustment occurs practically as soon as work begins. It is initiated by the *central nervous system, by way of the hypothalamus*. Electrical stimulation of the lateral hypothalamus of dogs, at the level of the mammillary bodies, produces autonomic responses that resemble in detail those of animals working on a treadmill. If the animal is anesthetized, locomotor movements and accelerated breathing can be observed during electrical stimulation of the hypothalamus. By changing the position of the stimulating electrode slightly one can also elicit autonomic and somatic reactions independent of one another. The responses are abolished by bilateral **lesions** of the neuronal regions that produce them when stimulated; a dog with such a lesion cannot adjust its cardiovascular system to working conditions (it tires rapidly on the treadmill). This finding indicates the existence in the lateral hypothalamus of neuronal structures controlling the modification of the circulation during muscular work. These hypothalamic regions are subject to **neocortical control.** We do not know whether the hypothalamus alone can accomplish this central-nervous adjustment; to do so, it would require a relatively specific afferent input from the skeletal musculature [53].

The cholinergic vasodilator system. The precapillary resistance vessels in the vascular bed of the muscles of some species (e.g., cat, dog, fox, goat) are innervated by cholinergic sympathetic neurons (cf. Table 6-1, p. 113). These neurons can be activated by the lateral ventral hypothalamus and adjacent parts of the central gray matter and tegmentum of the cranial mesencephalon; they act to increase the flow of blood through the musculature. They do not participate in homeostatic reflexes such as the baroreceptor reflex (p. 426). These postganglionic neurons are thought to inhibit the pacemaker cells of the smooth muscle in the larger precapillary resistance vessels, and thus open the vascular bed of the muscle [45].
The cholinergic vasodilation in muscles is probably an integral component of the hypothalamically organized *defensive behavior.* Cholinergic vasodilation can also be elicited by electrical stimulation of the *motor cortex,* an effect shown to be mediated by axons running from the cortex through the internal capsule to the hypothalamus. It is possible that this cholinergic vasodilation serves as a **preparatory action** to ensure *rapid delivery of nutrients to the musculature* to be activated by cortical command. Studies on cats indicate that following so-called emotional stimuli this vasodilator system can selectively dilate the vessels in active muscles. The system is also thought to exist in *man,* where it can be activated under **emotional stress.**

Hypothalamus and Behavior

Electrical stimulation of small areas in the hypothalamus, with microelectrodes, causes animals to exhibit characteristic behavior patterns. The diversity of such behavior resembles the range of natural species-specific behavior patterns of the animal concerned. Chief among them are *defense and flight behavior, eating and drinking* (nutritive behavior), *reproductive (sexual) behavior* and *thermoregulatory behavior.* These behavior patterns subserve **survival of the individual** and the **species.** Thus in a broad sense they can be considered as homeostatic processes. Each of them consists of somatomotor, autonomic and hormonal components.

Local electrical stimulation in the caudal hypothalamus (stimulus site 2 in Fig. 6-24), for example, elicits **defense behavior** in a waking cat. This behavior comprises typical somatomotor reactions such as arched back, hissing, spreading of the toes and extension of claws, as well as autonomic reactions such as increased respiration, pupil dilation and piloerection on back and tail. Blood pressure and muscle perfusion increase, whereas motility and blood flow in the intestines are reduced (Fig. 6-24, right). Most of the autonomic reactions are brought about by activation of adrenergic neurons in the sympathetic system. In addition to the *autonomic* and *somatomotor* reactions, hormonal factors contribute to defense behavior. **Catecholamines** are released from the adrenal medulla into the bloodstream (cf. pp. 116 f. and Fig. 6-5). Activation of the hypothalamo-hypophyseal system causes the release of **ACTH** from the adenohypophysis and thus the release of **corticosteroids** from the adrenal cortex.

Similar behavior patterns can be produced in *diencephalic* cats with hypothalamus intact, by natural (painful and non-painful) stimulation of the skin. Because these animals lack the whole forebrain, the behavior they exhibit has no reference to their surroundings. When the caudal hypothalamus is destroyed only fragments of such behavior can be elicited, by painful stimuli. These studies have shown that the neuronal substrate integrating this behavior is situated in the posterior hypothalamus.

The **nutritive behavior** produced by the hypothalamus is nearly complementary to the defense behavior. Nutritive behavior is elicited by local electrical stimulation of a hypothalamic area 2–3 mm dorsal to the "defense area" (stimulus site 1 in Fig. 6-24). An animal in which this behavior is induced exhibits all the characteristics of an animal in search of food; when it comes to a full dish it begins to eat even though it is satiated, and it chews on inedible objects. Examination of the autonomic parameters shows that the behavior is accompanied by increased salivation, intestinal motility and intestinal blood flow, and decreased muscle blood flow (Fig. 6-24). The characteristic changes in autonomic parameters during nutritive behavior bring about a certain autonomic adjustment to the event **food intake.** This behavior pattern is characterized by excitation of the parasympathetic innervation of the digestive tract.

Principle of hypothalamic organization. Systematic study of the hypothalamus with *local electrical stimulation* indicates that this structure contains neuronal substrates for regulation of a wide range of behavior patterns. Studies employing other methods, such as lesions or chemical stimulation, have supported and extended this conclusion.

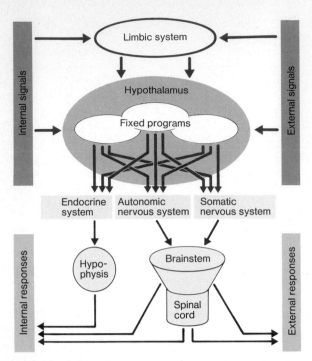

Fig. 6-25. Diagram of the functional organization of hypothalamic behavior patterns

For example, lesion of the area in the lateral hypothalamus in which electrical stimulation can induce eating behavior (the so-called feeding or hunger center; cf. p.314) causes aphagia (refusal of food), whereas lesion of the area in the medial hypothalamus that when stimulated inhibits eating behavior (the satiety center) elicits hyperphagia (excessive eating). *Chemical stimulation* of neuron populations can be achieved with substances that are candidate synaptic transmitters in the hypothalamus – for example, noradrenalin, acetylcholine, glycine, gamma-aminobutyric acid, neuropeptides. Microinjection of noradrenalin into the hypothalamus, for instance, dramatically increases food intake, whereas microinjection of acetylcholine can selectively elicit the intake of liquid [25].

The regions in the hypothalamus in which stimulation elicits behavior patterns overlap extensively. For this reason no one has yet succeeded in describing, neurophysiologically and neuroanatomically, the neuron populations responsible for the regulation of behavior patterns. For example, the hypothalamic nuclei revealed by neurohistological methods (cf. Fig.6-20) correspond only vaguely or not at all to the regions associated with particular behavior patterns by stimulation techniques. Thus the neuronal structures that integrate the response subunits to form behavior patterns must not be conceived as *anatomically well-defined* structures, as the terms "satiety center" and "hunger center" might suggest.
The neuronal organization in the hypothalamus that enables this small area of the brain to control the multitude of vital behavior patterns and neurohumoral regulatory processes remains a great puzzle. Presum-

ably functionally different groups of neurons in the hypothalamus are characterized by the specificity of their afferent and efferent connections, their synaptic transmitters, the spatial organization of their dendrites and other parameters. It must be assumed that the hypothalamic neural networks as yet inaccessible to us contain a large number of **programs.** Activation of these programs, by neuronal commands from superordinate brain structures (e.g., structures in the limbic system) and/or by signals from the sensory systems and from the interior of the body, would then produce the observed broad spectrum of behavior patterns and neurohumoral regulation (Fig. 6-25).

For a long time it was assumed that the cranial parts of the hypothalamus integrate somatic, autonomic and endocrine reactions to promote recuperation of the body and conservation of its energy, as well as digestion and excretion. This function was thought to be associated with excitation of the parasympathetic system, and the entire process was termed the **trophotropic reaction.** It was further assumed that activation of the caudal parts of the hypothalamus caused excitation of the adrenergic sympathetic system, mobilization of bodily energy and enhancement of performance capacity. This process was termed the **ergotropic reaction.** These concepts, introduced by Hess [14], imply that the hypothalamus consists of two *functionally and anatomically different systems,* the antagonism between sympathetic and parasympathetic found in the peripheral autonomic system being carried over into the hypothalamus. Many experiments performed in order to confirm or refute this hypothesis have contributed a great deal to our understanding of the functional significance of the hypothalamus. The hypothesis itself, however, appears too general to be able to explain the various functions of the hypothalamus.

Functional disturbances resulting from damage to the hypothalamus in man. Disturbances of hypothalamic function in man are most often caused by neoplasms (tumors), trauma or inflammation. Such damage is sometimes quite restricted in extent, producing isolated deficits in the anterior, intermediate or posterior hypothalamus. The functional disturbances the clinician observes in patients (with the exception of diabetes insipidus; cf. pp.310, 661) are complex phenomena. They also depend on whether the damage is acute (e.g., due to trauma) or chronic (e.g., due to a slowly growing tumor). Small acute injuries can cause notable functional disturbances even though the disturbance caused by slowly growing tumors does not become apparent until the damage has become extensive. The complex functions of the hypothalamus and the associated disorders are listed in Table 6-3. Disturbances of perception, memory and the sleeping/waking rhythm are in part brought about by damage to the ascending and descending systems from and to structures in the limbic system (cf. Figs.6-21 and 6-27 B) [26].

Table 6-3. Functional disturbances resulting from damage to hypothalamus in man. From [26]

	Anterior hypothalamus with preoptic region	Intermediate hypothalamus	Posterior hypothalamus
Function	Sleeping/waking rhythm, thermoregulation, endocrine regulation	Perception, caloric and fluid balance, endocrine regulation	Perception, consciousness, thermoregulation, complex endocrine regulation
Lesions: Acute	Insomnia, hyperthermia, diabetes insipidus	Hyperthermia, diabetes insipidus, endocrine disorders	Hypersomnia, emotional and autonomic disturbances, poikilothermia
Chronic	Insomnia, complex endocrine disturbances (e.g., pubertas praecox), endocrine disturbances resulting from damage to median eminence, hypothermia, no feeling of thirst	*Medial:* impaired memory, emotional disturbances, hyperphagia and obesity, endocrine disturbances *Lateral:* emotional disturbances, emaciation and loss of appetite, no feeling of thirst	Amnesia, emotional disturbances, poikilothermia, autonomic disturbances, complex endocrine disturbances (e.g., pubertas praecox)

6.6 Limbic System and Behavior

In a simplified view, the cerebrum consists of the neocortex and the limbic system. By its integral activity it generates goal-directed human behavior. In this process, the *neocortex* tends to regulate the precise spatiotemporal communication with the environment and the formal-intellectual and stereognostic capabilities, whereas the *limbic system* is more concerned with moods and incentives to action – that is, a person's motivational interactions and emotions – and the processes of learning and memory. The limbic system endows the information derived from the internal and external worlds with its particular significance to humans, and thus determines their characteristic purposeful behavior.

The limbic system comprises phylogenetically old parts of the telencephalon and the subcortical structures derived from them. Originally the term "la grande lobe limbique" was introduced by Broca [47]. This term at first denoted only cortical areas of the central nervous system, arranged in a bilateral *ring-shaped* belt bordering the neocortex (*limbus* is Latin for "border") and separating it from the brainstem and hypothalamus. It included the cingulate and hippocampal gyri as well as others close to the fibers from the olfactory bulb (Fig. 6-27 A). Because these structures were assumed to have an olfactory function, they were called the *rhinencephalon*. Recently MacLean [47, 48] has given the cortical and subcortical telencephalic structures described by Broca the purely descriptive name "limbic system". He proposed that these cerebral structures are a functional unit containing the neuronal substrate of the mechanisms of expression and generation of emotional behavior in mammals [48].

MacLean [48] proposed that the mammalian brain be subdivided into three systems on functional, neuroanatomical, ethological and phylogenetic grounds; these subdivisions are the *protoreptilian, paleomammalian* and *neomammalian* brains (Fig. 6-26). The **protoreptilian** brain consists of the brainstem, diencephalon and basal ganglia. It integrates stereotyped, largely innate behavioral patterns (instincts) that are important for survival. It is distinguished by a lack of flexibility and thus requires stability of the environment. The **paleomammalian brain** comprises the structures of the limbic system. According to MacLean, it is the first step in nature toward the development of consciousness. He also calls this brain *"visceral brain"* because of the large amount of information it receives from the interior of the body – information important in forming the content of memory and its affective shading. This brain is capable of overriding and modifying the genetically fixed phylogenetic behavioral repertoire; it contains the structures for species-specific behavior of mammals. The neomammalian brain consists of the neocortex. This brain can process signals from within the body at a largely unconscious level. It analyzes the signals from the environment in a spatiotemporal coordinate system and develops concepts and strategies for action. It is a brain that plans the future and modifies the "conservative", "traditional" strategies laid down in the paleomammalian brain.

This subdivision is speculative. There is no evidence that a reptile ever existed with a brain corresponding to the protoreptilian brain. As far as is known, all the living reptiles also have brain elements homologous to the structures of the limbic system and the neocortex. The argument in favor of subdividing the brain into three prototypes is that this subdivision reflects the association found between general behavioral functions of organisms and gross anatomical structures. Thus this brain model is a graphic expression of the hierarchical organization of brain and behavior.

Elements of the Limbic System

The **cortical components** of the limbic system are three-layered (allocortex) and five-layered (transitional cortex, mesocortex) at the transition to the six-layered neocortex (isocortex; cf. p. 146). They consist

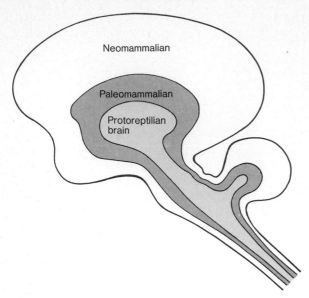

Fig. 6-26. Schematic illustration of the subdivision of the brain into three brain types. From MacLean [48]

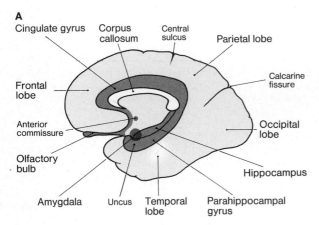

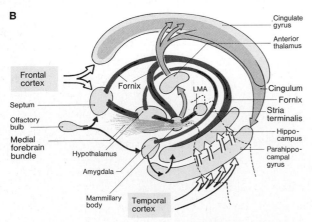

Fig. 6-27 A, B. Structures in the limbic system. **A** Curved arrangement of the limbic system around the edge of the neocortex. **B** Afferent and efferent connections of the limbic system. LMA limbic midbrain area

of the *hippocampus* (Ammon's horn, dentate gyrus and subiculum), *parahippocampal gyrus* (entorhinal area and presubiculum), *cingulate gyrus* (with subcallosal cortex) and old elements of the olfactory brain (olfactory bulb, olfactory tubercle, cortical areas above the amygdala). Many authors also include the orbitofrontal cortex, the insular cortex and parts of the temporal cortex in the limbic system. The *subcortical components* include the *amygdala*, the *septal nuclei* (with nucleus accumbens and Broca's diagonal band) and the *anterior thalamic nucleus*. Many authors also count the preoptic region, hypothalamus and mammillary bodies as part of the limbic system (Fig. 6-27).

The afferent and efferent connections of the structures in the limbic system, with neighboring structures and with one another, are extremely diverse, and not all of them are known (Fig. 6-27 B). Most conspicuous are the massive **reciprocal connections with the hypothalamus.** The hypothalamus and the mammillary bodies communicate with the hippocampus and the septum by way of the *fornix*, with the amygdala by way of the *stria terminalis* and *amygdalafugal bundle* (not shown in Fig. 6-27 B) and with the frontobasal parts of the olfactory brain by way of the *medial forebrain bundle*. By way of the hypothalamus and mammillary bodies, the limbic system makes connections with structures in the mesencephalon (the limbic midbrain area, LMA in Fig. 6-27 B; cf. Fig. 6-21) [15, 24].

A striking feature of the limbic system is its organization in *multiple circuits of excitation*. The circuit consisting of the parahippocampal gyrus, hippocampus, fornix, septum, mammillary body, anterior thalamus, cingulate gyrus and cingulum (Fig. 6-27 B) is probably a significant neuronal substrate of the emotions [48] and the formation of memory (cf. p. 164) [15, 16].

The limbic system communicates with the neocortex by way of the frontal and temporal regions (Fig. 6-27 B). The **temporal brain** mediates primarily information from the visual, auditory and somatosensory cortices to the amygdala and the hippocampus. The **frontal brain** is probably the most important neocortical control element of the limbic system. Moreover, it is the only neocortical region with direct neuronal connections to the hypothalamus [51].

Functions of the Limbic System

The limbic system controls emotional behavior and thus the complex of internal factors motivating animal and human actions. It brings about an *overall* improvement in **adaptation** to constantly changing surroundings. If this adaptation is disturbed, by pathological changes in or experimental interference with the limbic system, inappropriate behavior patterns result; that is, there are disturbances in the functional systems controlled by the limbic system, which have their neuronal substrate in the hypothalamus and upper mesencephalon – nutritive behavior, behavior to protect the individual and the species, and socio-sexual behavior. The regulation of these functional systems in a particular animal is manifest in its **species-specific behavior patterns.** In man, changes in the limbic system disrupt **emotional behavior patterns,** which are probably homologous to species-specific behavior. In the following paragraphs the functions of some limbic-system structures are discussed with reference to clinical and experimental examples.

Amygdala. In man the amygdala (or amygdaloid body) is a large, highly differentiated subcortical nuclear region deep within the temporal lobe (Fig. 6-27). Electrical stimulation of the various parts of the amygdala of the cat or monkey elicits in principle the same response patterns as are elicited by electrical stimulation of the hypothalamus (cf. p. 125), or inhibits these patterns. Such patterns include both elementary, homeostatic responses and behavior comprising all autonomic, endocrine and somatic reactions.

Bilateral destruction of the amygdala of an animal produces no serious disturbance of the homeostatic functions integrated in the hypothalamus. By contrast, the *behavior* of a bilaterally **amygdalectomized animal** is severely disrupted. Monkeys are no longer capable of functioning as members of social groups. They cannot recognize the social significance of the exteroceptive (especially visual, auditory and olfactory) signals that regulate social behavior, or relate them to their own affective states (moods), which regulate approach to or avoidance of other members of the group and are thus the building blocks of social interactions. Amygdalectomized monkeys avoid the other members of the group and seem anxious and insecure.

When kept alone in a cage the same monkeys develop symptoms of the classical Klüver-Bucy syndrome. This syndrome was first described by KLÜVER and BUCY [39] from their observations of Rhesus monkeys with both temporal lobes removed, including the uncus, amygdala and hippocampal formation (Fig. 6-27). The monkeys exhibited severe disturbance of affective behavior, consisting of the following symptoms: psychic blindness (inability to distinguish edible from nonedible objects); extreme oral tendencies (the monkeys grasp all objects with the lips and take them into the mouth) and abnormal feeding habits; hypersexuality; turning toward any object that comes into view; severe deficiency in fear and affective responses. The behavioral disturbances exhibited in the Klüver-Bucy syndrome of monkeys in a cage and by amygdalectomized monkeys in a social group are only apparently contradictory. From both sets of observations one can conclude that the an-

imals are incapable of recognizing the significance to their own behavior of sensory stimuli from the environment (especially visual and acoustic signals, in the case of primates) and cannot relate them to their own affective states. This failure disrupts the normal interaction between own behavior and the surroundings, particularly in the *social context* with members of the own group and with strangers [20].

The behavioral disturbances of the monkeys are thought to be caused by the bilateral interruption of information transfer between the **temporal lobes** and hypothalamic neuronal mechanisms, which eliminates the opportunity for evaluating sensory information in the context of affective state. In this view, the amygdala would be the brain structure responsible for such evaluation. Among the findings corroborating this view are the following:

1. In electrophysiological experiments the neurons in the amygdala can be activated, by way of the temporal lobes, by stimulation of the primary neocortical sensory areas.
2. Temporal-lobe epilepsy in man is characterized by complex sensorimotor and autonomic disturbances. In such cases of (focal) epilepsy the (pathological) excitation originates in the temporal lobes and causes excitation of the amygdala. At the onset of an attack the patients frequently experience complex differentiated hallucinations about past events, before the amygdala becomes excited; the same hallucinations can also be elicited in these patients by topical electrical stimulation of the temporal lobe [20, 23, 36].

The clinical and experimental observations in humans and animals indicate that the temporoamygdalar system contains important neuronal substrates for learned motivated behavior and emotions. In this system complex sensory information is presumably compared with corresponding information (the contents of memory) acquired in the past. The sensory information thus becomes significant to the organism, and by way of the amygdala brings about the activation of those affective behavior patterns that have proved appropriate in previous occurrences of equivalent environmental constellations. In this process the amygdala activates and/or inhibits the relevant hypothalamic mechanisms [20, 36].

We do not know how the neocortex is informed about affective states, or how the consciousness of emotions arises. The information may travel from the hypothalamus, mammillary bodies and limbic midbrain area through the anterior thalamus to the cingulate gyrus (Fig. 6-27 B) and through the mediodorsal thalamus to the frontal brain, or directly from the amygdala to the neocortex [24]. Moreover, we do not know how the organism learns to relate the exteroceptive signals important to it (especially in the social context) to its affective states. It has been proposed that information about the *environment* from the temporal cortex and information about the homeostatic state of the *internal milieu* from the hypothalamus converge on the neurons of the amygdala, changing the synaptic connectivity there. These items of memory must be very stable and enduring, so that permanent associations between environmental stimuli and motivated behavior patterns can be created [20, 36].

Emotions and the Limbic System

Although the term "emotion" is understandable to everyone, it cannot be given a precise scientific definition [19]. Emotions are understood to comprise our *feelings* and *moods* and their *expression* in our motor behavior and in the responses of the autonomic nervous system and the endocrine system. For example, when a person is watching an exciting film there are increases in blood pressure, heart rate, sweat secretion and the concentration of the catecholamines in the blood. The emotions comprise all the negative and positive affective states, from anxiety and fear to love and happiness. Feelings and moods can only be experienced introspectively. We become conscious of them and able to communicate them through our capacity for speech. On the other hand, the expression of these experiences in motor behavior and in the autonomic and endocrine reactions is accessible to *objective scientific observation,* and can be measured in various emotional states.

So far the attempt to describe objectively, and thus to classify, the different emotions by the accompanying pattern of motor, autonomic and endocrine reactions has failed. Only at a very gross level can emotions be treated in this way. This failure made futile two approaches that would have had important theoretical and practical consequences, as follows. 1. It became impossible to make an operational definition of emotions on the basis of autonomic parameters, excluding introspection and inference by analogy. 2. It proved impracticable to make an objective diagnosis of the affective disturbances in so-called psychosomatic conditions, from the pattern of peripherally observable autonomic and humoral disturbances.

The expression of the emotions is probably based largely on **inherited, inborn reactions** [6]. These reactions serve as *signals* to conspecifics and the members of other species, and have certainly conveyed biological advantages during evolution. For example, an enraged monkey with bristling hair is a more obvious signal to its conspecifics and other animals than one without bristling hair. Therefore the emotions can most probably be considered biologically as a category of *"species-specific behavior".* Emotions also act as inward-directed signals, in that they cause the individual to adjust itself to changes in the environment by developing new reactions.

The production of emotions is associated with the cognitive abilities of mammals and thus with *percep-*

tion and *evaluation* of sensory stimuli and with *memory.* The motor, autonomic and endocrine disturbances observed in various emotional states are on one hand the expression of such cognitive processes; on the other, these reactions can affect the emotions by afferent feedback. As yet there is neither a unified scientific theory of the emotions that is generally accepted nor a sufficiently precise idea of where and how the emotions arise and what their neuronal substrate is. Probably *all* structures of the limbic system, the hypothalamus, the limbic midbrain area and the frontal lobe participate in the development and differentiation of the emotions. For example, *organic brain disorders* (tumors, inflammations, systemic diseases) that affect these structures and injury to these structures by external forces frequently change the patient's emotional behavior. Conversely, when people are suffering from otherwise intractable and intolerable *behavioral disturbances* – compulsive neuroses, insatiable sexual drive, severe anxiety states, depression and so on – these conditions have been and still are ameliorated or cured by stereotaxic destruction of small areas in these brain structures. Structures removed or isolated in such treatment include the anterior cingulate gyrus, the cingulum, the fornix, the frontal-lobe tracts and nuclei in the thalamus, hypothalamus or amygdala. Such surgical intervention must of course not be undertaken lightly, in view of its irreversibility and the undesirable and in part unpredictable postoperative personality changes (cf. psychosurgery, p. 173).

A very common emotional disturbance with which the practicing physician is confronted is **anxiety.** It is characterized by unrest and agitation because the patient feels himself threatened by a real or imagined danger with which he cannot cope. Anxiety states are expressed in *motor disturbances* such as gesticulation and facial expressions, and in *autonomic disturbances* such as sweating, tachycardia, extrasystoles, hypertension, disturbances of the digestive tract (upset stomach, diarrhea), insomnia, dry mouth and dilated pupils. Anxiety can also be very discretely expressed, in a single autonomic disorder; in this case it is usually diagnosed as autonomic dystonia or as a psychosomatic disorder [19, 23].

Monoaminergic Systems and Behavior

Central organization of monoaminergic systems. The neuronal monoaminergic systems appear to be of great importance in the *global regulation* of animal and human behavior. The group includes *dopaminergic, noradrenergic* and *serotonergic* systems, which originate in the brainstem and innervate practically all regions of the brain.

When tissue is treated with aldehydes or glyoxylic acid the monoamines in it form complexes, which fluoresce at characteristic wavelengths (depending on the amine) under illumina-

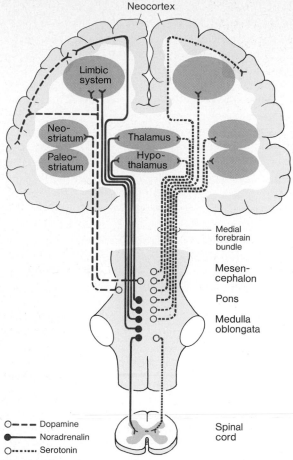

O— — — Dopamine
●——— Noradrenalin
O······· Serotonin

Spinal
cord

Fig. 6-28. Schematic diagram of the central monoaminergic systems. [Modified from ANDEN et al.: Acta physiol. scand. *67*, 313 (1966)]

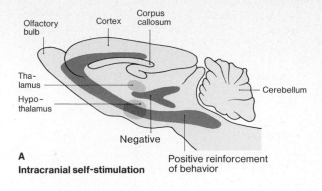

A
Intracranial self-stimulation

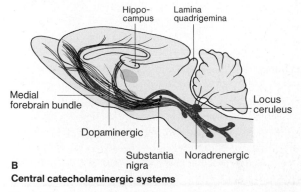

B
Central catecholaminergic systems

Fig. 6-29 A, B. Comparison of the brain areas, intracranial self-stimulation of which results in positive and negative reinforcement of behavior, with the course of the central catecholaminergic systems. **A** Intracranial self-stimulation. Positive reinforcement of behavior: light *red*. Negative reinforcement: dark red. **B** *Red:* noradrenergic system; black: dopaminergic system. Rat brain. Modified from OLDS [25]

tion with UV light. This property is exploited in *histofluorescence microscopy* to reveal selectively the somata, axons and nerve endings of the monoaminergic neurons in the CNS.

Noradrenergic neurons (Fig. 6-28, left) have cell bodies in distinct groups within the medulla oblongata and pons, especially in the *locus coeruleus*. Most of the ascending axons run in the *medial forebrain bundle*. The axons in the dorsal parts of the brainstem come chiefly from the *locus coeruleus*. They innervate various structures in the mesencephalon, thalamus and telencephalon, primarily the amygdala, hippocampus, cingulate gyrus, entorhinal cortex and neocortex. The innervation of the neocortex is very diffuse and uniform as compared with the dopaminergic innervation (see below). The more ventrally located axons in the brainstem innervate predominantly mesencephalic structures, the hypothalamus, preoptic area and olfactory bulb. Some of the noradrenergic neurons send their axons into the ventral, lateral and dorsal horns of the spinal cord (the substantia gelatinosa in particular), and into the cerebellum. Single

noradrenergic neurons in the locus coeruleus, with their collaterals, can project simultaneously to the neocortex, hippocampus, cerebellum and spinal cord.

The dopaminergic neurons (Fig. 6-28, left) originate in the ventral mesencephalon (mesotelencephalic dopaminergic system). The laterally situated neurons from the zona compacta of the *substantia nigra* innervate the neostriatum (putamen and caudate nucleus) and the nucleus accumbens. Destruction of these dopaminergic neurons causes *Parkinson's* disease (cf. p. 108). The neurons lying more medially in the ventral mesencephalon innervate primarily nuclei of the limbic system (amygdala, septum, olfactory tubercle) and allo- and neocortical areas (chiefly the *frontal cortex, cingulate gyrus* and entorhinal cortex). Most of the axons of dopaminergic neurons, like those of the noradrenergic neurons, pass through the *medial forebrain bundle*. Other dopaminergic systems with short axons, which project into the median eminence and probably participate in the liberation of releasing hormone, are located in the hypothalamus. In addi-

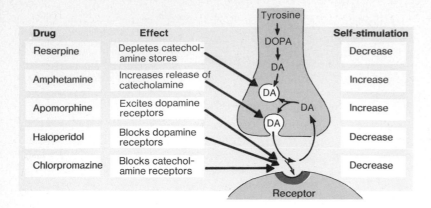

Drug	Effect	Self-stimulation
Reserpine	Depletes catechol-amine stores	Decrease
Amphetamine	Increases release of catecholamine	Increase
Apomorphine	Excites dopamine receptors	Increase
Haloperidol	Blocks dopamine receptors	Decrease
Chlorpromazine	Blocks catechol-amine receptors	Decrease

Fig. 6-30. Action of drugs on the central dopaminergic synapse, and their effects on intracranial self-stimulation (cf. Fig. 6-29)

tion, there is a periventricular dopaminergic system in the medulla oblongata, which projects chiefly to medial structures of the brainstem and to the diencephalon.

Serotonergic neurons (Fig. 6-28, right) have their somata in the median and paramedian midline nuclei *(raphe nuclei)* of the medulla oblongata, the pons and the lower mesencephalon. Their axons pass in part through the medial forebrain bundle, like the noradrenergic neurons innervating practically all of the diencephalic and telencephalic regions of the brain. Some of the serotonergic neurons project to the spinal cord and to the cerebellum [24, 49, 50, 58].

Monoaminergic systems and intracranial self-stimulation. By implanting a stimulating electrode in the *medial forebrain bundle* in the lateral hypothalamus of a rat and allowing the animal to stimulate itself by pressing a bar in the Skinner box (cf. Fig. 8-8, p. 185), one can use this intracranial stimulus as a reward to establish behavior by operant conditioning; the *intracranial stimulus reinforces* the desired behavior. The reinforcing action of the electrical stimulation is so great that the animals normally prefer it to any other kind of reinforcement, including food. Rats and monkeys are commonly observed to stimulate themselves by electrodes in the medial forebrain bundle until they are in danger of death from exhaustion. The bar-pressing rates can reach 7 000 per hour.

Systematic study of the whole brain by means of intracranial self-stimulation shows that stimulation is rewarding in practically the entire limbic system, the frontal lobe, the lateral hypothalamus and tracts of the mesencephalon, pons and upper medulla oblongata. The strongest effects, however, are obtained from the **medial forebrain bundle,** which links the upper mesencephalon, hypothalamus and limbic system (Fig. 6-29 A). In addition to the brain regions in which electrical stimulation provides positive reinforcement, there are others, electrical stimulation of

which is avoided. These regions are smaller in extent and are arranged **periventricularly in the di- and mesencephalon** (Fig. 6-29 A). There is some overlap between the regions for positive and for negative reinforcement.

Various experimental findings and theoretical arguments support the inference that the neuronal substrates, stimulation of which provides *positive or negative reinforcement* of behavior, are *not identical* to those in which specific homeostatic response patterns (pp. 135 f.) can be elicited [11, 25]. Therefore the two sets of structures providing positive and negative reinforcement have been given different names: the *pleasure and unpleasantness, approach and avoidance,* or *reward and punishment* systems. The existence of these systems supports the notion that pleasure and aversion are actively produced by excitation of the corresponding brain structures.

The results obtained in animals by the technique of intracranial self-stimulation also apply to **humans.** When patients are allowed to stimulate their own brains during neurosurgical operations they can elicit *pleasant or unpleasant feelings*. These feelings can be described by terms such as satisfaction, joy, relaxation and comfort on the one hand, and discouragement, restlessness, anxiety and fear on the other.

In the search for the neuronal substrates of positive reinforcement, in particular, it immediately became apparent that the brain areas in which **self-stimulation** is successful coincide almost entirely with those innervated by **catecholaminergic neurons** (cf. Fig. 6-29 A and B). The strength of the intracranial self-stimulation is roughly correlated with the density of the catecholaminergic innervation. This anatomic-topographic similarity of the two regions suggested that the catecholaminergic systems either are themselves the neuronal substrate of positive reinforcement of behavior or are synaptically connected with this substrate. This hypothesis is supported by the following findings. 1. Transection of the medial forebrain bundle reduces or abolishes intracranial self-stimulation by electrodes *cranial to the lesion*. 2. When 6-hydroxydopamine, a substance that selectively *destroys* catecholaminergic neurons, is injected into the ventricles or into central catecholaminergic structures, intracranial self-stimulation is abolished. 3. *Drugs* that interfere with catecholamine metabolism or affect storage, release or uptake of catecholamines, and those that interact with the postsynaptic catecholamine receptors, influence intracranial self-stimulation (Fig. 6-30) [11, 25].

It is not yet clear whether the dopaminergic or the noradrenergic system contributes more to intracranial self-stimulation and thus to positive reinforcement of behavior. Many arguments suggest that both systems are activated simultaneously. The neuronal mechanisms that bring about the behavioral changes when the catecholaminergic systems are activated are essentially unknown. It has not been ruled out that the central catecholamines in many parts of the brain do not act as transmitters at all, but rather serve as neuromodulators (cf. p. 68) [50].

Electrophysiological studies have shown that the noradrenergic neurons of the **locus coeruleus** (Figs. 6-28 and 6-29 B) have an *inhibitory* action in almost all the CNS regions they innervate. Because these neurons are activated during **stress** of all kinds, it is thought that their action is twofold: (i) to depress the activity of CNS structures during stress, so that the CNS is protected from overexcitation, and (ii) to keep the excitability of the neurons at an intermediate level, in order to ensure optimal signal transmission. In this regard it is interesting that the afferents to the locus coeruleus come from parts of the brain that regulate affective behavior – particularly from structures in the limbic system, from the hypothalamus and from the mesencephalon. The morphological, biochemical and electrophysiological characteristics of the noradrenergic neurons of the locus coeruleus closely resemble those of peripheral noradrenergic neurons. In the cortex, many noradrenergic fibers from the lower brainstem appear to innervate the arterioles and capillaries. These noradrenergic neurons may participate in regulating blood flow through the cortex. One might thus be tempted to regard them as a central sympathetic system [24, 27].

Monoaminergic systems and psychotropic drugs. Humans are very vulnerable to psychiatric disorders. About 1% of the population suffer from schizophrenia, and about 15–30% exhibit one of the various forms of depression at some time in their lives [23]. The genesis of these and other mental illnesses, and the central-nervous disturbances underlying them, are largely unknown. The disturbances are probably associated with higher-order CNS structures, predominantly those of the *limbic system*. In the last three decades a great number of *drugs* have been used to treat these diseases. Studies of the effects of these compounds on human and animal behavior (psychopharmacology) and on their neuronal structures (neuropharmacology) have shown that most psychotropic drugs influence, directly or indirectly, the central monoaminergic systems. Therefore the monoaminergic systems are thought to be involved in many or most mental diseases; either they themselves are disturbed, or they play some as yet unknown role in originating and determining the nature of such diseases, or mediate the effects of drug therapy.

Anxiety states, mental tension and extreme irascibility – accompaniments of both neuroses and organic diseases – are often treated with **tranquilizers** of the *benzodiazepine type* (Valium, Librium). These drugs lower the metabolic rate of the monoaminergic systems. Their suppressant action is thought to reside particularly in a reduction of serotonin metabolism (cf. Fig. 6-30) and thus, under some circumstances, in a damping of the central negative-reinforcement system (Fig. 6-29 A).

Depressions of the most diverse origin may have in common an inadequate activatability of central noradrenergic systems. *Antidepressive* drugs of the tricyclic type (e.g., imipramine) potentiate the action of noradrenalin and serotonin at synapses, by inhibiting presynaptic uptake. Drugs that empty the central catecholamine stores often cause depression (e.g., reserpine; cf. Fig. 6-30).

One of the most puzzling mental diseases, and one of the most severe and variable in its symptoms, is **schizophrenia.** This disorder is classified as an endogenous psychosis, and is roughly characterized by the following primary symptoms: impaired associative thinking, inappropriate affect (mood), withdrawal from the outside world, deficient communication and autistic behavior. Additional (secondary) symptoms important for the differential diagnosis of schizophrenia are auditory hallucinations, delusions of grandeur and other kinds of delusion. The central-nervous disturbances underlying this disease are unknown, but presumably they are in the area of the complex mutual adjustments of *perception, memory* and the *inner world* and thus amount to a disturbance of communication between the neocortex and the limbic system. A special role is played by the central **dopaminergic system** (Figs. 6-28 and 6-29 B). *Neuroleptic drugs* in the phenothiazine (e.g., chlorpromazine) and butyrophenone (e.g., haloperidol) series, used throughout the world in the treatment of schizophrenia, block the central dopamine receptors (Fig. 6-30). Drugs that increase the rate of dopamine release – for example, those in the amphetamine group (Fig. 6-30) – can produce a psychosis with symptoms practically indistinguishable from those of schizophrenia, or they exacerbate existing or latent schizophrenia [5, 17, 23, 56].

6.7　References

Textbooks and Handbooks

1. APPENZELLER, O.: The Autonomic Nervous System. 2nd Ed. Amsterdam–Oxford: North Holland Publishing Co. New York: American Elsevier Publishing Co. 1976
2. BÜLBRING, E., BRADING, A.F., JONES, A.W., TOMITA, T. (Eds.): Smooth Muscle. Baltimore: Williams & Wilkins 1970
3. BURNSTOCK, G., COSTA, A.: Adrenergic Neurons. London: Chapman and Hall 1975
4. CANNON, W.B.: The Wisdom of the Body. 2nd Ed. New York: W.W. Norton & Co., Inc. 1939
5. COOPER, J.R., BLOOM, F.E., ROTH, R.H.: The Biochemical Basis of Neuropharmacology. 3rd Ed. Oxford: University Press 1978
6. DARWIN, C.: The Expression of the Emotions in Man and Animal. London: John Murray 1872
7. DAVSON, H., SEGAL, M.B.: Introduction to Physiology, Vol. 3, Chapter 4, "Control mechanisms in the alimentary process" pp. 276–403. London: Academic Press, New York: Grune & Stratton 1976
8. FOLKOW, B., NEIL, E.: Circulation. New York–London–Toronto–Oxford: University Press 1971
9. GABELLA, G.: Structure of the Autonomic Nervous System. London: Chapman and Hall 1976
10. GILMAN, A.G., GOODMAN, L.S., GILMAN, A.: Pharmacological Basis of Therapeutics. 6th Ed. New York: Macmillan 1980
11. HALL, R.D., BLOOM, F.E., OLDS, J.: Neuronal and Neurochemical Substrates of Reinforcement. Neuroscience Research Program Bulletin. Cambridge, Mass.: MIT Press 1977
12. Handbook of Physiology, Section 7: Endocrinology, Vol. VI: Adrenal Gland. American Physiological Society, Washington, D.C. 1975
13. HAYMAKER, W., ANDERSON, E., NAUTA, W.J.H. (Eds.): The Hypothalamus. Springfield, Ill.: Ch.C. Thomas 1969
14. HESS, W.R.: Diencephalon. Autonomic and Extrapyramidal Functions. New York: Grune & Stratton 1954
15. ISAACSON, R.L.: The Limbic System. New York–London: Plenum Press 1974
16. ISAACSON, R.L., PRIBRAM, K.H.: The Hippocampus. Vol. 1: Structure and Development. Vol. 2: Neurophysiology and Behavior. New York–London: Plenum Press 1975
17. IVERSEN, S.D., IVERSEN, L.L.: Behavioral Pharmacology. New York–Oxford: Oxford University Press 1977
18. JOHNSON, R.H., SPALDING, J.M.K.: Disorders of the Autonomic Nervous System. Oxford–London–Edinburgh–Melbourne: Blackwell Scientific Publications 1974
19. LEVI, L. (Ed.): Emotions. Their Parameters and Measurement. New York: Raven Press 1975
20. LIVINGSTON, K.E., HORNYKIEWICZ, O. (Eds.): Limbic Mechanisms. New York–London: Plenum Press 1978
21. LIVINGSTON, W.K.: Pain Mechanisms. New York–London: Plenum Press 1976
22. MASTERS, W.H., JOHNSON, V.E.: Human Sexual Response. Boston: Little, Brown and Co. 1966
23. NICHOLI, A.M., Jr. (Ed.): The Harvard Guide to Modern Psychiatry. Cambridge, Mass.–London: The Belknap Press of Harvard University Press 1978
24. NIEUWENHUYS, R., VOOGD, J., VAN HUIJZEN, CHR.: The Human Central Nervous System. Berlin–Heidelberg–New York: Springer 1978
25. OLDS, J.: Drives and Reinforcements. Behavioral Studies of Hypothalamic Functions. New York: Raven Press 1977
26. REICHLIN, S., BALDESSARINI, R.J., MARTIN, J.B.: The Hypothalamus. Research Publication: Association for Research in Nervous and Mental Disease. Vol. 56. New York: Raven Press 1978

Research Reports and Reviews

27. AMARAL, D.G., SINNAMON, H.M.: The locus coeruleus: neurobiology of a central noradrenergic nucleus. Progr. in Neurobiology, 9, 147–196 (1977)
28. BARD, P.: Control of systemic blood vessels. In: MOUNTCASTLE, V.B. (Ed.): Medical Physiology, 12th Ed. St. Louis: C.V. Mosby Co., pp. 169–171 (1968)
29. BEACH, F.A.: Cerebral and hormonal control of reflexive mechanism involved in copulatory behavior. Physiol. Rev. 47, 289–316 (1967)
30. BELL, C.: Autonomic nervous control of reproduction: circulatory and other factors. Pharmacol. Rev. 24, 657–736 (1972)
31. BORS, E., COMARR, A.E.: Neurological disturbances of sexual function with special reference to 529 patients with spinal cord injury. Urol. Survey, 10, 191–222 (1960)
32. BURNSTOCK, G.: Purinergic nerves. Pharmacol. Rev. 24, 509–581 (1972)
33. FLEMING, W.W., McPHILLIPS, J.J., WESTFALL, D.P.: Postjunctional supersensitivity and subsensitivity of excitable tissues to drugs. Rev. Physiol. Biochem. & Pharmacol. 68, 55–119 (1973)
34. FURCHGOTT, R.F.: The classification of adrenoceptors (adrenergic receptors). An evaluation from the standpoint of receptor theory. In: BLASCHKO, H., MUSCHOLL, E. (Eds.): Handbook of Experimental Pharmacology, Vol. 33 "Catecholamines" pp. 283–335. Berlin–Heidelberg–New York: Springer 1972
35. FURNESS, J.B., COSTA, M.: The adrenergic innervation of the gastrointestinal tract. Ergeb. Physiol. 69, 1–51 (1974)
36. GLOOR, P.: Temporal lobe epilepsy: its possible contribution to the understanding of the functional significance of the amygdala and its interaction with neocortical-temporal mechanisms. In: ELEFTHERIOU, B.E. (Ed.): The Neurobiology of the Amygdala, pp. 423–457. New York: Plenum Press 1972
37. GROAT, W.C. de: Nervous control of the urinary bladder of the cat. Brain Res. 87, 201–211 (1975)
38. HAYWARD, J.N.: Functional and morphological aspects of hypothalamic neurons. Physiol. Rev. 57, 574–658 (1977)
39. KLÜVER, H., BUCY, P.C.: Preliminary analysis of functions of the temporal lobe in monkeys. Arch. Neurol. Psychiat. 42, 979–1000 (1939)
40. KOIZUMI, K., BROOKS, C.M.: The integration of autonomic reactions: a discussion of autonomic reflexes, their control and their association with somatic reactions. Ergebn. Physiol. 67, 1–68 (1972)
41. KUHN, R.A.: Functional capacity of the isolated human spinal cord. Brain 73, 1–51 (1950)
41. KURU, M.: Nervous control of micturition. Physiol. Rev. 45, 425–495 (1965)
43. LANGER, S.Z.: Presynaptic receptors and their role in the regulation of transmitter release. Br. J. Pharmacol. 60, 481–497 (1977)
44. LEVITZKI, A.: Catecholamine receptors. Rev. Physiol. Biochem. Pharmacol. 82, 1–26 (1978)
45. LISANDER, B.: Factors influencing the autonomic component of the defence reaction. Acta physiol. scand. Suppl. 351, 1–42 (1970)
46. LOH, L., NATHAN, P.W.: Painful peripheral states and sympathetic blocks. J. Neurol. Neurosurg. & Psychiatry 41, 664–671 (1978)
47. MacLEAN, P.D.: Psychosomatic disease and the "visceral brain". Recent developments bearing on the Papez theory of emotion. Psychosom. Med. 11, 338–353 (1949)
48. MacLEAN, P.D.: The triune brain, emotion and scientific bias. In: Intensive Study Program in the Neurosciences, Neurosciences Research Program. Chapter 23, p. 336–349. New York: Rockefeller University Press 1970
49. MOORE, R.Y., BLOOM, F.E.: Central catecholamine neuron systems: anatomy and physiology of the dopamine systems. Ann. Rev. Neurosci. 1, 129–169 (1978)
50. MOORE, R.Y., BLOOM, F.E.: Central catecholamine neuron systems: anatomy and physiology of the norepinephrine and epinephrine systems. Ann. Rev. Neurosci. 2, 113–168 (1979)
51. NAUTA, J.: The problem of the frontal lobe: a reinterpretation. J. Psychiat. Res. 8, 167–181 (1971)
52. NISHI, S.: Cellular pharmacology of ganglionic transmission. In: NARAHASHI, T., BIANCHI, C.P. (Eds.): Advances in General and Cellular Pharmacology, pp. 179–245. New York–London: Plenum Press 1976
53. RUSHMER, R.F.: Structure and Function of the Cardiovascular System. Philadelphia–London–Toronto: Saunders 1972
54. SATO, A., SCHMIDT, R.F.: Somatosympathetic reflexes: afferent fibers, central pathways, discharge characteristics. Physiol. Rev. 53, 916–947 (1973)
55. SCHUSTER, M.M., MENDELOFF, A.I.: Motor action of rectum and anal sphincters in continence and defecation. In: Handbook of Physiology Section 6: Alimentary Canal, Volume IV: Motility. American Physiological Society, Washington, D.C. pp. 2121–2145 (1968)
56. SNYDER, S.H.: Catecholamines as mediators of drug effects in schizophrenia. In: SCHMITT, F.O., WORDEN, F.G. (Eds.): The Neurosciences, Third Study Program, pp. 721–732. Cambridge, Mass.–London: MIT Press 1974
57. STARKE, K.: Regulation of noradrenaline release by presynaptic receptor systems. Rev. Physiol. Biochem. Pharmacol. 77, 1–124 (1977)
58. UNGERSTEDT, U.: Stereotaxic mapping of the monoamine pathways in the rat brain. Acta physiol. scand. Suppl. 367, 1–48 (1971)

7 Integrative Functions of the Nervous System

R. F. SCHMIDT

7.1 General Physiology of the Cerebral Cortex

Functional Histology of the Cerebral Cortex

Neurons in the cerebral cortex, cortical layers. The cerebral cortex is a thin, much-folded layer of neuronal tissue, the *surface area* of which is about 2200 cm^2 (corresponding to a square measuring 47 cm × 47 cm). Its *thickness* varies in different parts of the cerebrum, between 1.3 and 4.5 mm. Its volume is 600 cm^3. It is composed of **10^9 to 10^{10} neurons** plus a large but unknown number of glial cells [5, 6, 18, 44]. Within the cortex, layers in which cell bodies predominate alternate with others made up chiefly of axons, so that the freshly cut cortex has a striated appearance. In the typical cortex **6 layers** can be distinguished on the basis of the shape and arrangement of the cells; some of the layers can be subdivided into two or more sublayers (Figs. 7-1, 7-3).

More than 90% of the cerebral cortex is of this *basic 6-layered type,* which in phylogeny first appears with the mammals and therefore is called **neocortex:** because of its structure it is also called **isocortex.** The phylogenetically older **allocortex** has a different structure. It includes the *archipallium* (fascia dentata, Ammon's horn, subiculum), the *paleopallium* (prepiriform region, periamygdalar region, entorhinal region) and the *cortical derivatives* claustrum and amygdala [5, 6, 9, 16].
The layers in the **isocortex,** counting from the surface down, are as follows (Figs. 7-1, 7-3):

I. Molecular layer (plexiform layer). Fibers are abundant here, but there are few cells. The fibers form a dense plexus tangential to the surface.

II. External granular layer. Here small neurons varying widely in shape are closely packed, with small pyramidal cells (named for their shape) below them. The predominant orientation of the nerve fibers is tangential to the surface.

III. External pyramidal layer. The chief elements here are pyramidal cells of intermediate size, with the larger cells in the deeper parts of the layer.

IV. Internal granular layer. A loose array of small neurons of various sizes is penetrated by bundles of densely packed fibers tangential to the surface.

V. Internal pyramidal layer. Basically composed of medium-sized and large pyramidal cells, especially large in the precentral gyrus (Betz's giant pyramidal cells). Like all pyramidal cells these have long apical dendrites, extending as far as the molecular layer, whereas the basal dendrites spread out more or less tangential to the surface.

VI. Fusiform-cell layer. Predominantly spindle-shaped neurons. The inner part of this layer (VI b) merges with the white matter.

On the basis of the *positions of the cell bodies* in one or another of these layers of the isocortex **three classes of neurons** can be distinguished: the **pyramidal cells,** the **granule** or **stellate cells,** and the **spindle cells.** The first two of these classes comprise many subclasses. Some of the important connections of these neurons, with one another and with other neurons, are discussed in the context of Fig. 7-4.

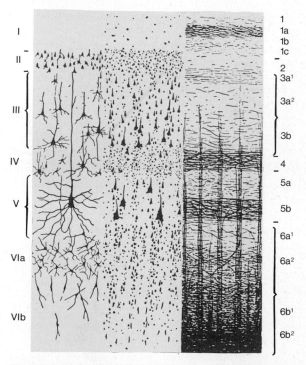

Fig. 7-1. Semidiagrammatic representation of the layered structure of the cerebral cortex, based on Golgi staining *(left),* Nissl staining *(middle)* and a myelin-sheath preparation (right). The layers are numbered from the surface down. Two common numbering systems are shown. Layers described in the text. (After BRODMANN and VOGT)

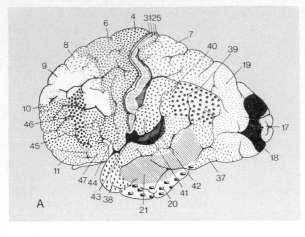

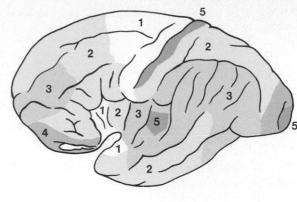

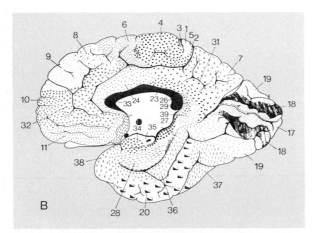

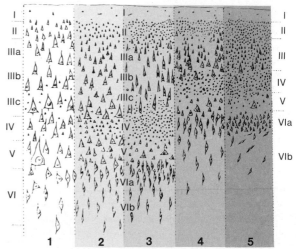

Fig. 7-2. Map of the cytoarchitectonic areas of the human cortex according to Brodmann. The different areas are identified by different symbols, and their numbers are indicated

Fig. 7-3. Basic types of neocortical cytoarchitecture *(bottom)* and their distribution in the cerebral cortex *(top).* 2, 3, 4: homotypical cortex; 1, 5: heterotypical cortex, of which 1 is agranular and 5 is granular. (After VON ECONOMO)

Cortical maps. Although the basic structural pattern of the isocortex is uniform, there can be considerable local variation. On the basis of cortical **cytoarchitectonics** alone – that is, the density, arrangement and shape of the neurons – Brodmann subdivided the cerebral cortex into about 50 areas (Fig. 7-2). Other maps are still more detailed (VON ECONOMO and VOGT [5, 6]). To a certain extent these histologically defined areas match the areas to which particular functions are ascribed on the basis of physiological experiments and clinical observations. Examples will be presented with reference to Fig. 7-3.

Differences in the arrangement of the nerve fibers – that is, **myeloarchitectonics** – have also been represented in cortical maps. On the whole, these are consistent with the cytoarchitectonic maps. Other features of cortical structure also vary in ways that can be used to characterize the different areas of cortex; these include the structure of the vascular system **(angioarchitectonics)**, the arrangement, nature and shape of the glial cells **(gliar-**

chitectonics)**,** and the chemical substances such as enzymes and transmitters that are found in the cells **(chemoarchitectonics)** [5, 6, 9].

Homotypical and heterotypical isocortex. VON ECONOMO groups the cytoarchitectonic cortical areas into *five basic types* (Fig. 7-3). The types 2, 3 and 4 in the lower diagram of the figure contain (to varying extents) all 6 layers, and therefore are called **homotypical.** By contrast, in mature cortex of Types 1 and 5 fewer than 6 layers are clearly identifiable; the cortex is **heterotypical.** In the *heterotypical cortex* of Type 1 there are no distinct granular layers (II and IV), whereas in Type 5 these layers are especially conspicuous, and the pyramidal-cell layers (III and IV) are very poorly developed. Therefore Type 1 is called **agranular cortex** and Type 5, **granular cortex** or **koniocortex.**

Agranular cortex is found particularly in regions where *cortical efferents* originate, for example, in the precentral gyrus and rostral to it (Fig. 7-3). It can thus be regarded as the **prototype of the motor cortex.** Conversely, the **granular** or koniocortex is found especially in areas in which the major sensory pathways terminate. It can therefore be classified as the **prototype of the sensory cortex.** The homotypical cortex, which in humans occupies a far larger area than the two heterotypical cortices together, in collaboration with subcortical structures participates chiefly in those complex processes that are termed **mental and psychological processes** in the broadest sense, which are subject to detailed investigation only in humans (cf. Fig. 7-25).

Fiber connections in the neocortex. The afferent and efferent connections of the cerebral cortex, in turn, can be assigned to a few basic types (cf. Fig. 7-4). The **cortical efferents** (corticofugal fibers) serve (i) as **projection fibers** to subcortical structures (for example, the corticospinal tract and corticopontine and corticothalamic pathways), (ii) as **association fibers,** passing to neighboring and more distant cortical areas in the *same hemisphere,* and (iii) as **commissural fibers,** providing a link to cortical areas in the *contralateral hemisphere.* The great majority of commissural fibers cross in the corpus callosum (cf. p. 161). They are very numerous; for example, in the cat there are about 700 000 fibers per square millimeter of corpus callosum.
The **cortical afferents** (corticopetal fibers) comprise both the *association and commissural fibers* from other parts of the cortex, mentioned above, and the **thalamocortical fibers,** the dominant if not **only afferents from subcortical structures.** (There is some evidence that corticopetal fibers from reticular structures reach the cortex with no thalamic relay, but these findings are still controversial).

Cortical circuits. On p. 103 the motor cortex was used to introduce the concept of histological and functional *cortical columns.* According to this concept, information processing in the cerebral cortex is essentially based on circuits arranged perpendicular to the surface [48]; it should be kept in mind, however, that the analysis of such cortical circuits is not nearly as advanced as, for example, that of certain circuits in the spinal cord (Figs. 5-7, 8, 10 and 11) or cerebellar cortex (Fig. 5-18, p. 98), so that they can be described only in very general terms (Fig. 7-4).

At a very schematic level, the arrangement of axons in the cortex provides a basis for distinguishing **four groups of neurons.** The first comprises cells with axons that leave the cortex as corticofugal fibers (see above; cells 1 to 5 in Fig. 7-4). A second group has short axons that terminate in the immediate vicinity of the soma (cells 8 to 10 in Fig. 7-4). The cells in the third group send their axons to the surface of the cortex, with branches to one or more cortical layers in passing (cell 11 in Fig. 7-4). The axons in the last group of neurons (cell 12 in Fig. 7-4) are almost all oriented horizontally.
Of the **corticopetal fibers** (on the left in Fig. 7-4), the *thalamocortical fibers in the direct sensory pathways* (specific thalamocortical afferents) end in a dense plexus in Layer IV (internal granular layer), sending no collaterals to other layers of the cortex (fibers a and b in Fig. 7-4). Other thalamocortical fibers, like fiber c in the figure, end in Layer I after giving off many collater-

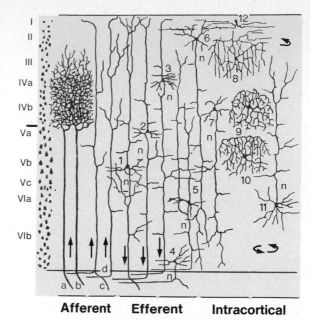

Afferent   Efferent   Intracortical

Fig. 7-4. Schematic representation of the neurons involved in cortical circuits. The fibers entering the cortex are labelled a to d; the origin of these afferents is discussed in the text. Neurons 1 to 5 are efferent neurons, the axons of which leave the cortex. The axons of the remaining cell types end intracortically. The neurites (axons) of the cells are labelled n. (After LORENTE DE NÓ in [6])

als. These fibers are often called "nonspecific." The *association and commissural fibers* (d in Fig. 7-4) also traverse all the layers. Their endings, however, lie mostly in the upper four layers, II and III in particular.

With regard to the **direction of information processing** in the cortex, given the termination regions of the afferent fibers a to d in Fig. 7-4, a simplified view of the situation is that the **superficial layers I to V serve chiefly in the reception and processing** of corticopetal information. In particular, the internal granular layer (IV), especially conspicuous in the granular cortex of the direct sensory projection areas (Fig. 7-3), seems to be a major end station for corticopetal afferents (Fig. 7-4, left). Conversely, the cell bodies of the most important *cortical efferents* tend to lie in the deeper layers (cells 1, 2, 4, 5 in Fig. 7-4) – for example, the pyramidal cells in Layer V. Thus on the whole the **deep layers V and VI** can be regarded as the **sites of origin of the cortical efferents.** Processing of the information flowing into the cortex thus occurs in **circuits** the essential organization of which is vertical, from the cortical surface to the depths (concept of functional cortical columns [48]). Transverse connections, horizontal to the surface (neuron 12 in Fig. 7-4), seem to play a minor role within the cortex. Transverse (horizontal) information transmission seems to be performed mainly by the association fibers.

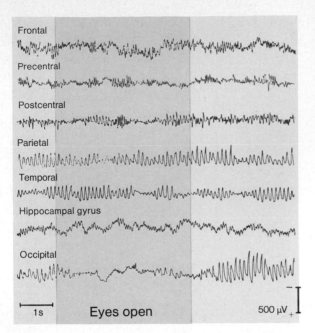

Fig. 7-5. Electrocorticograms of a resting, waking human, recorded from the indicated cortical areas with bipolar silver-chloride brush electrodes. The basic α rhythm predominates in the occipital and temporal cortex and all the parietal cortex except for the postcentral gyrus. More rapid activity is found in the more frontal regions, with a relatively pure β rhythm in the precentral gyrus. The occipital α rhythm is blocked by opening the eyes (cf. also Fig. 7-8). (From PENFIELD and JASPER [20])

This description of cortical-neuron connectivity leaves most questions open [4, 48]. There is no doubt, for example, that the regular layering of the cortex (Fig. 7-1) and its variation in different cortical areas, with certain layers strongly emphasized in certain areas (Figs. 7-2, 7-3), is of great functional significance; but at present the actual relationships are insufficiently understood. Although it is striking that the granular cortex predominates in the sensory areas, whereas in the motor areas agranular cortex with thick pyramidal-cell layers is found, it is not yet possible to draw more than the few rather general conclusions mentioned above from this comparison. Progress in this regard can be expected to result mainly from the further application of electrophysiological micromethods (see below) and the combination of these with histological procedures.

Electrophysiological Correlates of Cortical Activity

Properties of cortical neurons. Like motoneurons, neurons in the neocortex and hippocampus have been studied by intracellular recording with microelectrodes, and the **biophysical properties** of the cortical neurons have been found to be entirely comparable with those of the motoneurons. For example, the resting potentials of large and small pyramidal cells in the motor cortex of the cat are –60 to –80 mV, and the amplitude of the **action potential,** with a duration of 0.5–2 ms, is 60–100 mV. The action potentials are generated at the axon hillock of the cell, spreading

from there not only to the periphery but also over the soma and dendrites. **Membrane time constants and resistances,** insofar as they have been studied, are also of orders of magnitude commensurate with those of spinal neurons. Membrane depolarizations induced synaptically or by applied current, if they exceed the threshold, lead to repetitive discharge at frequencies depending on the degree of depolarization; here, again, the response closely parallels that of motoneurons. Thus the bioelectric phenomena observed in cortical neurons are presumably based on the same mechanisms as those in the neurons of lower structures. To the extent that differences in the bioelectrical properties have been noted, they can in most cases be ascribed to variations in geometrical structure [13, 18].

Synaptic activity of cortical neurons. As compared with the motoneuronal postsynaptic potentials illustrated in detail in Chapter 3 (cf. Figs. 3-8 and 3-9, pp. 59, 61), the cortical potentials are all longer in duration. **Excitatory postsynaptic potentials** often have a rise time of several milliseconds and a fall time of 10–30 ms, whereas **inhibitory postsynaptic potentials** usually last still longer, 70–150 ms. Spontaneous excitatory postsynaptic potentials can occur singly in cortical cells, but frequently appear in groups that can summate to form large depolarizing waves. Often records from a given neuron reveal excitatory postsynaptic potentials differing in rise time; these probably arise in synaptic structures at different distances from the recording electrode. Inhibitory postsynaptic potentials are less common than excitatory potentials in the spontaneously active cortex, and those that occur are of smaller amplitude. By contrast, after the activation of corticopetal sensory pathways large, long-lasting inhibitory postsynaptic potentials are frequently recorded, either in isolation or following excitatory synaptic potentials. The frequency of the **cortical impulse activity elicited by postsynaptic potentials** is low, even in waking animals. It is usually below 10 Hz, and not uncommonly below 1 Hz; the resting potentials of cortical cells usually fluctuate in the range 3–10 mV below threshold [31].

Electrocorticograms. When one records between two electrodes laid on the surface of the cerebral cortex, or between one such electrode and a reference electrode some distance away (e. g., on the earlobe), in humans (Fig. 7-5) and other vertebrates continuous *potential fluctuations* are observed, called the **electrocorticogram (ECoG).** Their frequencies are between 1 and 50 Hz, and their amplitudes are of the order of 100 µV or more (Fig. 7-5).

Under normal conditions **frequency and amplitude of the ECoG** depend fundamentally on the species of animal, the recording site (Fig. 7-5) and the degree of wakefulness. In **humans** in the awake but relaxed state the predominant activity is waves at 8–13 Hz, most pronounced over the occipital cortex; these are called *α waves.* When the eyes are opened (see the bottom trace in Fig. 7-5) the α waves disappear **(α blockade)** and are replaced by higher-frequency *β* **waves** (14–30 Hz) of lower amplitude. (For further phenomenological details see p. 151.)

Origin of the ECoG. The ECoG essentially reflects the **postsynaptic activity of the cortical neurons,** not the conducted impulse activity of these cells nor the activity of cortical glial cells. This conclusion is derived from many experiments in which the ECoG was recorded from cortical neurons with intracellular and extracellular electrodes simultaneously.

Simplifying matters, we can say that a *positive potential fluctuation* on the cortical surface is caused either by excitatory postsynaptic potentials in the deeper layers of the cortex or by inhibitory postsynaptic potentials in the superficial layers; conversely, a *negative potential fluctuation* is elicited by synaptic activity of the opposite kind at the various depths [31].

The *rhythmic activity of the cortex,* especially the α rhythm, is induced largely by the activity of deeper structures, especially the **thalamus** (Fig. 7-6). Unilateral ablation of the thalamus or deafferentation of the cortex (to isolate an area of cortex) causes the α waves to disappear ipsilaterally (Fig. 7-6 A, B). On the other hand, decortication leaves the rhythmic activity of the thalamus practically unchanged. Intrathalamic recordings indicate the existence of multiple **thalamic pacemakers** (Fig. 7-6 C), which by way of appropriate excitatory and inhibitory connections are capable of initiating and sustaining rhythmic activity. Their activity in turn is modified by thalamopetal influences. **Reticular structures** in particular have a *rhythm-generating (synchronizing)* and *rhythm-inhibiting (desynchronizing)* action on the thalamus, as described in greater detail in the discussion of the sleeping/waking cycle, Section 7.2 [1].

Evoked potentials. The electrical potential fluctuations recorded in the central nervous system as a response to the stimulation of receptors, peripheral nerves, sensory pathways or nuclei, or other central structures (e.g., nuclei, tracts, cortical areas) are called **evoked potentials** (Fig. 7-7). For example, after peripheral stimulation slow, positive-negative potential deflections can be recorded from the sensorimotor areas of the cortex (SI, SII; Fig. 7-7 B, D). These are called **primary evoked potentials.** Such potentials

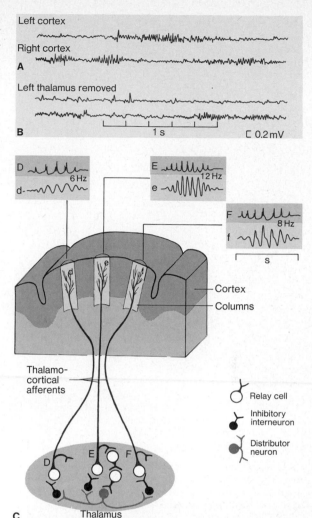

Fig. 7-6 A–F. Thalamic origin of the α rhythm. **A** Records of the electrocorticogram from the left and right motor cortex of the cat. **B** Like **A,** except that the left thalamus has been removed by suction. The rhythmic basic activity (α spindles under barbiturate anesthesia) has disappeared on the left but is unchanged on the right. **C** Model of the connections of thalamic pacemaker areas with the cortex (projection of D, E, F to d, e, f) and with one another. The individual areas are linked to one another by "distributor neurons." The duration and intensity of the inhibitory feedback within the individual pacemaker groups determines the basic rhythm of thalamic discharge (**D, E, F,** upper records) and of the electrocorticograms d, e, f thus induced (lower records). (After ANDERSEN and ANDERSSON [1, 31])

can be used, for example, to explore the somatotopic relationships between cortex and periphery, or to study the relation between the intensity of a peripheral stimulus and the cortical response. Evoked potentials can also provide evidence about the links among structures within the central nervous system – for example, the cortical association and commissural fibers [8, 9, 30].

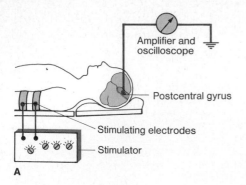

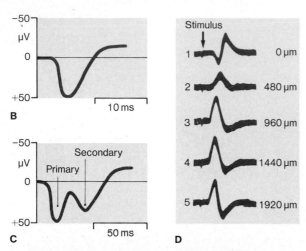

Fig. 7-7 A–D. Cortical evoked potentials recorded in human (**A–C**) and the cat (**D**). **A** Experimental arrangement. Instead of the electrical skin stimulus chosen here other stimulus modalities (mechanical, thermal) could be used. Recording is done with an EEG electrode on the scalp. **B** Primary evoked potential from the associated projection area in the postcentral gyrus. **C** Primary evoked and secondary evoked potential. Note the different time scales in **B** and **C**. **D** Cortical evoked potential recorded with a microelectrode. As the microelectrode is advanced to the indicated depths below the surface of the cortex (record 1, 0 μm) in steps of 480 μm (records 2–5), the potential changes polarity and latency. [B-D modified from Th. C. RUCH et al.: Neurophysiology, 2nd ed., W. B. Saunders: Philadelphia and London, 1965]

With regard to the **mechanism of origin of evoked potentials,** there is general agreement that they, like the waves of the electrocorticogram, basically reflect the *synaptic activity* rather than the impulse activity of neurons. For example, the change in an evoked potential observed as a microelectrode is advanced from the cortical surface to deeper layers (Fig. 7-7 D) – that is, the disappearance of the initial positive component in favor of an initial negativity with short latency – shows that the neurons of the external granular layer in particular are depolarized during this time (owing to excitation by afferent input), as would be expected from the discussion on p. 147.

Electrodes on the scalp of a **waking human** normally do not reveal single evoked potentials, because they are not sufficiently distinct from the spontaneous activity in the electroencephalogram (cf. p. 151). But if the peripheral stimuli are repeated several times and the subsequent potential fluctuations fed into a computer for averaging, the **averaged evoked potentials** stand

out clearly from the background of spontaneous activity. This method provides evoked potentials that can be used for clinical-diagnostic purposes. For example, they give an objective measure, and a means of monitoring the progress, of certain forms of hearing impairment. The evoked potentials produced by conditioning (expectancy potential; p. 107) and accompanying the initiation of voluntary movements (readiness potential; Fig. 5-27, p. 107) are also revealed only by the averaging of many individual responses.

Cortical DC potentials. Normally a maintained potential difference can be measured between the cortical surface and the white matter below it, or between the surface and a distant reference electrode; it amounts to several millivolts (surface negative). This **cortical DC or steady potential,** however, also exhibits *fluctuations,* though their frequency is considerably lower than that of the ECoG. For example, when one falls asleep the cortical surface becomes more positive; conversely, both arousal reactions and increases in activity of an already wakeful animal are accompanied by increased surface negativity. Local or general convulsive discharge and disturbances of the respiratory-gas supply (O_2 deficiency, CO_2 excess) also cause characteristic changes in the DC potential, the time course and polarity of which can be used for prognoses about the reversibility of cortical damage. Unfortunately, **clinical-diagnostic application** of these findings is nearly impossible, for the many sources of error (primarily electrode potentials of unknown origin) make the routine recording of DC potentials impracticable [13, 31, 43].

As to the **origin of the cortical DC potentials,** there is as yet no consistent interpretation. The voltage shifts that appear, for example, in association with the sleeping/waking cycle are very probably based on changes in the membrane potentials of cortical neurons. The other causes of cortical voltage changes listed above also probably involve neuronal structures, but other candidate generators are potential differences at the blood-brain barrier, the meninges or the glial cells [13, 31, 43].

The Electroencephalogram (EEG)

Definition, mechanism of origin. Continuous potential fluctuations are recordable not only from the surface of the exposed cortex (electrocorticogram; see above), but also from the *intact scalp* over the skull. The latter are called the **electroencephalogram,** abbreviated **EEG.** Hans Berger was the first to discover that it is possible to record the electrical activity of the human brain in this way. Between 1929 and 1938 he laid the foundations for the clinical and experimental application of this method. The **recording conditions** correspond basically to those for recording the elec-

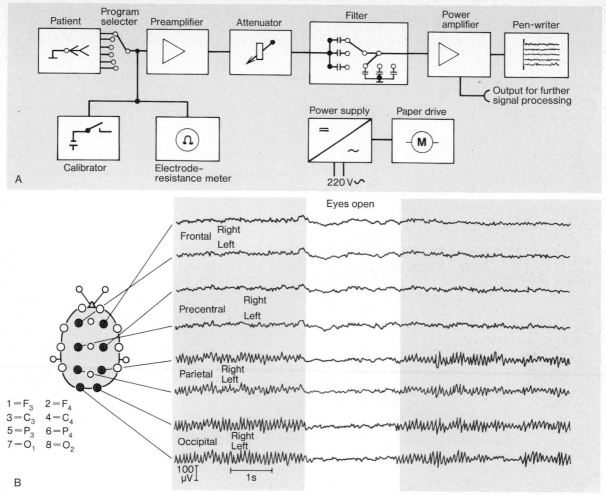

Fig. 7-8. A Block diagram of an electroencephalograph; an instrument has up to 16 recording channels in parallel, only one of which is shown here. **B** Normal EEG of a resting, waking human. Simultaneous eight-channel monopolar recording from the indicated sites on the skull. Opening the eyes blocks the α rhythm. Compare with Fig. 7-5. (After RICHARD JUNG)

trocorticogram. However, because of the electrical resistance of the tissues between the surface of the brain and the electrodes the amplitude of the potential fluctuations is reduced, and because the recording electrodes are further away from the potential generators (so that the recording is from a somewhat larger cortical area) the more rapid potential fluctuations are "averaged out." Therefore the EEG is smaller in amplitude than the ECoG, and somewhat lower in frequency. The mechanisms underlying the EEG, however, are those discussed with regard to the ECoG (p. 149).

Recording and interpreting the EEG. The recording of the EEG is a routine procedure used internationally for neurological diagnosis. To enable comparison, therefore, the positions of the recording electrodes (Fig. 7-8 B, left) and the recording conditions (paper speed, time constants and filters in the amplifier sys-

tem) have been **extensively standardized** [23]. The EEG is recorded either with a **bipolar** arrangement, between two recording electrodes placed on the skull, or with a monopolar arrangement, between a *recording* electrode on the scalp and a distant *reference* electrode (on the earlobe, for instance; Fig. 7-8). The record is **interpreted** primarily on the basis of the frequency, amplitude, shape, distribution and duration of occurrence of the waves contained in the EEG. This analysis can be done "by hand" or with the assistance of analog and digital devices. An example is given in Fig. 7-9. For further details the reader is referred to the literature [23].

Forms of the EEG; diagnostic significance. In the discussion of the ECoG (Fig. 7-5) mention was made of the fact that in a *healthy adult* resting with eyes closed the **basic α rhythm** (alpha waves, 8–13 Hz, averaging 10 Hz) predominates and is especially prominent in

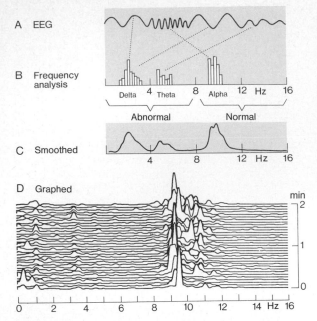

Fig. 7-9 A–D. Computer-assisted analysis of the EEG. Four-second-long sections of an EEG record (**A**) are broken down electronically into their frequency components (Fourier analysis, **B**) and after smoothing (**C**) are displayed in sequence from bottom to top (**D**). The resulting picture of an "EEG landscape" gives a graphic impression of both the frequency components in the record (plotted from left to right; **D** represents the α rhythm of a normal subject), and their variation in time (from *bottom* to *top*). [From BICKFORD, R.: J. Altered States Consciousness 1, 49 (1973)]

the occipital area (*synchronized EEG*, Fig. 7-8). When the eyes are opened, other sensory stimuli impinge, or mental activity is performed, the α waves vanish (**alpha blockade**) and higher-frequency β **waves** (beta waves, 14–30 Hz, averaging 20 Hz) of smaller amplitude appear; the EEG becomes *desynchronized* (Fig. 7-8). Other, distinctly slower waves of larger amplitude have been identified (Fig. 7-10, left), for example, the ϑ **waves** (theta waves, 4–7 Hz, averaging 6 Hz) and the δ **waves** (delta waves, 0.5–3.5 Hz, averaging 3 Hz), but they are not normally observed in a *waking adult*. The EEG of *children and juveniles,* by contrast,

is slower and more irregular, exhibiting δ waves even in the waking state. Otherwise, slow waves are observed in a healthy person only during sleep (cf. p. 155).

With regard to the *clinical significance* of the EEG, only a few examples will be given here [23, 26]. The records on the right in Fig. 7-10 illustrate a number of *seizure potentials* such as appear in epileptics, in particular. Other general changes, such as *slowing and irregularity in the recorded curves,* accompany diffuse organic brain diseases or follow cerebral trauma or metabolic intoxication (coma). Tumors, too, often produce (local) changes in the EEG. It should also be noted that many medications, especially psychoactive drugs, affect the EEG. A general extinction of the EEG *(isoelectric or flat EEG)* is increasingly being taken as a *criterion for death* in cases of doubt. That is, when modern methods of resuscitation succeed in overcoming an interruption of circulation and breathing, but the patient neither regains consciousness nor begins to breathe spontaneously, one suspects that the cerebral cortex and brainstem have been irreversibly damaged by the ischemia (deficient blood supply). This state of **brain death** is distinguished not only by the symptoms just described (flat EEG, unconsciousness, no spontaneous breathing) but also by the absence of a light response and the mydriasis (dilation) of the pupils and by areflexia, atony and unresponsiveness.

Cortex and brainstem have *low ischemia tolerance.* The maximal duration of ischemia that can be survived – the **resuscitation** or **structure-maintenance limit** – is only 3–8 min in the case of the cortex and 7–10 min for the brainstem. In other organs the resuscitation limit is considerably longer. For instance, it is 90 minutes for the myocardium, and 150 minutes for the kidney. Therefore these organs can be kept alive by resuscitation techniques even after brain death has occurred, so that in certain circumstances, especially when the brain death is the consequence of an accident to a healthy young person, they can be used for **organ transplants.**

Cerebral Activity, Metabolism and Blood Flow

The brain consumes about 50 ml O_2 per minute, roughly 20% of the total oxygen requirement of a resting person. Accordingly, the brain must be provided with around 15% of the cardiac output at rest, although it accounts for only 2.5% of the total body weight. But the rate of perfusion is by no means uniform in all parts of the brain. For one thing, far less

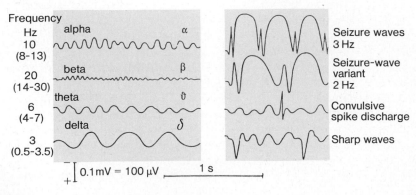

Fig. 7-10. Main forms of the EEG. On the left the different types of wave that can appear in a healthy person. On the right examples of seizure potentials, as recorded primarily from epileptics. The characteristic sequence of rapid and slow fluctuations is called a "spike-and-wave" complex. (After RICHARD JUNG)

blood flows through the white matter than through the cerebral cortex; for another, even the different parts of the cortex almost always receive at least slightly different amounts of blood. At rest (Fig. 7-11 A, B), with a typical α-wave EEG, *much more blood flows through the frontal regions than through the other cortical areas.* Slightly painful stimulation of the skin (C) causes the perfusion maxima to shift to the region of the parietal cortex – that is, to the primary sensory area. (At the same time there is a slight increase in overall blood flow through the brain.) The perfusion pattern changes in the same direction, even more distinctly, when the contralateral hand is actively opened

and closed (D). Reading aloud (E) results in a Z-shaped distribution of perfusion maxima, extending into the visual regions of the occipital lobe [33].

The regional changes in blood flow appear to be predominantly under **metabolic control.** "Metabolic" maps obtained by monitoring the uptake of radioactive glucose into the brain cells correspond to a great extent with the "blood-flow maps." The implication is that any regionally elevated neuronal activity, whether sensory, motor, or based on a form of thinking, is accompanied by enhanced metabolic activity of the neurons; the metabolites released in the process cause local vasodilation and thus increased blood flow.

Clinical experience reveals that in unconscious or comatose patients, or those with high-grade dementia or schizophrenia, the sensory, motor or mental deficits in each case are accompanied by decreases in both overall blood flow and in perfusion of the relevant regions [33]. Blood flow measurements can therefore be expected to acquire increasing clinical significance, especially if it proves possible to refine their resolution and to monitor parts of the brain below the surface as well.

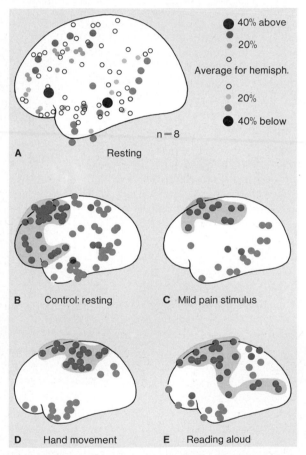

A Resting

B Control: resting **C** Mild pain stimulus

D Hand movement **E** Reading aloud

● 40% above
● 20%
○ Average for hemisph.
○ 20%
● 40% below

n = 8

Fig. 7-11 A–E. Measurement of regional blood flow by means of intraarterial injection of ^{133}Xe into the internal carotid artery (N. A. LASSEN and D. H. INGVAR). The uptake and washing out of this gas in the different regions of the brain is monitored with Geiger counters (as many as 245) mounted on the side of the head. With the help of a computer the blood flow is calculated and represented numerically or graphically. **A** Flow through the dominant hemisphere at rest. Means of 8 subjects. Deviation from the mean is indicated by the symbols shown on the right. **B** Like **A,** except that only those areas are shown that have blood flow at least 20% above or below the mean. **C-E** Change in regional blood flow during the indicated cerebral activities, represented as in **B.** Measurement by D. H. INGVAR et al. (From [33])

7.2 Waking and Sleeping

Circadian Periodicity as the Basis of the Waking/Sleeping Rhythm

The circadian oscillator. Nearly all living beings, from protozoans to humans, undergo rhythmical changes in the state of their organs and functions. These changes are often coupled to the 24-hour periodicity associated with the earth's rotation (but in some cases to the tides, the phases of the moon or the annual cycle), so that it has frequently been concluded that animal and human diurnal rhythms are a passive response of the organism to environmental periodicity. Recent experiments [7, 25, 27], however, have shown unequivocally that this rhythmicity continues even *after all environmental factors have been excluded.* The period of such a **free-running rhythm** is often shorter or longer than 24 h, a further indication that the cause of the rhythm lies not in the environment, but rather in endogenous processes (of unknown nature, summarized in the term "biological clock"). The endogenous periodicity thus corresponds only approximately *(circa)* to the natural duration of a day *(dies),* which has given rise to the adjective **circadian.** A free-running circadian rhythm does not die out for a long time (weeks, months); that is, it behaves like a self-excited oscillator. Normally the periodicity of this oscillator is **synchronized** with the 24-h cycle by **external signals**

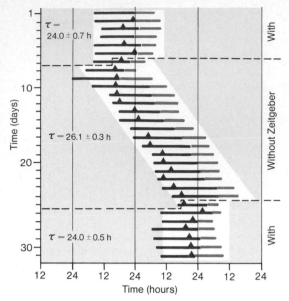

Fig. 7-12. Rhythm of waking *(red bars)* and sleeping *(gray bars)* of a subject in an isolation chamber with open door (social Zeitgeber) and in isolation (without Zeitgeber). Triangles: maxima of rectal temperature. τ = period of a complete waking/sleeping cycle. Measurements by J. ASCHOFF et al.

("Zeitgeber") such as the alternation between light and darkness or social factors.

Circadian periodicity in humans. More than 100 parameters of human organs and functions have been found to change cyclically with a 24-hour period [27, 40]. Body temperature, for example, is known to vary between a minimum in the early morning and a maximum, about 1–1.5° C higher, in the evening. But the most impressive diurnal fluctuation is the **waking/ sleeping cycle.** It comes as no surprise, then, that the many adjustments of the organism normally associated with the onset of sleep – for instance, the fall in body temperature, heart rate and respiratory rate (Fig. 7-14) – have been thought to be *causally* related to sleep. Many experiments have shown, however, that the diurnal rhythmicity of these and many other vegetative and physiological parameters is retained even during *sleep deprivation.* From these and other experiments it has been concluded that humans (and other highly organized metazoans) possesses **a considerable number of circadian oscillators** of somewhat different periods. It is only to the extent that these oscillators are synchronized either with one another or with external Zeitgeber that they depend on the waking/sleeping cycle.

Clear evidence of the **independent periodicity of vegetative rhythms** is provided by *studies of shift workers.* In these people, for example, the rhythms of body temperature and other parameters do not change phase even when night work is continued

for a long time, although the curve may be *distorted* by the night work. Evidently **social contacts** and **knowledge of the time of day** are more effective Zeitgeber for the phase of the circadian oscillators than the working rhythm and the resulting waking/sleeping behavior. One of the consequences of this conflict situation is that performance capacity continues to reach a minimum in the hours after midnight despite the demands of the job, so that mistakes and accidents are more frequent at this time (cf. p. 562).

Humans shut off from the environment (during experiments in underground bunkers or caves) also exhibit a **circadian periodicity,** with a cycle duration in most cases somewhat longer than 24 hours (Fig. 7-12). Here, again, differences in cycle length and the relative independence of individual oscillators can be demonstrated. For example, in Fig. 7-12 the maxima of body temperature (upward-pointing triangles) during the first days of free-running circadian periodicity are distinctly shifted from their positions in the synchronized waking/sleeping rhythm, which are retained for the first two days. This result suggests that these two oscillators are coupled to one another, their phase shift depending on the prevailing circumstances and in particular on the period of the system as a whole. In extreme cases, when the waking/sleeping rhythm in isolation acquires an especially long period (in isolated instances 48-hour cycles, or *bicircadian rhythms,* have been observed [25, 27]), vegetative functions become completely uncoupled *(internal desynchronization)* and continue to run with the original cycle of ca. 25 hours.

If the **rhythm of the external Zeitgeber is shifted once** – for example, shortened by a flight to the east or lengthened by a westward flight – the circadian systems often require several cycles to regain their normal phase relation to the Zeitgeber. The individual functions differ in the time required for resynchronization. Social and professional activity can rapidly be adjusted to the shifted Zeitgeber, but body temperature and other vegetative functions follow more slowly. This dissociation certainly must contribute to "jet lag", the temporary deterioration of performance that follows long-distance flights.

The ratio of the durations of activity and rest times within a circadian cycle is not kept constant. Remarkably, prolongation of the activity phase leads to shortening of the subsequent rest phase – that is, the average circadian period is kept as constant as possible (cf. Fig. 7-12). This finding is contrary to what would be expected on the basis of a fatigue hypothesis (sleep as recuperation), and is a sign that the **circadian periodicity is the primary process,** to which sleeping and waking are subordinate.

The **biological significance of the circadian rhythms** of humans and animals has tended to be underestimated. Circadian rhythmicity is evidently inherited, and is to be regarded as a phylogenetic adaptation to the temporal structure of our environment. This **internal** copy of the time program of the environment places the organism in a position to adjust itself **in advance** to the changes in environmental conditions to be expected at any time. The resulting advantages extend from the simple utilization of certain times of day for certain actions to the use of the "internal clock" for the actual measurement of time, an ability required, for example, by animals that orient by using the sun as a compass. Seen in this light, the **waking/sleeping rhythm** is not the cause, but rather one of the *side effects of endogenous circadian periodicity.* An explanation of the nature of these endogenous oscillators, which is just beginning to emerge [25, 27], will also bring us closer to an understanding of the mechanisms underlying waking/sleeping behavior.

Phenomenology of Waking and Sleeping

Human waking/sleeping behavior. Whereas a person who is awake is in active contact with the environment – for example, responds to stimuli with adequate actions – in sleep the contact with the environment is very much restricted. It is not entirely eliminated, however, for stimuli, especially those with a particular significance (key stimuli), can wake the sleeper. For example, the whimpering of an infant awakens its mother, though considerably louder traffic noise does not. Nevertheless, the traffic noise, like all noise, is detrimental to sleep, affecting its depth and the sequence of sleep stages, and thus impairs well-being in general. Therefore all disturbing environmental stimuli should be kept away from the bedroom.

Neither waking nor sleeping is a homogeneous state of consciousness. Just as in the waking state the amount of attention directed outward can vary considerably, there are distinct **stages of sleep.** The simplest and oldest measure of the **depth of sleep** is the *intensity of a stimulus* sufficient for awakening. The deeper the sleep, the higher the awakening threshold. Today the **EEG** is usually used to determine the depth of sleep. Four or five stages of sleep can be distinguished on the basis of the EEG pattern (Fig. 7-13), and there is widespread agreement on standard criteria for them [2, 15, 17 24]. On the whole, the EEG becomes progressively slower (more synchronized) as sleep becomes deeper, and in addition special formations such as sleep spindles and K complexes appear (see Fig. 7-13, Stages C and D). Deep sleep (Stage E) is uniquely characterized by slow, large-amplitude delta waves. During the *course of a night* the individual **stages of sleep are passed through several times,** three to five times on the average (Fig. 7-14). In general the maximal depth of sleep reached during each

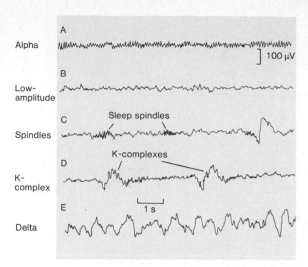

Fig. 7-13. Classification of the stages of human sleep on the basis of the EEG. *Stage A: relaxed waking;* α rhythm prevails. *Stage B: falling asleep;* α rhythm is diminished and shallow ϑ waves (theta waves) appear. *Stage C: light sleep;* further decrease in frequency until δ waves (delta waves) appear. Occasional "sleep spindles" (groups of waves at 12–15 Hz). *Stage D: moderately deep sleep;* δ waves and K complexes. *Stage E: deep sleep;* almost exclusively large, slow δ waves. The *REM stage* corresponds about to Stage B of the EEG. There are smooth transitions between the different stages. This classification is by LOOMIS et al. (1936); others also exist [15, 24]. From [46]

cycle decreases toward morning, so that at this time Stage E no longer appears [2, 14, 15, 17, 24, 46].

The many **vegetative functions with circadian periodicity** (cf. p. 154) are either unaffected by these rhythmic fluctuations in depth of sleep (e.g., body temperature) or phasic fluctuations are superimposed on their slow periodicity (e.g., heart rate and respiration in Fig. 7-14). This phasic modulation is especially apparent when the cycle passes through Stage B in the course of a night (but not during the initial falling asleep). Other reactions, in fact, can be observed only during these repeated B stages (e. g., penis erection in Fig. 7-14).

The *special nature of the repeated B stages* is also emphasized by the accompanying motor patterns. That is, during this period (as in the stage of deep sleep) there is essentially a complete loss of tone in the peripheral musculature (cf. EMG in Fig. 7-14). As an exception to this rule, *bursts of rapid eye movement appear* (cf. EOG in Fig. 7-14). These rapid eye movements are so characteristic of this stage that it is called the **REM stage.** The atony of the rest of the musculature can also be interrupted by brief twitches (of the facial muscles, for instance) during the REM bursts. The *awakening threshold* during REM sleep is about as high as during deep sleep, while the *EEG* resembles that at the *onset of sleep.* This apparent incon-

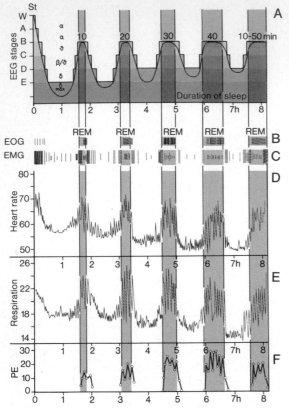

Fig. 7-14. Cyclic transitions among sleep stages during a night and associated changes in certain autonomic variables. Averages, highly schematic. From top to bottom: EEG stages, nomenclature according to Loomis et al. (1936). REM stages indicated by red background. EOG, electrooculogram; REM movements of the eyes marked by vertical lines; a few slow eye movements accompany falling asleep. EMG, electromyogram of the neck muscles; activity indicated by vertical lines. Heart rate: beats per minute. Respiration: breaths per minute. PE, penis erection. (From JOVANOVIĆ [14])

sistency has given rise to the terms **paradoxical sleep** and **desynchronized sleep** as synonyms for *REM sleep*. Often all the other stages together are called **NREM sleep** (non-REM sleep, also called *synchronized sleep* or *SW sleep* = slow-wave sleep). During normal sleep REM stages appear about every 1½ hours. Their duration averages 20 minutes and increases in the course of the night (Fig. 7-14).

The relative amounts of time spent waking and sleeping, like the proportions of REM and NREM sleep in the total sleeping time, undergo a characteristic **ontogenetic development.** The general trend in the course of a lifetime is not only a reduction in total sleeping time but also a considerable shortening in the relative duration of REM sleep. These durations can be found in Fig. 7-15. The sequence and duration of the other stages of sleep (not shown in Fig. 7-15) are also distinctly different in infants and small children than in adults. The large proportion of REM sleep in the former has suggested that these periods of elevated neuronal activity (desynchronized EEG like that during attentiveness; see, e.g., α blockade in Figs. 7-5 and 7-8) are important for ontogenetic development, for infants experience far fewer external stimuli than adults.

Sleep and dreams. When children and adults are awakened during or immediately after a REM stage they report considerably more often that they have just been dreaming than when they are awakened from NREM sleep. All who have done such experiments found a high percentage (60–90%) of **dream reports on waking from REM sleep,** whereas the percentage of dream reports on waking from NREM sleep was distinctly lower, on the whole, in the var-

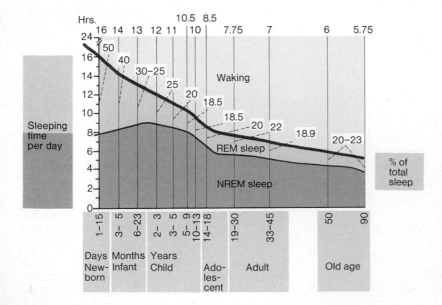

Fig. 7-15. Waking and sleeping times and the proportions of NREM and REM sleep during a human lifetime. Apart from the reduction in total sleeping time, the most notable change as a child grows is the marked reduction in the duration of REM sleep. (Modified from ROFFWARG et al. [45])

ious studies and had a greater range of variation (1–74%; see reviews in [2, 46]). It therefore seems certain that dreams very often or usually occur during REM sleep. But even during NREM sleep mental processes apparently take place in the brain. Dream reports, as stated above, are much less likely but other signs of psychological activity, such as *talking in one's sleep, sleepwalking* and the *"night terror"* of children occur mainly during NREM sleep [17].

Dreams can be influenced by preceding events. For example, water deprivation (thirst) increases the duration and intensity of the REM phases and the dreams experienced during them. A similar effect seems to appear when one watches an exciting movie or television play before going to bed. Moreover, when one is awakened each time a REM period begins and thus **deprived of REM sleep,** the REM phases in subsequent undisturbed sleep are longer and deeper, and dreaming is more intense – a sort of "catching up" effect. In these experiments it was noted that even when people or animals were deprived of REM sleep for a long time there were no long-lasting physical or mental consequences of the lack of REM sleep and thus of dreams, as various authors had at first expected [2, 17, 45]. External stimuli during REM sleep, especially acoustic stimuli, are occasionally incorporated into dreams. In the sleep laboratory such stimuli can be used as time markers for the dream reports. Their incorporation into dreams provides especially good support for the inference that the dreams actually do occur during the REM periods.

REM sleep appears to offer especially good conditions for dreaming. It is by no means a consequence of dreaming, for typical REM eye movements also occur under conditions in which complex hallucinatory visual perceptions cannot be reported and their existence is hardly conceivable – for example, in the unborn and, as mentioned above, the newborn (including newborn animals before the eyelids have opened), in anencephalic children (born without a functional cerebral cortex), and in adults with a nonfunctional cortex owing to disease or accident.

Despite the considerable increase, over the last three decades, in our knowledge about the psychophysiology of dreaming, most questions remain open. For example, we do not know whether mental processes take place continually during sleep or only from time to time. Given the plausible assumption that during each nightly REM period at least one and sometimes several dream episodes occur, it is immediately clear that each of us remembers only a fraction of his dreams (most of which are apparently quite simple and prosaic), but it remains to be discovered why we forget the rest so easily.

Disturbances of sleep [2, 17]. One form of sleep disturbance, harmless to the individual but often annoying to others, is **snoring.** Particularly when the sleeper is lying supine, the jaw sinks down and the tongue back, producing the characteristic

sounds. Unfortunately there is essentially no effective treatment. Nocturnal **grinding of teeth** (bruxism) is also frequently less disturbing to the sleeper than to those nearby, although in the long term the teeth may begin to be worn down and the supporting tissue damaged. The cause is unknown. Perhaps it is a phylogenetically old behavior pattern, one observed in animals which serves to sharpen the teeth. **Talking in one's sleep** is sometimes regarded as a sleep disturbance. But as mentioned above, it is more an expression of mental activity during sleep and is absolutely harmless in all respects.

Sleepwalking (somnambulism), too, is neither a pathological symptom nor – apart from occasional accidents – is it harmful. It can happen to people at any age, but is most common in children and young people. The eyes of the sleepwalker are open, gazing straight ahead – apparently into emptiness. No attention is paid to the surroundings. The movements are stiff and awkward. Sleepwalking, as mentioned above, usually occurs when the person has been in deep sleep, and is therefore not the motor expression of a dream. While the person is walking about an alpha-wave EEG is recorded, despite the open eyes. This seems to be a special form of waking, in which the conversion of sensory stimuli into motor activity is basically intact but the consciousness is excluded.

Bed-wetting (enuresis), which happens to about 10% of all children, practically always occurs during NREM sleep. Accordingly, when the children are awakened immediately thereafter they are confused and disoriented and can say nothing about having dreamed. The causes of bed-wetting are unknown. The fact that it is commonly – almost always – restricted to the juvenile stage indicates that a "weak spot" in the maturing brain for unknown reasons sets in motion the complicated behavioral mechanism of micturition just when the child is deeply asleep. Another phenomenon of childhood sleep, found predominantly between the third and the eighth years of life and only rarely after puberty, is **pavor nocturnus** ("night terror"). Suddenly, during sleep, the child sits up and begins to scream, appearing to stare at someone or something with eyes wide open. The face is pale and covered with sweat, and breathing is difficult. After a short time the child wakes up, recognizes its surroundings and, reassured, goes back to sleep. Adults can experience something similar with **nightmares.** A special variant of these is the **sleep paralysis** that occasionally occurs when waking up or falling asleep; for a short time it is absolutely impossible to make a movement. Often it happens when the person is fully conscious, and it tends to be more surprising than terrifying. But it can also be accompanied by startling or frightening hallucinations, such as the impression that a stone is lying or a person crouching on one's chest. As soon as the paralyzed person is spoken to or touched all symptoms vanish.

About 15% of all adults complain of **insomnia;** that is, they have the impression that they cannot sleep, or not long enough. This subjective sleep deficiency does not necessarily mean that the affected person objectively sleeps too little and suffers impaired health as a result of lack of sleep. In sleep laboratories it has been shown that such patients sleep more than they think. Moreover, in experiments on the **effects of sleep deprivation** it has turned out that although when sleep is prevented entirely transient physical and psychological changes occur as would be expected, partial sleep deprivation – for example, only five and a half hours of sleep per night for many weeks – causes slight or no detectable change in the performance and well-being of the subject. In other words, as long as the insomnia does not involve distinct shortening of total sleep duration for a long period, our present knowledge suggests that the condition does not necessarily represent a threat to health. The pharmacological treatment of insomnia should therefore be appropriately restrained.

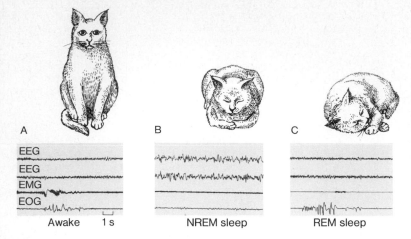

Fig. 7-16 A–C. Sleep stages in a mammal (cat). Records from top to bottom: EEG, electromyogram (EMG) of the neck musculature, electrooculogram (EOG). **A** Waking state; head-turning with eye movements in the middle of the record. **B** NREM sleep (synchronized sleep). **C** REM sleep, with bursts of rapid eye movement. Brief myoclonic twitches appear in the otherwise quiet EMG. The postures of the cat are typical of the different stages. (Measurements by W. BAUST)

Waking/sleeping behavior of animals. In addition to humans all the other **mammals** exhibit a form of sleeping behavior, in which NREM stages can be clearly distinguished from REM stages. The animal most commonly used for sleep research, the cat, spends about two-thirds of its life asleep, typically in sessions of 10–20 min of NREM sleep followed by 6 or 7 min of REM sleep. Whereas cats in NREM sleep can be easily awakened and still have appreciable muscle tone (as can be seen from the typical posture; cf. Fig. 7-16 B), during REM sleep (Fig. 7-16 C) the awakening threshold is much higher and the musculature is completely atonic (so that the animal lies on its side as in Fig. 7-16 C). In the cat, then, the REM stage is evident in the position of the body.

Phylogenetically *REM sleep is a relatively recent development* (Fig. 7-17). Fish and reptiles have no REM sleep. In birds the

phases of REM sleep are very brief (seconds), amounting to less than 1% of the total sleeping time. By contrast, all mammals spend a considerable fraction of their sleeping time in REM sleep. It is striking that hunting species (human, cat, dog) have distinctly more REM sleep (about 20% of the total on the average) than those that are hunted (rabbits and ruminants average 5–10%). The late appearance of REM sleep in phylogeny, however, is not recapitulated in **ontogeny**. On the contrary, like humans (cf. Fig. 7-15) other newborn mammals spend a larger proportion of their total sleeping time in REM sleep than they do later in life (Fig. 7-17). Thus whereas REM sleep is a feature only of highly developed brains it may, as mentioned with regard to Fig. 7-15, be of (still unknown) significance to the ontogenetic development of these brains.

Mechanisms of Waking and Sleeping

Like the causes of the circadian periodicity of other bodily functions, the *mechanisms of waking and sleeping* are almost entirely unknown. Although waking and sleeping affect the entire organism, they are basically determined by central nervous processes. In the narrow sense, therefore, the question takes the form "how does the neuronal activity of a waking brain differ from that of a sleeping brain, and what events determine the transition from one stage to the next?"

The distinction between waking and sleeping *cannot be narrowed down to a question* of which forms of cerebral activity are associated with *consciousness* and which are not, even though waking and consciousness are closely linked in the intact organism. That is, a sleeping/waking rhythm is found even in *creatures without telencephalon or diencephalon* – for example, anencephalic humans or chronically decerebrate mammals – and it is highly unlikely that animals lacking the cerebrum possess consciousness of any sort. Conversely, dreams indicate that sleep is not a state completely devoid of consciousness such as anesthesia or coma.

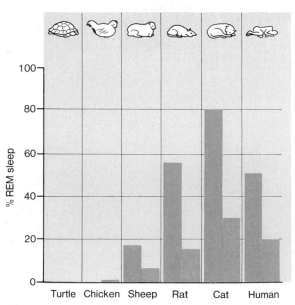

Fig. 7-17. Proportions of REM sleep in three classes of vertebrates, as percentage of total sleep duration. The complexity of the brain structures increases from left to right. In all mammals the percentage of REM sleep is at least twice as large in the newborn (*red* bars) as in the adult (*gray* bars). (From JOUVET [25])

Sleep is certainly also *not only the absence of the pattern of brain activity characteristic of waking,* a kind of "resting of the brain." On the contrary, all neurophysiological data indicate beyond doubt that the neuronal activity of the brain during the various stages of sleep is of a *complexity equal to that in the waking state.* This situation is apparent to some extent even in the EEG recordings, and dreams provide further evidence. Sleep – or, better, the individual stages of sleep – is thus a **succession of alternative forms of functional organization of the brain,** not the absence of coordinated neuronal activity.

This interpretation does not contradict the everyday experience that humans and animals have an **essential sleep requirement.** In speaking of such a requirement we are saying only that the forms of operation of cerebral neurons associated with sleep are (for unknown reasons) absolutely necessary to the well-being of the organism. The plausible view that tiredness and sleep are elicited primarily by the periodic accumulation, depletion or specific production of metabolic substances (sleep factors [19]) that circulate in the bloodstream and must be broken down or eliminated during sleep *(chemical theory of waking and sleeping)* is certainly not correct in this simple form. Evidence against this view includes not only the absence of any unequivocal demonstration of such substances, but in particular the observations of Siamese twins with crossed, mutual circulation but separate nervous systems. There is no mutual interaction between the sleeping/waking cycles of such twins. Moreover, in animal experiments the cerebrum can be separated from the rest of the CNS, or the two hemispheres can be separated by sagittal cuts; in these preparations sleeping/waking symptoms appear independently in the isolated parts of the brain.

Theories of waking and sleeping. In addition to the unsatisfactory **chemical theory** just mentioned, there have been other approaches to a theory of waking and sleeping; some have also been largely refuted, and some have received slight corroboration. They will be mentioned only briefly here.

The **deafferentation theory** was based on the idea that the activity of the CNS is induced and controlled primarily by sensory stimuli (simple reflex concept). It was supported by the observation that after decerebration at the level of the corpora quadrigemina (the *cerveau isolé* of Bremer), which eliminates all sensory inputs to the cerebrum apart from vision and olfaction, only a synchronized (sleeping) EEG remained. The basic postulate was that the waking state depends on a certain minimal level of cortical activity, and that this cortical tone is maintained or critically modulated by the sensory influx. This theory had to be discarded because in chronic *cerveau-isolé* preparations a sleeping/waking rhythm eventually reappears. Furthermore, thorough sensory deprivation of humans (in sleeping chambers where all acoustic, visual and proprioceptive stimuli are entirely excluded) causes a progressive decrease in the duration of sleep during the period of isolation, and patients with traumatic high paraplegia also sleep for abnormally short times. Finally, the concept that descending cortical tone keeps the organism awake is incorrect in view of the abovementioned fact that organisms lacking a cerebrum also exhibit waking/sleeping symptoms.

The **reticular theory of waking and sleeping** accounts for the last of these observations. It regards the cortex plus diencephalon as the primary seat of the processes responsible for the waking state, but at the same time ascribes to the **reticular formation of the brainstem** a unitary function – to maintain the level of excitation necessary for waking by sending out an ascending stream of activating impulses. This function is represented in the term *ascending reticular activating system,* abbreviated **ARAS.** The ascending pathways belonging to the ARAS are called **nonspecific projections** to distinguish them from the classical sensory specific projections. *Relatively large fluctuations* in the amount of ascending reticular activation are thought to be responsible for the transition from sleeping to the waking state and back. These fluctuations in turn are dependent on the sensory input to the reticular formation (by way of collaterals of the specific pathways on their way through the brainstem; here the theory is related to the deafferentation theory) and on the activity of descending pathways from cortex and subcortical structures, so that there is a reciprocal connection between brain and brainstem. During the waking phase *smaller fluctuations* in ARAS activity are thought to be responsible for subtle behavioral changes (e.g., degree of attentiveness).

The inference that there is a waking or arousal center in the reticular formation is based primarily on the following experimental observations: (i) *high-frequency* electrical stimulation of the reticular formation in brainstem and medulla oblongata elicits a waking reaction (arousal), revealed in the appearance of a desynchronized EEG. (ii) Destruction of the ascending reticular projections in the midbrain region, with or without transection of the specific sensory tracts, leaves the experimental animal in a coma. These findings, however, are opposed by others that make the **simple view of the reticular formation as the decisive waking center hardly tenable.** First, by changing the frequency of the electrical stimulus to the reticular formation, depending on the initial condition, sleep as well as arousal reactions can be elicited. Thus both a sleeping and a waking center must be postulated. Second, the neuronal activity of the reticular formation during sleep, especially during REM sleep, is no less than in the waking state (as the reticular theory postulates), but is only organized differently. Third, even the chronically isolated brain, which lacks a reticular formation, has a sleeping/waking rhythm, for which structures in the diencephalon seem to be particularly responsible. The reticular formation is therefore not indispensable for waking and sleeping (literature survey in [42]).

Finally, it should be mentioned that certain *monoam-inergic transmitter substances* – serotonin (5–HT) and noradrenalin (for biochemistry see pp. 66, 67) – evidently play a large role in the waking/sleeping cycle, so that a **biochemical theory of waking and sleeping** is beginning to take shape [34, 35]. The most important findings from animal experiments are as follows. **(i)** Neurons of the raphe nuclei in the brainstem contain large amounts of **serotonin.** When this supply is exhausted (for example, by poisoning of synthesis) the result is severe insomnia with a reduction in both REM and NREM sleep. Destruction of the raphe nuclei has a similar effect. This insomnia can be alleviated by administration of 5-hydroxytryptophan, the precursor of serotonin (the latter cannot cross the blood-brain barrier). **(ii)** Neurons of the *locus coeruleus* (in the lateral pontine reticular formation) contain large amounts of **noradrenalin.** Bilateral destruction of the loci coerulei causes a complete disappearance of REM sleep but has no influence on NREM sleep. **(iii)** If the serotonin and noradrenalin stores are both exhausted by administration of reserpine, both kinds of sleep (as would be expected from **(i)**) are eliminated. Subsequent administration of 5-hydroxytryptophan restores NREM sleep but not REM sleep, which is consistent with **(ii).** These findings indicate that *serotonin* is important especially for NREM sleep, and *noradrenalin* for REM sleep, and that normally REM sleep is possible only if preceded by NREM sleep. But experiments on humans with regard to serotonin and noradrenalin have given rather the reverse result: the amount of REM sleep is found to be greater, the higher the serotonin level and the lower the noradrenalin level. The reason for these discrepancies has not yet been discovered [17].

7.3   Neurophysiological Correlates of Consciousness and Speech

Consciousness in Humans and Animals

Behavioral characteristics of consciousness. The most impressive change in the state of our bodies in everyday experience is the return of **consciousness** when we awaken from sleep (or from anesthesia, coma or severe concussion). This state of *consciousness* with all its shadings, which can only be experienced introspectively and which is the essential feature of our existence, has been the object of many attempts at interpretation by both physiologists and psychologists, some of them very contradictory and still in flux [3, 8, 11, 12, 23, 28, 38, 47]. The physiologist can contribute

to this discussion by establishing the boundary conditions, from the *viewpoint of the natural sciences,* that determine whether consciousness is possible or not. To give an idea which of the observable aspects of human and animal behavior can serve as reference points for the existence of consciousness, some of them are listed here [18]:
1. Attentiveness and the ability to redirect attention appropriately.
2. The creation and employment of abstract ideas, and the ability to express them in words or other symbols.
3. The ability to estimate the significance of an act in advance and thus to have expectations and plans.
4. Self-recognition and the recognition of other individuals.
5. The presence of aesthetic and ethical values.

Certainly, the various aspects must be weighted differently, and some are predominantly or only observed in humans. But if they are accepted, at least provisorily, they imply that *consciousness is a property of both humans and animals.*

Phylogeny of consciousness. Not all animals have consciousness in the sense of the above definition. Whereas it can hardly be doubted that higher vertebrates (birds, mammals) with a *highly differentiated nervous system* exhibit one or several of the characteristics of conscious behavior listed above, animals with *very simple nervous systems* display such behavior patterns, if at all, only in isolated instances and in a sketchy form. Consciousness is thus *bound to complex neuronal structures* and cannot exist apart from these structures. But as the previous considerations may already have made clear, it is impossible to draw a sharp dividing line between animals with consciousness and those without. Rather, consciousness seems to develop roughly in parallel with the phylogenetic development of the nervous system. In other words, the animal kingdom comprises many gradations and extremely varied forms of consciousness, the human consciousness without doubt being by far the most differentiated form.

This view – that consciousness presupposes a correspondingly differentiated nervous system – suggests that during phylogeny consciousness of one form or another always evolves when simpler forms of neuronal activity (e.g., reflexes) no longer suffice to direct and control the organism. If this is so, the emergence of consciousness is a *necessary step in evolution,* absolutely required for the optimal adaptation of higher organisms to their environment [8, 22].

Functional and Structural Prerequisites for Consciousness

As far as *human consciousness* is concerned, only very simple and on the whole *entirely inadequate* statements can be made about the **functional prerequisites,** that is, the associated neuronal activity. Consciousness evidently requires an **intermediate activity level** in the central nervous structures involved, as represented, for example, by a desynchronized waking EEG.

Too little neuronal activity, as in anesthesia or coma, is incompatible with consciousness, and so is excessive neuronal activity like that in an epileptic seizure (EEG with spikes and waves; cf. Fig. 7-10) or under electroshock. It also seems certain that consciousness is possible only in the **interplay of cortical and subcortical structures;** each of these structures is incapable of creating consciousness by itself. The ascending reticular activating system (ARAS), as would be expected in view of its role in sleeping/waking behavior (p. 159), probably occupies a key position in this regard [8, 12].

Important insights into the **structural prerequisites** of consciousness have recently been provided by studies of Roger Sperry and his colleagues on patients in whom the corpus callosum and anterior commissure have been surgically transected in order to ameliorate otherwise uncontrollable epileptic seizures, or at least to restrict them to one half of the brain. The transection of the *commissural fibers* in these **split-brain patients** breaks all connections between the two cerebral hemispheres, leaving each to its own devices, so to speak. The postoperative behavior of these (about 20 so far) patients in everyday life is inconspicuous, and their intellect appears unchanged. At most one can detect a reduction in spontaneous activity on the left side of the body (of right-handed people) and an absence or attenuation of responses to stimuli (e. g., pushing) on that side. With carefully designed tests, however, Sperry and his coworkers have demonstrated considerable differences in the performance of the two halves of the brain [10, 11, 12, 25, 47].

To understand these tests, remember that because the ascending and descending tracts cross the midline the left half of the cerebrum is responsible for the somatosensory and motor supply of the right side of the body, and conversely. Moreover, because of the decussation in the optic chiasm the right half of the visual field projects to the left hemisphere and the left half, to the right hemisphere. By contrast, the central auditory pathways are partly crossed and partly uncrossed, so that each hemisphere is reached by both ipsilateral and contralateral auditory inputs.

With the apparatus shown in Fig. 7-18 separate visual signals (flashes of light, objects, writing) can be presented to the two halves of the visual field. In addition, the right or left hand can be used for tactile exploration or for writing without visual control. Visual and tactile sensory stimuli on the right are conveyed *only to the left half of the brain* (left hemisphere) in this situation, and vice versa. The most important results of these experiments are as follows.

When an object (e. g., a key or pencil) is projected into the **right half of the visual field,** the split-brain patient can *name* it or *pick it out* from other objects with the *right hand.* When words are projected into this half of

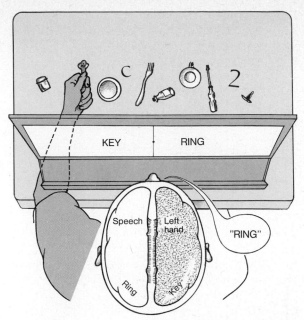

Fig. 7-18. Behavior of a split-brain patient during a test by Roger Sperry and his coworkers. The patient sits in front of an opaque milk-glass screen onto which objects or written words can be projected into the left, right or both halves of the visual field. The patient is told to fixate a point in the middle of the screen; the visual stimuli are presented briefly (0.1 s) so that a change in gaze direction, which would bring the stimulus into the other visual field, is prevented. In the test illustrated the patient reports (by way of his left, speaking hemisphere) that he has read the word RING in the right field of view. He denies having seen the word KEY in the left field, and he cannot name any object placed in his left hand. But he can use his left hand to select the correct object, though he says he has no knowledge of the object. If asked to name the object he has selected, the speaking hemisphere calls it "RING." (After SPERRY in [25])

the visual field he can *read* them aloud, *write them down* and again pick out the appropriate object with the right hand. When an object is placed in his *right hand* the results are consistent with the above; the patient can *name* the object and *write* its name down. In other words, the patient in these situations does not differ from a normal experimental subject.

When an object is projected into the **left half of the visual field** the split-brain patient **cannot name it.** But he is able to pick it out from other objects with the *left hand* when he is asked to do so. Even then, however, after a successful search, he cannot name the object, nor can he name it when it is placed in his **left hand.** He is unable to read aloud words projected into the left half of the visual field. But if the word is the name of an everyday object he can select the object with his left hand (Fig. 7-18). Again, even after having successfully located it, he cannot name it. In this situation, then, the patient can carry out certain tasks but he cannot express what he is doing verbally or in writing even on request.

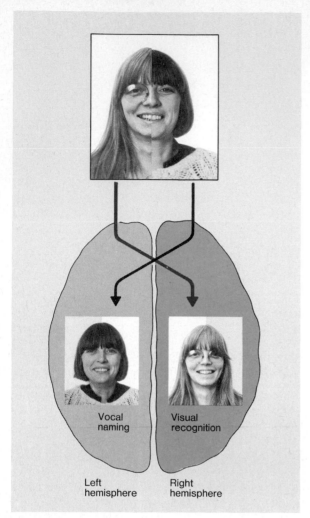

Fig. 7-19. The identification of faces by the left and right hemispheres of a split-brain patient. When the arrangement of Fig. 7-18 is used to present "composite portraits" as visual stimuli, each hemisphere supplements the half-face it sees to form a complete face, about which the other hemisphere knows nothing. When verbal identification of the face is required, as expected the left hemisphere dominates. In all other, nonverbal tests the right hemisphere is far superior to the left. Such tests include operations with complex geometrical figures that cannot be described verbally. (After SPERRY et al. in [25])

The most important **conclusion** from these results is the following. With regard to *speech* and *consciousness* the performance of the **left hemisphere alone** is indistinguishable from that of the two coupled hemispheres, either from the subjective viewpoint of the patient or by the objectively observable behavior. Therefore it (or as yet unknown parts of it) is to be regarded as the decisive neuronal substrate for speech and specifically human consciousness *in the normal brain as well* [11]. The **right hemisphere alone** cannot express itself verbally or in writing. The patient is evidently not conscious of the sensory, integrative and

motor processes taking place there. Separated from the left hemisphere, the right leads a life of its own of which the patient is only indirectly aware, by way of the sensory channels of the left hemisphere.

It is remarkable what the right hemisphere alone can do. It possesses a memory, for example, as well as visual and tactile form recognition, a capacity for abstraction and a degree of speech comprehension (commands given acoustically are carried out and simple words read; cf. Fig. 7-18). Some patients can even write or copy simple short words. (It remains an open question whether this understanding of speech was present preoperatively or was learned postoperatively.) In some respects, as in the identification of faces (Fig. 7-19) and in regard to spatial conceptualization and the understanding of music, the right hemisphere actually seems superior to the left. On the whole, the achievements of the right hemisphere are certainly better than those of any animal brain, even the monkey brain. Thus if we postulate consciousness in higher animals, as on p. 160, by the behavioral criteria listed there the **consciousness of the isolated right hemisphere is highly developed.** But because it is unable to express itself in speech, it is as little able as the animals are to communicate directly with others about its consciousness.

Neurophysiological Aspects of Speech

Lateralization of speech. Practically all our knowledge about the neurophysiology of speech is based on *clinical observations*. So far the greatest amount of information has been derived from studies in which speech disturbances could be correlated with the postmortem neuropathological determination of the underlying brain damage. But brain surgery, especially in combination with electrical stimulation of the exposed brain of a waking patient, and other methods of study have made valuable contributions. For example, the therapeutic transection of commissural fibers (split-brain operation) has shown that as a rule only the **left hemisphere** contains the regions necessary for speech. This had already been inferred from considerably older clinical-neuropathological findings, and it was for this reason that the left hemisphere was called the **dominant hemisphere.** The dominance of the left hemisphere over the right was assumed to extend to other functions, because motor skills are also distinctly lateralized, most people being *right-handed*. It was concluded further that the speech regions of *left-handed* people would as a rule be found on the right.

Neither generalization is correct. It is true that the speech regions of right-handers are practically al-

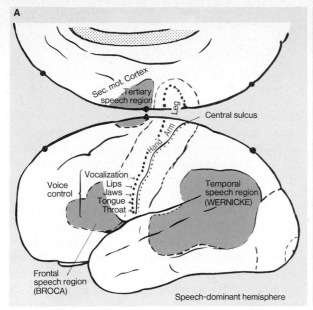

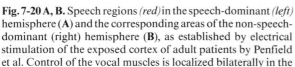

Fig. 7-20 A, B. Speech regions *(red)* in the speech-dominant *(left)* hemisphere (**A**) and the corresponding areas of the non-speech-dominant (right) hemisphere (**B**), as established by electrical stimulation of the exposed cortex of adult patients by Penfield et al. Control of the vocal muscles is localized bilaterally in the precentral gyri. Unlike the rest of the body, each half of the face is represented bilaterally. The temporal speech region probably extends less far into the temporal lobe than is shown in **A**. (After PENFIELD and ROBERTS [21])

ways on the left, but most left-handers also have them on the left, while in a few others they are on the right or bilateral [10, 21]. Moreover, because it is becoming ever clearer (mainly through the studies of split-brain patients) that in some respects the right hemisphere is superior to the left, it is more appropriate to speak of a *mutually complementary* **specialization of the two hemispheres** in which the left as a rule is **speech-dominant.**

Speech regions. Broca, over a hundred years ago, was the first to observe that lesions of the lower part of the third frontal gyrus on the left caused a *failure of speech* (aphasia) such that although speech is still understood the patients say hardly anything spontaneously. On command, hesitantly and with great effort, they can produce short sentences, reduced to the most essential nouns, verbs and adjectives (telegraphic speech). This form of aphasia is called **motor aphasia,** and the associated area of the brain is called **Broca's speech region.** As Fig. 7-20 shows, this area is immediately in front of the parts of the motor cortex that control the muscles of the face, jaws, tongue, palate and throat – the muscles necessary for *articulation.* But the motor aphasia that results from damage to *Broca's region* is not ascribable to paralysis of these muscles. Even direct damage to the facial region of the precentral gyrus (Fig. 7-20A, B; cf. Fig. 5-22, p. 102) causes only slight contralateral deficits, because the facial musculature is represented bilaterally

in the cortex and a unilateral deficit can be compensated by the opposite side.

Soon after Broca's discovery Wernicke described another type of aphasia, in which the *understanding of speech* is severely impaired but the spontaneous speaking by the patient is fluent, though distorted. This **sensory aphasia** is strikingly well correlated with damage to the temporal lobes, especially in the posterior part of the first temporal gyrus, in the immediate vicinity of the auditory cortex (Fig. 7-20 A).

The speech regions described by Broca and Wernicke were approximately confirmed by the experiments of Penfield and his coworkers, in which the exposed cortex was stimulated (Fig. 7-20). Electrical stimulation of these areas and of a third area overlapping roughly with the secondary motor area (MII) induces aphasia for the duration of stimulation. Words or sentences are never elicited by stimulation of these regions. This effect is distinct from that obtained by stimulation of the lateral precentral gyrus, in which stimulation on either side elicits *vocalization* (as a rule, vocal exclamations) [20, 21]. These findings also imply that the *speech functions are lateralized to one hemisphere* whereas the cortical areas responsible for articulation, the execution of speech, are bilateral (Fig. 7-20A, B). Accordingly, neurosurgical observations show that unilateral removal of the parts of the precentral gyrus associated with speaking never produces aphasia but rather, as just mentioned, often causes only astonishingly slight disturbances of speech. By contrast, when the *speech regions are removed* the result is aphasia of varying duration. The aphasic disturbance following removal of the third speech region (overlapping with MII) persists for some weeks. Removal of Broca's area brings about a more long-lasting aphasia, though even in an adult there is an improvement after months or years. Removal of the temporal speech region, however, produces permanent aphasia. The *temporal speech region,* viewed in this light, is the *primary* region [10, 12, 20, 21].

Aphasia, alexia, agraphia, acalculia. Disturbances of the expressive (motor) and receptive (sensory) speech functions and associated abilities such as writing, reading and calculating hardly ever appear in pure form, but rather in many different combinations. But the subdivision of aphasias into *motor* and *sensory,* depending on whether the *expressive* or *receptive* speech functions are most severely impaired, was and is clinically useful. A separate convenient distinction is that between **global aphasia,** in which both expressive and receptive functions are severely impaired, and **amnesic aphasia,** in which disturbances of *word-finding ability* predominate. The patient replaces the word he is looking for with a filler word ("the whatsis") or by a more general category ("bird" instead of pigeon) or by a circumlocution ("to write with" instead of pencil). For a more detailed description of the symptomatology of the various aphasias and for more recent attempts to characterize aphasias more precisely and to classify them, the reader is referred to the literature [18, 25, 26].

Disturbances of speech-related abilities – reading, writing and arithmetic – appear as side effects of aphasia; sometimes they are the chief symptoms, in which case they are called **alexia, agraphia,** and **acalculia,** respectively. Whereas alexia is more in the category of sensory aphasia, agraphia indicates a disturbance of expressive speech function. It is practically impossible to ascribe the various forms of aphasia to *particular locations* in the brain on the basis of clinical-psychological findings. The assignments originally made by Broca and Wernicke have proved to be oversimplifications, applicable only to a first approximation.

Aphasias as a consequence of gradual (e. g., arteriosclerosis) or sudden (e. g., stroke; p. 108) damage to the speech regions isolate the patient from his social environment. He cannot communicate with other people as he once could, and they in turn are usually not able to detect (especially with aphasia of slow onset) that the speech difficulty is not the result of altered personality structure but rather is due to damage in the parts of the brain responsible for speech. In other words, many aphasics are regarded by people around them as mentally ill. Particularly in the sensory aphasias a layman cannot readily discern that the obvious failure to understand speech, together with the uninhibited but more or less incoherent spontaneous speech, is not evidence of a disturbed mind. These patients suffer doubly and triply: from their aphasia, from the false interpretation of the nature of their illness, and from the lack (or incorrectness) of treatment.

Ontogenetic aspects. Once a child has learned to speak, destruction of the speech region in the left hemisphere causes complete aphasia. But after about a year the child begins to speak again. Now the speech is represented in the corresponding regions of the right hemisphere (cf. Fig. 7-20). This transfer of speech dominance from the left hemisphere to the right is possible only up to the tenth year of life, at the latest [25]. The original ability to establish the speech center in either hemisphere is lost at this age, probably for two reasons. First, the development of the *basic neuronal patterns* necessary for speech (which are also employed for later learning of a second language) is no longer possible. Second, the corresponding regions of the *non-speech-dominant hemisphere* at this time have already taken on other tasks, in particular that of spatial orientation and consciousness of the dimensions of the body itself and its relationship to the surroundings (Fig. 7-20 B). However, the plasticity of the brain exacts a price: patients whose right hemisphere has had to take over the task of speech in addition to the nonverbal functions just cited, because the left hemisphere was damaged in childhood, all have lower general intelligence and poorer speech abilities than a comparable sample of normal people [25].

7.4 Learning and Memory

The uptake, storage and retrieval of information are general properties of neuronal networks. Their *biological significance* as the basis of **adaptation of individual behavior to the environment** can hardly be overestimated. Without learning and memory neither the individual nor its species could survive, for successes could not be repeated by planning and failures could not be intentionally avoided. Accordingly, much attention has been directed to these phenomena in recent decades by neurobiologists; as yet, however, no even moderately satisfactory or comprehensive theories about the underlying mechanisms have emerged. It is certain that we store only a *very small part* of the events of which we are conscious, and these are only a small fraction of all our sensory inputs. It is also certain that we forget most of the information that once was stored. Both these mechanisms, *selection* and *forgetting,* protect us from being inundated with data, which would be just as detrimental as the lack of learning and memory.

At present we can make only a rough estimate of the **storage capacity of the human brain.** Comparisons between the storage capacity necessary for learning languages (4–$5 \cdot 10^7$ bits) and the number of neurons in the associated temporal areas ($3 \cdot 10^8$) indicate that about *10 neurons* are required to store *one bit of information.* Extrapolation of this result to the entire human cortex gives a total storage capacity of about $3 \cdot 10^8$ bits. This storage capacity would suffice for the permanent storage of about 1% of the information flowing through our consciousness, a value obtained from cybernetic considerations as follows[36]. The **information flow through consciousness** from the entire sensory system is less than 50 bits $\cdot$ s^{-1} under all conditions. For example, it is 40 bits $\cdot$ s^{-1} for quiet reading, 12 bits $\cdot$ s^{-1} for mental calculation, and 3 bits $\cdot$ s^{-1} for counting. Assuming an average value of 20 bits $\cdot$ s^{-1}, the total information flow in 70 years of 16-hour days is about $3 \cdot 10^{10}$ bits, a hundred times more than the available storage capacity as derived above. From all this material, **one percent** must be selected for **long-term storage.** It seems evident that the information selected will be primarily that most important to the individual for one reason or another – for example, for survival [36].

Uptake (learning) and storage (in memory) of information by the nervous system have been more thoroughly studied in recent decades than the problem of retrieval from storage (remembering). For the first two processes, therefore, the underlying mechanisms are beginning to be revealed, at least in outline. On the other hand, most of the processes underlying retrieval remain obscure, and we can say little about them here.

Human Memory

Forms of memory. Of the many data accumulated in recent decades by the experimental study of learning and memory, certain salient findings have found general acceptance and must be taken into account in any formulation of theories of learning and memory. The first of these is that it is easier to remember a *short* list (of nonsense syllables, for instance) than a *long* one. As banal as this assertion may appear, it serves to show that our memory does *not* operate like an electronic data bank or a magnetic tape, for both of these continue to take in information until the available capacity is fully occupied or until the storage process is stopped.

A second important point is that we tend to *store generalities* rather than details. For example, after reading this paragraph the message it contains – that **concepts are stored** – will remain in memory, whereas the verbatim formulation of this thought will be quite forgotten. When retrieval is desired, the opposite mechanism operates; that is, we remember the concept, and the speech mechanisms provide us with the verbal terms to express it. In this regard, too, the human memory processes differ distinctly from those of electronic data banks. The ability of humans to **verbalize concepts and ideas** and store them in this abstract form distinguishes the **human memory** decisively from those of animals, even the highest primates. It must be inferred at least that the human ability to store verbally coded material is supplementary to the nonverbal information storage of which both humans and animals are capable. This complication makes it more difficult to apply the results of animal experiments in interpreting human memory processes.

Third, there are good reasons to suspect that *storage in memory occurs in several steps,* which can be distinguished experimentally even though the underlying mechanisms are still largely unknown. According to these findings, our memory comprises at least two stages, a **short-term and a long-term memory.** Information in the short-term memory (for example, a telephone number one has just looked up) is soon forgotten unless it is transferred to the long-term memory by *practice.* Once in the latter it remains available for reference after quite a long time; the memory trace it has formed, the **engram,** is reinforced every time it is used. This fixing of the engram, so that an item of memory becomes progressively less likely to be lost, is called **consolidation.**

The following description of the human memory processes takes into account the concept of short- and long-term memory, extending it to correspond to the current state of our knowledge. These more recent findings include (i) the differential treatment of verbally and nonverbally coded material, (ii) a **sensory memory** preceding the short-term memory, and (iii) special memory mechanisms for the storage and retrieval of especially well consolidated material [32, 49]. These processes are summarized in Table 7–1.

Sensory memory. Sensory stimuli are first stored automatically, for a few hundred milliseconds, in a *sensory memory,* where they are examined, evaluated and either processed further or forgotten. Forgetting begins immediately after the information is acquired. The stored information can also be actively extinguished, or written over by information taken up shortly thereafter (Table 7–1, Fig. 7-21).

The experimental findings from which the existence of a sensory memory has been inferred are almost entirely in the realm of vision. For example, if a 16-letter array is presented for 50 ms and the subject is asked to recall the letters and to indicate which of the letters was marked by a dot, immediately after the presentation over 70% of the 16-letter array can be recalled. If the marking dot is projected after the letters rather than together

Table 7-1. Survey of human memory processes. Modified from ERVIN and ANDERS [32])

	Sensory memory	Primary memory	Secondary memory	Tertiary memory
Capacity	Limited by the information transmitted from receptor	Small	Very large	Very large
Duration	Fractions of a second	Several seconds	Several minutes to several years	Permanent
Entry into storage	Automatic during perception	Verbalization	Practice	Very frequent practice
Organization	Representation of the physical stimulus	Temporal ordering	Semantic and by spatiotemporal relations (Gestalt learning)	?
Access to storage	Limited only by speed of read out	Very rapid access	Slow access	Very rapid access
Types of information	Sensory	Verbal (among others?)	All forms	All forms
Types of forgetting	Fading and extinction	New information replaces old	Interference, proactive and retroactive	Possibly no forgetting

with them it becomes apparent that forgetting begins immediately and proceeds uniformly for 150 ms. Thereafter a plateau at the 25–35% level is reached, apparently because some of the letters have been transferred to a more permanent memory. Without this process the information stored in the sensory memory would be completely forgotten in about 250 ms. Tests with successive stimuli have revealed that in addition to this passive "fading" of information it can be actively "erased" by new information. All the results are the same regardless of whether the stimuli are presented to both eyes simultaneously or to one eye or the other in alternation, which is consistent with the notion of a single central visual memory [32].

The transfer of information from the short-lived sensory record to a more permanent memory can occur in two ways. One is by verbal coding of the sensory data, which the available experimental results indicate is the most common in adults. The other is a nonverbal way about which little is known, which must be used by small children and animals and also serves for the uptake of memory items that are difficult or impossible to express verbally.

Primary memory (Table 7–1). This memory serves for the **temporary storage of verbally coded material.** Its capacity is smaller than that of the sensory memory. The information is stored in the order of its arrival time. Forgetting occurs when the stored information is replaced by new items. Because the organism is continually processing information, the average duration of stay in the primary memory is short, only a matter of seconds. The **primary memory** corresponds roughly to the *short-term memory* mentioned above. *Nonverbally coded material* is not stored by the primary memory. It is transferred from the sensory memory to the secondary memory (see below) either

directly or by way of an intermediate storage mechanism of its own.

Transfer from the *primary memory* into the more permanent *secondary memory* is facilitated by **practice** – that is, attentive repetition and the corresponding circulation of the information in the primary memory (Fig. 7-21). The probability of transfer to the secondary memory depends on the duration of this practice.

Secondary memory (Table 7–1). This memory is a large long-term storage system. Only if it is stored there does information remain available for retrieval after a long time. So far there have been no wellfounded estimates of its capacity or of the duration of stay of the stored material. The information is stored according to its "significance." This *organizational difference* from the primary memory is clear in the nature of the mistakes that can occur during retrieval from storage. In the primary memory these usually amount to the confusion of phonetically similar sounds such as p and b, whereas in the secondary memory words of similar significance are confused. The two stores also differ in *speed of access;* retrieval from the primary memory is rapid and from the secondary memory, slow (searching through a large store takes more time).

Forgetting in the secondary memory appears to be based largely on interference with the learning process by other things learned previously or subsequently. In the first case the term **proactive inhibition** is used and in the latter, **retroactive inhibition.** Proactive inhibition seems to be the more important factor, since a greater amount of previously learned material is available. Viewed in this way, the blame for most of our forgetting must be placed on what we have learned before [18, 32].

Tertiary memory (Table 7–1 and Fig. 7-21). There are engrams – for example, one's own name or the ability to read and write or other skills employed daily – that as a result of years of practice are essentially *never forgotten,* even if through disease or injury the entire remaining content of memory is more or less erased. These engrams are also distinguished by *extremely short access times.* They appear to be stored in a particular form of memory, the **tertiary memory** [32]. In this concept, the **long-term memory** mentioned above corresponds to the secondary plus the tertiary memory.

Disturbances of Memory

Anterograde amnesia. The inability to learn newly acquired information – that is, to store it permanently where it is accessible for reference – is called **anterograde amnesia.** In the clinic this syndrome is called the *amnestic syndrome* or *Korsakoff's disease.* The patients (often chronic alcoholics) have nearly normal secondary and tertiary memory with respect to the time before the illness, and the primary memory is also functional. But they *cannot transfer information from the primary to the secondary memory.* Clinically, this situation is rather imprecisely called the loss of **"recent memory"** with retention of **"established (remote) memory."**
Pathological-anatomical and neurosurgical observations indicate that anterograde amnesia is caused in particular by bilateral damage to or removal of the *hippocampus and the structures associated with it.* These structures apparently play a key role in the *recoding and transfer* of information from the primary to the secondary memory. Because this process is also coupled with the selection of information for permanent storage, it must be assumed that the hippocampus and other limbic structures are especially involved in this activity [36, 41].

The thorough study by Brenda Milner and colleagues, over more than 15 years, of the highly intelligent patient H. M., who suffered **anterograde amnesia** following bilateral removal of the median parts of the temporal lobes [41], showed that the he could retain **simple material** (e.g., the number 584) for at least 15 minutes **by constant repetition** (in his primary memory). But if his attention was diverted only briefly the information was immediately lost forever. Tasks that exceeded the capacity of the primary memory – for example, finding and remembering the way through a peg maze with 28 steps from start to goal (Fig. 7-22 A) – could not be performed successfully even after many hundred trials. Not until the task was made much simpler

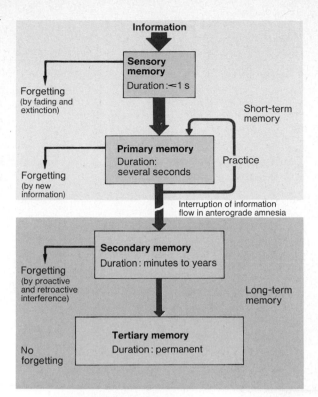

Fig. 7-21. Diagram of the information flow from the sensory (visual) to the secondary memory, by way of the primary memory. Verbal material is conveyed to the primary memory, where it is either repeated (practiced) or forgotten. Some of the practiced material reaches the secondary memory. Repetition facilitates transfer to the secondary memory, but it is not indispensable, nor does it guarantee transfer. (Modified from WAUGH and NORMAN [49])

(Fig. 7-22 B) could it be solved, and then only with the greatest effort since the patient was not able to remember the preceding practice session.
Anterograde amnesia appears to be particularly severe where verbal tasks are concerned, and **less pronounced for nonverbal tasks.** For example, the patient H. M. achieved practically normal performance in learning certain continuous motor tasks (Fig. 7-23). But even here, when *repeating the task he could never remember* having practiced it before. This, then, is a kind of learning in which no feeling of familiarity with the learned material develops. The normal learning curve for this kind of motor task indicates, as mentioned above, that this nonverbalizable information is transmitted from the sensory to the secondary memory not by way of the primary memory but by some other, unknown route. The inference that **verbal memory is chiefly affected in anterograde amnesia** is supported by the results of experiments employing classical and operant conditioning and others in which shape recognition is tested. In these experiments, as long as no verbal or verbalizable material was involved, the results were normal or nearly normal – but again *without the patients' remembering that they have learned anything* [32].
So far, unfortunately, *experimental lesions in animals have never produced a syndrome* comparable to human anterograde amnesia. Three main causes of this failure come to mind. (i) The disturbance in humans is limited to verbal or verbalizable material, so that it cannot become evident in animals. (ii) The experiments on animals done so far have used tests that cannot moni-

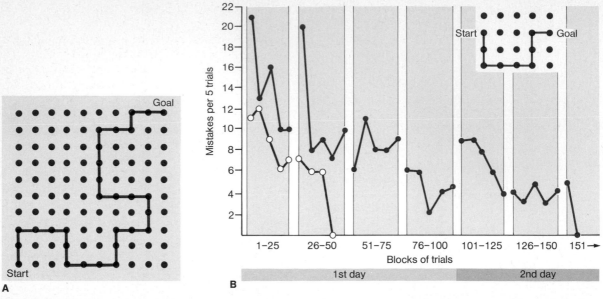

A

B

Fig. 7-22 A, B. Learning in a peg maze. **A** The black circles symbolize metal pegs on a wooden board. The subject must discover the correct path from start to goal (shown in *red*) and remember it. When an incorrect peg is touched a click sounds. A normal subject can learn to perform the task without mistakes three times in a row in twenty trials or less. Even highly intelligent patients with anterograde amnesia cannot solve the problem. **B** Learning by a patient with anterograde amnesia, with a smaller pegboard. Even this simple task was learned only after 155 trials *(red line)*. When the test was repeated two years later some retention was evident, but the patient could not remember having ever performed the task (From MILNER [41])

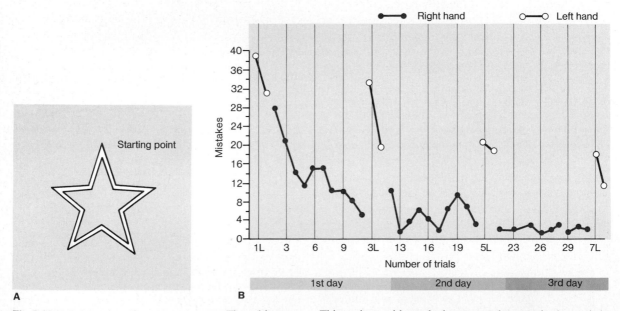

A

B

Fig. 7-23 A, B. Learning of a motor program. The subject sees the star in **A** and the pencil he is holding in a mirror, and must trace the star in the space between the two outlines (try it yourself!). Crossing either outline counts as a mistake. The learning curves in **B** were produced by the same patient as in Fig. 7-22. This patient, with marked anterograde amnesia, learned the task just as rapidly as a normal subject. Again, however, he could not remember ever having performed the task. (From MILNER [41])

tor accurately enough the transfer from the primary to the secondary memory. (iii) The role of the hippocampus and associated structures has changed during phylogeny (together with the development of speech?).

Retrograde amnesia. The inability to retrieve items stored in memory in the time before normal brain function was impaired is called **retrograde amnesia.** Well-known examples of its possible causes are mechanical shocks (concussion), stroke (apoplexy), electroshock (therapeutic or by accident) and anesthesia. All are associated with fairly generalized disruption of brain function, and it is not yet known which particular structural and functional disturbances give rise to retrograde amnesia.

In any case, the event that produces retrograde amnesia erases the content of the *primary memory.* Initially more or less large parts of the secondary memory are also lost, further back into the past the more severe the damage was. It is striking, however, that the forgotten time span later narrows and in some cases shrinks so far that no gap remains. Moreover, special techniques (e.g., hypnosis) can be used to recall forgotten material to memory. These and other findings make it seem likely that **retrograde amnesia** amounts mainly to **interference with access to the secondary memory** and less to a loss of the content of memory. The tertiary memory, as a rule, is unaffected even in severe cases of retrograde amnesia [18, 32].

Animal experiments relevant to retrograde amnesia have so far had results just as unsatisfactory as those designed to study anterograde amnesia. Among other techniques, these experiments employ general electroshock, local electrical stimulation (e.g., of the amygdala), rapid anesthesia, partial or complete *functional decortication* by temporary application of isotonic KC1 solution to the cerebral cortex (which causes local massive depolarization spreading into the surroundings, and thus inexcitability of the cortical neurons, called *"spreading depression"*), intense cooling of cortical areas, and the application of cholinesterase and protein-synthesis inhibitors. The aim in each case has been to produce retrograde amnesia or to disturb the process of consolidation; the results are extraordinarily inconsistent [29].

Hysterical amnesia. Occasionally patients with complete loss of memory are encountered who cannot remember who they are and what they have done prior to this moment in their lives. In these extremely rare cases one is dealing with an *exclusively functional* mental disturbance quite unlike the amnesias discussed so far. It is described by the term **hysterical amnesia.** The disorder is distinguished from the primarily organic amnesias (caused by damage to brain tissue) by three characteristics: 1. all personal data are forgotten, including even the person's own name; 2. the amnesia is global in nature and entirely unaffected by key stimuli (for example, returning the patient to his former surroundings or to the company of

relatives); and 3. the inability to remember past events persists even though new information can be remembered well.

Hysterical amnesia is rarely a conscious pretense – for example, to hide something or avoid punishment. Although it is always based at least in part on the desire to escape an emotional stress situation, the plunge into amnesia (usually occasioned by a spectacular external event) is not under conscious control. Moreover, the cause of the stress is not always to be sought in a social conflict situation.

Neuronal Mechanisms

The simplest and most intuitively appealing inference about the neuronal basis of learning is that an item of information is initially stored in the form of reverberating excitation (cf. Fig. 4-5) in a spatiotemporally organized pattern *(dynamic engram)*. This circulating excitation brings about **structural changes at the synapses involved** (consolidation to a *structural engram*). The content of memory can then be retrieved by corresponding activation of these synapses.

The *concept of reverberating excitation* is consistent with the subjective experience that we must *practice* material to be learned – that is, let it pass repeatedly through our consciousness – in order eventually to retain it. Morphological and electrophysiological findings indicate at least the possibility of such reverberation. But it is still an entirely open question whether such events are related to learning processes.

The **changes in synaptic efficiency** during and after tetanic stimulation have been discussed extensively (p. 74). Particularly in cases of *posttetanic potentiation,* which has been seen to last for many hours at certain *excitatory* synapses (e.g., in the hippocampus) and probably can persist considerably longer, it has long been thought that the altered synaptic properties may reflect changes in the nervous system associated with formation of a structural engram [11, 22]. This view is consistent with the fact that in the spinal cord, where only relatively brief posttetanic potentiation occurs (cf. Fig. 4-6 D, E, p. 74) no persistent learning is observed. The concept is also supported by the observation that when dendritic synapses in the mouse visual cortex are not used from birth onward (because the eye is removed or the animals are raised in darkness) they show histological and functional signs of degeneration – a decrease in functional capacity as a consequence of insufficient use [11].

The connection between use or non-use of synapses and their efficiency, however, must not be viewed too simply. Because the nervous system is continuously active throughout life, the eventual result of cumulative activity would be a considerable hypertrophy of all the synapses. Modifications of the original concept have been proposed to get around this difficulty. For example, it has been suggested that in the cerebellum only the *simultaneous activation* of mossy-fiber and climbing-fiber synapses on a Purkinje cell induces a synaptic learning process in the former [11].

The study of **changes in the electroencephalogram** has so far produced an abundance of interesting results but little insight into the neuronal mechanisms of learning and memory. As described on pp. 148 and 151, in the EEG of a waking, relaxed person slow α waves of 8–13 Hz predominate. A new stimulus, especially if unexpected, abolishes the α waves (α blockade), which are replaced by high-frequency β waves (14–30 Hz) of lower amplitude. At the same time other somatic and vegetative reactions appear (e. g., looking toward the stimulus source, increase in muscle tone, changes in heart rate). These changes together are called the **orienting response.** If the stimulus has no significance to the animal, the orienting response soon disappears upon repeated presentation. The process of becoming accustomed to the stimulus, regarded as a form of *negative learning* (the animal learns that the orientation response is not necessary for this stimulus) is called **habituation.** Habituation is specific to each stimulus.

Stimuli such as clicks, which at first do not produce α blockade, can do so when by Pavlov's *classical conditioning* technique (cf. p. 185) they are temporarily presented together with a stimulus that in itself elicits α blockade (the unconditioned stimulus; e. g., a light flash). Moreover, the cortical DC voltages (p. 150) can be influenced in this way; for example, the change in the cortical DC potential that normally occurs when a hungry cat is fed can be conditioned by visual or acoustic stimuli. In other words, animals and humans can learn, by classical conditioning, to modify the electrophysiological correlates of brain activity [18]. More recently, it has been possible to use *operant conditioning* (for definition and method see p. 185) to produce changes in the animal and human EEG (cf. below: learning in the autonomic nervous system). Therapeutic applications of such methods are conceivable – for example, to suppress pre-epileptic high-frequency discharge or to assist mental and emotional relaxation.

Studies using **simultaneous recording from several regions of the brain,** at the level of macro- and micropotentials, and combinations of such **recordings with observation of behavior** show that most learning processes are accompanied by changes in the activity of *many cortical and subcortical structures.* Moreover, during and after learning processes there are distinct *phase shifts* in the spontaneous rhythms of individual parts of the brain, which may indicate that the learning has induced a corresponding change in the leading pacemaker. The interpretation of these complex findings, however, in general remains a matter for vigorous debate [18].

Biochemical (Molecular) Mechanisms of the Engram

Since the coding of **genetic memory** in deoxyribonucleic acid (DNA) has been discovered, and the study of **immunological memory** has been similarly successful, there has been an incentive to look for molecular changes underlying **neuronal memory** that could be considered the basis of the engram.

Many experiments have been concerned with the question whether learning can bring about **changes in the ribonucleic acids** (RNA) of neurons and glial cells. Microtechniques that permit measurement of both the amount of RNA and the proportions of the four nucleotide bases of which RNA molecules are composed have in fact shown that there are changes in the proportions of these bases during certain learning processes (HYDÉN in [29]). But it cannot be ruled out – indeed, it is likely – that these changes are entirely nonspecific. To overcome this objection, further attempts have been made to demonstrate the possibility of **transfer of learned behavior** by this RNA; RNA extracted from the brains of trained populations of animals is injected into control animals. These experiments have so far provided no convincing evidence, whether for simple organisms like flatworms (planarians) or for fish and mammals [29].

Two further attempts to reveal the biochemical bases of neuronal memory deserve mention. First, in an approach just the opposite of those described above, an attempt has been made to interfere with formation of a structural engram in the cell or the cell membrane by **inhibiting the synthesis of RNA or protein** (for example, by administering actinomycin or puromycin). To the extent that these experiments have been successful, they too face the objection that a general inhibition of protein synthesis leads not only to a disturbance of engram formation but also to a general disruption of all cellular function. Second, from the brains of rats trained to avoid dark places (contrary to their natural preference) by punishment with electric shocks, a polypeptide has been isolated that when injected into normal rats (or into mice or fish) causes them to spend more time in the light. This polypeptide, called **scotophobin,** comprises 15 amino acids; it has since been synthesized (cf. Unger in [29]). It is not yet clear how these findings are to be evaluated. The experiments have not yet been confirmed by other researchers, nor has any other macromolecule been isolated that serves as an "information carrier" in learning another behavior pattern. Moreover, in part of its amino-acid chain scotophobin resembles ACTH, which increases the degree of wakefulness of the organism. If scotophobin were to do the same thing, it could enhance the ability to learn in a nonspecific way.

Learning in the Autonomic Nervous System

Since Pavlov's time it has been known that after a stimulus initially ineffective in itself has been coupled with an effective (unconditioned) stimulus, the *conditioned stimulus* becomes capable of eliciting changes

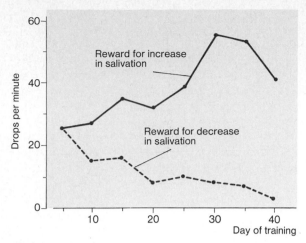

Fig. 7-24. Learning curves (average values) of thirsty dogs rewarded with water for increasing or decreasing their salivary secretion. It was remarkable that the group trained to increase the flow of saliva on the whole appeared more attentive and wakeful than the other group. (After MILLER and CARMONA in [39])

Attempts have also been made to influence autonomic processes in humans by the technique of operant conditioning. For example, if the subject of such an experiment is allowed to monitor his own heartbeat or its frequency by visual or audible signals, in general small changes in heart rate in the desired direction can serve as a reward and as an incentive to achieve larger changes. Such **biofeedback arrangements** are regarded as a promising therapeutic approach, by which disease processes in the organism can be ameliorated without the use of drugs. Successes have been reported, for example, in the treatment of disturbed heart rhythms, tension headache, migraine and difficulty in falling asleep (for control of EEG frequency see p. 170). But here, even more than in animal experiments, it should be kept in mind that many indirect influences can participate in changing the autonomic parameter under study.

in the behavior of effectors of the autonomic nervous system (heart, smooth muscles, glands). It was long thought that this very restricted form of learning was the only form of which the autonomic nervous system is capable. But application of the technique of **operant conditioning** (synonyms: Type II conditioning, trial-and-error learning, instrumental learning; cf. p. 185), in which the desired behavior pattern is reinforced by a reward, has shown that even in the autonomic nervous system far more extensive learning is possible. For example, in experiments on animals it has been possible to change over a wide range the secretion of saliva (Fig. 7-24), the heart rate, the tone of the intestinal musculature, the excretion of urine and the blood flow through the wall of the stomach [39].

The greatest difficulty encountered in studying the behavioral changes induced by operant learning in the autonomic nervous system is that the most easily measurable responses (e. g., heart rate) can also be affected *indirectly* by way of the skeletal musculature – that is, by changes in muscular work, muscle tone or diaphragm contraction. The same is true of more subtle indirect influence, such as the general degree of wakefulness and attentiveness of the experimental animal (cf. legend to Fig. 7-24). It has not always been possible to show conclusively that such indirect factors have been ruled out as crucial causes of the observed changes in the effectors of the autonomic nervous system. Although in many experiments learning occurred in the autonomic nervous system even after the skeletal musculature had been paralyzed with curare, there has been some criticism of the results [39].

7.5   The Frontal Lobes

It was relatively late in the course of evolution when there appeared a significant increase in those parts of the neocortex to which no direct sensory or motor functions could be ascribed. In humans these **"nonspecific areas"** take up by far the largest part of the cerebral cortex (Fig. 7-25). The nonspecific areas were originally referred to as *"association cortex"* or association areas, because of the widespread view that they represented a *corticocortical connection* between the sensory and the motor areas, thus contributing to the perception and processing of the acquired information and at the same time serving as the seat of the highest mental functions. But more recent histology has shown that corticocortical connections are relatively rare, and many stimulation and ablation experiments and careful clinical observations have since made it possible to delimit further the role of the nonspecific cortical areas. The *parietal* and *temporal* regions, for instance, are involved in part in the neuronal processes underlying speech and in part in the form and spatial recognition of the body and the outside world, with interesting differences between the left and right hemispheres (cf. pp. 161, 163 and Fig. 7-20). As to the **functions of the frontal lobe,** however, very little information is available, derived mostly from clinical observations (see below). For a long time the frontal lobe was believed to be the seat of the highest mental functions and of the human intelligence, but to date there is no solid experimental and clinical foundation for this view.

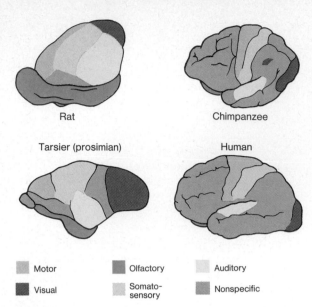

Rat   Chimpanzee

Tarsier (prosimian)   Human

■ Motor   ■ Olfactory   ■ Auditory
■ Visual   ■ Somato-   ■ Nonspecific
                   sensory

Fig. 7-25. Side view of the brains of mammals, to illustrate the massive increase in nonspecific cortex in the course of late phylogeny. In evaluating the relative proportions of the different cortical areas, the considerable absolute difference in size of the brains should be kept in mind. (After STANLEY COBB)

Connections of the frontal lobe. The frontal cortex in the narrow sense comprises Areas 9 to 12 on the dorsal and lateral surfaces of the frontal lobe (cf. Fig. 7-2, p. 146) as well as Areas 13 and 14 on the orbital surface. These *homotypical* cortical regions (cf. Fig. 7-3, p. 146) are rather misleadingly called the **prefrontal cortex.** The prefrontal cortex receives most of its afference from the **dorsal medial nucleus,** one of the *nonspecific thalamic nuclei* (cf. Fig. 9-9, p. 201). It also has extensive reciprocal connections with various parts of the limbic system, including the cingulate gyrus, the hippocampus, the amygdala and the hypothalamus. Therefore the prefrontal cortex has also been regarded as the **neocortical part of the limbic system,** its dorsal regions being connected more to the hippocampus and the ventral regions, more to the amygdala. Given that the limbic system plays a special role in the species-specific behavior of an organism (drives, motivation; cf. p. 138), it is perhaps justified to postulate that one of the tasks of the prefrontal cortex is the *learned control* of innate behavior patterns. This idea is supported by the fact that many patients with frontal-lobe damage are said to be unusually impulsive, uninhibited, irritable, euphoric or psychologically labile in other ways [12, 26].

Inferences from Frontal-Lobe Lesions in Humans

Patients with frontal-lobe lesions have normal scores on most of the standard *intelligence tests.* Often, however, they exhibit subtle personality changes, rather hard to describe, such as the *lack of motivation* and the *absence of firm intentions and plans based on foresight.* Moreover, they are often unreliable, crude or tactless, frivolous or irascible; as a result, despite their normal "intelligence," they can become embroiled in social conflicts (for example, while at work).

In *tests with tasks involving movement,* these patients are inclined to persist in a motor act they have begun, even when the rules of play have long since demanded that they do something else. In the task illustrated in Fig. 7-26 the patients are told, after each drawing, which geometric figure they should draw next. Although they understand this instruction (and can repeat it if asked), they frequently proceed to draw again a figure already drawn one or more times. Such persistence in what has been begun is called **perseveration.**

Perseveration is often accompanied by a *dissociation between verbal and other motor reactions.* For instance, if such a frontal-lobe patient is asked to press a button with the left hand when given a green signal and with the right hand when the signal is red, he will follow this instruction a few times and then begin to respond to both signals with one hand only or with either at random. Asked to repeat the instruction, he can do so correctly, but he does not correct his mistake. It appears as though the verbal instruction is not conveyed to the motor areas responsible for the movement of the hands. (Similar disparities are occasionally seen in everyday life – for example, when a person says "left" but turns to the right.) The tendency to perseveration is also reflected in learning experiments in which the patient has difficulty distinguishing a stimulus in a series from those that preceded it. Their behavior gives the impression that the preceding memory trace cannot make room for the next rapidly enough – that their problem is an *enhanced proactive inhibition* (cf. p. 166 and Table 7-1).

When tested with peg mazes (cf. Fig. 7-22) these patients also make far more than the average number of mistakes made by normal people or patients with other kinds of brain damage. In particular, they tend to carry on regardless of their mistakes, or to jump diagonally from peg to peg though this is prohibited by the rules. Here, again, they are conscious of their mistakes, but they are incapable of bringing their impulsive actions under control; the determination to reach the goal appears to outweigh all other motivations.

Frontal-lobe patients, then, find it difficult to change their behavior when the circumstances require it. The

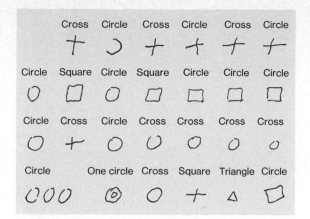

Fig. 7-26. Perseveration in the performance of motor tasks by four patients with frontal-lobe damage. Each line shows the patient's drawings in red, and above them the instructions given by the examiner. The first, second and fourth patients had tumors of the left frontal lobe, and the third had an abscess in the right frontal lobe. (From LURIA [37])

effectiveness of external constraints appears to be weakened, and when several external and internal motivations are in competition it is hard for the patient to change from one to another rapidly and appropriately. This conclusion from observations of behavior is consistent with that drawn above, in the context of the anatomical connections – that the prefrontal cortex is involved in the **learned control of inborn behavior patterns** and in **harmonizing external and internal motivations.**

Psychosurgery. In behavioral studies on chimpanzees (see below) it was noticed that animals that previously became enraged at their mistakes began to accept them calmly after the connections between frontal lobe and thalamus had been cut. A rather hasty application of these findings to humans by Moniz led to the performance of such operations on neuropsychiatric patients in the period 1940–1950. These **prefrontal lobotomies** or **leukotomies** were meant to treat mental disorders and intractable pain; in the latter case it was thought that the pain continued to be sensed but that its affective elements were considerably reduced.

Prefrontal leukotomy was always controversial and has since become obsolete – that is, unnecessary and no longer justified – owing to the introduction of effective psychoactive drugs. But its original acceptance as therapy marked the beginning of **psychosurgery,** the deliberate attempt to *affect human behavior by the destruction or removal of brain tissue.* In a broader sense electroshock treatments, long-term therapy with psychoactive drugs, and the insertion of electrodes into the brain should also be regarded as psychosurgery, because these procedures can also produce permanent alterations of brain tissue.

In view of the extent of our ignorance about the way the brain works and the functions of its individual components, the grounds for using psychosurgical procedures today are more empirical than theoretical. The most common operation at present appears to be **cingulotomy,** the stereotactic disconnection of the cingulate gyrus; it is performed to relieve intractable pain and to treat a number of mental disturbances such as de-

pression, severe anxiety states and compulsive neuroses. **Amygdalotomy** is used as a last resort to control aggressive behavior, though grave misgivings are expressed about such profound interference with personality. It should never be performed without painstaking examination of the individual case. There must be firm proof that despite the utmost effort none of the conventional psychiatric treatments have helped the patient for whom the operation is being considered, and that in the present state of knowledge there is a fair chance that limited psychosurgical intervention will succeed in improving his condition without causing any fundamental personality change.

Frontal-Lobe Symptoms in Animal Experiments

The systematic study of the effects of frontal-lobe lesions on the behavior of chimpanzees and other mammals has so far had two main results: (i) like humans, the animals show a strong tendency to **perseveration,** and (ii) they perform *tasks requiring delayed responses considerably more poorly* (see below). The latter defect cannot be demonstrated in humans, probably because the difficulties can be circumvented by verbalizing the task.

Many test arrangements have revealed the *tendency to perseveration* – for example, arrangements in which alternate switches are to be pressed in response to light signals. As in the experiments on humans described above (Fig. 7-26), rather than alternating, the animal continues for a long time to give the response first chosen. The *interpretation of this behavior* is analogous to that for humans (see above).

In the simplest case of a **delayed-response task,** a reward (e.g., a nut) is placed under one of two overturned cups while the animal is watching, and then an opaque screen is let down between the cups and the animal. After a predetermined time has elapsed the screen is raised again and the animal can look for the reward under one of the cups. Normal chimpanzees can readily solve this problem after a minute's delay, but animals with frontal-lobe lesions fail after a delay of only five seconds. One might well suspect that the difficulty lies in an impairment of (short-term) memory, but experiments have not supported this view. If the animal is kept in the dark during the waiting period, its performance improves, indicating that the stimuli to which it is exposed in the light during the delay crowd out the information about the position of the reward. That is, the animals suffer from **enhanced retroactive inhibition** (cf. p. 166 and Table 7-1), and find it difficult to pay enough attention to the crucial stimuli. This thesis of **increased distractability** of animals with prefrontal lobectomies is supported by still other evidence: the animals are usually hyperactive and hyperreactive; small doses of sedatives, such as barbiturates, have positive effects like that of darkening the room during the waiting period; and in tests with many stimuli or choice situations the results are particularly bad.

In general, all these findings can be summarized in the hypothesis that the prefrontal cortex is of major significance in the **development of behavioral strategies.** An inability to work out such strategies becomes especially clear whenever it is necessary to change behavior rapidly, and when there is a delay between the presentation of the problem and its solution, so that the additional input of information during this time must be appropriately incorporated into the behavioral strategy.

7.6   References

Textbooks and Handbooks

1. ANDERSEN, P., ANDERSSON, S.A.: Physiological Basis of the Alpha Rhythm. New York: Appleton-Centruy-Crofts 1968
2. ARKIN, A.M., ANTROBUS, J.S., ELLMANN, S.J. (Eds.): The Mind in Sleep. Psychology and Psychophysiology. Hillsdale, N.J.: Lawrence Erlbaum Assoc. 1978
3. BRAIN, LORD: Science and Man. London: Faber and Faber 1966
4. BRAITENBERG, V.: On the Texture of Brains. New York–Heidelberg–Berlin: Springer Verlag 1977
5. BRAZIER, M.A.B., PETSCHE, H.: Architectonics of the Cerebral Cortex. IBRO Monograph Series Vol.3. New York: Raven Press 1978
6. BRODAL, A.: Neurological Anatomy in Relation to Clinical Medicine. 2nd Edition. New York–London–Toronto: Oxford University Press 1969
7. BÜNNING, E.: The Physiological Clock. Circadian Rhythms and Biological Chronometry. 3rd Edition. New York–Heidelberg–Berlin: Springer Verlag 1973
8. BUSER, P.A., ROUGEUL-BUSER, A. (Eds.): Cerebral Correlates of Conscious Experience. Amsterdam–New York–Oxford: Elsevier 1978
9. CREUTZFELDT, O. (Ed.): Afferent and Intrinsic Organization of Laminated Structures in the Brain. Experimental Brain Research, Suppl.1, 1976
10. DIMOND, S.J., BLIZARD, D.A. (Eds.): Evolution and Lateralization of the Brain. Ann. New York Acad. Sci. 299, 1977
11. ECCLES, J.C.: The Understanding of the Brain. New York–St. Louis–San Francisco–Düsseldorf: McGraw Hill 1973
12. GAZZANIGA, M.S. (Ed.): Neuropsychology. Handbook of Behavioral Neurobiology, Vol.2. New York–London: Plenum Press 1979
13. JASPER, H.H., WARD, A.A., POPE, A. (Eds.): Basic Mechanisms of the Epilepsies. Boston: Little, Brown and Co. 1969
14. JOVANOVIĆ, U.J.: Normal Sleep in Man. Stuttgart: Hippokrates 1971
15. KOELLA, W.P.: Sleep – Its Nature and Physiological Organization. Springfield: C.C. Thomas 1967
16. LEONHARDT, H.: Human Histology, Cytology and Microanatomy. Stuttgart: Thieme 1977
17. MENDELSON, W.B., GILLIN, J.Ch., WYATT, R.H.: Human Sleep and its Disorders. New York–London: Plenum Press 1977
18. MOUNTCASTLE, V.B. (Ed.): Medical Physiology, Vol.II. 13th Edition. St. Louis: Mosby 1974
19. PAPPENHEIMER, J.R., KOSKI, G., FENCL, V., KARNOVSKY, M.L., KRUEGER, J.: Extraction of sleep-promoting Factor S from cerebrospinal fluid and from brains of sleep-deprived animals. J. Neurophysiol. 38, 1299 (1975)
20. PENFIELD, W., JASPER, H.: Epilepsy and the Functional Anatomy of the Human Brain. Boston: Little, Brown and Company 1954
21. PENFIELD, W., ROBERTS, L.: Speech and Brain Mechanisms. Princeton, N.J.: Princeton University Press 1959

22. POPPER, K., ECCLES, J.C.: The Self and Its Brain. Berlin–Heidelberg–New York: Springer Verlag 1978
23. RÉMOND, A. (Ed.): Handbook of Electroencephalography and Clinical Neurophysiology. Amsterdam: Elsevier Scientific Publishing Co. 1974 and in press
24. RECHTSCHAFFEN, A., KALES, A. (Eds.): A Manual of Standardized Terminology, Techniques and Scoring System for Sleep Stages of Human Subjects. Washington (D.C.): Publ. Health Service, U.S. Government Printing Office 1968
25. SCHMITT, F.O., WORDEN, F.G. (Eds.): The Neurosciences, Third Study Program. Cambridge, Mass.–London: The MIT Press 1974
26. WALTON, J.N.: BRAIN'S Diseases of the Nervous System. 8th Edition. Oxford: Oxford University Press 1977
27. WEVER, R.A.: The Circadian System of Man. Berlin–Heidelberg–New York: Springer 1979
28. YOUNG, J.Z.: An Introduction to the Study of Man. London–Oxford–New York: Oxford University Press 1974
29. ZIPPEL, H.P. (Ed.): Memory and Transfer of Information. New York–London: Plenum-Press 1973
30. ZÜLCH, K.H., CREUTZFELDT, O., GALBRAITH, G.C. (Eds.): Cerebral Localization. Berlin–Heidelberg–New York: Springer 1975

Research Reports and Reviews

31. CREUTZFELDT, O.: The neuronal generation of the EEG. In: RÉMOND, A. (Ed.): Handbook of Electroencephalography and Clinical Neurophysiology, 2/C. Amsterdam: Elsevier Scientific Publishing 1974
32. ERVIN, F.R., ANDERS, T.R.: Normal and pathological memory: data and a conceptual scheme. In: SCHMITT, F.O. (Ed.): The Neurosciences, Second Study Program, p.163. New York: Rockefeller University Press 1970
33. INGVAR, D.H.: Functional landscapes of the dominant hemisphere. Brain Research 107, 181 (1976)
34. JOUVET, M.: The states of sleep. In: Physiological Psychology. Readings from SCIENTIFIC AMERICAN, p.328. San Francisco: W.H.Freeman 1967
35. JOUVET, M.: The role of monoamines and acetylcholine containing neurons in the regulation of the sleep-waking cycle. Ergebn. Physiol. 64, 166 (1972)
36. KORNHUBER, H.H.: Neural control of input into long term memory: limbic system and amnestic syndrome in man. In: ZIPPEL, H.P. (Ed.): Memory and Transfer of Information, p.1. New York–London: Plenum Press 1973
37. LURIA, A.R.: The functional organization of the brain. In: Physiological Psychology. Readings from SCIENTIFIC AMERICAN, p.406. San Francisco: Freeman 1971
38. MACKAY, D.M.: Selves and brains. Neuroscience 3, 599 1978
39. MILLER, N.W.: Learning of visceral and glandular responses. Science 163, 434 (1969)
40. MILLS, J.N.: Human circadian rhythms. Physiol. Rev. 46, 128 (1966)
41. MILNER, B.: Memory and the medial temporal regions of the brain. In: PRIBRAM, K.H., BROADBENT, D.E. (Eds.): Biology of Memory, p.29. New York–London: Academic Press 1970
42. MORUZZI, G.: The sleep-waking cycle (Neurophysiology and neurochemistry of sleep and wakefulness). Ergebn. Physiol. 64, 1 (1972)
43. O'LEARY, J.L., GOLDRING, S.: D-C potentials of the brain. Physiol. Rev. 44, 91 (1964)
44. PAKKENBERG, H.: The number of nerve cells in the cerebral cortex of man. J. comp. Neurol. 128, 17 (1966)
45. ROFFWARG, H.P., MUZIO, J.N., DEMENT, W.C.: Ontogenetic development of the human sleep-dream cycle. Science 152, 604 (1966)
46. SNYDER, F., SCOTT, J.: The psychophysiology of sleep. In: GREENFIELD, N.S., STERNBACH, R.A. (Eds.): Handbook of Psychophysiology. New York: Holt 1972
47. SPERRY, R.: A modified concept of consciousness. Physiol. Rev. 76, 532 (1969)
48. TOWE, A.L.: Notes on the hypothesis of columnar organization in somatosensory cerebral cortex. Brain, Behavior and Evolution 11, 16 (1975)
49. WAUGH, N.C., NORMAN, D.A.: Primary memory. Psychol. Rev. 72, 89 (1965)

Part II
Sense Organs

8 General Sensory Physiology

J. Dudel

8.1 Basic Concepts

The field of general sensory physiology is concerned with the *principles* underlying the sensory abilities of humans and animals. This general approach is possible and useful because the various sense organs closely resemble one another in organization and function, in their connections to centers in the brain, and in the reactions they elicit. Moreover, for all sense organs there is the problem of "objective" and "subjective" aspects. We can observe and analyze the performance of a human or animal sense organ by the same procedures as in research on the circulatory system, for example; in so doing, we are studying **objective sensory physiology.** But we can go further and apply scientific analysis to our own sensations, produced by environmental phenomena with the mediation of the sense organs, and in this we can also draw upon the analogous experiences reported by other people. Here we are in the area of **subjective sensory physiology.** One of the basic concerns in general sensory physiology is to analyze these two aspects and evaluate their interdependence.

Objective and Subjective Sensory Physiology

Subjective sensory physiology is concerned with sensation and perception – activities of the human *mind.* Objective sensory physiology treats receptor potentials (cf. p. 26), the impulse frequencies in sensory centers of the brain and the like; all of these are in principle *material* phenomena, describable in physical and chemical terms. One may well wonder whether these two areas indeed have anything in common, whether the material and the mental are comparable or derivable one from the other. Questions at this level soon lead us to the basic themes of ontology and epistemology, which can be mentioned only briefly here.

Many schools of philosophy hold the human body to be in essence distinct from the human mind; from this point of view, objective and subjective sensory physiology are concerned with essentially non-comparable things. Other philosophical systems – for example, those with a materialistic slant – see no essential difference between body and mind, and would regard objective and subjective sensory physiology simply as different methods for observing the same object. There are epistemological positions corresponding to each of these ontological standpoints. One emphasizes the fact that everything a person knows has been learned by way of his senses. *Empiricists* or *positivists* (e.g., Aristotle, Hume, Wittgenstein) thus regard knowledge as the sum of all we have acquired by direct sensory experience, and postulate that general conclusions can be drawn by *inductive* inference from individual observations. But a strong case can be made for the opposite view – that it is logically impossible to base a general conclusion on a number of single observations. Having seen a thousand white geese, one is not therefore justified in concluding that *all* geese are white (POPPER [25]). Inference from observation cannot be generally valid in the absence of concepts, rules of logic, theories. The *idealistic* schools of epistemology hold these categories to be primary, a precondition of experience (e.g., Kant). To their extreme exponents (e.g., Hegel) only ideas are real and true. It is easy to see that these different epistemological approaches must involve quite different evaluations of objective and subjective sensory physiology.

From a methodological viewpoint physiology, working with the methods of the natural sciences, practices a form of **critical empiricism.** It relies on the observation of phenomena in the realm of the senses, but in full knowledge that any scientific observation presupposes a theory, and that any summary of such observations leads to scientific theories with implications that, as a rule, go beyond what has been documented by direct observation. The natural scientist dares to make such theories, but demands that their predictions should be testable by observations. Any theory is permissible as long as its *incorrectness can be demonstrated* in principle by observation or *experiment.* Theories in the natural sciences must be *falsifiable;* theories not meeting this criterion may be true, but they are "metaphysics" [25]. Therefore statements regarding the essential difference or identity of mind

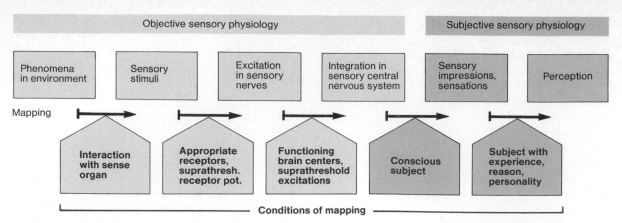

Fig. 8-1. Mapping in sensory physiology. The boxes represent basic phenomena of sensory physiology, and the arrows be-tween them indicate the mapping of one stage onto the next, under the conditions listed below each arrow

and matter are outside the scope of sensory physiology, for such statements are not falsifiable by observation. Causal relationship between subjective and objective sensory phenomena cannot be postulated in the framework of the natural sciences, although certain correlations can be discerned and checked by observation.

Recently POPPER and ECCLES [26] have developed an approach that borders on the kind of hypothesis found in the natural sciences. They postulate a "selfconscious mind" distinct from the body and the functions of the brain. The selfconscious mind has access to the information present in the brain, can bring it into consciousness, and can also intervene in and modify the operation of the brain. The most important function of the self-conscious mind is to select from the abundance of information received and stored, and from the manifold actions the brain is prepared to initiate integrating this to 'the unity of conscious experience from moment to moment'. Many aspects of this hypothesis are in principle falsifiable by observation, as is required of a hypothesis in the natural sciences.

The "mapping" relationship. So that we can define these correlations more precisely, we shall first set out in a general scheme the different levels in sensory physiology, from stimulus to perception (Fig. 8-1). Of the many and varied environmental influences to which we are exposed, some affect our sense organs. In this context they are called **stimuli** to the particular organs concerned. The stimuli give rise to potentials in *receptors,* which in turn cause *excitation* of afferent sensory nerve fibers (cf. p. 27). The activity of many of these afferent fibers is integrated in *sensory centers in the brain.* We have no subjective knowledge of these events in our nervous system. The first subjective sign that a simple stimulus has occurred is a **sensory impression;** light of wavelength 400 nm elicits the sensory impression "blue". Sensory impressions are the elements of sensation. A **sensation,** for example, might be described by saying "I see a blue area within

which are round white areas of different sizes." As a rule, the subject interprets its sensations, fitting them into what it has already experienced and learned; in this process, the sensation becomes a **perception.** The above sensation "I see a blue area ..." corresponds to the perception "There are cumulus clouds in the sky."

The chain of correspondences implied in the last paragraph, between environmental phenomena and their perception, is diagrammed in Fig. 8-1. The basic phenomena of sensory physiology, indicated in the square boxes, are connected by arrows. In this diagram the arrows stand not for a *causal* relationship, but the relationship we shall call **mapping** (*Abbildung,* cf. [4]). The concept "mapping" denotes that there is a defined and unique representation by which points on an object are associated with (or "mapped onto") points on another – or more generally in mathematical terms, a unique association between members of two sets ($x \varepsilon A \leftrightarrow \gamma \varepsilon \beta$). A sensory stimulus, for example, is mapped onto excitation in a nerve, and sensory impressions are mapped onto perception. The object itself is not the cause of its representation; the mapping may occur by means of a suitable device – for example, an aerial camera which projects an image of the object onto photographic paper. The mapping therefore is not only characterized by the object, but also by the special mapping conditions, the surveyor's instruments, the scale, the kind of projection, or the symbols of representation for specific details.

Therefore Fig. 8-1 also shows, beneath the arrows, the conditions of mapping at each level. Environmental phenomena are sensory stimuli only when they interact with a suitable sense organ. Similarly, the signals from a sense organ that are processed and integrated in the CNS become sensory impressions or sensations only if the CNS is associated with a conscious subject.

The mapping relationships indicated by the arrows in Fig. 8-1 in the realm of objective sensory physiology, from stimulus to integration in the CNS, can in principle be described as physical and chemical processes. In this sense the stimulus can be said to "cause" excitation in a sensory nerve. As discussed above, however, no such causal relationship can be postulated for the transition from the phenomena of objective sensory physiology to those in the subjective sphere. The direction of the arrow showing mapping of the CNS onto sensation in Fig. 8-1 is justified nevertheless, for a more or less normally functioning CNS is a prerequisite for sensation.

Basic Dimensions of Sensation

Having described the content of sensory physiology in the most general terms, we shall now begin to fill in the framework we have erected by considering the characteristics of the individual sensations. Each sensation (as well as the correlated responses in the sensory nervous system) has 4 basic dimensions: **spatiality, temporality, quality** and **intensity.** The first two of these relate the sensation or perception to the world or to one's environment. When something touches my skin I can locate its position on my body, and I perceive a light stimulus as coming from a definite spot in my visual field. Similarly, each sensation has a time component, a specifiable onset and duration. Spatiality and temporality, being dimensions of all material phenomena, also apply to objective sensory physiology.

Quality and modality. The third basic dimension, quality or modality, is the criterion by which the various sensations are distinguished. We do not experience our environment directly as a whole, but in discrete elements by way of specialized *sense organs* or *senses.* Among these are the traditional "five senses" sight, hearing, touch, taste and smell. The sense organ associated with each of these is capable of responding to a certain category of environmental influences, and of sending information about it to the central nervous system.

The ranges of stimuli to which our sense organs are specialized can be explained in phylogenetic terms. Only those environmental events are detected that were relevant to survival in the environment of the primates and higher mammals. Consider, for instance, the electromagnetic waves striking the surface of the body. We experience no sensation of γ rays, X rays or ultraviolet light. We can see, with our eyes, only light of wavelengths between 350 and 800 nm, to which the earth's atmosphere is relatively transparent. By contrast, we do not see infrared light; but we do sense long-wavelength heat rays by way of the heat sensors in the skin. The entire spectrum of radio waves elicits no sensations in humans. But other animals have adapted to habitats very different from ours by evolving other sense organs. For example, snakes that hunt at night have infrared sense organs with which they locate their prey, and many fish have organs extremely sensitive to changes in electric field strength.

Each sense organ mediates sensory impressions that, although they vary in intensity, are similar in quality. The *group of similar sensory impressions* mediated by a particular organ is called a **modality.** In addition to the classical "five senses" we are sensitive to such modalities as temperature, vibration and pain. The sense of equilibrium is another modality. There are also *enteroceptive* modalities; the sense organs mediating these are within the body, and serve to monitor the body's own state. Examples are the stretch or length receptors in the muscles, and the sense organs that measure the osmotic pressure in the cells (thirst), the CO_2 tension in tissue (shortness of breath) or the degree to which the stomach is stretched (hunger). We are barely conscious of the information such sensors provide, and tend to experience these modalities as "general feelings." Clearly the number of modalities far exceeds the five senses, although it cannot be stated precisely.

It is often possible to distinguish different kinds of sensory impression within a single modality; these are called **qualities.** For example, the visual sense comprises the qualities brightness (or position on the gray scale) and the colors red, green and blue. The audible qualities are tones of various pitch, and taste has the qualities sweet, sour, salty and bitter. In general there is a particular kind of sense organ for each modality, whereas the organic correlate of a quality is one of the specialized receptor types within a sense organ. In Fig. 8-2 these relationships are diagrammed for the sense of sight.

Intensity and quantity. The last of the basic dimensions of sensation to be discussed is its intensity or **quantity.** In the case of vision, for example, the quantity is the strength of the brightness sensation, and in the case of hearing it is the loudness of a tone. As discussed on p. 26, the organic correlate of the quantity of a sensory impression is the amplitude of the receptor potential or the frequency of the action potentials in the sensory nerve, as illustrated for the sense of sight in Fig. 8-2. Just as the degree of activity in a sensory nerve can be measured, one can also determine the quantity of a sensation; such procedures are a central topic of Section 8.4.

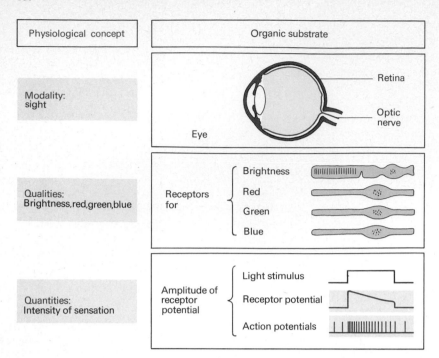

Physiological concept	Organic substrate
Modality: sight	Eye — Retina, Optic nerve
Qualities: Brightness,red,green,blue	Receptors for { Brightness, Red, Green, Blue }
Quantities: Intensity of sensation	Amplitude of receptor potential { Light stimulus, Receptor potential, Action potentials }

Fig. 8-2. Modality, quantity, quality and their organic substrates; the organ of sight is taken as an example

8.2 General Objective Sensory Physiology

This section is concerned with the generally applicable principles of the reception of stimuli and their processing in the nervous system. The function of the first element in the sensory system, the receptor, was treated in the context of the physiology of excitation (p. 26); here we shall concentrate on the operation of the sensory centers. The topic could also be approached from the viewpoint of *information processing*, for receptors receive information and the nervous system transmits, filters and integrates it. Because an extensive introduction to the terminology and concepts of information theory is required, a separate chapter has been devoted to this area; in Chapter 15 information theory and cybernetics are discussed in relation to the sensory system and motor control mechanisms.

Specificity of Sense Organs

The receptors in the sense organs are specialized to respond optimally to certain stimuli. One aspect of this specialization is the position of the receptor – for example, in the mucous membrane of the tongue or in a muscle. Moreover, most receptor cells contain special organelles that are extremely sensitive to certain stimuli and when stimulated cause the development of a receptor potential. Examples of these are the light-absorbing pigment layers in the outer segments

of the visual cells (cf. p. 244) and the cilia of the receptors in the auditory and static organs (cf. p. 275), which are easily deflected by fluid in motion. The stimulus forms to which a sense organ responds optimally are called the **adequate** stimuli.

But a sense organ does not respond exclusively to the adequate stimulus. All sense organs, for example, can be excited by electrical current. Similarly, most receptors respond to sharp pressure changes ("seeing stars" after being hit in the eye) and to changes in the chemical milieu (pH, oxygen deficiency). These are all examples of unphysiological stimuli, but even physiological non-adequate stimuli can elicit responses. A green receptor in the retina responds to strong red or blue light, but it is most sensitive to green light (cf. Fig. 11-20, p. 246). Indeed, when cutaneous senses are concerned it can be difficult to specify the adequate stimulus for a particular receptor. There are pressure receptors that respond to small pressure changes and are also sensitive to temperature changes. In such cases only a study of the central processing of the trains of impulses sent out by these and neighboring receptors can reveal the modality of the adequate stimulus. The specificity of the sense organs – the delimitation of modalities and qualities – is thus not achieved by specificity of the *receptors alone*. The adequate stimulus for a sense organ is also defined by the *central processing* of the signals from the receptors, by the correlation of the responses of receptors of the same kind and by comparison with the information arriving from nearby receptors of other modalities.

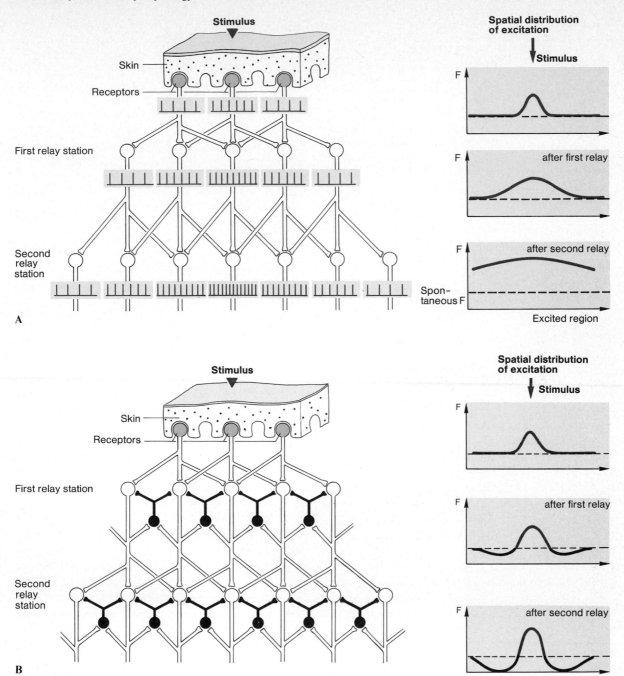

Fig. 8-3 A, B. Effect of lateral inhibition. **A** *Left:* diagram of the excitatory synaptic connections among 3 receptors and the interneurons at the next two higher levels. The inset over each axon shows its relative rate of discharge during stimulation. *Right:* distribution of the discharge rates F in the "excited region" around the stimulus site at the three levels. **B** The addition of inhibitory interneurons *(black)* narrows the higher-order discharge-rate distributions; on either side of the excited region the discharge rate is driven below the resting level by lateral inhibition *(black* sections of the curves)

Neuronal Connectivity in the Sensory System

The nerve fibers carrying signals from the receptors pass them on to centers in the brain by way of a series of synaptic relay stations. At these synapses summation and inhibition occur, and there is interaction among the signals of individual receptors. The classes of neuronal interconnections in this system have been treated in general in Chapter 4 ("Physiology of Small Groups of Neurons"); here we shall discuss only the way they affect the transmission of information to the centers.

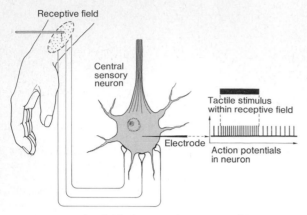

Fig. 8-4. Receptive field of a central neuron sensitive to touch stimuli on the skin of the forearm; the discharge rate of the neuron is elevated during stimulation

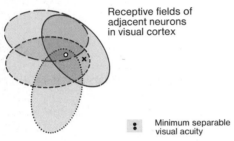

Fig. 8-5. Overlap among the receptive fields of adjacent neurons in the primary visual cortex. The point visual acuity is drawn to the same scale as the receptive fields

Fig. 8-3 shows a nerve net consisting of 3 receptors and the two next higher-order synaptic levels. The middle receptor increases its activity as the result of stimulation and excites the three neurons with which it makes synaptic connections. The result of this *divergence* is that the *"excited region,"* narrowly circumscribed at the level of the receptors, expands (Fig. 8-3 A, right). The stimulus becomes less precisely *localized*. On the other hand, divergence ensures that even the effects of weak stimuli on few receptors are passed on to higher levels by many fibers, so that many synapses are crossed in parallel. The neuronal network of Fig. 8-3 also demonstrates *convergence:* each neuron receives afferents from many other neurons. The convergence of the signals from many neighboring receptors causes *spatial summation* or *facilitation* of the synaptic potentials in this neuron. Thus even slight excitation of a few neighboring receptors can combine at their synapses with the sensory neuron and depolarize it to the threshold, so that action potentials are generated. Convergence thus also enhances the effects of weak stimuli. On the other hand, when an intense stimulus is applied over a large area the neurons in a convergent system soon reach their maximal state of excitation; *occlusion* occurs.

Inhibition. If the spread of neuronal activation shown in Fig. 8-3 A were to continue indefinitely the whole brain would soon be excited, and it would be impossible to discriminate among qualities and sites of stimulation. This situation is prevented by introducing *inhibition.* Fig. 8-3 B shows the neuronal network of 8-3 A with inhibitory interneurons (black) added. Only one type of inhibition is considered here, *lateral inhibition by negative feedback* (cf. p. 73), a particularly important feature of the sensory system. In the example of Fig. 8-3 B the lateral inhibition creates a zone of suppressed activity around the neurons on the central axis, which are maximally excited by the stimulus, and thus greatly restricts the extent of the excited region even at higher synaptic levels.

In a number of sensory systems superordinate centers can also exert inhibition. *Central inhibition* can act at the level of the receptors themselves. For example, the response of crustacean stretch-receptor cells (cf. Fig. 1–28) to stretch can be reduced by the activity of an inhibitory fiber [22]. In the auditory organ centrally controlled inhibition acts at various synaptic levels to adjust the sensitivity of the organ [17].

Receptive Field

In the last subsection we considered the flow of sensory information from the receptor through a series of relay stations. The opposite approach is also common in sensory physiology – to determine the receptors or points in space from which a particular higher-order cell can be excited. The set of points at the periphery at which specific stimuli can influence a cell is called its **receptive field** [5, 19]. Fig. 8-4 illustrates this concept for a central (e.g., thalamic) sensory neuron. Lightly touching the skin at various points reveals that the neuron changes its discharge rate only when points within the region of forearm skin shown in red are stimulated. This region is the receptive field of the neuron, with the quality "weak pressure stimulus."

The receptive fields of sensory neurons vary widely in extent. Some neurons have very small receptive fields; e.g., in the visual cortex for some neurons the retinal area within which a light stimulus is effective is only 0.02 mm^2. Other cells in the central nervous system can be influenced by cutaneous stimuli in a region as large as an entire leg, and touch, vibration and cold stimuli are all effective. That is, their receptive fields are not only large but comprise several modalities.

Overlap of receptive fields. All an individual sensory neuron "knows" about the location of a specific stimulus is that it is somewhere in the receptive field. The site of stimulation can be identified more accurately by comparison of the receptive fields of several cells, for the receptive fields of adjacent cells in a sensory center overlap extensively (Fig. 8-5). A particular stimulus site need not be in all these overlapping fields; for example, the small circle in Fig. 8-5 is in all four fields, whereas two do not contain the cross. A higher-order neuron appropriately connected to the neurons having the receptive fields shown here could determine the position of the cross relative to the circle with a precision much greater than would correspond to the size of a single receptive field. High point-separation acuity (or position-discrimination threshold; cf. p. 184) can be achieved only by the comparison of overlapping receptive fields.

Center and periphery of the receptive field. Having established that a neuron can be *influenced* at points in its receptive field, let us now consider the nature of this influence. The activity of the neuron can be either enhanced or inhibited, and as a rule the **center** and **periphery** of a receptive field are associated with *opposite* responses. For example, a stimulus in the center can elicit an *"on-response";* that is, the discharge rate rises during the stimulus and afterward transiently falls below the resting level (Fig. 8-6). If the stimulus in the center elicits an on-response, the effect of stimuli in the periphery is the reverse – an *"off-response"* (Fig. 8-6, left). A receptive field of this sort is an *"on-center"* field. *"Off-center"* fields, with the opposite organization, are just as numerous (Fig. 8-6, right) [21].

This receptive-field organization is based on lateral or **surround inhibition.** As shown in Fig. 8-3, such inhibition forms an inhibitory zone around the "excited region" produced by the stimulus; this distribution is equivalent to an *on-center* and an *off-periphery*. When the excitation elicited by a stimulus activates an inhibitory synapse, by analogy, an *off-center* receptive field results. The organization of the receptive field into a center and a periphery with the opposite characteristics sharpens the spatial discrimination ability of the brain centers and enhances *contrast* (cf. p. 189). At the boundary between center and periphery, where the response changes sharply over a small distance, moving stimuli are especially effective; they are also favored by the mechanism of *adaptation* (cf. Fig. 1-29).

The size and organization of the receptive field should not be regarded as an immutable property of a sensory neuron. The size of the receptive field can be reduced by centrally controlled inhibitory processes, and even the relative sizes of center and periphery can be altered. For example, an important mechanism in dark adaptation of the eye (p. 186) is the relative enlargement of the centers of the receptive fields of the retinal ganglion cells in dim light [10]. Such changes in the receptive field are possible because the fields reflect the synaptic organization of the centers involved, and the functional state of these synapses can be greatly modified by pre- or postsynaptic inhibition.

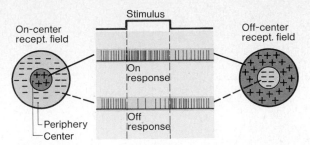

Fig. 8-6. The organization of receptive fields. All the points at which an "on-response" was elicited are marked +, and all those eliciting "off-responses" are marked –. The alteration of discharge rate during the two kinds of response is shown in the middle

Ontogenesis of the receptive field. The receptive-field concept implies complexity at several levels – the synaptic connections of a sensory cell with a population of receptors, the existence of specialization to particular qualities, and the possibility of centrally controlled functional changes in synaptic connections. We may well ask how these highly specialized and "reasonable" connections come into being. Experiments on newborn kittens have shown that connectivity as specific as the representation of "identical" points on the retinas of the two eyes in the receptive fields of cells in the visual cortex is already present at birth. This correct connectivity is lost, however, if the kitten does not practice seeing with both eyes during a critical period in early life [5, 20]. Evidently although very specific synaptic connections are *innate* these connections can be changed, by a *practice* or *learning factor,* during particular susceptible periods of an animal's development.

Intensity/Response Relationships

For central sensory cells it is possible to determine not only the quality and location of the adequate stimuli, but also the way the response is related to stimulus intensity. The relationship between impulse frequency F of the neuron and the suprathreshold stimulus intensity $(S-S_0)$ can usually be best described by the *power function*

$$F = k \cdot (S-S_0)^n,$$

as was found in the case of the receptors (p. 28) [29]. The exponent n can have various values; central cells can exhibit proportionality between stimulus and response $(n = 1)$, but in most cells the response becomes relatively smaller as the stimulus increases, so that n is smaller than 1.

Sensory neurons, like receptors, have a measurable **absolute threshold** S_0 to the adequate stimulus. This is

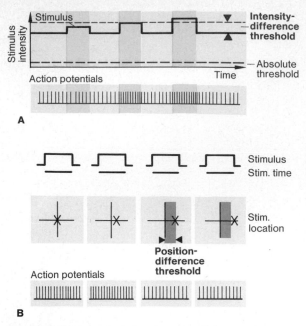

A

B

Fig. 8-7. A Measurement of an intensity-difference threshold. The maintained suprathreshold stimulus is incremented in steps *(above)*, the second of which is large enough to elicit a change in discharge rate *(below)*. **B** Measurement of a position-difference threshold. The position of a stimulus on a coordinate system is varied; the responses to stimulation at the first two sites are the same (bottom record), but stimulation at the third site elicits a detectably smaller response

Difference thresholds can be determined similarly for stimulus parameters other than intensity or position – for example, *time differences, pitch differences, color differences* and so on. In all cases the difference threshold depends not only on the sense organ, but also on the conditions of stimulation and in particular on the absolute stimulus intensity. In testing position-discrimination as in Fig. 8-7 B, for example, an increase (within limits) in the area stimulated would reduce the difference threshold. But the most important relation is the dependence of the intensity-difference threshold on stimulus strength.

Weber's law. Measurements of intensity-difference threshold as a rule show an increase as the absolute stimulus intensity increases. For many stimulus qualities there is a certain intensity range in which the *intensity-difference threshold* ΔS is proportional to the amplitude S of the whole stimulus. This relation is called **Weber's law:**

$$\Delta S/S = \text{const.}$$

For pressure stimuli on the skin, for example, throughout the (limited) range of intensities for which the rule holds the difference threshold is a 3% increase in pressure [1, 4, 9].

the smallest stimulus intensity that produces a detectable change in the discharge rate of the neuron. A more important property is the **difference threshold,** the *smallest change* in the stimulus parameter that produces a *measurable* change in the discharge rate of the sensory neuron. It is the difference threshold that concerns us here.

The measurement of an **intensity-difference threshold** is illustrated in Fig. 8-7 A. A suprathreshold maintained stimulus gives rise to impulse discharge at a constant frequency in a sensory cell. When the stimulus intensity is briefly increased in small steps, the first such increase produces no noticeable change in impulse frequency. The next, somewhat larger increase raises the impulse frequency, and thus corresponds to the intensity-difference threshold. Fig. 8-7 B illustrates the measurement of a **position-difference threshold.** The initial position is shown at the left: a stimulus at the center of a coordinate system (e.g., on the skin) causes a marked increase in the neuronal discharge. In the next trial the stimulus site is shifted slightly to the right, and the result is the same as in the initial situation. The third stimulus site is still further right, and the response is noticeably smaller than it was. This amount of stimulus-site displacement is therefore the position-difference threshold.

8.3 Stimulus and Behavior

When we hear an unexpected sound at one side we turn our heads in that direction; a deer in the wood behaves in just the same way. Monkeys in the zoo, when they see their keeper approaching at feeding time, become restless and noisy. When something appears in the way of a driver, braking and swerving are not his only responses – his heart speeds up and his muscle tone increases. In all these examples specific sensory stimuli give rise to more or less complex changes in the activity of the animal or person. Such activities, usually interpretable as goal-directed, are in general called **behavior.** Stimulus-elicited changes in behavior reflect responses of the nervous centers to sensory inputs at an even higher level of integration than that revealed by recordings from cells in the CNS, for in behavioral responses the sensory and motor systems are coupled. The observation of behavioral responses to sensory stimuli is thus a very effective method of *objective* sensory physiology. Some of the fundamental concepts and methods in this approach, which is also employed in *animal psychology, psychometry* and the *psychology of learning,* are discussed in the following paragraphs.

Conditioned Reflex and the Conditioning Process

Painful stimulation of the foot causes the leg to be withdrawn by bending at all its joints. This *flexor reflex* is innate and can be elicited in all animals regardless of their prior history. Such *unconditioned reflexes* are based on fixed connections in a chain of neurons from the receptor to the effector. In the context of sensory physiology the *acquired* or *conditioned reflexes* are of special interest. Here the functional connections between excited receptors and patterns of activity in effector organs are established by learning processes: an experienced driver brakes "automatically" when an obstacle appears.

Conditioning. The acquisition of conditioned reflexes by many animals can be followed in the laboratory. The first procedure of this sort is the "classical" *conditioning* developed by Pavlov. First an *unconditioned* reflex is triggered – for example, the flow of saliva in a dog when food is presented. Together with the stimulus for the unconditioned reflex another stimulus is presented – perhaps the ringing of a bell at the same time as the food appears. If this association of an arbitrary stimulus with an unconditioned reflex is frequently repeated, surprisingly soon the arbitrary stimulus alone suffices to elicit the reflex. Even in the absence of food the dog will begin to salivate when the bell rings. In the classical conditioning procedure the association of the adequate stimulus for an unconditioned reflex with an arbitrarily chosen test stimulus converts the latter to the effective stimulus for a *conditioned reflex*.

In classical conditioning the conditioned reflex is acquired passively. An animal acquires conditioned reflexes more easily by *active* participation during **operant conditioning** [2, 9]. In operant conditioning the animal is *rewarded* (by food, for example) when it makes the desired response to a stimulus – that is, the behavior to be established as a reflex. The reward *reinforces* the desired behavior, and the animal quickly learns to respond to the test stimulus with the correct conditioned reflex.

The desired behavior can also be negatively reinforced, by "punishing" undesired behavior (for example, by painful stimuli). However, operant conditioning is more successful with rewards. With regard to the nature and frequency of the rewards there are various strategies, which we cannot treat here.

Operant conditioning differs from training in that the guiding influence of humans should be eliminated as far as possible. Therefore conditioning is done by *apparatus* that automatically presents the stimulus, records the response and supplies the reward in accordance with preset criteria. A familiar device of this sort is the "Skinner box," which can be used for

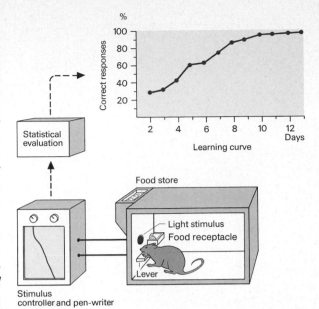

Fig. 8-8. Operant conditioning in the "Skinner box." When the controlling element turns on the stimulus (here a light) the animal can press the bar and is automatically rewarded with food. The stimuli and the resulting behavior are plotted by the pen-writer as a learning curve. Abscissa: days since the beginning of the learning experiment; ordinate: percentage of correct responses to the test stimulus

the conditioning of various species of small animals (Fig. 8-8).

Simple conditioned reflexes such as pressing a bar in response to a light stimulus are acquired very rapidly, as shown by the *learning curve* in Fig. 8-8; the percentage of correct responses rises sharply in the first few days, and the curve soon saturates near 100%. By making the task progressively more difficult one can develop far more complex behavior patterns than the response to a simple light stimulus – for example, the discrimination between a triangle and a square, regardless of size [14].

Devices for operant conditioning such as the Skinner box can be set up in large arrays, with the program of experiments automatically controlled by computer. The results are statistically significant at a high level of reliability. Such automated experiments permit considerable diversification of the stimuli, and are thus of great use in sensory physiology. But the procedure is also employed in other areas – for example, by experimental psychologists in the study of learning, by pharmacologists to determine the effects of psychopharmaceuticals, and by biochemists to examine the results of alterations in cerebral metabolism.

Measurement of Dark Adaptation by Operant Conditioning

When we suddenly go from a lighted room into a dark one we at first see *nothing*. After some minutes have passed the first contours become visible, and when

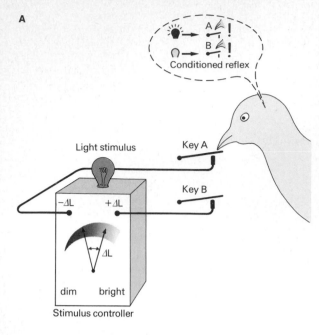

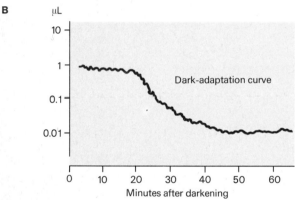

Fig. 8-9 A, B. Measurement of visual threshold of a pigeon in a behavioral experiment. **A** Diagram of the experimental arrangement: the pigeon pecks Key A when it sees light, and as a result the light intensity is reduced. Pecking of Key B, when no light is visible, increases the intensity of the next stimulus. **B** Gradual change in the threshold intensity after the bright background lighting is turned off. After [13]

we have been in the "dark" for a while we are often astonished to find that we can, after all, discern many details. This slow increase in sensitivity of the sense of sight following a decrease in light intensity is called *dark adaptation* (cf. p. 249). Here we describe an experiment in which *operant conditioning* is used for the quantitative determination of the visual threshold and the course of dark adaptation in a pigeon. In preparation for this experiment the pigeon must acquire two conditioned reflexes: to peck Key A of the arrangement in Fig. 8-9 A when it sees the *light stimulus* and to peck Key B when it sees *no light*. At the beginning of the experiment the pigeon sees the stimulus light glowing fairly brightly. In accordance with its

acquired reflex it will peck Key A several times, and at each peck the stimulus controller reduces the brightness of the light. Eventually the stimulus intensity falls below the visual threshold, and the pigeon begins to peck Key B. This activity causes the stimulus controller to increase the light intensity, and Key B is pecked only until the light again becomes visible. By alternating between the two keys the pigeon thus sets the light intensity so that it fluctuates about the *absolute visual threshold*.

The same apparatus can now be used to follow changes of threshold in time – e.g., the time course of *dark adaptation* [13]. For about the first 25 min after the initially lighted room has been darkened the pigeon sets the light at a relatively high intensity, indicating a threshold of 1 µL (Fig. 8-9 B). The threshold then falls rapidly, after about 1 h reaching a minimum near 0.01 µL. During this time, therefore, the visual sensitivity of the pigeon as monitored by its behavior has increased by about a factor of 100. The pigeon dark-adaptation curve so obtained closely resembles, in time course and amplitude, the subjectively measured human dark-adaptation curve (cf. Fig. 11-25, p. 249).

Behavioral tests of this sort can also be used in other kinds of experiments on animal thresholds [14]. For example, detailed studies have been made of the relation between absolute visual threshold and wavelength of the light, to determine the absorption curves of the visual pigments of various mammals, frogs, fish, birds and even cephalopods. Moreover, difference thresholds can be measured in this way for tone frequency and position. The operant-conditioning technique has made it possible to carry out very detailed analyses in animal sensory physiology. Many of the principles of subjective sensory physiology presented in the next section have analogs in animals, which such experiments reveal as relations between *stimulus* and *behavior*. Inasmuch as our verbal descriptions of subjective experiences can be regarded as highly specialized forms of behavior, the correspondence between these two kinds of experiment may provide at least a tenuous link between objective and subjective sensory physiology.

8.4 General Subjective Sensory Physiology

This section is intended primarily as an introduction to the methodology of the field of subjective sensory physiology, by describing certain quantitative experimental procedures. Again we are concerned with the basic dimensions of sensation – *quality, intensity, spa-*

tiality and *temporality* (p.179). Because the qualitative aspects of sensation have been treated extensively above, emphasis here will be placed on the intensity and the spatial and temporal aspects.

Measurement of the Intensity of a Sensation or Perception

In objective sensory physiology the response to a stimulus is assessed in physicochemical terms – as the amplitude of a receptor potential, for instance, or the frequency of action-potential discharge.

Intensities of sensation cannot be so measured. The criteria used here must be **intrinsic** to the sensation or perception itself; suitable subjective measures include the *absolute threshold* of the individual sensations and the subjectively experienced *difference threshold,* the "just noticeable difference" (JND) in sensation.

Weber-Fechner law. Weber investigated the amount by which two pressure stimuli on the skin must differ in order to produce a noticeable change in sensation. He found the difference threshold to be proportional to the relative increase in stimulus intensity $\Delta S/S$, where S is the initial intensity:

$$JND = k \cdot \Delta S/S$$

That is, over a certain range of stimulus intensity the just noticeable difference is a constant fraction of the stimulus intensity – a 3% increase in a pressure stimulus, 1–2% increase in brightness, or 10% increase in the concentration of a taste stimulus. This relationship, *Weber's law,* also applies to objectively measured difference thresholds – but in both cases only over a relatively small range of intensity.

On the assumption that Weber's law is generally valid the mathematician Fechner tried to relate the intensity of sensation to the stimulus intensity S by integrating Weber's law over S. He thus derived the **Weber-Fechner law:**

$$Sensation = K' \cdot \log S$$

This proportionality between sensation intensity and the logarithm of stimulus intensity has been called the **fundamental law of psychophysics.** It has been taken as the basis for logarithmic scales of the stimuli for certain sensations, the best-known of which is the phon scale for the intensity of tones. The Weber-Fechner law of course, like Weber's law, is valid only over a limited intensity range.

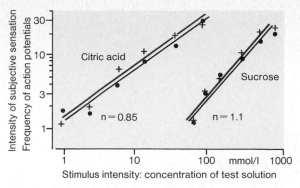

Fig. 8-10. Intensity of the subjective taste sensation *(red, crosses)* and discharge rate *(black, dots)* in fibers of the gustatory nerve as a function of the concentration of citric acid and of sugar solution. After[15]

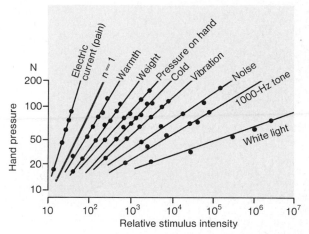

Fig. 8-11. Intensity of sensation as a function of stimulus intensity, as determined by cross-modality intensity comparison (force on a hand dynamometer matched to sensation intensity, ordinate). The exponents of the different power functions are given in Table 1. After[9]

Estimation of the multiple of a sensation intensity. One way to measure sensation by entirely subjective criteria is to define a standard sensation (the response to a standard stimulus) and have the subject estimate how many times greater a given sensation is as compared with the standard sensation. From repeated tests at different intensities one can construct a *ratio scale.* Often the sensation produced at the absolute threshold stimulus intensity is taken as the standard. The results of two such series of measurements are plotted in Fig. 8-10. Subjects tasted solutions of citric acid or sugar in the concentrations shown on the abscissa, and reported how much stronger than the standard solution the test solution tasted. These data are shown in red in Fig. 8-10. The scale of both abscissa and ordinate is logarithmic, and the data for the various test solutions can be closely approximated by straight lines of different slope. That is, these data can be described by power functions with different exponents, n = 0.85 for citric acid and n = 1.1 for sugar. In general, then,

Sensation $= K \cdot (S-S_0)^n$

The finding that strength of sensation is proportional to a power of the suprathreshold stimulus intensity that is specific to the quality of the sensory stimulus was first published by Stevens [9, 28, 29] and is generally called **Stevens' power function.**

As was noted for receptors and for central sensory cells (cf. Fig. 1-31 and p. 28), such power functions also apply to objectively measurable responses. In the experiment on which Fig. 8-10 is based it was possible to compare the subjective experience directly with an objective measure of the response. The subjects here were patients who because of hearing difficulties were undergoing middle-ear surgery (stapes mobilization). In the course of the operation the *chorda tympani* is exposed, and it was possible to record from taste fibers passing to the brain in this nerve and thus to determine the neural response to taste stimuli varying in intensity. These data, plotted in black in Fig. 8-10, can also be approximated by straight lines – lines with the same slope as those found by subjective estimates. In the case of these taste qualities, then, the *objectively* measured response and the strength of *subjective* sensation are describable by *Stevens' power functions with the same exponents n.* Similar results have been obtained for other sense organs.

Cross-modality comparison of intensity. Many people find it difficult to express intensities of sensation as multiples of a standard, as in the experiment of Fig. 8-10. The method of **cross-modality intensity comparison** avoids this problem. Here the strength of the sensation to be measured is expressed with reference to a sensation in another modality. For instance, the subject may be required to apply pressure to a dynamometer with his hand in an amount corresponding to the sensed brightness of a stimulus light. Plots of strength of sensation (represented by the force exerted) against stimulus intensity (Fig. 8-11) again give power functions varying in slope for different modalities, here arranged in order of decreasing slope from pain to light. The exponents of the functions are listed in Table 8-1 in the column "force comparison n_i." In parallel with the intermodal intensity comparison using hand force, the intensity of sensation was determined with a ratio scale as described in the preceding paragraphs, by comparison with a standard sensation of the same modality. The exponents n_r so measured are also listed in Table 8-1. In all cases n_r exceeds n_i, by a factor of about 1.7. The exponent n found for manual force is exactly 1.7, so that the exponents measured by cross-modality comparison with a dynamometer can be interpreted as the product of the exponent for manual force and that characteristic of the modality in question. Thus the two methods of measurement produce mutually consistent results, even though neither method would seem to be very accurate.

Measurement by means of difference-threshold steps. A third procedure for measuring the strength of sensation is based on finding the number of *"elementary sensations"* that would sum to give the sensation in question. A *difference-threshold step,* the increase in stimulus intensity that produces a just noticeable difference in sensation, can be regarded as an elementary sensation in this sense. The procedure in this case is first to determine the absolute threshold intensity for the stimulus quality being tested; this sensation is assigned the value N = 1. Then the stimulus intensity is raised until there is a noticeable increase in sensation, and the associated sensation is given the value N = 2. Starting with this new stimulus intensity, the JND is again determined, and so on until the sensation has risen to the level for which a measure is desired. For example, if 10 difference-threshold steps are required to reach this sensation strength, the strength of sensation is N = 10. With this procedure again, the intensities of stimulus and sensation are found to be related as *power functions,* the exponents of which agree well with those in Table 8-1.

Simultaneous Changes in Dimension

Stimuli have dimensions of space and time as well as intensity; a stimulus can cover a variable area and have a variable duration. How is the intensity of sensation affected by simultaneous changes in these dimensions of the stimulus? The simplest assumption would be a linear relation – that increases in area or duration have *additive* effects. This is the case, however, only in a very narrow range of near-threshold intensities.

Simultaneous dimensional changes near threshold. For the effectiveness of light stimuli in eliciting sensation at near-threshold intensities, it holds that the product of light intensity S and the area of the light surface A is constant [1, 4]:

$S \cdot A = $ const.

This rule applies as long as the angle subtended by the object is smaller than 3 minutes of arc. (A similar relationship is found for the responses of ganglion cells in

Table 8-1. The exponents n_r and n_i of Stevens' power functions for different stimuli. (From [28])

Form of stimulus	Stimulus range	Measured exponent		n_r/n_i
		Ratio scale n_r	Force comparison n_i	
Alternating electric current	0.29–0.73 mA	3.5	2.13	1.64
Temperature (warm)	2–14.5° C above neutral temp.	1.6	0.86	1.67
Weight of objects	0.28–4.8 N	1.45	0,79	1.83
Pressure on hand surface	2.5–25 N	1.1	0.67	1.64
Temperature (cold)	3.3–30.6° C below neutral temp.	1.0	0.6	1.67
60-Hz vibration	17–47 dB **re** threshold	0.95	0.56	1.70
Loudness of noise	55–95 dB **re** 0.0002 dyn/cm^2	0.6	0.41	1.46
Loudness of 1000-Hz tone	47–87 dB **re** 0.0002 dyn/cm^2	0.6	0.35	1.71
Brightness (white light)	56–96 dB **re** 10^{-10} lambert	0.33	0.21	1.57

the retina to near-threshold stimuli [10].) There is also a *multiplicative relation between light intensity* and *duration* for durations of 120 ms or less. Constant products of stimulus dimensions at the absolute threshold have been found for the senses of temperature, touch and hearing as well [3].

Suprathreshold stimuli of varied duration or area do not summate completely. For example, when the intensity of sensation is measured by successive difference-threshold steps, one finds that simultaneous change in intensity S and area A of a pressure stimulus elicits a sensation described by the equation

$$(\text{Sensation})^2 = S^2 + A^2$$

[12]. This "pythagorean" sum of squares is smaller than $(S + A)^2$ by the factor $2 \cdot S \cdot A$ – that is, the summation is incomplete. This relation has also been shown to hold for vision and hearing, in limited ranges [4].

Quantitative analysis of the effects of *simultaneous changes* in different stimulus dimensions of the intensity of sensation is particularly important because such complicated stimulus changes resemble the *natural stimuli* in our surroundings more closely than the change of intensity or a spatial parameter in isolation. Within one's visual field, as a rule, the location, area and brightness of a stimulus change together; when we feel an object there is simultaneous variation in the pressure and area of contact. One practical consequence of the multiplicative relation between stimulus intensity and area described above is that a warning signal – a sign on a highway, perhaps – that must be recognized quickly should have the largest possible area.

Spatial Dimension of Sensation; Contrast

The third dimension to be discussed here is that of position and extent in space. Again, changes in these stimulus parameters can produce quantitatively

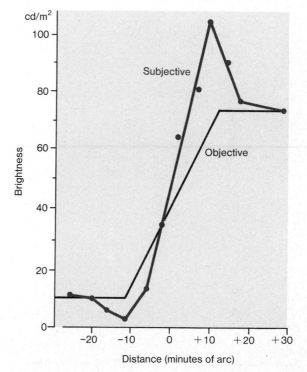

Fig. 8-12. Contrast enhancement. Transition from a dark area on the left to a light area on the right; the curves represent values along a line perpendicular to the edge (abscissa). Ordinate: brightness of the surface. The *black* curve shows the objective brightness distribution measured with a photometer and the *red* curve, the subjective distribution. The latter was obtained by having the subject set a comparison area to a brightness perceived as equal to that at each position on the test pattern. After [23]

measurable changes in sensation. For example, one can find a resolution threshold, the smallest distance between two stimulus points at which they can just be detected as separate; one can also measure the difference in sensation as stimulus area is changed by counting the difference-threshold steps that correspond to this change in sensation. These procedures will not be discussed further here; instead, we shall

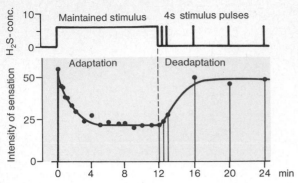

Fig. 8-13. Adaptation of an olfactory sensation. Top *(black),* stimulus amplitude (hydrogen sulfide concentration $6.5 \cdot 10^{-6}$ by volume); bottom *(red),* intensity of sensation, estimated as a multiple of a standard intensity by 4 subjects in 10 trials each. After[6]

turn to an important special feature of the spatial dimension, contrast.

In a physical sense, **contrast** denotes the relative brightness of two adjacent areas of a picture, and analogous definitions apply to other sensory modalities. A visual stimulus with defined contrast was used in the experiment of Fig. 8-12 – a surface, the brightness of which changes uniformly over 20 minutes of arc, from 10 cd/m^2 to 70 cd/m^2. When the strength of the subjective brightness sensation is measured for various parts of the picture, the red curve is obtained. The intensity of sensation departs from the physical brightness distribution in both directions such that the sensed difference between the two intensities at the boundary is greater than the actual physical difference; in the sensation, **contrast is enhanced.** Contrast enhancement can be demonstrated by a simple experiment: put any light and dark surfaces side by side and look at the boundary between them; just next to the boundary line the light area appears lighter, and the dark area darker, than over the rest of the surface. These light and dark stripes in a high-contrast picture are called *Mach bands.* The phenomenon of contrast enhancement is found not only for vision but also for the auditory, cutaneous and gustatory senses; it is a general property of sensation [11]. Contrast enhancement increases the capacity for spatial discrimination. The effectiveness of this mechanism is obvious when one compares the "washed-out" appearance of a woodland scene in a photograph with the much greater contrast in the direct sensory impression.

Sensory cells give responses analogous to the contrast enhancement we find in sensation. For example, when stimulated by patterns like that in Fig. 8-12 afferent fibers from the *Limulus* eye [27] and retinal ganglion cells of cats discharge at rates correspond-

ing to the sensation-intensity curve [18]. The phenomenon is brought about by lateral inhibition and by the organization of the receptive field, with reciprocal responses in center and periphery (cf. Figs. 8-3 and 8-6). When the receptive field of a neuron is entirely within the uniformly illuminated light area the center and periphery are stimulated equally, and the response of the neuron corresponds to the sum of excitation and lateral inhibition. But if the receptive field is at the edge of the bright area, with some of its inhibitory surround in the dark area, the lateral inhibition of the neuron is reduced. This neuron will therefore be more strongly excited than the first, and the relatively high discharge rate of the neurons at the edge of the light area is thereby explained.

Time Dimension of Sensation; Adaptation

The last of the dimensions of sensory stimuli to be discussed is time. The duration of a stimulus has a marked effect on the strength of the sensation (p. 189). *Time-difference thresholds* can be found for stimuli of different duration, and with periodic stimuli one can measure a *fusion frequency,* the lowest frequency at which the stimuli are not sensed as separate. It turns out that sense organs are relatively sluggish and not very useful for precise measurement of time.

One feature of sensations elicited by prolonged stimuli that is almost routinely encountered is **adaptation,** a change in the intensity of sensation during or following the stimulus. Fig. 8-13 illustrates adaptation to the smell of hydrogen sulfide. Immediately after the subject is exposed to this odor he estimates its intensity to be 56. During the next few minutes, although the concentration of the substance remains constant, the strength of the sensation falls sharply, reaching a constant level of ca. 20 after about 5 minutes. The *recovery* from adaptation is also shown in the figure; after the stimulus has been removed it is presented briefly at intervals, and at each presentation sensitivity is seen to have increased. The time course for recovery of subjective sensitivity is similar to that for adaptation.

Adaptation has been found for all sensory modalities except pain, each modality having a characteristic degree and time course of adaptation. In reducing the sensitivity during a long stimulus, adaptation favors the detection of changes in a stimulus. Sense organs are much more sensitive to dynamic processes than to static situations. We don't feel the ring on a finger, but are immediately aware of a fly landing next to it. *Adaptation* and spatial *contrast enhancement* are *analogous* mechanisms, each assisting the perception of changes in stimulus parameters in its own dimension. Both facilitate the selection and perception of the crucial items in the flood of information sent out by the sense organs.

Processes of adaptation are also of common occurrence in objective sensory physiology. Most receptors adapt (cf. Fig. 1-29), and adaptation is also evident in the decline in discharge rate of central neurons during a maintained stimulus (Figs. 8-4 and 8-6) and in experiments on animal behavior (Fig. 8-9). The time courses of adaptation found in central neurons usually agree quantitatively with those of the associated sensations.

Affective and Intentional Aspects of Perception

In addition to the 4 dimensions just discussed, sensory perceptions often have affective components, which can be expressed by the word pairs pleasant/unpleasant, comforting/disturbing, beautiful/ugly and so on. These components may dominate in the case of odors, which we can often describe with no better terms than "refreshing" or "disgusting." The *intensity* of the affects produced by perception can be measured by methods like those for measuring the intensity of the perception itself. Fig. 8-14 shows the result of an experiment with nude subjects in a room where the air temperature was +4°C. They were irradiated with infrared light so that the effective temperature at the body surface was as shown on the abscissa, and asked to report the degree of *discomfort* – the amount by which their well-being was disturbed – at each temperature. They did this either by *estimating* a numerical value for discomfort (red curve, procedure of Fig. 8-10) or by a *cross-modality intensity comparison* (black curve, procedure of Fig. 8-11). The two curves nearly coincide. Discomfort was least between 22° and 26°C, a range corresponding roughly to the normal skin temperature. Warming or cooling outside this range caused a sharp increase in discomfort; the exponent for cooling was 1.7, about as high as that for the sensation of pain (Fig. 8-11). One could think of pain as an extreme level of discomfort. Feelings of comfort or discomfort usually affect our behavior. We avoid excessive cold and heat, and seek out pleasant warmth. The abrupt rise in discomfort during cooling may well function to warn us of the danger of hypothermia.

To conclude this introduction to subjective sensory physiology, we shall consider the influence of *intention* on perception. Sensation and perception are not passive responses of the subject to the environment; *active participation* is involved. It is this willing of sensation that makes it a personal event, causes it to occupy my *personal time* and become part of my own ex-

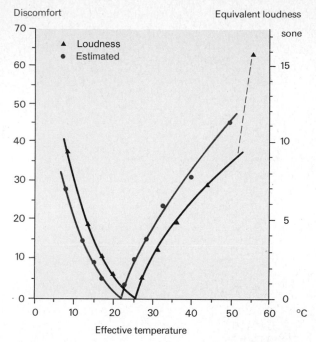

Fig. 8-14. "Discomfort" as a function of temperature. Abscissa: "effective skin temperature" produced by irradiating the subject (in air at 4°C) with an infrared lamp set at different intensities. The degree of discomfort at each temperature was estimated by the subjects (*circles, red* curve and ordinate) or indicated by setting a sound source to the equivalent loudness (*triangles, black* curve and ordinate). Effective temperatures of 22°–24°C were felt to be neutral. After [6]

perience; and because this experience is repeatable – and thus predictable – it can become a basis for my *actions* [3]. This active property of sensation has been formulated in a modern theory of the relation between the intensities of stimulus and sensation, as follows:

'perception is regarded as an internal, outwardly directed, adaptive or "matching" response to stimulation, generated within the organizing system that determines the current "state of readiness" of the organism. On this view the perceived intensity of a stimulus should reflect, not the frequency of impulses from the receptor organ, but the magnitude of internal "organizing activity" evoked to match, or in some other sense "counterbalance," that frequency.' [24]

8.5 References

Textbooks and Handbooks

1. CARTRETTS, E. C., FRIEDMANN, M. P. (Eds.): Handbook of Perception, Vols. 1 & 2. New York-London: Academic Press 1974
2. GROSSMANN, P.: A Textbook of Physiological Psychology. New York-London-Sidney: John Wiley and Sons pp. 1–932 (1967)

3. Handbook of Sensory Physiology, Vol. I: Principles of Receptor Physiology (LOEWENSTEIN , W. R., ed.). Berlin–Heidelberg–New York: Springer 1971
4. HENSEL, H.: Allgemeine Sinnesphysiologie, Hautsinne, Geschmack, Geruch. Berlin-Heidelberg-New York: Springer 1971
5. KUFFLER, S. W., NICHOLLS, J. G.: From Neuron to Brain. Sunderland, Mass.: Sinauer Associates 1976
6. MARKS, L. E.: Sensory Processes. New York-London: Academic Press 1974
7. MILNER, P. M.: Physiological Psychology. London-New York-Sydney-Toronto: Holt, Tinehart and Winston pp. 1–531 1971
8. RUCH, F. L., ZINBARDO, P. G.: Psychology and Life, 9th Ed. Glenview, Illinois-London: Scott, Foresman and Co. 1975
9. STEVENS, S. S.: Psychophysics. New York-London-Sydney-Toronto: John Wiley 1975

Research Reports and Reviews

10. BARLOW, H. B., FITZHUGH, R., KUFFLER, S. W.: Change of organization in the receptive fields of the cat's retina during dark adaptation. J. Physiol. (Lond.) 137, 338 (1957)
11. v. BÉKÉSY, G.: Mach band type lateral inhibition in different sense organs. J. gen. Physiol. 50, 519 (1967)
12. BERSTRÖM, R. M., LINDFORS, K. O.: Experimental demonstration of the euclidean-pythagorean structure and the quadratic metrics in the perceptual manifold of the cutaneous tactile sense. Acta physiol. scand. 44, 170 (1958)
13. BLOUGH, D. S.: Dark adaptation in the pigeon. J. comp. Physiol. Psychol. 49, 425 (1956)
14. BLOUGH, D. S., YAGER, D.: Visual psychophysics in animals. In: Handbook of Sensory Physiology, Vol. VII/4: Visual Psychophysics (JAMESON, D., HURVICH, L. M., Eds.) Berlin-Heidelberg-New York: Springer 1972
15. BORG, G., DIAMANT, H., STRÖM, L., ZOTTERMANN, Y.: The relation between neural and perceptional intensity: a comparative study on the neural and psychophysical response to taste stimuli. J. Physiol. (Lond.) 192, 12 (1967)

16. ECKMAN, G., BERGLAND, B., BERGLUND, V., LINDFALL, T.: Perceived intensity of odor as a function of time of adaptation. Scand. J. Psychol. 1967, 177. Cited by ENGEN, T.: Olfactory Psychophysics. In: Handbook of Sensory Physiology, Vol. IV: Olfaction (BEIDLER, L. M., Ed.) Berlin-Heidelberg-New York: Springer 1971
17. FEX, J.: Auditory activity in centrifugal and centripetal cochlear fibers in cat. Acta physiol. scand. 55, Suppl. 189 (1962)
18. FIORENTINI, A.: Mach-band phenomena. In: Handbook of Sensory Physiology, Vol. VII/4: Visual Psychophysics (JAMESON, D., HURVICH, L. M., Eds.) Berlin-Heidelberg-New York: Springer 1972
19. HARTLINE, H. K.: The receptive fields of optic nerve fibers. Amer. J. Physiol. 130, 690 (1940)
20. HUBEL, D. H., WIESEL, T. N.: The period of susceptibility to the physiological effects of unilateral eye closure in kittens. J. Physiol. (Lond.) 206, 419 (1970)
21. KUFFLER, S. W.: Discharge patterns and functional organization in mammalian retina. J. Neurophysiol. 16, 37 (1953)
22. KUFFLER, S. W., EYZAGUIRRE, C.: Synaptic inhibition in an isolated nerve cell. J. gen. Physiol. 39, 155 (1955)
23. LOWRY, E. M., DePALMA, J. J.: Sine wave response of the visual system. I. The Mach phenomenon. J. Opt. Soc. Amer. 51, 740 (1961)
24. McKAY, D. M.: Psychophysics of perceived intensity: a theoretical basis for Fechner's and Stevens' laws. Science 139, 1213 (1963)
25. POPPER, K. R.: The Logic of Scientific Discovery. 3rd Ed. London: Hutchinson 1968
26. POPPER, K. R., ECCLES, J. C.: The Self and Its Brain. Berlin-Heidelberg-New York: Springer 1977
27. RATLIFF, F., HARTLINE, H. K.: The responses of Limulus optic nerve fibers to patterns of illumination on the receptor mosaic. J. gen. Physiol. 42, 1241 (1959)
28. STEVENS, S. S.: The psychophysics of sensory function. Amer. Scientist 48, 226 (1960)
29. STEVENS, S. S.: Sensory power functions and neural events. In: Handbook of Sensory Physiology, Vol. I: Principles of Receptor Physiology (LOEWENSTEIN, W. R., Ed.) Berlin-Heidelberg-New York: Springer 1971

9 Somatovisceral Sensibility: Processing in the Central Nervous System

M. ZIMMERMANN

Underlying the subjective sensations are objectively measurable events in the nervous system. Receptors transform stimuli into trains of nerve impulses, conducted to the central nervous system along afferent nerves. The trains of impulses are modified in various ways at several successive levels, by the excitatory and inhibitory synapses in populations of neurons. These central nervous events are denoted by the general terms "processing" and "integration" of sensory information. Our conscious perceptions are only a small fraction of the output of this integrating system; we are quite unaware of most of the afferent information flow. This chapter is concerned with the central processing of the afferent impulses from receptors in skin and viscera – the somatovisceral input – as an example of central sensory systems in general.

9.1 Survey of the Central Structures for the Processing of Somatosensory Information

First consider the block diagram of Fig. 9-1, a highly schematic and simplified representation of the paths of afferent information flow, the stations along them and their functions. The physical states of the external and internal milieu are conveyed to the nervous system when adequate stimuli activate receptors in skin and viscera. Within the central nervous system we can distinguish two levels of processing of the signals from these receptors: the level of the *afferent* systems, and the level of the *integrative* and *efferent* systems.

The **afferent** or **sensory** subdivision of the central nervous system can be traced through several stations in the spinal cord, brainstem, thalamus and cortex. Various ascending pathways are used – parallel paths, so to speak. The peripheral sensory surface, the complete set of cutaneous and visceral receptors, pro-

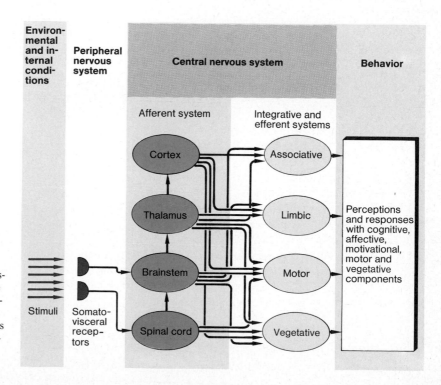

Fig. 9-1. Schematic survey of the neuroanatomical and functional systems for the conduction and processing of sensory information from skin and viscera. The proposed subdivision of the central nervous processing stations into a central afferent system and integrative and efferent systems is meant as an introductory aid, and not as a *complete* classification of all central nervous functions

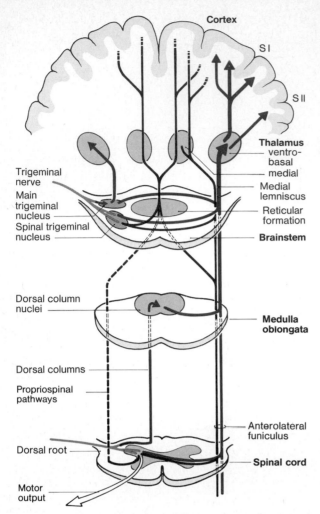

Cortex

SI

SII

Thalamus
— ventro-
— basal
— medial

Trigeminal
nerve

Main
trigeminal
nucleus

Spinal trigeminal
nucleus

Medial
lemniscus

Reticular
formation

Brainstem

Dorsal column
nuclei

Medulla
oblongata

Dorsal columns

Propriospinal
pathways

Anterolateral
funiculus

Dorsal root

Spinal cord

Motor
output

Fig. 9-2. Survey of the anatomy of the somatosensory system (schematic). *Red:* specific (lemniscal) pathways; *black:* nonspecific (extralemniscal) pathways. The *arrows* denote somatotopic maps, i.e. topographically ordered projections of a peripheral sensory surface onto the associated region of the central nervous system. SI, SII: first and second somatosensory projection area of the cortex

jects to the thalamus and to the cortex; this mapping of the periphery onto thalamus and cortex produces a somatotopic organization of the central afferent system. In the following sections of this chapter the details of this sensory subdivision will be treated.

Now we turn to the second level of central nervous processing (Fig. 9-1), the **integrative** and **efferent** side. The block diagram distinguishes among four functional systems, which receive input from the sense organs after preprocessing in the central sensory system. The functions of these four regions, which overlap anatomically to some extent, are discussed in other chapters of this book. They are the association system (pp. 163, 171), the limbic system (p. 137), the motor system (p. 81) and the autonomic system (p. 111). The complex, largely unexplored interaction of

these brain regions must be viewed as the basis of our behavior. With regard to sensory stimuli, behavior consists of perceptions and responses with *cognitive* (involving conscious recognition), *affective* (involving feelings), *motivational* (involving drives), *motor* and *vegetative* components.

All sensory systems (vision, hearing, taste, smell, vestibular) are fundamentally organized along the lines of Fig. 9-1. There is always a delimitable *sensory* level in the central nervous system which – perhaps with the exception of the olfactory system – includes a projection to thalamus and cortex. The information about the environment processed by the central sensory systems is passed on to the *integrative* and *efferent* systems. Among the important functions of these systems are the collation and integration of signals from *several* sensory systems and of *stored* information (memory). As yet we have very little basic knowledge about the integrative systems. From the great diversity of our behavior (including perception) we must conclude that information processing here is very complex.

The Specific and Nonspecific Afferent Somatosensory Systems

It has proved useful in studying sensory systems – the somatosensory system in particular – to subdivide the afferent, centripetal pathways and the associated central stations into the phylogenetically young *specific system* and the phylogenetically old *nonspecific system* [9]. Here the adjectives "specific" and "nonspecific" label a number of contrasting functional properties that particularly characterize one or the other system. As an introduction, we propose the following definition: "specific" is applied to those central nervous components of a sensory system with an anatomically and neurophysiologically identifiable main input from *only one peripheral sensory surface.* Specific systems that have been thoroughly studied so far include those related to the mechanoreceptors of the skin, and to the receptors of the eye and of the inner ear. By contrast, in a nonspecific system the afferent input is not so clearly defined; the system is excited by convergence from several sensory surfaces (polymodal or *polysensory convergence*). First we shall describe the anatomy of the two systems, with reference to Fig. 9-2; functional details will be discussed in later sections.

Anatomy of the specific somatosensory system. The specific component of the somatosensory system (the red elements in Fig. 9-2) is called the *lemniscal system,* because the medial lemniscus is one of its important tracts (from the medulla oblongata to the thalamus). It consists of pathways clearly distinguishable anatomically and neurophysiologically, by which spinal and trigeminal cutaneous afferents project to two cortical regions in the parietal lobe, the first and second somatosensory areas (SI and SII; cf. Fig.9-9, p. 201).

SI receives its afferent input from the skin of the opposite (contralateral) side, whereas the afferents to SII come from both sides of the body (bilateral). The ascending signals are conducted rapidly, over at least three synaptic relays. The main pathway is as follows: dorsal column of the spinal cord, dorsal column nuclei in the medulla (first synapse), medial lemniscus, ventrobasal nucleus of the thalamus (second synapse), areas SI and SII of the cortex (third synapse). Part of the anterolateral funiculus – the neospinothalamic tract, a conspicuous feature in primates (monkeys, apes and man) – is also included in the lemniscal system (Fig.9-2, 9-7).

A particular characteristic of this system is its *somatotopic arrangement*, the orderly spatial (topographic) mapping or projection of the skin (the peripheral sensory surface) onto all the relay stations. The details of this projection are discussed below (p. 203).

The lemniscal system is particularly well developed in primates. It is the anatomical substrate for the *sense of touch* and all the sensory abilities (conscious and unconscious) that involve discrimination of the *spatial details* of a stimulus.

Anatomy of the nonspecific system. The nonspecific component of the somatosensory system is called the *extralemniscal* or nonlemniscal system. It is less well defined anatomically (Fig.9-2, black) than the lemniscal system, and is thus somewhat inconsistently described in the literature. Its most important elements are parts of the reticular formation of the brainstem and certain nuclei of the medial thalamus, called nonspecific thalamic nuclei. The chief spinal pathways for somatovisceral input to these centers are the spinoreticular and paleospinothalamic tracts, in the anterolateral funiculus. But they also receive sensory inputs from all other systems (polysensory convergence, not shown in Fig.9-2; cf. Figs.9-7, 9-8).

The nonspecific system makes connections with practically all regions of the cerebral cortex. These connections are *diffuse* – that is, not precisely delimited in space – with little or no somatotopic organization; typically they are slowly conducting, probably because they comprise many synaptic relay stations in series. In addition there are connections to the centers of vegetative control in the brainstem and hypothalamus, to the limbic system and to the subcortical motor centers.

The nonspecific system is thought to participate in the following aspects of *perception:* perception of pain, affective shading of perception (desire, aversion), control of the state of consciousness (e.g., sleeping/waking) and orienting responses (toward novel stimuli).

The nonspecific system has not yet been satisfactorily described, particularly with regard to the functional categories illustrated in Fig.9-1. This situation results partly from its inaccessibility to experimental study. Recent research suggests strongly that the concept of the nonspecific system must be revised [5, 26].

The subdivision of the somatosensory system into specific (lemniscal) and nonspecific (extralemniscal) by no means implies that these subsystems can be activated separately or that clearly distinct perceptual phenomena can be ascribed to them. On the contrary, the various sensory stimuli encountered in daily life activate both components, and the interactions of the two are many and varied.

9.2 Connections of Afferents in the Spinal Cord

The dermatome. The cutaneous afferents, together with those from muscles, joints and viscera, enter the spinal cord by way of the dorsal roots. There is an orderly spatial (topological) arrangement along the cord (Fig.9-3); the cutaneous afferents in each dorsal root innervate a circumscribed region of skin called a **dermatome.** There is considerable overlap between adjacent dermatomes, owing to the rearrangement of fiber bundles that occurs – especially in the plexuses (e.g., lumbo-sacral) – as the fibers grow into the periphery. A peripheral nerve contains fibers from several adjacent dorsal roots, and each dorsal root contains fibers from various nerves. Because of this reorganization the region innervated by a dorsal root is less clearly delimited than that innervated by a peripheral nerve branch. Whereas transection of a peripheral nerve causes a sensory deficit in a restricted area, transection of a single dorsal root tends rather to thin out the innervation of an area without causing a marked deficit. Dorsal root transection (rhizotomy) sometimes is performed as therapy for the relief of pain; because of the overlap among dermatomes it is usually necessary to cut several adjacent dorsal roots.

Neurophysiology of the Dorsal Horn

The afferents from trunk and limbs make synaptic connections with spinal neurons in the dorsal part of the gray matter of the spinal cord, the *dorsal horn*

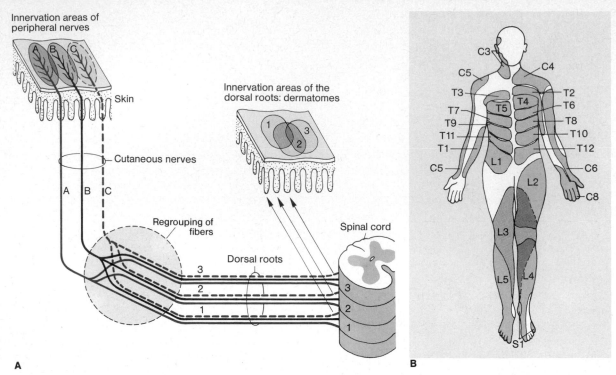

A

B

Fig. 9-3 A, B. Regions innervated by cutaneous nerves and dorsal roots. **A** Rearrangement of the afferent fibers (highly schematic). The cutaneous nerve branches (A, B, C) innervate sharply delimited regions with little overlap. Because the peripheral nerve fibers are redistributed among the spinal nerves, the cutaneous innervation areas of the dorsal roots (dermatomes 1, 2, 3) are less well defined; they have greater overlap.

B Dermatomes in man. The cutaneous innervation areas of the dorsal roots (i.e., the dermatomes) of successive segments of the spinal cord are shown on alternating sides of the body. To clarify the extent to which adjacent dermatomes overlap, L3 (lumbar 3) is shown on both legs. After FOERSTER, O., cited by LEWIS, T.: Pain. New York: MacMillan 1942]

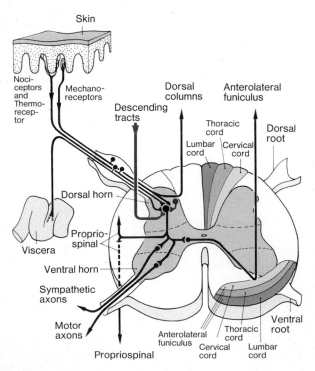

(Fig. 9-4). Some of the thick myelinated fibers (Groups I and II) also send branches, called *collaterals,* into the ascending dorsal column (see below).

The dorsal horn is the first relay and processing station in the somatovisceral system [16]. The four functionally distinct outputs from the dorsal horn are shown in Fig. 9-4 – (i) long ascending tracts, in particular the *anterolateral funiculus* (cf. p. 198), (ii) short fibers in the propriospinal tracts, which provide ascending and descending connections with neighbor-

Fig. 9-4. Connections of cutaneous and visceral afferents in the spinal cord. Entering through the dorsal roots, the afferents synapse with dorsal horn neurons which pass the information on to efferents in the same segment (sympathetic and muscle efferents) and to ascending pathways; one of the latter, the anterolateral funiculus (ascending to brainstem and thalamus) is shown here. Collaterals of Group II afferents ascend directly in the dorsal white matter to the medulla oblongata (dorsal column pathway). Two inhibitory influences on the dorsal horn neuron are indicated *(red):* descending inhibitory activity and spinal inhibitory interneurons. On the right, the topographic segregation of fibers of the ascending pathways in the cervical cord is shown

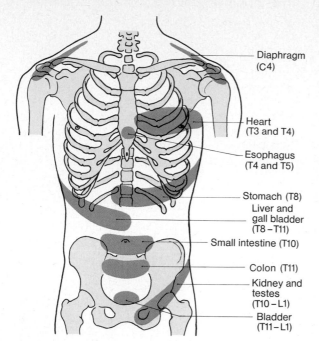

Fig. 9-5. Location of Head's zones of internal organs, and their relations to dermatomes. These zones correspond approximately to those in Fig. 6-12 which have been described by other observers. [From EWALD, G.: Neurologie und Psychiatrie. München: Urban und Schwarzenberg 1964]

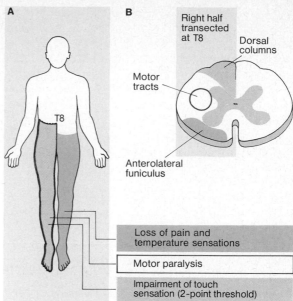

Fig. 9-6 A, B. Neurological deficits following unilateral transection of the spinal cord (Brown-Séquard syndrome). A Transection of the right side in segment T8 results in ipsilateral motor paralysis and impairment of the sense of touch (marked increase in the two-point threshold), and contralateral abolition of the senses of pain and temperature. B Cross section of the cord at the level of segment T8, showing the three spinal pathways, interruption of which causes the deficits listed in A

ing segments, and fibers making synaptic connections with (iii) motoneurons and (iv) sympathetic (preganglionic) neurons. By way of the last two outputs, the cutaneous and visceral signals are involved in the spinal *motor* and *autonomic reflexes* (pp. 83 and 122).

The dorsal horn neuron in Fig. 9-4 represents many thousand neurons in each segment of the spinal cord; in general an individual neuron does not make all four of the efferent connections shown. The neuronal connectivity in the dorsal horn conforms to the general principles of the physiology of small groups of neurons (pp. 71–75). A feature of special importance here is the *convergence of afferents from skin and viscera* onto the same neurons. Because of this convergence, afferent activity from the viscera (in biliary colic, for example) is ascribed by the patient to a false site of origin, on the body surface. Every internal organ is associated with a particular area of skin **(Head's zone)** on the basis of the spatial arrangement of the converging afferents from skin and viscera. Pain originating in the viscera but apparently coming from the body surface is called *referred pain* (p. 230). In diagnosing cases of pain, the physician can obtain useful evidence as to the affected internal organ by carefully identifying the Head's zone involved [3, 4].

An important feature of neuronal connectivity in the

dorsal horn is the presence of inhibitory synapses (red in Fig. 9-4). The excitability of the dorsal horn neurons receiving input from the skin and viscera can be modified by *inhibition* [32, 34]. Inhibition can be produced, for example, by stimulating the afferent myelinated fibers or by activating descending pathways from various parts of the brain (cf. Fig. 9-15). Both these inhibitory mechanisms are thought to be involved in various methods of pain therapy – for example, in transcutaneous electrostimulation and in acupuncture. However, inhibition is continuously operating as an essential part of central nervous system function.

Ascending Pathways in the Spinal Cord

Unilateral transection of the spinal cord (as in an accident) causes characteristic neurological deficits called the **Brown-Séquard syndrome.** This syndrome (Fig. 9-6A) consists of sensory impairment on both sides of the body below the lesion, with paralysis of voluntary movement on the side of the lesion (ipsilateral). The impairment of sensation is different on the two sides of the body; *ipsilaterally* the sense of *touch* is affected (as indicated, for example, by an increase in the two-point threshold; cf. Fig. 10-3, p. 213), and *contralaterally pain and thermal stimuli* are no longer perceived. These effects are considered to result from interruption of tracts in the white matter (Fig. 9-6 B) – the descending motor pathways (paralysis), the dorsal column (ipsilateral tactile input) and the anterolateral column (input from contralateral pain and temperature sensors). Ipsilateral to the lesion sensitivity to pain and temperature persists, and on the contralateral side tactile perception is nearly normal. Characteristic losses of some kinds of sensation but not others, called "dissociations" of sensation, are diagnostic of various spinal-cord lesions.

The dorsal column and its nuclei. The dorsal column consists of *direct collaterals* of ipsilateral myelinated dorsal root fibers (Groups I and II) coming exclusively from sensitive, specialized mechanoreceptors (in muscles, skin, joints and viscera). It is the most important spinal pathway for the specific (lemniscal) somatosensory system, a route for the rapid and accurate transmission, to thalamus and cortex, of signals about mechanical stimulation of the skin and the positions of the joints. Some of these signals are processed into conscious perceptions, in the categories of **tactile sensibility** (sense of touch) and *deep sensibility*. A special feature of the perception of mechanical skin stimuli mediated by the dorsal column is *localization acuity,* together with the spatial identification of objects (stereognosis). Movements, especially those of tactile exploration of the environment, are guided with the aid of feedback signals from skin, muscles and joints – again by way of the dorsal columns [2, 28]. People with dorsal column lesions therefore have a severely impaired ability to identify objects by active touch and to recognize numbers written onto the skin.

The axons of the dorsal column terminate in a nuclear region of the medulla, the **dorsal column nuclei** (cuneate and gracile nuclei). Here they synapse chiefly with large neurons that send axons to the contralateral thalamus by way of the *medial lemniscus.* These are called relay neurons, to distinguish them from interneurons with axons that do not leave the dorsal column nucleus. The processing involved in synaptic transmission to the relay neurons is such that the afferent information at this level has the following characteristics: (i) Preservation of receptor specificity; only afferents of the same receptor type converge on a neuron. (ii) Large safety factor in synaptic transmission; even single impulses in an afferent fiber can cause postsynaptic impulse discharge. (iii) Somatotopic organization; there is an orderly spatial representation of the periphery in the relay nucleus (cf. p. 201). (iv) Afferent inhibition (lateral inhibition, p. 73). (v) Small receptive fields. (vi) Descending control inputs, from the cerebral cortex in particular (p. 208).

These properties are also characteristic of the subsequent relay stations in the lemniscal system (cf. p. 202).

Anterolateral funiculus. The anterolateral funiculus consists of ascending axons of neurons, most of which have their somata in the contralateral gray matter of the dorsal horn (Fig. 9-4). It is the classical spinal pathway for the *perception of pain and temperature;* when it is cut, these sensations disappear (Fig. 9-6). Severe pain that cannot be adequately treated by other means can be alleviated by surgical transection of the anterolateral funiculus (chordotomy) [14]. The deficits are associated with the dermatomes (and the corresponding visceral innervation areas) of all the dorsal roots contralateral and caudal to the place where the spinal cord is cut (Fig. 9-6 A).

Within the ascending pathways, the axons from a particular segment run side by side. As a result the column is *layered* (Fig. 9-4); as new axons enter they become aligned between the gray matter and the axons already present. The individual laminae are not as sharply delimited as they appear in Fig. 9-4, however. Because of this topographic arrangement, when the anterolateral funiculus is superficially damaged (by injury or a tumor) in the cervical spinal cord neurological deficits might first appear in the lower half of the body.

There are three subdivisions of the anterolateral funiculus, differing in the supraspinal sites at which the axons terminate (Fig. 9-2): two phylogenetically old tracts, the *spinoreticular* and *paleospinothalamic* (both extralemniscal), and the young *neospinothalamic* (red in Fig. 9-2). The latter is well developed in primates. It is counted as part of the lemniscal system because it conveys information from the skin, in a somatotopic projection, by way of the ventrobasal nucleus of the thalamus to the somatosensory cortical areas of SI and SII.

Neurons of the anterolateral funiculus [16]. In view of the significance of the anterolateral funiculus in pain and temperature perception, it is surprising that it contains only a few axons of specific nociceptive and thermosensitive neurons. Most of the axons come from neurons that can also be excited by light mechanical stimuli (multimodal neurons). It is still not clear whether the few specific pain- and temperature-sensitive neurons suffice to transmit these qualities, or whether the information necessary for the perception of pain and temperature is filtered out of the activity of the multimodal neurons in the brain [32].

Other pathways. Three long tracts (not shown in Fig. 9-2) will be mentioned only briefly here, for their physiological role is unknown. The two *spinocerebellar tracts* transmit mechanoreceptive information from skin, muscles and joints to the cerebellum, where it is used, for example, in the coordination of complex movements. Functionally, these are part of the motor system. The *spinocervical tract* (dorsolateral in the spinal cord) is found chiefly in carnivores (e. g., cats) and is thought to be the functional equivalent of the neospinothalamic tract, poorly developed in these animals; because of its supraspinal connections (e. g., to the somatosensory cortical area SI) it is considered part of the lemniscal system [3].

Of all the ascending pathways in the extralemniscal system, the least is known about the series of short *intersegmental (propriospinal) connections* that carry information within the spinal cord (dashed black line in Fig. 9-2). The results of transection at carefully selected sites in experimental animals [23] indicate that this multisynaptic pathway is diffusely distributed over the cross section of the spinal cord, and that as it ascends there are multiple crossings to the opposite side and back again. This pathway is thought primarily to subserve the sense of pain; its existence could explain the observation that even after bilateral chordotomy sensations of pain persist or recur.

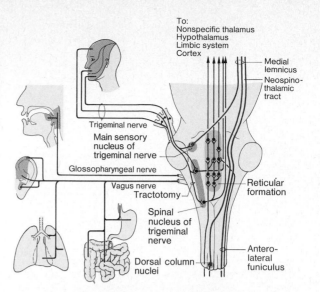

Fig. 9-7. Survey (diagrammatic) of the somatosensory structures in the brainstem, including the central afferent system of the trigeminal nerve and its ascending pathways, the reticular formation and the tracts ascending from the spinal cord. *Red:* pathways of the specific (lemniscal) system. *Black:* pathways of the nonspecific (extralemniscal) system. Afferents of the vagus and glossopharyngeal nerves also belong to the somatosensory system. Their central connections are not drawn. Tractotomy is the surgical transection of trigeminal afferents of the spinal nucleus for relief of pain (trigeminal neuralgia)

9.3 Somatosensory Functions of the Brainstem

The brainstem, consisting of the medulla oblongata, pons and midbrain (Fig. 9-7; cf. Fig. 5-13), is the origin of most of the cranial nerves. It is crowded with distinct nuclei having sensory, motor and vegetative functions, between which all the ascending and descending pathways linking brain and spinal cord, as well as cerebrum and cerebellum, must find their way. In this section the afferent system for somatosensory input from the head (the trigeminal system) is discussed, along with the reticular formation – a main constituent of the nonspecific system.

The Trigeminal Nerve and Its Connections

The head is innervated by 12 pairs of **cranial nerves,** most of which join the central nervous system in the brain stem and the diencephalon. The fifth cranial nerve, the trigeminal, in its three branches (*trigeminal*) carries afferents from the face and mouth region (Fig. 9-7). It innervates the skin, teeth, oral mucosa, tongue and cornea. The seventh cranial nerve (the facial) also, to a lesser extent, contains somatosensory afferents from the head. Cranial nerves IX and X

(glossopharyngeal and vagus) contain visceral afferents from the organs of circulation, respiration and digestion. The somatovisceral afferents, then, are distributed among the spinal nerves and cranial nerves V, VII, IX and X.

Sensory trigeminal nuclei and ascending pathways. Afference from the trigeminal nerve passes through synaptic relays in two nuclei, islands of gray matter in the pons and medulla called the *nucleus of the spinal tract* and the *principal sensory nucleus* (Fig. 9-7). The nucleus of the spinal tract corresponds functionally to the dorsal horn of the spinal cord, whereas the principal sensory nucleus corresponds to the dorsal column nuclei of the spinal afferents. This correspondence extends to the postsynaptic connections; mechanoreceptive, thermoreceptive and nociceptive information is carried from the spinal nucleus by fibers running to the reticular formation and the thalamus, like the fibers in the anterolateral funiculus that carry information from the spinal cord. The only afferents terminating in the principal sensory nucleus are those of low-threshold mechanoreceptors; the postsynaptic axons join the medial lemniscus.

In the brainstem, the information supplied by the trigeminal nerve is integrated into *motor reflexes* of the head musculature and into numerous *vegetative re-*

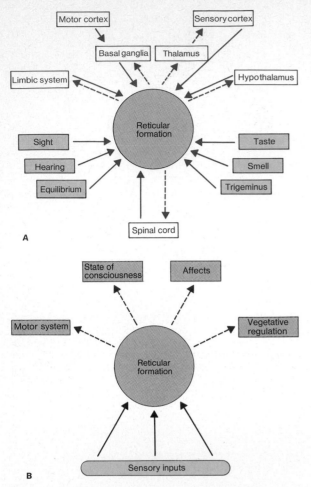

A

B

Fig. 9-8 A, B. Reticular formation: connections and functions. **A** Diagram of the afferent and efferent connections of the reticular formation, based on anatomical and physiological findings; note the great diversity of inputs and outputs. **B** Contributions of the reticular formation to functional systems

flexes. Especially in mammals, the trigeminal system performs vital functions – in tactile exploration of the environment, feeding, sound production and so on. It is already well developed at the time of birth, and carries the sensory signals that initiate feeding behavior. The trigeminal system provides the infant with its first sensory experience of the environment.

The perception of facial *pain* and *temperature* seems to be associated chiefly with processing in the *caudal* part of the nucleus of the spinal tract, as has been concluded from the sensory deficits following surgical interruption of the afferent nerves to this nucleus. This operation (tractotomy, Fig. 9-7) is carried out to alleviate pain in the facial region [14].

The Reticular Formation

The reticular formation, an elongated structure within the brainstem [1, 5, 6, 10, 15, 26], is an important sta-

tion in the ascending *nonspecific system* (Fig. 9-7); cf. Fig. 9-2, p. 194). The many afferent and efferent connections of this region are diagrammed in Fig. 9-8 A. The somatovisceral afferents arrive by way of the *spinoreticular tract* (anterolateral funiculus), probably also by *propriospinal* (polysynaptic) pathways, and by corresponding pathways from the nucleus of the spinal trigeminal tract (Fig. 9-7). The reticular formation also receives input from all the other afferent cranial nerves – that is, from essentially all sense organs. Additional afference derives from many other parts of the brain, such as the motor and sensory areas of the cortex, the thalamus, and the hypothalamus. The efferent connections are also manifold, with pathways descending to the spinal cord and ascending, by way of the nonspecific thalamic nuclei, to the cortex, hypothalamus and limbic system.

The diversity of the afferent connections is also evident at the level of the single neuron. Microelectrode recordings in the reticular formation have revealed that most units synapse with two or three of the afferents of different origin shown in Fig. 9-8 A. This *polysensory convergence* is a characteristic feature of reticular neurons. Other properties are the large receptive fields, often bilateral on the body surface, the long latency of the response to peripheral stimulation (due to multisynaptic conduction), low response reproducibility (stochastic fluctuations in the number of action potentials produced by repeated stimuli), and temporal facilitation with multiple stimulation. All these properties are opposite to those of neurons in the specific nuclei – the lemniscal neurons, in the somatosensory system (cf. pp. 197, 202). The neurons of the reticular formation are thus examples of *nonspecific* or *extralemniscal neurons*.

The varied *functions of the reticular formation* are not yet completely understood. As diagrammed in Fig. 9-8 B, it is thought to participate in a number of processes that can be summarized as follows: (i) control of the level of consciousness by influencing the activity of cortical neurons and thus, for example, contributing to sleeping/waking behavior (key phrase: ascending reticular activating system, ARAS, cf. p. 159); (ii) mediation of the affective-emotional aspects of sensory stimuli, particularly the pain signals carried by the anterolateral funiculus, by passing on the afferent information to the limbic system; (iii) vegetative control functions, including mediation of many vital reflexes (circulatory, respiratory, swallowing, coughing, sneezing reflexes) in which several afferent and efferent systems must be coordinated with one another; (iv) involvement in postural and goal-directed movement, as an important component of the brainstem motor centers (p. 93).

This list makes clear the impossibility of drawing sharp lines in the reticular formation to distinguish the central sensory system and the integrative systems, in the sense of Fig. 9-1 (p. 193). It has recently become evident that several regions within the reticular formation can be defined on the basis of their anatomical, functional and chemical properties (for example, the serotonergic raphe nuclei). It is to be expected that as our knowledge of the reticular formation expands the concept of the nonspecific system can be revised.

9.4   The Thalamus

The brainstem is a phylogenetically old center for the control of vital vegetative functions; afferent information can be integrated into this process by way of the reticular formation. By contrast, the thalamus can be regarded as the gateway for afferent inputs from all systems to the phylogenetically younger cerebral structures, which make possible goal-directed, conscious behavior.

Anatomical and Functional Survey

In the higly diagrammatic summary of Fig. 9-9, the right thalamus is subdivided into several functionally and/or anatomically distinguishable nuclei. Most of the thalamic nuclei are linked to cortical areas by massive tracts; this connectivity is indicated in Fig. 9-9 by lines connecting identically shaded structures. Simplifying the situation, we can separate the thalamic nuclei into four classes, as follows [1, 10, 15]:
1. Specific relay nuclei for the somatosensory, visual and auditory afferent systems (red),
2. Nuclei of the nonspecific system (black),
3. Nuclei with predominantly motor functions (light red),
4. Nuclei with associative functions (various shades of gray).
Assignment of the thalamic nuclei to classes 2, 3 and 4 is uncertain in some cases. The reader should therefore regard this scheme as an aid to orientation rather than as a fixed functional classification.

1. The *specific nuclei of the sense organs* (dark red) are relay stations for the particular sensory information concerned. They project to the sensory areas of the cortex, but are also reciprocally under the control of the same cortical regions (cf. pp. 203, 207). The specific nuclei for the visual and auditory systems, the lateral and medial geniculate bodies (LGB, MGB), are treated in Chapters 11 and 12 together with the corresponding cortical areas. The specific somatosensory

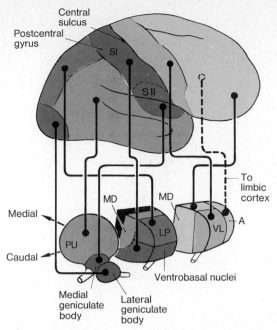

Fig. 9-9. Thalamus: anatomical subdivisions and connections to the cortex, illustrated by a highly schematic drawing of the right thalamus. Some of the nuclei are labelled: PU, pulvinar; LP, nucleus lateralis posterior; MD, nucleus medialis dorsalis; VL, nucleus ventralis lateralis; A, nucleus anterior. The anatomical and functional associations with areas of the right cortex are indicated by lines and color correspondence. The thalamic nuclei can be subdivided into 4 functional groups: specific sensory nuclei *(dark red)*, nonspecific nuclei *(black)*, association nuclei *(various shades of gray)* and motor nuclei *(light red)*

nucleus is the ventrobasal nucleus (VB); it is connected with cortical areas SI and SII on the parietal lobe.

2. Chief among the *nonspecific nuclei* (black) are the *medially* situated regions bordering on the third ventricle and the *intralaminar nuclei,* which include the centrum medianum (not shown in Fig. 9-9). These are functionally associated with the brainstem reticular formation (p. 200) and, like it, receive afference from all sense organs. The main inputs from the spinal cord arrive from the anterolateral funiculus, directly by the paleospinothalamic tract, and by way of the reticular formation. The nonspecific thalamic nuclei have also been held responsible for the perception and evaluation of pain stimuli, but no conclusive evidence has been provided by either stimulation experiments or surgical lesions. Stimulation of the nonspecific nuclei has shown that they make efferent connections with all areas of cortex, as well as with the hypothalamus and limbic system. For all the other thalamic nuclei, stimulation experiments have indicated a more narrowly circumscribed cortical projection, about as shown in Fig. 9-9. The nonspecific thalamic nuclei are regarded as secondary distribution stations for affer-

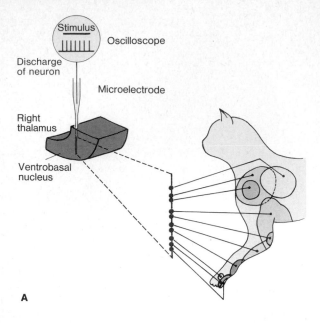

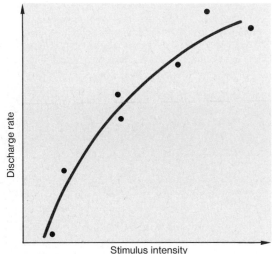

Fig. 9-10 A, B. Functional properties of neurons in the ventro-basal nucleus of the thalamus. **A** The microelectrode track shown in the cross section of the right thalamus (schematic) is an example from an experiment on the cat in which the activity of 10 neurons was recorded at the positions indicated; their receptive fields were on the skin of the left foreleg, as shown. Mechanical stimulation in the receptive field causes discharge of the neuron. **B** Example of the relation between intensity of a mechanical stimulus (e.g., pressure on the skin or velocity of hair movement) and discharge rate of a thalamic neuron
A: Modified from Poggio and Mountcastle: Bull. Johns Hopkins Hosp. 106, 266 (1960)

ent information converging on the reticular formation (cf. Figs. 9-2 and 9-8).

3. One important *motor nucleus* (light red) is the nucleus ventralis lateralis (VL), which connects the cerebellum and the basal ganglia with the motor cortex. Lesions made surgically at appropriate positions in the VL can alleviate motor disorders (e.g., Parkinson's disease).

4. The term *"association nucleus"* (gray shading) is applied to those thalamic nuclei that have distinct connections to cortical areas but cannot be assigned to a single sensory system. They participate in the higher integrative processes of the brain (cf. Fig. 9-1). Representatives of the group shown in Fig. 9-9 include three nuclei, each related to one of the major association areas of the cortex – the pulvinar (PU) is connected chiefly to the association field of the parietal and temporal cortex, the nucleus lateralis posterior (LP) is connected to the parietal cortex, and the nucleus medialis dorsalis (MD) is connected primarily to the frontal lobe. The nucleus anterior (A) is also shown here as an association nucleus; it is related to the limbic cortex (cingulate gyrus, on the median surface of the hemisphere).

The Specific Thalamic Nucleus of the Somatosensory System

Because of its anatomical position (cf. Fig. 9-9), this is called the **ventrobasal nucleus** (VB) or ventrobasal complex [9, 29, 30]. It is subdivided into the VPL (nucleus ventralis posterolateralis) and VPM (nucleus ventralis posteromedialis). The neuronal representation of the body is in the VPL, and that of the face in the VPM; the pathways leading to the VPL are the *medial lemniscus* and the *neospinothalamic tract,* and those to the VPM are the corresponding tracts from the trigeminal nuclei. The ventrobasal nucleus is the second synaptic relay station of the lemniscal system (cf. Fig. 9-2).

The following paragraphs describe characteristic *properties of VB neurons.* These are typical examples of lemniscal neurons; almost all their properties are opposite to those of the extralemniscal neurons (cf. p. 200).

Most of the neurons from which one records with microelectrodes in the ventrobasal nucleus are excitable by mechanical stimulation of the skin. In an experiment on an anesthetized cat, for example, as the electrode was slowly advanced within the right thalamus a series of neurons was found with the following functional characteristics (Fig. 9-10):

(i) Each neuron could be activated only by stimuli in a particular region of skin on the left foreleg, the *receptive field* of the neuron. (ii) The receptive fields of the VB neurons are smaller, on the average, the further distal their position on the leg. This presumably is one of the neurophysiological prerequisites for the high *spatial resolution* measured in behavioral experiments in which the animal explored objects with the forepaw. (iii) Neighboring regions of the body project to neighboring parts of the VB nucleus. This is yet another instance of the *somatotopic organization* mentioned above, an organization even more clearly defined in the subsequent projections to the SI field of the cerebral cortex. (iv) Each neuron is excited by a single type of receptor – for example, slowly adapting pressure receptors or hair-follicle receptors in the skin. (v) The intensity of a peripheral stimulus is encoded in the mean discharge rate of the neuron, as in the receptors (p. 26).

In such experiments on anesthetized animals, the neurons of the ventrobasal nucleus (like those at other stations of the lemniscal system) are found to reflect quite accurately the activity of the peripheral receptors. This is not the case in a waking animal, where the sensory input to the nervous system is supplemented by many other neuronal inputs from other parts of the brain; under anesthesia, the latter are suppressed. This complication is one reason for the gaps in our knowledge about the processing of sensory information in the thalamus and other somatosensory regions of the brain. To obtain a rough idea of the magnitude of the processing possible in ventrobasal relay neurons, consider the number of synapses available for the purpose: only 8% of all the synapses in this nucleus are occupied by the terminals of medial-lemniscus fibers, so that the great majority (92%) evidently subserve the flow of information within the nucleus coming, for example, from other subcortical regions and from the cortex via the abundant corticifugal axons [29].

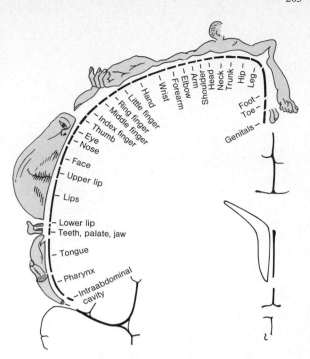

Fig. 9-11. Somatotopic organization of the human somatosensory cortex SI. The symbols drawn over the brain cross section (at the level of the postcentral gyrus) and the associated labels show the spatial representation of the body surface on the cortex, as found by local electrical stimulation of the brains of waking patients. (From [11]; cf. Fig. 5-22, p. 102)

9.5 Somatosensory Projection Areas in the Cortex

The ventrobasal nucleus (VB) of the thalamus is connected, by both ascending and descending axons, with the two cortical areas called SI and SII (where S stands for somatosensory; cf. Fig. 9-9). SI is on the *postcentral gyrus,* immediately posterior to the central sulcus, a deep furrow lying transversely on the cerebral hemisphere. SII is on the upper wall of the lateral sulcus, which separates the parietal and temporal lobes. SI, phylogenetically younger than SII, is of great significance in the higher mammals (especially primates); it mediates all those functions of the somatosensory system that depend on good *spatial discrimination ability* (cf. Fig. 10-3, p. 213).

Topographic Organization of the Somatosensory Cortex

The periphery of the body is projected onto the SI of the opposite side in a remarkably well organized way, termed **somatotopy.** A somatotopic arrangement is also evident at lower levels of the somatosensory system (the lemniscal tracts and nuclei, especially the ventrobasal nucleus of the thalamus; cf. Fig. 9-10). In this mapping, adjacent parts of the entire *contralateral* body surface are represented in adjacent areas on the surface of the postcentral gyrus. There are several methods of studying the arrangement of SI: local electrical stimulation of the human cortex, surgical intervention, measurement of evoked potentials, and recording from single neurons.

Electrical stimulation of SI in man. Some neurosurgical operations require that a site of disturbance be located in the waking patient (with local anesthetization of the incision), by local electrical stimulation of the cortex. Such stimulation of SI elicits perceptions, the origins of which are referred by the patient to particular peripheral regions. Systematic plotting of the sites of perceptions elicited at different sites in SI produces a map of the somatotopic organization illustrated symbolically in Fig. 9-11 (the "sensory homunculus"). The somatotopic arrangement is a conspicuously *distorted* representation of the periphery; the mouth and hand regions, in particular, are disproportionately large. These are the regions that in man have an especially dense peripheral innervation.

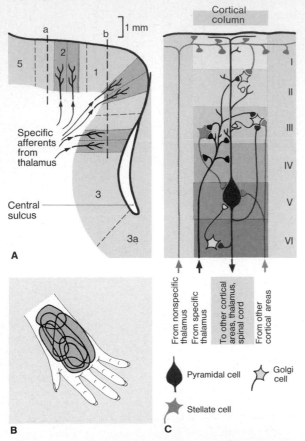

Fig. 9-12 A–C. Columnar arrangement of cortical neurons. **A** Sagittal section through the postcentral gyrus; the numbers indicate the cytoarchitectural subdivisions according to Brodmann (cf. p. 146). In each of the areas 1, 2 and 3 two adjacent columns are shown, with their specific thalamocortical afferents (schematic). Lines a and b show directions of electrode penetration, one parallel to the columns and one transverse. **B** Receptive fields (monkey hand) of 7 neurons encountered as the microelectrode advanced through Area 2 along line a (modified from [9]). **C** Diagram of the arrangement of neurons in a column. The functional congruity of the neurons in all layers (I–IV) can be partially explained in neuroanatomical terms: The terminals of the specific thalamocortical afferents and the dendritic trees of the pyramidal cells are limited in lateral extent (0.2–0.5 mm, approximate diameter of the columns in SI). Interneurons of the cortex (Golgi cells, stellate cells) usually spread over still smaller regions. By contrast, the nonspecific thalamocortical afferents in the cortex (especially those to layer I) branch extensively, allowing neither somatotopic projection nor columnar organization of the activity they mediate

Physiologically, these regions are distinguished by their high *spatial discrimination capacity* (measurable, for example, by the two-point threshold; cf. Fig. 10-3, p. 213). A causal relationship is evident here; the more receptors and central neurons there are per mm^2 sensory surface area, the better is the spatial resolution in the neuronal processing of information about the stimulus.

There is also a somatotopic projection in SII, but it is less well defined. SII further differs from SI in that both sides of the body are represented in each hemisphere; the projection is bilateral.

In animals with other highly specialized sensory surfaces, the cortical projection is distorted correspondingly. In the rat, for example, the greatest area in SI is occupied by the projection of the vibrissae (tactile hairs around the mouth). Mechanoreception by the vibrissae is probably more important than vision to the rat, as a means of recognizing its surroundings.

Evoked potentials. By exposing the cortex of an experimental animal, one can record evoked potentials in response to peripheral stimulation – the summed activity of populations of neurons (cf. Fig. 7-7, p. 150). After a brief latency (rapid lemniscal path with at least three synapses) the primary evoked potential appears. Its amplitude, for stimulation at a given peripheral site, is maximal in a circumscribed area of SI (and SII). Thus the somatotopic representation can be mapped by systematically plotting the potential maxima associated with various stimulus sites, and these maps correspond to those obtained by local stimulation of the human cortex (Fig. 9-11). The secondary evoked potential, which appears with a longer latency (Fig. 7-7, p. 150), has a complex time course, is not somatotopically arranged, also appears in regions other than SI and SII, and is very variable (e. g., depends strongly on level of anesthesia). It reflects various events: slow afferent conduction by way of the reticular formation or subcortical "detours", and intracortical conduction from SI to association areas.

Neuronal Organization of the Somatosensory Cortex

Columns of cortical neurons. When a microelectrode is advanced on a track perpendicular to the surface of the sensory cortex (Line a in Fig. 9-12 A), the neurons successively encountered often have identical or broadly overlapping receptive fields (Fig. 9-12 B). When advanced at an angle to the surface (Line b) it encounters several such populations of neurons, each usually having a receptive field distinctly separated from those of the others. It has been deduced from these and other findings that the sensory cortex, like the motor cortex (p. 103), is arranged in units, columns of neurons perpendicular to the surface [9, 18, 24, 30, 31]. Six columns are diagrammed in Fig. 9-12 A. The anatomical basis of these columns (0.2–0.5 mm in diameter) is the limited horizontal extent of the terminals of afferent neurons from the ventrobasal thalamic nucleus, together with the preferred vertical orientation of the pyramidal-cell dendrites (Fig. 9-12 C).

Receptor-specificity of the columns. By selective adequate stimulation – for example, of three different types of cutaneous receptor (SA, RA and PC receptors; cf. Figs. 10-5 to 10-8, pp. 214–215) – it was shown that the neurons in a column are frequently excitable only by one type of receptor (Fig. 9-13). The columns are evidently functional units corresponding to the location and nature of a mechanical stimulus.

Thermosensitive neurons are also found in the projection areas SI and SII, but it is not yet clear whether they are arranged in columns. The existence of specific *nociceptive neurons* in SI and SII is in debate; in the studies in which they have been reported, they are a very small proportion (less than 3%) of the total population [32].

Neuronal processing in the cortex. In theory, because of the large number of neurons within it (up to ca. 10^5), a column has considerable capacity for the processing of information from the periphery. It has been proposed that there is a sort of hierarchy among the neurons in the column, based on diverse excitatory and inhibitory interactions. This hypothesis is supported by many experimental observations, which suggest that the cortical neurons are either simple ("low in the hierarchy") or complex ("higher in the hierarchy").

Simple neurons. The discharge pattern of these neurons reflects quite closely that of the associated receptor type. An example of a simple neuron is shown in Fig. 9-13. The shaded area RA is the envelope of the tuning curves (cf. legend of Fig. 9-13) of single SI neurons excited by RA receptors (p. 214). The RA receptors themselves have the same tuning curves; thus the properties of the receptors determine the behavior of the (simple) SI neurons.

Complex neurons. Cortical neurons that respond to peripheral stimuli with discharge patterns not closely reflecting the discharge pattern of the associated receptors will here be called complex neurons. It is thus a very broad category, comprising a variety of different neurons. Among them are neurons responding specifically to stimuli that *move* linearly over the surface of the skin, with a maximal response to a particular direction of motion. Such neurons have been found in SI and SII, and in the association areas of the parietal cortex (areas 5 and 7 of Brodmann) [6].

The *thermosensitive* cortical neurons found in the monkey are also complex neurons. Some respond only when the skin tem-

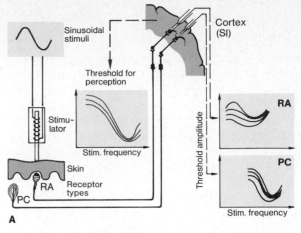

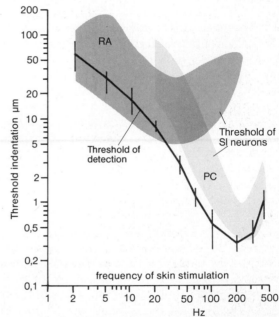

Fig. 9-13 A, B. Threshold of cortical neurons and of perception, with mechanical stimulation of skin. **A** The monkey hand was stimulated mechanically with a vibrator, producing sinusoidal deformation of the skin at various frequencies. In cortex area SI of the (anesthetized) monkey two functionally different types of neurons (RA, PC) were found to be excited by the skin stimulus. **B** The minimal skin stimulus amplitude required to excite the neurons (threshold in μm, ordinate) depends on stimulus frequency (abscissa); the neurons have characteristic tuning curves as indicated by the differently shaded areas. The *red* curve (± standard deviation shown for each mean) represents the threshold (in μm) for detection of the stimulus by a waking animal in an operant-conditioning experiment (p. 185). [Data from Mountcastle et al.: J. Neurophysiol. 32, 452 (1969); J. Neurophysiol. 35, 122 (1972)]

perature changes, while others signal only the stationary temperature. Thus the phasic-tonic behavior of single thermoreceptors (cf. Fig. 10-15, p. 224) has disappeared from the responses of these cortical neurons. Nor do thermosensitive cortical neurons exhibit the discharge peak at temperatures around 26 °C that is characteristic of cold receptors. Another kind of complex thermosensitive neuron has been found in the rat cortex. Here the discharge rate jumps between maximal and minimal when the temperature of the skin in the receptive fields is changed by ca. 2° C (threshold detectors).

These examples of simple and complex neurons demonstrate that cortical processing results in a neuronal representation or filtering out of information concerning widely varying parameters of peripheral stimuli. This ability of the neuronal arrays in the cortex to extract information, called **feature detection** [13], has been particularly thoroughly studied in the visual cortex (cf. p. 252).

Efferent connections of SI. Area SI, like all other regions of the cortex, sends out many efferent axons (Fig. 9-12 C). These efferents are thought to carry information about peripheral stimuli, in processed form, to other parts of the central nervous system. Connections exist between SI and the following regions (the main function thought to be associated with each connection is given in parentheses): *motor cortex* (feedback control of movement), *parietal association fields* (visual-somatosensory integration), *contralateral* SI and SII (bilateral cooperation), and *thalamus, dorsal-column nuclei, spinal cord* (efferent control of afferent pathways; cf. p. 208).

Cortex area SII. This area, considerably smaller than SI, lies at the lateral end of the postcentral gyrus, in the upper wall of the sylvian fissure. Here the somatotopic representation of the body surface is *bilateral*. The neuronal columns usually have receptive fields on both sides of the body, often symmetrically positioned. SII is thought to play a special role in the sensory and motor coordination of the two sides of the body (e.g., grasping or exploring with both hands) [13].

Cortex and Perception

Here we discuss some of the many findings that show the activation of SI neurons to be a prerequisite for precise tactile discrimination and conscious perception of the spatiotemporal events on the skin surface. However, excitation of SI does not always result in conscious perception; for example, peripheral stimulation elicits primary evoked potentials in an anesthetized person (cf. Fig. 7-7, p. 150), who has no conscious perception of them.

Cortex stimulation in man. As described above (p. 203), local electrical stimulation of SI or SII in a waking patient gives rise to perceptions that appear to originate at the periphery [6, 11, 23]. Stimulation of the visual and auditory projection areas similarly causes

visual and auditory perception, respectively, whereas conscious perception is not elicited by electrical stimuli anywhere else on the cortex. The perceptions elicited by near-threshold point stimulation of SI are mostly described by the patients as "like those caused by natural stimuli to the body". A range of experiences are described: simple receptor-specific sensations (vibration, heat, cold), sensations of moving stimuli both on the skin and in the interior of the limbs, and sensations of joint movement. Sensations of pain are rarely reported.

Lesions of the cortex. When the human cortex in SI is destroyed by injury or surgically removed for therapy, perceptual deficits appear. Stimuli to the skin can still be perceived as such, but the ability to localize them and to recognize spatial details is impaired. The severity of the deficits depends on the extent of the cortical lesion. Here again, the somatotopic arrangement is evident.

After a fairly long time the deficits become less severe. This improvement is thought to result from a capacity of other cortical regions (e.g., area 5 of the parietal cortex) to take over the functions of SI [6, 23].

Correlations between neurophysiology and psychophysics. One of the modern branches of neurophysiological research is directed toward establishing a quantitative relationship between perception and the states of activation of single neurons or populations of neurons [25, 33]. The results often permit conclusions as to the neuronal substrate of perception. Study of the *correlations* between neurophysiology and psychophysics is illustrated by the experiment of Fig. 9-13. The hand of a monkey is stimulated by an electrically driven vibrator, which produces mechanical deformation of the skin with a sinusoidal time course; the frequency of the sinusoid is variable. With the animal anesthetized, the activity of neurons in the hand area of SI was recorded; the threshold stimulus intensity for neuronal discharge was measured over a range of frequencies of skin deformation. Two types of tuning curves were found (shaded areas in Fig. 9-13), each associated with a particular type of *simple cortical neuron.* The RA neurons are excited by RA receptors in the skin, and the PC neurons by PC receptors (cf. Fig. 10-8, p. 215). Later the *thresholds for detection (perception)* of the same sinusoidal skin stimuli (red in Fig. 9-13) were measured in the same animals, in the waking state, by operant conditioning (cf. Fig. 8-8, p. 185).

The threshold curve for perception follows closely the lower outline of the neuronal tuning curves (shaded areas in Fig. 9-13 B), which indicate the thresholds of SI neurons. One inference from the quantitative agreement between neuronal threshold and perception threshold is that these SI neurons are elements in the process by which mechanical stimuli to the skin are perceived.

The *human perception threshold* for sinusoidal deformation of the skin follows the same curve as that of monkeys (red curve in Fig. 9-13 B). The implication is that the neuronal mechanisms underlying perception of mechanical skin stimuli are similar in the two species. Human subjects distinguish different *qualities* of sinusoidal mechanical skin stimulation; depending on frequency, it is perceived as "fluttering" (below 40 Hz) or "vibration" (above 40 Hz) [9]. The two frequency ranges so discriminated match the ranges in which the tuning curves of the RA neurons and the PC neurons, respectively, coincide with the perception threshold (Fig. 9-13). It therefore seems plausible that the difference in quality of perception of such stimuli is correlated with the existence of these two types of SI neurons (and peripheral receptors).

9.6 Control of Afferent Input in the Somatosensory System

At all stations in the central nervous system, afferent information can be influenced and changed (modulated). On one hand, afferents can reciprocally inhibit one another within a central structure (afferent inhibition); on the other, inhibitory or facilitatory effects can be induced by other parts of the central nervous system (ascending or descending influences). Several examples of afferent inhibition are discussed elsewhere in the book – autogenic inhibition and antagonist inhibition in spinal motor system, and lateral inhibition in many sensory systems (cf. pp. 181, 247, 305). The following section is concerned with functions of descending inhibition, which plays an important role in the somatosensory system [6, 32, 34].

Centrifugal control of afferent pathways. We have noted on several occasions that sensory systems must not be regarded as one-way streets for the transmission of information from the periphery to the cortex; on the contrary, the intermediate processing of such information involves a number of influences of more central origin, conducted in the opposite direction. These *centrifugal* influences can be either *excitatory* or *inhibitory*. The diagram of Fig. 9-14 A summarizes (in red) the currently recognized *descending inhibitory pathways* in the somatosensory system. Descending effects originate in two distinct parts of the brain – the cortex and the brainstem, especially the midbrain.
The descending inhibition from the cortex influences the synaptic transmission of sensory information in the contralateral spinal cord, the contralateral dorsal-

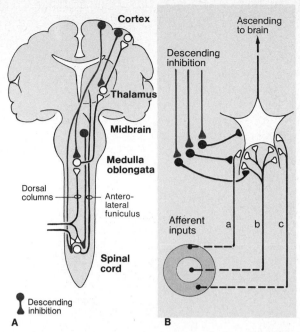

Fig. 9-14 A, B. Centrifugal control by descending inhibition in the somatosensory system. **A** At the synapses in the dorsal horn of the spinal cord, the dorsal-column nuclei and the ventrobasal nucleus of the thalamus, afferent information can be modified by descending inhibition (inhibitory tracts and synapses shown in *red*). Descending inhibitory influences originate, e.g., in the somatosensory cortex SI, the motor cortex, and the periaqueductal gray of the midbrain. **B** The size of the receptive field of a neuron in the central sensory system can be changed by inhibition; strong inhibition prevents the afferents from the marginal receptive field *(gray)* from exciting the neuron, for they (a and c) make fewer synaptic contacts with it than do the afferents (b) from the field center *(light red)*. When afferents from different types of receptor (a, b) converge on a neuron in the central somatosensory system, selective inhibition of one or the other can change the modality mediated by the neuron

column nuclei, and the ipsilateral thalamus (ventrobasal nucleus in particular). From the midbrain, several systems of descending inhibition act on transmission in the dorsal horn of the spinal cord; this action is predominantly bilateral.
What can these systems of descending inhibition achieve? The functional influences on afferent information flow known so far can be summarized as follows:
1. The *threshold* for synaptic transmission is raised by descending inhibition. One result of this action may be that trivial information (e.g., maintained stimulation by clothing) is suppressed.
2. The size of the *receptive field* of a central neuron is diminished by the elevation of threshold for synaptic transmission (Fig. 9-14 B). That is, the inhibition of the neuron first affects the afferents from the periphery of the receptive field (afferents a and c in

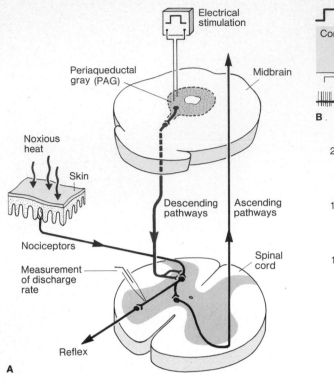

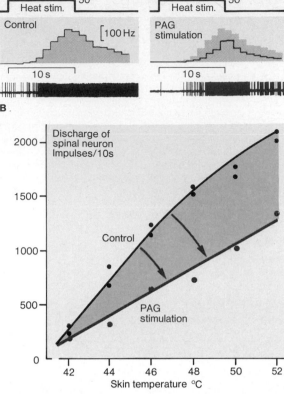

Fig. 9-15 A–C. Inhibition of somatosensory information in the spinal cord by midbrain stimulation. **A** Diagram of the descending system and the experimental method for studying it. A stimulating electrode is implanted in the periaqueductal gray (PAG) of the midbrain of an experimental animal. Nerve impulses are recorded from single neurons in the spinal cord, in response (for example) to noxious heat stimuli to the skin in the neuron's receptive field. The information about the heat stimuli

can be inhibited in the spinal neuron via descending pathways. **B** Discharge of a spinal neuron upon heating of the skin (50 °C, 10 s duration) before *(left)* and during *(right)* electrical stimulation of the PAG. **C** Relation between discharge rate of the spinal neuron (ordinate) and intensity of the heat stimulus (skin temperature, abscissa) before (*black* curve) and during (*red* curve) PAG stimulation. [After CARSTENS, YOKOTA and ZIMMERMANN: J. Neurophysiol. 42, 558 (1979)]

Fig. 9-14 B), which because they make fewer synaptic contacts with the neuron are less effective. The afferents from the center of the field (b in Fig. 9-14 B), with a greater number of synaptic contacts, can still excite the neuron.

3. Change in the *modality* of a neuron on which different kinds of afferents converge (a and b in Fig. 9-14 B). The inhibition can block preferentially one type of afferent (e.g., mechanoreceptors vs. nociceptors, or cutaneous vs. muscle afferents).

4. The sensitivity of afferent information transmission is reduced. An example of such *sensitivity control,* or range-setting, is given in the following.

Sensitivity control of afferent transmission by descending inhibition. Fig. 9-15 shows how the afferent information from cutaneous receptors can be inhibited at neurons in the spinal cord, by electrical stimulation in the periaqueductal gray matter of the midbrain. As

indicated in Fig. 9-15 A, this inhibitory influence is mediated by a descending pathway; it can act directly (as shown) or indirectly (by way of spinal inhibitory interneurons) on the spinal relay neurons (i.e., postsynaptic inhibition) as well as on the presynaptic endings of the afferent fibers from the skin (i.e., presynaptic inhibition; cf. p. 63).

The cutaneous stimulus in this example is a noxious heat stimulus, signalled to the spinal cord by nociceptors. The *intensity* of such stimuli (temperature of the skin) is encoded approximately linearly in the discharge rate of the spinal neurons (Fig. 9-15 C). Stimulation in the midbrain reduces the discharge rate of the spinal neuron associated with a given heat stimulus (Fig. 9-15 B), so that the slope of the characteristic curve for intensity coding is reduced (Fig. 9-15 C). Here the descending inhibition can be regarded as a mechanism for sensitivity control at an afferent relay station.

In terms of information technology, the change in slope of the intensity characteristic (Fig.9-15C) can be interpreted as an *amplification adjustment* or gain control in the transmission of afferent information. As in an electronic amplifier with variable gain, information (here the discharge frequency signalling heat stimuli) about all the input intensities is decreased by the same factor, depending on the degree of inhibition.

So far descending inhibition has been studied chiefly by *electrical stimulation* in the part of the brain of interest (as in Fig.9-15). We do not yet know much about the way such inhibitory systems are activated naturally. One of their functions is thought to be assisting *attentive behavior*. It has been suggested that in some cases the information ascending from the spinal cord can itself activate the descending inhibition. This would be a case of *recurrent inhibition* (feedback inhibition), differing from spinal recurrent (Renshaw) inhibition (cf. Fig.4-4, p. 73) in that a supraspinal loop is involved. In this special case of feedback inhibition the effect on the intensity characteristic (Fig.9-15C) amounts to *automatic range-setting;* the slope of the curve (or the gain during transmission at the relay neuron) is determined by the intensity of the afferent neuronal information itself. This mechanism is comparable, for example, to the automatic gain control in the input amplifier of a cassette recorder.

Influences of motor systems on afferent information. Motor centers can also exert a considerable centrifugal influence on the signals from receptors. Consider the control of the muscle spindle by the γ-fiber system, the oculomotor system essential to visual perception, the movement of the fingers during tactile examination, and the changes of muscle tone in the middle-ear apparatus. These qualify as motor mechanisms of *centrifugal modification of the sensory channel,* serving the same general purpose as the above-mentioned influences of descending systems on sensory information transmission within the central nervous system. From all these examples it should be evident that the central nervous system is involved in perception not only as the passive receiver of peripheral information but as an active participant, influencing, controlling and filtering the flow of information in a variety of ways.

9.7 References

Textbooks and Handbooks

1. BRODAL, A.: Neurological Anatomy in Relation to Clinical Medicine, 2nd Ed. New York–London–Toronto: Oxford University Press 1964
2. GORDON, G. (Ed.): Active Touch. Oxford–New York–Toronto–Sydney–Paris–Frankfurt: Pergamon Press 1978
3. HANSEN, K., SCHLIACK, H.: Segmentale Innervation, ihre Bedeutung für Klinik und Praxis. Stuttgart: Thieme 1962
4. HEAD, H.: Studies in Neurology. London: Oxford University Press 1920
5. HOBSON, J.A., BRAZIER, M.A.B. (Eds.): The Reticular Formation Revisited. New York: Raven Press 1979
6. IGGO, A. (Ed.): Somatosensory System. Handbook of Sensory Physiology, Vol.2. Berlin–Heidelberg–New York: Springer 1973
7. KORNHUBER, H.H. (Ed.): The Somatosensory System. Stuttgart: Thieme 1975
8. MILNER, P.M.: Physiological Psychology. London–New York–Sydney–Toronto: Holt, Rinehart and Winston 1970
9. MOUNTCASTLE, V.B. (Ed.): Medical Physiology, Vol.1. 14th Ed. St.Louis–Toronto–London: The Mosby Company 1980
10. NIEUWENHUYS, R., VOOGD, J., VAN HUIJZEN, C.: The Human Central Nervous System. Berlin–Heidelberg–New York: Springer 1978
11. PENFIELD, W., RASSMUSSEN, T.: The Cerebral Cortex of Man. New York: Macmillan 1950
12. RUCH, T.C., PATTON, H.D.: Physiology and Biophysics. I. The Brain and Neural Function. Philadelphia–London: Saunders 1979
13. SCHMITT, F.O., WORDEN, F.G. (Eds.): The Neurosciences. Third Study Program. Cambridge (Mass.)–London: MIT Press 1974
14. WHITE, J.C., SWEET, W.M.: Pain and the Neurosurgeon. Springfield Ill.: Thomas 1969
15. WILLIAMS, P.L., WARWICK, R. (Eds.): Functional Neuroanatomy of Man. Edinburgh–London–New York: Churchill Livingstone 1975
16. WILLIS, W.D., COGGESHALL, R.E.: Sensory Mechanisms of the Spinal Cord. New York–London: Plenum Press 1978
17. ZOTTERMAN, Y. (Ed.): Sensory Functions of the Skin in Primates. Oxford–New York–Toronto–Sydney–Paris–Frankfurt: Pergamon Press 1976

Research Reports and Reviews

18. ARMSTRONG-JAMES, M.: The functional status and columnar organization of single cells responding to cutaneous stimulation in neonatal rat somatosensory cortex SI. J. Physiol. *246,* 501 (1975)
19. AZULAY, A., SCHWARTZ, A.S.: The role of the dorsal funiculus of the primate in tactile discrimination. Exp. Neurol. *46,* 315 (1975)
20. BOIVIE, J., PERL, E.R.: Neuronal substrates of somatic sensation. In: International Review of Physiology, Vol.3, Neurophysiology I (HUNT, C.C., Ed.), p.303. London: Butterworths 1975
21. FERRINGTON, D.G., ROWE, M.: Differential contributions to coding of cutaneous vibratory information by cortical somatosensory areas I and II. J. Neurophysiol. *43,* 310 (1980)
22. FOERSTER, O.: Symptomatologie der Erkrankungen des Rückenmarks und seiner Wurzeln. In: Handbuch der Neurologie (BUMKE, O., FOERSTER, O., Eds.), Vol.5, p.1. Berlin: Springer 1936
23. FOERSTER, O.: Sensible corticale Felder. In: Handbuch der Neurologie (BUMKE, O., FOERSTER, O., Eds.), Vol.6, p.358. Berlin: Springer 1936
24. JONES, E.G., WISE, S.P.: Size, laminar and columnar distribution of efferent cells in the sensory-motor cortex of monkeys. J. comp. Neurol. *175,* 391 (1977)
25. KNIBESTÖL, M., VALLBO, Å.B.: Intensity of sensation related to activity of slowly adapting mechanoreceptive units in the human hand. J. Physiol. *300,* 251 (1980)
26. SIEGEL, J.M.: Behavioural functions of the reticular formation. Brain Res. Review *1,* 69 (1979)
27. VIERCK, C.J.: Absolute and differential sensitivities to touch stimuli after spinal cord lesions in monkeys. Brain Res. *134,* 529 (1977)
28. WALL, P.D.: The sensory and motor role of impulses travelling in the dorsal columns towards cerebral cortex. Brain *93,* 505 (1970)

29. WELKER, W. I.: Principles of organization of the ventrobasal complex in mammals. Brain Behav. Evol. *7*, 253 (1973)

30. WHITE, E. L.: Thalamocortical synaptic relations: a review with emphasis on the projections of specific thalamic nuclei to the primary sensory areas of the neocortex. Brain Research Reviews *1*, 275 (1979)

31. WOOLSEY, T. A., WELKER, C., SCHWARTZ, R. H.: Comparative anatomical studies of Sml face cortex with special reference to the occurrence of "barrels" in layer IV. J. comp. Neurol. *164*, 79 (1975)

32. ZIMMERMANN, M.: Neurophysiology of nociception. In: International Review of Physiology, Vol. 10, Neurophysiology II (PORTER, R., Ed.), p. 179. Baltimore: University Park Press 1976

33. ZIMMERMANN, M.: Mechanoreceptors of the glabrous skin and tactile acuity. In: Studies in Neurophysiology presented to A. K. MCINTYRE (PORTER, R., Ed.), p. 267. Cambridge: Cambridge University Press 1978

34. ZIMMERMANN, M.: Peripheral and central nervous mechanisms of nociception, pain, and pain therapy: facts and hypotheses. In: Advances in Pain Research and Therapy, Vol. 3 (BONICA, J.J., LIEBESKIND, J. C., ALBE-FESSARD, D. G., Eds.), p. 3. New York: Raven Press 1979

10 Somatovisceral Sensibility: Cutaneous Senses, Proprioception, Pain

R. F. Schmidt

The sensory modalities of the skin and associated structures – *mechanoreception, thermoreception* and *nociception* (sensation of pain) – together with *proprioception* and the *pain sensibility of the body as a whole* – constitute the category **somatovisceral sensibility.** A common feature of all these modalities is that their receptors are not grouped in a discrete sense organ (such as the eye or ear) but as a rule are scattered over and in the body; moreover, their afferent fibers do not form special nerves (such as the optic and stato-acoustic nerves) but rather are distributed among many peripheral nerves and central tracts (cf. previous chapter).

The *performance of the somatovisceral systems* is entirely comparable with that found for any other sensory modality. Thus the term "lower senses," once commonly applied to the somatovisceral modalities (perhaps to indicate the absence of complicated special sense organs), is misleading and should no longer be used.

10.1 Mechanoreception

This section is concerned with the reception and processing of mechanical stimuli to the skin – that is, with **mechanoreception** (synonym: *sense of touch;* this term, as one of the "five senses," formerly comprised all the cutaneous senses). Mechanoreception comprises a number of qualities, the names of which are also part of everyday language – for example, the sensations of *pressure, touch, vibration* and *tickle.* In the following, after the subjectively measurable properties of mechanoreception are discussed, it will be shown that the skin contains a number of *mechanosensitive receptors* with varying properties, such that each type appears to be especially well suited to mediate one or another quality of mechanoreception.

Subjectively Measurable Properties of Mechanoreception

When a bristle (animal or nylon) is used to touch the skin at different places, it becomes evident that light pressure stimuli (in the 1–5 mN range; calibrated as

in Fig. 10–1 A) give rise to sensations of pressure or touch only at certain points on the skin. These points are called **touch points.** Their distribution on the human skin was studied in detail toward the end of the last century (VON FREY, GOLDSCHEIDER). An example is shown in Fig. 10-18, p. 228. Regions of skin with particularly dense arrays of touch points include the fingertips and lips, whereas the distribution of touch points on upper arms, thighs and back is particularly sparse.

The measurements required to find the touch points in an area of the skin and determine their thresholds to pressure stimuli are informative, but intricate and laborious; a further disadvantage is that with punctate stimuli it is difficult to make direct comparisons

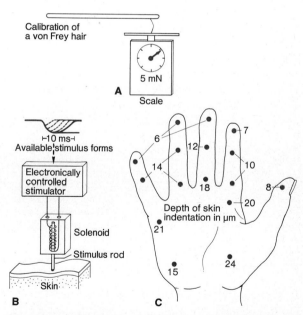

Fig. 10-1 A–C. Threshold and distribution of mechanosensitivity on the skin. **A** Calibration of a "von Frey hair"; the force (in millinewtons) at which the hair or the (nylon) bristle just bends is measured. A graded set of such stimulus hairs can be used to determine the thresholds and distribution of the touch points, and the thresholds and receptive fields of mechanoreceptors. **B** Example of mechanical stimulation of the skin with an electronically driven rod or stylus. **C** Distribution of the sensation thresholds to stimuli of the form shown in **B**, expressed in micrometers of indentation. (After Lindblom and Lindström, from [16])

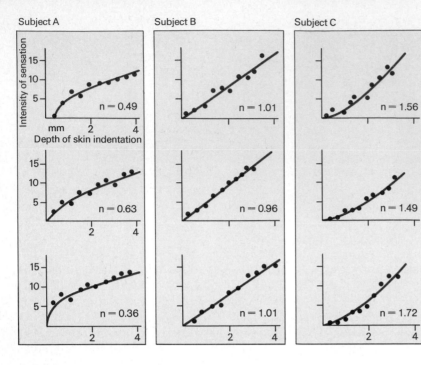

Fig. 10-2. Psychophysical intensity functions, showing the relationship between pressure sensation and stimulus intensity. Pressure pulses 1 s in duration were applied to the inner surface of the hand with the apparatus shown in Fig. 10-1 B, and the depth to which the skin was indented was measured. The three subjects (A), (B) and (C) assigned to the stimuli numerical values reflecting the intensity of their sensations. Each experiment was repeated three times (the three curves in each column). The solid curves are power functions fitted to the data points, having the exponents shown on the right of each diagram. (After Knibestöl and Vallbo, from [16])

with the larger-area stimuli encountered in everyday life. Modern mechanical stimulators permit the variation of form, duration and intensity of the stimuli over a wide range, using interchangeable rods that contact the skin over different areas. The **tactile sensation thresholds** obtained with such a stimulator, applying stimuli of the form shown in Fig. 10-1 B to the inner surface of the right hand, are shown in Fig. 10-1 C. The data here represent the minimal depth of skin indentation (in micrometers) necessary to produce a just detectable sensation of touch.

Thus skin indentations of the order of only 0.01 mm (10 μm) on the inner surface of the hand suffice to produce tactile sensations. The thresholds found at the fingertips are distinctly lower than those over the rest of the surface. This result agrees with everyday experience. But it is surprising to find that the thresholds of the tips of the index and middle fingers are not appreciably different from those of the other fingers. The same study revealed – again rather unexpectedly – that the tactile thresholds of the blind do not differ distinctly from those of normal subjects (however see spatial thresholds, p. 213).

Psychophysical intensity function. With suprathreshold mechanical skin stimulation, one can measure the dependence of sensation intensity upon stimulus intensity by the psychophysical methods described on pp. 186–189. Fig. 10-2 serves as an example of such an investigation. It shows the results for three subjects (A, B, C) in a graph relating the amplitude of a pressure stimulus (abscissa) to the subjectively experienced stimulus intensity (ordinate). This **intensity function** was obtained three times for each subject; the results showed clearly that the function is re-

markably reproducible for a given individual, but varies widely among different individuals. This finding is evident in the exponents of the power functions fitted to the data. In evaluating intensity functions of this kind (for further examples see Figs. 8-10 and 8-11), it is therefore necessary to take account not only of the conditions of the experiment but also of the interindividual differences in subjective sensation.

The spatial resolution of pressure/touch sensations. By measuring *spatial difference thresholds* (using a pair of calipers with rounded tips or the like) one can easily show that the ability to resolve stimuli applied to the skin either simultaneously or in succession is far from being uniform over the whole skin, and corresponds to the variation in density of touch points. Fig. 10-3 shows examples of **simultaneous spatial thresholds** – the averages found for adults (black bars) and those of a 12-year-old boy, almost all of which are somewhat lower. The **successive spatial thresholds** are distinctly lower; that is, sequential stimuli are better resolved than simultaneous stimuli. The successive thresholds are often only a quarter of the simultaneous thresholds – for example, 1 mm instead of 4 mm. This *improved spatial resolution* of successive stimuli is also reflected in the fact that surface characteristics of an object can be discerned considerably more easily by stroking it than by leaving the fingers in contact without moving them. The *reasons for this difference* lie partly in the mechanical properties of the skin, but mostly in the way it is innervated and the central connections of the afferent nerve fibers (cf. p. 219).

Plasticity of spatial thresholds. The spatial acuity of mechanoreception is not an immutable characteristic. It has long been known that with practice, even in a matter of hours, spatial thresholds can be reduced to about half. When one stops practicing, this *improvement of spatial resolution* is lost within a few months. The blind are especially well known for their ability to identify small objects (for example, the raised dots in a Braille text) rapidly and accurately by touch. Typesetters have similar abilities. When the spatial threshold in an area of skin is reduced by practice, the reduction is found not only in and around this area but also in the corresponding area of skin on the other side of the body, though here it is not as pronounced. The spatial threshold along the long axis of a limb is higher (worse) than that in the perpendicular direction. Factors that can *impair spatial resolution* include, for example, (i) reduced blood flow or congestion of venous blood in the skin, (ii) too frequent testing of spatial threshold, (iii) general fatigue, (iv) cooling of the skin.

Tests of mechanoreception. In *routine clinical examination* of mechanosensibility the usual **test for touch sensation** is to stimulate the skin with a wad of cotton or the like and ask the patient what is felt and where the stimulus is located. The *discrimination between pointed and dull* is tested by touching the skin with the tip or head of a glass-head pin, in irregular sequence. Another standard procedure is to ask the patient to *identify numbers written on the skin;* a dull stylus (pinhead, fingertip) is used to write first large and then gradually smaller numbers.
Vibration sensation is tested with a tuning fork placed in contact with a bony area (e.g., elbow or shinbone). In an experiment or for more precise examination, it is better to use a solenoid driven by a sine-wave generator. As a rule two characteristics are tested. One is the *absolute threshold* for a conscious sensation of vibration. This threshold, like that of the Pacinian corpuscles (cf. p. 215 and Fig. 10-7), is minimal at ca. 150–300 Hz. The minimal vibration amplitude required in this range is of the order of 1 μm, and is thus in the range of threshold sensitivity of the Pacinian corpuscles (cf. Fig. 10-7). The other characteristic tested is the *difference threshold for changes in vibration frequency.* This difference threshold is lowest in the range of low stimulus frequencies, and rises sharply at frequencies above 100 Hz. In all clinical measurements the *two sides of the body should be compared* if at all possible, so that even slight differences are detected. Note, however, that clinical examination – a relatively summary procedure in any case – is often hampered by the patient's failure or inability to cooperate [15].

Cutaneous Mechanoreceptors

For over 100 years the touch points have been thought to correspond to receptors embedded in the skin below the touch point. Therefore experiments on man and animals have been designed to study the *physiological function and histological structure* of cutaneous receptors and to correlate them with one another. In the case of *mechanoreception* the attempt has largely succeeded. It seems that in both the hairy and the hairless skin of man and monkey, and to some extent in other mammals, there are only *three main types* of mechanoreceptors (with myelinated afferents); their responses, structure and physiological significance are discussed in the following paragraphs [2, 4, 7, 9, 10, 12, 14].

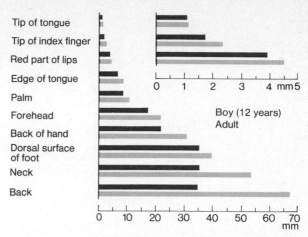

Fig. 10-3. Simultaneous spatial thresholds of adults *(gray bars)* and a 12-year-old boy *(red bars).* The inset at upper right shows the simultaneous spatial thresholds of the three skin areas at the left, with the abscissa expanded by a factor of 10. The length of the bars indicates, for each region of the body, the smallest distance between two simultaneously applied point stimuli for which the two points are still detected as separate. (After WEBER and after LANDOIS)

Pressure receptors (intensity detectors). In hairy and hairless (glabrous) skin there are *receptors* sensitive exclusively or primarily to *pressure stimuli,* which adapt only *slowly* to the pressure stimulus. Examples of these slowly adapting receptors, or **SA receptors,** are shown in Figs. 10-4 and 10-5. The *discharge rate* of these receptors is *proportional to stimulus intensity* at each point in time during the stimulus. In a double logarithmic coordinate system (Fig. 10-5 B) the relation between stimulus intensity I and discharge rate R can be represented by a straight line at all times, indicating that this relation is a power function of the form $R = I^n$ (cf. p. 188). In terms of function, such receptors probably serve as **intensity or displacement detectors,** measuring the strength of a mechanical stimulus to the skin or the depth of skin indentation. Simultaneously, because even after a long time they are not completely adapted (Fig. 10-5 A), the SA receptors also indicate the *duration* of a pressure stimulus.

Touch receptors (velocity detectors). When a hair (e.g., on the back of the hand) is touched a sensation is produced only while the hair is moving; the intensity of the sensation mediated by the hair-follicle receptors depends on the *velocity* of hair movement and not on its amplitude. In hairless skin, too, there are receptors with velocity-dependent responses. An example is shown in Fig. 10-6. The discharge rate of this receptor during ramp stimuli depends in particular on the *rate of indentation* by the stylus. In a double logarithmic coordinate system (D) the impulse rate is a linear function of indentation velocity (i.e., the first deriva-

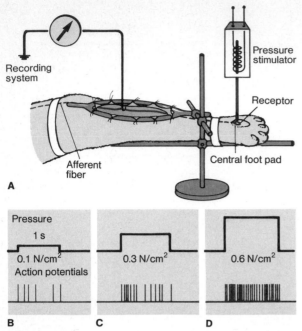

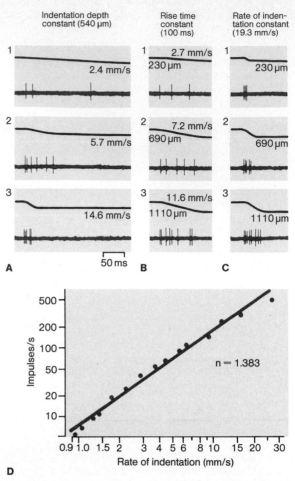

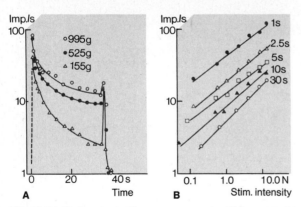

Fig. 10-4 A–D. Experiment on the stimulus-response behavior of cutaneous receptors. **A** Diagram of the experimental setup; a cat's paw is positioned so that the central pad is upward and weights can be set on it. **B, C, D** Impulses (action potentials) of a pressure receptor (SA receptor) in the hairless sole of the cat's paw (lower, *red* records) during stimulation with various weights (i.e., stimuli of constant force; upper records). The SA receptor was not spontaneously active

Fig. 10-5 A, B. Response of a pressure receptor (SA receptor) to various constant-force stimuli. **A** Time course of receptor discharge (ordinate in impulses/s, logarithmic scale) during three stimuli 40 s in duration (abscissa) at intensities indicated by the symbols in the graph. **B** The relation between stimulus intensity (abscissa) and frequency of receptor discharge (ordinate) at various times after stimulus onset. Both axes are logarithmic. The threshold stimuli at each time during the maintained stimulus were subtracted from the applied intensities. Each point in **A** and **B** is the average of ten individual measurements

Fig. 10-6 A–D. Responses of a velocity detector (RA receptor) in bird skin. As the original records *(red)* show, action potentials appear only during the movement phase of the stimuli (*black* ramps). The varied stimulus parameters are indicated for each stimulus trace. With *constant indentation amplitude* but increasing velocity (**A** 1–3) the discharge rate rises but the duration of discharge is reduced. With constant rise time (**B** 1–3) the discharge rate increases as the velocity and amplitude of indentation change simultaneously. With *constant indentation velocity* (**C** 1–3), although the duration of the discharge increases with stimulus amplitude, the discharge rate stays nearly constant. Thus this receptor was sensitive only to the velocity component of the stimulus. **D** shows the quantitative relation between indentation velocity (abscissa) and the mean impulse frequency (ordinate), in double logarithmic coordinates. The data are fit by a power function with the exponent n = 1.383. The straight line corresponds to the mathematical regression line (measurements by K.-M. GOTTSCHALDT)

tive of distance with respect to time); that is, the relation between *discharge rate* of the receptor and *indentation velocity* is also described by a *power function*. These receptors can be called *velocity detectors*. During square-wave stimuli like those in Fig. 10-4, these receptors adapt within 50-500 ms. They can thus be called moderately *rapidly adapting* receptors (**RA receptors**).

Receptors such as pressure receptors, which mediate primarily the intensity of a stimulus and not its change in time, used to be called **proportional receptors** *(P receptors)* in analogy with technical sensors. Accordingly, receptors with responses like those of the touch receptors were frequently called **differential recep-**

tors *(D receptors),* and intermediate forms were called *PD receptors* or **PD sensors.**

Vibration receptors (acceleration detectors). Fig. 10-7 A, B shows the responses of the third receptor type to *square-wave stimuli.* Both stimuli equal to the threshold intensity (A) and those several times greater (B) elicit only one impulse; the receptor adapts *very rapidly.* Thus it can signal neither the depth nor the velocity of indentation. But with *sinusoidal stimulation* (Fig. 10-7 C, D) each cycle of the sine wave elicits an action potential; the minimal amplitude of the sinusoidal oscillation necessary to give a 1:1 response decreases greatly as the stimulus frequency rises. Thus in the double logarithmic plot (E) the slope of the line relating threshold amplitude S_T to stimulus frequency f is about minus two in the range 30–200 Hz. This relation can also be written as $S_T =$ const. $\cdot f^{-2}$, which indicates that the *adequate* stimulus to these receptors is the second derivative of indentation depth with respect to time, i.e. the *acceleration* of skin displacement. We can therefore call these receptors **acceleration detectors.** They can be excited by stimuli to hairy and glabrous skin. At frequencies above 200 Hz the threshold of the receptors rises again, and at frequencies above 400 Hz it is no longer possible to elicit impulses in a 1:1 relation.

Histological structures and afferent innervation of the mechanoreceptors. In the adipose tissue of the subcutaneous layer of glabrous (Fig. 10-8 A) and hairy (B) skin there are neuronal endings enclosed in a relatively large structure with layers like an onion, composed of connective tissue and Schwann cells. These are the **Pacinian corpuscles** (synonym: Vater-Pacini corpuscles). There is convincing experimental evidence that these Pacinian corpuscles are the **acceleration detectors,** which therefore are also called **PC receptors.** Apart from the subcutaneous tissue they are also found, in varying numbers, in the tendons and fascia of the muscles, in the periosteum, in the joint capsules and in the mesenteries.

The moderately rapidly adapting **velocity detectors** in *glabrous* skin are the *Meissner corpuscles,* also called *Meissner's tactile corpuscles,* in the papillae of the corium (Fig. 10-8 A). In the hairy skin velocity detectors take the form of hair follicle receptors (Fig. 10-8 B). Various subtypes of these hair follicle receptors have been found in mammals, but it is not yet certain whether all of them are present in man.

The slowly adapting **intensity detectors** of the *glabrous* skin are the **Merkel cell complexes or Merkel disks.** They lie in small groups in the lowermost layers of the epidermis, where it extends down between the papillae of the corium (Fig. 10-8 A). Merkel cell complexes

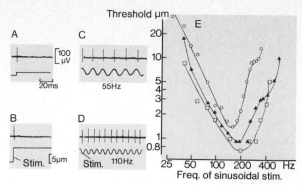

Fig. 10-7 A–E. Responses of Pacinian corpuscles (acceleration detectors, PC receptors). **A–D** Responses of a Pacinian corpuscle to mechanical square-wave stimuli differing in intensity (**A, B**) and mechanical sinusoidal stimuli at 44 and 110 Hz (**C, D**). The amplitudes of the sinusoidal stimuli are just above the threshold for a one-spike-per-cycle response. The calibrations apply to all records. **E** Threshold (ordinate) of three PC receptors as a function of the frequency (abscissa) of mechanical sinusoidal stimuli. The stimuli were applied at the site of maximal sensitivity of each receptor (sole of cat's paw). Both scales are logarithmic

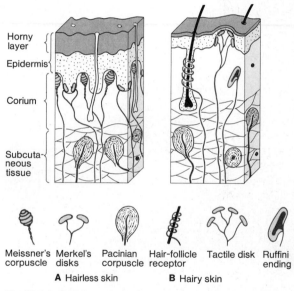

Fig. 10-8 A, B. Schematic drawing of the structure and position of mechanoreceptors in hairless (**A**) and hairy (**B**) skin. For details see text

are also found in *hairy* skin, but here they lie in special **dome corpuscles** elevated above the surrounding skin surface, also called *Pinkus-Iggo tactile corpuscles.* With a height of ca. 0.1 mm and a diameter of 0.2–0.4 mm, these corpuscles are just discernible by the unaided eye. In addition to the dome corpuscle, another slowly adapting **intradermal receptor** (Iggo's Type II) is found in the deeper layers of the dermis of hairy and glabrous skin; its histological correlate is the **Ruffini corpuscle.**

All the mechanoreceptors described so far are supplied by **myelinated afferent nerve fibers** of Group II (diameter 5–10 μm, conduction velocity 30–70 m/s; cf. Table 1–2, p. 24). The connections of these nerve fibers in the spinal cord, ascending tracts and thalamocortical projections of the sensory periphery are discussed in Chapter 9.

Mechanosensitive free nerve endings in the skin. Along with *myelinated* (Groups II and III) afferents, each cutaneous nerve contains *unmyelinated* (Group IV) fibers amounting to 50% or more of the total. Some of these are efferent *postganglionic sympathetic fibers,* and some are *afferent* fibers terminating in *free nerve endings*. The receptor functions of these free nerve endings are not yet entirely clear. Some may be *temperature receptors,* and many are probably nociceptors (cf. pp. 224 and 228). A number of them have been shown to respond specifically to low-intensity tactile stimuli. In experiments on animals such **mechanoreceptors** have been found in the hairy skin and – though only rarely – in glabrous skin.

Because of the low *conduction velocity of the Group-IV fibers* (ca. 1 m/s), as a rule several hundred milliseconds elapse between the application of a stimulus and the arrival of the afferent impulses in the central nervous system. Many reflexes induced by mechanical stimuli, and usually one's subjective sensations, have shorter latencies than the conduction times of the afferent impulses in Group-IV fibers. For this reason alone it can be concluded that these fibers are not involved in such processes, at least not at the outset.

Tests of the *response behavior of mechanosensitive Group-IV receptors* show that, in contrast to the intensity detectors discussed above, their responses to skin stimuli at a *given intensity* are extremely *variable*. Thus the *accuracy* with which these receptors measure stimulus intensity is low. The number of discriminable intensity steps is less than 3, usually 2. The average *information capacity* with respect to stimulus intensity is thus ca. 1 bit per stimulus. This low value suggests that these receptors may be **threshold detectors** – sensors that signal only the presence of a stimulus at a certain position on the skin. Moreover, recent studies have shown that they may participate especially in mediating weak **moving mechanical stimuli** on the skin (crawling insects). It has also been proposed that they, alone or with other receptors, play a role in the **sensation of tickle,** but as yet there are no clear-cut physiological findings in support of this proposal.

Receptive fields and innervation density of mechanoreceptors. The area within which a stimulus of defined intensity can excite a mechanoreceptor is called the **receptive field** of the receptor. The stimulus intensity ordinarily used to outline the receptive field is a few times the threshold intensity. In some cases the receptive field as so defined coincides approximately with the anatomical extent of the receptor (e. g., dome cor-

puscles), and in others stimuli at a great distance from a receptor can excite it (e. g., Pacinian corpuscles). The situation is the same for the **receptors of other modalities** of somatovisceral sensibility.

As to the **density of innervation** of the individual areas of skin, there are as yet few, mainly indirect indications (e. g., from the measurement of difference thresholds; Fig. 10-3). Quantitative descriptions of the **divergence** and **convergence** of afferent nerve fibers and the receptors they supply are also few. It is likely that two to three dome corpuscles are innervated by a single afferent nerve fiber, each collateral of which supplies all the Merkel cells (30–50) within the dome corpuscle. A far greater degree of divergence and convergence is found in the hair follicle receptors, for one afferent fiber can supply several hundred hair follicles, and each follicle is innervated by many afferent fibers. Considerable **species differences** in the innervation of corresponding areas of skin further complicate the picture.

The **relative numbers of the different mechanoreceptors** in the skin have also been estimated in only a few cases. Such estimates indicate that in the hairy and hairless skin of the monkey and probably of man, the *velocity detectors* are clearly in the majority. This makes sense in view of the fact that changes in the constellation of stimuli are more important to the organism, as a rule, than the absolute intensity, duration or frequency of a stimulus. Therefore the velocity or RA receptors are also called **novelty detectors.**

Receptor Function and Mechanoreception

It seems plausible that each of the sensations pressure, touch and vibration is mediated by one of the main types of mechanoreceptor: the intensity, velocity and acceleration detectors, respectively. The inference is strongest in the case of the Pacinian corpuscles, which at stimulus frequencies above 60 Hz appear to be responsible mainly for the sensation of vibration. But the mechanical stimuli to which the skin is ordinarily exposed, except for the vibration stimuli just mentioned (60–800 Hz), as a rule stimulate **several mechanoreceptor types simultaneously** to different degrees, depending on the stimulus. Thus the resulting sensations cannot be ascribed to a particular type of receptor. Correspondingly, in everyday experience the differences between pressure and touch sensations are hard to define. (For further comments on the physiology underlying experience of the tactile world see p. 220.)

Some years ago, when the technique of using metal microelectrodes to record transcutaneously from single afferent nerve fibers in the human skin was introduced, it became possible to make simultaneous psychophysical and neurophysiological measurements. With this method it has been shown that very weak tactile stimuli (of the order of 4 μm in amplitude), which when applied to the fingertip excite only a single RA receptor, suffice to produce a sensation. By contrast, stimuli to the inner surface of the hand must be well above the mechanoreceptor threshold in order to elicit a sensation (cf. Fig. 10-1 C). This difference demonstrates that the central nervous system "pays more attention" to impulses from mechanoreceptors in skin areas important to the sense of touch than to impulses from less important regions.

10.2 Proprioception

In the conscious state we are constantly aware of the positions of our limbs with respect to one another. We know when our joints move, either passively by the action of external forces or actively by the action of our own muscles. We can also state fairly accurately the amount of *resistance* opposing any movement we make. These abilities together are called **proprioception,** because the stimuli to the receptors involved **(proprioceptors)** are derived from the body itself and not from the surroundings [3, 9, 12, 21]. The term **deep sensibility** is also used, reflecting the fact that most of the proprioceptors are not superficially located, but lie rather in the muscles, tendons and joints (the labyrinth receptors are also in this category, and in the strict sense the visceral receptors are included as well).

Qualities of Proprioception

Sense of position. Even without visual assistance it is usually possible to know very precisely the positions of one's limbs and the orientation of their parts with respect to one another. This *quality of proprioception* is called the **sense of position.** Strictly speaking, the sense of position informs us of the *angle at each joint:* from this information the overall orientation of the limbs is derived. Subjective experience shows that the *sense of position exhibits little or no adaptation.*

The *positions of the joints* as a rule – that is, without special practice – cannot be described with even rough accuracy in degrees of angle or in any other verbal form. But we can easily demonstrate the precision with which we are informed of the relative positions of the different parts of our limbs by the following two experiments. First, any position taken by one limb, whether adopted actively or imposed passively (by an experimenter),

can be imitated without visual control by the corresponding limb on the other side. Second, we can accurately indicate with a finger any specified point on a limb, without visual control.

Sense of movement. When we change the angle of a joint without visual control, we are aware of both the direction and the velocity of the movement. This *quality of proprioception* is called the **sense of movement.** *Active* movement at a joint by musucular contraction is perceived as well as passive movement by another person. The *perception threshold of the movement sense,* as in the case of other sensory modalities, depends both on the *amount* of change of angle and on the *rate* of change.

In the case of *passive* movement the *perception threshold* is distinctly lower (better) at the proximal joints than at the *distal* joints. For example, the threshold for movement at the shoulder joint is 0.2–0.4 ° with a minimal velocity of 0.3 °/s, whereas the corresponding values for the middle joint of a finger are 1.0–1.3 ° at 12.5 °/s (GOLDSCHEIDER. To obtain a *measure of the sensitivity* of the passive movement sense, one can multiply the minimal necessary change in angle by the minimal rate of change. Evaluated in this way, for example, the shoulder joint is over forty times as sensitive as the finger joints.
With *active* joint movements, the *perception threshold* is somewhat – but for practical purposes negligibly – lower (better) than when the movement is passive (GOLDSCHEIDER. But under certain conditions it can be shown that the evaluation of active joint movements is subject to a number of *illusions.* In particular, the velocity of the movement seems not to be perceived very accurately; for example, when one attempts to make a symmetrical movement with both hands at the same time, one hand often moves further than the other without the discrepancy being intended or perceived.

Sense of force. By tying strings to a number of objects that differ from one another in weight by 10% or more, and then lifting them by the strings, one can demonstrate that weight differences of this magnitude are easily detected. To make this discrimination, we estimate the *amount of muscle force* we must expend to raise the objects and hold them in the air. This *quality of proprioception* – the ability to estimate muscle force, which is necessary for making movements or maintaining the position of a joint – is called the **sense of force.** Because the muscle force necessary in any situation depends on the resistance opposing the movement, and because proprioception informs us about the amount of resistance, the term *resistance sense* could be used as a synonym for the sense of force; it has not, however, been generally accepted.

In determining experimentally the *abilities of the sense of force,* one inevitably encounters difficulties in eliminating or controlling contributions from cutaneous mechanoreceptors. However, it can easily be shown that the *discriminatory ability* of the sense of force is distinctly better then that of the pressure sense of the skin. It is considerably more difficult to estimate the weight of an object if it is set on the skin than if it is lifted – a fact that everyone turns to advantage in ordinary life. For the sense

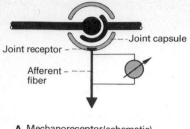

A Mechanoreceptor(schematic)

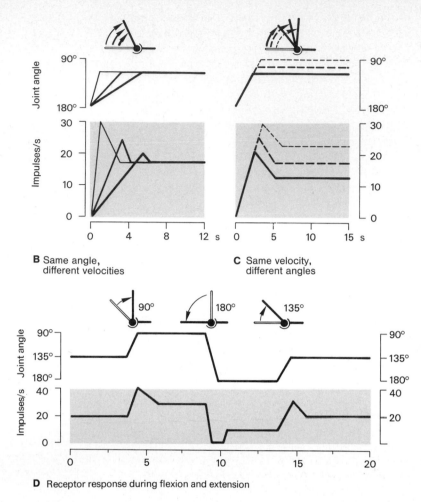

B Same angle,
different velocities

C Same velocity,
different angles

D Receptor response during flexion and extension

Fig. 10-9 A–D. Responses of joint receptors. **A** Experimental arrangement. **B** Joint position changed by a fixed amount at three different velocities. **C** Joint moved from an initial position to three different final positions, with constant velocity of movement. **D** Behavior of a receptor as the joint is moved back and forth. This receptor responds to flexion with an increased discharge rate; others give mirror-image responses. (Schematic, adapted from BOYD and ROBERTS). Recently, evidence is accumulating that joint receptors of the type shown here are rare. The majority of joint receptors seem to be only activated at the extremes of joint excursion. The matter needs further clarification

of force, again, a number of conditions are known to induce *illusions*. Two of these in particular must be kept in mind during experiments on the sense of force: (i) in comparing weights with a "standard weight" it is not irrelevant which is tested first, because there is a tendency to underestimate the second weight, especially when the tests are done in rapid succession; (ii) the ability to discriminate is usually better when the weights are presented in the order light-to-heavy than when the reverse order is used. On the whole, however, the sense of force is distinguished by *great accuracy* and *precise reproducibility,* and for this reason it is a favorite choice as the standard in cross-modality intensity comparisons (cf. Fig. 8-11).

Proprioceptors

The senses of position and movement could be mediated by receptors in the skin overlying the joints, which is compressed or stretched by joint movements. By locally anesthetizing these areas of skin, however, it has been shown that the *cutaneous receptors* play only a small role in sensing position and movement; moreover, it is clear that they cannot be involved in the sense of force. It follows that the *proprioceptors must be situated in extracutaneous struc-*tures. Chief among these are the muscles, tendons and joint capsules. The properties of the **muscle spindles** and **tendon organs** are discussed in detail elsewhere (pp. 83–86), so that we shall consider only the **joint receptors** here [21].

Receptors of the joint capsules. Within the joint capsules are receptors with discharge rates that change both in **proportion to the position of the joint** at rest and in **proportion to the velocity** of movement; the receptor discharge adapts *little or not at all* while a constant joint position is maintained. Fig. 10-9 gives examples of the responses of such receptors when the joint position is changed at different angular velocities (B) or to different final positions (C), or when flexion and extension alternate (D).

The receptors shown in Fig. 10-9 respond to flexion with an increase in discharge rate and to extension with a decrease. But there are about as many receptors with the mirror-image behavior, decreasing their activity during flexion and increasing it during extension. At joints with many degrees of freedom there are sets of receptors with mirror-image responses for practically every direction of motion (inward rotation, outward rotation, abduction, adduction).

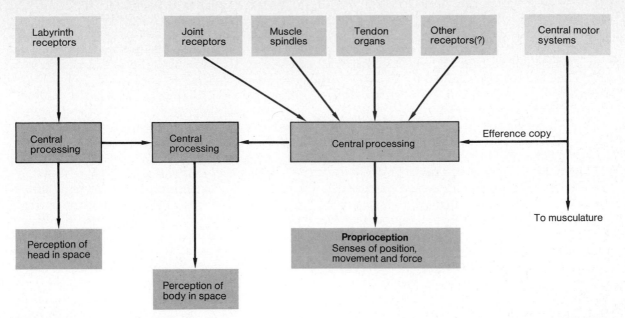

Fig. 10-10. Perception of deep sensibility *(red* shading) by way of proprioceptors, the afferent signals of which are processed together (integrated) with the motor efference copies in the sensory centers for the senses of position, movement and force. The information coming from the receptors in the equilibrium organ, when processed together with the proprioceptive input, gives rise to the perception of the body in space

The joint receptors usually respond over a range of angles smaller than those shown in Fig. 10-9. In most cases there are only a few degrees between zero and maximal discharge. The advantage is that the individual receptor has a *large* dynamic range for *slight* changes in angle – that is, whenever the joint position is in its activity zone, the receptor signals the position with great accuracy. *Overlap of the activity zones* of all the receptors in the population ensures that every joint position is signalled to the central nervous system. The *integrative processing* of this afferent information begins in the corresponding *sensory relay nuclei below the cortex.* In the *thalamus,* for example, neurons have been found with discharge rate that accurately reflects joint position over more than 90 °. There must be considerable precisely organized *convergence* on such a neuron of many joint receptors (and/or muscle or tendon receptors) in the joint concerned.

Histology: The *histological structure* of joint receptors of the kind shown in Fig. 10-9 is not entirely clear. The joint capsule contains receptors of the *Ruffini type* (cf. textbooks of histology); these are the prime candidates. The ligaments also contain receptors of similar appearance, the *Golgi type,* as well as a few *paciniform corpuscles.* True Pacinian corpuscles, in small numbers, tend to be located in the connective tissue loosely surrounding the joint rather than in the joint capsule itself. All these receptors are supplied by myelinated afferent nerve fibers of Groups II and III. In addition, there are free nerve endings with unmyelinated afferents (Group IV or C fibers). Their function is unknown. It is likely that they are involved in the transmission of joint pain.

Central integration. Although it was implicit in the preceding paragraphs that the perception of deep sensibility could originate primarily in the *receptors discussed in the previous section,* it has also been suggested that appropriate *feedback from motor efferents* (efference copy; see below) is extensively involved. Until recently the latter view was supported mainly by the failure to demonstrate any participation of muscle spindles and tendon organs in conscious sensation; thus for the sense of force in particular, but also for the senses of position and movement, it appeared that no adequate peripheral receptor system was available. But since electrophysiological experiments have demonstrated a *cortical representation of the Ia afferents,* and since it has been shown that *selective stimulation of the muscle spindles* (by vibration of the tendon) *in humans gives rise to impressive illusions about the actual position of the joints,* the earlier objections to participation of the muscle receptors in conscious sensation appear to have been largely refuted [11, 17, 21, 25, 27].

We may therefore conclude that the simultaneous systematic activation of various receptor systems and their central integration have primary responsibility for the perception of deep sensibility (Fig. 10-10). Perhaps the *joint receptors* are of greatest importance in the perception of *position* and *movement;* as far as the *sense of force* is concerned, the *muscle spindles* are the prime candidates, though the *tendon organs* and *other receptors* in the muscles, skin and connective tissue may be involved in ways as yet unclear or unknown.

An important aspect of central nervous integration, though we know little about it as yet, is that the central motor systems apparently send a "carbon copy" of their activity to the nervous structures responsible for the perception of deep sensibility (right in Fig. 10-10) – the **efference copy** of von Holst. These efference copies give advance notice of the intended muscular activity and the movements that will result. They can be used to **eliminate the ambiguity in afferent information** that can arise, for instance, in the muscle spindles owing to γ-fiber activity; other receptors (e.g., mechanoreceptors in the skin near joints) can send out ambiguous signals because they are activated by external stimuli as well as by movement.

A second way to **eliminate ambiguity** of afferent input is a directed **efferent inhibition,** exerted by the motor relay nuclei on the sensory relay nuclei. A third method is the reciprocal influence of receptive inputs on one another – that is, **afferent inhibition.** Both efferent and afferent inhibition occur in practically all sensory nuclei, from the spinal cord to the thalamus [26].

The structure of the tactile world and consciousness of the body (body scheme). *Deep sensibility* and *mechanoreception,* and to a certain extent *cutaneous thermoreception,* together enable us to **construct the three-dimensional tactile world,** about which our chief source of information is the hand, as it moves to touch and feel objects. Our concepts of space are formed largely by visual perceptions, but many features of our environment are accessible predominantly or exclusively to tactile exploration. For example, think of properties such as liquid, sticky, firm, elastic, soft, hard, smooth, rough, velvety and many others. An important point is that these properties are discerned poorly, if at all, by passive touching (laying the object on the motionless hand, or the hand on the object), whereas if the **hand is moved** one has little trouble in recognizing structure and form. The superiority of the „feeling" hand over the motionless one derives in part from the activation of many more cutaneous receptors, adaptation of which is partially or completely circumvented, so that detailed information about distortion of the skin is sent centrally. Moreover, when the hand moves, proprioception contributes its share to the recognition of the shape and surface properties of the objects touched.

The overall subjective impression of the **position of the body in space** is basically obtained by integrative evaluation of the information conveyed by the *sense of position* with that from the *labyrinths* (equilibrium organs) about the *position of the head* in the earth's gravitational field (Fig. 10-10). An important sub-aspect of our nonvisual concept of space is the *conscious awareness of the spatial extent of one's body in its surroundings,* often called the **body scheme.** This body scheme is astonishingly firmly fixed, and apparently is in part independent of afferent input from the proprioceptors. Consider, for example, the fact that even after partial or complete amputation of a limb the great majority of patients still feel the missing limb for a long time, often for the rest of their lives. The illusion is frequently so persuasive that the patient experiences the **phantom limb** more intimately than the remaining one. In many cases the patient is able to "move" the phantom limb at will (influence of efference copy?), and in others, feels it to be in an unalterable, permanent position. It often happens that somatosensory sensations arise in the phantom limb, such as the feeling that one has bumped into the edge of a table while crossing the room. Unfortunately, some of these sensations are unpleasant; occasionally they are so painful that the **phantom-limb pain,** which is difficult to alleviate therapeutically, becomes a heavy or even unbearable burden on the patient (cf. also p. 231). (Phantom sensations can also follow the loss of other organs, such as the female breast, the penis or an eye.)

In addition to the direct somatosensory thalamocortical projection areas (cf. p. 203), *spatial abstraction, synthesis and orientation functions* also involve particularly those **unilateral parietal and temporal cortex areas** and associated thalamic nuclei that correspond to the *speech regions* on the speech-dominant side (Fig. 7-20, p. 163). As a rule these functions are predominantly located in the right half of the brain (cf. p. 162). Injury in these regions leads to spatial disorientation states called visuo-spatial agnosia [15]. The symptoms are diverse. For example, these patients lose their way even in familiar surroundings, or they are quite unable to make three-dimensional drawings of simple objects, such as a house. Occasionally there is also a partial loss of the consciousness of the body. Such patients can *completely ignore the existence of the left half of the body* (**left-side neglect**) and cease to care for it; for example, they shave or make up only the right side of the face, or dress themselves only on the right side.

10.3   Thermoreception

Cutaneous thermoreception (synonym temperature sense) has two objectively and subjectively demonstrable qualities – the senses of **cold** and **warmth.** Among the evidence for these distinct qualities in man are the following findings. There are specific cold and warm points in the skin, at which only sensations of cold or warmth can be elicited. Reaction-time measurements have indicated higher conduction velocities for sensations of cold than for warmth. By selective blocking of nerves it is possible to prevent either the cold sensation alone or the warm sensation alone. Finally, there are specific cold and warm receptors in the skin, which not only serve as sensors for conscious sensations of temperature but also participate in the thermoregulation of the body. In the latter task they are supplemented and reinforced by temperature sensors in the central nervous system (e.g., hypothalamus and spinal cord). As a rule we are not conscious of the activity of these central thermoreceptors; they will not be discussed here (but cf. p. 540).

In the analysis of thermoreception it has proved helpful to study those physiological processes that can be recorded while the skin temperature is constant separately from those recorded during a change in skin temperature. Accordingly, in the following discussion of psychophysical results first the **static** and then the **dynamic** temperature sensations will be considered; the same sequence will be followed in the discussion of the thermoreceptors themselves.

Cutaneous Temperature Sensations

Static temperature sensations (constant skin temperature). When one gets into a warm (ca. 33 °C) bath one first experiences a distinct *sensation of warmth*. This sensation fades away after a short time, more rapidly than the bath cools. If one emerges from the bath briefly and then reenters it, the sensation of warmth is renewed. The opposite phenomenon is also familiar; the first sensation after one jumps into a pool of water at ca. 18 °C on a hot summer day is that the water is cool. After a short time, however, the *sensation of coolness* gives way to a *neutral sensation*. At least in an *intermediate range of temperatures,* then, warming or cooling give rise only temporarily to the respective sensations of warmth or cold. In this range of temperatures there is an essentially **complete adaptation** of temperature sensation to the new skin temperature. The temperature range within which complete adaptation of the temperature sensation occurs is thus a **neutral zone** (sometimes called the "comfort" zone). Above or below this neutral zone, permanent sensations of heat or cold are produced even when the skin temperature is kept constant for a long time (the best-known example is perhaps feeling that one's feet are cold for hours at a time). The upper and lower temperature limits of the neutral zone are 36 °C and 30 °C, respectively, for a skin area of 15 cm². When smaller areas of skin are studied the zone expands,

and with larger areas it becomes narrower (an indication of central summation of the impulses coming from the thermoreceptors). In experiments with naked humans in a climate-controlled room, the neutral zone is ca. 35 °–33 °C [16].

Measurements of the **time course of adaption** to stepwise changes of skin temperature within the neutral zone have shown, as illustrated in Fig. 10-11, that with *small* temperature steps adaptation is *rapid* (e.g., 1 min with a step from 31.5 °C to 30 °C), whereas with large step changes the **adaption time** greatly increases (e.g., 20 min with a step from 31.5 °C to 23 °C). As the comparison between the (subjective) *adaptation times* (red bars in Fig. 10-11) and the *time to equilibration of skin temperature* (gray bars) shows, the two times are not the same. When the thermode makes a small temperature step the temperature sensation has adapted before the skin temperature has stabilized, whereas with large temperature steps the reverse occurs [5].

The **maintained sensations of warmth** experienced at constant skin temperatures above 36 °C are more intense, the higher the skin temperature. At temperatures of more than 43°–44 °C the sensation of

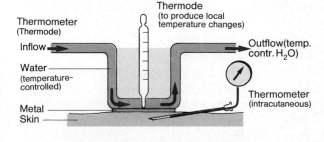

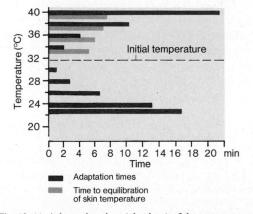

Fig. 10-11. Adaptation time (abscissa) of the temperature sensation (*red* bars) following stepwise change in thermode temperature from 31.5 °C to the value shown on the ordinate. The *gray* bars indicate the time required for the skin temperature to stabilize. The small-area thermode was placed on the inner side of the forearm, about 10 cm from the elbow. The area of skin in contact with the thermode contained 11 warm points and 130 cold points. (From data of HENSEL, H.: Physiologie der Thermoreception. Ergebn. Physiol. *47,* 166, 1952)

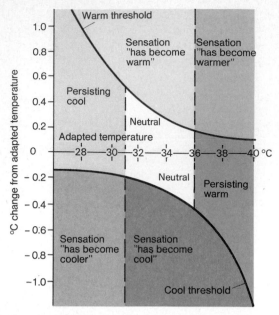

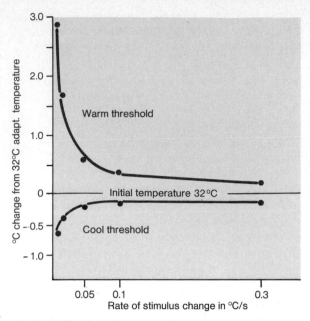

Fig. 10-12. The dependence of thresholds for sensations of warmth and cold upon the initial skin temperature. Starting at the temperatures shown on the abscissa, to which the skin had been adapted for some time, the skin temperature had to be changed by the number of degrees shown on the ordinate in order to elicit a sensation of cold or warmth. The diagram is valid for all temperature changes at a rate of more than 6°/min. (After KENSHALO in [16])

Fig. 10-13. The dependence of cold and warmth thresholds on the rate of temperature change. The initial temperature in all cases was 32 °C. (After KENSHALO in [16])

warmth gives way to a painful heat sensation (heat pain). Similarly, when large areas are cooled to temperatures below 30 °C the **maintained cold sensation** increases in intensity, the colder the skin. Actual cold pain sets in at skin temperatures of 17 °C or less, but at skin temperatures as high as 25 °C the cold sensation has an unpleasant component, especially when fairly large areas of skin are affected. (Man is a tropical creature, intolerant of skin temperatures much below 30 °C).

Recent studies of the **static temperature sensation on the inner surface of the hand** indicate that there, even with very long adaption time (30 min or more) within the temperature range 25 °– 40 °C, reproducible estimation of skin temperature is possible; that is, there is **no complete adaption.** Subjects estimate the set temperature of the skin most accurately when it is 37 °C; at higher and lower temperatures the temperatures estimated were distinctly above or below the correct value, respectively. The skin temperatures 25 °C and 27 °C were estimated to be 10 °C! In these experiments temperatures around 34 °C were felt to be neither cold nor warm, so that this region can be regarded as a (very narrow) neutral zone. At 37 °C the subjects had a pleasant, maintained sensation of warmth (HENSEL in [16]).

Dynamic temperature sensations. The temperature sensations experienced while the skin temperature is changing are basically determined by three parame-

ters – the initial temperature of the skin, the rate of temperature change, and the size of the skin area affected by the stimulus.

The **influence of the initial temperature** on the threshold for a sensation of warmth or cold is shown in Fig. 10-12. At low skin temperatures – for example, 28 °C – the threshold for a warmth sensation is high and that for a cold sensation is low. If the initial temperature (abscissa) is shifted upward, the warmth thresholds decrease and those for cold increase. In other words, a cool skin (e. g., 28 °C) has to be cooled further by less than 0.2 °C to convert the maintained cold sensation into the sensation "has become colder." But the same skin must be warmed by almost 1 °C before a sensation of warmth occurs. Correspondingly, if the initial temperature is 38 °C a slight warming (< 0.2 °C) elicits the sensation "has become warmer," whereas the skin must be cooled by around 0.8 °C to produce a cold sensation.

A peculiarity of this response that is not apparent in Fig. 10-12 should also be mentioned. When the change is such that the temperature moves out of the neutral zone (31 °–36 °C in Fig. 10-12), cooling or warming cause a shift from a neutral sensation to a sensation of cold or warmth. On the other hand, if the skin is warmed up from a temperature of 28 °C (for example), before reaching the warmth threshold shown in Fig. 3-12 the subject says that the skin is *"less cool"* and then *"neutral."* Conversely, when the skin is cooled down from a high temperature, the first feelings are "less warm" and then "neutral," before a sensation of cold appears. These **sensations of decreasing intensity** of an existing cold or warmth sensation are distinctly different from those described as the occurrence of a sensation of warmth or cold.

A final conclusion to be drawn from Fig. 10-12 is that at a **given skin temperature,** depending on the stimulus conditions, sensations of **either warmth or cold** can be produced. For example, when the initial temperature is 32 °C warming by 0.5 °C gives rise to a sensation of warmth, whereas cooling by 0.5 °C from an initial 33 °C produces a distinct sensation of cold. You can easily convince yourself of the phenomenon just described by repeating Weber's three-bowl experiment; fill one bowl with cold, one with lukewarm, and the last with warm water and then put one hand in the cold water and the other in the warm water. Now if you move both hands to the bowl with the lukewarm water, you will have a clear sensation of warmth in one hand and of cold in the other.

As Fig. 10-13 shows, the **rate of temperature change** has only a slight effect on the warmth and cold thresholds, as long as the change is more rapid than 0.1 °C/s (6 °C/min). With slower temperature changes both thresholds increase steadily. The increase continues when the temperature changes at rates even slower than those shown in Fig. 10-13. For example, cooling of the skin by 0.4 °C/min (0.0067 °C/s) from a starting temperature of 33.5 °C gives rise to a sensation of cold only after the temperature has fallen by 4.4 °C, 11 min after the change was begun. When cooling is very slow, then, a person may not notice that *large regions of skin have become quite cold* (with concomitant loss of heat from the body), especially if his attention is distracted by other things. It is conceivable that this factor is involved when one **catches a cold.**

With respect to the **size of the skin area** affected by a change in temperature, the thresholds to cooling or warming of small areas are higher than when large areas are stimulated; moreover, with a given suprathreshold change in skin temperature the intensity of the sensation increases with the stimulated area. Thus in both the threshold and the suprathreshold region there is a central nervous **spatial facilitation** of the impulses coming from the thermoreceptors. This is especially clear in experiments in which the stimulus is given bilaterally. For example, when heat stimuli are applied simultaneously to the backs of both hands, the threshold is lower than when either hand is stimulated alone.

Cold and Warm Points; Spatial Thresholds

The sensitivity of the human skin to cold and warmth is localized at different points in the skin; that is, there are **cold points** and **warm points.** These are distributed over the skin in varying density, though on the whole they are less numerous than the touch points of the mechanoreceptor system. There are clearly *more cold points* than warm points. For example, the hand surfaces have 1–5 cold points per cm² but only 0.4 warm points per cm². Both are most densely distributed in the most temperature-sensitive region of the skin, the face. Here there are 16–19 cold points per cm², whereas the warmth sensitivity in this region cannot be resolved into individual points – it forms a *sensory continuum.*

In accordance with the low density of cold points and the even lower density of warm points, the **simultaneous spatial thresholds to temperature stimuli** are high. The spatial thresholds for cold stimuli are lower than those for warm stimuli. Moreover, there are considerable differences between the longitudinal and transverse directions. For example, on the thigh the simultaneous spatial threshold for warm stimuli in the longitudinal direction is 26 cm and in the transverse direction, 9 cm; the corresponding values for cold stimuli are 16.5 and 2.9 cm.

Cold and Warm Receptors

Properties of specific thermoreceptors. In primates and other mammals, and in many other species as well, the presence of **specific thermoreceptors** has been established conclusively. They share the following characteristics [2, 5, 7, 16, 18, 19]:

- Maintained discharge at constant skin temperatures, with discharge rate proportional to skin temperature (static response, Fig. 10-14).
- A rise (or fall) in discharge rate during a change in skin temperature (dynamic response, Fig. 10-15).
- Insensitivity to nonthermal stimuli.
- Threshold sensitivity comparable to the human sensation thresholds to thermal stimulation of the skin.
- Small receptive fields (1 mm² or less), each afferent fiber supplying only one or a few warm or cold points.

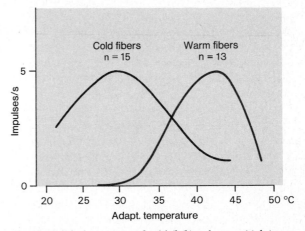

Fig. 10-14. Discharge rates of cold *(left)* and warm *(right)* receptors in the monkey skin at constant skin temperature. The action potentials were recorded from thin filaments of the associated nerves, as in the sketch of Fig. 10-4. The data are means of the steady discharge frequencies of the populations (size indicated in figure) of cold and warm receptors. (After KENSHALO in [16])

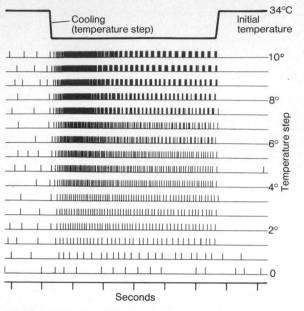

Fig. 10-15. Behavior of a cold receptor during brief cooling temperature steps. The initial and final temperature was 34 °C for each record. The amplitude of each cooling step is given in °C on the right. Particularly when the steps are large, the PD behavior immediately after the cooling and the grouping of impulses as the lower temperature is maintained are clearly evident. Records from a filament of the median nerve to the skin of a monkey, made with the technique shown in Fig. 10-4. [From DARIAN-SMITH et al.: J. Neurophysiol. *36*, 325 (1973)]

– Conduction velocities below 20 m/s, in some species as low as 0.4 m/s.

Responses at constant skin temperature. Fig. 10-14 shows the discharge rates of thermoreceptors at *constant* skin temperatures (abscissa). The mean static frequencies of the two populations (cold and warm receptors) form "bell-shaped" curves, with the maximal activity of the cold receptors at about 30 °C and that of the warm receptors at about 43 °C. (The individual activity maxima of single cold receptors lie between 17 °C and 36 °C; those of single warm receptors are between 41 °C and 47 °C.)

Responses during change of skin temperature. The dynamic responses of a cold receptor during cooling and rewarming are shown in Fig. 10-15. Comparison of this figure with Fig. 10-14 reveals that the discharge rate of a thermoreceptor depends not only on temperature *(proportional sensor)* but also on the rate of change of temperature *(differential sensor)* – a property to be expected from the results of the subjective experiments described above. The behavior of the *warm receptors* during temperature changes is the mirror image of that of the *cold receptors*. Warming causes them to discharge at a higher rate, and during

cooling there is an undershoot in frequency, followed by return to a steady level.

Note that in general the **peaks of the dynamic sensitivity ranges** of the thermoreceptors correspond roughly to the peaks of the static sensitivity ranges; that is, for a given temperature step the dynamic response, like the static response, depends greatly on the initial temperature. However, the dynamic sensitivity range is broader than the static range. For example, a cold receptor that is silent at maintained temperatures between 40 ° and 38 °C discharges as the temperature is changed from 40 ° to 38 °C. Because of these properties of the dynamic responses, when the **temperature is changed in the region of the core temperature of the body** there are simultaneous changes in discharge rate of the warm and cold receptors, even though the static sensitivity is minimal in this region (Fig. 10-14). The presence of these two receptor populations rather than one homogeneous population of thermoreceptors offers the advantage that considerably more detailed information about thermal events at the skin can be signalled to the CNS. Finally, it should be mentioned that the **temperature at the receptor** alone determines its response. The direction of the *temperature gradient* in the skin plays no role. Whether a receptor is stimulated from the surface of the skin or from below (e.g., by intraarterial injection of a cold or warm liquid), the response is the same.

Grouped discharges. Whereas most thermoreceptors discharge continuously within their static sensitivity range, the *cold receptors of primates* in particular exhibit regularly grouped discharges in the intermediate sensitivity range (Fig. 10-15); the number of groups per unit time and the number of impulses per group depend on the temperature in a characteristic way. It remains an open question whether, and to what extent, this information in addition to the mean discharge rate is utilized by the central nervous system.

Nonspecific thermoreceptors. In addition to the thermoreceptors described above, mammals have receptors that can be excited by both *pressure* and *cooling*. But even when sharply cooled they discharge only briefly and at a low frequency, whereas they are very sensitive to pressure. These are probably *intensity detectors* with a certain degree of cold sensitivity. Perhaps their behavior explains why the colder of two otherwise identical weights placed on the hand surface appears heavier than the warmer weight (Weber's illusion).

Histology. It has not yet been possible to make a complete assignment of thermoreceptor function to specific *histological structures*. In the human skin, the *cold receptors* appear to lie within and just below the epidermis, with the *warm receptors* more in the upper and middle layers of the corium. In the facial skin of the cat free nerve endings of thin myelinated fibers (Group III) have been shown to be the histological substrate of the cold receptors [7].
Afferents. On the whole, *thermoreceptors* in the skin are apparently supplied predominantly by **Group IV fibers** (i.e., unmyelinated fibers). In mammals, including primates, this appears to hold for all *warm receptors,* whereas some of the cold receptors, as just mentioned, consist of **Group III** fibers (hence the more rapid reactions to cold stimuli mentioned on p. 221).

Receptor Function and Thermoreception

There is no doubt that the activity and changes in activity of thermoreceptors are responsible for temperature sensations. However, as will be apparent in the following comparison of the receptive and subjective responses, receptor activity is reflected in consciousness only after considerable **central nervous integration** of the influx from the periphery. The spatial summation of temperature stimuli mentioned above is one indication of such processing.

As Fig. 10-14 shows, both warm and cold receptors discharge impulses when the skin temperature is kept constant within the *subjective neutral zone* (31 °–36 °C). Thus thermoreceptor activity, at least at low frequencies, does not necessarily give rise to subjective sensations. Sensations arise only if impulses reach the central nervous system at a sufficient rate. The **maintained sensations of warmth** above 36 °C can be interpreted in this sense, as a result of the steadily increasing discharge rates of the warm receptors as temperature rises; above 43 °C, because of the additional excitation of heat receptors, the sensation of warmth gives way to a painful heat sensation. The **maintained cold sensations** below 31 °C, on the other hand, cannot be so simply ascribed to the increase in the static discharge of the cold receptors. That is, the lower limit of the neutral zone and the position of the maximal average discharge rate of the cold receptors are practically the same. Furthermore, the average discharge rates at 25 °C and 33 °C, for example, are about the same, but at the lower temperature there is a lasting sensation of cold and at the higher, a neutral sensation. In this case, then, *additional information is required* to decide on which side of the bell-shaped curve the actual skin temperature lies. One way in which this could be derived is from the presence or absence of *simultaneous discharge of the warm receptors;* alternatively, the CNS could make use of the fact that many cold receptors tend to discharge in *short bursts* in their intermediate frequency range (cf. Fig. 10-15). As a final example of the central modification the peripheral inputs undergo before they are reflected in consciousness, remember that the time course of **subjective adaptation** to a new skin temperature extends over **many minutes** (Fig. 10-11), whereas the **thermoreceptors** adapt to a new temperature within a **few seconds** (Fig. 10-15). Evidently the central nervous activity induced by the transient afferent influx dies out slowly.

Special Forms of Thermoreception

A common feature of the sense of temperature is the occurrence of **after-sensations.** For example, if one presses a cold metal rod against the forehead for about 30 s and then removes it, a distinct feeling of cold persists even though the skin is warming up again, so that a feeling of warmth might be expected. Weber, who studied this phenomenon, believed that the persistent cold sensation came from a spread of the cooling into the surrounding skin. But direct recordings from thermoreceptors have shown that when they have been greatly cooled the cold receptors continue to discharge during rewarming – at first even at an increasing rate (HENSEL). The after-sensation is thus a "normal" cold sensation. Corresponding sensations of warmth have also been described. Very strong warm stimuli (e.g., too-hot bath water) often elicit a **paradoxical sensation of cold.** This is presumably based on the fact that the cold receptors, normally silent above 40 °C, discharge again transiently when *rapidly warmed to more than 45 °C.*

The **heat sensation** that occurs regularly at skin temperatures above 45 °C is not yet entirely understood in terms of neurophysiological correlates. It appears, however, that there are special heat receptors (Fig. 10-19). Because the *heat sensation* also has a painful character, and because heat stimuli are injurious, the heat sensation is more appropriately considered a quality of pain than one of thermoreception. A strong negative affective component also characterizes the sensations of **oppressive closeness** and of **chill.** Both are accompanied by autonomic reflexes: sweating and vasodilation in the former, and shivering and vasoconstriction in the latter. These are ordinarily elicited either by external stimuli or by psychological causes, though more rarely pathological processes in the CNS may be implicated.

Clinical examination. Usually this is confined to observing the sensations of cold and warmth elicited by two test tubes, one filled with hot water and the other with ice water. Spatially delimited disturbances of the sense of temperature can be diagnostic of spinal-tract damage or blocking. Usually the sense of pain is also affected, because the pain afferents pass centrally along the same paths (see p. 198). Under such conditions mechanoreception and proprioception may be unaltered.

10.4 Somatic and Visceral Pain

Unlike the other sensory modalities, pain contributes little to our information about the environment. Rather, it informs us about threats to our bodies, for it is activated by **noxious** (tissue-damaging) stimuli. This specific protective function is not available via the other modalities, so that the sense of pain is *indispensable for a normal life.* Pain is also the modality of greatest importance in medicine, for it is this effect of noxious influences that brings the patient to the physician: *the pain hurts.*

Qualities of Pain

Pain can be categorized in terms of a number of qualities, defined either by the site of origin of the pain or by its nature. In Fig. 10-16 these *qualities* are shown in the red boxes. The major subdivision of the modality **pain** is that into the qualities **somatic** pain and **visceral** pain.

Somatic pain. If somatic pain originates in the skin it is called **superficial pain;** if it comes from the muscles,

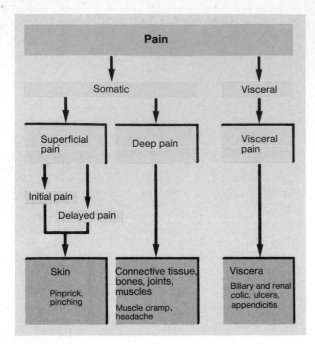

Fig. 10-16. Pain qualities (*red* background). The localization of each quality is indicated (*gray* background), with examples of specific forms of pain

bones, joints or connective tissue it is called **deep pain.** Superficial and deep pain are thus (sub)qualitites of somatic pain.

If superficial pain is produced by piercing the skin with a needle, the subject feels a sharp *"flash"* of pain, a readily *localizable* sensation that fades away rapidly when the stimulus stops. This **initial pain** is often followed, particularly at high stimulus intensities, by a **delayed pain** with a latency of 0.5–1.0 s. The delayed pain has a *dull (burning) character,* is more *difficult to localize* and dies out more *slowly;* a good example is the pain felt in response to the squeezing of an interdigital fold.

The most familiar example of *deep pain* is **headache,** probably the commonest form of pain experienced by humans. Deep pain is dull in nature, is poorly localizable as a rule, and tends to radiate into the surroundings.

Headache takes many forms; it can be an illness on its own or a symptom accompanying other diseases. In the relevant literature *over 20 different forms of headache* are described, though with one exception the different groups are not sharply delimited and therefore not standardized. The single exception is the severe headache called **migraine,** distinguished primarily by its periodic recurrence and by the fact that it is usually unilateral, with a distinct onset and end. It is brought about by a temporary change in the tone of the smooth musculature of the blood vessels, the cause of which is unknown; the result is abnormal blood flow through the affected part of the brain. Thus migraine represents the vasomotor type of headache.

In addition to the differences just discussed, between initial pain and delayed or deep pain, there is another important difference, with regard to **affective** and **autonomic responses** to pain and **participation** in the painful situation. Delayed pain and especially deep pain (such as migraine) are accompanied by feelings of aversion or even illness, and they often elicit autonomic responses such as nausea, sweating and a drop in blood pressure. Initial pain, by contrast, gives rise to escape reflexes such as withdrawal of a foot that has stepped on a sharp object (it would of course make little sense to run away from deep pain).

Visceral pain. As diagrammed in Fig. 10-16, **visceral pain** is a major quality distinct from somatic pain. This pain, too, tends to be dull or diffuse in character and it resembles deep pain in that similar autonomic responses accompany it. It is remarkable that when the viscera are exposed under local anesthesia they can be squeezed or cut without pain as long as the parietal peritoneum and the mesenteric roots are not stimulated. But rapid or extensive stretching of the hollow organs elicits severe pain. Moreover, spasms or strong contractions of smooth muscle are painful, especially when they are associated with inadequate circulation (ischemia). Other peculiarities of visceral pain are discussed on p. 231.

Measurement of the Intensity of Pain; Adaption to Pain

Experimental research on pain in humans and animals encounters many special problems [1, 2, 4, 5, 8, 12, 20, 28]. These begin with the fact that practically all tissue-damaging **(noxious)** stimuli give rise to pain, so that *no single adequate stimulus* for pain can be specified. Moreover, because of the injurious nature of painful stimuli, the *constancy of stimulus conditions* usually demanded in experimental procedures cannot always be achieved. *Comparison of subjective sensations* in humans with the *neurophysiological correlates* measured in animals is also difficult; moreover, painful stimuli can be applied to humans or animals for experimental purposes only within relatively narrow limits. Finally, it must be kept in mind that the *affective reactions* to pain are often more important to patient and physician than the *physiological aspects,* with which we are chiefly concerned here. For example, the subjective intensity of pain depends not only on the intensity of the stimulus but also on the extent to which it preoccupies the subject. Redirection of attention can weaken the sensation of pain and in extreme situations (the stress of an accident, wounding in battle, hypnosis) actually abolish it [6, 13, 29].

Whether animals suffer pains comparable to those experienced by humans cannot be determined with absolute certainly, as likely as it may seem. As an admission of this fundamental epistemological difficulty, it has become customary to use the term **noci-ception** for the sensory modality of animals that in humans gives rise to the conscious experience of pain. Accordingly, pain receptors are better termed **noci-ceptors.**

Mechanical pain stimuli. Various methods have been devised for *measuring the intensity of superficial pain* in humans. One example is illustrated in Fig. 8-11, a plot of the increase in intensity of the pain produced by *electrical stimulation of the skin* as found by cross-modality comparison. The threshold for **dull superficial pain** caused by pressure stimuli (mechanical pain, using a rod with an end area of 0.78 cm²) was found to be ca. 550 g/cm² on the forehead. As the stimulus intensity was increased to 6600 g, as many as 15 levels of intensity could be discriminated. These measurements were used to construct a **pain-intensity scale** (Hardy et al.), in which 2 intensity-difference steps were set equal to one **dol,** giving a total intensity range of 7.5 dol for dull presssure pain.

Thermal pain stimuli. *Warm stimuli* – especially thermal radiation, which avoids simultaneous mechanical stimulation – have been widely used for *measurement of pain thresholds.* Such **heat pain** is first sensed when the skin temperature reaches 43 °– 47 °C, usually 45 °C. As the skin temperature is further increased, as many as 21 difference steps (that is, 10.5 dol) can be distinguished before the pain sensation becomes maximal. The threshold for thermal pain is independent of sex, age and sociological origin.

Chemical stimuli, as a rule, are ineffective when placed in direct contact with the skin. Therefore in experiments an irritant pad is used to raise a blister, which is then removed to expose the underlying tissue. This tissue, the basal layer of the epidermis, can then be rinsed with test solutions. This procedure and local intraarterial injections to measure deep pain and visceral pain have aroused great interest, especially because of the possibility that they might reveal a **pain substance** common to all pains that is released from the tissue by the noxious agent. The results of the various chemical experiments done so far can be summarized in simplified form as follows. There are a number of substances naturally occurring in the body that in appropriate concentrations induce pain; they include acetylcholine, serotonin, histamine (itch stimulant), H^+ ions from pH 6, K^+ ions from 20 mmol/l, as well as plasmakinins such as bradykinin and other polypeptides of unknown composition. Nevertheless it is unclear which of these substances are involved in producing pain *in vivo*. In any case, a number of them can reach pain-inducing concentrations in the body. Altogether, the results suggest that there is **no single pain substance** [1, 2, 24].

Adaption to pain. In addition to the character and intensity of plain, the most *clinically* important aspect is whether the sensation of pain adapts. Subjective experience tends to indicate a **lack of adaptation** (headaches and toothaches can last for hours). An experiment to *measure adaptation* to heat pain is shown in Fig. 10-17. Subjects are required to adjust the intensity of radiation from an infrared source warming the forehead such that it is always just at threshold. The skin temperature is then a measure of the pain threshold. As the record in Fig. 10-17 shows, the skin temperature hardly changes at all in the course of the

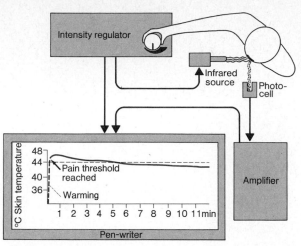

Fig. 10-17. Apparatus for the study of pain stimulation. Infrared rays warm a blackened area of skin on the subject's forehead. The skin temperature is monitored by a radiation sensor (photocell) and recorded on a pen-writer. After HARDY: J. appl. Physiol. *5,* 725 (1953). The red curve shows dependence of the pain threshold (average values) on duration of the heat stimulus. The subjects are required throughout the experiment to regulate the intensity of the radiation themselves, to a level such that the temperature of the forehead is just felt to be painful. The initial overshooting of skin temperature, beyond the pain threshold, is caused by the inertia of the equipment. [After GREENE and HARDY: J. appl. Physiol. *17,* 693 (1962)]

experiment. The slight change that is observed is a reduction in skin temperature – that is, the radiant intensity at which the subject just sensed pain became progressively lower. This result implies that rather than adaptation there is a **sensitization** of the stimulated area of skin. Thus neither everyday experience nor the results of experiments on heat pain give any indication of the existence of adaptation to pain.

Neurophysiological Basis of Pain

Specificity of the sense of pain. During the past hundred years, three main hypotheses have been proposed regarding the mechanism of peripheral coding of painful stimuli. These are the *intensity,* the *pattern,* and the *specificity theories;* only the last of these has received sufficient experimental support [14].

The intensity and pattern theories were formulated because the variety of painful stimuli – that is, the lack of a single adequate stimulus – led to the assumption that there were no special pain receptors (nociceptors). Rather, it was thought, pain always occured when the low-threshold mechanoreceptors and thermoreceptors were stimulated above a certain intensity. According to the **intensity theory,** nociceptive stimuli elicit volleys of impulses at particularly *high frequencies* in the low-threshold receptors; according to the **pattern theory** such stimuli produce *special pat-*

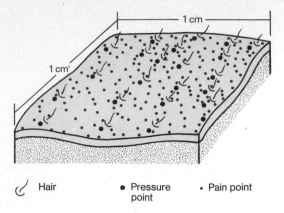

Hair   • Pressure point   · Pain point

Inside of forearm

Fig. 10-18. Pain and pressure points on the human skin. The location of the pain points was determined with von Frey hairs. [From STRUGHOLD: Z. Biol. *80*, 376 (1924)]

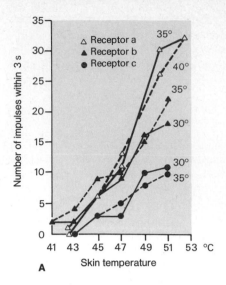

A

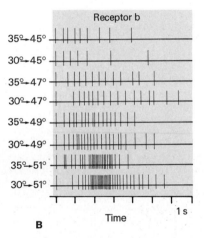

B

Fig. 10-19 A, B. Responses of polymodal nociceptors of the facial skin of the rhesus monkey to heat stimuli. **A** Dependence of the discharge of three receptors on the final temperature of heat stimuli within the associated receptive field. The ordinate indicates the number of impulses discharged within the 3 s following the first impulse after application of the stimulus. The initial temperatures for each of the 6 experiments are shown on the right of the curves. **B** Discharge patterns of the receptor b in response to temperature increases from 30 ° or 35 °C to the indicated final temperatures. Each record begins with the first impulse elicited by the stimulus. [After BEITEL and DUBNER: J. Neurophysiol. *39*, 1160 (1976)]

terns of impulses, differing from those discharged in response to noninjurious stimuli. In both proposals the central nervous system would decode the altered afferent input as a sensation of pain. By contrast, the **specificity theory** postulates (in complete analogy with the other sensory modalities) the **existence of special nociceptors (pain receptors),** which respond only to high-intensity stimuli and thus give rise directly to the pain sensation.

The gate-control theory of pain [23] is a modern special case of the pattern theory. For a number of years it aroused considerable interest, especially in the clinic. Basically, the proposal was that in the presence of painful peripheral stimuli a tonic spinal presynaptic inhibition of afferent fibers, which acted as a gate, was suppressed; with the gate thus opened, it would become possible for the nociceptive impulses to be conducted centripetally. Experiments did not succeed in confirming this hypothesis, and in fact its fundamental postulates were refuted. The gate-control theory has therefore been discarded [26].

Pain points. As was found for mechano- and thermoreception, the skin is not uniformly sensitive to pain, but rather exhibits **pain points** (Fig. 10-18). These are distinctly more numerous than either *pressure points* (9:1 in Fig. 10-18) or *cold* and *warm points* (10:1). This finding alone makes it likely that the nociceptors are *not identical* with the other cutaneous receptors.

Nociceptors *(pain receptors).* Since the formulation of the specificity theory, it has been possible to record the activity of receptors in humans and animals that respond, as the theory demands, not to low-intensity stimuli but only to those at intensities high enough to damage tissue. These must be regarded as special **nociceptors. In the skin,** so far, purely mechanosensitive, purely thermosensitive, and mechano- plus ther-

mosensitive nociceptors have been found. The latter, called *polymodal nociceptors,* are apparently more common than the other two types in human skin. Examples of the responses of polymodal nociceptors to warm and heat stimuli are shown in Fig. 10-19. The receptors do not respond to cold or warm stimuli below 41 °C. But if the skin is warmed to 45 °C or more the receptors discharge at a rate that clearly increases as the temperature rises. Because painful heat sensations occur at skin temperatures above 45 °C (cf. p.

227), these receptors, like the purely thermosensitive nociceptors, can also be called **heat receptors.** Recently **skeletal muscle** has been found to contain not only *polymodal nociceptors* but also specifically *mechanosensitive* and specifically *chemosensitive* nociceptors [24]. The latter are excited exclusively or predominantly by the substances listed on p. 227 as chemical pain stimuli.

In **cardiac muscle,** especially when *local blood flow is restricted* (ischemia), the excitation of nociceptors produces the painful condition known as **angina pectoris.** It is not yet known which of the changes caused by the inadequate circulation in the tissue (e.g., abnormal contractions, oxygen deficiency, increased concentration of metabolites) is responsible for exciting the cardiac nociceptors.

The smooth-muscle walls of the **hollow viscera** evidently contain many **visceral nociceptors.** These receptors respond in part to passive stretch, and in part to active contraction of the smooth musculature. When this contraction is isometric – that is, without length change (e.g., when the exit from the organ is blocked) – the visceral nociceptors are activated especially strongly. Extremely severe pain is experienced subjectively under these conditions; clinical examples of this category are the *biliary colic* and *renal colic* produced by obstruction of the bile duct or a ureter, respectively. *Ischemia* can also lead to severe visceral pain; in this case it is not known whether the pain is caused by the mechanical or the chemical changes produced in the tissue. The **lung,** too, contains many nociceptors, which are activated by stimuli such as irritant gases or dust particles.

Histology. Of the two basic types of nerve endings in the skin, the corpuscular and free nerve endings, the latter are much more common. Thus the large number of pain points in itself suggests that pain reception is mediated by **free nerve endings,** and this inference is supported by numerous other findings. For example, ulcerous cutaneous tissue, in which only pain and no other sensations can be elicited, has been found to contain only free nerve endings. The cornea, tympanum and dental pulp also contain only free nerve endings, and in these tissues pain is more readily elicited than any other sensation. In certain conditions of impaired peripheral innervation in which patients report only pain sensations, only free nerve endings are found. Furthermore, in the viscera and elsewhere in the body free nerve endings are found at sites where pain can be elicited by appropriate stimuli. However, these correlations definitely do not imply that all free nerve endings are nociceptors. As described above, many receptive units with Group-III and Group-IV afferent fibers are specifically sensitive to mechanical or thermal stimuli, and these prob-

ably all have free rather than corpuscular endings. The **free nerve endings,** then, are **not a homogeneous population** functionally, and the absence of histological differentiation *by no means* indicates the absence of *functional specificity*. This specificity is likely to be associated with the differentiation of *molecular structures* inaccessible to observation in the light or electron microscopes.

Afferent nociceptive fibers. In the case of **superficial pain in the skin** it appears that the receptors that mediate the *initial pain* are Group-III fibers, and those for *delayed pain* are Group-IV fibers. Because the latter conduct considerably more slowly than the former, the difference in latency of the two pain sensations is evidently due primarily to the different *conduction velocities* of the two groups of fibers.

In humans the following findings support the notion that Group-III fibers mediate initial pain and Group-IV fibers, delayed pain. (i) When conduction in a nerve is blocked by **mechanical pressure,** the thick fibers are affected first and the thin fibers somewhat later. As long as only the Group-II fibers are blocked, both qualities of superficial pain persist. But as soon as the Group-III fibers are blocked, the initial pain disappears, leaving only the delayed pain. (ii) When a nerve is blocked with a **local anesthetic** (e.g., Novocaine) to which the Group-IV fibers are more sensitive than the Group-III fibers, the reverse phenomenon is observed; the delayed pain disappears before the initial pain. (iii) **Electrical stimulation** of exposed cutaneous nerves at intensities such that Group-III fibers are excited produces sharp pain sensations. But if the myelinated fibers are blocked and a stimulus intensity appropriate to Group IV is used, the result is a dull burning pain, subjectively so unpleasant that it is described as difficult to endure.

In **skeletal muscle** as well the *nociceptors* appear to be predominantly or exclusively Group-III and -IV fibers [24]. Most of the afferent fibers from the **viscera** are unmyelinated; it is not yet known which of them serve for *visceral reflex regulation* and which are involved in *visceral pain*.

10.5   Special and Abnormal Forms of Pain; Pain Therapy

Special Forms of Pain

Projected pain. A sharp blow to the ulnar nerve, where it passes superficially over the elbow, produces unpleasant sensations difficult to describe (tingling

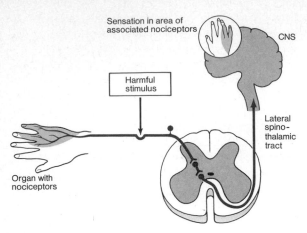

Fig. 10-20. The origin of projected pain (schematic)

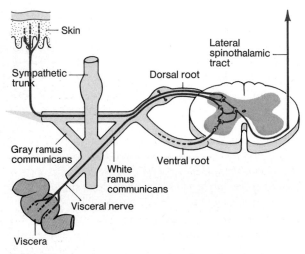

Fig. 10-21. The reflex pathway underlying referred pain. Some of the pain afferents from the viscera synapse in the spinal cord with the same neurons of the lateral spinothalamic tract on which cutaneous pain afferents terminate

and the like) in the areas supplied by this nerve, the ulnar parts of the distal forearm and the hand. Evidently the activity elicited in the afferent nerve fibers at the elbow is **projected** by the central nervous system (that is, by our consciousness) into the regions served by these afferent fibers, because we have learned that such sensory impulses normally come from the receptors in this region. We find it difficult to *interpret* the resulting sensations because the pattern of impulses produced by direct mechanical stimulation of the nerve is not ordinarily encountered.

Projected sensations can occur in all sensory modalities. Apart from the harmless example just discussed, **projected pain** is clinically important and of common occurrence. The way it arises is diagrammed in Fig. 10-20. One such condition frequently encountered in the clinic is the compression of spinal nerves

at the entrance into the vertebral canal, owing to damage of the intervertebral disks (the "slipped disk" syndrome). The centripetal impulses thus abnormally produced in nociceptive fibers generate pain sensations that are projected into the area supplied by the stimulated spinal nerve. (There may, of course, also be pain in the region of the disk itself.) In *projected pain,* then, the site at which the noxious agent acts is not that at which the pain is sensed.

Neuralgia. Far more serious than acute projected pains are those produced by continuous irritation of a nerve or a dorsal root (by pinching, pressure, overstretching). The chronic, direct nerve injury causes *"spontaneous" pains* that often come in waves or *attacks*. Usually, as would be expected for projected pain, they are *restricted to the region supplied by the affected nerve or root*. This condition is called **neuralgia** or **neuralgic pain.** Unfortunately, very little is known about the way in which local damage to a nerve leads to neuralgic pains. Accordingly, it is difficult to treat such conditions, especially if the process damaging the nerve is not corrected adequately or in time. Particularly agonizing forms of intractable neuralgia are those that occur not as a sign or symptom of obvious nerve damage, but rather *without discernible cause*. The prime example of such cryptogenic (the word denotes "of obscure origin") neuralgia is cryptogenic **trigeminal neuralgia,** a condition as difficult for the patient to bear as for the physician to alleviate.

Causalgia. For unknown reasons, nerve injury (especially secondary to bullet wounds) can give rise to chronic tormenting pains in the region supplied by the injured nerve, associated with vasomotor and sudomotor disturbances of the innervated region and with progressive trophic changes in the affected tissue. This complex of symptoms is called **causalgia.**

Referred pain. The sensation produced by nociceptive stimulation of the viscera is often localized not (or not only) in the internal organ, but rather in distant superficial sites. Such pain is called **referred pain.** The referral is always to parts of the periphery supplied by the same segment of the spinal cord as the affected internal organ. That is, with respect to the skin surface, the pain is referred within the associated **dermatome** (cf. Fig. 9-5, p. 197). Many organs are supplied by more than one spinal segment; in such cases, the pain is referred to several dermatomes. Together, these are the **Head's zone** of the organ concerned. A well-known example is that of pain originating at the heart but appearing to come from the chest and a narrow strip along the medial aspect of the left arm. Because the relationship between dermatomes and internal organs (innervation from the same spinal segment) is known, such referred pain is an important *aid to diagnosis* (cf. also pp. 196 and 197).

The **production of referred pain** probably occurs as illustrated in Fig. 10-21. Some of the pain afferents from the skin and the internal organs that enter a given spinal segment are connected with the same neurons of origin of the spinothalamic tract (cf. Fig. 9-4,

p. 196). Excitation of such cells is interpreted as pain at the periphery because this interpretation is usually appropriate in the body's *experience*. When an internal organ is diseased, there is often a further consequence of the convergence of nociceptive afferents from the organ and the associated dermatome upon neurons in the pain pathway – **hyperesthesia** (oversensitivity) of the skin in the dermatome. The reason is that the excitability of the spinal interneurons is increased by the visceral impulses, so that a stimulus to the skin causes greater than normal central activity (facilitation).

Other interactions between the somatic and autonomic nervous systems. There appear to be still other interactions between the somatic and autonomic systems, apart from referred pain, which we do not yet entirely understand. An example is the *therapeutic effect of heat* applied to the skin, in certain diseases of internal organs. The warmth does not act directly on the internal organ (the blood serves as a coolant to prevent warming of the deep tissues), but probably has a reflex effect by way of the warm receptors in the skin (cf. p. 223).

Stimulation of *visceral pain receptors* often produces an increase in the **tone of skeletal muscles,** and in extreme cases can lead to reflex **maintained contraction** (muscle spasms). Activity in polysynaptic reflex paths excites not only motoneurons in the associated segment, but also those of other functionally related muscles. Pain in the abdominal cavity, for example, produces tension in the muscles of the abdominal wall, and such patients often lie with knees drawn up, because the flexor muscles of the legs are excited by the same afferents. A marked, prolonged *increase in muscle tone* produces **muscle pain** and **tenderness** of the muscle. Such pains are found not only in cases of organic illness, about which they can provide important evidence, but also during psychological stress. A typical example is headache combined with painful tension of the dorsal neck musculature, which disappears once the source of psychological stress is resolved or when the patient is given appropriate psychotherapy. The mechanism by which such pain arises in the muscles is unknown. High muscle tone reduces blood flow through the muscle, which probably plays a role in the production of pain (perhaps via the accumulation in the tissue of metabolites with noxious effects).

Itch. It may be that *itch* is a special form of pain sensation elicited in particular stimulus conditions. This interpretation is supported by the fact that a sequence of itch stimuli at high intensity leads to sensations of pain; moreover, an interruption of pain conduction in the anterolateral funiculus is accompanied by a loss of itch sensation, whereas a disturbance of the senses of pressure and touch (transmitted in the dorsal columns) leaves the itch sensation unaffected. It has also been shown that the skin is sensitive to itch only at discrete points, and that these **itch points** correspond to the *pain points*. But other considera-

tions suggest that itch is a sensation *independent* of pain, which may have receptors of its own. For example, the sensation of itch can be elicited only in the outermost layers of the epidermis, whereas pain is produced in the deeper layers of the skin as well. It is also possible, using suitable techniques, to generate all degrees of itch without pain and vice versa. Finally, it appears to be a prerequisite for the occurrence of an itching sensation that a chemical substance, perhaps **histamine,** be released. An intradermal histamine injection elicits severe itching, and in skin injuries that lead to itching histamine is set free in the skin.

Peripheral and Central Disturbances of Nociception

Hyperalgesia, hypalgesia, analgesia. A few hours after the skin has been damaged by intense ultraviolet radiation (sunburn) or other noxious agents (heat, freezing, X-rays or abrasion), the skin becomes reddened *(vasodilation)* and its sensitivity to mechanical stimuli is increased. This hypersensitivity is called **hyperalgesia.** The pain threshold is lowered, and even stimuli ordinarily painless (such as the friction of clothing) are perceived as unpleasant or painful. Hyperalgesia and vasodilation can last for days. It seems plausible that they are caused by the local liberation of a chemical substance such as *histamine* from damaged cells in the tissue, but the relevant findings are extremely varied. A raised threshold to pain **(hypalgesia)** and complete loss of pain sensitivity **(analgesia)** usually occur only in combination with disturbances or deficits in other modalities of cutaneous sensation. In the simplest case, for example, transection or blockade (e.g., with Novocaine) of a skin nerve produces both local analgesia and disappearance of sensation in the other modalities. (A lowered or elevated threshold to all sensory modalities of the skin or mucosa is called **hyper-** or **hypoesthesia,** respectively, and complete elimination of sensitivity, as in conduction blockade, is called **anesthesia.**

Disturbances in the processing of pain. Chronic pains, regardless of their origin, cause unknown *changes in the central nervous system that favor the occurrence of these pains.* Perhaps this phenomenon amounts to an (entirely undesired) *learning process,* the ultimate result of which is that very *small external stimuli* or even the *spontaneous internal fluctuations in excitability* of the central nervous system suffice to release the painful state in its entirety. This sort of **dissociation of the pain sensation from the external pain stimulus** was mentioned on p. 220 as one of the symptoms of the phantom-limb experience. **Phantom pains** can be very persistent and agonizing; in such cases the patient almost always feels that the phantom limb is in a cramped, stiff position, interestingly, one which would also cause an intact limb to hurt. Often it can be shown that the phantom pains are *completely independent of sensory input* from the stump. Then it is certain that they "originate" in the CNS, just like the other phantom sensations. The same is true of chronic forms of **trigeminal neuralgia,** in which touching or moving a circumscribed *"trigger zone"* in the skin (for example, one corner of the mouth) elicits a pain attack. Chewing, swallowing, speaking or yawning can be torture to such patients. Often the patients are so severely tormented by these pains that they consider suicide.

Pathological processes in the *central structures* involved in the processing of pain tend to produce not deficits but rather alterations in the sensation of pain; normal experience of pain is possible only with unimpaired activation of both the cortical and the subcortical pain systems. For example, if the sensory ventral nuclei of the thalamus are diseased, pain sensations are particularly unpleasant and give the subjective *impression of oversensitivity to pain* **(hyperpathia).** Moreover, the patients often experience severe spontaneous pains in the associated (i.e., contralateral) half of the body **(thalamic pain).** The *affective aspect of pain* can also be changed by central damage. For example, patients with severe frontal-lobe lesions may scarcely notice pain as long as they are distracted and kept occupied, even though the pain thresholds are entirely unchanged. In **pain asymbolia,** usually caused by simultaneous defects in the frontal lobe, insula and parietal lobe, the affective evaluation of and motor responses to pain stimuli deteriorate to such an extent that the patients repeatedly expose themselves to the same harmful stimuli and often mutilate themselves as a result. Bilateral lesions or ablation of the temporal lobe in monkeys produce a similar syndrome.

It should be pointed out here that many purposeful and affectively *normal responses* to painful stimuli are apparently not innate, but rather *must be learned* by the juvenile at an early stage of development. If these experiences are missed in early childhood, the appropriate responses are very difficult to learn later. This has been demonstrated in animal experiments. Young dogs protected from all harmful stimuli in the first 3 months of life were incapable of responding appropriately to painful stimuli, and later learned to respond only slowly and incompletely [22]. Similar observations have been made with a baby chimpanzee.

Permanent **congenital insensitivity to pain** has been observed occasionally in humans (NATHAN in [4]). In such conditions either there is an absence of all reaction to painful stimuli, comparable to pain asymbolia, or the nociceptive Group-III and -IV afferents (and in some cases the associated spinal nuclei and tracts) are absent.

Pain Therapy

Somatic approaches to the treatment of pain include *physical, pharmacological* and *neurosurgical* measures [1, 6, 13, 15, 20, 29]. Such treatment is always appropriate once the pain has fulfilled its function as an indicator of damage; pain therapy, when carried out properly, often makes a crucial contribution to rapid recovery. But also in incurable conditions – indeed, here in particular – the alleviation or elimination of pain is important.

Physical measures that may be indicated in various situations are immobilization, cold or warm wrappings, diathermy (shortwave radiation to warm deeper tissues), massage, and exercises to reduce stiffness. **Drugs** can act at many levels. The generation and conduction of impulses in pain fibers can be prevented at the periphery *(local anesthesia),* or transmission of activity in the ascending pathways can be blocked (e.g., *lumbar anesthesia).* The excitability of the central neurons involved in pain can be suppressed (by *general anesthesia* in the extreme case). Finally, there are drugs that act on those structures responsible for the emotional state of the patient so as to bring about a more emotionally neutral attitude to the pain, making it easier to bear. The **neurosurgical measures** – which because they are irreversible should be reserved for chronic pain conditions, and which because of their many side effects require great experience – will not be enumerated here. In the whole, interruption of the anterolateral column of the spinal cord, by transection of the anterior contralateral quadrant *(chordotomy),* is one of the most successful operations; others, such as transection of the pathways from the thalamus to the frontal lobe *(leukotomy),* are no longer performed because of their severe disadvantages (cf. p. 173).

Inhibition of pain. Certain recent approaches to the treatment of pain, some of which have already been tried on humans, offer great promise. In these, advantage is taken of the spinal afferent inhibitory interactions (cf. p. 182) and of the descending control systems that influence afferent input (cf. p. 207), to inhibit undesired nociceptive inputs. The procedure is either to stimulate cutaneous nerves electrically *(transcutaneous electrostimulation)* or to implant stimulating electrodes surgically in the relevant tracts (dorsal columns of the spinal cord) or nuclei (in the central gray matter around the brainstem ventricle), to allow external activation of these neurons.

Acupuncture (the Latin *acus* = needle) may be a pain-treatment method related to transcutaneous electrostimulation. However, the underlying mechanism is still unknown, and it has not yet been possible to separate the pronounced pyschological, hypnotic and mystical components. In this ancient Chinese teaching, which goes back 4000 years, there are 750 puncture points arranged in twelve longitudinal lines on the body surface, the meridians. In these lines there is continuous circulation of a certain amount of vital energy *ch'i,* consisting of the antagonists *yang* (bright, warm) and *yin* (dark, cold); perfect balance between yang and yin constitutes the ideal state of health. Whereas acupuncture for **therapeutic purposes** (when organ function is impaired) requires only that the needles be stuck into the appropriate points (or burning of a moxa (*Artemesia* fibers) cigarette over the points, called *moxibustion,* or massage or electrical stimulation), in order to obtain an **analgesic effect** the puncture needles must be turned constantly or a repetitive electric current must be passed through them – in other words, continual stimulation of the (mechano)receptors in the puncture area is necessary. This kind of pain inhibition is reminiscent of other procedures such as "gritting one's teeth" or the application of heat, in which the activation of other receptor systems is employed to inhibit the central action of the pain afferents. But outside of China, at least, acupuncture has so far had only limited success.

10.6   References

Textbooks and Handbooks

1. BONICA, J.J., LIEBESKIND, J.C., ALBE-FESSARD, D.G. (Ed.): Advances in Pain Research and Therapy, Vol.3, pp. 1–956. New York: Raven Press 1978
2. DE REUCK, A.V.S., KNIGHT, J.: Touch, Heat and Pain. London: J. & J. & A. Churchill Ltd. 1969
3. FULTON, J.F.: Physiology of the Nervous System. London–New York–Toronto: Oxford University Press 1943
4. GORDON, G. (Ed.): Somatic and Visceral Sensory Mechanism. British Medical Bulletin *33,* 89–182 (1977)
5. HENSEL, H.: Allgemeine Sinnesphysiologie. Hautsinne, Geschmack, Geruch. pp. 1–345. Heidelberg: Springer 1966
6. HILGARD, E.R.: Pain Perception in Man. In: HELD, R., LEIBOWITZ, H.W., TEUBER, H.L., (Eds.): Handb. Sensory Physiology, Vol. VII, Perception, pp. 849–875. Berlin–Heidelberg–New York: Springer 1973
7. IGGO, H. (Ed.): Handbook of Sensory Physiology, II. Somatosensory System. Berlin–Heidelberg–New York: Springer 1973
8. JANZEN, R., KEIDEL, W.D., HERZ, A., STEICHELE, C. (Eds.): Pain. Stuttgart: Georg Thieme 1972
9. KORNHUBER, H.H. (Ed.): The Somatosensory System. Stuttgart: Georg Thieme 1975
10. LOEWENSTEIN, W.R. (Ed.): Handbook of Sensory Physiology. I. Principles of Receptor Physiology. Berlin–Heidelberg–New York: Springer 1971
11. MATTHEWS, P.B.C.: Mammalian Muscle Receptors and their Central Actions. London: Edward Arnold Publishers Ltd. 1972
12. MOUNTCASTLE, V.B.: Medical Physiology. Vol I. 13th Edition Saint Louis: The C.V.Mosby Company 1974
13. STERNBACH, R.A. (Ed.): The Psychology of Pain. New York: Raven Press 1978
14. WILLIS, W.D., COGGESHALL, R.E.: Sensory Mechanisms of the Spinal Cord. pp.1–485. New York–London: Plenum Press 1978
15. WALTON, J.N.: BRAIN's Diseases of the Nervous System. 8th Edition. Oxford: Oxford University Press 1977
16. ZOTTERMAN, Y. (Ed.): Sensory Functions of the Skin in Primates. Oxford: Pergamon Press 1976

Research Reports and Reviews

17. GOODWIN, G.M., McCLOSKEY, D.I., MATTHEWS, P.B.C.: The contribution of muscle afferents to kinaesthesia shown by vibration induced illusions of movement and by the effects of paralysing joint afferents. Brain *95,* 705–748 (1972)
18. HENSEL, H.: Neural processes in thermoregulation. Physiol. Rev. *53,* 948–1017 (1973)
19. JOHNSON, K.O., DARIAN-SMITH, I., LAMOTTE, C., JOHNSON, B., OLDFIELD, S.: Coding of incremental changes in skin temperature by a population of warm fibers in the monkey: correlation with intensity discrimination in man. J. Neurophysiol. *42,* 1332 (1979)
20. KERR, F.W.L., CASEY, K.L.: Pain. Neurosciences Research Program Bulletin 16, 1–207. Cambridge, Mass.: The MIT Press 1980
21. McCLOSKEY, D.I.: Kinesthetic Sensibility. Physiol. Rev. *58,* 763–820 (1978)
22. MELZACK, R., SCOTT, T.H.: The effects of early experience on the response to pain. J. comp. Physiol. Psychol. *50,* 155–161 (1975)
23. MELZACK, R., WALL, P.D.: Pain mechanisms: A new theory. Science *150,* 971–979 (1965)
24. MENSE, S., SCHMIDT, R.F.: Muscle pain: which receptors are responsible for the transmission of noxious stimuli? In: ROSE, F.C. (Ed.): Physiological Aspects of Clinical Neurology. Oxford: Blackwell 1977
25. PHILLIPS, C.G., POWELL, T.P., WIESENDANGER, M.: Projection from low-threshold muscle afferents of hand and forearm to area 3a of baboon's cortex. J. Physiol. *217,* 419–446 (1971)
26. SCHMIDT, R.F.: Control of the access of afferent activity to somatosensory pathways. In: IGGO, A. (Ed.): Handb. Sensory Physiology. Vol.II. Somatosensory System. pp.151–206. Berlin–Heidelberg–New York: Springer 1973
27. SHERRINGTON, C.S.: The muscular sense. In: SCHÄFER's Textbook of Physiology. London–Edinburgh: Pentland. Vol.2, 1002–1025 (1900)
28. SWEET, W.H.: In: Handbook of Physiology, Section 1. Neurophysiology. Vol.1, pp.459–506. Washington, D.C.: American Physiological Society 1959
29. WEISENBERG, M.: Pain and pain control. Psychological Bulletin *84,* 1008–1044 (1977)

11 Vision and Eye Movements

O.-J. GRÜSSER

11.1 Light and Sight

Electromagnetic radiation at wavelengths between 400 and 750 nm is perceived by humans as **light.** The light source most important to us is the sun. In a rainbow, we see the yellowish-white light of the sun separated into its components, the *spectrum* of wavelengths; the long-wavelength components appear red to us, and the short-wavelength components blue-violet (Fig. 11-1). The term **monochromatic** light is applied to radiation in any very narrow band within this spectrum.

Objects in our surroundings reflect light to different degrees. The difference in luminous intensity (or luminance) of adjacent structures determines their physical *contrast* (C); $C = (I_b - I_d)/(I_b + I_d)$, where I_b is the luminance of the brighter surface and I_d, that of the darker surface. Vision is based primarily on the perception of bright/dark contrasts rather than absolute luminance. *Color contrast* enables us to distinguish objects with physical contrast $C = 0$ if they differ in the degree to which they reflect particular parts of the spectrum.

The mean luminance of man's natural environment varies widely: 10^{-6} cd $\cdot$ m^{-2} (cd = candela) under an overcast night sky, 10^{-3} cd $\cdot$ m^{-2} in starlight with no moon, 10^{-1} cd $\cdot$ m^{-2} on a clear night with full moon, and as much as 10^7 cd $\cdot$ m^{-2} in bright sunshine. The visual system adjusts to this enormous range of intensities by various *processes of adaptation,* discussed on p. 245; 249. The relative range of energy within which vision is possible is at most $1 : 10^{11}$. But with constant illumination variation in the reflectances of the surroundings requires the visual processes to adapt only within a range of ca. $1 : 40$ [9, 14, 24, 28].

The Duplicity Theory of Vision

Adaptation to the widely differing conditions of ambient lighting is facilitated by the organization of the retina, in which there are two receptor systems with different absolute thresholds **(duplicity theory).** Vision is mediated by the **rods** in dim light and at night **(scotopic vision),** and by the **cones** under daytime lighting conditions **(photopic vision).** Scotopic and photopic vision differ fundamentally with regard to two elementary *qualities* of visual sensation (cf. p. 259), the perception of *color* and the perception of *brightness gradation.* By starlight objects appear *colorless, but differ in brightness,* whereas in photopic vision both color and brightness can be distinguished. The *spectral-sensitivity* curve of the eye also shifts with the transition from scotopic to photopic vision. The spectral brightness curve (Fig. 11–1) for scotopic vision has a maximum at ca. 500 nm, and that of photopic vision is at ca. 555 nm [16].

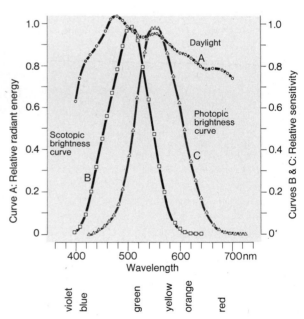

Fig. 11-1. Spectrum of sunlight on the earth's surface (A) and spectral sensitivity of the human visual system (B, C). Curve A was obtained by measuring the relative energy of daylight under a cloudless sky in the visible region of the electromagnetic radiation. The scotopic (B) and photopic (C) brightness curves are the means of measurements on many observers with normal vision (standard curves of the International Color Society), as follows. First the *relative energy* required to produce the sensation "equally bright" with various monochromatic light stimuli was measured. The results were then normalized by setting the energy value for the most effective wavelength (500 nm for scotopic vision, 555 nm for photopic vision) equal to 1. Curves B and C thus represent the reciprocal of the relative radiant energy

Active Seeing

Active movements of the eyes and head play an important role in vision. This active element finds expression in terms such as "survey", "scan", "look around" and the like. By voluntary and involuntary gaze movements we explore our visual environment. The amplitude and direction of the eye and head movements depend not only on the internal state of the observer (attentiveness, interest) but also on the visual stimulus patterns (cf. p. 267). When a specially designed optical system is used to "stabilize" an image on the retina, so that despite the eye movements it always falls on the same spot on the retina, we find that within a few seconds colors and contours can no longer be perceived. If one then shifts the image on the retina, visual perception can be restored. In the following discussion the *interaction* of motor and sensory mechanisms in vision will at first be ignored, but we shall return to it in the concluding section, after the oculomotor system has been described [41].

11.2 The Eye and Its Dioptric Apparatus

The Structure of the Eye

The dioptric apparatus. The optical system of the eye is a compound lens system, which forms a reversed, reduced image of the outside world on the retina. The dioptric apparatus consists of the transparent **cornea,** the anterior and posterior chambers (containing the aqueous humor), the **iris** (which forms the pupil), the **lens** (surrounded by a transparent lens capsule) and the **vitreous body,** which occupies most of the space within the eyeball (Fig. 11-2). The vitreous body is a clear gel composed of extracellular fluid with collagen and hyaluronic acid in colloidal solution [6, 31].

The retina. The sensory surface of the eye, the **retina,** arises in ontogeny as part of the diencephalon. Covering the inner surface of the posterior part of the eyeball, it consists of several layers – pigment epithelium cells, photoreceptors (the signal-input layer) and four different classes of nerve cells – throughout which blood vessels and glial cells are distributed. The **ganglion cells** constitute the output layer of the retina. Their axons, initially unmyelinated, run through the retina to the papilla, cross the **sclera** of the eye through the lamina cribrosa, and then form the **optic nerve** (Fig. 11-2). The human optic nerve contains about a million axons, most of them myelinated, surrounded by glial cells and connective tissue.

The fovea. At the posterior pole of the eye the human retina exhibits a small pit, the *fovea centralis.* Here, in contrast to the rest of the retina, the receptor layer (as viewed from the vitreous body) is not covered by the other retinal neurons. The fovea is the place where vision is most acute; when an object is **fixated,** its image is formed there [24, 27, 31].

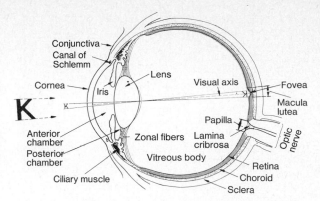

Fig. 11-2. Horizontal section through the right eye (diagrammatic)

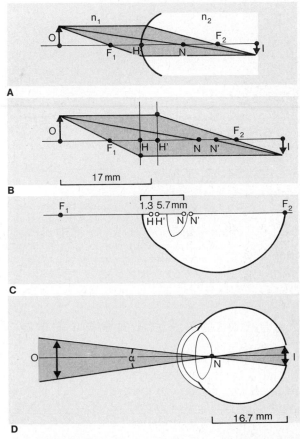

Fig. 11-3 A–D. *Production of an image by a simple optical system, schematic and reduced eye.* **A** Paths of rays from object to image in a simple optical system. F_1, F_2, focal points; H, principal point; N, nodal point; O, object; I, image; index of refraction n_2 > n_1. **B** Simplified ray paths in a *compound, centered* optical system that has been *reduced* to two principal planes H, H' and two nodal points N, N'. **C** Schematic eye according to Gullstrand. **D** Reduced eye. The points H and H' in the schematic eye have been superimposed, as have N and N'. The distance N–I is 16.7 mm. From this distance and the angle α the size of the image (I) on the retina can be calculated: 1 degree of arc at the object (O) = 0.29 mm on the retina

Tears

The outer surface of the cornea is covered with a thin film of tears, which improves the optical properties of its superficial structure. The tears are produced continually in small amounts by the lacrimal glands and distributed uniformly over the cornea and conjunctiva by the movements of the eyelids. Some of the fluid evaporates into the air, and the rest flows through the nasolacrimal ducts into the nasal cavity. The tears protect the cornea and conjunctiva from drying out, and simultaneously act as a lubricant between the eyeball and lids. When a foreign body comes between the lids and the eye it stimulates the mechanoreceptors in the cornea and conjunctiva, with fibers in the trigeminal nerve, causing a *reflex* increase in tear secretion. The purpose of tear production in this case is to rinse the object out of the eye, with the help of more frequent blinking. Tears taste salty; in composition they correspond approximately to an ultrafiltrate of plasma. In addition they contain enzymes effective against pathogenic organisms, and thus offer the eye some protection against infection. Finally, tear secretion in man has a further significance as a means of *expressing emotion,* during crying.

Neural control of tear secretion. Most tear-secretion reflexes are triggered by receptors in the eye region, which send signals to the brainstem by way of the first branch (ophthalmic nerve) of the trigeminal nerve. But we know from everyday experience that stimuli outside the eye region can reflexly increase tear secretion (e. g., toothache, mechanical stimulation of the nasal epithelium, strong taste or odor stimuli, or stimuli that elicit coughing). The secretion of tears is controlled by parts of the autonomic nervous system (cf. p. 112). The parasympathetic ganglion cells, the axon terminals of which control tear secretion, lie in the *pterygopalatine ganglion.* The preganglionic axons reach this ganglion by way of the *greater petrosal nerve;* the somata of these cells lie in the pontine region of the brainstem. These neurons are excited by hypothalamic and limbic systems as well as by signals from neurons in the sensory trigeminal nucleus (reflex activation). The sympathetic innervation of the lacrimal glands is controlled by neurons in the upper thoracic cord, the signals from which reach the lacrimal glands by way of neurons in the *superior cervical ganglion* and sympathetic nerve fibers running along the cerebral arteries.

The Production of an Image on the Retina

Foundations of physical optics. The simplest optical system is the **camera obscura,** a device in which a small aperture creates a reversed image. The image is sharp only if the aperture is very small, so that the intensity of the image is very low. The aperture can be made larger if a convex lens is mounted behind or in front of it. The image then produced on the "receptive surface" is reversed and reduced. This principle is realized in the imaging of the surroundings on the retina by the compound optical system of the eye: the air-cornea interface acts as a lens in front of the aperture (pupil, adjusted by the iris), and there is a biconvex lens behind the aperture (Fig. 11-2) [9, 13, 24, 25].

Refraction and focal length. When a ray of light strikes an interface between two transparent media of different refractive index (n), it is bent by an amount depending on the angle of incidence (Fig. 11-3 A). All the rays parallel to the optical axis of a spherically curved interface (the line through the principal point H in Fig. 11-3 A; see below) are bent in such a way as to converge at the focal points (F_1, F_2). The **refractive power** of the system depends on the radius of curvature r of the interface and the refractive indices (n_1, n_2) of the two media. When parallel rays from the medium with smaller refractive index (n_1) pass through the interface they converge at focal point F_2 in the medium with greater index. The **focal length** "behind" the lens (f_2, the distance H-F_2)is

$$f_2 = \frac{n_2 \cdot r}{n_2 - n_1} \quad [m] \tag{1}$$

When parallel rays cross the interface in the opposite direction they converge at F_1, so that the focal length "in front" of the lens is

$$f_1 = \frac{n_1 \cdot r}{n_2 - n_1} \quad [m] \tag{2}$$

These equations are strictly valid only for a small (Gaussian) area about the optical axis. The **optical axis** is the line connecting the focal points F_1 and F_2, and the principal point H is the point at which this line intersects the interface. The **nodal point** N is the center of the sphere of which the interface is a part. The refractive power RP of the interface is defined as

$$RP = \frac{1}{f} \tag{3}$$

When the focal length f is given in meters, the unit of refractive power is the **diopter** (D).

The refractive power RP_1 of a lens with two refractive surfaces can be calculated by Gullstrand's formula, as follows:

$$RP_1 = RP_f + RP_b - \frac{d}{n} \cdot RP_f \cdot RP_b \quad [D] \tag{4}$$

where RP_f is the refractive power of the front surface of the lens and RP_b that of the back surface, d is the distance between the two refractive surfaces in meters, and n is the refractive index of the medium between the refractive surfaces.

Image formation. A spherical lens with focal length f, given an object d_o meters away, produces an image of that object d_i meters away on the opposite side of the lens. If the lens is surrounded on all sides by the same optical medium, it holds that

$$\frac{1}{f} = \frac{1}{d_o} + \frac{1}{d_i} \tag{5}$$

If the object is at infinity, or at a sufficiently great distance, then $1/d_o \rightarrow 0$, so that the image distance d_i is equal to the focal length f of the lens. Focal length can thus be found by measuring the image distance for infinitely distant objects.

Image formation by the dioptric apparatus of the eye. The data required for calculating image formation in the eye are summarized in Table 11-1. The air-cornea interface, according to Eq. (2), has the **object-side focal length** f_e

$$f_c = \frac{n_1 \cdot r_1}{n_c - n_1} = \frac{7.7}{0.376} \approx 20.5 \quad [mm] \tag{6}$$

where n_c is the refractive index of the cornea. The refractive power RP_{ac} of the front surface of the cornea is thus $1/0.0205 =$

Table 11-1. Schematic eye. (After GULLSTRAND)

Indices of refraction:

Air	$= 1.00$
Cornea, n_c	$= 1.376$
Aqueous humor and vitreous body, n_h	$= 1.336$
Lens, n_1	$= 1.414$ (unaccommodated, U)
Lens	$= 1.424$ (accommodated, A)

	Radius of curvature (mm)	Distance from pole of cornea (mm)
Front corneal surface	7.7	0
Back corneal surface	6.8	0.5
Front lens surface	10.0 (U)	5.6 (U)
Front lens surface	5.3 (A, max)	5.2 (A, max)
Back lens surface	6.0 (U)	7.2
Back lens surface	5.3 (A, max)	7.2
Retina		24.4
1st principal point H		1.35
2nd principal point H'		1.60
Anterior nodal point N		7.05
Posterior nodal point N'		7.30
Image-side focal length		22.78 (U)
Object-side focal length		–17.05 (U)

48.8 D. The interface between cornea and aqueous humor causes the light rays to diverge, because $n_h < n_c$ (Table 11-1). From Eqs. (1) and (3) we find that the refractive power RP_c of this interface is -5.9 D. Gullstrand's formula (Eq. 4) can now be used to calculate the total refractive power RP_{co} of the system air-cornea-aqueous humor from RP_{ac}, RP_c and $d = 0.5$ mm: $RP_{co} = 43$ D. The *object-side focal length* f_{co} of the whole cornea system is found by Eqs. (1) and (3):

$$f_{co} = \frac{n_h}{RP_{co}} = \frac{1.336}{43} \doteq 31 \quad [mm] \tag{7}$$

The lens. To obtain a sharp image on the fovea 24.4 mm from the pole of the cornea, the *additional refractive power* of the lens of the eye is required. This biconvex lens consists of several lamelliform layers, differing in both radius of curvature and refractive index; the latter increases progressively from the *periphery to the core* of the lens. That is, the lens is optically inhomogeneous. The experimentally determined **total index** given in Table 11-1 is greater than the individual indices of the lens layers. The refractive power RP_1 of the lens in its flattest state was found by Gullstrand to average 19.1 D.

Total refractive index of the eye. From the refractive power of the cornea RP_{co} and that of the lens RP_1, the total refractive power RP_e of the dioptric apparatus of the eye can be calculated, using Gullstrand's formula (Eq. 4, with $d = 5.6$ mm and $n = n_h = 1.336$). RP_e is found to be 58.6 D. The image-side focal length of the whole dioptric apparatus – the critical parameter of image formation in the eye – is thus

$$f_i = \frac{n_h}{RP_e} = \frac{1.336}{58.6}[m] = 22.8 \quad [mm] \tag{8}$$

The schematic eye. The diagrammatic representation of the imaging process in a *compound optical system* is facilitated by determining the *cardinal points* (for details see textbooks of physical optics). In this schematization of the optical system the effects at all optical interfaces are represented by two principal planes (H, H'), two nodal points (N and N') and two focal points (F_1, F_2; Fig. 11-3 B). Gullstrand determined the values listed in Table 11-1 for the human eye (Fig. 11-3 C). The distance from the pole of the cornea to the posterior principal point (1.60 mm) and the image-side focal length f_i of the eye (22.8 mm) together give the cornea-to-fovea distance (24.4 mm).

The reduced eye. A further simplification is the reduced eye (Fig. 11-3 D), in which H coincides with H' and N with N'. In the reduced eye the distance from the nodal point N to the retina is 16.67 mm. From this value and the visual angle α subtended by the object the size of the image on the retina can be estimated.

Regulatory Processes in the Dioptric Apparatus

The refractive power of the lens and the diameter of the pupil can be altered by neurally controlled smooth muscles.

Pupil responses. Normally both pupils are round and of equal size. The mean pupil diameter decreases with advancing age.

Light response. When the ambient illumination is constant, the amount of light entering the eye per unit time is proportional to the *area of the pupil*. Reflexes cause the pupils to become larger, the lower the ambient light intensity. When a person in daylight closes his eyelids for 10–20 s, the pupils enlarge; when he opens them again, the pupils become smaller. This **light response** can be further differentiated by separately illuminating the two eyes (Fig. 11-4). When one eye is illuminated, within 0.3–0.8 s its own pupil constricts **(direct light response),** and that of the unilluminated eye constricts as well **(consensual light response).** The light response is clearly a useful regulatory mechanism, for it reduces the amount of light incident on the retina when the surrounding light intensity is high (e. g., in bright sunlight), and in dim light increases the light reaching the retina, by pupil dilation. The sensors in this negative-feedback **control circuit** are the retinal receptors, and the controlled variable is pupil diameter. In young people the diameter of the pupil can vary from 1.5 to ca. 8 mm, changing the relative amount of light entering the eye by a factor of about 30. In comparison to the range of mean environmental luminance discussed on p. 234, however, the regulation provided by change in pupil diameter is slight.

Near-vision response (convergence response). The diameter of the human pupil also depends on the *distance* of the object fixated. When an experimental subject initially looking into the distance shifts his gaze to an object 30 cm away, his pupils become con-

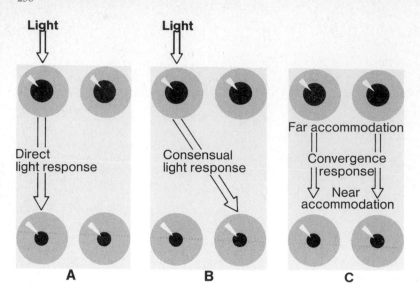

Fig. 11-4. *Diagram of the pupil responses* (direct and consensual light responses and accommodation response). The arrows symbolize illumination of one eye

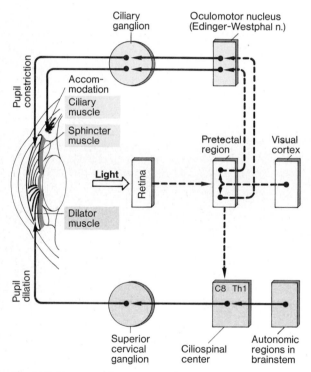

Fig. 11-5. *Diagram of innervation of iris musculature and ciliary muscle.* The neurons of the efferent sympathetic nervous system are shown in *red,* and those of the efferent parasympathetic nervous system in *black*

Function and innervation of the pupillomotor muscles (Fig. 11-5). The pupil responses are brought about by two smooth-muscle systems in the iris. By contraction of the annular *sphincter muscle* in the iris the pupil becomes smaller **(miosis),** whereas contraction of the *dilator muscle,* with fibers arranged radially in the iris, widens it **(mydriasis).** The sphincter muscle is innervated by parasympathetic nerve fibers arising in the ciliary ganglion, behind the eye. The preganglionic fibers originate in *pupillomotor neurons* in the Edinger-Westphal nucleus, the "autonomic" part of the oculomotor nucleus in the brainstem, and pass to the orbit along with the other fibers in the oculomotor nerve. The state of activity of the pupillomotor neurons in the Edinger-Westphal nucleus is controlled by nerve cells in the pretectal region (Fig. 11-5). Axons from the ganglion-cell layer of the retina and from the visual cortex (Areas 18 and 19) terminate in this region. The dilator muscle, on the other hand, is innervated by sympathetic nerve fibers that are excited by neurons in the **ciliospinal center** of the spinal cord, at the level of the 8th cervical segment and the 1st to 2nd thoracic segments. Axons from the ciliospinal center run in the cervical sympathetic chain to the superior cervical ganglion, where they synapse with the postganglionic neurons; their axons pass to the orbit along the *internal carotid* and *ophthalmic arteries,* and run in the ciliary nerve to the eye. The state of activation of the ciliospinal center depends on the general level of autonomic tone.

Clinical significance of the pupil response. The diameter of the pupils and the pupil responses are important diagnostic signs, for they can indicate lesions of the retina and the optic nerve as well as lesions in the brainstem (oculomotor region), the cervical cord, or the regions through which the pre- and postganglionic pupillomotor fibers run (deep neck region, sphenoid bone and orbit). The autonomic innervation of the iris muscles also accounts for the dependence of pupil size on age, psychological factors, attentiveness and degree of fatigue [13, 32].

Accommodation. In the human eye adjustment of the refractive power of the dioptric apparatus to the distance of the fixated object **(accommodation)** is brought about by changing the curvature of the lens, its *front surface* in particular. The amount of curvature depends on the elasticity of the lens and on the

stricted. Because the visual axes of the two eyes converge, as a rule, when one looks at a nearby object (cf. p. 265), this pupil constriction is also called the **convergence response.** This adjustment of the pupil to a near object is accompanied by an increase in the refractive power of the lens (discussed below). As in a camera when the aperture is reduced, the *depth of focus* in the eye increases when the pupil constricts.

forces acting on the lens capsule. The passive elastic forces of the ciliary apparatus, the choroid and the sclera are imposed upon the lens capsule by the fibers of the **ciliary (Zinn's) zonule.** The mechanical tension of the sclera in turn depends on the intraocular pressure, the chief source of this tension (cf. p. 242). When the tension in the zonule fibers increases the lens is stretched and thus flattened. The influence of these passive elastic forces on the lens is modified by the ciliary muscle, which encircles the lens (Figs. 11-2, 11-6). The smooth muscle fibers of this muscle are oriented radially, circularly and meridionally and are supplied by autonomic, chiefly parasympathetic nerve fibers. When the ciliary muscle contracts it reduces the elastic force exerted on the lens by the zonule fibers, so that the tension in the lens capsule is less. The front surface of the lens, in particular, becomes more strongly curved, and the refractive power of the lens increases; it is in a state of **accommodation.** When the ciliary muscle relaxes the lens is **unaccommodated**; when least curved its refractive power is lowest. In this state a normal eye forms a sharp image on the retina of objects at an infinite distance (far point = ∞ m).

Range of accommodation. The increase in refractive power (in diopters) as the focus is changed from the far point to the near point is called the **range of accommodation.** It is greatest in the young, 14 diopters at most. It follows from Eqs. (3) and (5) that such an eye, when maximally accommodated, can bring objects at a distance of $1/14$ m = 0.07 m = 7 cm into sharp focus on the retina. With advancing age the lens becomes progressively less elastic owing to water loss, so that its ability to change refractive power and thus its accommodation amplitude are reduced. The near point gradually moves away from the eye, so that older people with otherwise normal eyes need reading glasses **(presbyopia**; Fig. 11-7) [21, 24, 25, 29].

Neural control of accommodation. The preganglionic parasympathetic axons (cf. p. 112) of the accommodation system, like those of the pupillomotor system, originate in cells of the Edinger-Westphal nucleus and pass to the ciliary ganglion. The adequate stimulus for a change in accommodation is a **blurred image** on the retina. This property of the stimulus pattern is presumably detected by neurons in the foveal projection region of the visual cortex (Area 18), a region that makes connections with the Edinger-Westphal nucleus (Fig. 11-5). The peripheral autonomic synapses at the ciliary muscle and muscles in the iris, like other synapses in the autonomic nervous system, can be influenced by drugs. If an **atropine** solution is dripped into the connective-tissue sac behind the eyelid it diffuses to the iris and the ciliary body and blocks signal transmission at the parasympathetic synapses, so that

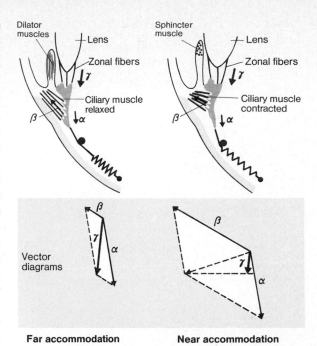

Fig. 11-6. *Diagram of ciliary-muscle action.* When the ciliary muscle contracts, the elastic tension in the zonule fibers is reduced and the curvature of the lens increases *(accommodation).* Reduction of ciliary-muscle tone allows the tension in the elastic tissue of the choroid to be transferred more strongly to the lens capsule by way of the zonule fibers, and the curvature of the lens is decreased. In the vector diagrams α is the elastic tension of the choroid, β is the force component contributed by the ciliary muscle, and γ is the *resultant vector* in the direction of the zonule fibers. The size of the pupil changes with the state of accommodation. In the fully accommodated eye the sphincter muscle of the pupil is contracted, and in the unaccommodated eye the contraction of the dilator muscle is increased

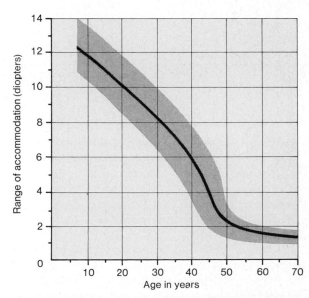

Fig. 11-7. *Amplitude of accommodation* (ordinate; shading represents standard deviation) of observers with normal vision at different ages (abscissa). (After Graff, 1954)

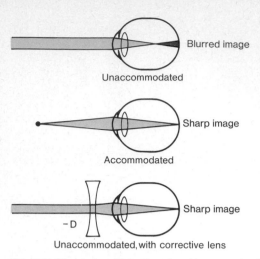

Fig. 11-8. *Myopia* (nearsightedness) and its correction by a concave lens (−D). The length of the eyeball is exaggerated for clarity ("axial myopia")

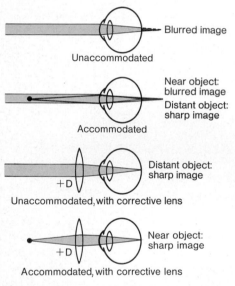

Fig. 11-9. *Hypermetropia* (farsightedness) and its correction by a convex lens (+D)

the lens becomes unaccommodated and the pupil expands. **Neostigmine** (cf. p. 57), on the other hand, causes constriction of the pupils and accommodation [13, 21, 31, 32].

Optical Defects and Refractive Anomalies

The lens system in a modern camera can produce a considerably better image than the dioptric apparatus of the eye. The physicist and physiologist HERMANN V. HELMHOLTZ (1821–1894) once wrote that if he should receive an optical instrument so carelessly constructed as the eye, he would send it back to the

maker. The "physiological" deficiencies in focussing by the eye discussed here, however, are largely compensated by neuronal contrast mechanisms (cf. p. 249).

Astigmatism. The corneal surface is not rotationally symmetric about the optical axis, for the vertical curvature is usually somewhat greater than the horizontal curvature. As Eq. (1) indicates, this discrepancy results in an angle-dependent difference in refractive power *(astigmatism* or *astigmia)*. If the difference is no greater than 0.5 D, the condition is called "physiological" astigmatism.

Spherical aberration. The cornea and the lens of the eye, like all simple lenses, have shorter focal lengths in the peripheral regions than in the central part around the optical axis. The resulting *spherical aberration* causes blurring of the image. The smaller the pupils the more the peripheral rays are excluded and the less distortion is caused by spherical aberration.

Chromatic aberration and accommodation. As do all simple lenses, the dioptric apparatus refracts short-wavelength light more strongly than long-wavelength light *(chromatic aberration)*. Therefore greater accommodation is required for sharp focussing of the red parts of an object than for the blue parts. It is because of this difference that blue objects appear to be further away than red ones at the same objective distance. The builders of Gothic churches often exploited this physiological illusion in their stained-glass windows, by making the background blue and the figures other colors, so that one sees an apparent spatial separation between figures and background.

Stray light and clouding of the dioptric apparatus. The lens and the vitreous body contain structural proteins and macromolecular substances in colloidal solution. Therefore a slight *diffuse dispersion* of the light occurs in the dioptric apparatus. But this *stray light* impairs visual perception only with very bright stimuli (cf. p. 250). Even in a healthy eye there are *cloudy areas in the vitreous body,* visible against a white wall as small disks or irregularly shaped small gray spots. When the eye moves they seem to flit like gnats across the light background. In older people the water content of the lens can decline so greatly that the structure of the remaining material becomes condensed, making the lens opaque *(senile cataract)*. Removal of the lens enables these patients to see normally when they are fitted with spectacles having a strong convex lens (ca. +13 D for long-distance vision).

Myopia. The total refractive power of the dioptric apparatus of a normal, unaccommodated eye is 58.6 diopters (cf. p. 237). With this refractive power an infinitely distant object is focussed sharply on the retina when the distance between the pole of the cornea and the fovea is 24.4 mm. If the axial length of the eyeball is greater, distant objects cannot be seen sharply because the plane of focus is *in front* of the fovea (**nearsightedness, myopia**). A nearsighted person must wear glasses with concave lenses (negative refractive power) to see sharply at a distance (Fig. 11-8).

Hypermetropia. If the axial length is too short for the refractive power of the dioptric apparatus, a condition of "farsightedness" (**hyperopia** or **hypermetropia**) exists. The hypermetropic person can see distant objects clearly by near-accommodating to some extent, but his accommodation range is not sufficient to allow sharp focussing of nearby objects. Convex lenses (positive refractive power) are required to compensate this defect (Fig. 11-9) [13, 25, 29].

Measurement of Refractive Errors and Prescription of Corrective Lenses

Objective measurement of refraction. The procedure called **retinoscopy ("shadow test")** is capable of establishing refractive power with a precision of ca. 0.5 D. A pencil of parallel light rays is projected from a **retinoscope** at a distance of ca. 1 m into the unaccommodated eye of the patient (Fig. 11-10). Observing the light reflected by the retina, the physician sees the shadow of the edge of his own pupil (or of the aperture of the retinoscope).

In the diagram illustrating retinoscopic examination (Fig. 11-10) each illuminated point on the retina is assumed to act as a light source for the rays reflected out of the eye. One such point source is shown in each drawing of Fig. 11-10. When the physician turns the retinoscope, the reflected beam of light and the shadow also move. From the direction of movement of the shadow one can determine whether the rays reflected from the patient's eye converge *in front* of the examiner's eye. They do so when the far point of the eye being examined lies between the eyes of physician and patient. If the far point of the patient's eye is outside this range, the reflected beam and the shadow turn in the direction of rotation of the retinoscope. In order to measure refraction, the examiner holds lenses of increasing (positive or negative) diopter number until the direction of movement of the shadow reverses. The refractive error of the patient's eye can be determined from the diopter number of the lens that produced the reversal; if the retinoscope is at a distance of 1 m from the patient's eye, 1 D must be subtracted from the diopter number of the lens.

Subjective measurement of refraction. The vision-testing charts described on p. 255 can be used to determine refraction subjectively. The patient views a chart monocularly from a distance of 6 m. With a nearsighted patient, lenses of progressively increasing − D values are placed in front of the eye until visual acuity becomes optimal. The refractive power of the lens giving this result is about equivalent to the refractive error. A hypermetropic patient, as a rule, can see optimally at a distance without a corrective lens. In this case convex lenses (+ D) are placed in front of the eye until acuity deteriorates. Then, once the near point

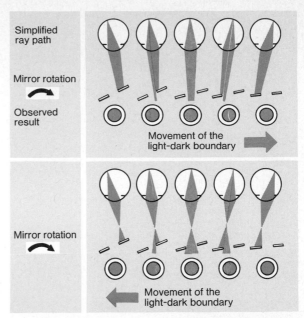

Fig. 11-10. Simplified diagram of the use of light reflected from the retina to determine refraction (retinoscopy; from Axenfeld-Serr as cited by Leydhecker). *Black:* shadow seen in the pupil region. *Red:* the pupil glows orange. *Top:* In *hypermetropia* or *emmetropia* the far point (focal point of the rays emerging from the eye) is behind the examiner. Therefore the light/ shadow boundary moves *with* the movement of the mirror as the physician turns it from left to right. *Bottom:* In *myopia* the far point of the patient's eye lies between the physician and the patient. The movement of the light/shadow boundary as perceived by the physician is thus *against* the direction of retinoscope movement

has been determined, the degree of hypermetropia can be determined from the diopter number of the lens [21, 29].

Spectacles. The corrective lens and the eye together form a compound optical system to which Eq. (4) applies. If a corneal contact lens is worn instead of spectacles with *concave lenses,* the term d in Eq. (4) becomes smaller – that is, the refractive power of the *corneal contact lens* can be somewhat lower than that of the lens in a pair of glasses. When fitting spectacles care must be taken to ensure that (when the patient looks straight ahead) the optical axes of eye and corrective lens coincide. To this end, the distance between the right and left pupils (56–70 mm) must be measured and the frame of the lenses selected correspondingly.

The *size* of the retinal image depends on the strength of the corrective lens. If the refraction of the left eye is not identical to that of the right, complete correction produces images of different sizes on the retinas, which can impair **binocular vision** (cf. p. 257). In this case a compromise must be found between optimal correction and undisturbed binocular vision. The difference in refractive power of the two lenses should not exceed 3 D.

Labels in figure:
Simplified ray path
Mirror rotation
Observed result
Movement of the light-dark boundary
Mirror rotation
Movement of the light-dark boundary

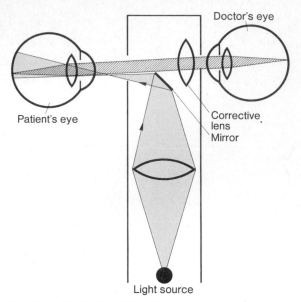

Fig. 11-11. Highly simplified diagram of the use of the *direct ophthalmoscope* (upright image)

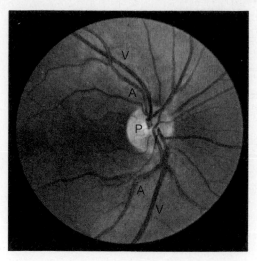

Fig. 11-12. *Back surface of the eye* (part of right retina) as seen in the direct ophthalmoscope. A, branches of the central artery of the retina; V, branches of the central veins of the retina; P, papilla of the optic nerve; F, fovea centralis. (From W. LEYD-HECKER, Grundriß der Augenheilkunde, 20th Ed., 1979)

Pronounced "regular" **astigmatism,** in which there is a systematic variation in curvature along different meridians of the cornea, can be corrected by a **cylindrical** lens. "Irregular" astigmatism is produced by irregular deformations of the cornea, and is better compensated by contact lenses.

Examination of the Interior of the Eye with the Ophthalmoscope

When an animal in the dark looks into the headlights of a car, the driver can see the animal's eyes "glowing", because the light is reflected from the back surface of the eyeball. The technique of **ophthalmoscopy** takes advantage of this reflection of light. A simplified diagram of the paths of the entrant and reflected rays is shown in Fig. 11-11. The examiner must relax his eye as though looking into the distance in order to see the retina clearly; refractive errors of his own or the patient's eye must be corrected by lenses. An example of what one sees under these conditions is shown in Fig. 11-12. The **papilla,** the retinal **vessels** and the inner surface of the retina appear in an upright image enlarged about 15 times, because the dioptric apparatus acts as a magnifying lens.

To see a **reversed image** of the retina the physician uses an indirect ophthalmoscope at a distance of ca. 80 cm. The parallel rays of light emerging from the patient's eye are focussed by a convex lens of + 13 to + 15 D, to give a reversed, real image of the retina. The physician accommodates to this image. In this method the image is magnified only about 4 ×, but

the advantage is that a larger part of the retina is in view and the peripheral areas of the retina are more readily visible than in the case of a non-reversed image.

Intraocular Pressure

The external shape of the eye and the relative positions of the components of the dioptric apparatus are nearly constant. This stability is provided by the firm **sclera** and the constancy of the **intraocular pressure** [32, 38, 54].

The secretion of aqueous humor. The pressure within the eyeball depends primarily on the amount of aqueous humor continuously produced and drained away. By *ultrafiltration* (cf. p. 618) plasma fluid from the blood capillaries in the ciliary body moves into the extracellular space within the ciliary body (Fig. 11-2); the epithelial cells of the ciliary body then **secrete** it, as aqueous humor, into the posterior chamber of the eye.

The aqueous humor flows from the posterior chamber into the anterior chamber, and from there passes over the trabecular meshwork at the edge of the chamber (the iridocorneal angle), through Schlemm's canal, and into the venous system. The intraocular pressure is constant when the amount of aqueous humor drained off through Schlemm's canal per unit time exactly equals that produced by the ciliary body. When the production rate is normal but the outflow is restricted, the intraocular pressure rises. A pathological increase in intraocular pressure is called **glaucoma.** In chronic glaucoma (glaucoma simplex) the mechanically weakest part of the wall of the eye – the lamina cribrosa – bulges **outward,** damaging the blood supply of the optic nerve fibers. The beginning of optic nerve fiber impairment is seen by the development of a characteristic extrafoveal *scotoma (p. 256). In an attack of* **acute glaucoma** ("narrow-angle glaucoma") the iridocorneal angle becomes blocked, the intraocular pressure rises sharply and blood flow through the retina is impaired. As a consequence of the reduced blood flow, the retina can suffer temporary or permanent damage, with blindness.

The elastic forces in the iris are transmitted to the iridocorneal angle (Fig. 11-2) in such a way that when the iris is stretched (the pupil constricted) the trabecular meshwork and Schlemm's canal are expanded. For this reason drugs that cause pupil constriction increase the rate of aqueous-humor outflow, and those that expand the pupil (e. g., atropine) reduce it. Thus when glaucoma is suspected pupil-dilating medications are to be strictly avoided.

Tonometry. Intraocular pressure can be determined indirectly by measuring the degree to which the cornea is indented by a stylus of specified diameter and weight **(impression tonometry)** or by measuring the force required to flatten a small area of the corneal surface **(applanation tonometry).** The intraocular pressure is considered to be pathologically high when it is above 22 mm Hg (2.93 kPa) in repeated measurements. In an attack of acute glaucoma it can exceed 60 mm Hg (8 kPa) [32, 38].

11.3   Signal Reception and Processing in the Retina

The layer of receptor cells in the vertebrate eye is on the side of the retina away from the vitreous body, in close contact with the pigment epithelium cells that constitute the boundary between the vascular system of the choroid and the receptor cells; the pigment epithelium cells thus influence the metabolism of the latter. Between the receptors and the vitreous body are the layers of horizontal cells, bipolar cells, amacrines and ganglion cells (Fig. 11-13).

The Transduction Process in Vision

Structure of the photoreceptors. In the human eye the receptor layer consists of ca. 120 million rods and 6 million cones, distinguishable by their histological features (Fig. 11-13). The *receptor density* (number of receptors per unit area) is highest in the middle of the fovea in the case of the cones, whereas the rod density is greatest in the parafoveal region. There are no rods in the fovea centralis (Fig. 11-14). Rods and cones are similar in structure in that each has an outer segment consisting of about a thousand membranous disks (rods) or infoldings (cones). The outer segment is joined to the remainder of the cell by a narrow cilium (Figs. 11-13, 11-15). Seen in cross section, the outer segments of the photoreceptors form an extremely regular mosaic pattern. In the middle of the fovea the diameter of the cone outer segments is about 2 μm, which corresponds to a visual angle of ca. 0.4 minutes of arc (Fig. 11-3 D) [8, 13].

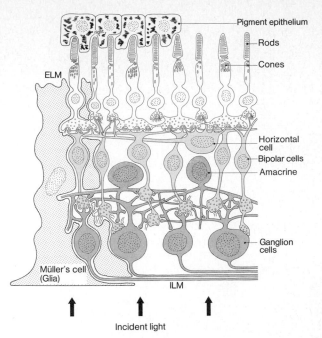

Fig. 11-13. *Diagram of the structure of the primate retina,* from electron micrographs. ELM, external limiting membrane; ILM, internal limiting membrane. [Based on an illustration of DOWLING and BOYCOTT, Proc. Roy. Soc. (Lond.) *166,* 1966]

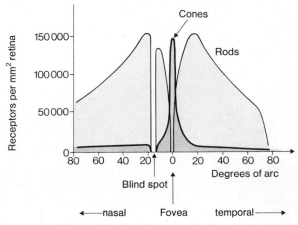

Fig. 11-14. Distribution of the cones and rods over the retina (schematic). Ordinate, receptor density (no./mm^2 area); abscissa, distance from fovea

Visual pigments. The molecules of the visual pigments are embedded in a regular array within the lipid double layer of the membrane disks in the outer segments (Fig. 11-15). A retina dissected out in the dark, or a solution of the rod visual pigment (**rhodopsin,** or "visual purple"), looks red because rhodopsin absorbs green and blue light especially strongly. This property can be measured exactly by determining the **spectral absorption curve** or *spectral extinction curve* of the visual pigment. "Absorption" refers to the differ-

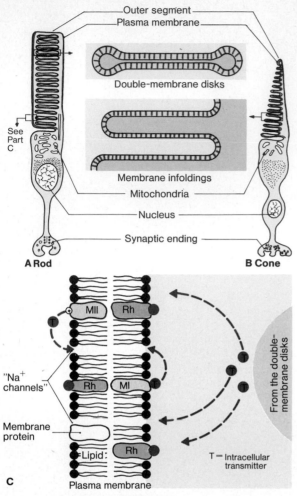

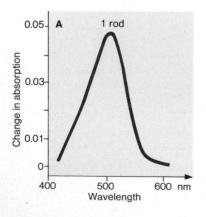

Fig. 11-15 A–C. Diagram of the structure of a rod **(A)** and a cone **(B)** in the vertebrate retina, with enlarged diagrams of the membrane of the disks in the outer segments of the rods, and of the membranous infoldings in the outer segments of the cones. Diagram of the structure of the disk or plasma membrane of photoreceptors **(C)**. It is not yet clear whether rhodopsin (Rh) is embedded in the lipid double layer of the membrane in pairs *(above)* or singly *(below)*. MI, metarhodopsin I, M II, metarhodopsin II (cf. Fig. 11-17). From [42]

ence between the amount of light incident on the solution under study (I_i) and the amount that emerges on the other side (I_o). The "extinction" of a solution is the logarithm of the ratio of I_i to I_o. The measurement of extinction offers the advantage that the resulting curves vs. wavelength, properly normalized, are independent of the absolute concentration of the pigment in the solution. A rhodopsin solution has two absorption maxima, one in the visible range at ca. 500 nm and the other in the ultraviolet, at ca. 350 nm.

The extinction curves of the visual pigments of single rods and cones can be found by **microspectrophotometry:** Under microscopic control a very small pencil of light is projected through the isolated outer segments of the photoreceptors in a piece of retina excised during surgery, and highly sensitive photocells are used to measure the light absorbed at different wavelengths (Fig. 11-16). The results are as follows:
(i) The visual pigments of the rods and cones have different spectral extinction curves.
(ii) The extinction curve for the rods corresponds to that of rhodopsin, and matches to a close approximation the curves for the spectral sensitivity of scotopic vision (Fig. 11-1).
(iii) There are *3 cone types* differing in their visual pigments.
Chemical analysis has shown that rhodopsin consists of a glycoprotein (opsin) and a chromophore group, 11-*cis*-retinal (Fig. 11-17). Retinal is the aldehyde of Vitamin A_1 (retinol) [5, 6, 8, 22].

Bleaching and regeneration of the visual pigment following light absorption. *The transduction process in the photoreceptors* begins with the *absorption* of a photon by a pigment molecule in the π-electron region of the conjugated double bonds of retinal (Fig. 11-17 A). As a result the rhodopsin molecule is raised to a higher energy level and oscillates more strongly. With a probability *(quantum efficiency)* of 0.5–0.65, **stereoisomerization** of the retinal ensues; in a process requiring several stages, 11-*cis*-retinal is converted to all-*trans*-retinal, with a change in the bond between retinal and opsin. By lowering the temperature of the preparation or of the rhodopsin solution one can ar-

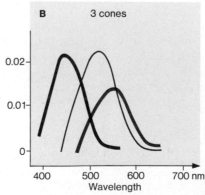

Fig. 11-16. *Results of microspectrophotometric measurements* of the spectral absorption of single receptors in the human retina (specimens from operations). The curves represent difference spectra (i.e., the difference in spectral absorption before and after bleaching). Three types of cone can be distinguished. [Schematized from BROWN and WALD, Science *144*, 45 (1964)]

rest this process at different stages for closer analysis (Fig. 11-17 B). At the stage of the conversion of metarhodopsin I to metarhodopsin II there is a change in conformation of the pigment molecule that also involves opsin and probably results in the "activation" of Ca^{++} ions. These ions are loosely bound either to metarhodopsin or to neighboring protein molecules in the membrane. In exchange for the Ca^{++} released in this reaction, the metarhodopsin II molecule takes up protons. The Ca^{++} ions, or transmitter molecules activated by them, diffuse from the disks of the rods to the plasma membrane of the outer segment or, in the case of cones, from one part of the plasma membrane to another (Fig. 11-15). There they bring about a reduced *conductance* for small ions, sodium in particular. These events explain the production of the *secondary receptor potential* discussed below.

The several-stage process of rhodopsin breakdown ends with the formation of *retinol* and *opsin* (Fig. 11-17 B). In an energy-consuming reaction involving a chain of enzymes rhodopsin is reconstituted from either retinal or retinol and opsin. With a constant average incidence of photons on the retina an *equilibrium* is eventually established between the rate of light-induced pigment bleaching and that of (chiefly enzymatically controlled) pigment regeneration. This dynamic equilibrium shifts toward higher pigment concentrations as the amount of light incident on the retina is reduced. This is the *photochemical* contribution to the familiar experience of *dark adaptation* (cf. p. 234).

The primary receptor potential of the photoreceptors. The *conformational change* in the visual-pigment molecule brings about an electrical potential of extremely short latency ($\ll$ 1 ms), the primary receptor potential (*early receptor potential,* ERP; Fig. 11-18). It consists of various components, which can be isolated by lowering the temperature to different levels. At temperatures below 0° C (Fig. 11-18) the component associated with the stereoisomerization (metarhodopsin I → metarhodopsin II) is isolated.

The secondary receptor potential. A secondary receptor potential (*late receptor potential,* LRP) is elicited by illumination of photoreceptors in the vertebrate retina, a **hyperpolarization** of the rod or cone membrane potential is observed. The receptor cell membrane potential varies from − 25 to − 40 mV measured in the dark. The amplitude of hyperpolarization increases with the intensity of the light stimulus (Fig. 11-19). The late receptor potential of the rods has a slower time course than that of the cones. The rod system is therefore more sluggish than the cone

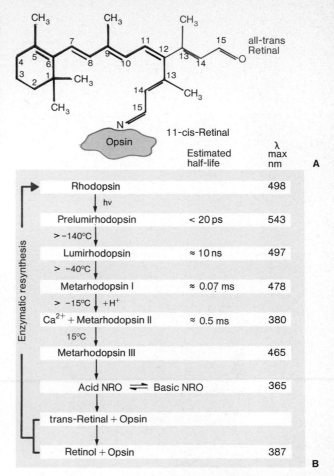

Fig. 11-17. **A** Structural formula of 11-*cis*-retinal and its isomer (all-*trans* form) after stereoisomerization. The binding of retinal to opsin, shown diagrammatically here, probably occurs by way of the carbon atom 15 and a nitrogen bridge. **B** Breakdown and reconstitution of rhodopsin after photon absorption. NRO, N-retinylidene opsin

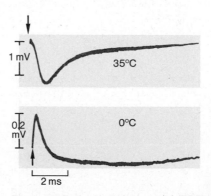

Fig. 11-18. Early receptor potential (ERP) of the ground squirrel, recorded at two different temperatures (after PAK and EBREY: J. gen. Physiol. *49* (1966)). The amplitude of the various components of the ERP rises about in proportion to the logarithm of the light-flash intensity over 2–3 $\log_{10}$ units. The brief light flashes are indicated by arrows

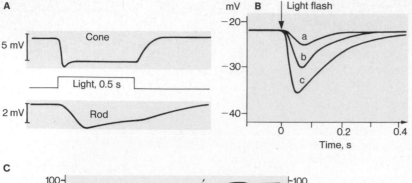

Fig. 11-19 A–C. *Late receptor potential of the photoreceptors of the vertebrate retina.* **A** Intracellular recording of the receptor potentials of a cone and a rod in the vertebrate retina, diagrammatic. **B** Receptor potential of a cone in the turtle retina in response to light flashes (10 ms duration) of increasing intensity. Relative stimulus strength a = 1, b = 4, c = 16. **C** *Intensity function* of the receptor potential of a single cone in the turtle retina. The relative amplitude (A, ordinate) increases in proportion to the logarithm of relative stimulus intensity (I, abscissa) over a narrow range. **B** and **C** after BAYLOR and FUORTES: J. Physiol. (Lond.), *207* (1970). **C** also includes a schematic curve representing the relation between activation of a retinal on-center ganglion cell and light intensity

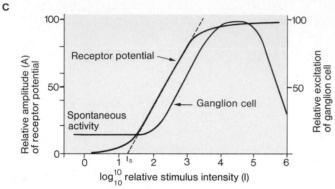

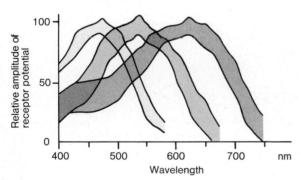

Fig. 11-20. *Spectral sensitivity* of the receptor potentials of the fish retina. Means (with standard deviation) of measurements from three different classes of cones are shown (After TOMITA, 1970)

system, a property also reflected in the fact that the upper frequency limit of the rods when stimulated with intermittent light is lower than that of the cones (cf. p. 251). The intracellularly measured *spectral sensitivity* of the three different classes of secondary cone potentials in animals with color vision is consistent with the results of microspectrophotometry, and confirms the trichromatic theory of color vision (cf. p. 261 and Figs. 11-16 and 11-20). The spectral sensitivity of the receptor potentials of the rods has a maximum at ca. 500 nm, as does the spectral absorption curve of rhodopsin.

Generation of the hyperpolarizing receptor potential of rods and cones can be represented by the following

model: The conformational change in the pigment molecules "activates" Ca^{++} ions or "secondary" intracellular transmitter molecules, which reach a "Na^+ channel" in the cell membrane of the photoreceptor outer segments by diffusion. By interaction between the transmitter molecules and the lipoprotein molecules at the Na^+ channels, the channels are "plugged" and the *sodium conductance* of the membrane decreases. As compared with other nerve cells or sensory receptor cells in the body, the photoreceptor membrane in the dark (in the absence of adequate stimulation) has a relatively high Na^+ conductance, so that a *dark current* through the membrane is produced by the flow of Na^+. Under illumination the sodium conductance and the dark current decrease, and the hyperpolarizing receptor potential is the result (Fig. 11-19 A, B). This hypothesis concerning the intracellular transmission of the transduction process to the plasma membrane of the outer segments offers the advantage that it also explains why the secondary receptor potential of the cones has a shorter latency and more rapid time course than that of the rods (Fig. 11-19 A). That is, the activated transmitter molecules have a shorter distance to travel to the nearest Na^+ channels in the cones than in the rods. In the rods most of the pigment molecules are in the *disk membrane* of the outer segment, whereas in the cones they are embedded in the infoldings of the cell membrane itself (Fig. 11-15 A, B). In the rods, the transmitter molecules released 1–2 ms after photon absorption must diffuse to the cell membrane before interaction with the Na^+ channels can occur.

The intensity of a stimulus light I_s (number of photons incident per unit time and unit area) is related to the amplitude A of the secondary receptor potential as follows:

$$A = \frac{\alpha I_s}{1 + k_i \cdot I_s} \quad [mV] \tag{9}$$

This *hyperbolic equation* can be approximated for a small range of intermediate intensities by a logarithmic function that is also known as the Weber-Fechner law in general sensory physiology (cf. p. 187):

$$A = k \log I_s/I_0 \quad [mV] \tag{10}$$

where I_0 is the threshold intensity and depends on the state of adaptation. The constants α and k in Eqs. (9) and (10), respectively, change as a function of the wavelength of monochromatic light; this relation corresponds approximately to the spectral absorption curves of the visual pigments in the rods and cones (Figs. 11-16, 11-20) [5, 8, 22, 36, 42].

The Corneoretinal Potential and the Electroretinogram (ERG)

Macroelectrodes record two functionally distinct kinds of electrical potentials from the eye as a whole – the **steady potential** between the cornea and the relatively negative retina, and the **electroretinogram (ERG).** The steady corneoretinal potential derives largely from the electrical potential difference between the scleral side of the pigment cells and the inner segments of the photoreceptors. That is, it reflects the sum of the currents flowing through the plasma membrane of the pigment cells and photoreceptors, and therefore it changes with state of adaptation.

The ERG is a voltage fluctuation consisting of several "waves" (a, b, c, d; Fig. 11-21), which is elicited by an increase or decrease in the light falling on the retina. The a-wave presumably arises by summation of receptor potentials, the slower b-wave primarily by membrane-potential changes in the glial cells (Müller cells), and the c-wave by membrane-potential changes in the pigment epithelial cells at "light on"; the d-wave is produced by the change in the photoreceptor and bipolar-cell membrane potentials at "light off" (off-effect). With light stimuli of over 0.3 s duration the c-wave begins during the stimulus and the off-effect is superimposed on it. With brief light flashes, the b- and d-waves coincide [8, 10].

Receptive Fields of Retinal Ganglion Cells

The neuronal network in the retina. The signals from the receptors are transmitted to the bipolar and horizontal cells by synaptic contacts (Fig. 11-13); "processing" in these cells occurs by slow membrane-po-

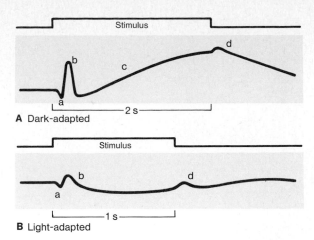

Fig. 11-21. *Electroretinograms of the human retina.* Schematized from recordings of Hanitzsch et al. [Vision Res. 6, 245 (1966)]

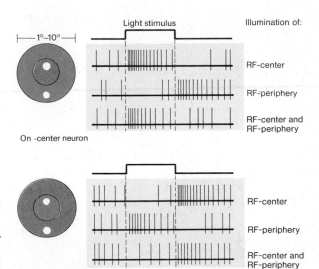

Fig. 11-22. *Functional organization of receptive fields of the ganglion cells in the mammalian retina.* For analysis of the receptive fields spots of light (shown in *white*) are projected into either the RF-center or the RF-periphery. Light stimuli elicit different responses of the *on-center* and *off-center* neurons. When both parts of the receptive field are illuminated simultaneously, the excitatory and inhibitory processes associated with illumination of the center and periphery summate. However, the response elicited by stimulation of the RF-center predominates

tential changes. The signals from the bipolar cells are transmitted to the dendrite membranes of the ganglion cells, either directly or by way of the amacrines. As a rule, each ganglion cell receives input from several bipolar cells. Close examination of Fig. 11-13 shows, for example, that in the section of retina illustrated each ganglion cell is connected, directly or indirectly, with many of the receptors, bipolar cells, horizontal

Fig. 11-23. Patterns demonstrating visual simultaneous contrast

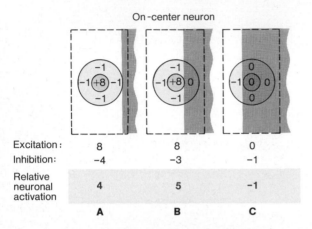

On-center neuron

	A	B	C
Excitation:	8	8	0
Inhibition:	−4	−3	−1
Relative neuronal activation	4	5	−1

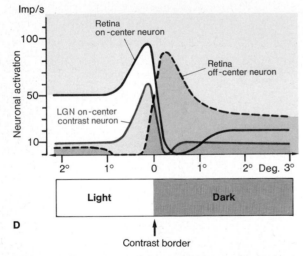

Fig. 11-24 A–D. *Diagram of the mechanisms underlying simultaneous contrast. A–C* The activation of an on-center neuron depends on the position of a light/dark boundary within the RF. The maximal activation is produced at Position **B,** where the light/dark boundary coincides with the boundary between RF-center and RF-periphery. The numbers indicate relative excitation, neglecting spontaneous discharge. **D** Dependence of the activation of visual neurons on the position of a light/dark boundary in the receptive field (abscissa). The schematized curves represent the responses of retinal on-center and off-center neurons and of on-center contrast neurons in the lateral geniculate nucleus. (After Baumgartner [35] and Eysel and Grüsser [12])

cells and amacrines. The extent of anatomically demonstrable **signal convergence** is greater, the further toward the periphery of the retina the ganglion cell is located. Signal convergence depends on the size of the dendritic tree of a ganglion cell and on the spatial extent of the lateral processes of the horizontal cells and amacrines. These two classes of neurons are responsible for the transmission of **lateral-inhibition signals** (cf. p. 181) [12, 18, 19].

Because *one* photoreceptor is usually connected to *several* bipolar cells and these in turn make contact with several ganglion cells, there is also a considerable degree of **signal divergence** in the retinal neural network. But as the relative numbers of receptors (about 125 million) and ganglion cells (about 1 million) show, in the human retina signal convergence predominates.

Receptive fields. The convergence and divergence of connections within the retina are the basis of the **receptive fields (RFs)** of retinal ganglion cells. The RF is that area on the retina within which a suitable visual stimulus pattern can excite or inhibit a neuron. The RFs of the neurons in the visual system are often composed of regions differing in their functional properties. The excitatory and/or inhibitory processes initiated at the various points within an RF are spatially summated by the ganglion cell [8, 12, 18, 19].

Classes of retinal ganglion cells. In the light-adapted mammalian retina, *achromatic* light stimuli reveal two classes of retinal ganglion cells, each with *antagonistically* arranged RF. **On-center neurons** respond to illumination of the RF-center with depolarization and thus with an increase in the neuronal discharge rate (Fig. 11-22). By contrast, illumination of the RF-periphery (like "light off" in the RF-center) elicits hyperpolarization of the membrane potential and inhibition of the neuronal discharge. When center and periphery are illuminated simultaneously, the response from the center dominates, but it is weaker than it would be if the center had been stimulated alone, for the excitation from the center and the inhibition from the periphery are summed. The receptive fields of the **off-center neurons** have just the opposite arrangement (Fig. 11-22). The adequate stimulus for excitation of an off-center neuron is a decrease in luminance in the RF-center or an increase in luminance in the RF-periphery.

Stimulus intensity and neuronal response. Given a constant average state of adaptation, the discharge rate of an on-center neuron, like the amplitude of the receptor potential (Fig. 11-19C), increases with the intensity of the light stimulus over 2–3 $\log_{10}$ units. The response to very intense stimuli falls off again, because of strong inhibitory effects. The rate of impulse discharge in the off-activation of an off-center neuron is also related, by a logarithmic function, to the amplitude of the preceding (negative) intensity step at "light off".

Time course of neuronal excitation. In both the on-center and the off-center ganglion cells two types of response can be distinguished. "Sustained" neurons or X-neurons stimulated with an adequate change in light intensity respond with maintained activation, whereas "transient" neurons or Y-neurons exhibit only a brief on- or off-activation, a few seconds in duration. A third class of retinal ganglion cells (W-neurons) responds strongly only to moving stimulus patterns. Stationary light stimuli elicit a short on- and off-activation in W-neurons.

Neurophysiological Basis of Simultaneous Contrast

We now come to the first example of **correlation** between visual perception and the activation of certain classes of neurons in the visual system. Regardless of the epistemological limits of such psychophysical correlation, its value lies primarily in the opportunity to predict one response from the other, if the correct "mapping" of the neurophysiological data onto the results of experiments in perception psychology is known (cf. p. 178). In the following this mapping is assumed to be such that activation of the on-center neurons has the *meaning* "brighter" with respect to the site of its receptive-field center, whereas activation of the off-center neurons has the meaning "darker". The strength of the subjective sensation "brighter" or "darker" is evidently linearly correlated with the mean neuronal discharge rate.

Fig. 11-23 illustrates **visual simultaneous contrast.** A gray field on a white background appears to be darker than the same field on a dark background. Along the black/white boundary the light part seems somewhat lighter and the dark part, somewhat darker than the areas further from the boundary (border contrast, Mach band). The functional organization of the RF of retinal ganglion cells offers an explanation of simultaneous contrast (Fig. 11-24), as follows. Activation of the retinal neurons by a light/dark boundary depends on the position of the boundary in the receptive field. Neuronal activation is strongest when the light/dark boundary is at the transition point between RF-center and RF-periphery. The activation of the off-center neurons reaches a maximum when the RF-center is on the darker side of the boundary, and the activation of the on-center neurons is maximal when their RF-center is on the lighter side of the boundary. The average activation of all the on- and off-center neurons in the region of a light/dark boundary has a spatial distribution corresponding to the curve of perceived simultaneous contrast.

Simultaneous contrast provides partial functional compensation of the physiological errors of the diop-

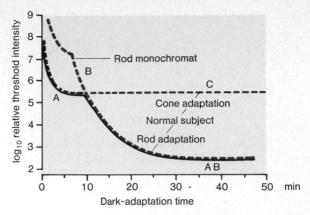

Fig. 11-25. *Human dark-adaptation curve.* (A) Curve of the means for 9 normal subjects. (B) Dark-adaptation curve of a completely color-blind person, measured for the part of the retina 8° above the fovea centralis. (C) Dark-adaptation curve for the cone system of a subject with normal color vision (fovea, red light stimulus). For curve (B) the time axis (abscissa) should be shifted to the right by 2 min. (A and B drawn from data of E. AUERBACH, Vision Research Laboratory, Jerusalem, 1973)

tric apparatus described on p. 240. Moreover, simultaneous contrast is an important mechanism in the perception of shape, because **visual acuity** (p. 255) depends not only on the density of the receptor raster, but also on simultaneous contrast [12, 13, 14, 18, 19].

Light/Dark Adaptation, Overstimulation, Afterimages

Dark adaptation. When the average ambient illumination changes, the sensitivity of the visual system adjusts to the new conditions. A person who steps from a brightly lighted room into outdoor darkness is at first unable to see the surrounding objects, but after a while their outlines become visible. During dark adaptation the **absolute sensitivity** of the visual system slowly increases, but visual acuity is always considerably reduced in the dark-adapted state. The time course of dark adaptation can be found by repeated measurements of the threshold light intensity (Fig. 11-25). The slow rate of adaptation is well matched to the gradual dimming of the ambient light during the evening twilight. As dark adaptation proceeds the rod system becomes considerably more sensitive than the cone system. After more than 10 min of dark adaptation the rod-free fovea centralis is less sensitive than the extrafoveal retina. The absolute visual threshold is not reached until one has been in the dark for more than 2 hours; in this state the threshold intensity of light stimuli projected onto a large area of the retina is 1–4 photons per minute per receptor [8, 14, 16, 28].

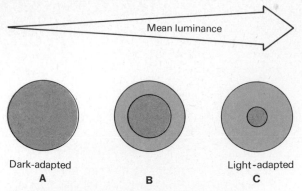

Mean luminance

Dark-adapted   Light-adapted
A   **B**   **C**

Fig. 11-26. *Relation between the functional organization of the RF of a retinal on-center ganglion cell and the state of adaptation.* The RF-center becomes relatively smaller, the higher the luminance to which the eye is adapted. In the dark-adapted state the antagonistic organization of the RF disappears, and light stimuli produce excitation everywhere within the field

Fig. 11-27. *Patterns to demonstrate afterimage production.* When one fixates the center of the geometric figure on the right for ca. 30 s and then looks at the center of the circle on the left, one sees a negative *afterimage* of the right-hand figure

Adaptation and visual acuity. Even within the *photopic* range visual acuity (p. 255) decreases with reduction of the mean ambient intensity:

Print as small as this can be read only if the page is well illuminated.

The dependence of contrast perception and visual acuity on average luminance can be explained by a change in the organization of the RFs of retinal ganglion cells. That is, the RF-centers become functionally smaller, the greater the mean luminance of a stimulus pattern (Fig. 11-26), because of the relative increase in lateral inhibition. Under conditions of scotopic adaptation there is no demonstrable antagonistic organization of RF-center and RF-periphery. When illuminated, all the receptors within the entire RF cause excitation of on-center neurons and inhibition of off-center neurons. Summation of the excitation over an extensive area of the retina, together with an increase in concentration of visual pigment in the receptors, is an important mechanism for increasing the sensitivity of the retina during dark adaptation.

Light adaptation. The inverse of dark adaptation, called **light adaptation,** is considerably more rapid. When a dark-adapted person enters a brightly lighted room, his visual system adjusts to the new ambient illumination within a few seconds, though his eyes may be dazzled briefly.

Mechanisms of light/dark adaptation. In addition to the shift of the equilibrium between bleached and unbleached pigment in the photoreceptors (p. 245), certain neuronal mechanisms play an important role in light/dark adaptation. Vision is "switched" from the cone system to the rod system by neuronal mechanisms. The increase in area of the RF-centers of retinal ganglion cells is brought about by adaptation-dependent processes of lateral inhibition, in which the horizontal cells and amacrines participate. The dependence of **pupil size** on mean ambient intensity, discussed on p. 238, is also a neuronal component of light/dark adaptation.

Local adaptation and afterimages. Local adaptation occurs when circumscribed areas on the retina are illuminated at different intensities, even though the average ambient luminance remains constant. After the center of the geometrical pattern in Fig. 11-27 has been fixated for ca. 30 s, if the gaze is shifted to a white or gray background a negative **afterimage** appears for several seconds. In the negative afterimage what was light in the original pattern appears dark, and what was dark appears light. Those parts of the retina on which the image of the dark parts of the pattern lay have become more sensitive than the nearby regions corresponding to the light parts of the image during the fixation period.

Afterimages persist for a long time when a retinal area has been illuminated strongly or for a sufficiently long period. Local adaptation to **colored stimulus patterns** produces afterimages in the *complementary color* (p. 262):

"As I entered an inn toward evening, and a buxom maid with a dazzling white face, black hair and scarlet bodice came into my room and stood at a little distance from me, I gazed at her intently in the half-light. Then when she moved away I saw on the white wall opposite me a black face surrounded by a bright glow, and the clothing of the completely distinct figure appeared a beautiful sea-green" (W. v. GOETHE, *Zur Farbenlehre,* I, 52).

After exposure to brief flashes of light one perceives a rapid succession of positive (light) **periodic afterimages** (2–4 afterimages within 2 s), brought about by oscillatory excitatory and inhibitory processes in the retinal neuron system [43].

Overstimulation. Sudden strong illumination of the retina – for example, by the headlights of an oncoming car at night – can cause a positive afterimage so intense that form vision is temporarily disrupted; the visual threshold is elevated and contrast perception reduced. When the eyes are dazzled in this way a **reflex closing of the lids** is brought about by way of subcortical visual centers affecting neurons in the facial nucleus.

The Temporal Properties of Transmission in the Retina

The **flicker-fusion frequency** (critical flicker frequency, CFF) is the frequency of an intermittent light stimulus just great enough to give **no impression of flickering.** In the range of **scotopic intensities** (rod vision) the maximal CFF is 22–25 light stimuli per second. In the photopic range the CFF rises about in proportion to the logarithm of the luminance and of the area stimulated, to a maximum of ca. 80–100 light stimuli per second. The psychophysically measured CFF is determined largely by the temporal properties of retinal transmission. The flicker-fusion frequency measured at the retinal ganglion cells is subject to the same laws as the subjective flicker-fusion frequency. Intermittent light stimuli in a frequency range between 5 and 15 Hz elicit a particularly strong activation of retinal nerve cells, causing a strong excitatory input to the brain. Therefore in some epileptic patients flickering light can trigger convulsions [17].

11.4   Signal Processing in the Central Visual System

The Central Visual Pathway

Anatomy. Visual information is carried to the brain by the axons of the retinal ganglion cells, which form the optic nerves. The right and left optic nerves coalesce at the base of the skull in the **optic chiasm** (Fig. 11-28), in which the nerve fibers from the nasal half of each retina cross to the opposite side. The fibers from the temporal half of each retina continue ipsilaterally, together with the crossed axons from the contralateral optic nerve, as the **optic tract.** The optic tract leads to the first central stations of the visual pathway – the **lateral geniculate nuclei,** the **superior colliculi,** the **nuclei of the accessory optic tract** and the **pretectal region** of the brainstem. The axons of the geniculate cells run through the **optic radiation,** predominantly to the **primary visual cortex** (striate area, or Area 17 of the occipital cerebral cortex). The primary cortex makes connections with the **secondary** (Area 18) and **tertiary** (Area 19) **visual cortex** and with the superior colliculi.

Topological organization of the visual pathway. The axons and the various nerve-cell layers in the central visual pathway exhibit topological organization. That is, just as a certain geographical region is represented on a map, the image of the environment projected onto the retina is represented in a systematic way in the spatial pattern of excitation of the neurons in the lateral geniculate, superior colliculus and visual cortex. In contrast to a map – with a scale, say, of 1 : 100,000 so that a centimeter anywhere on the map corresponds to a kilometer in nature – the topological projection of the retina is *nonlinear.* The small region of the fovea centralis is projected onto a far larger region of the visual cortex than is an area of equal size in the periphery of the retina.

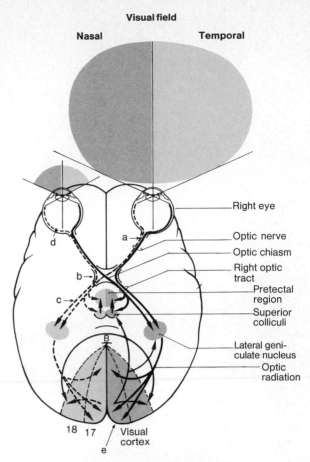

Fig. 11-28. *Diagram of the visual pathway in the human brain.* The efferent connections between the visual cortex and subcortical structures are shown on the right side. The visual-cortex areas on the left and right halves of the brain are connected with one another by axons running through the corpus callosum (CC). The arrows labelled with letters indicate possible sites of lesions producing the visual-field deficits shown in Fig. 11-35

Signal Processing in the Superior Colliculi

The nerve cells in the superior colliculi respond preferentially to moving visual patterns, and some of them are **directionally sensitive.** The latter are activated only if the stimulus pattern moves through the RF in a certain direction. The neurons of the colliculi are arranged in "columns" perpendicular to the collicular surface. Within each column all the neurons have RFs in the *same part of the visual field*. In the deeper layers of the colliculi are nerve cells that are activated shortly *before* eye movements and that presumably function in the *motor control of gaze direction* (cf. p. 269).

Stimulation of a small region of the superior colliculus in the monkey by chronically implanted fine microelectrodes elicits **eye movements.** The receptive fields of these nerve cells can be determined. When the cells are stimulated, the eye moves in

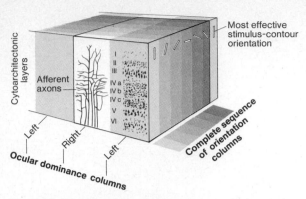

Fig. 11-29. Diagram of the "horizontal cytoarchitectonic layers" (I–VI), the ocular-dominance columns and the orientation columns in the visual cortex (Area 17) of the rhesus monkey. (Schematized from Hubel and Wiesel, 1977)

such a way as to bring the image that was in their receptive fields into the fovea centralis. The deep layers of neurons in the colliculus evidently function as a "foveal centering system", controlled by connections between the visual cortex and the colliculi (Fig. 11-28). The foveal centering system controls the reflex head and eye movements that are triggered by the sudden appearance of a moving object in the periphery of the visual field [2, 19, 44, 55, 56]. Under natural stimulus conditions the excitation of movement-sensitive retinal ganglion cells leads to an activation of superior-colliculus neurons (p. 268).

Signal Processing in the Lateral Geniculate Nucleus (LGN)

Within the LGN axons of the optic tract terminate in six layers, three associated with the ipsilateral eye and three with the contralateral eye. Many nerve cells of the LGN, like the retinal ganglion cells, have concentrically arranged receptive fields (Fig. 11-22). Achromatic light/dark patterns reveal two different classes of neurons in the LGN: **"contrast neurons"** and **"light/dark neurons".** In both classes there are about equal numbers of on-center and off-center neurons. The contrast neurons, because of the predominance of lateral inhibition, give little or no response to diffuse light stimuli but respond strongly to a light/dark contour within the RF (Fig. 11-24). Activation of the light/dark neurons, on the other hand, depends on the mean luminance of the visual stimulus pattern in the receptive field as a whole [12, 18].

In mammals with color vision, such as the monkey, some of the LGN neurons have receptive fields with a **color-specific organization.** Monochromatic light stimuli elicit excitation or inhibition, depending on wavelength; in some cases the spectral sensitivity of the RF-center differs from that of the RF-periphery (cf. p. 262).

Signal Processing in the Visual Cortex

The neuron systems of the retina and the LGN evaluate visual signals in terms of their chromatic properties, spatial contrast distribution and average luminance in the various parts of the visual field. A further "structuring" of the afferent visual signals is achieved by the neuron systems in the visual cortex. In each of three different regions of the occipital cerebral cortex – the primary, secondary and tertiary visual cortex – the entire contralateral half of the visual field is represented (Fig. 11-28). Microelectrode recording in higher mammals has made it possible to analyze signal processing by the neuronal networks in the visual cortex in considerable detail. Such experiments have revealed that only part of the nerve cells, especially those in the cytoarchitectonic layer IVc of the primary visual cortex (Fig. 11-29), have concentric receptive fields similar to that of LGN-neurons and respond to simple light/dark stimuli. The nerve cells in the other layers respond only to **contours** in certain orientations, **interruptions of contours,** and so on. It is evident that the response patterns of cortical visual neurons represent a further "specialization" in visual signal processing. The degree of specialization is characterized by the receptive-field properties: a distinction is made among **simple, complex** and **hypercomplex** receptive fields.

The functional architectonics of the visual cortex. The nerve cells in the visual cortex (Areas 17, 18 and 19), as in most other parts of the cerebral cortex, are arranged in 6 clearly distinguishable *cytoarchitectonic* layers parallel to the surface of the cortex (Fig. 11-29). Some of the afferent axons from the lateral geniculate nucleus terminate in all layers of the primary visual cortex (Area 17). Their main projection area, however, is Layer 4, which is subdivided into the sublayers a, b and c. To understand the neuronal mechanisms of binocular integration it is important to bear in mind that in Layer 4 there is still a functional separation of the signals from the right and left eyes. That is, if illumination of the receptive field in the left eye excites a neuron in Layer 4, illumination of the corresponding receptive field in the right eye inhibits this neuron. This effect is presumably one of the neuronal components contributing to *binocular rivalry* (p. 258). By contrast, the neurons of the other cytoarchitectonic layers in the primary visual cortex receive predominantly excitatory connections; they are activated by axons from LGN-cells connected with the left or the right retina. In these cortical neurons there is a more or less pronounced binocular summation of excitation, with the signals from one of the two eyes dominating in many cases.

The nerve cells of the visual cortex are arranged not only in layers parallel to the surface, but also in functional layers *perpendicular* to it. The receptive fields of the nerve cells within a vertical layer or "column" are all in the same part of the retina. Neurons in adjacent columns have partially overlapping receptive fields. This geometrical arrangement is an instance of the retinotopic organization mentioned on p. 251. For the nerve cells in an *ocular-dominance column* the signals from either the right or the left eye dominate (Fig. 11-29). Within an ocular-dominance column there is a further level of differentiation, into narrower vertical columns; in each of these, the entire vertical array of nerve cells has receptive fields with similar "axial orientations". The axes of the receptive fields of nerve cells in neighboring **"orientation columns"** change progressively as the distance between the columns increases (Fig. 11-29). The properties of receptive-field organization of cortical nerve cells now to be discussed must be understood in the context of this anatomical organization. Neurons with so-called simple receptive fields are found chiefly in Layer 4; visual processing in the other layers of the primary visual cortex as well as in the secondary and tertiary cortex (Areas 18 and 19) is based on neurons with complex or hypercomplex receptive fields [50, 51, 59].

Simple receptive fields. Some of the nerve cells in Area 17 have "simple" receptive fields with on- or off-zones arranged concentrically or side by side (Fig. 11-30). Diffuse illumination of the entire receptive field elicits little or no activation in most of these neurons. The **axial orientation** of a field with a longitudinal boundary between the on- and off-zones is the direction of the boundary. A light/dark contour activates the neuron most strongly when it is on and parallel to the boundary between the on- and off-zones.

Complex receptive fields. Nerve cells with complex receptive fields are activated only if differentiated stimulus patterns are projected onto the RF. Such patterns include *light/dark contours* in particular orientations and *contour interruptions* of a certain extent. Complex RFs as a rule are subdivided into a **excitatory receptive field** (ERF) and an **inhibitory receptive field** (IRF). When the ERF and IRF are stimulated simultaneously there is little or no activation of the neuron (Fig. 11-30). Areas 18 and 19 contain, in addition to neurons with complex RFs, others with *hypercomplex* receptive fields. These nerve cells are activated only when light/dark contours in a particular orientation *and* with a limited extent, contour interruptions or intersecting contours (corners) are projected into the ERF (Fig. 11-30).

In primates Area 18 is divided into functionally different regions, called V2, V3 and V4. In these regions there are, on the one hand, areas in which the neuronal responses are highly color-selective, and on the other hand areas in which the neurons are predominantly movement-specific. Further processing of visual information occurs in the parietal cerebral cortex (Area 7), which controls the eye and hand movements involved in grasping objects. Still other visual association regions are found

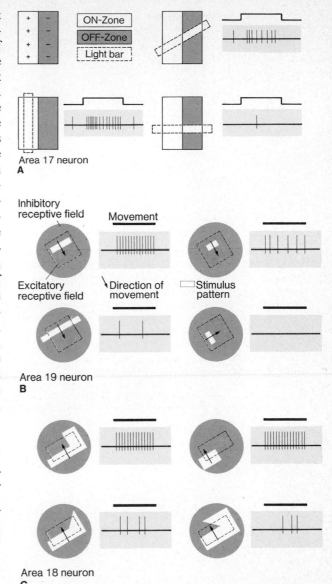

Area 17 neuron
A

Area 19 neuron
B

Area 18 neuron
C

Fig. 11-30 A–C. *Discharge patterns of single neurons in the visual cortex.* **A** Neuron with *simple* receptive field, on- and off-zones arranged in parallel. **B** Neuron with *complex* receptive field. The greatest activation is produced by a moving, tilted bar of light of limited extent. **C** Neuron with *hypercomplex receptive field*. Maximal activation is elicited by *two contrast boundaries* meeting at right angles. The stimulus patterns in each case are shown in *white*. In **B** and **C** the arrows show the *direction of movement* of the stimulus patterns. (Schematized from data of HUBEL and WIESEL)

in the lower and middle temporal lobes. In the midregion of the primate temporal lobe a small cortical field has recently been found in which the neurons respond preferentially to visual patterns representing faces or parts of faces (eyes, nose, mouth). Presumably humans, too, can perceive and recognize faces only if the function of a specialized cortical region in the occipito-temporal region is undisturbed. Bilateral lesions in this region, or a unilateral lesion in combination with a lesion of the corpus callosum, give rise to the (rare) symptom called **prosopagnosia**:

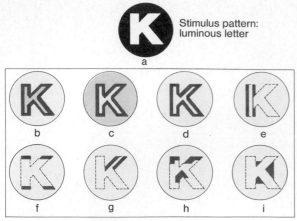

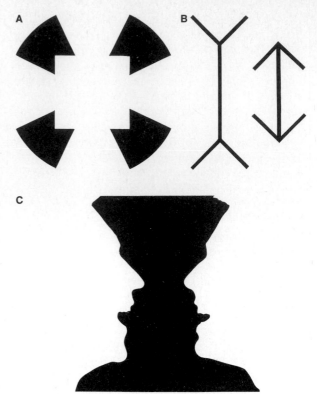

Fig. 11-31 a–i. Diagram of the excitation elicited by a luminous letter K (cf. Fig. 11-2) in various neuronal layers of the retina and in the central nervous system. **a** Image of the luminous letter on the retina, and spatial pattern of excitation in the receptor layer of the retina. **b** and **c** Pattern of excitation in the output layer of the retina (ganglion cells). In **b** to **i** the excitation is denoted by red bars. **b** On-center neurons, **c** off-center neurons. **d** Pattern of excitation in the neurons of the lateral geniculate nucleus and of layer IV of the visual cortex. The contours of the luminous letter elicit excitation of the nerve cells. **e** to **i** Pattern of excitation in various neuron layers and different nerve-cell classes in the primary, secondary and tertiary visual cortex. These nerve cells are stimulated only by contours in certain orientations, with certain interruptions of angle or contour. The illustration greatly simplifies the neurobiological situation; the spatial distribution of excitation in the various nerve-cell layers of the cerebral cortex is not a linear transformation of the stimulus pattern

Fig. 11-32. A Example of *visual shape completion* (white square). **B** Müller-Lyer illusion; the objective lengths of the two vertical lines are equal. **C** Pattern to demonstrate *alternation of figure and background*. The viewer sees either a black "candlestick" on a white background or two smiling profiles on a black background (negative of a silhouette)

these patients are no longer capable of recognizing previously familiar faces.

Movement sensitivity of cortical neurons. Neurons with complex or hypercomplex RFs respond to changes in position or to **moving stimulus patterns** more strongly than to motionless patterns. This movement sensitivity can be interpreted as an adaptation to the eye movements constantly present in normal seeing. The "cerebral picture" of the stationary world is constructed from ever-changing retinal images (cf. p. 267). Some of the movement-sensitive cortical neurons control the **sampling** movements of the eyes discussed on p. 267, by way of connections via the superior colliculi and the pulvinar or direct cortico-pontine axons, and regulate accommodation and pupil size by way of connections with the pretectal region (cf. p. 238) [12, 18, 19, 49, 50, 51, 59, 60].

Neurophysiological Bases of Shape Perception

Contours of particular orientation and length, contour interruptions and angles are optimal stimulus patterns for the activation of the different classes of neurons in the visual cortex. In each class, the spatial pattern of neuronal excitation represents a particular feature of the stimulus pattern. The stimulus pattern

"K", for example, gives rise to the spatial distributions of excitation diagrammed in Fig. 11-31 for the retina, the contrast neurons of the LGN, and the various classes of cortical neurons. Because of the nonlinear projection of the retina onto the visual cortex (cf. p. 251), the spatial distribution of excitation in a class of cortical neurons is not as uniform as shown in Fig. 11-31 [12, 18, 19].

Optical illusions. Some of the familiar **optical illusions** can be explained by the organization of the receptive fields of cortical visual neurons. For example, an observer viewing Fig. 11-32 A without preconceptions sees a white square on a somewhat darker background. The compelling impression of a complete outline is presumably caused by the excitation of cortical neurons with complex receptive fields that (like the neuron of Fig. 11-30 C) respond maximally when contours in a certain orientation intersect. The Müller-Lyer illusion, shown in Fig. 11-32 B, indicates that even for the "simple" perception of the length of a line the excitation of cortical neurons with complex receptive fields plays a role, for one's impression of the length of the vertical line is affected by the angle between it and the lines pointing out to the side.

Figure and background in shape perception. Looking at Fig. 11-32 C one sees either the silhouette of a black vase (or

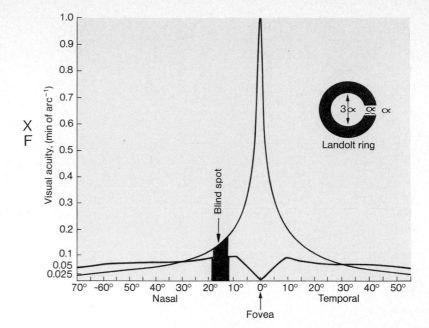

Fig. 11-33. *Dependence of visual acuity (ordinate) on position in the visual field (abscissa). Black curve: photopic vision, red curve: scotopic vision.* Visual acuity was measured with the Landolt ring (inset). This figure can be used to demonstrate the blind spot, by viewing the cross F monocularly with the right eye from a distance of ca. 32 cm. Then the Landolt ring falls in the blind spot and is no longer seen

candlestick) on a white background or two white profiles smiling at one another against a black background. It is impossible to perceive the black figure and the white profiles *simultaneously* as shapes. If one continues to gaze at the picture one cannot prevent figure and background from alternating. Thus visual form recognition involves neuronal operations in the higher visual centers other than signal processing by the complex and hypercomplex neurons discussed above.

Constancy of shape and size. As a rule we see the things in our surroundings unchanged in shape and size, even if the angular extent and shape of their images on the retina change. For example, when a boy cycles past he always seems the same size, regardless of distance. The wheels of the bicycle are still perceived as circular even when their images on the retina have become narrow ellipses. In the phenomenon of **shape- and size-constancy,** experience helps to determine how we see our environment. In the case of size-constancy there are additional neuronal mechanisms independent of experience. Evidently the degree of *convergence* and *accommodation,* which depends on the distance between the eye and the object viewed, is a factor in the central processing of visual information. Spherical lenses and prisms can be combined in such a way that when an object is viewed through them the functional coupling of accommodation and convergence is eliminated. In this experiment an object that forms an image of constant angular extent on the retina appears smaller, the more the eyes converge and/or the more strongly they accommodate. Such findings suggest a **feedback** of the signals from the neuron systems controlling convergence and accommodation (cf. p. 238) to the sensory parts of the central visual system.

Visual agnosia and alexia. The multiple mapping of the retinal pattern of excitation onto the spatial excitation patterns of cortical neurons constitutes an important mechanism for the visual **preprocessing of symbols** in the brain. We do not yet know what neuronal operations are responsible for the eventual **symbol recognition** – the discrimination of an "A" from a "B" or of a tulip from a daffodil – of which the brain is capable. It is known that signals are transmitted from the neuron systems in the visual cortex to higher association fields in the parietal cortex. If oc-

cipito-parietal association fields are damaged, visual shape recognition is disturbed **(visual agnosia).** Functional failure of certain visual association fields of the left hemisphere of the brain associated with the sensory speech region can result in an isolated impairment of reading ability **(alexia).**

The Measurement of Visual Acuity

The image of an object fixated with the eyes in the normal position is projected onto the fovea centralis of each eye. Everyday experience teaches us that in photopic vision acuity is greatest in the region of the fixation site and decreases from there to the periphery of the visual field (Fig. 11-33). The physician ordinarily determines visual acuity at the point of greatest acuity, by instructing the patient to fixate a standardized target. The most common measure of visual acuity in North America and parts of Europe is the Snellen fraction:

$$V = d/D \qquad (11)$$

where d is the distance at which a symbol can be discriminated, and D is the distance at which that symbol subtends one minute of arc. The symbols in this case are letters in a Snellen chart. In practice, the chart is set at a standard distance from the patient, usually 20 feet, and D is calculated from the size of the smallest letters the patient can read. For people with normal vision D is the same as the test distance, so that the Snellen fraction is 20/20.

An alternative procedure is to determine the angular extent α of the gap in a Landolt ring that is just detectable by the subject. The visual acuity, or "visus", is then given by $V = 1/\alpha$ and has units of (minutes of arc)$^{-1}$. The visus for normal acuity (discrimination of a target subtending 1 minute of arc) is thus 1/minute of arc.

When visus is measured after refractive errors have been corrected with glasses the result is called **visus con correctione**(visus c. c.), and that measured without glasses is called **visus sine correctione** (visus s. c.).

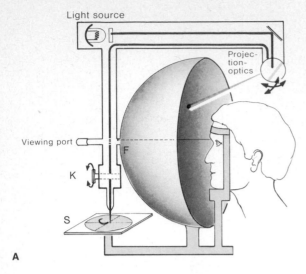

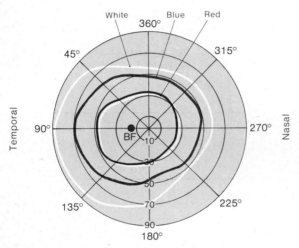

B Visual field of the left eye

Fig. 11-34. A *Perimeter apparatus,* diagrammatic. The field of view **B** is measured monocularly. The eye of the patient is positioned at the center of the perimeter hemisphere. The patient fixates a point at the pole of the perimeter. The examining physician checks his fixation by looking through the viewing port and moves a light spot over the perimeter surface by adjusting the projection optics with the knob K. The light spot can have various sizes, luminances and colors. The subject makes a signal as soon as he sees the light spot, and its position at this time is recorded on a card on the stage S. **B** Result of a measurement of the normal visual-field boundaries with white, blue and red light. BS, blind spot. The fixation point is the center of the concentric circles, which demark distance from the fixation point (in degrees of arc)

The decrease in acuity from the fovea to the periphery in photopic vision is caused by three factors:
(i) The quality of the image formed by the dioptric apparatus is better in the region of the fovea than in the peripheral region.
(ii) The density of cones is greatest in the fovea (Fig. 11-14).
(iii) The size of the receptive fields of retinal and cortical neurons increases with distance from the fovea.

Contour acuity and point acuity. Tests of visual acuity with Snellen charts or Landolt rings also test the perception of contour and shape. **Contour acuity** is always greater than **point acuity.** Point visual acuity is the reciprocal of the distance (in minutes of arc) by which two small points of light must be separated in order to be just detected as separate. Contour visual acuity is the reciprocal of the smallest interruption in a contour (in minutes of arc) that can be detected as a step in the intensity scale [13, 24, 29].

Measurement of the Visual Field by Perimetry

The monocular visual field is the part of the visual environment perceptible with one gaze-fixed motionless eye. The total visual field comprises all points in space that can be perceived with both (motionless) eyes. Within the total visual field is a region that can be seen with both eyes, the **binocular visual field,** on either side of which is a region visible by only one eye, the monocular crescent. Even with the head motionless, of course, a region greater than the "total" visual field can be brought into view by eye movements (field of gaze).

The loss of visual sensation in one part of the visual field is called a visual field defect. When a visual field defect is surrounded by normal visual field, it is called **scotoma.** Visual field defects can be caused by damage to either the retina or the visual pathway. The boundaries of the normal or abnormal visual field are mapped and the locations of scotomas identified by means of **perimetry** (Figs. 11-34. 11-35). For precise perimetry the state of adaptation and the size, intensity and spectral composition of the stimulus light must be exactly defined. From the nature of the visual field defects the physician can deduce the site of damage within the visual pathway – assuming, of course, that he knows the anatomical relationships discussed on p. 251.

The visual field in the light-adapted state is greater for light/dark perception than for color perception (Fig. 11-34). The color blindness of the extreme periphery of the visual field results from the low number of cones in this part of the retina (Fig. 11-14). In the visual field of each eye there is a physiological scotoma, the **blind spot.** This spot coincides with the place (the papilla) where the optic nerve passes out of the eye through the sclera; here there is no retina. The reader can demonstrate for himself the existence of the blind spot by means of Fig. 11-33 [3, 32].

The Visual Evoked Potential (VEP)

Perimetry, measurement of visual acuity and tests for shape perception are **subjective methods** of diagnosing damage in the retina or higher visual centers. The results of such measurements depend partly on the willingness of the patient to cooperate. The first steps toward **objective testing** of the function of the retina and the central visual system have been taken in recent years, with the development of methods for measurement of the ERG (cf. p. 247) and the **visual evoked potential** (VEP). The VEP is recorded by *electroencephalography* from the back of the head; it is elicited by repeated stimulation of the retina with patterns of defined intensity, extent and location in the visual field. Because the individual VEP is small and superposed on intrinsic rhythms of the electroencephalogram (p. 149), many successive responses are averaged by computer to give sufficiently reliable data. Different stimulus patterns, and monochromatic stimuli of constant energy but different wavelength, evoke VEPs with different properties (Fig. 11-35). In one of the most common neurological diseases, multiple sclerosis, the latency and amplitude of the VEP-waves are altered. Measurement of the VEP is thus of considerable diagnostic value [26].

One useful application of the VEP involves the presentation of checkerboard patterns generated on a TV screen. An electronic system simultaneously changes all the white squares to dark and all the dark to white, at a frequency of 1–5 Hz, so that a change of pattern is produced while the mean luminance in the stimulus field remains constant. The angular extent of the dark and white fields can be changed, to allow an objective estimate of visual acuity by means of the evoked potential.

11.5   Binocular Vision

Depth perception. When an object is viewed monocularly and binocularly in alternation, it appears basically the same except that binocular vision provides a greater **impression of spatial depth.** Because the eyes are located at different places on the head, their geometrical and optical properties cause the images of the surroundings on the two retinas to be different. This difference is an important factor in depth perception. The binocular difference decreases with increasing distance from the fixated object; therefore depth perception is poorer, the further away the objects being viewed [13, 15, 24].

The discrepancy between the images of the visual world on the two retinas can easily be detected in the following experiment. Hold your arm out straight and look at the thumb monocularly, with the left and right eyes in alternation. At each change of fixation the thumb appears to jump to a different position against the background. That is, as seen with the right eye the thumb covers certain objects in the space behind it, and as seen with the left eye it covers others.

Monocular depth perception. A certain amount of "three-dimensional" vision is possible even with one eye. In this case depth perception is based on the differences in size of familiar objects, occlusion by interposition, perspective and parallactic shifts when the head is moved. Binocular depth perception at distances > 6 m is also based on these signals.

The horopter. Despite the differences in mapping of the visual world onto the two retinas, objects in one's

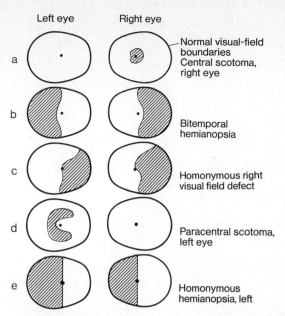

Fig. 11-35a–e. *Typical visual-field deficits,* diagrammatic. Possible sites of origin of the deficits are **a** right retina (fovea centralis) or right optic nerve, **b** optic chiasm, **c** left optic tract or left central visual system, **d** left retina or left optic nerve, **e** right optic tract or right central visual system. The locations of these lesions are shown in Fig. 11-28

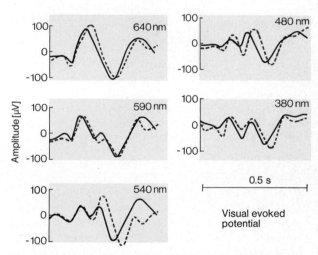

Fig. 11-36. *Visual evoked potential (VEP)* in two subjects (*black* and *red* curves). Brief flashes of monochromatic light at different wavelengths (480 and 640 nm) were presented at the beginning of each record. Each curve represents the averages of 30 responses. (After SHIPLEY et al., Vision Res. 1972)

surroundings are seen as *single*. The geometry of **binocular fusion** is based on the existence of **corresponding points** in the two retinas – that is, points functionally associated with one another – being excited by the same stimulus pattern. (As we shall see, however, central mechanisms also contribute to "single vision".) The positions of corresponding points on the

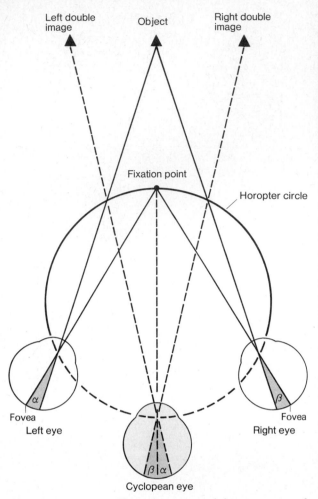

Left double image   Object   Right double image

Fixation point

Horopter circle

α   β

Fovea   Fovea
Left eye   Right eye

β | α

Cyclopean eye

Fig. 11-37. *Diagram of binocular vision and the construction of the cyclopean eye.* When an object is outside the horopter its image is projected to the right of the fovea in the left eye and to the left of the fovea in the right eye. In this case, binocular viewing gives an *uncrossed double image,* the position of which can be found by mapping the retinas of the left and right eyes onto the imagined retina of the cyclopean eye

Double vision. If one eye is displaced slightly with the finger while one views an object binocularly, different parts of the object are projected onto the foveae of the two eyes; the object is seen double. The images of objects in the visual field that are *not* on the horopter fall on *non*-corresponding retinal points and thus can also be perceived as **double.** The positions of these double images can be found from Fig. 11-37; here the object (the black triangle) is outside the horopter, so that its image lies to the left of the fovea on the retina of the right eye, and to the right of the fovea on the retina of the left eye. From the positions of the two images in the cyclopean eye one can find the positions in space of the apparent double objects. With an object in the position shown in Fig. 11-37 the double images are **uncrossed** – the left eye sees the object to the left of its actual position (and of the fixation point), and the right eye sees it to the right. **Crossed double images** appear when the object is between the eye and the horopter.

The production of crossed and uncrossed double images can be observed by the **two-finger experiment.** With a white wall as background, hold your right index finger about 20 cm away from your eyes in the horizontal plane and your left index finger about 20 cm behind the right index finger. When you fixate the closer of the two fingers, the one further away is seen double. Now close left and right eye in alternation, and you will find that you see **uncrossed double images** of the left finger. Next fixate the more distant finger; now the closer finger appears double, and alternate monocular fixation reveals that the **double images are crossed.**

In this experiment the "tolerance limit" for binocular fusion can also be found. Fixate the nearer index finger and bring the more distant one up until it touches the nearer one. Now the more distant finger appears single. As you move the more distant finger slowly away, you will see it "fall apart" and become double a few centimeters behind the closer, fixated finger.

Binocular rivalry. One might conclude from the preceding considerations that all the objects in sight that are not on the horopter at any moment must be seen double, because their images do not fall on corresponding areas of the retina. But ordinarily when the visual environment is well structured such disturbing double images are not perceived. One of the mechanisms by which seeing double is prevented is the relatively low visual acuity of the peripheral retina (cf. p. 255). The perception of double images is also suppressed by a **binocular** inhibitory mechanism in the central visual system.

This "binocular rivalry" can be observed for the region of the fovea in the following experiment. Hold a paper tube about 30 cm long and 3–4 cm in diameter in front of each eye. Now

retinas can be found by construction of the "cyclopean eye" (Fig. 11-37). The cyclopean eye is defined as a structure in which the retinas of the two eyes are superimposed in such a way that the foveas coincide and the coordinates of each retina correspond to those with the eyes in the normal position in the head while looking forward.

The image of an object falls on corresponding points in the two retinas if the object is on the **horopter.** The horopter is the curved surface on which lie the nodal points (p. 235) of the optical systems of the two eyes (and of the cyclopean eye) and the fixation point; for each fixation point there is a different horopter, defined by the relative orientations of the optical axes (i. e., the position of the fixation point) [15]. The horizontal section through the horopter is the *horopter circle* (Fig. 11-37).

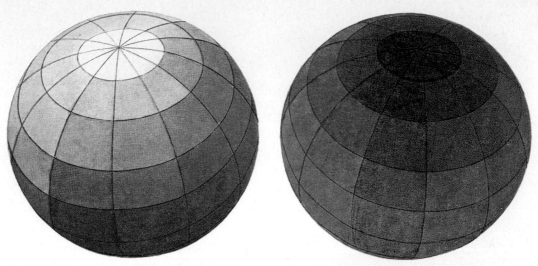

Fig. 11-38. *The color sphere* of Ph. O. RUNGE (1810), a non-metric representation of color space

when you look through these tubes with both eyes simultaneously, fixating a quarter with one eye and a postage stamp with the other, you do not see a single "quarterstamp". As a result of binocular inhibition, perception of the stamp alternates in time with perception of the coin. Sometimes parts of the two are seen simultaneously, but they are always *next to one another* rather than superimposed.

Horizontal disparity and binocular fusion. With the head in the normal position, a three-dimensional object at a finite distance from the eye is, for geometrical-optical reasons, projected onto the retina in such a way that the images on the left and right retinas are shifted horizontally. This difference is called **horizontal disparity**. In the example of Fig. 11-37 the horizontal disparity of the two images equals the sum of the angles $\alpha + \beta$. A binocularly viewed object breaks up perceptually into two images when a certain degree of horizontal disparity is exceeded. The degree of horizontal disparity *below* this tolerance limit contributes to the impression of spatial depth. Binocular fusion *and* depth perception thus occur when the points of an object are imaged on corresponding **areas** in the two retinas and do not exceed a certain horizontal disparity. The extent of these corresponding retinal areas probably corresponds to the size of the excitatory receptive fields of binocularly activated neurons in the visual cortex (cf. p. 253).

Strabismus. When a fixated object is not projected onto corresponding areas in the two foveae, the situation is called squint or **strabismus.** Strabismus of sudden onset, owing to paralysis of an extrinsic eye muscle (p. 264), causes the appearance of **double images** with every eye movement involving the paralyzed muscle. Accurate description of the double images (position, crossed or uncrossed) seen when the patient looks in different directions is an important diagnostic aid in determining which of the extraocular muscles is affected. When squinting occurs in early childhood as a result of disturbances in the coor-

dination of binocular eye movements, **strabismic amblyopia** usually develops in one eye: differentiated visual stimuli are seen only with one eye, whereas shape recognition by the amblyopic eye is greatly impaired. This deficit is caused not by a disturbance of retinal function in the amblyopic eye, but rather by a change in the processing of signals in the central visual system. Strabismus can often be prevented from developing into amblyopia by various means – correction with lenses of the hyperopia that is often present, exercising the eye muscles, and if necessary surgical correction of the squint in preschool children [3, 13, 15, 32].

11.6 Color Vision

Colors and the Measurement of Color

The phenomenon of color vision makes it especially clear that perception depends not only on the stimulus and the receptors, but also on processing within the nervous system. The different regions of the visible spectrum (Fig. 11-1) appear differently colored to us, with a *continuous* change in sensation over the range violet, blue, green, yellow and red. On the other hand, we perceive colors – the purple tones produced by a mixture of red and blue light – that are not present in the spectrum. Very different physical stimulus conditions can give rise to identical color perceptions; spectral yellow, for example, cannot be distinguished from a certain **additive mixture** of spectral green and spectral red (cf. p. 260).

The **laws of color vision** derived from psychophysical measurements describe the *phenomenological structure* of color perception. For over 100 years theories of the physiology of color vision have been developed from these laws, and for the last 25 years or so it has

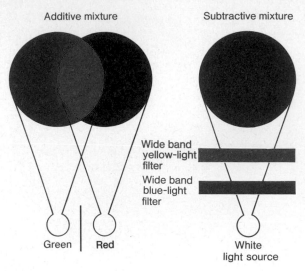

Additive mixture   Subtractive mixture

Wide band
yellow-light
filter

Wide band
blue-light
filter

Green | Red   White
light source

Fig. 11-39. Diagram of an *additive* and a *subtractive* color mixture

been possible to test these theories directly by electrophysiological recording from single receptors and nerve cells of the visual system.

The phenomenological structure of color perception. The visual world of a person with normal color vision exhibits an enormous variety of color nuances. About 7 million different **color valencies** can be distinguished. These can be grouped in two great classes: **chromatic and achromatic valencies.** The **achromatic valencies** comprise the "natural series" from the brightest white through the various shades of gray to the deepest black sensation, produced by simultaneous contrast (p. 249). The **chromatic valencies** of the *surface colors* of objects are characterized by three phenomenological attributes: **hue, saturation** and **lightness.** In the case of luminous color stimuli (e. g., a colored light source) the dimension "lightness" is replaced by the **luminance** (brightness). On p. 234 it was noted that monochromatic light stimuli of the same energy but different wavelengths give rise to different sensations of brightness. The spectral brightness curves (or spectral sensitivity curves) for photopic and scotopic vision (Fig. 11-1) are constructed from systematic measurements of the radiant energy necessary to give different monochromatic light stimuli an equal subjective brightness.

The **hues** form a "natural" **continuum** that can be represented qualitatively as a *color circle* with the sequence red, yellow, green, blue, purple and back to red. *Hue* and *saturation* together determine the **chromaticity** or shade of a color. Saturation is determined by the content of white or black. Spectral red mixed with white, for example, gives the shade pink. The color valencies can be represented in a three-dimen-

sional "color solid". Fig. 11-38 shows an early, non-metric representation of one kind of **color solid,** the *color sphere* of the German painter PHILIPP OTTO RUNGE (1810). Every color valency is represented by a particular place on or in the color sphere, which can be used to describe the most important **qualitative** properties of color perception, as follows.
1. The perception of all color valencies in the color solid forms a continuum; that is, adjacent color valencies merge with one another without stepwise changes.
2. Every position in the color solid can be precisely defined by three quantities.
3. The color solid has a polar structure – the **complementary colors** black-white, green-red and blue-yellow are arranged as opposing pairs.

In the modern **metric** color systems the perception of color is subdivided according to the "dimensions" hue, saturation and lightness, taking due account of the *color-mixing laws* discussed below, to give steps of identical sensation. In metric three-dimensional systems the simple color sphere is deformed into a non-spherical color solid. The goal of these metric color systems (in Germany the DIN color system DIN-Norm 6164 by M. RICHTER is used) is not a physiological *explanation* of color vision but rather an unambiguous *description* of color perception. Nevertheless, when a comprehensive physiological theory of color vision is put forward (there is none as yet) it will have to account for the structure of the metric color systems.

Color mixtures. An **additive** color mixture is produced when light of different wavelengths falls onto the same spot on the retina. In the *anomaloscope,* an instrument used for the diagnosis of disturbances in color vision (cf. pp. 263 f.), one color (e. g., spectral yellow, 589 nm) is projected onto one half of a circle and a mixture of colors (e. g., spectral red, 671 nm, and green, 546 nm) onto the other. An additive color mixture can be found that will give a sensation identical to the spectral color, by the following *"color-mixing equation"* (Fig. 11-39):

$$a \cdot (\text{red}, 671) + b \cdot (\text{green}, 546) \cong c \cdot (\text{yellow}, 589)$$
$$(11)$$

The symbol $\cong$ signifies *equivalence of sensation* and has no mathematical significance; a, b and c are luminosity coefficients. A person with normal color vision would set the coefficient of the red component at about 40, and that of the green component at 33 relative units (the yellow component being 100).

When two monochromatic light stimuli, one between 430 nm and 555 nm and the other between 492 nm and 660 nm, are mixed additively, the hue of the resulting color mixture is either white or corresponds to a spectral color at a wavelength *between* those of the mixed light stimuli. But if the wavelength of one of the monochromatic lights is above 660 nm and that of the other is below 430 nm, **purple hues** are produced that cannot be found in the spectrum.

The color white. For every hue in the color circle there is another hue in the circle that when mixed with the first gives the color **white.** The constants (weighting factors a and b) of this mixing equation

$$a\{F_1\} + b\{F_2\} \cong K\{white\} \tag{12}$$

depend on the definition of "white". The hues in any pair F_1, F_2 that satisfies Eq. (12) are called **complementary colors.**

Subtractive color mixing. Subtractive color mixing differs from additive color mixing, being a purely physical process. When white light is sent through a broad-band yellow filter followed by a broad-band blue filter, the resulting subtractive color mixture is green, because only the green part of the spectrum is passed by both filters (Fig. 11-39). A painter who mixes pigments is producing a subtractive color mixture, because the individual pigment granules act as chromatic broad-band filters.

Trichromacy. In the case of normal color vision, any given hue (F_4) can be produced by additive mixing of three suitably chosen hues F_1–F_3; this situation is described by the unique and sufficient sensation equation

$$a\{F_1\} + b\{F_2\} + c\{F_3\} \cong d\{F_4\} \tag{13}$$

By international convention the **primary colors** F_1, F_2 and F_3 chosen for construction of the modern color systems are spectral colors with the wavelengths 700 nm (red), 546 nm (green) and 435 nm (blue). For additive mixing to give the color **white** the weighting factors a, b, c of these primary colors are related as

$$a + b + c = d = 1 \tag{14}$$

The results of experiments in sensory physiology based on Eqs. (11) through (14) can be represented geometrically by the **chromaticity diagram** shown in Fig. 11-40 ("color triangle"). This diagram differs from the three-dimensional representations in that it omits the lightness dimension. The color resulting from mixture of two colors in the diagram lies on a straight line between the two. Pairs of complementary colors can be found with this diagram by drawing straight lines through the "white point" (E).

The colors seen while watching **color television** are produced by additive mixing of three hues selected in analogy with Eq. (13) [9, 13, 14, 28, 33].

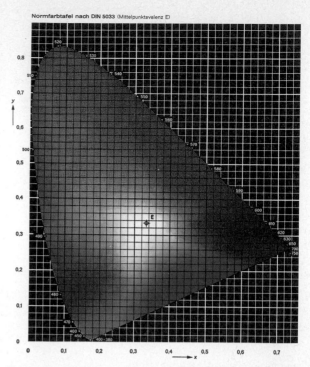

Fig. 11-40. *Chromaticity diagram* according to the standard DIN 5033. The white region surrounds the point E. The base of the "color triangle" is made up of the purple hues. The *additive mixed colors* composed of two arbitrary colors A and B lie on the line connecting A and B. *Complementary colors* are on lines through the point E

Theories of Color Vision

The two most important theories of color vision are described briefly in the following. Once there were vigorous disputes between their supporters, but today the two can be regarded as complementary theoretical interpretations of color vision. Each applies "correctly" to a different level of the afferent visual system. The synthesis of these rival theories was proposed 80 years ago by JOHANNES V. KRIES, in his **zone theory.**

The trichromatic theory of color vision. From Eq. (13) and the chromaticity diagram it follows that color vision is based on three independently acting physiological processes. The trichromatic theory of color vision (YOUNG, MAXWELL, HELMHOLTZ) postulates **three different cone types,** which operate as independent receiver systems in photopic vision; their combined signals are processed in a neuronal brightness system and a neuronal color system. This theory is supported by the color-mixing laws as well as many observations in sensory psychology. For example, at the lower limit of photopic sensitivity only three hues can be distinguished in the spectrum – red, green and blue.

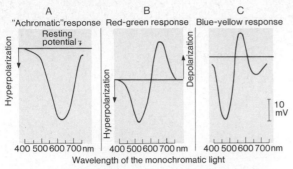

Fig. 11-41 A–C. *Dependence of the membrane potential of three different horizontal cells in the fish retina on the wavelength of monochromatic light stimuli (abscissa).* The wavelength of monochromatic light stimuli of equal energy is changed slowly. **A** Horizontal cell that responded with hyperpolarization in all regions of the spectrum. **B** Red-green horizontal cell; green light causes hyperpolarization and red light, depolarization. **C** Yellow-blue horizontal cell. The level of the resting membrane potential is shown by a black line in each graph. The amplitude of hyperpolarization is plotted below this line, and that of depolarization above it. [After SPEKREIJSE and NORTON: J. gen. Physiol *56* (1970)]

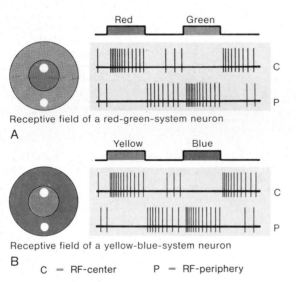

C = RF-center   P = RF-periphery

Fig. 11-42 A, B. *Simplified diagram of the spatial organization of 2 receptive fields* in either the ganglion-cell layer of the retina or the lateral geniculate nucleus of a mammal with color vision. **A** Nerve cell of the red-green system. **B** Nerve cell of the yellow-blue system. In color-specific receptive fields there is an antagonistic organization of RF-center and RF-periphery

The microspectrophotometric measurements of single cones shown in Fig. 11-16 and the color-specific response of the cone receptor potentials in the retinas of animals with color vision (Fig. 11-20) can be regarded as the first objective confirmation of the three-receptor hypothesis of color vision [5, 13, 16].

The opponent-process theory. A gray area enclosed by a luminous green ring acquires a light red hue as a re-

sult of **chromatic simultaneous contrast.** It follows that color-specific lateral inhibitory or excitatory processes in the visual system participate in color perception, for the spectral composition or the light reflected from the gray surface is not altered when the green surround is added. Chromatic simultaneous contrast and chromatic successive contrast (afterimages; cf. p. 250) are interpreted by the **opponent-process theory** proposed by HERING in the 19th Century. HERING inferred four **primary colors** *(Urfarben)* – red, yellow, green and blue – coupled by two processes, each antagonistically organized: the **green-red process** and the **yellow-blue process.** A third opponent process was required for the achromatic complementary colors **black** and **white.** Hering called these color pairs "opponent colors" *(Gegenfarben)* because of the polarized nature of the perception of these colors; that is, there is no "greenish red" and no "bluish yellow".

The opponent-process theory thus postulates antagonistic, color-specific neuronal mechanisms. For example, if green excites a color-specific neuron, red must inhibit it. These opponent processes proposed by HERING are in part detectable in the responses of nerve cells directly connected to the receptors. Some vertebrates with color vision have red-green horizontal cells (cf. p. 243), the resting membrane potential of which becomes hyperpolarized when their receptive field is illuminated with spectral stimuli between 400 and 600 nm, and depolarized when stimulated with spectral light of over 600 nm. Horizontal cells of the yellow-blue system are hyperpolarized by spectral light below 530 nm and depolarized by spectral light between 530 and 620 nm (Fig. 11-41). The ganglion-cell layer of the retina and the lateral geniculate nucleus also contain nerve cells with color-specific responses. As the opponent-process theory predicts, illumination of the RF-center by one part of the spectrum excites these cells, while another part inhibits. The spectral sensitivity of the RF-periphery is the mirror image of that of the RF-center in some cases, but in others it is the same (Fig. 11-42).

From the neurophysiological findings simple neuronal circuit diagrams can be derived to explain how three independently operating cone systems could be interconnected to produce the color-specific neuronal responses in the higher-order neuron systems. In these circuit diagrams, as in v. KRIESS' zone theory, the trichromatic theory is taken to be valid at the receptor level while the opponent-color theory applies to higher-order neuron systems [8, 14, 16].

Disturbances of Color Vision

The pathological changes that impair color perception can affect the visual pigments, signal processing in the photoreceptors or at higher levels, or the spectral transmittance of the dioptric apparatus. In the color-vision disturbances of genetic origin discussed below both eyes are almost always affected, though there are very rare cases of typical color-vision disturbance in only one eye. The latter individuals can describe the subjective perceptions of disturbed color vision, because they can compare the different sensations they experience with the right and left eyes.

Anomalies of trichromatic vision. The conditions called **anomalies** are relatively mild forms of color-vision impairment; they are inherited as a recessive trait carried by the X chromosome. Color-anomalous individuals are all trichromats – that is, like people with normal color vision, they require three primary valencies (as in Eq. 13) to describe completely the colors they see. However, they can distinguish fewer color valencies than normal trichromats, and in color-matching they use the red and green parts of the spectrum in different proportions. To satisfy the sensation equation (11) by adjusting the anomaloscope, **protanomalous** subjects add more than the normal proportion of red to the color mixture, and **deuteranomalous** subjects add more green than normal. In the very rare cases of **tritanomaly** the yellow-blue system is disturbed.

Dichromats. The various forms of dichromatopsia are also inherited with the X chromosome as recessive traits. Dichromats can describe **all** the hues they see with only two spectral colors (by the process of Eq. 13). In both **protanopes** and **deuteranopes** the red-green system is disturbed. The spectral brightness curve (Fig. 11-1) for photopic vision is shifted with respect to the normal curve. Protanopes have a maximum at 520 nm, and the maximum for many deuteranopes is at 580 nm. The protanope confuses red with black, dark gray, brown and in some cases, like the deuteranope, with green. The spectrum has achromatic regions between 480 and 495 nm as seen by the protanope, and between 495 and 500 nm as seen by the deuteranope. The very rare **tritanopes** confuse yellow and blue; the blue-violet end of the spectrum appears to them as shades of gray to black. The tritanope perceives an achromatic band in the spectrum between 565 and 575 nm [8, 16, 28, 33].

Total color blindness. Less than 0.01% of the population are completely color-blind. These monochromats see the world about as a person with normal color vision sees it in a black-and-white film – in various shades of gray. Monochromats usually have impaired light adaptation in the photopic region. Because their eyes are easily dazzled, monochromats discern

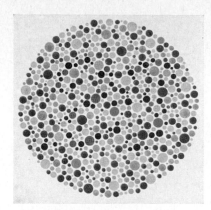

Fig. 11-43. Example from the series of "pseudo-isochromatic" charts of Ishihara. A person with normal color vision perceives the number 26, whereas the protanope sees "6" and the deuteranope, "2"

shapes poorly in daylight, which gives rise to the symptom of *photophobia*. Therefore totally color-blind people wear dark sunglasses even in normal daylight. Their visual acuity (p. 255) in the fovea centralis is reduced to less than 0.1 (minute of arc)$^{-1}$. There is usually no histologically detectable abnormality in the cones of the monochromat retina. Because monochromats have the normal spectral brightness curve in the scotopic region (Fig. 11-1), it is thought that their cones contain rhodopsin as the visual pigment; their dark-adaptation curves (Fig. 11-25, p. 249) are consistent with this view.

Disturbances of the rod system. People with abnormal rod systems perceive colors normally but their capacity for dark adaptation is severely restricted. The cause of this "night blindness" or *nyctalopia* can be a dietary deficiency of Vitamin A$_1$, the precursor of retinal (p. 244).

Diagnosis of abnormal color vision. Because color-vision disturbances are carried by the X chromosome, they are much more common in men than in women. About 0.9% of the male population are protanomalous, 1.1% are protanopic, 3–4% are deuteranomalous and 1.5% are deuteranopic. Tritanomaly and tritanopia are extremely rare. About 0.3% of the female population are deuteranomalous, and 0.5% protanomalous.

Because normal trichromatic color vision is essential for many professions (e. g., pilots, locomotive drivers, fashion designers) all children should be tested for color vision before they begin training for a particular kind of work. One simple test uses the "pseudo-isochromatic" charts of Ishihara (Fig. 11-43). These charts show areas covered with spots of different sizes and colors arranged to form letters or numbers. Spots of different colors are at the *same lightness levels*. People with disturbed color vision cannot see some of the numbers, depending on the colors that form them. By testing a sufficient number of hue combinations, with several Ishihara charts, color-vision impairment can be detected quite reliably. Precise diagnosis of disturbances in color vision is possible by color-mixing tests based on Equations (11) through (13).

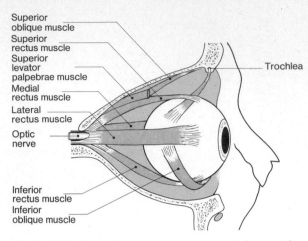

Superior
oblique muscle
Superior
rectus muscle
Superior
levator
palpebrae muscle
Medial
rectus muscle
Lateral
rectus muscle
Optic
nerve
Trochlea
Inferior
rectus muscle
Inferior
oblique muscle

Fig. 11-44. *Positions of the extraocular muscles and the eye within the orbit* (diagrammatic)

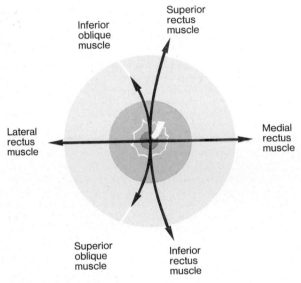

Inferior
oblique
muscle

Superior
rectus
muscle

Lateral
rectus
muscle

Medial
rectus
muscle

Superior
oblique
muscle

Inferior
rectus
muscle

Fig. 11-45. *Diagram of the actions of the extraocular muscles.* The arrows indicate the movement of the front pole of the eye (middle of the cornea) produced by contraction of each of the 6 muscles in isolation (from HERING)

11.7   Eye Movements, Movement Perception and Sensorimotor Integration in Vision

The motor apparatus of the eye. The human eye is moved by six extrinsic (extraocular) muscles, which are innervated by three cranial nerves: the *trochlear nerve* (IV) innervates the superior oblique muscle, the *abducens nerve* (VI) innervates the lateral rectus, and the *oculomotor nerve* (III) innervates the remaining four extraocular muscles (medial, inferior and superior rectus and inferior oblique) as well as the voluntarily contractible levator muscles of the upper eyelid (Fig. 11-44). Damage to one of these three cranial nerves results in *paralysis of the eye muscles* it innervates. The most important sign of eye-muscle paralysis is that the patient *sees double* when looking in a direction such

that the paralyzed muscle would normally contract to move the eye.

The cells of origin (motoneurons) of the three motor cranial nerves listed above are grouped as "nuclei" in the brainstem. The state of excitation of these motoneurons is controlled primarily by the nerve cells in the "gaze control centers" of the **paramedian pontine reticular formation (PPRF)** and the **mesencephalic reticular formation (MRF)** of the brainstem. The activity of these nerve cells determines the way in which the six extrinsic muscles of the left and right eyes interact. For normal binocular vision even the briefest glance must be coordinated so that the *same* object is focussed on the *fovea centralis* of each eye (cf. p. 258).

Fig. 11-45 diagrams the actions of the individual eye muscles to produce eye movement. The *primary action* is the movement produced by contraction of the muscle when the eye is initially in the resting position (looking forward). The directions in which the lateral rectus (outward turning or *abduction* of the eye) and medial rectus (inward turning, or *adduction*) muscles pull are almost independent of initial eyeball positon. By contrast, the actions of all the other eye muscles depend on the momentary position of the eyeball in the orbit (for details see textbooks of anatomy). It is also evident in Fig. 11-45 that an exactly *vertical* upward rotation of the eye, for example, can be brought about only by the simultaneous contraction of the inferior oblique and superior rectus muscles, with a simultaneous decrease in tone (corresponding to the rules for *antagonistic innervation;* cf. p. 86) in the superior oblique and inferior rectus muscles.

Measurement of Eye Movements

Eye movements can be recorded relatively simply in the *electro-oculogram* (EOG). This procedure makes use of the steady corneoretinal potential (cf. p. 247; Fig. 11-46). The eye is an electrical dipole, with the positive pole at the front and the negative pole at the back; as the eye rotates within the orbit each pole comes closer to one or the other of a pair of recording electrodes positioned at the nasal and temporal edges of the orbit *(horizontal EOG)* or at the upper and lower rim *(vertical EOG),* causing the voltage difference between the two electrodes to change. If only the *conjugate* horizontal movements of the two eyes are of interest, as in clinical *electronystagmography,* the electrodes on both sides are positioned at the temporal rim of the orbits.

The Binocular Coordination of Eye Movements

With regard to *gaze control* – that is, the movements of the two eyes together and of the eyelids, to allow fixation of different points in space – three different programs can be distinguished (Fig. 11-47):

1. The eyes can move with their axes in parallel, in **conjugate eye movements** upward, downward, or toward the left or right.
2. Shift of the fixation point between a near and a more distant position requires **vergence movements,**

in which the movement of one eye is approximately the mirror image of that of the other, relative to the head coordinates. When a point at a great distance is fixated the visual axes are parallel. When the gaze is shifted to a nearby object the visual axes converge *(convergence movement)*. Subsequent shift to an object further away requires a *divergence movement* in which the axes move apart. Vergence movements and conjugate eye movements occur simultaneously when, for instance, one shifts one's gaze from a faraway object on the right to a nearby object on the left.

3. **Cyclorotatory eye movements** in the frontoparallel plane accompany tilting of the head to the side. Even when the head is tilted rapidly through a large angle they amount to little more than 10° (cf. p. 278).

The Temporal Properties of Eye Movements

Saccades. When we look freely about us our eyes move in quick jerks (saccades) from one fixation point to the next. The saccades are separated by *fixation periods* lasting from 0.15 to ca. 2 s (Fig. 11-48). The amplitude of the saccades can be a few minutes of arc (microsaccades) or many degrees (e.g., when looking from the right to the left half of the field). The mean angular velocity of the eyes rises with saccade amplitude and amounts to 200–600°/s. The duration of a saccade ranges from 10 ms to ca. 80 ms, and is approximately proportional to its amplitude. Saccades of more than 10–15° are usually accompanied by supplementary head movements. During a voluntary visual search of the surroundings the head moves first and the eyes follow with a slightly delayed saccade. On the other hand, if a moving object appears suddenly in the peripheral visual field it triggers a *reflex shift of gaze* in which the first event is a saccade by the eyes. During the subsequent head movement the eyes move in the orbits in such a way that the fixated object remains focussed on the fovea (Fig. 11-48 D).

Fixation periods. Because an *eye tremor* a few minutes of arc in amplitude is always present (frequency components predominantly between 20 and 150 Hz), the eyes move slightly even during the fixation periods. During prolonged voluntary fixation slow "drifts" occur, which move the fixation point away from the fixated object. Microsaccades compensate the drifts and bring the object back into proper fixation.

Smooth eye movements. When a *moving* object is fixated, smooth *pursuit movements* of the eyes are required. The angular veocity of eye rotation here

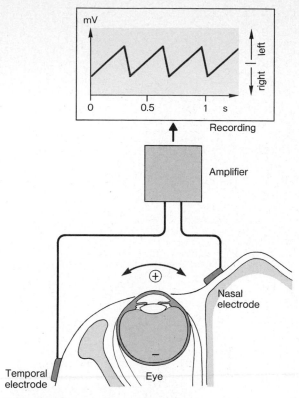

Fig. 11-46. *Diagram of the electrode positions in electro-oculography*

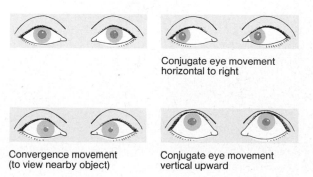

Conjugate eye movement horizontal to right

Convergence movement (to view nearby object)

Conjugate eye movement vertical upward

Fig. 11-47. *Conjugate eye movements and vergence movements*

corresponds approximately to that of the fixated object as long as it does not move more rapidly than 60–80°/s.

Small correction saccades are superposed on the smooth pursuit eye movements at variable intervals between 0.3 and about 2 seconds. The image of a fixated point on the object then remains within about 2° from the fovea. With object velocities above 80°/s the pursuit movements of the eyes are distinctly slower than the angular velocity of the moving object, so that its image moves across the retina. With object velocities between 80° and 180°/s the retinal displacement

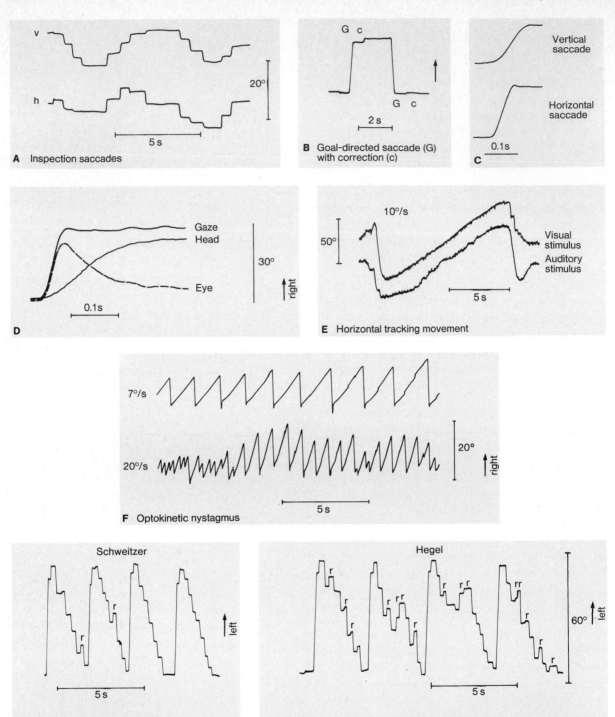

Fig. 11-48 A–H. *Electro-oculographic recordings of eye movements in man.* **A** Horizontal saccades when subject looks around freely. **B** Large goal-directed horizontal saccade (G) with small corrective saccade (C). **C** Horizontal and slower vertical saccades. **D** Eye and head movement recorded when a rhesus monkey reflexly shifts its gaze to a small light stimulus appearing suddenly in the right visual field (after E. Bizzi, Scientific American, October 1974). **E** Horizontal pursuit movements in tracking stimuli in a dark room: a small (0.2° diameter) horizontally moving light spot or a small loudspeaker moving at the same speed while emitting white noise. **F** Horizontal optokinetic nystagmus elicited by a moving pattern of stripes. **G** Horizontal eye movements in reading a text simple in both style and content (ALBERT SCHWEITZER's "Aus meiner Kindheit und Jugendzeit") and **(H)** a simply written text with difficult content (G. F. HEGEL's "Einführung in die Philosophie"). During reading of the conceptually more difficult text regression saccades *(r)* from right to left occur much more frequently, and the total number of saccades per line is greater while the speed of reading declines. (After GHAZARIAN and GRÜSSER, 1977)

of the image is compensated by additional large saccades.

These pursuit movements are normally coordinated with following movements of the head. Within certain limits, then, the *shift of gaze* resulting from the combination of head and eye movement corresponds to the movement of the object being viewed. Eye and head movements are coordinated in the gaze-control centers of the brainstem, which receive information about head position and movement not only from the vestibular receptors of the inner ear (p. 274) but also from the mechanoreceptors of the cervical joints. Pursuit movements of the eyes can also be elicited in the dark, by *auditory stimuli* (Fig. 11-48 E). Such movements are less regular than visual pursuit movements and, even at fairly low angular velocities of the moving stimulus, are interrupted by saccades.

If a motionless object is fixated and the head is moved, the eyes perform slow pursuit movements in a direction opposite to that of head motion. This can be readily observed in the mirror, as follows. Fixate the pupil of one of your eyes in the mirror and turn your head slowly to the right or left, up or down. The eyes move uniformly in the orbits, and appear to be standing still in space. These smooth eye movements are controlled by visual and vestibular inputs (cf. p. 268).

Optokinetic nystagmus. A periodic alternation between saccades and slow pursuit movements (nystagmus) occurs when a subject fixates a uniformly moved visual stimulus pattern. The same thing occurs, for instance, when a person riding in a railway car looks out the side window at objects in the (apparently) moving scenery. Both eyes simultaneously follow the visual pattern as it appears to move in a direction opposite to that of the train; the angular velocity of the eye movements depends on the speed of the train and on the distance of the object fixated. When the object is no longer in view a saccade returns the eye to a new, more central fixation point, which is then tracked by the subsequent smooth eye movement. This *optokinetic nystagmus* (OKN) is also produced when a person observes a measuring stick moved in front of him in a horizontal or vertical direction and tries to read the numbers. For more precise diagnostic or experimental measurement of OKN, horizontal or vertical light/dark stripes are moved, either attached to a cylinder around the subject or projected onto a hemicylinder in front of him. Parameters varied in such tests are the angular velocity and the direction of motion of the striped pattern. The *direction of nystagmus,* by convention, is the direction in which the eye moves during the quick phase (the saccade). For example, if a pattern of vertical stripes is moved to the right it elicits slow pursuit movements of the eyes to the right and quick phases to the left – that is, a left optokinetic nystagmus. By testing OKN one can obtain a quantitative measure of disturbances in the gaze-control system (Fig. 11-48 F).

Eye movements in viewing complex stimulus patterns.
The eye movements discussed so far have been predominantly vertical or horizontal. But when one gazes about in visually structured surroundings eye movements occur in all directions, and vergence

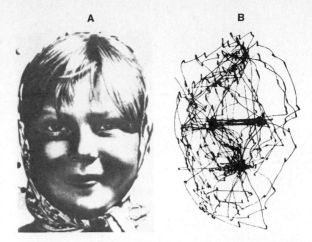

Fig. 11-49 A, B. *Two-dimensional plot of eye movements during viewing of a face* **(B).** An experimental subject looked at the photograph **(A)** for several minutes. (After YARBUS, 1967)

movements (cf. p. 265) are also present. When an experimental subject looks at a detailed picture, he changes his fixation point at intervals of from 0.2 to 2.0 s. Plots of these eye movements in two dimensions (Fig. 11-49) reveal that they, and the intervening fixation points, are determined chiefly by the *contours, contour interruptions, or contour overlap areas* in the stimulus pattern. Moreover, when one views a human face the eyes and the mouth are favorite fixation points. The first glance at a new face, as a rule, is directed toward the right eye, followed by saccades to the left eye and the mouth. When one looks at scenery the *horizon* is preferentially fixated. These examples show that gaze control is determined not only by the physical properties of the stimulus pattern but also by the "significance" of the visual signals to the observer. If a picture is observed long enough the sampling movements of the eyes create a "movement image" of the stimulus pattern (Fig. 11-49). The frequency of fixation of a particular spot is a measure of the "conspicuousness" of particular substructures in the pattern. Here "conspicuousness" is determined both by the stimulus pattern and by the state of the observer. Psychologists involved in advertising have tried to use eye-movement recordings to learn how well certain visual structures in advertisements "catch the eye" – a measure of their subliminal effectiveness.

Eye movements in reading. A particularly regular form of eye movement occurs during reading: the eyes move over the lines in rapid saccades, with fixation periods 0.15 to 0.5 s in duration between the saccades (Fig. 11-48 G, H). When the scanning process reaches the end of the line being read, the eyes make a single saccade to the left, back to the beginning of the next line. The amplitude and frequency of the reading saccades depend on the format of the text (size, subdivisions, system of capitalization), but are also influenced by the reader's understanding of

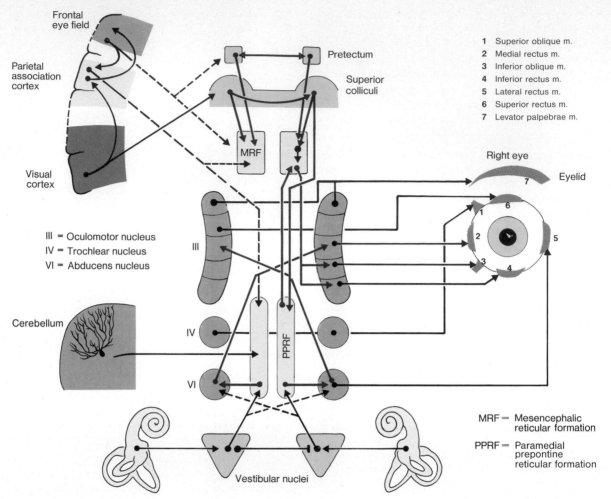

Fig. 11-50. *Diagram of the connections from and to the gaze-control and oculomotor centers of the brainstem, and of the innervation of the extraocular muscles*

the text. If the style of writing is unclear or the content difficult to comprehend, **regression saccades** occur more often (Fig. 11-48 H); these are saccades opposed to the normal direction of reading. The eye movements of a child learning to read also show many regression saccades. When *reading aloud* the amplitude of the saccades is reduced and thus the number per line is increased.

Adults who have completed a so-called "speed-reading" course do not exhibit the eye movements shown in Fig. 11-48 G, with fairly uniform sequences of saccades from left to right. Their eyes "jump" within a line and between the lines, and sometimes irregularly back and forth. Although this method of reading may raise the average rate of reading slightly, it is doubtful whether an increase in the amount of information absorbed per unit time is achieved, unless the text is very simple and its content highly redundant, as is frequently the case in political statements, etc.

The Neuronal Control of Eye Movements

Slow pursuit movements, saccades and fixation periods are different binocularly coordinated motor patterns. The varying programs for these different move

ments are controlled by different discharge patterns of the nerve cells in the gaze-control centers of the brainstem.

a. Horizontal eye movements. The horizontal eye movements are controlled by oculomotor neurons in the *paramedian pontine reticular formation* (PPRF, Fig. 11-50). Patients with a *unilateral lesion* in this region suffer from **paralysis of horizontal gaze movement** toward the side of the lesion. If the right PPRF is damaged, for example, when the patient intends to gaze straight ahead *both eyes* look slightly to the left of the midline; moreover, the patient can no longer voluntarily glance to the right or follow with his eyes objects moving toward the right. But if the patient turns his head to the left while fixating an object it is possible for the eyes to turn to the right, proving that the muscles themselves are not paralyzed. When the head moves to the left the receptor cells in the horizontal semicircular canals are excited. The vestibular-nucleus neurons are then activated by the primary afferent vestibular fibers (p. 274, Fig. 11-50) and in turn excite, by both mono- and polysynaptic routes, the motoneurons of the right lateral rectus and left medial rectus muscles, while the antagonists of these muscles are inhibited (horizontal "vestibulo-ocular reflex"; cf. p. 278).

b. Vertical eye movements. The vertical movements are also controlled by a neuronal system in the PPRF. The connections between these neurons and the eye-muscle nuclei, however, are indirect, by way of the *mesencephalic reticular formation* below the superior colliculi (MRF, Fig. 11-50). A *bilateral lesion* in the MRF causes paralysis of vertical eye movement, such that *voluntary* upward or downward rotation of the eye is no longer possible. But if the head is actively or passively tilted forward or back, vertical eye movements are elicited by the excitation of the receptors in the anterior vertical semicircular canals. This vertical vestibulo-ocular reflex is predominantly mediated by direct connections from the vestibular nuclei to the eye-muscle nuclei.

c. Excitatory inputs to the gaze-control regions of the brainstem. The gaze-control regions in the mesencephalic and pontine reticular formation are integration centers for incoming excitatory signals of diverse origin, all of which influence the eye movements. From the *superior colliculi* (Fig. 11-50) come signals serving chiefly to control the reflex changes in gaze direction elicited by moving objects that appear suddenly in the periphery of the visual field. The frontal eye field of the premotor cortex (Area 8; Fig. 7-2, p. 146) influences the gaze control system of the brainstem by way of connections, the details of which are as yet unknown. Electrical stimulation of the frontal eye field in one half of the brain produces conjugate horizontal eye movements to the opposite side. When a cerebral convulsion begins with a "focus of excitation" in this region, the patient is compelled to look "away from the focus".

Indirect connections by way of the cerebellar and vestibular nuclei mediate the influence upon gaze direction of the *Purkinje cells* in the flocculus of the cerebellum (p. 99). Lesions in the cerebellum chiefly disturb the smooth pursuit movements and the fixation periods, but the saccades may also deteriorate, becoming less precise. Patients suffering from large cerebellar lesions have disturbances of gaze holding and saccadic dysmetria. The cerebellum receives visual information mainly by way of the nucleus of the optic tract and the superior colliculi, and processes these inputs together with vestibular and proprioceptive signals.

The *visual fields of the cerebral cortex* (primarily Areas 18 and 19 of the visual cortex) participate in the control of eye movement chiefly by way of connections with the superior colliculi and the pretectal region of the brainstem. The voluntary eye movements required to follow irregularly moving objects (as in watching a butterfly flutter about a bush) are controlled primarily by these corticofugal neuronal connections. In man, undisturbed function of the visual cortex is a prerequisite for normal optokinetic nystagmus.

Eye movements, however, depend not only on visual stimuli but also on the internal state, attentiveness and interest of the observer. As everyone knows, of the multitude of different objects about us we choose to fixate on those of particular interest at the moment. The neurons responsible for this function are in the parietal cerebral cortex (especially in Area 7; cf. Fig. 7-2, p. 146). This part of the cortex includes nerve cells activated 50–200 ms before the saccades and during slow following movements. If this cortical region becomes nonfunctional on one side, no or lowered attention is paid to visual stimuli in the field of view contralateral to the affected part of the brain and the gaze is rarely directed to this side (visual neglect), even though there is no demonstrable disturbance of the *visual field* (cf. p. 257).

Because during reading the difficulty of the text determines the sampling movements of the eyes, the temporoparietal integrative cortex of the dominant hemisphere, including Wernicke's region (Fig. 7-20, p. 163) – a region important for the understanding of language – must also be assumed to influence eye movements. The neuronal systems mediating this influence, however, are unknown.

Reflex changes in eye movements occur, as mentioned above, whenever the position of the head is changed so as to excite receptors in the semicircular canals or macula organs (p. 275). These reflex eye movements are brought about by direct connections linking the neurons in the vestibular nuclei with the motoneurons of the eye muscles and with the gaze-control regions of the PPRF and MRF (Fig. 11-50). The oculomotor reflexes triggered by vestibular activity normally assist in "keeping" the fixation point while the head is actively moved. They are influenced by signals from the receptors in the neck joints to the vestibular nuclei or gaze-control regions. In the waking human the vestibulo-ocular reflexes are usually subordinate to other "voluntary" commands. But if *pathological excitation* of the receptors in the vestibular system or of the neurons in the brainstem vestibular nuclei should occur, this alone can determine the eye movements even when the person is awake. The result is vestibular nystagmus, dizziness when turning and a sensation that the stationary surroundings are moving. All of these disrupt spatial orientation (cf. p. 279).

Neurophysiology of the Control of Eye Movements and Gaze Direction

a. Horizontal eye movements. The anatomy of the gaze-control and oculomotor systems in the human brainstem closely resembles that of other primates. Therefore the results of microelectrode recordings in alert rhesus monkeys can contribute greatly to our understanding of gaze control in man.

Neuronal control of horizontal eye movements

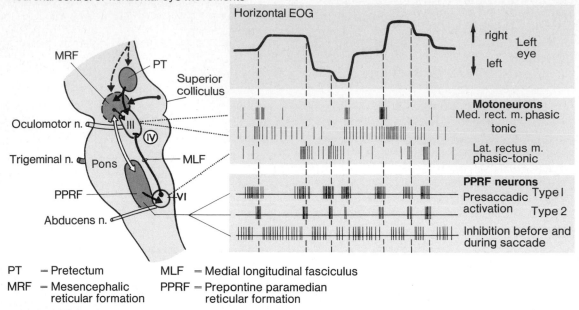

PT   = Pretectum
MRF = Mesencephalic
        reticular formation

MLF = Medial longitudinal fasciculus
PPRF = Prepontine paramedian
        reticular formation

Fig. 11-51. *Examples of neuron types found in the gaze-control and oculomotor centers of the brainstem, the activation of which is correlated with saccades or fixation periods.* (Schematized from publications by BÜTTNER, BÜTTNER-ENNEVER and HENN, 1975–1978)

In the PPRF of the rhesus monkey four classes of neurons have been found, the activity of which is correlated with horizontal eye movements (Fig. 11-51). *Type I* (long-lead burst neurons) exhibit a marked increase in activity 100–120 ms before each saccade, lasting until the saccade is nearly completed. In *Type II* (short-lead burst neurons) the onset of presaccadic activation occurs 12-20 ms before the beginning of the saccade. The activation of *Type III* (burst-tonic neurons) also begins 12–14 ms before each saccade, but in this case it extends into the fixation period, during which the activity is greater, the more the eye departs horizontally from the midline toward the ipsilateral side. The neurons of *Type IV* (saccade-pause neurons), finally, have spontaneous activity interrupted briefly before and during the saccade and returning to the relatively high initial level during the fixation periods (Fig. 11-51).

The neurons of Types I–III control the state of excitation of the motoneurons of the ipsilateral abducens nucleus, which in turn determines the state of contraction of the lateral rectus muscle. In addition to the motoneurons, the abducens nucleus comprises interneurons that excite the motoneurons of the contralateral medial rectus muscle by way of axons running in the medial longitudinal fasciculus (MLF in Fig. 11-51), and have inhibitory connections to the motoneurons of the ipsilateral medial rectus and contralateral lateral rectus muscles. This arrangement illustrates well the principle of antagonistic innervation.

Like the muscles of the limbs (cf. p. 60), the eye muscles are innervated by *phasic* and *tonic* motoneurons as well as intermediate forms. The cell bodies of the phasic motoneurons are larger than those of the tonic neurons; their axons innervate the thick muscle fibers of the extraocular muscles, which contract chiefly during saccades. The tonic motoneurons have thinner axons, with motor end-plates (p. 51) on the thinner, striated muscle fibers in the extraocular muscles. Histological studies have shown that these thinner muscle fibers lie in a layer near the orbit. As discussed in the chapter on muscle (p. 40), the thinner muscle fibers belong to the system for sustained tone ("maintenance work"). They therefore exert tension even during the periods of fixation.

b. Vertical eye movements. In addition to the neurons activated *before horizontal saccades* the PPRF contains neurons that discharge at a high rate shortly *before vertical saccades*. The axons of these cells pass to the rostral part of the MRF (Fig. 11-50), another gaze-control region. Here again there are nerve cells of Types II and III, activated *before vertical saccades*. These nerve cells send their axons to the motoneurons of the superior rectus, inferior rectus and inferior oblique muscles. Like those in the abducens nucleus (described above), these motoneurons in the oculomotor nucleus are of three kinds – phasic, tonic and phasic-tonic.

The Perception of Movement

Visual movement perception is a distinct *quality* of the sensory modality vision. It involves processing by "movement-specific" neuron systems in the visual cortex. Displacement of an image across the retina is not the only input analyzed here, for movements of the eyes, head and body must also be taken into account.

Thresholds for the perception of movement. Movement is the displacement of an object relative to a reference system regarded as motionless. There is both an upper and a lower velocity threshold for the visual detection of movement of an object with respect to a motionless background; these thresholds depend on the size of the moving object, the lighting conditions and the structure of the background. Sensitivity to movement within the visual field, like visual acuity, decreases with increasing distance of the excited part of the retina from the fovea contralis. Nevertheless, moving stimuli in the periphery of the visual field are *more conspicuous* than those in the region of the fovea. The first appearance of a moving object in the periphery as a rule triggers reflex movements of the eyes and head, which bring the image of the new object into the foveal region (cf. p. 252). The low-velocity threshold of foveal movement sensitivity in photopic conditions is 0.2–0.8 minutes of arc/s. The threshold rises when the moving object is in an otherwise visually "empty" field – for example, a small moving light source in an otherwise dark room. The movement of the sun in a cloudless sky is not detected, even when the eyes are protected from the brilliant light by dark sunglasses, whereas the movement of the sun setting behind trees or buildings on the horizon (ca. 0.25 minutes of arc/s) is just detectable if one pays close attention. With angular velocities of up to 300–400 degrees/s not only is the movement detected, but its direction as well. Above this range, up to ca. 600 degrees/s, one is aware of movement in the visual field but cannot tell the direction. Objects moving at still higher velocities appear to us only as light/dark stimuli, and give no impression of movement.

Adaptation of movement perception. After looking at a moving visual pattern for some time, one underestimates its velocity. The same thing happens when an observer himself has moved uniformly and linearly for a long time – for example, after driving over a long straight section of highway. In this case direct visual perception is a poor indicator of one's actual velocity. A person who ignores this phenomenon may be moving at a dangerous speed when he enters the curve of the exit ramp. Recordings from movement-specific neurons in the mammalian visual cortex have revealed adaptation effects suggesting that this neuronal adaptation might be the neurophysiological correlate of the psychological adaptation that leads to misestimation of movement velocity.

Movement aftereffects. One sign of the adaptation of movement-sensitive neuron systems is the presence of aftereffects following prolonged observation of a moving stimulus pattern. For example, if one gazes for 2–3 minutes at a piece cut out of a sheet of newspaper and placed on the rotating turnable of a phonograph, a motionless object viewed subsequently (e. g., a picture on the wall) appears to turn in a direction opposite to that of the rotation of the previous movement stimulus.

Phi-phenomena. When two stationary stimuli are projected onto different regions of the retina in rapid succession (with an interval of 20–200 ms), an *apparent movement* is seen. This *phi-phenomenon* occurs even if the first stimulus differs in form from the second. The movement seen when watching a motion picture is a series of phi-phenomena produced by the rapid sequence (18–24/s) of stationary images projected onto the screen. The responses of movement-specific visual neurons in the visual cortex to sequentially presented patterns in this frequency range resemble those to real movement of a stimulus pattern.

Movement Perception and Motion of the Observer

Objects are perceived to move relative to a reference system that is perceived as stationary. One's own body can serve as the reference system. If a person stands on a bridge and looks down at a river flowing rapidly under it, after a while he begins to feel that he himself is moving, together with the bridge, in a direction opposite to that of the flowing water. Similarly, a motionless observer surrounded by a horizontally rotating cylinder with vertical stripes has a subjective sensation that his body is rotating in the direction opposite to the cylinder movement. These experiences result from the direction-specific activation of neurons in the vestibular nuclei by visual signals elicited by the stimulus pattern. Excitation is probably sent from the retina to the vestibular neurons by way of the nucleus of the optic tract and the cerebellum. The connections between visual and vestibular neurons also underlie the dizziness one can experience when exposed to prolonged optokinetic stimulation while sitting still.

Eye Movements and Movement Perception

The movement of a visual pattern is perceived by *motionless* eyes when the image of the moving object moves across the retina. But the motion of a moving object is also perceived when its image remains *in the same place* on the fovea while the object is being followed by the eyes. On the other hand, when the direction of gaze is *shifted voluntarily* no movement of stationary objects is perceived even though during the

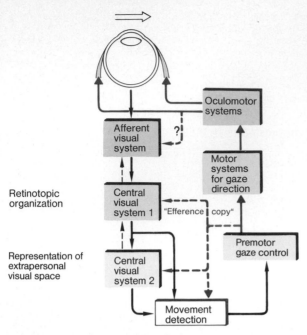

Fig. 11-52. Block diagram of the interaction of afferent visual signals and the signals fed back within the central nervous system (efference copy) from the premotor systems for gaze control. Interaction between efference copy and reafference presumably also occurs at a cerebral level onto which the extrapersonal space, rather than the retina (retinotopic organization), is mapped. The perceived movement is the sum of the afferent signals (movement of the retinal image) and the opposed signals of the efference copy. (After BEHRENS and GRÜSSER, 1979)

saccades their images are displaced on the retina. By contrast, if the eye is moved passively by pushing it lightly with a finger, the resulting displacement of the retinal image does cause the surroundings to be perceived as moving. Moreover, during nystagmus elicited by vestibular overstimulation or alcoholic intoxication the displacement of the retinal image during the slow phase of the nystagmus is perceived as movement of the surroundings. Finally, an afterimage can also be perceived to move; in this case there is definitely *no* possibility of retinal image motion and there is no visual reference system for relative movements whatsoever. That is, by fixating for some time a spot *next to* a bright light bulb and then darkening the room, one can produce a positive afterimage 1–2° to the side of the fovea, which seems to move *in the direction* of the eye movement when one tries to fixate it.

On the basis of such observations one of the pioneers of vision research, HERMANN VON HELMHOLTZ (1864), concluded that visual processing in the brain must include *comparison of the efferent motor commands for eye and head movements with the afferent visual signals from the retina*. This mechanism was formulated more precisely in the model of the *reafference principle* by v. HOLST and MITTELSTAEDT; it is

presented in the form of a block diagram in Fig. 11-52. The central commands to change the direction of gaze are transmitted to the motor eye-muscle nuclei by way of the gaze-control regions, and cause the two eyes to move. The result of this movement is a displacement on the retina of the images of all stationary objects, but no object movement is perceived because a copy of the efferent signals controlling the eye movement **(efference copy)** is retained within the central nervous system, where comparison with the signals reflecting retinal image displacement can establish the cause of the displacement. On the other hand, if a small, uniformly moved object is followed by the eyes (Fig. 11-48 E), the displacement of the retinal image is negligible but the movement is seen. Again, comparison of the retinal signals and the efference copy is thought to underlie the perception of movement.

The interaction between efferent motor signals and sensory (reafferent) signals formulated in the reafference principle is an example of the intermeshing of motor and sensory components in perception, as mentioned at the beginning of this chapter. Moreover, it is an advantage to the physiologist that the physiological phenomena interpretable by the reafference principle can be measured quantitatively [37].

11.8   References

Textbooks and Handbooks

1. BAKER, R., BERTHOZ, A. (Eds.): Control of Gaze by Brain Stem Neurons. Amsterdam–New York: Elsevier 1977
2. BACH-Y-RITA, P., COLLINS, C.C., HYDE, J.E. (Eds.): The Control of Eye Movements. New York–London: Academic Press 1972
3. CARPENTER, R.H.S.: Movement of the Eyes. London: Pion 1977
4. DESMEDT, J.E.: Visual Evoked Potentials in Man: New Developments. Oxford: Clarendon Press 1977
5. DARTNALL, H.J.A. (Ed.): Photochemistry of Vision. Handbook of Sensory Physiology, Vol. VII/1. Berlin–Heidelberg–New York: Springer 1972
6. DAVSON, V.: The Eye. 3 Vols. London: Academic Press 1962
7. DICHGANS, J., BIZZI, E. (Eds.): Cerebral Control of Eye Movements and Motion Perception. Basel: Karger 1972
8. FUORTES, M.G.F. (Ed.): Physiology of Photoreceptor Organs. Handbook of Sensory Physiology, Vol. VII/2. Berlin–Heidelberg–New York: Springer 1972
9. GRAHAM, C.H. (Ed.): Vision and Visual Perception. New York–London–Sidney: J. Wiley 1965
10. GRANIT, R.: Sensory Mechanisms of the Retina. London: Oxford University Press 1947
11. GRANIT, R.: Receptors and Sensory Perception. New Haven: Yale University Press 1955
12. GRÜSSER, O.-J., KLINKE, R. (Eds.): Pattern Recognition in Biological and Technical Systems. Berlin–Heidelberg–New York: Springer 1971
13. VON HELMHOLTZ, H.: Handbuch der physiologischen Optik. 2nd Ed. Hamburg–Leipzig: L. Voss 1896. Translation: SOUTHHALL, J.P.C. (Trans.), Treatise on Physiological Optics, 3 Vols. Rochester: Optical Society of America 1924–1925

14. HERING, E.: Grundzüge der Lehre vom Lichtsinn. Berlin: Springer 1920. Translation: HURVICH, L. M., JAMESON, D. (Trans.), Outlines of a Theory of the Light Sense. Cambridge, Mass.: Harvard University Press 1964

15. HOFMANN, F. B.: Die Lehre vom Raumsinn des Auges (1920). Berlin–Heidelberg–New York: Springer 1970 (reprint)

16. JAMESON, D., HURVICH, L. M. (Eds.): Visual Psychophysics. Handbook of Sensory Physiology, Vol. VII/4. Berlin–Heidelberg–New York: Springer 1972

17. JUNG, R.: Neurophysiologische Untersuchungsmethoden. In BERGMANN, G. v. (Ed.): Handbuch der Inneren Medizin, Vol. V/1, 4th Ed. Berlin–Göttingen–Heidelberg: Springer 1953

18. JUNG, R. (Ed.): Central Processing of Visual Information. A: Integrative Function and Comparative Data. Handbook of Sensory Physiology, Vol. VII/3 A. Berlin–Heidleberg–New York: Springer 1973

19. JUNG, R. (Ed.): Central Processing of Visual Information. B: Visual Centers in the Brain. Handbook of Sensory Physiology, Vol. VII/3 B. Berlin–Heidelberg–New York: Springer 1973

20. KOMMERELL, G. (Ed.): Disorders of Ocular Motility. München: J. F. Bergmann 1978

21. LANDOLT, E.: Die Untersuchung der Refraktion und der Akkommodation. In: Graefe-Saemisch's Handbuch der gesamten Augenheilkunde, 3rd Ed., Untersuchungsmethoden, Vol. 1. Berlin: Springer 1930

22. LANGER, H. (Ed.): Biochemistry and Physiology of Visual Pigments. Berlin–Heidelberg–New York: Springer 1973

23. LENNERSTRAND, G., BACH-Y-RITA, P.: Basic Mechanisms of Ocular Motility and Their Clinical Implications. Oxford: Pergamon Press 1975

24. LINKSZ, A.: Physiology of the Eye. Vol. I: Optics. Vol. II: Vision. New York: Gruner und Stratton 1950–1952

25. MÜTZE, K., NEHRLING, B., REUTTER, J.: Brillenglasbestimmung. Zürich: Verlag für Augenheilkunde und Optik 1972

26. PERRY, N. W., CHILDERS, D. G.: The Human Visual Evoked Response. Method and Theory. Springfield, Ill.: Ch. C. Thomas 1970

27. POLYAK, S.: The Vertebrate Visual System. Chicago: University of Chicago Press 1957

28. RUBIN, M. L., WALLS, G. L.: Fundamentals of Visual Science. Springfield, Ill.: Ch. C. Thomas 1969

29. SMELSER, G. K.: The Structure of the Eye. New York–London: Academic Press 1961

30. SPIGEL, I. M. (Ed.): Readings in the Study of Visually Perceived Movement. New York: Harper and Row 1965

31. WALLS, G. L.: The Vertebrate Eye and Its Adaptive Radiation. New York–London: Hafner 1963

32. WALSH, F. B., HOYT, W. F.: Clinical Neuroophthalmology. 3rd Ed. Baltimore: William and Wilkins 1969

33. WRIGHT, W. D.: The Measurement of Colour. 3rd Ed. London: Hilger and Watts 1964

34. YARBUS, A. L.: Eye Movements and Vision. New York: Plenum Press 1967

Research Reports and Reviews

35. BAUMGARTNER, G., HAKAS, P.: Die Neurophysiologie des simultanen Helligkeitskontrastes. Pflüg. Arch. ges. Physiol. *274*, 489 (1962)

36. BAYLOR, D. A., FUORTES, M. G. F.: Electrical responses of single cones in the retina of the turtle. J. Physiol. (Lond.) *207*, 77 (1970)

37. BEHRENS, F., GRÜSSER, O.-J.: Smooth pursuit eye movements and optokinetic nystagmus elicited by intermittently illuminated stationary patterns. Exp. Brain Res., *37*, 537 (1979)

38. BILL, A.: Uveoscleral drainage of aqueous humour in human eyes. Exp. Eye Res. *12*, 275 (1971)

39. BÜTTNER, U., BÜTTNER-ENNEVER, J., HENN, V.: Vertical eye movement related unit activity in the rostral mesencephalic reticular formation of the alert monkey. Brain Res. *130*, 239 (1977)

40. ECKMILLER, R., MACKEBEN, M.: Pursuit eye movements and their neural control in the monkey. Pflügers Arch. *377*, 15 (1978)

41. GERRITS, H. J. M., VENDRIK, A. J. H.: Eye movements necessary for continuous perception during stabilization of retinal images. Bibl. Ophthal. *82*, 339 (1972)

42. GRÜSSER, O.-J.: Grundlagen der neuronalen Informationsverarbeitung in den Sinnesorganen und im Gehirn. Informatik-Fachberichte Vol. 16, 234. Berlin–Heidelberg–New York: Springer 1978

43. GRÜSSER, O.-J., GRÜSSER-CORNEHLS, U.: Periodische Aktivierungsphasen visueller Neurone nach kurzen Lichtreizen verschiedener Dauer. Pflüg. Arch. ges. Physiol. *275*, 292 (1962)

44. GRÜSSER, O.-J., GRÜSSER-CORNEHLS, U.: Neurophysiologie des Bewegungssehens. Bewegungsempfindliche und richtungsspezifische Neurone im visuellen System. Ergebn. Physiol. *61*, 178 (1969)

45. HENN, V., COHEN, B.: Eye muscle motor neurons with different functional characteristics. Brain Res. *45*, 561, (1972)

46. HENN, Y., COHEN, B.: Quantitative analysis of activity in eye muscle motoneurons during saccadic eye movements and positions of fixation. J. Neurophysiol. *36*, 115 (1973)

47. HENN, V., COHEN, B.: Coding of information about rapid eye movements in the pontine reticular formation of alert monkeys. Brain Res. *108*, 307 (1976)

48. HAGINS, W. A., PENN, R. D., YOSHIKAMI, S.: Dark current and photocurrent in retinal rods. Biophys. J. *10*, 380 (1970)

49. HUBEL, D. H., WIESEL, T. N.: Receptive fields and functional architecture of monkey striate cortex. J. Physiol. (Lond.) *195*, 215 (1968)

50. HUBEL, D. H., WIESEL, T. N.: Cell sensitive to binocular depth in Area 18 of the macaque monkey cortex. Nature *225*, 41 (1970)

51. HUBEL, D. H., WIESEL, T. N.: Functional architecture of macaque visual cortex. Proc. Roy. Soc. (Lond.) *B 198*, 1 (1977)

52. HYVÄRINEN, J., PORANEN, A.: Function of the parietal association area 7 as revealed from cellular discharge in alert monkeys. Brain *97*, 673 (1972)

53. LYNCH, J. C., MOUNTCASTLE, V. B., TALBOT, W. H., YIN, T. C. T.: Parietal lobe mechanisms for directed visual attention. J. Neurophysiol. *40*, 362 (1977)

54. PEDERSON, J. E., GREEN, K.: Aqueous humor dynamics: experimental studies. Exp. Eye Res. *15*, 277 (1973)

55. SCHAEFER, K.-P.: Mikroableitungen im Tectum opticum des frei beweglichen Kaninchens. Arch Psychiat. u. Z. ges. Neurol. *208*, 120 (1966)

56. SCHILLER, P. H.: The role of the monkey superior colliculi in eye movement and vision. Invest. Opthal. *11*, 451 (1972)

57. TOMITA, T.: Electrical activity of vertebrate photoreceptors. Quart. Rev. Biophys. *3*, 179 (1970)

58. WURTZ, R. H., GOLDBERG, M. E.: The primate superior colliculus and the shift of visual attention. Invest. Ophthal. *11*, 441 (1972)

59. ZEKI, S. M.: Cells responding to changing image size and disparity in the cortex of the rhesus monkey. J. Physiol. (Lond.) *242*, 827 (1974)

60. ZEKI, S. M.: Colour coding in the superior temporal sulcus of rhesus monkey visual cortex. Proc. Roy. Soc. Lond. *B 197*, 195 (1977)

61. ZEKI, S. M.: Simultaneous anatomical demonstration of the representation of the vertical and horizontal meridians in Areas V2 and V3 of rhesus monkey visual cortex. Proc. Roy. Soc. Lond. *B 195*, 517 (1977)

12 Physiology of the Sense of Equilibrium, Hearing and Speech

R. KLINKE

This chapter is concerned with the physiology of two phylogenetically related sense organs. Not only are the organs of **equilibrium** and **hearing** close together anatomically, lying side by side in the petrous bone to form the **inner ear;** they are also derived from the same structure in evolution. Because in man the most important means of communication, speech, is mediated by the auditory organ, the **physiology of speech** is also treated in this chapter.

12.1 Physiology of the Sense of Equilibrium

Physiology of the Peripheral Sensory Apparatus

Introductory comments on anatomy. The vestibular organ is one part of the **membranous labyrinth,** which constitutes the inner ear; the other part is the organ of hearing (Fig. 12-1). The membranous labyrinth is filled with a fluid, the **endolymph,** and surrounded by another fluid called the **perilymph** (their compositions are given on p. 281). There are two morphological subunits of the vestibular organ – the **macula or-**

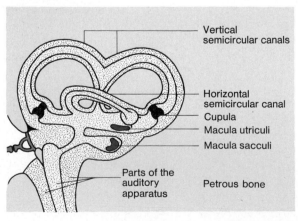

Fig. 12-1. Diagram of the vestibular labyrinth. The lymph spaces are in communication with those of the cochlear labyrinth

Labels in figure:
Vertical semicircular canals
Horizontal semicircular canal
Cupula
Macula utriculi
Macula sacculi
Parts of the auditory apparatus
Petrous bone
Perilymph
Endolymph

gans *(macula utriculi* and *macula sacculi),* also called **statolith organs,** and the **semicircular canals** *(horizontal* plus *anterior* and *posterior vertical* canals). In the region of the maculae, and in the semicircular canals near the so-called ampullae, there is a sensory epithelium within which the receptors are embedded. The sensory epithelium is covered by a gelatinous mass made up largely of *mucopolysaccharides.* In the macula organs this mass lies over the sensory cells like a pillow, and contains calcium-carbonate deposits in the form of minute **calcite crystals.** Because of these stony inclusions it is called the **otolith membrane.** In the semicircular canals the gelatinous mass is more a sheet-like membrane. This structure, the **cupula,** contains no crystals.

The receptors and the adequate stimulus. The sensory cells in the vestibular organ are of two morphologically different types [19], which evidently do not differ appreciably in their physiological properties. Both have submicroscopic hairs **(cilia)** on the free surface, and for this reason are called hair cells (Fig. 12-2). In the electron microscope it is possible to distinguish the **stereocilia,** of which each receptor cell bears about 60–80, from the **kinocilium;** each receptor has one kinocilium. The receptors are secondary sensory cells; that is, they have no neural processes of their own, but are innervated by afferent fibers from the nerve cells in the **vestibular ganglion,** which together form the vestibular nerve. Efferent nerve fibers also terminate on the receptor cells. The afferent fibers transmit information about the state of excitation of the peripheral organ, from the receptors to the CNS. The efferent fibers change the sensitivity of the receptors, but the significance of this influence is not yet entirely clear [31]).

Records from single afferent fibers in the vestibular nerve reveal a relatively high, regular **resting activity** – neuronal discharge produced in the absence of external stimuli. If the gelatinous structure is experimentally displaced with respect to the sensory epithelium, the background activity can be increased or decreased, depending on the direction of displacement. The change is brought about as follows: The cilia extend deeply into the mass, so that when it moves with respect to the sensory epithelium they are bent. This shearing of the bundle of cilia is the adequate stimulus to the receptor. When the direction of shear is toward the kinocilium (Fig. 12-2) the associated afferent nerve fiber is activated – that is, its discharge rate increases. If the bundle is bent in the opposite direction the discharge rate is reduced [19, 27]. Shear in a direction perpendicular to this axis is ineffective. The information is transmitted from the receptor cell to the afferent nerve ending by way of a receptor potential and an as yet unidentified synaptic transmitter.

The crucial point here is that *shearing* (bending) of the cilia is the adequate stimulus for the vestibular receptors, which increases or decreases the activity in the afferent nerve depending on the direction of shear. Thus there is a receptor-cell **orientation,** morphological with respect to the arrangement of the cilia and functional with respect to the effect on their activity.

The natural stimuli to the macula organs. As we have seen, the cilia of the receptor cells project into the otolith membrane. Because of the calcite crystals it contains, the otolith membrane has a considerably higher specific gravity (ca. 2.2) than the endolymph (ca. 1) filling the rest of the interior of the utricle or saccule. Their mechanism of action is based on this fact. If the organ is subjected to **translational (linear) acceleration,** the forces of inertia acting on endolymph and otolith membrane differ, because of their different density (force = mass · acceleration; the mass per unit volume of the otolith membrane is considerably greater than that of the endolymph). Therefore the whole otolith membrane slides very slightly over the sensory epithelium, just as a loose object slips forward in a car when the brakes are applied suddenly, because of its inertia. As a result the cilia are sheared, and the adequate stimulus is applied to the receptor [19].

A ubiquitous form of translational acceleration is the **acceleration due to gravity.** The macula organs are constantly under the influence of gravity. When the body is erect with the head held normally, the macula utriculi is about horizontal, so that the otolith membrane applies no shear force to the underlying sensory epithelium. But when the head is tilted the macula utriculi is tipped at an angle, and the heavy otolith membrane slides a short distance over the sensory epithelium – the cilia are bent and the receptors are stimulated. Depending on the direction in which the head is inclined, the discharge rate in the afferent nerve fibers will either increase or decrease. The situation is in principle the same in the macula sacculi, but they are roughly vertical when the head is in the normal position (cf. Fig. 12-1). Thus for every posi-

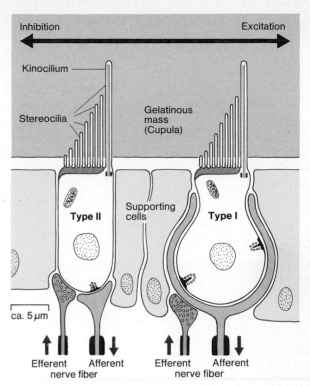

Fig. 12-2. Schematic drawing of two receptor cells in the sensory epithelium of the vestibular organ, with the associated nerve fibers. When the bundle of cilia is bent toward the kinocilium the discharge rate in the afferent nerve increases, and when the cilia are bent away from the kinocilium it is reduced

tion of the skull in space each otolith membrane has a certain position with respect to the underlying sensory epithelium. As a result, each head position is associated with a certain constellation of excitation in the nerve fibers, which is evaluated in the central parts of the vestibular system [17, 27]. In this way the organism obtains information about the position of the head in space. This is the most important task of the macula organs, although they of course respond to any other translational acceleration that may be imposed, in addition to that due to gravity. Because the cilia within the sensory epithelium of a macula are oriented in different directions, there is no general correlation between direction of head tilt and degree of nerve-fiber activation.

The natural stimuli to the semicircular canals. The second possible kind of adequate stimulus to the vestibular-receptor cilia is realized in the semicircular canals (Fig. 12-3). Even though the actual shape of the canals in the body is not a perfect circle (Fig. 12-1), in principle they operate as closed circular channels filled with endolymph. In the region of the ampulla the outer wall is lined with sensory epithelium (Fig. 12-3). Here the cupula, deeply penetrated by the cilia of the receptor cells, projects into the endo-

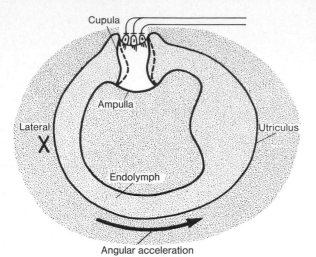

Fig. 12-3. Diagram of the left horizontal semicircular canal, seen from above. Except for the swelling that indicates the utricle, other parts of the labyrinth are not shown. Angular acceleration in the direction of the arrow (imagine that you are turning the book counterclockwise) deflects the cupula as shown by the dashed lines. If the head is tilted back the horizontal semicircular canal is brought into a vertical position (as though the book were set upright). In this situation warming at position X causes convective flow of the endolymph, which deflects the cupula in the same way (cf. p.278)

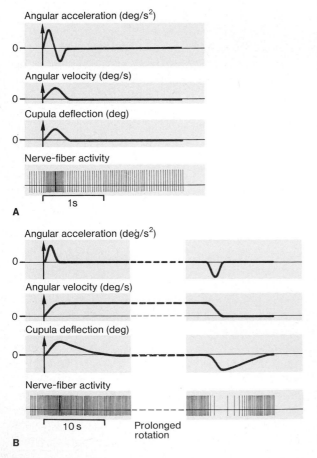

lymph. Lacking mineral inclusions, the cupula in a semicircular canal is of **exactly the same density** as the endolymph. Translational acceleration therefore does not affect the organ; when the body is accelerated in a straight line the relative positions of canal, cupula and cilia are unchanged. The effect of **angular** (rotational) **acceleration** is different. When the skull is rotated out of a resting position, the semicircular canals of course rotate with it, but because of its inertia the endolymph within them at first does not. Therefore the cupula, which recent research has shown to be suspended across the canal by fusion to the canal wall [30], is deflected in a direction opposite to that of the rotation as shown in Fig. 12-3. This deflection exerts a shear force on the cilia and thus changes the activity in the afferent nerve. In the horizontal canals all the receptors are oriented such that the kinocilium is toward the utricle. Therefore the activity in the afferent fibers is increased when the cupula is deflected toward the utricle *(utriculopetally)*. In the left horizontal semicircular canal, this happens during rotation to the left. In the vertical canals a *utriculofugal* deflection of the cupula (away from the utricle) activates the nerve fibers. Again, the activity of these fibers is evaluated in the CNS. From the discharge pattern in the afferent nerves of the total two × three canals, the brain extracts the information as to the angular acceleration acting on the skull. Because the head can be rotated about all three spatial axes – nodded forward or backward (pitch), tilted to right or left (roll), and turned about the long axis of the body (yaw) – it is necessary to have three semicircular canals. As required, they lie in planes roughly perpendicular to one another. In clinical examination (cf. p.278) it is important to know that the so-called horizontal semicircular canal is not exactly horizontal; its front edge is raised by ca. 30 degrees.

Peculiarities of cupular mechanics. First consider what happens to the cupula during a brief angular acceleration, as occurs in daily life when we turn our heads. It is evident in Fig. 12-4A that the deflection of the cupula does not correspond to the angular acceleration but rather to the momentary angular veolocity. Accordingly, the change in neuronal discharge rate as compared with the spontaneous rate approximates the change in angular velocity rather than the change in acceleration, even though the forces causing deflection of the cupula are forces of acceleration. By the time this brief movement is over the cupula has re-

◄

Fig. 12-4 A, B. Deflection of the cupula and activity in an afferent nerve fiber, with **A** brief rotation (e.g., turning the head) and **B** prolonged rotational movement (e.g., rotating chair). Note different time scales in **A** and **B**

turned to the starting position and the afferent nerve fiber is again discharging at the resting rate. Fig. 12-4B shows the fundamentally different behavior during prolonged rotation (for example, on a revolving chair). The initial acceleration builds up to a constant angular velocity, which is maintained for a long time. The cupula is deflected at first; during the phase of uniform rotation it slowly returns to the resting position, because the initially motionless endolymph is gradually set in motion by its friction against the canal wall. Eventually there is no further difference between the movement of the head and that of the endolymph. The elasticity of the cupula then brings it back to the resting position; at this point no further forces are acting to displace it. A rapid interruption of the constant-velocity rotation again deflects the cupula, now in the opposite direction. In other respects, however, this deflection has the same characteristics as that at the beginning of movement. A relatively long time (10–30 s) is required for the return to the resting position in each case.

The difference between the responses of the cupula to short and to long stimuli arises from the mechanical properties of the system cupula-endolymph, which behaves – though only to a first approximation – like a highly damped torsion pendulum [27]. But it should always be kept in mind that the forces leading to cupula deflection are **always exclusively** forces of acceleration, even though during the brief angular accelerations most common under physiological conditions the deflection of the cupula is proportional to angular velocity rather than angular acceleration.

The concept of cupular mechanics just described has recently become generally accepted [29, 30, 34], replacing the previous "swinging-door" model of cupular motion. It has also recently become clear that the deflection of the cupula under physiological conditions is very small. In experiments on animals rapid rotation of the body by only 0.005°, which deflects the cupula by even less than that angle, is a stimulus well above the threshold of the receptor cells in the canals [29].

The Central Vestibular System

The primary afferent nerve fibers in the vestibular nerve terminate chiefly in the region of the vestibular nuclei, in the medulla oblongata. On each side there are four different nuclei, distinct from one another both anatomically and functionally: the *superior* (BEKHTEREV'S), *medial* (SCHWALBE'S), *lateral* (DEITERS') and *inferior* (ROLLER'S) vestibular nuclei. The inputs to these nuclei from the vestibular receptors do not in themselves provide unambiguous information

about the position of the body in space, because the angle of the head, movable at the neck joints, is independent of that of the trunk. The CNS must know the position of the head relative to the trunk and take it into account in determining the position of the body as a whole. Therefore the vestibular nuclei receive additional neuronal inputs *from the neck receptors* (muscles and joints) [17]. If these connections are interrupted experimentally, the resulting disturbances of equilibrium resemble those following destruction of a labyrinth (cf. p.279). Somatosensory inputs from other joints (arm, leg) are also present.

The fibers leaving the vestibular nuclei make connections in other parts of the central nervous system that enable the reflexes necessary to maintain balance. These pathways are as follows [3, 17]:

a. The **vestibulospinal tract,** which ultimately influences γ-motoneurons of the extensors in particular, though some of the fibers go to α-motoneurons.
b. Connections to the **motoneurons of the cervical cord,** corresponding in principle to the vestibulospinal tract.
c. Connections to the **oculomotor nuclei** (cf. Fig. 11-51, p.270), which mediate the eye movements elicited by vestibular activity. These fibers run in the medial longitudinal fasciculus.
d. Tracts to the **vestibular nuclei on the opposite side,** by means of which the inputs from the two sides can be processed jointly.
e. Connections to the **cerebellum,** the archicerebellum in particular (see below).
f. Connections to the **reticular formation,** by way of which the reticulospinal tract is influenced; the latter is yet another (polysynaptic) route to the α- and γ-motoneurons.
g. Tracts via the **thalamus** to the **postcentral gyrus** of the cortex, which subserve the conscious processing of vestibular inputs and thus conscious orientation in space.
h. Fibers to the **hypothalamus;** these fibers are chiefly involved in the production of kinetoses (movement sicknesses; cf. p.279).

Its many neuronal connections, of which only the most important have been listed above, enable the vestibular system to play a central role in generating the motor outputs for posture and direction of gaze. The other main part of the CNS involved in these processes is the cerebellum, which receives some primary vestibular afferents (so-called direct sensory cerebellar pathway) in addition to the secondary vestibular neurons mentioned above. Both the primary and the secondary vestibular afferents (in mammals) termi-

nate as mossy fibers (cf. p.98) on the granule cells of
the nodulus and flocculus (archicerebellum) and in
parts of the uvula and paraflocculus (which belong to
the paleocerebellum). The granule cells excite the
Purkinje cells in these regions, and the axons of these
Purkinje cells project back into the vestibular-nucleus
region. The control circuit thus established regulates
the fine tuning of the vestibular reflexes. When the
cerebellum becomes nonfunctional owing to disease
these reflexes are disinhibited, with symptoms such
as increased or spontaneous nystagmus (cf. below
and the section on oculomotor regulation, p.264) and
disequilibrium, manifest by a tendency to fall, a strad-
dling walk, and overshooting movements, especially
in walking. These symptoms are part of the syndrome
called *cerebellar ataxia.*

The discharge patterns of the neurons in the vestibular-nucleus region are as diverse as their anatomical
connections, so that details are outside the present
scope. The interested reader is referred to the specialized literature [3, 19, 27].

The Vestibular Reflexes; Clinical Tests

Static and statokinetic reflexes. Equilibrium is maintained reflexly, without the primary participation of
consciousness. The reflexes involved are subdivided
into two groups, **static** and **statokinetic** reflexes. The
vestibular receptors and somatosensory inputs, especially those from proprioceptors in the neck region,
are responsible for reflexes in both groups. The **static
reflexes** bring about particular positions of the individual limbs with respect to one another, or of the
body in space – *postural and attitudinal reflexes,* respectively. The vestibular inputs for the static reflexes
are the macula organs. A static reflex easily visible in
cats, because of their vertical pupils, is **compensatory
rolling of the eyes,** which appears when the head is
turned about the long axis of the body (e. g., left ear
down). The pupils keep very close to the vertical position, the eye rolling in a direction opposite to that of
head rotation. This reflex is also present in man. The
statokinetic reflexes are responses to movement stimuli that in themselves take the form of movements.
They can be elicited by the semicircular canals and
the macula organs. These reflexes are treated in greater detail on p.96; one example is the turning of a falling cat to land on its feet.

One statokinetic reflex, **vestibular nystagmus,** de-
serves further discussion because of its special clinical importance. This is an *eye movement* elicited by
vestibular stimulation, which turns the eyes **against**
the direction of rotation so as to maintain the original
direction of gaze. Before the eyes have reached the

limit of their movement range they are suddenly
flicked back **in** the direction of rotation so that the
gaze is directed at a new region in space. This rapid
phase is followed by another **slow** movement against
the direction of rotation (cf. optokinetic nystagmus,
p.267).

When the body is turned about the vertical axis the
horizontal semicircular canals are essentially the only
part of the organ affected. Therefore deflection of the
cupulae of the two horizontal canals produces **horizontal nystagmus.** The direction of the two (quick and
slow) nystagmus components depends on the direction of rotation and thus on the direction of cupular
deflection; by convention, the direction of the nystagmus is designated by the direction of its quick phase.
That is, in a "right nystagmus" the quick phase is to
the right.

During passive rotation two factors tend to elicit nystagmus – the stimulation of the vestibular apparatus,
and the movement of the visual field with respect to
the subject. The vestibular nystagmus and the "optokinetic" nystagmus elicited by visual input act synergistically. The neuronal connections involved are
shown in Fig. 11-51, p.270.

Diagnostic significance of nystagmus. Nystagmus is used clinically as a *test of vestibular function,* usually in the form of **"postrotatory"** nystagmus. The subject is seated on a rotating chair
and turned at a constant speed for a long time. Then the movement is suddenly stopped. Fig.12-4 shows the behavior of the
cupula when such maintained rotation is interrupted. The stop
causes a deflection of the cupula in the direction opposite to
that in which it was deflected at the onset of movement, and this
deflection elicits a nystagmus. The term *postrotatory nystagmus*
is used for the nystagmus associated with the cessation of prolonged uniform motion. The direction of postrotatory nystagmus can be deduced from the record of cupular deflection; it
must be **opposite** to the direction of the previous motion. Records of the eye movements resemble those of optokinetic nystagmus (cf. Fig. 11-48, p.266). Such records are called **nystagmo-
grams.**
In testing postrotatory nystagmus it is important to eliminate
the possibility of **visual fixation,** for in optomotor reactions visual inputs predominate over vestibular inputs and under some
conditions could suppress nystagmus. For this reason the patient wears glasses with very strong convex lenses and a built-in
light source *(Frenzel's spectacles).* These make the patient myo-
pic and unable to fixate, while allowing the physician to observe easily the movement of the eyes. Glasses to prevent visual
fixation are also necessary for clinical tests for the presence of
spontaneous nystagmus – the first, simplest and most important
procedure in the clinical examination of vestibular function.
Another clinical procedure to elicit vestibular nystagmus is
thermal stimulation of the horizontal semicircular canal. It offers the advantage that each side can be tested separately. The
head of the seated subject is tilted back by ca. 60°, so that the
"horizontal" canal is precisely vertical. Now the **external meatus** of the ear is rinsed with cold or warm water. The outer edge
of the semicircular canal is very close to the meatus, and there is
sufficient heat transfer to cool or warm it. When warmed, endolymph has a lower specific gravity; the warmed part of the endolymph therefore rises, creating a current through the canal

which deflects the cupula and causes nystagmus (cf. Fig. 12-3, warming at **X**). Because of its origin, this form is called **caloric nystagmus.** Rinsing with warm water causes nystagmus toward the treated side, and cold water produces nystagmus in the opposite direction. The nystagmus of people with vestibular disorders differs qualitatively and quantitatively from the norm. It should also be mentioned that the slow phase of nystagmus is elicited by the vestibular system, the quick return movement being brought about by the pontine reticular formation (cf. p. 270).

The function of the macula organs can be tested by observing the eye-rolling response to head tilt.

Disorders of the vestibular system. Strong excitation of the vestibular apparatus is often associated with unpleasant sensations – dizziness, vomiting, sweating, rapid pulse etc. The term **kinetosis** (motion sickness) is applied to these symptoms [18]. Kinetoses are most likely to result from the action of stimulus constellations to which the organism is unaccustomed (for example, at sea). Coriolis accelerations are particularly effective in this regard, as are any discrepancies between visual impressions and signals from the vestibular apparatus. Infants and patients without labyrinths do not exhibit kinetoses.

Acute interruption of labyrinthine function on one side causes nausea, vomiting, sweating and the like, nystagmus toward the healthy side and vertigo toward the healthy side. There is also a tendency for the patient to fall toward the affected side. But often the clinical picture is complicated by ambiguity in the directions associated with dizziness, nystagmus and falling. In some diseases, such as Menière's syndrome, in which there is excessive pressure within the endolymph space on one side, the initial result is stimulation of the receptors, which naturally causes symptoms opposite to those of receptor destruction described above. In contrast to the dramatic effects of acute vestibular disorders, the **chronic elimination of one labyrinth** is relatively well compensated. The central vestibular system can habituate so as to reduce the response to unusual states of excitation [3, 27]. This adjustment is especially successful when other sensory channels provide corrective inputs – visual or tactile, for instance. Thus the difficulties experienced in the chronic condition become more pronounced in the dark.

Bilateral acute malfunction is rare in man. In animal experiments the symptoms are far less severe than those of unilateral destruction, for when the neuronal inputs to the vestibular nuclei are interrupted on both sides, symmetry still prevails.

Weightlessness (in space travel) does not affect the semicircular canals. The gravitational forces acting on the otoliths, however, are eliminated; therefore in all the maculae the otolith membrane takes a position determined by its own elastic properties. The resulting constellation of excitation never occurs on earth and has occasionally led to kinetosis, particularly during head movements [27, 28]. Habituation to the weightless state proceeds rapidly, but it must be kept in mind that astronauts are highly trained in this regard as in others, and perhaps are so little affected for this reason.

12.2   Physiology of Hearing

The customary distinction between the physical and biological aspects of hearing is reflected in the terminology of this field. The term "acoustic" and its derivatives are used with reference to the physical properties of sound and to the mechanical devices or anatomical structures that affect these properties, whereas "auditory" refers to the physiological processes in hearing and their anatomical correlates.

The Physical Properties of the Sound Stimulus (Acoustics)

Sound is an oscillation of the molecules[1] of an elastic medium, propagated through the medium as a longitudinal pressure wave. Air is one such medium. The oscillations in general are set up by oscillating bodies – for example, a tuning fork or loudspeaker cone – that impart energy to the surrounding medium by accelerating the adjacent molecules.

These pass the oscillation energy on to molecules a little further away, and so on. The process expands as a wave with the sound source at its center, with a velocity of ca. 335 m/s in air. Oscillation of the molecules creates zones in which molecules are densely packed and other zones containing fewer molecules. Accordingly, the pressure in these zones is higher or lower than average. The amplitude of this pressure variation is called **sound pressure.** Sound pressure can be measured with suitably designed microphones, and either its effective value (cf. a textbook of physics) or its time course can be recorded and used to characterize the sound. Like other pressures, sound pressure is given in N/m^2 (= Pa). In acoustics, however, it is customary to use a relative measure, the so-called **sound pressure level** (SPL). It is expressed in decibels (dB), as follows. The sound pressure of interest p_x is compared with the arbitrarily chosen (because it is near the human threshold) reference sound pressure $p_o = 2 \cdot 10^{-5} \ N/m^2$, by taking the ratio p_x/p_o. The logarithm (to the base 10) of this ratio is multiplied by 20. The complete definition is thus

$$\text{sound pressure level} = 20 \cdot \log_{10} \frac{p_x}{p_o} \ [dB]$$

The logarithmic scale was chosen because it makes the wide range of audible sound pressures considerably more manageable. The "20" has a simple explanation: the log of a ratio of sound power (I) was originally defined as a "bel" (in honor of Alexander Graham Bell), in which there are 10 dB. The sound pressure p, however, can be more easily measured than power. Because power is proportional to the pressure amplitude squared ($I \propto p^2$) and $\log p^2 = 2 \cdot \log p$, one ends up with the above equation. Corresponding definitions are generally applied in com-

---

[1] The molecules are also of course constantly in Brownian motion of considerable amplitude, upon which the oscillations that concern us here are superimposed.

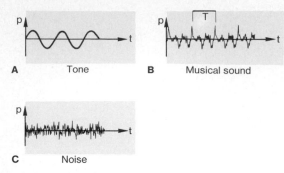

Fig. 12-5 A–C. Time course of the sound pressure of a tone (**A**), a musical sound (**B**) and a noise (**C**). T is the period of the fundamental frequency in the musical sound; there is no period in the noise

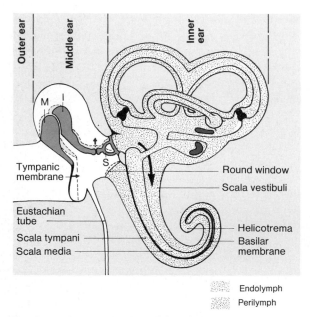

Fig. 12-6. Schematic drawing of the middle and inner ear. M, malleus; J, incus; S, stapes. The dashed lines show one extreme position occupied by the tympanum-ossicle apparatus during an oscillation cycle. The full red line represents the basilar membrane

munications technology. As an example of the use of the above equation, the sound pressure level of a tone with sound pressure $p_x = 2 \cdot 10^{-1}$ N/m² is found as follows:

$$\frac{p_x}{p_0} = \frac{2 \cdot 10^{-1}}{2 \cdot 10^{-5}} = 10^4$$

sound pressure level $= 20 \cdot \log_{10} 10^4 = 20 \cdot 4 = 80$

Thus the sound pressure $2 \cdot 10^{-1}$ N/m² corresponds to a sound pressure level of 80 dB. Similar calculations show that doubling the sound pressure increases the sound pressure level by 6 dB, and increasing sound pressure by a factor of 10 adds 20 dB. The ordinates on the left in Fig. 12-8 illustrate the relation-

ship between sound pressure and sound pressure level.

In acoustics it is customary to specify that one is using "dB SPL" because dB scales are widely used for other phenomena (voltages, for example) and with other arbitrary reference values. The appended "SPL" emphasizes that the numbers were obtained as described by the above equation, with the reference pressure $p_0 = 2 \cdot 10^{-5}$ N/m².

Sound intensity is the amount of energy passing through a unit area per unit time. It is given in W/m². 10^{-12} W/m² in a plane sound field corresponds to $2 \cdot 10^{-5}$ N/m².

The frequency of a sound is expressed in hertz (Hz); one hertz is equal to one cycle per second. A sound has the same frequency as its source as long as the source is not moving in space.

When a sound is composed of only a single frequency it is called a **tone.** Fig. 12-5 A shows the time course of the sound pressure in this case. Pure tones, however, practically never occur in everyday life; most sounds are made up of several simultaneous frequencies (Fig. 12-5 B). Usually this mixture consists of a fundamental frequency plus several harmonics, integral multiples of the fundamental frequency. Such sounds have a **musical** quality. The fundamental is reflected in the period of the complex sound-pressure wave (T in Fig. 12-5 B). Because different sound sources produce harmonics to differing extents, the quality of sounds at a given fundamental frequency can vary; the abundance of subtle shadings produced by an orchestra arises in this way [17, 20]. A sound comprising very many unrelated frequencies is called **noise** (Fig. 12-5 C), or "white noise" if essentially all frequencies in the audible range are equally represented. No periodicity is detectable in the sound-pressure record of a noisy sound.

Anatomical Bases of the Process of Hearing; the Peripheral Ear

The sound waves are channeled into the auditory system by way of the **external ear,** traveling along the external auditory meatus to the eardrum or **tympanic membrane** (cf. Fig. 12-6). This delicate membrane, with a mother-of-pearl sheen, closes off the meatus and forms a partition between it and the **middle ear,** which is also filled with air. Within the cavity of the middle ear is a chain of three flexibly linked **ossicles,** the *hammer (malleus), anvil (incus)* and *stirrup (stapes).* The "handle" of the hammer is firmly fused to the eardrum, and the foot-plate of the stapes (which really does look like a stirrup) fits into an opening in the petrous bone, the oval window. There the stapes bor-

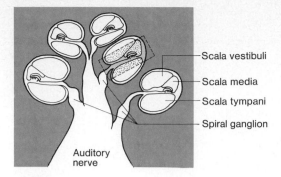

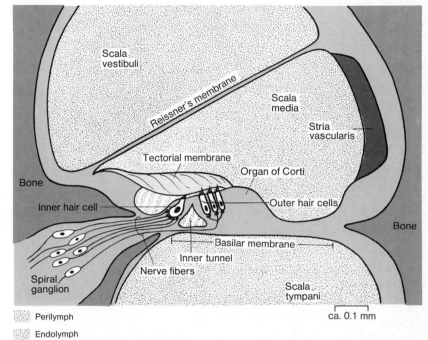

Fig. 12-7. Schematic section through the cochlea. The upper part of the figure gives an impression of the relative positions of the different parts of the cochlea, the spiral ganglion and the auditory nerve. The lower part shows the most important elements in one turn of the spiral, and the various lymph spaces. The composition of the subtectorial lymph has not been definitely determined

ders the **inner ear.** The sound energy is transmitted from the eardrum to the inner ear by way of the malleus, incus and stapes, as these structures oscillate in synchrony with the eardrum. The cavity of the middle ear communicates with the pharynx by way of the eustachian tube. Whenever one swallows, the tube opens, ventilating the middle ear and equalizing its air pressure with that of the atmosphere. When inflammation causes the mucous membranes in this region to swell, opening of the tube is impeded. Then if the external air pressure should change (as in an airplane) or if the air is reabsorbed from the middle-ear cavity, the resulting pressure differences are felt as "pressure on the ears." The pressure in this air space is also an important factor in diving; the diver must try, by pressing or swallowing, to match it to the increased external air pressure. If the attempt fails, the eardrum is in danger of rupturing.

The inner ear is embedded in the petrous part of the temporal bone. It comprises the organs of equilibri-

um and of hearing. Because of its shape the auditory organ is called the **cochlea** (Latin for "snail shell"). The cochlea consists of three parallel canals coiled together. These are the **scala tympani, scala media** and **scala vestibuli.** *Scala tympani* and *scala vestibuli* communicate with one another at the **helicotrema** (Fig. 12-6). They are filled with **perilymph,** a fluid resembling extracellular fluid in its composition and thus containing much Na^+ (ca. 140 mmol/l [5]). It is probably an ultrafiltrate of plasma. There are sites of communication between the perilymph and the cerebrospinal-fluid spaces, but their functional significance, if any, is unknown. In any case, the CSF and the perilymph are very similar in chemical composition.

The *scala media* is filled with **endolymph.** This fluid is rich in K^+ (ca. 145 mmol/l) and thus resembles an intracellular fluid [5]. The peri- and endolymphatic spaces of the cochlea communicate with the respective spaces of the vestibular organ (cf. Fig. 12-6). At the oval window the foot-plate of the stapes adjoins

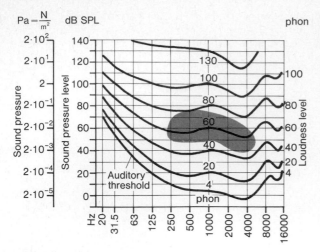

Fig. 12-8. Curves of equal loudness level (isophones) according to the standard DIN 45630. The ordinates on the left give the equivalent values of sound pressure and sound pressure level. The *red shading* indicates the speech region (see text)

the perilymph of the scala vestibuli; the opening is sealed off by an **annular ligament,** so that no perilymph can leak out. At the base of the scala tympani is another opening to the middle ear, the **round window.** This window is sealed by a fine membrane to prevent leakage of perilymph.

Fig. 12-7 shows a cross section through the cochlea. The scala vestibuli is separated from the scala media by **Reissner's membrane,** and the **basilar membrane** separates the scala media from the scala tympani. A thickened ridge running along the basilar membrane, the **organ of Corti,** contains the *receptors* surrounded by supporting cells. These again are hair cells, but they have only stereocilia; in the receptors of the organ of Corti the kinocilium is regressed [9]. A distinction is made between **inner** and **outer hair cells.** The latter are arranged in three rows, whereas the inner hair cells form a single row. In man there are about 3 500 inner and 12 000 outer hair cells [9].

Here, as in the vestibules, the hair cells are secondary sense cells. The afferent nerve fibers innervating the hair cells come from the bipolar cells of the **spiral ganglion,** which lies at the center of the cochlea; the central processes of these cells run to the CNS. About 90% of the nerve fibers in the spiral ganglion terminate on inner hair cells, each of which thus makes contact with many nerve fibers [38]. Only the remaining 10% of fibers innervate the far more numerous outer hair cells. These fibers must branch extensively in order to supply all the outer hair cells, though the many receptors supplied by one such fiber are all fairly close to one another. Altogether, the auditory nerve contains ca. 30 000 to 40 000 afferent fibers [9]. The organ of Corti also receives efferent fibers. Their functional significance is uncertain [31], though it is

known that they can inhibit the activity of afferent fibers.

Over the organ of Corti lies the **tectorial membrane,** a gelatinous mass attached to the inner wall of the cochlea in the region of the central bone, and to the organ of Corti. The stereocilia of the outer hair cells adhere at their ends to the underside of the tectorial membrane. Probably the cilia of the inner hair cells also contact the tectorial membrane, though considerably less rigidly, but this question is not yet definitely settled [32].

On the outer side of the scala media is the **stria vascularis** – a region well supplied with blood, as its name implies, and highly active metabolically. It plays an important role in *providing energy* to the cochlea and determining the composition of the endolymph. Various ion pumps here, including one for K^+, maintain the ionic milieu and the positive potential (cf. p. 286) in the endolymph [5]. Some diuretics (drugs that increase the output of urine) have ototoxic side effects that can lead to deafness. They act on the kidney by poisoning certain ion pumps in the tubule epithelia (cf. p. 641), which are responsible for the reabsorption of salts. Evidently some of the ion pumps in the stria operate on principles similar to those in the kidney and are thus also poisoned by these drugs.

Psychophysics of Auditory Sensations

Auditory thresholds. Sound must exceed a certain sound pressure level in order to be heard. This **auditory threshold** is frequency-dependent, the human ear being most sensitive in the range 2 000–5 000 Hz. In the higher and lower frequency ranges considerably higher sound pressure levels are required to exceed the threshold.

Loudness. A tone at any frequency, once the threshold has been passed, is sensed as becoming louder as the sound pressure increases. The relationship between the (physically defined) sound pressure level and the subjectively experienced **loudness level** can be described quantitatively. That is, a subject can be asked not only if a tone is audible (above threshold) but also whether two sequentially presented tones of the same or different frequency sound **equally loud** or not. For example, a test tone and a reference tone at 1 000 Hz are presented one after the other, and the subject is told to adjust a potentiometer so as to change the loudness of the reference tone until it seems the same as that of the test tone. When this is achieved, the two tones are said to have the same loudness level. The loudness level of a sound is expressed in **phon** – the sound pressure level of a

1 000-Hz tone that sounds equally loud. Thus if the 1 000-Hz tone has been set at 70 dB SPL when the subjective sensation of loudness equals that produced by a test tone, the test tone has the loudness level 70 phon. Because it is used as the standard, a 1 000-Hz tone necessarily has *identical* dB and phon values, as can be seen in Fig. 12-8. This figure also shows **equal-loudness contours** above the threshold curve, plotted from the average responses of a large, international sample of healthy young subjects. All the tones on one of these curves are regarded as equally loud, regardless of their frequency. Such curves are also called **isophones.** The threshold curve is also an isophone, for all the tones on it seem equally loud – just above threshold. The mean auditory threshold of healthy people is 4 phon; individuals, of course, can depart from this average in either direction.

Intensity-difference thresholds. Because the phon scale is based on subjective reports it is of interest to know how precise these reports are – that is, how different the sound pressures of two tones (which for simplicity should have the same frequency) must be to be judged unequal in loudness. Experiments designed to measure this **intensity-difference threshold** have shown that it is very small. Two tones at the same frequency are said to differ in loudness when their sound pressure levels differ from one another by only 1 dB. In the upper intensity range the difference can be even smaller [20].

The phon scale in itself tells nothing about the *increase* in subjective loudness as sound pressure level rises. The phon scale was constructed by asking subjects only to say when a test and a reference tone seem equally loud; the way the loudness of a given tone changes is not examined at all. But the relationship between loudness and sound pressure is of interest, for to evaluate disturbing noises one must know something about the increase in the sensation of loudness. To reveal such relationships, subjects were required to adjust a test tone at 1 000 Hz so that it was n times as loud (e.g., 2 times or 4 times) as a reference tone set by definition at 1 000 Hz and 40 dB SPL. From the sound pressure levels so obtained one can describe quantitatively the strength of the sensation; this unit of loudness is the **sone.** A tone that seems four times as loud as the standard (1 000 Hz, 40 dB) has a loudness of 4 sones, a tone half as loud has a loudness of 0.5 sones, and so on.

It turns out that above 30 dB SPL the loudness sensation is related to sound pressure by a power function with exponent 0.6 for 1 000 Hz (Stevens' power function; cf. p. 188 and [20]).

This is equivalent to saying that at 1 000 Hz and above 30 dB the sensation of loudness doubles when the sound pressure increases by 10 dB. Note that doubling the sound pressure amounts to an increase of only 6 dB, and thus does not double the loudness; rather, the sound pressure must be roughly tripled. This in turn, because $I \propto p^2$, means that the sound intensity must be raised by a factor of ten to double the loudness sensation. Ten musical instruments, all playing the same tone at the same level, sound only twice as loud as one playing alone.

Because the loudness level (in phon) of a given tone is by definition determined by comparison with a 1 000-Hz tone, the loud-

ness in sones of a tone can be calculated from its loudness level and the loudness function of a 1 000-Hz tone [20]. In this indirect way the loudness level provides information about loudness sensations. To this extent, for the technical measurement of disturbing noise, it is justified to use a simplified procedure which provides an approximation of the loudness level.

Devices to measure sound pressure level and loudness level. As was stated at the outset, isophones are derived from psychophysical experiments. It follows directly that the phon values of a sound cannot simply be measured by a physical method like those used for sound pressure – a physically defined entity measurable by suitable microphones and amplifiers (sound-level meters). To obtain at least approximate measurements of loudness level one can use sound-level meters incorporating frequency filters, with filter characteristics described roughly by the hearing threshold or other isophones. The device is thus made differentially sensitive to different frequencies, in nearly the same way as the human ear. It is less sensitive in the low-frequency and high-frequency ranges. There are three internationally accepted filter curves, designated A, B and C. When results obtained with such a device are reported one must indicate which of these curves was used, by adding the letter to the dB reading. For example, a measurement might be given as 30 dB (A), a value approximately equal to 30 phon. The filter curve A is designed to match the auditory threshold curve and should actually be used only in the low-intensity region. However, to simplify the measurement procedure practically all data are now given in dB (A), even if additional error is introduced. Similarly, for simplification, measurements of disturbing noise are done with the dB (A) filter although strictly speaking the sone scale should be used. For example, the noise of an idling car is about 75 dB (A).

Sound trauma. If the sound pressure level of a sound is greatly increased the eventual result is a sensation of *pain* in the ear. Experiments have shown that pain coincides with a loudness level of about 130 phon. Moreover, such intense sounds cause not only pain but also reversible loss of hearing (TTS, temporary threshold shift) or – if exposure is prolonged – even irreversible damage to the ear (permanent threshold shift, sound trauma). The damage is incurred by the sensory cells and the microcirculation in the cochlea. In fact, sound trauma can be caused even by sounds at considerably lower intensities if the exposure is long enough. Long-term exposure can be expected to cause injury if the intensity is 90 dB (A) or more.

The hearing of a worker regularly exposed to sound exceeding this level is therefore endangered, and must be protected by sound-damping devices (earplugs or ear muffs). Without this protection the person will become hard of hearing in a matter of years.

Subjective reactions to noise. Apart from sound trauma – objectively demonstrable damage to the inner ear by loud sounds – sound can have distinct harmful subjective effects (though these too may be accompanied by objective symptoms such as elevated blood pressure or insomnia). The "annoyance" caused by a sound depends a great deal on a person's psychological attitude toward the sound source. For example, a tenant in an apartment block may feel seriously disturbed by the piano playing of another tenant, even though they live two floors apart, other tenants have no complaints, and the loudness level of the music in the apartment of the aggrieved person is low. It is difficult to find general rules to prevent annoying noise, and the guidelines offered in civil regulations are often an unsatisfactory compromise [11].

Audible range and speech region. The audibility of a tone, as Fig. 12-8 shows, depends on its frequency as well as its sound pressure. A healthy young adult can hear frequencies from 20 Hz to 16 000 Hz (16 kHz). Frequencies above 16 kHz are called **ultrasound,** and those lower than 20 Hz **infrasound.** The audible range of man thus extends from 20 Hz to 16 kHz and from 4 phon to 130 phon. This is the **audible area** enclosed by the top and bottom curves in Fig. 12-8. In the middle of this area are the frequencies and intensities produced in speaking. This smaller area, shaded red in Fig. 12-8, is called the **speech area.** For speech to be adequately understandable, transmission systems (e.g., the telephone) must transmit frequencies at least in the range 300 Hz to 3.5 kHz. In older people sensitivity to high frequencies regularly declines, a phenomenon known as **presbycusis.**

Frequency-difference threshold. As we know from everyday experience, we can evaluate a tone not only by its loudness but also by its **pitch,** which is correlated with the frequency of the tone. We call a tone "high" when its frequency is high, and conversely. The ability to discriminate the pitches of tones heard in succession is astonishingly good. In the optimal range, around 1 000 Hz, the **frequency-difference threshold** is 0.3%, or about 3 Hz [17, 20].

Musical sounds composed of several frequencies can also be assigned a particular pitch; in general they are regarded as having the same pitch as a pure tone at a frequency equal to the fundamental frequency of the sound [17].

The ordinary musical scale is based on the octave, a doubling of frequency. In equal-tempered tuning the octave is divided into 12 equal steps, each differing from the next by the factor $\sqrt[12]{2} = 1.0595$. This difference is considerably greater than the threshold difference given above. Nevertheless it is interesting to find that when two pure tones are presented simultaneously their frequencies must be much further apart than the sequentially discriminable difference for two components to be detectable [14, 17]. Evidently the two simultaneously stimulated regions of the inner ear (cf. p. 285) must be separated by a certain minimal distance if they are to be resolved.

This finding corresponds to the formation of "critical bandwidths". For example, the auditory system has been found to be incapable of resolving pure tones within a range of about a third of an octave (the critical bandwidth); such tones fuse to give the sensation of a single sound. The loudness of this sensation increases regularly with the number of subcomponents, but the pitch sensed by the subject remains the same. The sound energy within a critical bandwidth is thus integrated, resulting in a unitary sensation.

The critical bandwidth – about a third on the scale – is astonishingly large, for it means that two *pure* tones separated by almost a third cannot be resolved. (In the case of mixed tones the situation is of course different; for example, it is easy to tell that two adjacent keys on a piano have been struck simultaneously, for the harmonics accompanying the fundamentals of each are not all within a single critical bandwidth.)

The human audible range comprises about 24 critical bandwidths. For further information see [17, 20].

When two tones sound at the same time the thresholds to the two are reciprocally affected. For example, during presentation of a steady tone at 500 Hz and 80 dB SPL, tones at other frequencies are not heard at the intensities on the auditory threshold curve of Fig. 12-8. Far higher sound pressures are required – in this example, about 40 dB SPL for a 1 000-Hz tone [14, 20]. This phenomenon is called masking. It is of considerable practical significance, because in daily life important acoustic information, such as a conversation, may be masked by background noises so that it cannot be understood. Further details about psychoacoustic phenomena can be found in [14, 17, 20, 37].

The Role of the Middle Ear

As described above, the eardrum is set into oscillation by sound and passes the energy of oscillation along the chain of ossicles to the perilymph in the scala vestibuli. Sound transmitted by this route is said to be **airborne.**

Airborne sound must be transmitted form the air to the fluids in the inner ear. When sound passes from air to liquid most of the arriving sound energy is ordinarily *reflected,* because the two media differ in their characteristic acoustic impedances. In the middle ear, however, the **tympanum-ossicle apparatus** effectively matches the acoustic impedances of air and inner ear to one another, considerably reducing the losses by reflection. The mechanism corresponds roughly to treating the objective lens of a camera so as to reduce reflection of light at the air-glass interface. The *impedance matching* is achieved by two mechanisms in particular: 1. The area of the eardrum is considerably larger than that of the stapes foot-plate. Because pressure = force/area, the pressure at the oval window is higher than at the eardrum. 2. An additional pressure increase is brought about by the differing lengths of the lever arms in the chain of ossicles. Thus the system operates like a transformer, though still other factors are also involved – the masses and elasticities in the transmission chain, and the curvature and oscillatory properties of the eardrum. The net effect of the impedance-matching mechanism is an improvement of hearing by 10–20 dB, depending on the frequency range, which is the equivalent of doubling to quadrupling the loudness sensation. The transmission properties of the tympanum-ossicle apparatus are frequency-dependent. Transmission is best in the intermediate frequency range, which accounts in part for the shape of the threshold curve.

But a sensation of sound also occurs when an oscillating body such as a tuning fork is placed directly on the skull, so that the primary energy transmission is to the skull bones. This process is called **bone conduction.** As will be shown in the next section, excitation of the inner ear requires fluid motion like that produced by the stapes movement induced by airborne sound. Bone-conducted sound produces such fluid motion in two ways. First, zones of compression and rarefaction traveling through the oscillating skull bones displace fluid from the voluminous vestibular labyrinth into the cochlea and back again (compression theory). Second, the tympanum-ossicle apparatus has a certain mass, and because of its inertia oscillation of the ossicles lags behind that of the skull bones. The stapes therefore moves relative to the petrous bone, exciting the inner ear (mass-inertia theory). But a number of features of bone conduction are still unclear or disputed; for further information see [9].

Although bone conduction does not contribute appreciably to hearing in everyday life, it is very useful as a diagnostic aid to the physician (cf. p. 291).

The **middle-ear muscles,** the tensor tympani and the stapedius, insert on the malleus and stapes. The reflex contractions of these muscles that accompany exposure to sound impair transmission, because they change the impedance of the middle ear. This mechanism cannot provide effective protection against excessively loud sounds, although such a possibility has been discussed. The functional significance of the middle-ear reflexes remains obscure.

Auditory Processes in the Inner Ear

Mechanical events. When the stapes is set into oscillation by sound entering the ear, it transmits sound energy to the perilymph in the scala vestibuli (cf. Fig. 12-6). Because the fluids of the inner ear are incompressible, there must be some structure permitting pressure equilibration. This structure is the round window; the membrane of the round window moves out as the stapes moves in, and vice versa. At the same time, the movements of the stapes displace the adjacent, basal part of the scala media, with the Reissner's and basilar membranes enclosing it, from the resting position; it swings up and down, toward the scala vestibula and scala tympani in alternation. For simplicity, in the following discussion we shall refer to the scala media with its bounding membranes simply as the *endolymphatic duct.* This displacement of the endolymphatic duct at its base generates a

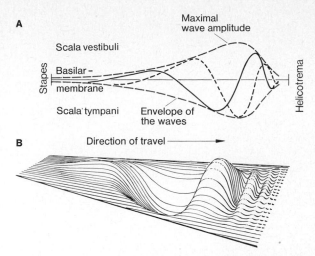

Fig. 12-9. A Diagram of a traveling wave, showing the wave contour at two different times. The envelope shows the maximal amplitude of the wave generated by a fixed frequency, at the different sites on the cochlea. **B** Three-dimensional representation of the wave (modified from [9])

wave, which passes along the duct from stapes to helicotrema like a wave along a taut horizontal rope. In Fig. 12-9 A two states of such a wave are shown, with the endolymphatic duct represented by a single line. Because the stapes is continually in oscillation during a sound, there is a steady succession of waves along the endolymphatic duct to the helicotrema. These are called **traveling waves** (cf. [5]). The stiffness of the basilar membrane decreases from the stapes to the helicotrema. Therefore the velocity of wave propagation becomes progressively lower as the helicotrema is approached, and the wavelength decreases. For the same reason, the amplitude of the waves traveling toward the helicotrema at first increases (Fig. 12-9), becoming very much larger than in the stapes region where the waves originated. However, because of the damping properties of the liquid-filled inner-ear channels the waves are soon attenuated; they rapidly decrease in amplitude and ultimately disappear, usually before they have reached the helicotrema. Somewhere between the sites of origin and extinction of the waves, then, there must be a place where the amplitude is maximal (Fig. 12-9). This *amplitude maximum* is found at a **different position for each frequency** – the higher the frequency, the closer to the stapes, and the lower the frequency, the closer to the helicotrema. The existence of this maximum results in a mapping of each frequency in the audible range onto **one** particular **place** in the endolymphatic duct (or on the basilar membrane). This situation is described by the term **frequency dispersion.** The sensory cells are most excited at the site of the oscillation maximum, so that different frequencies excite different sense cells **(place theory).**

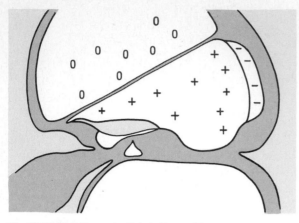

Fig. 12-10. Standing potentials in the cochlea

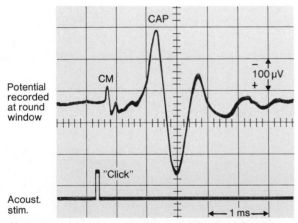

Fig. 12-11. Cochlear microphonic potential (CM) and compound action potential in the auditory nerve (CAP) recorded at the round window when a click is presented to the ear

These wave movements can be observed directly in the microscope with high sound pressures, and with sound pressures in the physiological range they can be demonstrated by means of the Mössbauer effect, a capacitive probe or laser light. With low-intensity sound the wave amplitudes are extraordinarily small. From data obtained in the intermediate range of sound pressures one can extrapolate to find the amplitude maxima in the threshold region; displacements of ca. 10^{-10} to 10^{-11} m have been estimated [5, 35].

The transduction process at the hair cells. As was shown in the preceding section, because of the mechanical properties of the cochlea exposure of the ear to a particular sound frequency causes the basilar membrane to oscillate with appreciable amplitude only at a single, narrowly delimited place, in the region of the amplitude maximum. Among the events then occurring at this place are **relative movements** of the basilar and tectorial membranes. Because the cilia of the outer hair cells make firm contact with the tectorial membrane [32], the resulting shear force bends them – the adequate stimulus for these hair cells, as for those in the vestibular organs. Presumably the inner hair cells are also excited in this way. But if the contact between their cilia and the tectorial membrane should prove not functionally rigid, the implication would be that they are bent by flow of the subtectorial fluid.

Bending of the cilia triggers the *transduction process,* by which minuscule mechanical deformations of the hair-cell membrane or of the cilia are converted to neuronal excitation. An initial prerequisite for this process is the **endocochlear potential.** Measurements with microelectrodes show that the endolymph space is positively charged (ca. $+ 80$ mV) with respect to the scala vestibuli and to the other extracellular spaces in the body. The stria vascularis and the organ of Corti are negatively charged (ca. $- 70$ mV; cf. Fig. 12-10). The potential measurable in the organ of Corti is probably the intracellular potential of the hair and supporting cells. The positive endocochlear potential is maintained by energy-supplying processes in the stria vascularis. It is thought that shearing of the cilia changes the membrane resistance of the hair cells in synchrony with the stimulus. Because of the standing (i.e., steady) potentials there is a large potential difference between the endolymph space and the interior of the hair cells, at least 150 mV; therefore these stimulus-synchronized changes in membrane resistance must produce local ion currents that change the membrane potential of the hair cell – they build up "receptor potentials" (the so-called **battery hypothesis** [5]). To record these receptor potentials in the hair cells is difficult, but it has been done [36]. It is simpler to place macroelectrodes near the receptors, in the scala tympani or at the round window; these record a potential called the **cochlear microphonic** (Fig. 12-11). This potential behaves like the output voltage of a microphone, reflecting the changes in sound pressure quite accurately. A tape recording of speech made not with a microphone but by picking up the microphonic potentials of an experimental animal is entirely understandable. The cochlear microphonic is probably the sum of all the extracellularly recordable receptor potentials. It follows the sound stimulus (i) with practically no latency, has (ii) no refractory period or (iii) measurable threshold, and is (iv) not subject to fatigue; in all these respects, it does not behave like a nerve action potential.

The ion currents generated by bending of the cilia cause the release of a transmitter at the bases of the hair cells. This transmitter, the chemical nature of which is not yet known [31a], excites the afferent nerve fibers. When a click (a brief pressure pulse) is presented to the ear the fibers in the auditory nerve are activated synchronously, and a compound action potential can be recorded at the round window in addition to the microphonic potential. More prolonged sounds elicit asynchronous discharge, which does not sum to form a discrete action potential. Fig. 12-11 shows the cochlear microphonic (CM) and compound action potential (CAP) elicited by a click. This record was obtained from a cat, but similar potentials can also be recorded in humans when – as is sometimes necessary for diagnostic purposes – an electrode is inserted through the eardrum and positioned near the round window [24].

The coding of sound in auditory-nerve fibers. Each nerve fiber in the auditory nerve comes from a narrowly circumscribed region of the cochlea, or from a single inner hair cell. Because certain places along the cochlea are associated with certain frequencies, it follows that each nerve fiber is maximally excited by a specific frequency – the **characteristic frequency** of the fiber. That is, a single fiber in the auditory nerve is most readily excited by presentation of sound at this characteristic frequency. If the ear is stimulated with other frequencies, this fiber cannot be activated, or is activated only by appropriately increasing the sound pressure level. This situation is illustrated in Fig. 12-12, a plot of threshold vs. stimulus frequency for two different fibers. The criterion for threshold is an increase above spontaneous activity by a certain amount. Each fiber can be activated by the frequencies and intensities within the shaded region. The **tuning curves** outlining these regions have a narrow, sharply tuned part where the threshold is low and another part covering a broad high-threshold range of frequencies. The sharp tuning in the highly sensitive part cannot be explained by the measured movements of the basilar membrane. It must either be assumed that the basilar membrane oscillates differently in response to threshold sound pressures than to those large enough to produce measurable movement, or one must postulate an additional, active filter process that sharpens the tuning [6]. In any case, it is clear that the cochlea is very vulnerable to damage, and the nerve fibers coming from a damaged cochlea have high threshold and poor frequency selectivity. If a sound stimulus comprises several frequencies, all the associated groups of nerve fibers are stimulated. The *duration* of a sound stimulus is encoded in the duration of neural activity, and its *intensity* by the level of activity. As sound pressure increases, so does the discharge rate of the neurons. Each fiber can be activated only up to a certain discharge rate, beyond which it saturates. However, high sound pressure

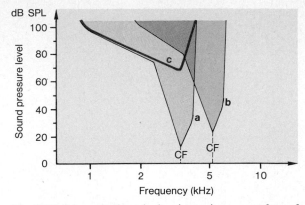

Fig. 12-12. Schematized graph, showing tuning curves of two afferent fibers in the auditory nerve (a, b) with different characteristic frequencies (CF). Curve c is typical of a pathological fiber, such as are found in cases of inner-ear damage

levels not only increase the discharge rate of the fibers already firing, but also bring adjacent, previously unexcited fibers into action. This recruitment is also apparent in Fig. 12-12; both fibers are activated when the sound is in the area where the curves overlap. In summary, then, we can say that at the level of the primary afferent fibers the sound stimulus is broken down into its frequency components. The individual components excite the associated afferent fibers. At higher stations in the auditory pathway the neurons behave differently.

With tones at frequencies up to ca. 4 kHz, the neuronal discharge in the auditory nerve tends to occur at particular phases of the sound-pressure cycle ("phase-locked" discharge). It seems that the organism can evaluate and so make use of this temporal structure of the discharge pattern. Certain psychoacoustical phenomena [37] indicate that the organism does not derive a pitch sensation exclusively from the frequency composition of a sound stimulus as analyzed by dispersion along the cochlea (place theory), but in some circumstances also utilizes the temporal structure of the stimulus – the regularly recurring sound-pressure peaks (so-called *periodicity analysis*). In addition, experiments in which the auditory nerves of deaf patients were stimulated electrically have shown that the neuronal discharges elicited by periodic electrical stimuli are processed to give a pitch sensation.

Nothing is known about the differences in properties and functions of the inner and outer hair cells. There are various hypotheses, but not one of them has yet been confirmed experimentally. It is certain that the inner and outer hair cells are separately innervated, but microelectrode recordings from fibers in the auditory nerve have not revealed two different fiber populations. Because 90% of the afferent fibers come from the inner hair cells [38], and the remaining 10% are thin and unmyelinat-

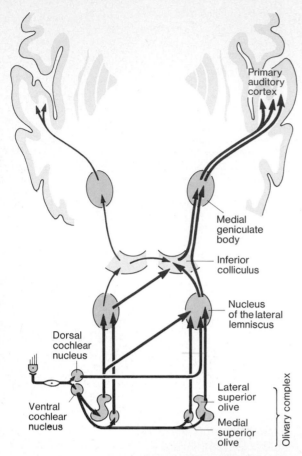

Fig. 12-13. Greatly simplified diagram of the auditory pathway, showing only the tracts originating on one side. The centrifugal tracts are omitted

ed, it is possible that all of the experimental results have been obtained from the inner-hair-cell fibers. Fibers found in such experiments have a low threshold, very close to the auditory threshold of the animal concerned. It follows that the hypothesis proposing that the inner hair cells have a higher threshold than the outer is presumably incorrect. Moreover, intracellular recordings from inner hair cells have shown that their tuning characteristics are largely consistent with those of the afferent fibers [36]. The properties of the outer hair cells, on the other hand, are not yet known.

The Central Auditory System

Anatomy of the auditory pathway. Fig. 12-13 is a much simplified diagram of the auditory pathway. For clarity, only pathways from the left ear are included. Each arrowhead indicates a synapse with a higher-order neuron. To avoid overcrowding of the picture, recurrent collaterals and interneurons are not shown, although connectivity of this sort is common throughout the auditory system.

The primary afferent fibers bifurcate, sending one end into the **ventral cochlear nucleus** and the other in-

to the **dorsal cochlear nucleus.** The fine structure of these nuclei, the dorsal one in particular, is very complicated [9, 23]. From the ventral nucleus a ventral tract runs to the olivary complexes of the same and the opposite side (the superior olive with the lateral, S-shaped nucleus and the medial nucleus). The nerve cells of the olivary complex thus receive inputs from both ears. It is at this neuronal level that the opportunity to compare acoustic signals acting on the two ears with one another first arises. We shall return later to these comparisons, which are done predominantly in the **medial superior olive.** From the dorsal cochlear nucleus a dorsal tract crosses to the opposite side and there terminates in the **nucleus of the lateral lemniscus.** The ascending projections of the cells of the olivary complex are both ipsilateral and contralateral. After synaptic relay the auditory pathway proceeds through the **inferior colliculus** and the **medial geniculate body** to the **primary auditory cortex,** in the transverse temporal gyri in the upper part of the temporal lobes (Heschl's gyrus). This region corresponds to Brodmann's area 41; most of it is concealed in the depths of the sylvian fissure. Adjacent to the primary auditory cortex are other projection fields of the auditory system, called the secondary auditory cortex (Brodmann's area 42). Up to the primary cortex, then, the pathway consists of at least 5 or 6 neurons, and because of additional relay stations and recurrent collaterals not shown in the diagram of Fig. 12-13 even longer chains are possible. Further details can be found in [9]. Finally, in addition to the afferent pathways the auditory system comprises centrifugal, efferent fibers, which have been omitted from Fig. 12-13 [31].

The excitation of central neurons in the auditory system. Whereas the primary afferent neurons in the auditory nerve are excitable by pure tones, very simple acoustic stimuli, neurons at higher levels in general are not. The neurons in the **ventral cochlear nucleus** still behave like those in the auditory nerve; here pure tones at suprathreshold intensities always excite the neurons, which have sharp tuning curves and short latencies. Therefore these are called "primary-like" cells. But in the **dorsal cochlear nucleus** the picture is fundamentally altered [25, 40]. Although most of the neurons here can also be excited by pure tones, their response patterns vary widely. As an example, Fig. 12-14 shows responses of fibers leaving the dorsal cochlear nucleus, in each case to a 50-ms tone at the characteristic frequency of the neuron. The neuron in Fig. 12-14 A behaves like a primary fiber, but the others are quite different. Some neurons in the dorsal cochlear nucleus can be inhibited by sound, and others are excited by certain frequencies and

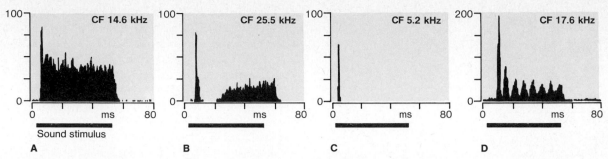

Fig. 12-14. Discharge patterns of 4 neurons in the dorsal cochlear nucleus, in response to a 50-ms tone at the CF, after [21].

Abscissa: time; *ordinate:* number of nerve action potentials

inhibited by slightly different frequencies. Still others are particularly responsive to tones of changing frequency (so-called frequency-modulated tones), although they also respond to pure tones. The anatomical bases of these complex responses are collateral connections, some excitatory and some inhibitory.

The *functional implication* is evidently that the neurons respond particularly well to certain features of the sound stimulus, contributing to pattern recognition even at this early station in the pathway. At higher levels such specificity becomes progressively better developed.

The further away from the cochlea in the auditory pathway, the more complex the sound patterns required to activate the neurons [25]. Many cells do not respond at all to pure tones. In the *inferior colliculus,* for example, there are cells excitable only by frequency-modulated tones with particular directions and degrees of modulation. Other cells in the inferior colliculus respond to a tone only if it is amplitude-modulated – that is, if its intensity changes. In this case, too, the modulation must often have certain properties in order to excite the neuron.

In general, we can say that the information contained in a sound stimulus is multiply recoded as the neuronal excitation passes the various stations in the auditory pathway. In the process, different types of neuron extract particular properties of the sound stimulus, so that the higher neurons each activates respond more or less specifically to this property alone.

In everyday life we are hardly ever confronted with pure tones. The sounds we hear are made up of various frequency components, which can change continually and independently. The amplitude of such sounds can change as well as the frequency, their duration varies, they begin and end abruptly or gradually, they can be repeated or not, their source can be nearby, far away or moving, and so on. People can evaluate all these properties of a sound, at least if their hearing has been suitably trained. Neuronal processes underlying such evaluation have been found especially in the **auditory cortex** [40]. For exam-

ple, in the primary auditory cortex some neurons respond only to the onset of a sound stimulus and others, only to its end. Still others fire only when the sound has lasted for a certain time, and others are excited only by repeated sounds. Some neurons are activated only if the stimulus is frequency- or amplitude-modulated in a particular way. Many can be activated by a broad frequency band – that is, by noises – and others have tuning curves with one or several sharp minima. Most of the cortical neurons are activated by the contralateral ear, but some respond to ipsilateral stimulation and others only when both ears are stimulated simultaneously. A considerable percentage of the neurons in the primary auditory cortex cannot be excited at all under laboratory conditions; presumably these neurons are highly specific, responding only to stimuli too complicated to be reproduced by the experimental equipment [40].

On the whole, the responses of cells in the *primary auditory cortex* resemble those of the complex or hypercomplex neurons in the visual cortex (cf. pp. 252–254). They are evidently involved in auditory pattern recognition – a process of fundamental importance, for example, in understanding speech. Indeed, cells have been found in the auditory cortex of monkeys that respond predominantly to certain conspecific communication sounds. But the properties of these neurons often depend on other, unknown parameters as well, so that their responses are subject to unpredictable variability [33].

Because the auditory cortex is located there, brain lesions involving the temporal lobes cause difficulty in understanding speech, in spatial localization of a sound source (see below) and in the identification of temporal patterns of sound. However, such injuries do not affect the ability to discriminate frequencies and intensities. Details about the central information processing involved in hearing can be found in [4, 40].

Recent studies have shown that the tonotopic organization found in the cochlea is preserved at all higher stations in the auditory system, including the cortex [22]. The tonotopic organization of the primary auditory cortex – that is, a systematic ar-

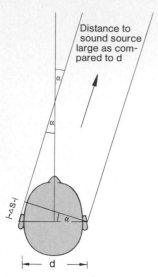

Fig. 12-15. Calculation of conduction-time differences in directional hearing (see text)

rangement by sound frequency – had previously been denied.

Another result contradicting earlier assumptions is that in the higher-level auditory neurons there is evidently no appreciable sharpening of tuning. The tuning curves of the primary neurons in the auditory nerve are already extraordinarily sharp, if the experimental animals are in optimal physical condition.

Auditory orientation in space. The central auditory system also makes an important contribution to *spatial orientation.* We know from ordinary experience that the direction of a sound source can be specified quite closely. This capability requires both ears (**binaural** hearing). The physical basis of **directional hearing** is the circumstance that one ear is usually further away from a sound source than the other. Because sound is propagated with finite velocity it arrives **later** at the more distant ear; moreover, its **intensity** there is lower, and the auditory system is able to detect intensity differences as small as 1 dB [2]. Fig. 12-15 illustrates the method of calculating differences in conduction time. The difference in distance is $\Delta s = d \cdot \sin \alpha$, where d is the distance between the two ears and α is the angle of the sound source with respect to the receiver. The time delay Δt is then $\Delta t = \Delta s/c$, where c is the speed of sound. Delays of as little as $3 \cdot 10^{-5}$ s can be reliably detected; this corresponds to a divergence of the sound source from the midline by ca. 3°. Under optimal conditions angles only half as large can be identified.

In both psychophysical and neurophysiological experiments it can be shown that directional hearing is in fact based on **differences in conduction time and intensity.** When earphones are used for independent stimulation of the two ears, delay or intensity reduction of the signal to one ear produces a spatial sensa-

tion – the sound is localized in the other ear. But a delay can be compensated by simultaneously increasing the intensity at the same ear; in this case the sound still seems to be in the middle of the head [2]. Similar results are obtained in neurophysiological experiments. In the *superior olive,* the first station at which inputs from the two sides come together, there are neurons that behave similarly with regard to the timing and intensity of a stimulus [25]. They are maximally excited when the sound presented to one ear is louder than **and** precedes that at the other ear. In the **inferior colliculus** there are two cell types, maximally excited when the acoustic signal is presented to the two ears either with a certain time difference or with a certain intensity difference respectively. Activation of such a cell signifies that the sound source is at a specified angle in space. In the **auditory cortex** there are also cells that can be activated only if the sound source is at a particular location. If the auditory cortex is destroyed spatial orientation is impaired [2]. However, there is as yet no good explanation of the way the central nervous system manages to detect minimal time differences of the order of 10^{-4} s.

Conduction-time and intensity differences do not suffice to determine whether the sound source is in front of the head or behind it, above or below. To make this decision we require an accessory device, the pinna of the ear. The pinna has a directional characteristic, "distorting" a sound signal in a particular way depending on the position of the sound source. This property is turned to advantage in localizing sounds. In a technical application of this phenomenon one can use an artificial head with microphones in the position of the eardrums to make excellent stereophonic recordings [2].

Adaptation in the auditory system. The auditory system, like other sensory systems, exhibits the phenomenon of **adaptation.** Both the peripheral ear and central neurons are involved in this process. Adaptation is manifest in an increased auditory threshold (**temporary threshold shift, TTS**). It is not a useless or undesirable mechanism, for it results in a reduction of the difference threshold and thus assists differentiation of our auditory experiences. The reason for this improvement is that in the adapted state the isophones are shifted upward and at the same time move closer together. For further information see [20].

Pathophysiology of Auditory Defects

Hearing difficulties and deafness greatly change the life of the affected person, and are therefore of great clinical significance. The causes of hearing impairment can be grouped into three categories.

1. Disturbance of sound conduction. Here the damage affects the middle ear, the sound-conducting apparatus. In cases of inflammation, for example, the tympanum-ossicle apparatus does not transmit the usual amount of sound energy to the inner ear. As a result,

AUDIOGRAM

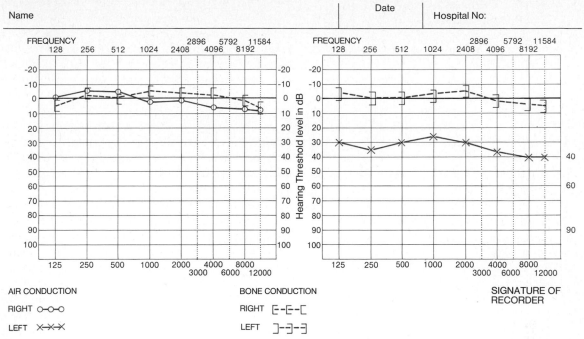

Fig. 12-16. Audiogram of a patient with impaired sound conduction on the left side

hearing deteriorates even though the inner ear may be intact.

2. Disturbance of sound sensation (sensorineural hearing loss). In this case the hair cells of the organ of Corti are damaged, so that either the process of transduction or the release of transmitter is disturbed. The net result is interference with the transmission of information from the cochlea to the CNS. This type of inner ear damage may be caused by noise trauma, or ototoxic drugs such as certain antibiotics or diuretics.

3. Retrocochlear damage. This group includes conditions in which both middle and inner ear are intact. Either the central part of the primary afferent nerve fibers or other parts of the auditory pathway are damaged (e. g., by a brain tumor).

The process of testing a patient's hearing ability is called **audiometry.** A variety of tests are available to demonstrate damage and indicate its site (for details see [16]).

The most important clinical test is **threshold audiometry.** Various tones are presented to the patient by a single earphone. The physician begins with an intensity certain to be subthreshold and gradually raises the sound pressure until the patient reports hearing a sound. This sound pressure is then recorded in a

graph (Fig. 12-16) called an *audiogram.* In the preprinted form the normal auditory threshold is represented by a straight line labelled "0 dB." In contrast to the graph of Fig. 12-8, higher thresholds (which amount to hearing loss) are plotted below the zero line, to indicate by how many dB the threshold of the patient differs from normal. Note that these are not sound pressure levels, which would be given in dB SPL. When the threshold of a patient is a certain number of dB above normal, he is said to have a hearing loss of that many dB. As a practical demonstration, try closing both ears with your fingers. The hearing loss produced in this way is about 20 dB (in doing this experiment, of course, care must be taken not to produce too much noise with the fingers themselves). The clinical procedure employing earphones tests the reception of *airborne sound. Bone conduction* can be tested similarly by using, instead of the earphones, an oscillating object placed on the mastoid process on the side to be tested, so that the oscillation is transmitted directly to the skull bones. By comparing the threshold curves for air and bone conduction one can distinguish between middle-ear deafness and inner-ear deafness.

Middle-ear deafness is a **disturbance of sound conduction.** The inner ear is not damaged. In this condition, therefore, a hearing loss is measured with airborne sound (cf. Fig. 12-16) while the threshold to bone-conducted sound is normal, for the sound energy

transmitted by the bones arrives at the hair cells without the assistance of the middle ear.

Inner-ear deafness arises from damage to the hair
cells, the middle ear remaining intact. In this case the
thresholds to both airborne and bone-conducted
sound are raised, as both are transduced by the same
receptor process. Retrocochlear damage also raises
the threshold for both types of conduction.

With the aid of a tuning fork (customarily 256 Hz) impaired conduction can very simply be distinguished
from inner-ear or retrocochlear damage, as long as
one knows which ear is affected **(Weber's test).** The
stem of the oscillating tuning fork is set on the middle
of the skull. A patient with inner-ear damage reports
hearing the tone on the healthy side, whereas with
middle-ear damage it is lateralized to the affected
side.

There is a simple explanation of this phenomenon in the case of
inner-ear damage. The damaged receptors produce less excitation in the auditory nerve, so that the tone seems louder in the
healthy ear, and this difference gives rise to a directional impression (cf. p. 290). In the case of middle-ear damage two simultaneous processes are involved. First, the affected middle
ear is usually altered by inflammation so that the ossicles become heavier. This improves the conditions for excitation of the
inner ear by bone-conducted sound. Second, because of the impaired conduction less of the sound in the environment reaches
the inner ear, so that the ear is adapted to a lower noise level; its
receptors are more sensitive than those on the healthy side.
These two factors act synergistically in a patient with middle-
ear damage to make the tone sound louder on the affected
side.

The **Rinne test** compares air and bone conduction for the same
ear. The oscillating tuning fork is placed on the mastoid process
(bone conduction) until it is no longer heard, and then held just
outside the ear (air conduction). A person with normal hearing
or impaired sensation hears the tone again (Rinne positive), and
one with impaired conduction does not hear it (Rinne negative).

Hearing loss in older people is a routine occurrence in civilized
countries. This condition, called presbycusis, first becomes apparent in the high-frequency range. A 60-year-old, on the average, can expect to have a hearing loss of ca. 40 dB at 8 kHz and
ca. 30 dB at 4 kHz. The damage is of the cochlear-retrocochlear
type, and often extends to frequencies important for understanding speech [16]. It remains debatable whether it is really a
normal concomitant of aging or is caused by effects of civilization.

In contrast to threshold audiometry, other test procedures examine the ability of the auditory system to
differentiate among suprathreshold sounds. In
speech audiometry a tape recording of spoken numbers or standardized syllables is played to the patient,
to test his **understanding of speech.** With inner-ear
damage complete understanding cannot be achieved
even with high sound pressures, because in this condition the tuning curves of the auditory-nerve fibers
are altered (see below).

If hearing is impaired on one side, measurement of
so-called **recruitment** enables one to decide whether

the organ of Corti is affected. Sounds are presented
through earphones, and the sound pressure levels
producing sensations of equal loudness in the two
ears are compared. The threshold of the affected ear
is elevated, so that initially it requires higher sound
pressure. Thereafter, if the organ of Corti is damaged,
a given increase in perceived loudness is produced by
a smaller increase in sound pressure at this ear than at
the healthy ear. As sound intensity is further increased a level is eventually reached at which the two
ears mediate identical loudness sensations at identical sound pressures ("positive recruitment"). With
middle-ear or retrocochlear damage, recruitment
does not occur [16].

There are a number of other tests that measure the increase in perceived loudness with other methods; the
results of these are explained in the same way as recruitment. One of them is the **SISI test** (Short Increment **S**ensitivity **I**ndex): during presentation of a
maintained tone 20 dB above the auditory threshold
the intensity is briefly raised by 1–5 dB. Patients with
inner-ear damage can detect an increment as small as
1 dB, whereas healthy people require as much as
5 dB.

Finally, hearing can also be tested by recording the
brainstem and cortical potentials evoked by acoustic
stimuli. The EEG deflections produced by several
single stimuli are added by a computer, so that the
background activity that otherwise obscures the potential fluctuations elicited by a single stimulus are
averaged out and the responses are revealed. The average curves so obtained comprise several potentials
varying in latency, the number of which depends on
the technique selected to suit the purpose of the study
(**E**voked **R**esponse **A**udiometry, **ERA**). The early potentials have latencies below 10 ms [24, 39]. They are
thought to originate in the various auditory nuclei of
the brainstem, though this interpretation does not necessarily apply to all components. In any case, there
can be no doubt that the potentials reflect the specific
processing that occurs in the basal parts of the auditory pathway. Although these potentials can also be
used to determine auditory threshold, the method is
considerably better suited for fine neurological diagnosis. It enables the examiner to infer the extent to
which the neuronal processes following an acoustic
stimulus are intact. Disorders in the brainstem region
alter these potentials.

The later potentials (latencies around 150 ms) are less
specific, and in recent times have not been regarded
as of practical significance.

Mechanism of inner-ear damage. Although the causes of inner-
ear damage may be very diverse, animal experiments have
shown that in all cases the result is that the thresholds of individual fibers in the auditory nerve are raised and their tuning is

less sharp [26]. The tuning curve of one such pathological fiber is shown in Fig. 12-12. This change affects very many or even all fibers, at least in a particular frequency range. It explains the increase in auditory threshold and also the deterioration of frequency discrimination, which ultimately makes it difficult to understand speech. The relatively flat tuning curves also offer an explanation of recruitment, as follows. The fibers are not excited at all when the sound pressure level is low. But once the threshold has been passed further increase in sound pressure rapidly activates many fibers, for a flat tuning curve implies low frequency selectivity. Soon just as many fibers are activated as in the healthy ear, and at sound pressures above this level the test tone seems equally loud in both ears.

12.3   Physiology of the Speech Apparatus

The significance of speech to man has been pointed out above. In this section we consider one area in the field of speech physiology, the physiology of the peripheral speech apparatus. The interesting central nervous processes that constitute the real foundation of "speech," failure of which disturbs the communication system far more than damage to the peripheral apparatus, will not be discussed here; mention is made of them on p. 162.

Basic Properties of the Acoustic Signal Produced in Speaking

Everyday experience tells us that the voices of different people can vary in "pitch." For example, the voice of a man is about an octave deeper than that of a woman. Moreover, a speaker is capable of changing his own pitch, and a singer still more so. Now, if someone sings the syllables "la la la …" (to the tune, perhaps, of "Row, row, row your boat") the vowel sound /a/ is clearly identifiable in each syllable, even though the "pitch" of the sung tone changes. Conversely, we can keep the pitch constant and change the vowel sound in successive syllables. A listener will be quite aware that the pitch is maintained while the syllables vary. Thus the acoustic signal produced during speaking or singing and analyzed by the auditory system must contain at least two independently variable parameters, of which one provides information about pitch and the other, information about the phonemic content – for example, by transmitting certain characteristics of the vowel sound /a/. This is indeed the case. The two parameters are produced by two fundamentally different mechanisms. The mechanism controlling pitch is called **phonation** and is located in the larynx; its physical basis is oscillation of the vocal cords. The mechanism that determines phonemic structure is called **articulation.** It takes

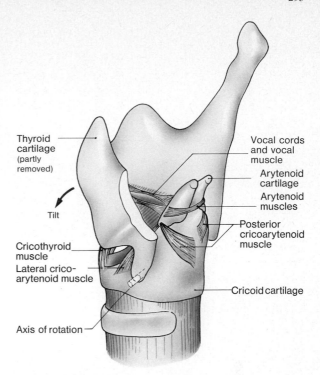

Thyroid cartilage (partly removed)

Tilt

Cricothyroid muscle

Lateral crico-arytenoid muscle

Axis of rotation

Vocal cords and vocal muscle

Arytenoid cartilage

Arytenoid muscles

Posterior cricoarytenoid muscle

Cricoid cartilage

Fig. 12-17. Schematic drawing of the larynx and its musculature, with part of the thyroid cartilage removed. The *arrow* shows the direction in which the thyroid cartilage can tilt

place in the oral cavity (in some cases also the nasopharyngeal region). Here the physical basis is the resonance of the hollow spaces. That the two mechanisms are in fact distinct is evident in whispering (p. 295). The whispering voice cannot be assigned any pitch, for the processes of phonation are eliminated and only articulation is done. In speaking, sequences of characteristic sounds are produced. These sounds, the elements of speech, are called **phonemes.** They are described by a system of phonetic symbols, to which we shall return below.

Phonation

Functional anatomy of the larynx. The larynx is the upper end of the trachea (Fig. 12-17). It consists of the annular **cricoid cartilage,** the **thyroid cartilage** and the paired **arytenoid cartilages.** The thyroid cartilage can move with respect to the cricoid cartilage in two ways – by sliding forward, and by tilting forward and down. The arytenoid cartilages are seated on the upper rear edge of the cricoid cartilage, where they can (i) be rotated about their long axes, (ii) be moved toward or away from one another by sliding over the cricoid cartilage (cf. Fig. 12-18), and (iii) be tilted forward. Between the thyroid cartilage and the vocal processes of the arytenoids are the two **vocal cords,** folds of membranous tissue enclosing ligaments; the gap between them is the **glottis.** Air must pass through this opening both in breathing and in speaking. The laryngeal muscles are of special functional significance. The **cricothyroid muscle** is ventrally situated, between the cricoid and thyroid cartilages. The **cricoarytenoid**

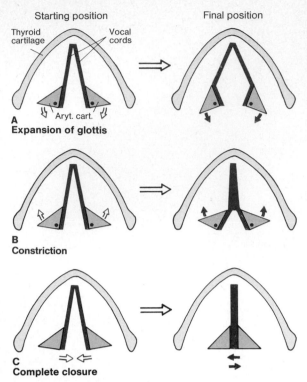

Fig. 12-18 A-C. Schematic illustration of the operation of the laryngeal muscles. The larynx is drawn about as it appears when examined with an inserted mirror; the thyroid and arytenoid cartilages and the vocal cords are shown. **A** Expansion of the glottis by the posterior cricoarytenoid muscle. **B** Constriction by the lateral cricoarytenoid, leaving only a small triangular gap. **C** Complete closure by the arytenoid muscles

muscle consists of two parts on each side, the lateral part passing from the arytenoid cartilage to the lateral surface of the cricoid cartilage, and the posterior part passing to its posterior surface. The **arytenoid muscles** join the two arytenoid cartilages at their dorsal surfaces. The **vocal muscles** are within the vocal folds, passing from the thyroid cartilage to the arytenoids. Lateral to each is another muscle, the thyroarytenoid.

The larynx is supplied by two branches of the vagus nerve. The superior laryngeal nerve contains sensory fibers from the mucosa and motor fibers to the cricothyroid muscle. The inferior laryngeal nerve is the terminal branch of the recurrent nerve, with the motor supply to the remaining laryngeal muscles and sensory fibers from the subglottal region.

The role of the laryngeal muscles is to adjust the *width of the glottis* and the *tension of the vocal cords* as required for phonation. Their action is assisted by that of other muscles that can exert, directly or indirectly, force on the larynx – for example, the sternohyoid muscle. The glottis is expanded by the posterior cricoarytenoid muscle, which pulls the arytenoid cartilages apart and turns their vocal processes to the sides (cf. Fig. 12-18). The gap is narrowed by the arytenoid muscles, the lateral cricoarytenoids and the thyroarytenoids. The **tension** of the vocal cords, finally, is regulated by the cricothyroid and vocal muscles. The

cricothyroid muscles tip the thyroid cartilage forward (cf. Fig. 12-17), moving it further away from the vocal processes of the arytenoid cartilages, so that the vocal cords are stretched. The vocal muscles, on the other hand, increase the tension of the vocal cords by the change in the modulus of elasticity associated with their contraction. During normal respiration the posterior cricoarytenoid muscles keep the glottis wide open (cf. Fig. 12-18).

Mechanism of phonation (voice production). The first step in speaking or singing is to prepare to exhale. Unlike the situation in normal breathing, however, the glottis is closed or only slightly open. As a result a higher pressure builds up in the thorax than would be the case in normal expiration (subglottal pressure). It is always in the range above 40–60 Pa (4–6 cm H_2O) and can easily reach 200 Pa (20 cm H_2O) or more. If the glottis is closed, the vocal cords are pushed apart by this pressure. At that moment air flows through the glottis into the oropharyngeal cavity. The glottis amounts to a *bottleneck* in the expiratory tract, at which the flow velocity of the expired air is far higher than in the trachea. It follows from Bernoulli's law that the air pressure here will be very low; therefore the glottis closes again, and the process begins anew. The vocal cords thus perform **Bernoulli oscillations.** The airstream is continually interrupted in the rhythm of these oscillations, producing an audible sound – the voice – with a fundamental frequency ("pitch" in common parlance) corresponding to the rate of airstream interruption.

Because the airstream cannot be sinusoidally modulated by the opening and closing of the vocal cords the sound produced is not a pure tone, but a mixture rich in harmonics [1, 8]. The number of glottal openings or closings per unit time, and thus the fundamental frequency of the sound, depends primarily on the tension of the vocal cords, and only secondarily on the subglottal pressure. Both parameters, however, can be changed by the laryngeal and thoracic musculature. The higher the tension in the vocal cords (or the higher the subglottal pressure), the higher the fundamental frequency of the sound produced. In this way the fundamental frequency of the sound produced in speaking or singing can be changed at will. This is the procedure underlying our first introductory example, in which the vowel sound /a/ is to be sung at different "pitches." On the basis of the anatomical differences in the larynx – the length of the vocal cords in particular – that cause variation in this oscillatory behavior, voices are classified as **bass, tenor, alto** and **soprano.** Within each of these ranges various **registers** can be distinguished.

For a singer to produce and hold a "tone" the contractions of the muscles involved must be extremely finely coordinated. Among the mechanisms participating in this control are proprioceptors in the laryngeal muscles and the mucosa, and auditory feedback. The results are astonishingly good; practiced singers can repeat a test tone with a frequency error less than 1%. The situation becomes especially difficult when it is necessary to change the intensity of a tone while maintaining the pitch. Because the increasing subglottal pressure required to raise the intensity also slightly raises the frequency, the cricothyroid muscle must be relaxed to compensate, by reducing the tension of the vocal cords. That this actually occurs can be demonstrated by electromyographic recording of the activity of the muscles concerned.

In singing sounds of considerable intensity can be produced; a soprano voice (measured at a distance of 1 m) can easily exceed a sound pressure of 100 dB SPL.

The abovementioned auditory feedback is extraordinarily important. Children born deaf do not learn to speak, because they lack this auditory stimulus. Therefore it is important to prescribe a hearing aid for children congenitally hard of hearing while they are still infants. Hearing difficulty can be suspected when a child in its second year of life pays no attention to familiar sound stimuli, and when at the end of the first year the infantile babbling is not replaced by syllables and simple word sounds, the vocalizations instead becoming less frequent or ceasing altogether. Even when a person becomes deaf as an adult, speech deteriorates appreciably.

In **whispering** the vocal cords do not oscillate. They lie close together, leaving only a small triangular opening in the region of the arytenoid cartilages (cf. Fig. 12-18). The air passing through this opening makes a noise that can be used for articulation and thus produce the whispering "voice."

Articulation

Functional anatomy of the "vocal tract." Emerging from the glottis, air first enters the oropharyngeal cavity, which in this context is called the **vocal tract.** Comprising the pharyngeal, nasal and oral cavities, its form is very variable. The nasopharynx and adjacent part of the throat can be separated from the oropharynx by the soft palate (velum). The *configuration* of the oral cavity can be changed considerably by altering the positions of tongue and jaws. Moreover, the tongue can form a hump to divide the oral cavity into two spaces (Fig. 12-19). The palatal musculature, the chewing musculature, and especially the tongue musculature are responsible for these changes. The tongue can occupy practically every conceivable position within the mouth, with the help of both its internal muscles and those that radiate into it from various sites of origin on bones, or are so arranged as to shift the position of the tongue bone.

Mechanism of articulation. The periodic interruption of the airstream at the glottis is not the only acoustic

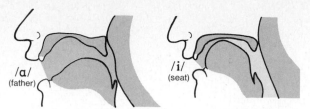

Fig. 12-19. Oropharyngeal space during pronunciation of /a/ and /i/

Table 12-1. Vowels in the English language (adapted from [1])

Front vowels (tongue forward)		Middle vowels (tongue in the middle)		Back vowels (tongue back)	
/i/	seat	/ɜ/	dirt	/ɑ/	cart
/I/	bit	/ʌ/	hut	/ɒ/	rod
/ɛ/	head	/ə/	the	/ɔ/	cord
/æ/	hat			/ʊ/	would
				/u/	rude

event in phonation. At other places where the respiratory tract narrows, if the velocity of expiration is high enough, turbulence produces a relatively weak noise, comprising a broad range of frequencies. The spaces in the vocal tract have particular **natural frequencies** of their own, depending on their momentary configuration. These are the frequencies produced when the air in these spaces is set into oscillation. For example, by tapping your cheek with a finger while the mouth is in different positions, you can make the different natural frequencies of the oral cavity audible (try this in a quiet room!). The noise produced at constrictions in the tract and the overtone-rich sound of the voice produced at the vocal cords also contain these frequencies. When the natural frequencies are present the vocal tract **resonates** [1, 7], amplifying these frequencies to above-threshold intensities so that they are distinctly audible. Each of the spaces formed in the many different configurations of the vocal tract has a different natural frequency. At each articulation position – that is, each particular position of jaw, tongue, and velum – quite specific frequencies or frequency bands are heard as soon as the cavities begin to resonate [1, 7, 12, 15]. The frequency bands characteristic of the different positions are called **formants.** They depend **only** on the configuration of the vocal tract, and not on the voice produced in the larynx. It is very easy to demonstrate experimentally that resonance phenomena are the essential factors in articulation, by breathing not air but another gas with a sound-conducting velocity different from air (e.g., helium). Under these conditions the resonance properties of the vocal tract are altered; speech becomes

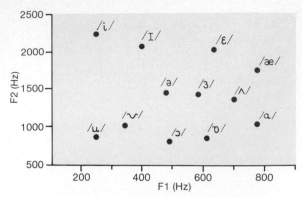

Fig. 12-20. Frequency of the second formant versus frequency of first formant for the vowels of English spoken by a typical male speaker. (From [1])

almost incomprehensible, even though the vocal-cord oscillations are unchanged.

Vowels. In normal speaking the vowels are produced by voiced resonance of the vocal tract; the configuration of the vocal tract is relatively stable, and the mouth is open to emit the sound [1, 7]. When the vowels in the English language are spoken, the velum is normally closed and the nasopharyngeal space does not oscillate with the oral cavity. The **formants** associated with this resonance are responsible for the facts that the vowel sound /a/ in our introductory example is recognized as such regardless of pitch or of the speaker, and that it and the other vowel sounds can be distinguished from one another. The formants are thus the acoustical equivalent of a particular vowel (or some consonants). Fig. 12-19 gives an example of the configuration of the oral cavity when the vowel sounds /a/ and /i/ are spoken. Depending on whether and where the tongue subdivides the cavity, spaces of different sizes and thus different formant frequencies are formed. In general a vowel sound is determined by at least two formants. Table 12-1 summarizes the vowels used in English, and Fig. 12–20 shows the associated formant frequencies of the first and second main formants (from [1]). The other frequently occurring formants are of low intensity and are not considered here.
By trying out different mouth positions it is easy to see how changes in the configuration of the oral cavity produce the transition from one vowel to another.

Diphthongs and semivowels. These phonemes resemble the true vowels except that the position of the vocal tract is not stable; it changes during articulation. Examples of diphthongs are the /ɛi/ in *pay* or the /ɑi/ in *high*. The transition is more rapid in the semivowels (or glides) – for example, /j/ in *you* or /w/ in

*w*all. These two phonemes start out like an /i/ or /u/. The consonants /r/ and /l/ are also in this phonetic group.

Consonants. This group includes a large number of phonemes, in the formation of which the vocal tract is not stable and the sound is not necessarily emitted through the mouth. They can be either voiced (i. e., accompanied by vocal-cord oscillation) or voiceless (without oscillation of the vocal cords). In general the vocal tract is more constricted than during vowel production, and the particular kind of constriction – by means of teeth, lips and tongue – determines which consonant is pronounced. A distinction is made between **fricatives** and **plosives** (or **stop consonants**).
The **fricatives** are accompanied by turbulent airflow at the constriction, which produces an audible sound. If the constriction is formed between the upper teeth and the lower lip (labio-dental), the consonants /v/ or /f/ are produced. Pressing the tip of the tongue against the upper teeth (dental) produces /ð/ and /θ/. /z/ and /s/ are produced by putting the upper and lower teeth close together and placing the tip of the tongue against the upper row (alveolar). If the tongue is shifted toward the hard palate (palatal) /ʒ/ and /ʃ/ are produced. Finally, /h/ is produced by a half-open position of the glottis (glottal). The various consonants are listed in Table 12-2.
The **plosives** are produced by the abrupt opening of the completely closed vocal tract, which suddenly releases the pressure in the lungs. Again, the site of the closure determines which stop consonant results (Table 12-2). If the tract is closed by the velum, /g/ and /k/ are produced. The individual plosives often differ hardly at all in frequency spectrum. Here the time course of the sound is the crucial factor in identifying the phoneme (cf. Fig. 12-21).

Nasals. In pronouncing the nasal consonants the nasopharyngeal cavity is wide open and the sound is emitted through the nose (as is easily demonstrated by closing the nose with the fingers: /m/ and /n/ cannot be produced for very long under these circumstances).

Sound Spectrography

Speech can be picked up by a microphone and broken down into its frequency components by a set of band-pass filters. The record of the frequency composition of sound as a function of time, the **sound spectrogram** (Fig. 12-21), is a representation of the acoustic characteristics just discussed, especially the formants. Time is on the abscissa, and frequency on

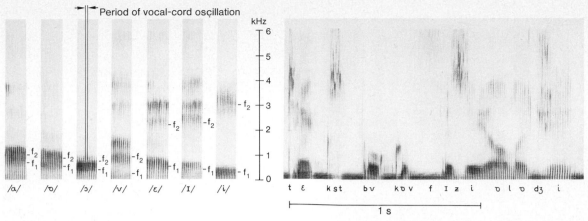

Fig. 12-21. Sonagram of the vowels /ɑ/, /ɒ/, /ɔ/, /ʊ/, /ɛ/, /ɪ/, /i/ and the phrase /textbook of physiology/. The abscissa represents time, and the ordinate the frequencies in the range 0–6 kHz in the composite sounds. The darker the shading, the more sound energy in a particular frequency band. f = formant (Recordings by courtesy of Dr. W. A. AINSWORTH)

the ordinate; the darkening indicates the time at which certain frequencies appear in the spoken sound. The darker the mark, the greater the sound energy in the designated frequency range. The formants are clearly distinguishable in the diagram. It is also evident that plosives (/t/) and fricatives (/s/, /z/) have a broad frequency spectrum with high-frequency components.

Speech Impediments

The complicated mechanism of speaking can be disturbed at many sites. A major distinction is that between *peripheral* and *central* disturbances. **Peripheral disturbance** is frequently caused by unilateral or bilateral paralysis of the laryngeal muscles, due to paralysis of the recurrent nerve. Slight damage causes hoarseness, whereas complete bilateral paralysis makes phonation impossible **(aphonia).** Because in this condition the glottis cannot be actively widened (paralysis of the posterior cricoarytenoids), breathing is considerably hampered. Nevertheless, verbal communication is still possible by **whispering,** because formant articulation is not affected. Even after surgical removal of the larynx patients can learn a method of speaking, called **esophageal speech.** Air is swallowed into the esophagus, and when it is released it makes a noise that sets the cavities of mouth and throat into resonant oscillation, producing the formant corresponding to the positions of the articulation structures. Electronic speech aids can also replace phonation in laryngectomized patients. In these, a generator produces a rasping noise, and when the device is pressed against the floor of the mouth resonant oscillations are induced. Because the vocal tract can still be put into the configurations required for articulation formants can be produced, giving tolerably understandable speech.

But if the musculature of tongue and throat fail to function properly speech is often severely impaired, because the formants can no longer be produced. An example is the "doughy" speech in bulbar paralysis, a neurological disease affecting the motor nuclei of the cranial nerves so as to damage the innervation of the tongue musculature.

Table 12-2. Consonants in the English language (adapted from [1])

Voiced			Unvoiced	
Fricatives				
Labio-dental	/v/	van	/f/	fix
Dental	/ð/	this	/θ/	thick
Alveolar	/z/	zoo	/s/	sat
Palatal	/ʒ/	azure	/ʃ/	ship
Glottal			/h/	hat
Stop consonants				
Labial	/b/	bat	/p/	pig
Alveolar	/d/	dog	/t/	tell
Velar	/g/	get	/k/	kick
Vocals				
Labial	/m/	man		
Alveolar	/n/	null		
Palatal-velar	/ŋ/	sing		

A congenital cleft palate also prevents the production of normal formants, because the mouth and throat cavities communicate through the gap. The remedy is surgical closure of the opening.

A major cause of **central speech disturbances** is destruction of Broca's speech center. In this case the ability to speak is lost even though the primary motor cortex for the speech musculature, the corresponding cranial nerves and their nuclei, and the peripheral apparatus are all completely intact. This condition is called **motor aphasia** (cf. p. 163). Further discussion of speech impediments can be found in [12].

12.4   References

Textbooks and Handbooks

1. AINSWORTH, W.A.: Mechanisms of Speech Recognition. Oxford: Pergamon 1976
2. BLAUERT, J.: Räumliches Hören. Stuttgart: Hirzel 1974

3. BRODAL, A., POMPEIANO, O. (Eds.): Basic Aspects of Central Vestibular Mechanisms. Amsterdam: Elsevier 1972
4. BULLOCK, T.H. (Ed.): Recognition of Complex Acoustic Signals. Berlin: Dahlem Konferenzen 1977
5. DALLOS, P.: The Auditory Periphery. New York–London: Academic Press 1973
6. EVANS, E. F., WILSON, J. P.: The Frequency Selectivity of the Cochlea. In: MØLLER, A. R. (Ed.), Basic Mechanisms of Hearing, pp. 519–551. New York: Academic Press 1973
7. FLANAGAN, J.L.: Speech Analysis, Synthesis and Perception. 2nd Edition. Berlin–Heidelberg–New York: Springer 1972
8. GREEN, D.M.: An Introduction to Hearing. Hillsdale: Lawrence Erlbaum Ass. 1976
9. KEIDEL, W.D., NEEF, W.D. (Eds.): Handbook of Sensory Physiology, Vol.V,1 (1974), Vol.V,2 (1975), Vol.V,3 (1976). Berlin–Heidelberg–New York: Springer
10. KORNHUBER, H.H. (Ed.): Handbook of Sensory Physiology, Vol.VI,1, Vol.VI,2. Berlin–Heidelberg–New York: Springer 1974
11. KRYTER, K.D.: The Effects of Noise on Man. New York–San Francisco–London: Academic Press 1970
12. LENNEBERG, E.H.: Biological Foundations of Language. New York: Wiley 1967
13. LUDVIGSEN, C., BARFORD, J.: Sensorineural Hearing Impairment and Hearing Aids. Stockholm: Almquist & Wiksell 1978, Scandinavian Audiology, Suppl.6
14. MOORE, B.C.J.: An Introduction to the Psychology of Hearing. London: Academic Press 1982
15. PROCTOR, D. F.: Breathing, Speech and Song. Wien: Springer 1980
16. RINTELMANN, W. F.: Hearing Assessment. Baltimore: University Park Press 1979
17. ROEDERER, J.G.: Introduction to the Physics and Psychophysics of Music. New York: Springer 1975
18. REASON, J.T., BRAND, J.J.: Motion Sickness. New York: Academic Press 1975
19. WILSON, V.J., MELVILL JONES, G.: Mammalian Vestibular Physiology. New York: Plenum 1979
20. ZWICKER, E., FELDTKELLER, R.: Das Ohr als Nachrichtenempfänger. 2nd Edition. Stuttgart: Hirzel 1967

Research Reports and Reviews

21. ADAMS, J.C.: Single unit studies on the dorsal and intermediate acoustic striae. J. comp. Neurol. *170,* 97–106 (1976)
22. AITKIN, L.M.: Tonotopic organization at higher levels of the auditory pathway. International Review of Physiology, Neurophysiology II, *10,* 249–279 (1976)
23. BRAWER, J.R., MOREST, D.K., KANE, E.C.: The neuronal architecture of the cochlear nucleus of the cat. J. comp. Neurol. *155,* 251–300 (1974)

24. DAVIS, H.: Principles of electric response audiometry. Ann. Otol., Rhinol., Laryngol., Suppl.28, Vol.85, No.3, Part 3, 4–96 (1976)
25. EVANS, E. F.: Neuronal processes for the detection of acoustic patterns and for sound localization. In: SCHMIDT, F.O., WORDEN, F.G. (Eds.), Neurosciences, Third Study Program, p.131. New York: MIT Press 1974
26. EVANS, E. F., KLINKE, R.: Reversible effects of cyanide and furosemide on the tuning of single cochlear nerve fibres. J. Physiol. *242,* 129–130 P (1974)
27. GOLDBERG, J.M., FERNANDEZ, C.: Vestibular mechanisms. Ann. Rev. Physiol. *37,* 129–162 (1975)
28. GRAYBIEL, A., MILLER II, E.F., HOMICK, J.L.: Experiment M 131. Human vestibular function. In: Proceedings of the Skylab Life Science Symposium NASA TMX – 5 G 154, pp. 169–220, 1974
29. HARTMANN, R., KLINKE, R.: Discharge properties of afferent fibres of the goldfish semicircular canal with high frequency stimulation. Pflügers Arch *388,* 111–121 (1980)
30. HILLMAN, D. E., McLAREN, J W.: Displacement configuration of semicircular canal cupulae. Neuroscience *4,* 1989–2000 (1979)
31. KLINKE, R., GALLEY, N.: Efferent innervation of vestibular and auditory receptors. Physiol. Rev. *54,* 316 (1974)
31a. KLINKE, R.: Neurotransmitters in the cochlea and the cochlear nucleus. Acta otolaryng. *91,* 541–554 (1981)
32. LIM, D.J.: Fine morphology of the tectorial membrane. In: PORTMANN, M., ARAN, J.M. (Eds.), Inner Ear Biology, pp. 47–60. INSERM, Paris 1977
33. MANLEY, J.A., MÜLLER-PREUSS, P.: Response variability of auditory cortex cells in the squirrel monkey to constant acoustic stimuli. Exp. Brain. Res. *32,* 171–180 (1978)
34. OMAN, C.M., YOUNG, L.R.: The physiological range of pressure difference and cupula deflections in the human semicircular canal. Acta otolaryng. (Stockh.) *74,* 324 (1972)
35. RHODE, W.S.: Some observations on cochlear mechanics. J. Acoust. Soc. Am. *64,* 158–176 (1978)
36. RUSSELL, I.J., SELLICK, P.M.: Intracellular studies of hair cells in the mammalian cochlea. J. Physiol. *284,* 261–290 (1978)
37. SMALL, A.M.: Periodicity pitch. In: TOBIAS, J.V. (Ed.), Foundations of Modern Auditory Theory, p.3. New York: Academic Press 1970
38. SPOENDLIN, H.: Innervation densities of the cochlea. Acta otolaryng. (Stockh.) *73,* 235 (1972)
39. THORNTON, A.R.D.: Properties of brainstem evoked responses. Rev. Laryng. (Bordeaux) *97,* 591–601 (1976)
40. WEBSTER, W.R., AITKIN, L.M.: Central auditory processing. In: GAZZANIGA, M.S., BLAKEMORE, C. (Eds.), Handbook of Psychobiology, p.325. New York: Academic Press 1975

13 Taste and Smell

H. Altner and J. Boeckh

13.1 Characterization of the Chemical Senses

The sensations of taste and smell are derived from a selective and highly sensitive reaction of specialized sense cells to the presence of the molecules of certain compounds. In a broader sense, specific reactions to molecules – a hormone (p.658), for instance, or a neurotransmitter (p.65) – are characteristic of many cells and tissues. But gustatory and olfactory sense cells act as exteroceptors; their reactions to molecules provide important information about external stimuli, which is processed in areas of the brain reserved for these senses and which gives rise to sensations. Other chemoreceptive cells serve as enteroceptors – for example, to measure CO_2 (p.484).

Taste and smell can be characterized and distinguished by morphological and physiological criteria. The most clear-cut difference between the two senses lies in the classification of their respective stimulus qualities (Table 13-1). Other characteristics, such as sensitivity or the physical properties of the adequate stimulus, differ in certain respects but with some overlap.

In comparison to other senses, taste and smell exhibit a high degree of **adaptation** (cf. Fig. 8-13, p.190). The excitation in the afferent pathways declines markedly during a maintained stimulus, and perception is correspondingly diminished; for example, after only a short time in a scented environment we stop perceiving the smell. An equally characteristic property of the chemical senses is the high sensitivity to certain stimuli. The **quantitatively** processable range of stimulus intensities, on the other hand, is small (ca. 1:500), and the difference threshold is high. The exponent in Stevens' power function $E = K \cdot (S-S_0)^n$ is 0.4–0.6 for odors and about 1 for taste stimuli (cf. Fig. 8–10, p.187).

Primary processes and chemical specificity. The first event in stimulation of a chemoreceptor is now gen-

Table 13-1. Subdivision and characterization of the chemical senses

	Taste	Smell
Receptors	Secondary sense cells	Primary sense cells; endings of cranial nerves V (IX and X)
Position of receptors	On the tongue	Nose and throat
Afferent cranial nerves	VII, IX	I, V (IX, X)
Stations in central nervous system	1. Medulla oblongata 2. Ventral thalamus 3. Cortex (postcentral gyrus) Connections to hypothalamus	1. Olfactory bulb 2. Telencephalon (prepiriform area) Connections to limbic system and hypothalamus
Adequate stimulus	Molecules of organic and inorganic substances, mostly nonvolatile. Stimulus source near or in direct contact with sense organ.	Molecules of almost exclusively organic, volatile compounds in gas form, becoming dissolved only at receptor. Stimulus source usually at a distance.
Number of qualitatively distinguishable stimuli	Small 4 basic qualities	Very large (thousands), in many poorly-defined quality classes
Absolute sensitivity	Relatively low At least 10^{16} or more molecules/ml solution	Very high to some substances (10^7 molecules per ml air, as little as 10^2 or 10^3 in animals)
Biological characterization	Contact sense Used for testing food and control of food intake and processing (salivary reflexes)	Long-distance sense Used to test environment (hygiene) and food, and by animals in foraging, communication, reproduction. Strong emotional weighting

erally thought to be an interaction based on weak binding forces between the stimulus molecule and a *receptor protein.* Proteins with the character of enzymes have been isolated from taste organs; their substance-specificity and turnover dynamics are the same as those of the receptors themselves. The subsequent events leading to the electrical response of the cell membrane are unknown. Each receptor cell responds very selectively to a particular group of substances. Slight changes in the structure of a substance can alter its sensory quality or render it ineffective. It is likely that the effectiveness of a molecule is crucially affected by its size (e.g., chain length) and the distribution of electrical charge within it (e.g., the positions of functional groups). But the fact that in many cases molecules that are quite different chemically elicit the same olfactory sensations remains unexplained. For example, the three following compounds all smell musky despite their structural differences (cf. BEETS in [1]).

CH—(CH$_2$)$_7$
‖   C = O
CH—(CH$_2$)$_7$

Civetone

O$_2$N

NO$_2$

5.7-Dinitro-indan   1.3.4.6.7.8-Hexahydro-cyclopenta[f]-2-benzopyran

It has been proposed that chemoreceptors bear **reception sites** specific to particular groups of substances. This view is supported by cases of partial anosmia, the selective failure to perceive a limited number of odors, quite closely related chemically (cf. p.304). The selective action of certain drugs on taste organs can be interpreted similarly. When potassium gymnemate, a substance from the Indian plant *Gymnema silvestre,* is placed on the tongue the perception of sweetness alone is eliminated – sugar "tastes like sand." A protein contained in the fruit of the western African plant *Synsepalium dulcificum* changes acid flavors to sweet, so that lemon tastes like orange (cf. KURIHARA in [1]). Placing cocaine on the tongue causes the loss of all four taste qualities at different times, in the following order: bitter, sweet, salty, sour.

13.2   The Sense of Taste

Receptors and Neurons

The **gustatory sense cells** *(taste cells)* in adults are on the surface of the tongue. Together with supporting cells, in groups of 40–60 elements, they form **taste buds** in the epithelium of the lingual papillae (Fig. 13-1). Large vallate papillae at the base of the tongue contain as many as 200 taste buds each, whereas the smaller fungiform and foliate papillae on the anterior and lateral parts of the tongue each contain only a few. Altogether, an adult has a few thousand taste buds. **Glands** between the papillae secrete a fluid that rinses the buds. The distal parts of the receptor cells, which are sensitive to the stimuli, are convoluted to form *microvilli.* These project into a common chamber that communicates with the exterior by a pore on the surface of the papilla (Fig. 13-1). The stimulus molecules reach the taste cells by diffusing through this pore.

Like other secondary sense cells, the taste cells produce a receptor potential when stimulated. This excitation is transmitted synaptically to **afferent fibers** in **cranial nerves,** which conduct it to the brain in the form of nerve impulses. The nerves involved are the **chorda tympani,** a branch of the **facial nerve** (VII) that innervates the anterior and lateral parts of the tongue, and the **glossopharyngeal nerve** (IX) to the posterior part (Fig. 13-2). By branching, a single afferent fiber

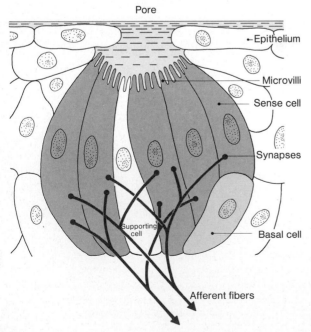

Pore

←Epithelium

Microvilli

Sense cell

Synapses

Supporting cell

Basal cell

Afferent fibers

Fig. 13-1. Schematic drawing of a taste bud embedded in a lingual papilla, showing basal cell, sense cells, supporting cell and afferent fibers of the associated cranial nerve

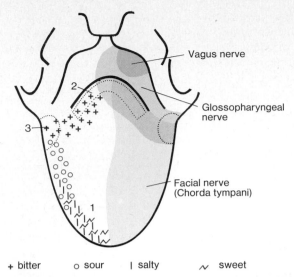

+ bitter   o sour | salty   ∿ sweet

Fig. 13-2. Schematic drawing of the human tongue, showing the afferent innervation by different cranial nerves (shading) and the distribution of the papillae (1 fungiform, 2 vallate, 3 foliate). The inhomogeneous distribution of taste qualities is indicated by symbols

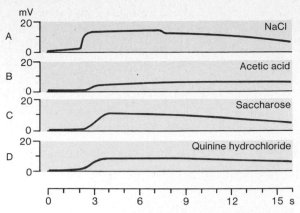

Fig. 13-3 A-D. Intracellularly measured receptor potentials of single gustatory sense cells on the tongue of a frog. Stimuli: **A** 0.5 mol/l NaCl, **B** 0.016 mol/l acetic acid, **C** 0.25 mol/l sucrose, **D** 0.004 mol/l quinine hydrochloride. (Modified from Sato, in [1])

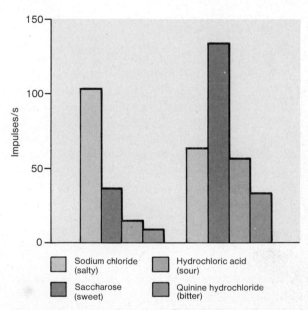

Fig. 13-4. Responses of two single fibers, in the chorda tympani of a rat, to various substances: 0.1 mol/l NaCl, 0.5 mol/l sucrose, 0.01 N HCl, 0.02 mol/l quinine hydrochloride. (Modified from Sato, in [12])

receives excitation from the receptor cells of various taste buds.

There is a remarkably high taste-cell **turnover rate**; the life span of a cell is about 10 days, after which it is replaced by a new receptor derived from a basal cell. The new taste cells become associated with the afferent fibers in such a way that the specificity of the fibers is unchanged. The mechanisms that ensure this match between receptor and fiber are not yet known (cf. Oakley in [12]).

Reactions of the cells and fibers. A single **taste cell** in most cases responds to substances representative of several taste qualities (Fig. 13–3), generating a corresponding pattern of excitation in the afferent fiber (Fig. 13-4). This specific pattern is called the *"taste profile"* of the fiber. Many fibers in Nerve IX give particularly strong responses to bitter stimuli; those in Nerve VII are more excited by salt, sugar or acid stimuli (cf. p. 302), one class of fibers responding more strongly to sugar than to salt, another more strongly to salt than to sugar, etc. This taste-specific difference in level of excitation in different fiber groups contains the information about **taste quality** – that is, the kind of molecule. The overall level of excitation in the population of fibers contains the information about **stimulus intensity** – that ist, the concentration of the molecules.

Central neurons. The **taste fibers** of Nerves VII and IX terminate in, or in the vicinity of, the **solitary nucleus** of the *medulla oblongata*. This nucleus makes connection, by way of the medial lemniscus, with the **thalamus** in the region of the *ventral posteromedial nucleus*. The third-order neurons pass through the internal capsule and terminate in the region of the *postcentral gyrus* of the **cerebral cortex**. Processing in these stations results in the presence of increasing numbers of highly taste-specific neurons. A certain number of cortical cells respond only to substances of a single taste quality. The positions of these neurons indicate a degree of spatial organization on the basis

Table 13-2. Characteristic taste substances and their effectiveness in eliciting taste sensations in man. (From PFAFFMANN, in [1])

Quality	Substance	Threshold (mol/l)
Bitter	Quinine sulfate	0.000008
	Nicotine	0.000016
Sour	Hydrochloric acid	0.0009
	Citric acid	0.0023
Sweet	Sucrose	0.01
	Glucose	0.08
	Saccharin	0.000023
Salty	NaCl	0.01
	CaCl$_2$	0.01

of effective taste quality. Other neurons in these centers respond not only to taste, but to thermal or mechanical stimulation of the tongue as well.

Gustatory Ability in Man

The qualities. Humans basically discriminate 4 taste qualities: **sweet, sour, bitter, salty.** These are quite well characterized by representative compounds (Table 13-2). A sweet taste is associated chiefly with naturally occurring sugars such as sucrose or glucose, and NaCl tastes salty; other salts, such as KCl, taste salty and bitter at the same time. Such **mixed sensations** are also characteristic of many natural taste stimuli, and correspond to the nature of their components. For example, orange tastes sweet and sour, grapefruit sour, sweet and bitter. Substances with a sour taste are acids; many plant alkaloids have a bitter taste.

Zones of specific sensitivity can be spatially demarcated on the tongue. Bitter stimuli act primarily on the *base* of the tongue, and the other qualities act at the *side* and *tip* in overlapping regions (Fig. 13–2; cf. p. 301).
There is no unequivocal correlation between the **chemical properties** of a substance and its **gustatory action.** For example, not only sugars but also lead salts taste sweet, and the most effective sweet stimuli are artificial sweeteners such as saccharin. The *perceived quality* of a substance, moreover, depends on its *concentration.* Table salt in low concentrations tastes sweet, and is purely salty only when more concentrated. Sensitivity to bitter substances is remarkably high. Because such substances are often poisonous, it makes sense that one should be warned of even small concentrations in water or food. Fairly strong bitter stimuli readily elicit *vomiting* or *retching reflexes.* The **emotional components** of taste perceptions

vary widely, depending on the condition of the body. A person with a salt deficiency finds food acceptable even though its salt concentration is so high that a normal person would reject it.

The sense of taste is evidently quite uniform in **mammals in general.** Behavioral experiments have shown that other mammals discriminate the same taste qualities as man does. However, single-fiber recordings have revealed certain abilities beyond the scope of the human taste sense. For example, in cats *"water fibers"* have been found, which either respond only to water or have a taste profile that includes water along with other qualities as an effective stimulus (cf. SATO in [1]).

Biological significance. The biological role of the sense of taste is not only to *test the edibility of food* (see above); tastes also affect the process of digestion. Connections with autonomic efferents form reflexes that enable taste inputs to control the secretion of digestive glands. Not only is the amount of secretion influenced, but also its composition – depending, for example, on whether a sweet or salty taste predominates in the food.
As one **grows older** gustatory ability declines. Consumption of drugs such as caffeine and heavy smoking also reduce taste sensations.

13.3   The Sense of Smell

The surface area of the nasal mucosa is increased by conchae, ridges that project from the side into the nasal cavity. The **olfactory region** containing most of the

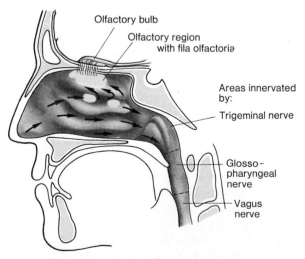

Fig. 13-5. Schematic drawing of the human nose and throat cavities (sagittal section). The olfactory region is restricted to the upper and middle conchae. The regions innnervated by the trigeminal (V), glossopharyngeal (IX) and vagus (X) nerves are indicated

sense cells is restricted to the upper concha, although the middle concha bears small islands of olfactory epithelium (Fig. 13-5).

Receptors

The **olfactory cells** are primary, bipolar sense cells, sending out two processes – at the apex a dendrite bearing **cilia,** and at the base an axon. The internal structure of the cilia differs from that of normal kinocilia; incapable of active movement, they are embedded in the layer of mucus that covers the olfactory epithelium. Odor substances carried in by the respired air can come into contact with the membranes of the cilia, the most likely site of the interaction between stimulus molecule and receptor. The axons run to the olfactory bulb in bundles, the *fila olfactoria*. In addition, the entire nasal mucosa contains free endings of the *trigeminal nerve,* some of which also respond to odor stimuli. In the throat region, olfactory stimuli can excite fibers in the glossopharyngeal and vagus nerve (Fig. 13-5). The mucus layer over the olfactory epithelium protects it from drying out; it is continually replenished by secretion and distributed by the movement of the kinocilia in the surrounding epithelial regions.

Odor molecules are conveyed to the receptors periodically, during inspiration through the nostrils. To a lesser extent, odors can move to the olfactory epithelium from the oral cavity, by diffusion through the choanae. While eating, therefore, one experiences mixed sensations in which gustatory and olfactory sensations are combined. Sniffing, a conspicuous behavior of many mammals, can considerably increase the intake of air and thus the concentration of stimulus molecules in the mucosa.

Altogether the human olfactory region, ca. 10 cm² in area, contains about 10^7 receptors. The number of receptors in other vertebrates is greater (e. g., $2.2 \cdot 10^8$ in a German shepherd dog). Olfactory cells, like taste cells, are regularly replaced; presumably, then, not all the cells are functional at the same time.

Electrodes in contact with the vertebrate olfactory epithelium record slow potentials of complex form and a few millivolts amplitude during odor stimulation. These **electroolfactograms** (EOG; Fig. 13-6; cf. OTTO-SON in [1]), like electroretinograms (ERG), represent the summed activity of many units, so that they give no information about the properties of the individual receptors. Recording from *single receptors* in the olfactory mucosa of vertebrates has been accomplished only occasionally (Fig. 13-6). Such records show that the spontaneous discharge rate of these cells is very low, only a few impulses per second, and that each re-

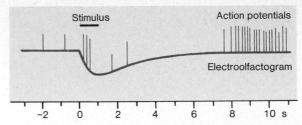

Fig. 13-6. Simultaneous recording of electroolfactogram *(red)* and action potentials of a single receptor in the olfactory epithelium of the frog during stimulation with nitrobenzene. Duration of stimulus *(black)* 1 s. (From GESTELAND, in [1])

Table 13-3. Distinguishing characteristics of odor classes. (From AMOORE and SKRAMLIK)

Odor class	Known representative compounds	Smells like	"Standard"
Floral	Geraniol	Roses	d-1-β-phenyl-ethylmethyl-carbinol
Ethereal	Benzyl acetate	Pears	1,2-dichlor-ethane
Musky	Muscone	Musk	3-methyl-cyclopentade-can-1-one
Camphor	Cineole, camphor	Eucalyptus	1,8-cineole
Putrid	Hydrogen sulfide	Rotten eggs	Dimethylsulfide
Pungent	Formic acid, acetic acid	Vinegar	Formic acid

ceptor responds to a large number of substances. As in the recording of taste profiles (cf. p. 301), it is possible to construct *response spectra* of single sense cells (cf. GESTELAND in [1]).

Odor Qualities

Humans can distinguish the smell of thousands of different substances. The olfactory sensations can be arranged in groups on the basis of certain similarities, so that **odor** or **quality classes** can be defined. However, this classification is by no means as clear-cut as that of taste qualities. The uncertainty in such categorization is evident in the widely varying number of classes proposed by the different authors. Quality is even less well correlated with chemically definable properties than in the case of taste stimuli (cf. p. 302). As Table 13-3 shows, the odor classes as a rule are named for the natural sources of the odor substances,

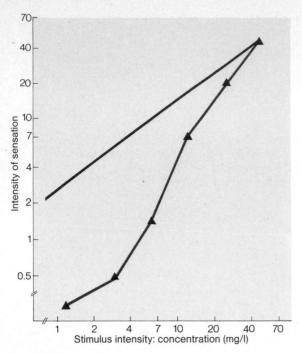

Fig. 13-7. Increase in intensity of sensation with increasing stimulus intensity (stimulus: propanol), unadapted *(straight black line)* and after adaptation to pentanol *(black triangles, red curve)*. (Modified from CAIN and ENGEN, in [11])

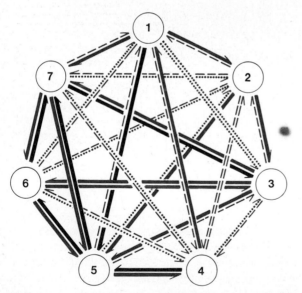

Fig. 13-8. Cross-adaptational relationships among 7 odor substances (1 citral, 2 cyclopentanone, 3 benzyl acetate, 4 safrole, 5 m-xylene, 6 methyl salicylate, 7 butyl acetate). As a rule the reciprocal interactions are not equally strong. The degree to which the detection threshold is raised is indicated by the connecting lines as follows: *black lines,* very large increase; *red continuous lines,* large increase; *red dashed lines,* moderate increase; *red dotted lines,* slight increase in threshold. (Modified from KÖSTER [6])

or for typical representatives; the classes can be characterized by "standard odors."

So far no neurophysiological basis for assigning odor substances to quality classes has been found. The view that groups of closely related odor substances can be distinguished from one another is supported by cases in which a person's ability to smell is partially impaired (**partial anosmia;** cf. p. 300). In this disorder the thresholds to certain odor substances are elevated; at least some such cases are genetic in origin. Often the thresholds to several substances are affected, and as a rule these prove to belong to the same odor class. Experimental data relevant to odor classification can also be obtained by analysis of *cross-adaptation.* These experiments are based on the observation that when prolonged exposure to an odor results in decreased sensitivity to that substance, the thresholds to certain other substances are raised as well (Fig. 13-7). By testing the degree to which the threshold to any arbitrary odor substance is affected by previous presentation of other substances, as well as the reciprocal interaction, one can construct a diagram of cross-adaptational relationships (Fig. 13-8). This procedure, however, does not provide an unequivocal, detailed organization of the great variety of odor substances [6].

When interpreting human olfactory sensations, it must be kept in mind that the fibers of the *trigeminal nerve* that terminate in the nasal mucosa also respond to odor substances and contribute to these sensations, as do the endings of *glossopharyngeal-* and *vagal-nerve fibers* in the throat (Fig. 13-5). These sensations, not mediated by the olfactory nerve, persist when the olfactory epithelium becomes nonfunctional – for example, as a result of infection (flu), tumors (craniotomy), or skull traumata. In such cases, together termed **hyposmia,** thresholds are considerably higher than normal, but the ability to discriminate among the odors that are detected is only slightly diminished. In hypogonadotropic hypogonadism (Kallmann's syndrome) olfaction is mediated entirely by these cranial nerves, for in this congenital disorder the olfactory bulbs are aplastic. Noxious thermal and chemical stimuli, depending on their nature and mode of action, can cause reversible or irreversible acute or chronic hyposmias or anosmias.

Sensitivity, Coding

The human sense of smell is very sensitive, even though some animal olfactory organs are known to perform still better. Table 13-4 gives the concentrations of two odor substances that just suffice to elicit a sensation in man. With very low concentrations the sensation is unspecific; only at somewhat higher concentrations can an odor be not only detected but identified. For example, the smell of skatole at low concentrations is regarded as not at all unpleasant, whereas above a certain limit the typical repulsive smell of this substance is manifest. Therefore a distinction is made between the **detection threshold** and the **recognition threshold.**

Thresholds of this sort, determined by reported sensations or the behavioral responses of animals, cannot establish the *sensitivity of single receptors.* However, knowing the spatial extent of the human olfactory organ and the number of sense cells within it, one can estimate their sensitivity. Such estimates indicate that an individual sense cell becomes depolarized and produces an action potential in response to a single odor molecule, or at most a few molecules. Of course, a behavioral response results only when sufficient receptors are activated to raise the signal-to-noise ratio in the sensory input above a certain critical level. Experiments on animals, insects in particular, in which the relevant parameters are more easily monitored and the responses of the receptors can be recorded electrophysiologically, have provided convincing evidence of the monomolecular response of the single sense cell.

Coding. The coding of odor stimuli by the receptors can as yet be described only to a first approximation. The first consideration is that the individual receptor cells respond to a fairly large number of different odor substances. Accordingly, the receptors (like gustatory receptors) have overlapping response profiles. Thus each odor substance would be associated with a specific pattern of excitation in the population of sense cells. For a given pattern, the concentration of the odor substance would be reflected in the overall level of excitation.

Central Processing

Olfactory bulb. Histologically, the olfactory bulb is subdivided into several layers characterized by cells of particular shapes that send out certain types of processes, with typical kinds of connections among these processes. The essential features of information processing in the olfactory bulb are (i) marked **convergence** of the sense cells upon the mitral cells, the second-order neurons in the auditory pathway, (ii) extensive **inhibitory mechanisms,** and (iii) **efferent control** of the incoming excitation. In the layer of the glomeruli the axons of about 1000 olfactory cells terminate on the primary dendrites of one *mitral cell* (Fig. 13–9). These dendrites also make reciprocal

Table 13-4. Detection threshold to butyric acid and butyl mercaptan. (From NEUHAUS and STUIVER)

Substance	Molecules per ml air	Concentration at stimulus source
Butyric acid	$2.4 \cdot 10^9$	10^{-10}
Butyl mercaptan	10^7	$2.7 \cdot 10^{-12}$

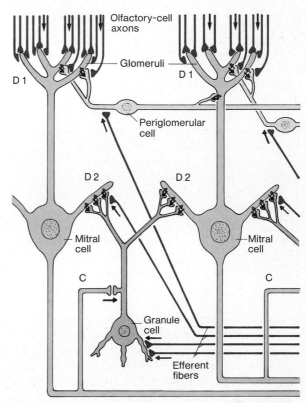

Fig. 13-9. Survey of the neuronal connections in the olfactory bulb. In the glomeruli the olfactory-cell axons terminate on the primary dendrites (D1) of the mitral cells. Periglomerular cells and granule cells make reciprocal synapses on the primary and secondary (D2) dendrites of the mitral cells. C, collaterals. The direction of synaptic transmission is indicated by arrows (excitation, *black;* inhibition, *red*). (Combined and modified from SHEPHERD, in [13])

dendrodendritic synapses with the *periglomerular cells.* The mitral-to-periglomerular-cell contacts are excitatory, and those in the opposite direction exert an inhibitory influence on the mitral cells. The axons of the periglomerular cells terminate on the mitral-cell dendrites of adjacent glomeruli. This arrangement makes possible a modulation of the local dendritic response; it mediates *self* or *surround inhibition.* The *granule cells* also make reciprocal dendrodendritic synapses with mitral cells, in this case with the secondary dendrites; these influence impulse generation in the mitral cells. Here, too, the synapses directed toward the mitral cell are inhibitory, so that the reciprocal contacts subserve self inhibition. Finally, the granule cells make contact with mitral-cell collaterals as well as with *efferent (bulbopetal) axons* of various origins. Some of the centrifugal fibers come from the contralateral bulb, by way of the anterior commissure.

The special feature of inhibition by the granule cells, which lack axons, is that in contrast to the typical Renshaw inhibition these cells can be partially activated – that is, with a spatial gradation. This pattern of highly complex interactions is entirely comparable to the situation in the retina, although the retinal processing is based on a different kind of cellular organization [13].

Central connections. The axons of the *mitral cells* form the *lateral olfactory tract,* among the destinations of which are the *prepiriform area* and the *piriform lobe.* Synapses with higher-order neurons provide connections to the *hippocampal formation* and, by way of the amygdaloid complex, to the autonomic nuclei in the *hypothalamus.* Neurons responding to olfactory stimuli have also been found in the reticular formation of the mesencephalon.

The influence of olfaction on other functional systems. The direct connection to the limbic system (cf. p. 138) explains the marked **emotional component** of olfactory sensations. Odors readily give rise to feelings of enjoyment or aversion (hedonic components of sensation), and the affective state of the organism is altered correspondingly. Moreover, the significance of olfactory stimuli in *control of reproductive behavior* should not be underestimated, although the results of animal experiments – especially the olfaction-blocking experiments on rodents – cannot be applied directly to humans. Animal experiments have also shown that the responses of neurons in the olfactory pathway can be altered by testosterone injection. Thus the flow of excitation is also under the influence of the sexual hormones.

Functional disorders. In addition to the states of impaired olfaction called hyposmia and anosmia (cf.

p. 304), olfactory sensations may arise in the absence of odor substances **(olfactory hallucinations)** or odors may be incorrectly perceived **(parosmia).** Olfactory hallucinations of unpleasant character (cacosmia) are experienced primarily by schizophrenic patients.

13.4 References

Textbooks and Handbooks

1. BEIDLER, L. M. (Ed.): Chemical Senses. Part 1: Olfaction, Part 2: Taste. Handbook of Sensory Physiology, Vol. IV. Berlin–Heidelberg–New York: Springer 1971

Research Reports and Reviews

2. DENTON, D. A., COGHLAN, J. P. (Eds.): Olfaction and Taste, Vol. V. New York: Academic Press 1975
3. EISENBERG, J. F., KLEIMAN, D. G.: Olfactory communication in mammals. Ann. Rev. Ecol. Syst. *3,* 1 (1972)
4. HAYASHI, T. (Ed.): Olfaction and Taste, Vol. II. Oxford–London–New York–Paris: Pergamon Press 1967
5. JAENICKE, L. (ed.): Biochemistry of Sensory Functions. 25. Mosbacher Koll. Ges. Biol. Chemie. Berlin–Heidelberg–New York: Springer 1974
6. KÖSTER, E.: Adaptation and Cross-Adaptation in Olfaction. Rotterdam: Bronder 1971
7. LE MAGNEN, J., MacLEOD, P. (Eds.): Olfaction and Taste, Vol. VI. London–Washington DC: Information Retrieval 1977
8. MOULTON, D. G., BEIDLER, L. M.: Structure and function in the peripheral olfactory system. Physiol. Rev. *47,* 1–52 (1967)
9. OHLOFF, G., THOMAS, A. F. (Eds.): Gustation and Olfaction. London–New York: Academic Press 1971
10. OTTOSON, D., SHEPHERD, G. M.: Experiments and concepts in olfactory physiology. In: ZOTTERMAN, Y. (Ed.): Sensory Mechanisms. Progress in Brain Res., Vol. 23. Amsterdam: Elsevier 1967
11. PFAFFMANN, C. (Ed.): Olfaction and Taste, Vol. III. New York: Rockefeller University Press 1969
12. SCHNEIDER, D. (Ed.): Olfaction and Taste, Vol. IV. Stuttgart: Wiss. Verlagsges. 1972
13. SHEPHERD, G. M.: Synaptic organization of the mammalian olfactory bulb. Physiol. Rev. *52,* 864 (1972)
14. WOLSTENHOLME, G. E. W., KNIGHT, J. (Eds.): Taste and Smell in Vertebrates. London: Churchill 1970
15. ZOTTERMAN, Y. (Ed.): Olfaction and Taste, Vol. I. Oxford–London–New York–Paris: Pergamon Press 1963

14 Thirst and Hunger: General Sensations

R. F. SCHMIDT

The feeling of thirst we experience when we have not drunk enough liquids, and the feelings of hunger when we have not eaten recently, cannot be ascribed to a particular sense organ or part of the body. For this reason they are called **general sensations.** Other examples of general sensations are tiredness, shortness of breath, and sexual appetite. From the viewpoint of sensory physiology, a characteristic they all share is that they can be elicited by one or more *adequate stimuli originating within the body itself* rather than in its environment. These stimuli are detected by receptors, some of which are still unknown, and thus produce the associated general sensations (Fig. 14-1 A). For example, we shall see below that intracellular osmotic hypertonicity can be sensed, giving rise to thirst (Fig. 14-1 B).

Such adequate stimuli not only elicit the general sensations but also induce **drives** directed toward correcting the deficiency that has been detected. This activity is controlled by the sensations to some extent, and to some extent is independent of them (Fig. 14-1 A). Water deficiency thus leads not only to a sensation of thirst, but also to the search for water and to the removal of the deficiency by drinking (Fig. 14-1 B). In general terms, the *satisfaction of a drive eliminates the cause of the general sensation* (Fig. 14-1 A).

From a *biological viewpoint* the drives associated with general sensations serve to ensure survival of the individual or species. As a rule, therefore, they must be satisfied. They are inborn and need not be learned. But during a lifetime they are modified by numerous influences, especially at the more advanced phylogenetic levels. These influences act at various points in the overall process (cf. Fig. 14-1 A, B). No description of drives and their modification can be given here; only those aspects of thirst and hunger related to sensory physiology will be discussed, as examples of the category of general sensations.

14.1 Thirst

The Origin of Thirst

Conditions under which a sensation of thirst appears. The adult human body consists of about 70%–75% water by weight (without taking account of the fat deposits). This water content is maintained within very narrow limits. Normally it fluctuates by only about $\pm$ 0.22% of the body weight, or ca. $\pm$ 150 ml in a man weighing 70 kg. If the body loses water amounting to more than 0.5% of its weight (ca. 350 ml for a person weighing 70 kg) thirst results [2, 5, 6, 10, 11]. (Usually people drink without being thirsty; cf. p. 310).

The physiological forms of water loss (urine, sweat, water vapor in the exhaled air) together cause water to be lost from the extra- and the intracellular compartments, with a concomitant, though normally slight, *hypertonicity.* Moreover, the *secretion of saliva* is reduced, causing the **feeling of dryness** in mouth and throat so characteristic of thirst. Assuming the presence of suitable receptors, then, water deficiency in the body could be measured (i) by the volume or osmotic pressure of the *cells,* (ii) by the volume or osmotic pressure of the *extracellular fluid,* and (iii) indirectly by the reduction of *saliva secretion* and the resulting dryness of the oral and pharyngeal mucosa. Most experiments designed to test these alternatives have been done on animals, the amount of water drunk by the animals being taken as an indicator of the degree of experimentally produced thirst [2, 5, 6, 8, 9, 10].

Adequate stimuli for the sensation of thirst. Following intravenous infusion of a hypertonic NaCl solution, a dog drinks twice as much water as it does after i. v. infusion of an osmotically equivalent solution of urea. In the former case, because the cell membranes are impermeable to Na^+ ions, water leaves the cells. But the cell membranes are readily permeable to urea, so that when it is injected, the concentrations in the intracellular and extracellular spaces equilibrate, with a

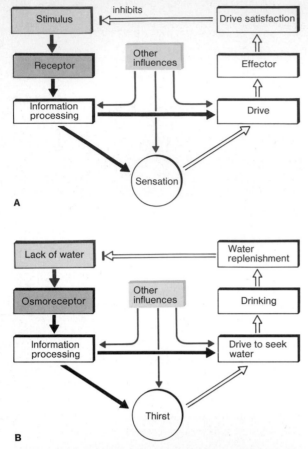

A

B

Fig. 14-1 A, B. Diagram of the relationship between general sensations and drives. **A** General representation of the origin of general sensations and drives. **B** Production, by water deficiency, of the feeling of thirst and of the drive to find water. Other receptors, in addition to the osmoreceptors, contribute to the sensation of thirst (cf. Fig. 14-2). The vertical red bars at the tips of the top arrows indicate that satisfaction of the drive (the provision of water in B) leads to elimination of the stimulus (water deficiency in B)

distinctly smaller change in volume and tonicity of the cells. This finding has been confirmed by repetition of the experiment, with many modifications, on a wide variety of mammals. The inference to be drawn is that **reduction of cell volume** (the *salt content* of the cells remaining constant) elicits thirst [9, 10].

If the amount of Na^+ in the extracellular space is experimentally reduced (for example, by a change in diet or by peritoneal dialysis), the extracellular compartment loses water; part is released from the body and part diffuses into the cells. Under these conditions thirst is experienced despite the increase in cell volume. (A hunger for table salt also appears [2].) If the total volume of the extracellular fluid is reduced without changing the NaCl concentration, thirst is also induced. We conclude that decrease in volume of the extracellular fluid also elicits thirst. Experi-

ments have shown that the effects of the above two factors are **additive,** so that *simultaneous decrease in cell volume and in extracellular fluid* gives rise to **intense thirst** [10].

The **dryness of the mouth** accompanying essentially all forms of thirst is caused, as mentioned above, by the *reduced secretion of saliva*. It reflects the water deficit and, contrary to previous opinion, appears to be a **symptom** rather than a cause of the general feeling of thirst. This is demonstrated by the following findings. Moistening the mouth and throat surfaces does not eliminate the sensation of thirst, though it can relieve it somewhat. Nor can thirst be relieved or prevented by local anesthesia of the oral mucosa, or even by complete denervation of the mouth and throat region. Finally, congenital absence of the salivary glands (in humans) or their surgical removal (from animals) has no appreciable effect on water consumption.

All the conditions giving rise to *thirst* simultaneously lead to the **release of ADH** (antidiuretic hormone or vasopressin; cf. p.662). Conversely, excessive drinking causes inhibition of ADH release and hence water diuresis [9].

Receptors and Central Mechanisms

Intracellular receptors. The neural structures chiefly responsible for regulating salt/water balance are located in the diencephalon, especially in the **hypothalamus and its vicinity.** There are numerous **osmoreceptors,** particularly in areas in *front* of the hypothalamus, which are activated by the increased *intracellular* salt concentration when the cell loses water. The injection of very small amounts (less than 0.2 ml) of hypertonic solutions of NaCl into certain parts of this region, for example, causes goats to begin drinking 30–60 s later, and to continue for 2–5 min, consuming 2–8 liters of water. Electrical stimulation of the same neural structures also elicits prolonged drinking. In many experiments the ablation or coagulation of certain constellations of hypothalamic structures has resulted in reduction or cessation of drinking even though body water is depleted. All these results indicate that **osmoreceptors in the diencephalon,** especially in the areas anterior to the hypothalamus, serve as *sensors* for the thirst induced by **cellular water deficiency** (Fig. 14-2). Neuronal structures in the hypothalamus evidently play a crucial role in processing the information from these osmoreceptors [3, 5, 9, 12].

Extracellular receptors. As far as the sensors underlying the *thirst elicited by lack of water in the extracellular space* are concerned, we have only suggestions and indirect evidence. At present it appears most likely that **stretch receptors** in the walls of the large veins near the heart, in addition to their influence on the circulation, also participate in the regulation of water balance and the induction of thirst (Fig. 14-2). The hypothalamus is an important processing center for signals carried in vagal afferents from the stretch receptors to the CNS. Moreover, there is evidence that the neuronal mechanisms giving rise to thirst are supplemented by **hormonal factors.** Extracellular dehydration causes the release of **renin** and thus the formation of **angiotensin II** (cf. p. 634). Intravenous administration of angiotensin II or its direct application to various parts of the hypothalamus, including the subfornical organ, elicits intense thirst. It seems certain, therefore, that angiotensin II plays a role in hypovolemic thirst, but at the moment its precise position and significance in the complex of mechanisms underlying thirst are unclear [2, 10, 11].

Receptors in mouth and throat. The *dryness of the mouth caused by reduced flow of saliva is signalled by receptors in the oropharyngeal mucosa* (Fig. 14-2). Experiments on animals have shown that various kinds of receptors are present there (mechanoreceptors, cold and warm receptors, and perhaps water receptors), but the extent to which each participates in eliciting this **peripheral component** of thirst is not known. If these receptors are stimulated when there is no general water deficiency in the body, as may happen as a result of speaking, smoking, breathing through the mouth or eating very dry food, the **false thirst** they elicit can be satisfied by moistening the oral mucosa; in the case of genuine thirst, as mentioned above, this procedure may lessen the feeling of thirst, but cannot eliminate it.

Central integration. Thirst is thus a general sensation based on the combined action of many receptor types, some in the periphery and others in the central nervous system itself. The **diencephalon,** the hypothalamus in particular, appears to play a dominant role in integrating this multitude of afferent inputs. We do not know how accurately the results of experiments on animals can be applied to humans, nor do we know which central structures give rise to the sensation of thirst. One may assume that the relationships diagrammed in Fig. 14-2 are indicative of those operating in humans [3, 9, 10, 12].

The sensation of thirst does not adapt. Again, animal experiments have corroborated this subjective experience. The amount of water consumed after i.v. injection of hypertonic saline solution has been shown to be independent of the rate of infusion. In other words, the thirst elicited by the injection of a specific amount of solution was the same whether the NaCl concentration rose very slowly or very rapidly. As a rule, because thirst does not adapt, the only way to alleviate the sensation is to consume water (cf. Fig. 9-1 B).

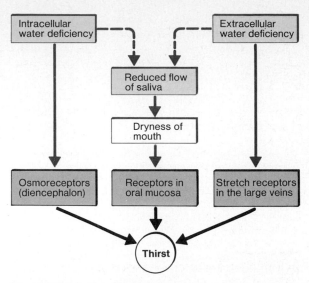

Fig. 14-2. Production of the sensation of thirst. The receptors involved are marked by the gray shading. Above them their adequate stimuli are indicated. Dryness of the mouth is an indirect consequence of intracellular and extracellular lack of water

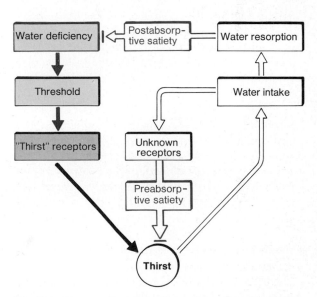

Fig. 14-3. Diagram of preabsorptive and postabsorptive satiety resulting from water intake. The receptors shown in Fig. 14-2 are indicated here by the single box labelled "thirst" receptors

The Quenching of Thirst

Preabsorptive and postabsorptive satiety. There is a considerable delay between the moment drinking is begun and the time the water deficiency is abolished for the water must first be absorbed. But it is a common observation, and one repeatedly confirmed in animal experiments, that the feeling of thirst ceases (i.e., drinking is stopped) long before compensation of the water deficiency in the extracellular and intracellular compartements is possible. **Postabsorptive satiety** is preceded by **preabsorptive satiety,** a mechanism to prevent the intake of excessive water until the absorbed water becomes effective (Fig. 14-3). Experiments on animals have shown that this *preabsorptive mechanism* operates with *great precision,* for the amount of water drunk corresponds quite closely to that actually required [1, 10].

The **receptors and underlying mechanisms of preabsorptive satiety** are not known. A dog with an esophageal fistula drinks about twice as much water as a normal dog with the same water deficit, and then stops drinking for 20–60 min. Therefore drinking itself, or the associated motor and sensory processes, causes a certain transient relief of thirst. Stretching of the stomach by the liquid consumed also appears to be important. Water poured directly into the stomachs of rats and other animals causes an equivalent reduction of the amount of water drunk. But the associated neural mechanisms remain unclear [9, 10].

The thirst threshold. Once the thirst has actually been quenched, by *compensation* of the relative (excessive salt intake) or absolute water deficit *(postabsorptive satiety),* a certain time elapses before the sensation of thirst recurs, even though there is a steady, slow physiological loss of water. There is thus a *threshold* for thirst, equivalent – as mentioned at the outset – to the loss of an amount of water corresponding to ca. 0.5% of the body's weight. This **thirst threshold** prevents slight water losses from inducing a thirst sensation. Physiologically, then, the water content of the human body fluctuates at least between a *maximum following postabsorptive satiety* and a *minimum* that in the ideal case is *just below the thirst threshold.* But the normal fluctuations in water content of the human body are often greater than this, for we frequently consume more liquid than necessary and we cannot always satisfy our thirst as soon as it becomes noticeable.

Primary and secondary drinking. Drinking that results from an absolute or relative lack of water in one of the fluid spaces of the body is called **primary drinking,** while drinking with no apparent necessity for water replenishment is called **secondary drinking.** The latter is normally the usual way that water is supplied! In general we (and other mammals) tend to consume the physiologically required water in advance. For example, liquid is drunk *during and after eating,* and we seem to have learned to *adjust the amount drunk* to the kind of food eaten; if it is salty we drink more, even though no sensation of thirst has yet occurred. *Habits* also appear to play a role, but our information about the mechanisms by which we estimate our water requirements in advance is very sparse. In any case, *primary drinking* is basically an *emergency response* seldom experienced by people leading well-regulated lives.

Clinical Thirst

An increase in thirst during illness can be the consequence of abnormally large water loss, with the thirst mechanisms functioning normally. On the other hand, it can indicate disturbances of the thirst mechanisms or of control of salt/water balance. Outstanding examples of the first case are the *water losses* due to continual vomiting or to severe diarrhea, as occurs in cholera (the English physician THOMAS LATTA was the first, in 1832, to quench the thirst of cholera victims by intravenous administration of fluid – a procedure which alleviated all the symptoms of the disease at once. Another example of the first case is diabetes insipidus, in which the lack of antidiuretic hormone (ADH) causes the body to excrete many liters of hypotonic urine per day. These patients, if untreated, suffer from unquenchable thirst, and their entire daily routine revolves about the constant need to drink. Further details of the many aspects of clinical thirst are available in textbooks of pathophysiology and clinical medicine.

14.2 Hunger

Origin of the Sensation of Hunger

Short-term and long-term regulation of food intake. Both humans and animals normally adapt their food intake to changing needs, depending on the amount of work done, the climate, and the nutritional value (energy content) of their food. This **short-term regulation** of food intake is superimposed on a **long-term regulation** that makes up for temporary inadequacies in the diet and ensures a return to the normal body weight. For example, when animals are fattened by *force-feeding* and then returned to normal conditions, they eat distinctly less than control animals. As the animals return to their original control weights, their food consumption slowly increases. Conversely, *after a period of fasting* the original body weight is regained by temporarily increased food consumption [1, 3, 4, 7].

Factors eliciting hunger. Subjective experience indicates that hunger is a general sensation localized in (or projected to) the stomach region; it appears when the stomach is empty, and vanishes or gives way to a **feeling of satiety** once the stomach is filled with food. Some early students of the problem postulated that hunger is elicited by **contractions of the empty stomach.** This view is supported by the observation that the stomach, in addition to the ordinary contractions by which food is processed and transported, contracts still more powerfully when it is empty, and these contractions are closely correlated with the occurrence of hunger. The contractions may be detected by **mechanoreceptors in the stomach wall** (Fig. 14-4).

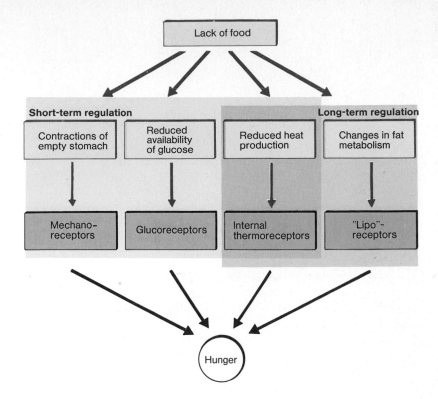

Fig. 14-4. Production of the sensation of hunger. The receptors involved are shown below their adequate stimuli. The factors and receptors involved in short-term and long-term regulation of food intake, respectively, are grouped by gray-shaded areas

But the influence of empty-stomach contractions on hunger should not be overestimated; when the stomachs of animals are experimentally *denervated* or *surgically removed,* the eating behavior is hardly affected. The contractions of the empty stomach are one factor in the sensation of hunger but a dispensable one [2, 4, 8].

Glucostatic hypothesis. The glucose dissolved in the blood appears to play a crucial role in eliciting hunger. (With regard to the hormonal control of the blood glucose level and the availability of glucose to the cells see p. 681) Experiments have shown that reduced **availability of glucose** (not the blood glucose level itself) is closely correlated with feelings of hunger and powerful contractions of the stomach. Evidently this factor is a critical parameter in the development of hunger. The **glucostatic hypothesis** is further supported by various experimental findings indicating that **glucoreceptors** probably exist in the diencephalon, liver, stomach and small intestine (Fig. 14-4); they signal the reduced availability of glucose and thereby elicit hunger [3, 4, 8, 14, 16].

Thermostatic hypothesis. The **thermostatic hypothesis** of the generation of hunger is less well supported than the glucostatic hypothesis. It is based on the observation that warm-blooded animals consume food in amounts inversely proportional to the temperature of the environment. The thermoreceptors within the body could act as sensors for integration of the over-

all energy balance. A *decline in total heat production* would then cause the **internal** thermoreceptors to trigger the sensation of hunger (Fig. 14-4). It can be shown experimentally that local cooling and warming in the diencephalon, the seat of the central thermoreceptors, can bring about changes in feeding behavior as predicted by this hypothesis; but other, less specific interpretations cannot be ruled out [4].

Lipostatic hypothesis. Excessive food intake leads to the deposition of fat in the body, and if food is insufficient the fat deposits are used up. Assuming the existence of **liporeceptors,** such departures from the ideal weight of the body could be monitored by way of the intermediate products of the associated fat metabolism and interpreted as hunger or satiety signals (Fig. 14-4). There is some good experimental evidence for the lipostatic hypothesis, in particular the above mentioned observation that force-fed animals subsequently eat less than under control conditions, until their fat deposits are gone [4, 13, 16].

The elicitation of hunger and short/long-term regulation. The lipostatic hunger mechanism, as shown by the experiment just described, serves chiefly in the *long-term regulation* of food intake, whereas the contractions of the empty stomach and the glucostatic mechanism are primarily involved in *short-term regulation.* The thermostatic mechanism possibly participates in both (cf. the gray shading in Fig. 14-4). With such a variety of physiological mechanisms subserv-

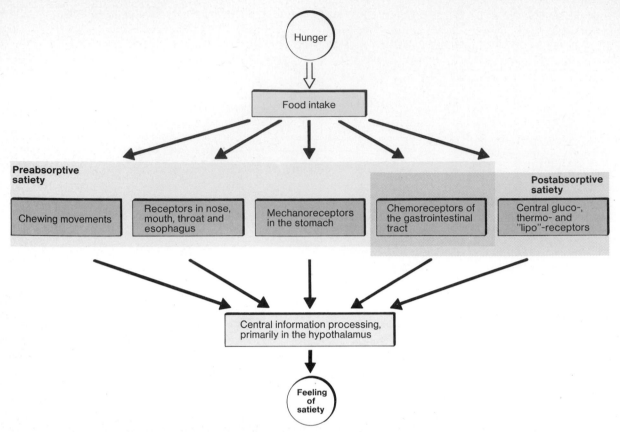

Fig. 14-5. Production of the feeling of satiation by food intake. The factors and receptors involved in preabsorptive and postabsorptive satiety are grouped within the gray-shaded areas. Chewing movements can contribute to preabsorptive satiety by way of a direct central efference copy of the motor patterns, by way of the activation of receptors during chewing (e.g., muscle spindles, tendon organs), or both together

ing the feeling of hunger, even under the most complex conditions the sensation of hunger and the feeding drive ensure the consumption of food in appropriate amounts.

Food intake without hunger. Humans are not the only animals that eat when not hungry; other warm-blooded animals also eat amounts of food that depend not only on the amount actually required or on psychological factors (p. 313), but also on when the next mealtime is expected and on the amount of energy likely to be consumed in the meanwhile. This sort of **predictive food intake** does not compensate an existing deficit (as discussed above), but rather **covers in advance the expected energy expenditure.** Such behavior corresponds to predictive water intake (secondary drinking, p. 310), which is the normal way in which water is supplied to the body.

Satiety

Preabsorptive and postabsorptive satiety. As in the case of drinking, food consumption by humans and animals is usually stopped long before absorption of the food from the digestive tract has eliminated the energy deficit that originally led to hunger and feeding. All the processes that cause an organism to end its meal are together termed **satiety.** The **feeling of satiation,** as everyone knows, is something more than just the disappearance of hunger; among its unique aspects (some of which are associated with pleasure) is the distinct feeling of **fullness** if too much food has been eaten. The *feeling of satiation* gradually recedes as time passes after a meal and eventually, after a neutral period, gives way to renewed hunger. Thus we can infer that satiation is initially **preabsorptive** (i.e., results from processes associated with food intake itself), whereas the subsequent **postabsorptive satiety** prevents the immediate recurrence of hunger.

Factors in preabsorptive satiety. Animals with an esophageal fistula feed for considerably longer periods than before the operation, and repeat their meals at shorter intervals. The **stimulation of olfactory receptors, gustatory receptors and mechanoreceptors** in the nose, mouth, throat and esophagus during feeding, and possibly the **act of chewing** itself, thus apparently contribute to preabsorptive satiety (Fig. 14-5), although the data available at present suggest that their influence on initiating and maintaining satiety is slight. Another factor seems to be the **stretching of the stomach** by the food (Fig. 14-5); if the stomach of an experimental animal is filled through a fistula or tube before its mealtime, there is a reduction in the oral food intake that partially compensates the filling. The *degree of compensation* depends not on the nutritional value of the food, but rather on the volume of the initial stomach content and the time it was introduced. In the extreme case, if large amounts of high-energy food are put directly into the stomach shortly before the scheduled mealtimes, oral food consumption can be inhibited completely for weeks. The above factors are supplemented by the **effects of chemoreceptors** in the stomach and upper small intestine (Fig. 14-5), which are apparently sensitive to the glucose and amino-acid content of the food. For example, while food is being eaten the glucose level in the blood rises by an amount related to the carbohydrate content of the food. This response could also of course be elicited hormonally, but the presence of *glucoreceptors and amino-acid receptors* in the intestinal wall has been demonstrated electrophysiologically [1, 3, 4, 8].

Factors in postabsorptive satiety. The **chemoreceptors in the digestive tract** just mentioned may also be involved in postabsorptive satiety, because they can signal the concentrations of utilizable nutrients still remaining in the intestine. But all the enteroceptive sensory events introduced during the discussion of hunger contribute to the process. The **increased availability of glucose, increased heat production** as the food is processed, and the **changes in fat metabolism** affect the corresponding central receptors (on the right in Fig. 14-5); the effects are the reverse of those giving rise to hunger (red shading in Fig. 14-4). **Hunger** and **satiety** are thus to a certain extent two sides of the same coin. The (short-term) sensation of hunger triggers eating ("go" signal) and the feeling of (preabsorptive) satiety brings it to an end ("stop" signal). But the amount of food eaten and the duration of the pauses between meals are also determined by the processes we have called "long-term regulation of food intake" and "postabsorptive satiety" – processes, as we now realize (cf. Figs. 14-4 and 14-5), that overlap more or less extensively.

Psychological Factors in Hunger; Appetite

In addition to the above *physiological factors,* a number of **psychological factors** are involved in the control of feeding behavior, which we can mention only briefly here. For example, the time at which food is eaten and the amount consumed are determined not only by one's hunger but also by many other things, including the habit of eating at "mealtimes" and the amount and palatability of the food offered. Our desire for certain food is called **appetite.** It can be part of the feeling of hunger, but it can also appear independently (e. g., at the sight or presentation of particularly delicious food). Appetite often has a *somatic basis,* as in the case of the craving for salty food when the body has lost salt, but it can also be independent of physical needs; in the latter case it reflects innate or acquired *individual preferences* for certain foods. Such preferences in turn, as well as the (often highly consistent) *rejection* of other foods, are formed by the regional availability of certain kinds of food and modified by the standards of the individual's particular culture; these are usually rooted in religion, although they may be rationalized subsequently. Viewed in this light, the "palatability" of a dish – the predominant elements of which are its smell, taste, consistency, temperature and the way it is prepared and served – depends very much on our **affective attitude** toward it. Examples can easily be found at regional, national and international levels [1, 15].

Finally, we should mention the major role the *neuroses* and *psychoses* can play in food consumption. Excessive eating, or the refusal of food, is often used as a substitute satisfaction or protest when the difficulty actually lies in the areas of other drives. The best known example is **anorexia nervosa,** a form of abstinence from eating most common in females at puberty; this disturbance in development of the psyche can be so severe as to result in death by starvation.

Central Mechanisms of Hunger and Satiety

The **hypothalamus** is apparently the most important central *relay and integration structure* for hunger and satiety. Bilateral destruction of small amounts of tissue in certain ventromedial regions of the hypothalamus causes extreme *obesity* in experimental animals as a result of overeating. On the other hand, destruction of more lateral areas can result in refusal to eat and eventually death by *starvation*. These striking findings, and comparable results of local electrical stimulation by way of electrodes implanted in the hypothalamus, have long attracted the attention of researchers so strongly to the hypothalamus that very little is yet known about the *significance of other brain structures* in the regulation of food intake. On the basis of the experiments just mentioned, it might be proposed that the entire central information processing is localized in two hypothalamic "centers," a ventromedial **"satiety center,"** the destruction of which results in disinhibition of a lateral **"hunger center"** and hence in compulsive eating; conversely, destruction of the "hunger center" would give rise to a permanent feeling of satiation, causing all food to be rejected henceforth [4, 8, 12, 16]. This, however, is certainly an oversimplification. That higher centers of the brain must also be involved is indicated, for instance, by the anticipatory eating and drinking mentioned above; among the structures implicated are the **limbic system** and the cortical areas associated with it (cf. p. 138). Finally, it should not be overlooked that eating and drinking are complex motor acts, demanding correspondingly extensive participation of the **motor system.** The limbic (especially hypothalamic) motivation areas probably have access to the motor centers by way of the central catecholaminergic systems, which project from the brainstem to cerebellum, basal nuclei and cortex (p. 140). These projections may thus be an important link between the drives and their expression in motor patterns [4].

14.3   References

Textbooks and Handbooks

1. CODE, C. F. (Ed.): Handbook of Physiology. Section 6: Alimentary Canal. Vol. I: Control of Food and Water Intake. Washington: American Physiological Society 1967

2. FITZSIMONS, J. T.: The Physiology of Thirst and Sodium Appetite (Monographs of the Physiological Society, No. 35). Cambridge, England: Cambridge University Press 1979
3. MORGANE, P.J. (Ed.): Neural regulation of food and water intake. Ann. N. Y. Acad. Sci. *157*, 531 (1969)
4. NOVIN, D., WYRWICKA, BRAY, G.A. (Eds.): Hunger. Basic Mechanisms and Clinical Implications. New York: Raven Press 1976
5. PETERS, G., FITZSIMONS, J.T., PETERS-HAEFELI, I., (Eds.): Control Mechanisms of Drinking. Berlin–Heidelberg–New York: Springer 1975
6. WOLF, A. V.: Thirst: Physiology of the Urge to Drink and Problems of Water Lack. Springfield, Ill.: Ch. C. Thomas 1958

Research Reports and Reviews

7. ANAND, B. K.: Nervous regulation of food intake. Physiol. Rev. *41*, 677 (1961)
8. ANDERSSON, B.: Receptors subserving hunger and thirst. In: NEIL, E. (Ed.): Handbook of Sensory Physiology, Vol. III/1. Berlin–Heidelberg–New York: Springer 1972
9. ANDERSSON, B.: Regulation of water intake. Physiol. Rev. *58*, 582 (1978)
10. FITZSIMONS, J.T.: Thirst. Physiol. Rev. *52*, 468 (1972)
11. FITZSIMONS, J.T.: The physiological basis of thirst. Kidney International *10*, 3 (1976)
12. HAYWARD, J. N.: Functional and morphological aspects of hypothalamic neurons. Physiol. Rev. *57*, 574 (1977)
13. KENNEDY, G.C.: Interactions between feeding behavior and hormones during growth. Ann. N. Y. Acad. Sci. *157*, 1049 (1969)
14. MAYER, J.: Regulation of energy intake and body weight: glucostatic theory and lipostatic hypothesis. Ann. N. Y. Acad. Sci. *63*, 15 (1955)
15. PILGRIM, F.J.: Human food attitudes and consumption. In: CODE, C. F. (Ed): Handbook of Physiology. Section 6: Alimentary Canal, Vol. I: Control of Food and Water Intake, p. 139. Washington: American Physiological Society 1967
16. RABIN, B. M.: Ventromedial hypothalamic control of food intake and satiety: a reappraisal. Brain Res. *43*, 317 (1972)

15 Cybernetic Aspects of the Nervous System and Sense Organs

M. Zimmermann

The field of *cybernetics* is concerned with the processes of **communication** and **regulation.** The theoretical structures on which it rests – information theory [12] and control theory [6] – were originally formulated in the context of technology, but their contribution to biology is steadily increasing. The application of these methods to living systems (called *biocybernetics* in Europe) provides a readily comprehensible, and frequently quantitative, description of biological functions; in many cases it deepens our understanding of the underlying relationships. Because so many processes of communication and control in organisms involve the *nervous system,* the biocybernetic approach has been emphasized most strongly in the areas of neurophysiology and sensory physiology [1, 2, 6, 10]. In the following sections, examples from these areas are used to introduce the elements of cybernetics.

15.1 The Sensory System in Terms of Information Theory

The Concept of Information Theory

The basic concept from which information theory is developed is represented by the block diagram of Fig. 15-1. Here the flow of information is indicated by a series of functions – information source, sender, transmission channel, receiver, user – which can be disturbed at various points (e. g., by noise in the transmission channel). This simple concept can be applied to all kinds of information transmission, in the realms of both technology and biology.

The meaning of "information." In information theory the term **information** denotes only the *measurable,* mathematically formulatable content of a message; it is the quantifiable *reduction of uncertainty* about an event.

The following example illustrates this usage of the word. When one of a fair pair of dice is thrown, one of six equally likely numbers comes up. The probability of each – which is all the player knows before the throw – is $p = \frac{1}{6}$. Thus each time the player throws, he removes the same amount of uncertainty; each throw has the same measurable information content.

Equal probability of all possible outcomes, as in a dice game, is a special case. Usually the events x_i have different *probabilities* $p(x_i)$. The less common a particular event x_i is – that is, the smaller $p(x_i)$ is – the greater the reduction in uncertainty when x_i occurs, and thus the greater the *information content* of the event x_i. The information content of an event x therefore can usefully be expressed by the reciprocal of its probability $p(x)$, $1/p(x)$. The measure of information is defined on this basis (see p. 317).

Semantic information. The *significance* or meaning of an item of information to the user need not be equivalent to its information content, as the term is used here. In a dice game, for example, the subjective significance of the different numbers varies, depending on all sorts of factors (the kind of game, previous experiences, the other players). These aspects, not accounted for by information theory, are termed *semantic* information.

Symbols, coding, and disturbance of information. Information is *transmitted* by sets of **symbols** (e. g., the letters of the alphabet, the numbers 0 to 9), from which the information source (Fig. 15-1) makes a selection.

Usually these symbols are *encoded* in the sender, into other symbols more convenient for transmission

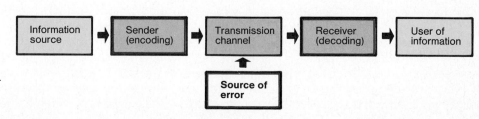

Fig. 15-1. Diagram illustrating the basic concept of information theory

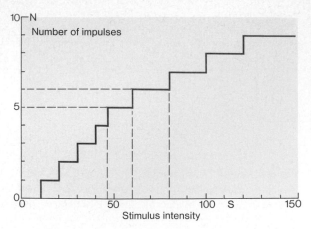

Fig. 15-2. Coding of stimulus intensity S in nerve impulses. During a stimulus of a given duration an integer number N of action potentials is generated in the receptor (ordinate), so that the curve relating response to stimulus intensity (abscissa) is a staircase function

(e.g., frequency-modulated electromagnetic waves in the case of an FM radio transmitter). **Coding** in general is the unequivocal assignment of the members of one set of symbols to those of another (for example, the assignment of Morse signals to the letters of the alphabet). In the receiver the transmitted information is *decoded* and passed on to the user.

A central element of the concept of information theory is the possibility of **disturbance of information transmission.** *Disturbance can occur at the sender (during coding), in the transmission channel and in the receiver (decoding). All the possible sources of disturbance* are represented in Fig. 15-1 by a single source, acting on the transmission channel. One of the tasks of information theory is to establish *coding algorithms* that prevent *loss of information due to disturbances* (cf. p. 319).

Now we shall consider how the concept of Fig. 15-1, discussed in general terms so far, can be applied to *information transmission in the nervous system.* Nerve fibers carry information encoded in nerve impulses. The transmission channel is thus a nerve fiber, the sender a receptor, the source of information external stimuli, and the receiver a synapse on a central neuron; the central neuron itself can be regarded as the user.

The Ideal Receptor: Coding and Information Content

Coding in a receptor. The physically measurable parameters of stimuli (e.g., intensity of pressure on the skin, position of a stimulus on the peripheral sensory surface, wavelength of light and sound stimuli) are items of information. Chapter 1 gives an example

(Fig. 1-30, p. 28) of the way a stimulus parameter determines the response of a receptor; as stimulus intensity changes, the discharge rate of the afferent fiber changes in the same direction. In this case the information *"stimulus intensity"* is encoded in the information *"mean frequency of nerve impulses."* This way of coding, comparable to *frequency modulation* in information technology, is found in receptors of various modalities; pressure receptors in the skin, muscle spindles, baroreceptors in the arteries, and photoreceptors in the retina all convert the intensity of their adequate stimulus into the mean frequency of a train of impulses. The *nerve-impulse frequency* is evidently a universal *information carrier*. Because the afferent fiber of a given receptor always makes contact with a particular set of neurons in the central nervous system, the signal is interpreted appropriately – the information is identified.

Information content of receptor discharge. The information content of a message is associated with the number of states that can be distinguished following coding. Consider the example of stimulus-intensity coding in a receptor. If the response of the receptor to a stimulus is either *no* impulse or *one* impulse, it can convey information about *two levels* of stimulus intensity: no impulse = intensity below threshold, one impulse = intensity above threshold. If the possible number of impulses per stimulus is 0, 1 or 2, the user can distinguish three states of stimulus intensity. In general, if a stimulus elicits a maximum of *N impulses* in the afferent fibers, the receptor can in theory signal *N + 1 different intensity levels* to an impulse counter in the CNS. This situation is illustrated in Fig. 15-2. Because the discharge number N in the afferent fiber (ordinate) must be an integer, a plot of N vs. stimulus intensity S (abscissa) gives a staircase curve. In an *ideal receptor,* which responds to a maintained stimulus by discharging impulses at a *constant* rate, the impulse number N is the product of the *discharge frequency* f and the *observation time* t: $N = f \cdot t$. Thus the number of distinguishable stimulus-intensity levels in the nerve-fiber signal is

$$N + 1 = f_m \cdot t + 1 \qquad (1)$$

where f_m is the *maximal* discharge rate of the receptor. From this relationship it follows theoretically that the number of discriminable steps of intensity increases with the maximal frequency f_m and with the length of the observation time t, during which the afferent discharge is evaluated in the central nervous system (or by the observer in a physiological experiment). An upper limit of f_m is set by the refractory time of the nerve fiber. In the case of a receptor with *spontaneous* discharge (with no detectable external stimulus) at frequency f_0, f_m in Eq. (1) and all following equations must be replaced by f_m-f_0.

The Technological Unit of Information

The *quantitative measure of information content* used in information technology is the **logarithm** of the number n of distinguishable states of an information source. In defining this measure, the logarithm to the base 2 was chosen ($\log_2$ or ld; ld n $= \log_{10}$ n$/\log_{10}$ 2). The following considerations demonstrate the appropriateness of this definition.

Binary symbols. As noted above, the transmission of information requires a set of symbols from which the information source makes a selection. In the simplest case the set comprises just two symbols, called **binary symbols** (e.g., 0 and 1). With these, the information source can signal a decision between two alternatives (e.g., yes/no). Binary systems are particularly convenient from a technical viewpoint (light/dark, switch position on/off, hole/no-hole in a punched tape, etc.). This is one of the reasons for the choice of the information content of the binary symbol as the **unit of information.** The elementary quantity of information transmitted by a single binary symbol is **one bit.** A bit is a very small amount of information. If more extensive messages are to be transmitted with binary symbols, several symbols must be strung together; when binary digits are used in this way to form *words,* the "alphabet" consists of the "letters" 0 and 1. The word length (the number of binary digits per word) is a direct measure, in bits, of the information transmitted: a word composed of two binary digits can transmit two bits, 3 bits are transmitted with 3 digits, and so on. The number of words that can be constructed with 2 binary digits is $2^2 = 4$, as follows: 00, 01, 10, 11. With 3 digits $2^3 = 8$ word combinations are possible: 000, 001, 010, 011, 100, 101, 110, 111. With **m** binary digits per word there are n $= 2^m$ possible combinations; that is, we can send n $= 2^m$ *different* signals, each with an information content of **m bits.**

Nonbinary symbols. Information content can be determined as discussed above even in cases in which *any arbitrary symbols* serve as carriers of information, for any desired set of symbols can be represented by binary symbols. To obtain an unequivocal association (coding) of a set of *n symbols* with a set of binary words, the latter must have an average word length *m = ld n* binary symbols.

The reader can convince himself of this by considering the coding of the letters of the alphabet in binary words of equal length.

To encode all the letters, the binary word length required is the next integer larger than ld 26, which is 5 ($2^5 = 32$).

If an arbitrary symbol can be replaced by a binary word, then one may say that it has the same information content (in bits) as the associated binary word. The *average* information content I of one symbol in a set of n symbols is **I = ld n.**

In this introduction to the basic concepts of information theory we have simplified matters considerably. The strict definition of information content takes account of the probability p (x_i) of occurrence of each symbol x_i of an information source. The information content I (x_i) is defined as

$$I(x_i) = ld \frac{1}{p(x_i)}$$

The *mean* information content H (x) of each of the n symbols of an information source (also called the *entropy* of the information source) is the arithmetic mean of the I (x_i):

$$H(x) = \sum_{i=1}^{n} p(x_i) \cdot ld \frac{1}{p(x_i)}$$

If all n symbols are *equally* probable, then p (x_i) $= 1/n$; it can easily be shown that then H $=$ I $=$ ld n, as in the above discussion. Thus this relationship holds only when all the symbols of an information source occur with equal frequency. The remainder of the discussion will be limited to this special case. For more extensive treatments of information theory the reader is referred to the specialized literature (e.g., [12, 13]).

Information Transmission in an Ideal Receptor

The relationships discussed in the previous section also apply to coding in a receptor. Here the set of symbols is the number of discriminable states of the afferent nerve discharge. The information content with regard to stimulus intensity in the example of Fig. 15-2 is thus I $=$ ld (N + 1) $=$ ld 10 $=$ 3.3 bits. In a receptor capable of responding to stimulation with a maximal frequency f_m the *information content* re *stimulus intensity* in general is

$$I = ld(f_m \cdot t + 1) \tag{2}$$

The relationship between I, f_m and observation time t is shown in Fig. 15-3 (black curves, black ordinate scale). It is evident that the information content I increases with both f_m and t. Although the maximal frequency f_m is a fixed property of a receptor, by prolonging the observation time t the information about intensity of a prolonged constant stimulus can in theory be made arbitrarily precise. In practice, however, this possibility is limited by two factors. First, the afferent discharge is accumulated by the central nervous processor only over a limited period (the integration time for decoding). Second, in a real receptor

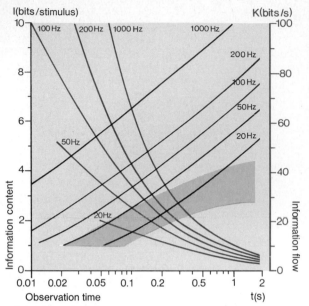

Fig. 15-3. Information content I in bits/stimulus (left ordinate, *black* curves) and information flow K in bits/s (right ordinate, *red* curves) of an ideal receptor as a function of the observation time t, measured in seconds (abscissa). The parameter distinguishing the curves in each set is the maximal discharge frequency f_m (in Hz) of the receptor. Curves calculated from Eqs.(2) and (3). The *red shaded* region indicates the information content of mechanosensitive cutaneous receptors as a function of t. (After the author's observations of cat slowly adapting mechano-receptors of the skin – SA receptors – and [29, 30])

(cf. p. 319) the increase in information content with observation time t is less than would be expected from Equation (2) (red shading in Fig. 15-3). For these reasons, only observation times of ca. 1 s or less are of practical significance.

Information flow is defined as the amount of information transmitted in a channel per unit time, in bits/s. Applying this definition to an ideal receptor, the information flow K obtained from Equation (2) is

$$K = \frac{I}{t} = \frac{1}{t} \cdot ld(f_m \cdot t + 1) \tag{3}$$

This relationship is plotted in Fig. 15-3 (red curves, red ordinate scale). As observation time t is *reduced,* the information flow *increases.* To understand the reason for this increase, consider that as t becomes shorter it is possible to evaluate successive segments of the impulse train at increasingly frequent intervals – in the case of an ideal receptor, 1/t times per second. As t is reduced, the information flow in an ideal receptor reaches a maximum K_m when $f_m \cdot t_0 = 1$ (that is, when in the time interval t_0 no more than a single impulse occurs); then it holds that

$$K_m = f_m \, bits/s$$

The *maximal information flow* can be called the *channel capacity.*

Information Transmission in a Real Receptor

Imprecise coding, noise. A real receptor achieves neither the theoretical number of discriminable stimulus-intensity levels found above nor the information content I and information flow K calculated from that number. Experiments reveal that for a *given* stimulus intensity the discharge rate of a receptor *varies* in successive measurements. Fig. 15-4 shows the discharge of a pressure receptor in the cat foot with different stimulus intensities. It is evident in (A) that the discharge rate, carrier of the information "stimulus intensity," fluctuates randomly for no apparent reason. Such *fluctuations* of the information carrier in general are called **noise** by information technologists. They always *diminish* the ability of a channel to transmit information and thus amount to a source of disturbance (cf. Fig. 15-1).

To estimate the amount of information *lost* due to noise in the coding process, consider the experimentally measured coding relationship graphed in Fig. 15-4 B. Each point represents the result of a single measurement like those in (A), but with an observation time of 5 s. The number of discriminable states

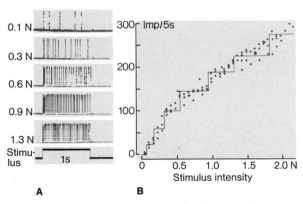

A   B

Fig. 15-4 A, B. Noise in the coding process. **A** Original record of the discharge of a pressure receptor in the sole of the cat's paw (SA-receptor) in response to stimuli 1 s in duration, delivered by a stylus with an area of 1 mm²; intensity, measured in newtons (N), increases from top to bottom. **B** Discharge rates (impulses/5 s, ordinate) measured in many records like those in **A**, as a function of stimulus intensity (abscissa). The stimulus duration was 5 s in these experiments. The staircase curve drawn through the scattered data shows approximately the number of intensity steps that can be distinguished in the discharge of the receptor

can be estimated by drawing a *staircase curve* through this field of dots; there are 8 steps (the first at 0 impulses), and thus 3 bits/stimulus.

The rationale for this *graphic method* of finding information content is as follows. Two stimulus intensities can be reliably distinguished if all the impulse numbers associated with one of them (ordinate in Fig. 15-4 B) are different from those associated with the other. The "worst case," which represents the *minimum discriminability available,* is given by the staircase curve of maximal step height that can be drawn in the experimentally measured field of dots. In some studies of this kind the minimal discriminability of stimulus intensities is taken to correspond to a certain overlap of discharge rates rather than complete disjunction [28, 30]. The number of discriminable stimuli calculated in this way is somewhat larger than that found by the graphic method.

If our receptor were to behave like an *ideal* frequency modulator (an ideal receptor, without noise; cf. pp. 27, 317), under the conditions of the experiment in Fig. 15-4 B ca. 300 steps of stimulus intensity would be discriminable, and the information content would be 8.2 bits/stimulus (cf. Eq. 2). In this example of a real receptor, then, 8.2 bits–3 bits = 5.2 bits are lost due to noise.

The largest values so far obtained for information content per stimulus in receptor discharge were found in de-efferented muscle spindles; primary endings can transmit 4.8 bits per 1-s stimulus, and secondary endings actually transmit 6.3 bits [22]. With the γ-efferents intact these figures are considerably smaller – 2.7 and 4.7 bits per stimulus, respectively.

Observation time, information flow. Experimental variation of the observation time t also reveals departures from the behavior of an ideal receptor. With a real receptor, prolongation of t does *not* indefinitely increase its information content, contrary to the prediction of Eq. (2) [29, 30]. For example, pressure receptors in the cat's paw (Fig. 15-4) have essentially reached the maximum (3 bits/stimulus) when t is only ca. 1 s. The red-shaded area in Fig. 15-3 shows the range in which the *experimentally* measured information content per stimulus changes with observation time t, for certain kinds of cutaneous mechanoreceptors (measured, e.g., as in Fig. 15-4). Although these receptors can discharge at rates as high as several hundred Hz, they evidently perform little or no better than an ideal receptor with a maximal discharge rate of 20 Hz. The attainable *information flow in real receptors* is also far less than theoretically predicted by Eq. (3) (Fig. 15-3, red curves). Among the highest values found experimentally are ca. 6 bits/s for pressure receptors (SA receptors) in the cat's paw, 30 bits/s for rapidly adapting (RA) mechanoreceptors in the cat's paw, and at least 15 bits/s for primary muscle-spindle endings (estimate based on the data in [22] and [29]);

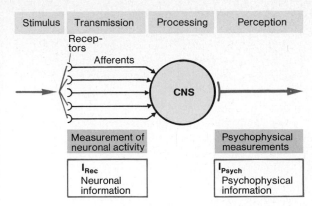

Fig. 15-5. Correlation between neuronal and psychophysical information. The information about the environment contained in the discharge of one or more receptors (I_{Rec}) can be determined in neurophysiological experiments. In psychophysical studies of human subjects the same stimuli can be used to determine the psychophysical information I_{Psych}. I_{Psych} is based on the central nervous processing of I_{Rec}, so that comparison of the two might provide some in right into the mechanisms underlying neural information processing

sensitive mechanoreceptors in the hairy skin of the cat's paw, with unmyelinated fibers, can transmit only ca. 0.1 bits/s.

Redundancy

The imprecise coding in a real receptor (due to noise) reflects a *disturbance* of information transmission. Can one identify principles of nervous-system operation that can *compensate* for such disturbance? In communications technology the methods available for protecting information against loss make use of the concept of redundancy. As an illustration of this notion, first consider an example from the field of linguistics. Try to decipher the following sequence of letters:

T.. ne.v. .mp.ls. .s t.. s.mb.l
f.r inf.r.at..n tr..sm.s.ion

The information contained in this sentence is discernible even though 45% of the letters are missing; written language contains *more* symbols than are necessary for the meaning to be detected with certainty. This *excess of symbols* is called redundancy; it is measurable in bits. Calculations based on the frequency of occurrence of the 26 letters of the alphabet in English text have shown that the information rate approaches an upper limit of only *1.5 bits per letter*. Theoretically, the average information content of each of the 26 letters in the alphabet is *ld 26 = 4.7 bits* (neglecting the differences in probability of occurrence);

the redundancy in this case therefore averages 4.7 bits − 1.5 bits = *3.2 bits per letter.*

This may at first appear to be an extravagant *waste of symbols,* but that is only one aspect of redundancy. Its advantages become clear when the transmission channel is *disturbed* – for example, with a bad telephone connection, noisy radio reception, or messy handwriting. Here the redundancy in a language ensures that a text can be recognized when only a fraction of the symbols are identifiable. Information theory provides a quantitative treatment of the fact that *information transmission is the more secure against disturbance, the greater the redundancy built into the coding.*

Redundancy in the nervous system. One effective way of using redundancy to protect against noise consists of transmitting the information over two or more channels in *parallel*. This possibility is realized in the nervous system. In the periphery the density of the receptors is usually so high that even point stimuli excite *several fibers*. In such *parallel transmission* the extent to which the information content is in fact utilized depends on the nature of the central nervous processing (cf. Fig. 15-5). Only a few studies have as yet been directed to this question [18, 29]. Under the simplifying assumption that evaluation involves *summation* of the impulses in all excited fibers, the information about stimulus intensity available to an "ideal observer" can be calculated from the *variability of the summed discharge* [18] – for example, by the method sketched in Fig. 15-4 B. If the sources of disturbance of the individual receptors (i. e., the stochastic fluctuations in discharge rate) are *independent* of one another, the information content of the summed discharge is *greater* than that of a *single* receptor. *Redundancy by transmission in parallel fibers compensates for disturbance of coding in the receptor.* Moreover, parallel transmission secures the information not only against disturbance by imprecise coding, but also against *partial damage* to nerve pathways, in which some of the axons from a particular region of the sensory surface are interrupted.

Redundancy is achieved by parallel transmission in the central nervous system as well. But here new factors enter. The axons carrying information in parallel lines from a peripheral point often run in *separate ascending pathways* (e.g., dorsal columns and neo-spinothalamic tract). In addition, because of the divergence and convergence in synaptic relay stations the parallel channels may be cross-connected, by which redundancy is increased.

But when information about stimulus intensity is so thoroughly protected, the number of channels available to represent different stimulus sites is reduced,

and a *loss* of information about stimulus *location* ought to result. *Lateral inhibition* (pp. 73, 181) can be regarded as a compensating mechanism in this situation; by limiting to varying degrees the spread of signals into parallel lines on the way from periphery to CNS, lateral inhibition determines whether the information about stimulus intensity or that about stimulus location receives the greater protection.

Neurophysiology and Psychophysics

Information theory is also applied in psychology [4], especially in the area of psychophysics. Recent research has shown that *comparison* of quantitative studies in neurophysiology and psychophysics is an extremely valuable aid to understanding the function of the nervous system [18, 20, 24, 31, 32]. The novelty of this approach lies in the comparison, under *identical conditions of stimulation,* of the information contained in the *discharge* of afferent or central neurons with that involved in the *subjective recognition and discrimination capacities* of people in psychophysical tests (Fig. 15-5). So far, psychophysical performance has been compared with neuronal information for the following cutaneous senses: threshold for detection (perception) of a mechanical stimulus to the skin (cf. p. 206, Fig. 9-13), frequency-discrimination capacity with the same stimuli [20, 24], subjectively perceived (estimated) intensity of pressure stimuli [11], and difference-threshold for cold stimuli [18]. In these studies the quantitative comparison revealed, among other results, the type of receptor responsible for transmitting information about the stimulus parameter of interest.

Neuronal intensity coding and psychophysics. We shall now consider in detail the last two experiments in the above list. Slowly adapting receptors in the monkey hand transmit 3.3 bits/stimulus (i. e., 10 distinguishable steps) of information about stimulus intensity [11] (I_{Rec} in Fig. 15-5). Humans subjectively estimating stimulus intensity under the same stimulus conditions can distinguish no more than 8 intensity steps (3 bits/stimulus; I_{Psych} in Fig. 15-5). From these results it follows, as a *theoretical limiting case,* that the information about stimulus intensity encoded by a *single receptor* suffices for the *subjective measurement* of stimulus intensity; the information carried by the other excited fibers would then be redundant, and could help to compensate for losses due to noise in synaptic transmission [22, 29].

The second experiment is an example of a situation in which the information content of a *population of receptors* is *fully utilized* in a psychophysical discrimination task (i. e., there is no redundancy). Here the ability of human subjects to *discriminate cold stimuli* (hand) was compared with the *information content of cold receptors* in the monkey hand [18]. In these experiments, for example, two cold stimuli were presented by a thermode (1 cm² area) at an interval of 10 s. With a temperature drop from 34 °C to about 29 °C, a trained subject could detect a *difference* between the two stimuli if the final temperatures differed by at least 0.05 °C (difference threshold). Analysis of the *variability* in cold-receptor discharge revealed that a single receptor is *not* sufficiently precise to provide the neurophysiological basis of the difference threshold found in the psychophysical experiment. Under the assumption that the central nervous system can extract the information "intensity of a cold stimulus" from the *sum* of the responses of many receptors, it was calculated that practically *all* the cold-receptor fibers (ca. 50) in the stimulated area of skin are required for the observed discrimination capacity; the information is transmitted without redundancy.

These examples illustrate the ability of the central nervous system to utilize the information coming from the periphery in *different degrees,* depending on the task. Comparative studies of this sort, especially if the activity of central neurons is also measured, offer considerable promise for advancement of our knowledge of the neuronal bases of sensory perception.

15.2 The Spinal Motor System Interpreted as a Control Circuit

One of the functions of the spinal stretch reflex is to keep the *length* of a muscle **constant** (p. 86). Because **control systems** in general are designed to keep things constant, it is useful to describe the stretch reflex in the language of *control theory* [16]. This section serves at the same time as an introduction to basic concepts of this area of technology, which when applied to *biological regulatory processes* (e.g., blood pressure, respiration, temperature, water balance; see the relevant chapters in this book) have facilitated our understanding [1, 8, 10, 16, 17, 26].

The Terminology of Control Theory

Survey. We shall begin by explaining the basic terms used to describe a *control circuit,* with reference to the general *block diagrams* of Fig. 15-6 A and the concrete example of room-temperature control. The **controlled variable** is a *state* that is to be kept constant (room temperature, in our example). The physical structures

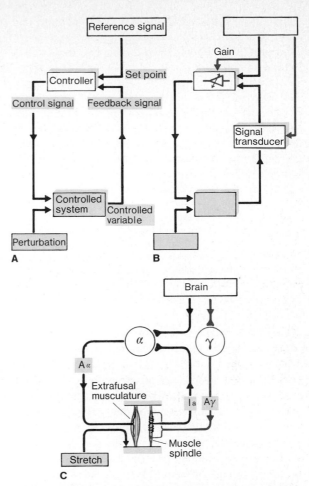

Fig. 15-6 A, B. Block diagram of a simple control system. The lines ending in *arrowheads* show the direction in which influence is exerted among the elements of the control system; there is a reciprocal interaction between controller and controlled system. The controlled variable is a state that must be kept constant. **B** Block diagram of an expanded control system (new parts shown in red); here, in contrast to **A,** the reference signal affects the controller and the transducer of the feedback signal. One action of the reference signal is to alter the controller gain. **C** Diagram of the stretch reflex

within which regulation occurs are the *controlled system* (room with heater). A *sensor* (thermometer) measures the current value of the controlled variable, and sends an appropriate *feedback signal* to the *controller* (thermostat). The controller compares the current value with a *reference signal* (desired temperature); this operation is a form of computation, and in general one finds that controllers have the properties of a computer. If the feedback signal differs from the reference signal, the *error* causes the controller to initiate corrective measures. It does so by sending a *control signal* to a device capable of appropriately altering the situation, the controlling element or *effector* (heater with variable fuel feed). Control signals are sent out continuously until the feedback and reference signals match. Factors that cause the controlled variable to depart from the set point given by the reference signal are called *perturbations* (e. g., loss of heat from the room).

The essential feature of a control circuit is thus the closed-loop arrangement, operating so that any disturbance of the controlled variable is automatically corrected. Because the overall function of the loop in principle amounts to minimizing the deviation of the controlled variable from the set point given by the reference signal, the term *negative feedback* is used.

Open-loop systems. The standard elements of a control system can also be arranged in an open circuit, *without feedback* (e. g., no signal representing current temperature). Such a system can compensate for a disturbance that is known in advance (e. g., an estimated amount of cooling at night), but not for a variable, unpredictable disturbance (e. g., loss of heat due to changing weather and the opening of doors and windows at irregular intervals).

More elaborate control circuits. In Fig. 15-6 B the basic block diagram is modified to illustrate additional properties of a control circuit – in particular, one applicable to the stretch reflex. Here the controller of Fig. 15-6 A has been provided with *variable gain;* the *gain of the controller* determines its *sensitivity* to differences between the feedback and reference signals. The influence of gain on the function of the control circuit is described later, in the discussion of the stretch reflex (pp. 323 and 324).

In Fig. 15-6 B the feedback signal passes through a *transducer,* which encodes the information from the sensor. Coding of information in the transmission of both the feedback and the control signal is such a common feature of control systems that block diagrams usually do not show the transducers explicitly. We shall refer to this element, however, in analyzing the stretch reflex (p. 326).

Regulators and servomechanisms. So far we have been concerned with the ability of a control system to keep a controlled variable at a constant preset level. A system functioning in this way is usually called a *regulator.* Now we turn to the mode of operation in which the *set point is changed* arbitrarily. We change the set point, for example, when we turn the temperature selector on the thermostat for room heating. The controller's response to a change in the *reference signal* is in principle the same as to a change in the feedback signal; the *difference* between the two is measured and the controlling element acts on the controlled variable until it has reached the new set point. Closed-loop systems designed so that the controlled variable will follow changes of the reference signal are called *servomechanisms.*

An alternative way of feeding the reference signal into the control circuit is also shown in Fig. 15-6 B; here the reference signal modifies the action of the *transducer* on the feedback signal. This use of the reference signal is not common in technology, but as we shall see (p. 326) it corresponds to the role of the γ-efferents to the muscle spindle.

The Stretch Reflex as a Control System

To apply the concept of regulation to the stretch reflex, we first consider a classical experiment of Sherrington. A muscle with its nerves to the spinal cord intact is given a certain extra load, and the resulting change in length is noted. It is evident that the muscle develops extra contractile force (reflex tonus) so as to oppose the passive length change that would otherwise be induced by the load; the length of the muscle is thus kept approximately constant. A *regulator mechanism* is operating here.

The *elements* of this *control circuit* are as follows (Fig. 15-6):

Controlled system	Muscle with tendons and joint
Controlled variable	Muscle length L
Controller	α-motoneuron
Effector	Extrafusal musculature
Control signal	Frequency F_α in the α-motoneuron
Sensor with transducer	Muscle spindle
Feedback signal (coded)	Frequency F_{Ia} in the Ia fiber
Reference signal	Excitation of motoneurons, descending from supraspinal levels
Perturbations	Gravity, muscle fatigue, loads

Analysis of the static control circuit. A control circuit is analyzed by *opening the loop,* interrupting either the connection between sensor and controller or between controller and effector. In this condition the properties of each element in the circuit can be measured in isolation.

Effector. We shall first examine the characteristics of the element that actually makes the required adjustment, beginning with a nerve-muscle preparation as described on p. 52. The motor nerve (the A α-fibers) is stimulated electrically at various intensities and frequencies. The different levels of stimulus intensity excite different numbers of A α-fibers; the correspondingly incremented activation of motor units is known as recruitment (cf. p. 41). By recruitment and by changing the stimulus frequency one can vary over a wide range the total number F_α of the efferent action potentials passing along a motor nerve per unit time. The resulting graded contraction of the muscle can be evaluated by plotting length L as a function of frequency F_α ($L = f(f_\alpha)$) as in Fig. 15-7 A. Because we are interested in the control of muscle length under varying loads (perturbations), we have plotted the *characteristic curves* for two different loads, P_1 and P_2, with $P_2 > P_1$.

The change in L caused by increasing the load can be compensated by increasing F_α. But because of the elasticity and fatigability of the muscle, it is impossible to establish a specific muscle length (and thus a particular body posture) exclusively by sending out a particular efferent signal (discharge rate of α-motoneurons). There must be continuous feedback to inform the central nervous system about the length of the muscle – that is, a closed loop is required.

Feedback. The *actual muscle length* at each moment is measured by the *muscle spindles* and encoded in nerve impulses. Because of the possibility of intrafusal contraction by way of the γ-efferents, the coding is ambiguous; this property is utilized when the system operates as a servomechanism to change muscle length (p. 326). Fig. 15-7 B shows *characteristic curves of a muscle spindle* – that is, the relationship between muscle length L and discharge rate F_{Ia} of the muscle spindles. The two curves were obtained under different conditions of intrafusal contraction, as indicated by the levels of excitation γ_1 and γ_2 of the γ-efferents ($\gamma_2 > \gamma_1$). The signal transducer in the modified block diagram of Fig. 15-6 B performs a corresponding function.

Controller. The characteristic curve of the controller, here taken to be linear, is shown in Fig. 15-7 C (Curve 1). It is the relationship $F_\alpha = f(F_{Ia})$, where F_{Ia} and F_α are *summed* frequencies – the total number of afferent or efferent action potentials per second in the muscle nerve. The controller curve can change its position in the diagram of Fig. 15-7 C, either by a *parallel shift* (Curve 3) or by a *change in slope* (Curve 2). The functional significance of such curve displacements in the operation of the control circuit are discussed below.

The relationships in Fig. 15-7 B and C can be combined to give a function $F_\alpha = f(L)$; that is, a certain change in muscle length causes a certain change in discharge rate of the α-motoneurons, as plotted in Fig. 15-7 D (Curve 1). By definition, the change in efferent discharge ΔF_α for a given change in length ΔL depends on the *slope* of the curve. By analogy with technical devices, we can speak of the controller as

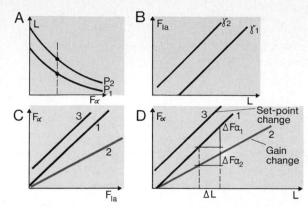

Fig. 15-7 A–D. Characteristic curves of isolated elements of the muscle-length control circuit. **A** Muscle length L as a function of impulse frequency F_α in the motor nerve, for two loads ($P_1 < P_2$). The dashed line shows how L changes with load, if F_α remains constant. **B** Coding characteristic of the muscle spindle: frequency F_{Ia} of the afferent fiber as a function of muscle length L, for two different levels of γ-efferent activity ($\gamma_2 > \gamma_1$). **C** Characteristics of the α-motoneuron: discharge rate F_α as a function of discharge rate F_{Ia} of the muscle-spindle afferents that make synaptic contact with the α-motoneuron. Position of the curve depends on the excitability of the motoneuron, and can be altered either by a parallel shift (transition from Curve 1 to Curve 3) or change in slope (1 to 2). **D** Relationship between muscle length L and discharge rate F_α of the α-motoneuron, obtained by combination of the diagrams in (**B**) and (**C**). The three lines are as in (**C**); a change ΔL causes different changes $\Delta F_{\alpha 1,2}$, depending on the slope of the characteristic

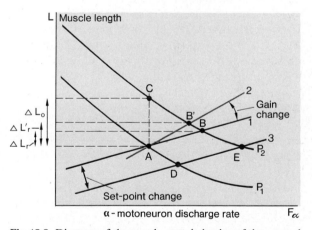

Fig. 15-8. Diagram of the steady-state behavior of the control system for muscle length L, obtained by superposition of Fig. 15-7 A and D in the F_α-L coordinate system. Further discussion in text

having a certain **gain** or amplification factor; the steeper the slope of the characteristic curve, the higher the gain. Changes in controller gain (Curve 2 in Fig. 15-7 C, D) can be caused by a change in the excitability of the α-motoneuron (Fig. 15-7 C) or by a change in the sensitivity of the muscle spindle induced by the γ-efferents (cf. p. 326); both effects can be mediated by descending pathways from the brain.

Closing the loop. From the characteristic curves obtained under open-loop conditions we can find the *static* properties of the *closed control system.* To do this, one superimposes the curves of the controller (Fig. 15-7 D) and the effector (Fig. 15-7 A), both of which represent a relationship between L and F_α, with opposite directions of action (Fig. 15-8). The only final states the controlled variable can reach are those that lie on both curves; the stable value of the controlled variable is represented by the point of *intersection* of the curves for *controller* and *effector* (point A for load P_1). If the load changes from P_1 to P_2 (perturbation), a new stable value is adopted (B in Fig. 15-8). A slight change in muscle length ΔL_r is associated with this new value. If the controller were inoperative the same change in load would give the final length C; in this case the change in length ΔL_0 is much greater. Obviously, the smaller ΔL_r is, the better the regulator is functioning. The quality of regulation can be described by the *regulation factor R:*

$$R = \frac{\Delta L \text{ with regulation}}{\Delta L \text{ without regulation}} = \frac{\Delta L_r}{\Delta L_0}$$

In the example of Fig. 15-8, measurement of these gives a regulation factor of about R = 0.13. Technical control systems can achieve far smaller values. The quality of regulation is critically dependent on the *gain of the controller;* with low gain (Curves 2 in Figs. 15-7 D and 15-8) the length change $\Delta L_r'$ for a given increase in load is greater – the regulation is poorer (point B' in Fig. 15-8). In this case the regulation factor, calculated from the distances $\Delta L_r'$ and ΔL_0, is 0.40.

Change in Gain of the Length Controller

Anything that *changes the gain* of the controller influences the regulation. Many supraspinal and segmental effects on the stretch reflex can be understood as operating in this way [5, 16, 23, 25].

Gain adjustment by inhibition. We have seen in another context that *inhibition* can be interpreted as a means of changing the amplification involved in synaptic transmission (cf. Fig. 9-15, p. 208). Examples of inhibition in the stretch reflex are the inhibition of the motoneuron by the tendon organs, inhibition by the Ia fibers of the antagonistic muscle, and Renshaw inhibition. Examination of the curves in Fig. 15-8 reveals that inhibition impairs regulation by *reducing the gain* of the controller (transition to Curve 2), so that there is a greater increase in length $\Delta L_r'$ following

increase of the load from P_1 to P_2. This can be a useful effect, for with lower gain the regulation is less "stiff" and the muscle *more compliant.* Increased compliance is desirable, for example, if a muscle is the antagonist and has to give way during movement of the joint. The stretch reflex of the antagonist muscle usually is not completely inactivated, but its gain is reduced. As a result, it can have a *braking action.* Autogenic inhibition by the tendon organs can also be regarded as a form of gain reduction in the control circuit – one which in the extreme can practically eliminate length regulation. Thus sudden strong stretching of the tendon causes the joint to buckle, like a pocket knife folded beyond the critical point: the clasp-knife reflex.

When tonic descending inhibition is abolished by pathological changes in the *supraspinal* central nervous system the gain of all the stretch-reflex control circuits can become so large that there is continual tonic activation even of antagonistic muscle groups *(spasticity)*[25].

Autogenic inhibition is often regarded as a circuit for the regulation of muscle tension (tension-control system [8, 9, 17]; cf. p. 89), superimposed on the length-control system. Without going into the matter further, we can mention here that the superposition of the two control circuits can be brought about by a subtractive and/or multiplicative processing of γ-motoneuron excitation and inhibition. The mechanism for gain adjustment proposed here implies multiplicative processing. It is likely that both mechanisms collaborate in the stretch reflex.

Dynamic Properties of Control Systems

So far we have considered only the static (steady-state) properties of the control system. Here we show that regulation is fundamentally characterized by the *temporal properties* of the system: disturbances should be compensated as rapidly as possible.

The dynamics of a control system or of its components are studied by imposing well defined disturbance. For analysis of our muscle control circuit, we shall use a *step function* (Fig. 15-9).

Open loop. In Fig. 15-9 the effects of a step increase in lenght (Fig. 15-9 A) are shown at various points in the open circuit. Fig. 15-9 B shows the step response of the muscle spindle – that is, the feedback signal after coding in the transducer. The dashed curve (Curve 1) is the response if the sensor output is proportional to the change in muscle length *(proportional sensor);* the secondary endings of the muscle spindle (Group II) usually behave in this way. The continuous red curve (2) is the response of a primary muscle-spindle ending (Ia); here the overshooting, dynamic portion of the discharge at the onset of muscle stretch is a measure of the *rate of stretch* – that is, of the first derivative of movement with respect to time [9]. In the later part of the response the discharge frequency F_{Ia} is proportional to the amount of stretch. In technological terms, therefore, the primary muscle-spindle ending (Ia) is a *proportional-differential (PD) sensor*.

Fig. 15-9 C shows the time course of the *control signal* F_α in response to a stepwise disturbance of muscle length L. Here, again, PD behavior is observed, due in part to the characteristics of the muscle-spindle response and in part to the fact that the α-motoneuron also exhibits PD behavior; thus we are dealing with a *PD controller*. The large transient component at the beginning of the response of the α-motoneuron (Curve 2) is further enhanced by the change in *gain* of the controller, which is high at the beginning of the discharge and subsequently brought down by the onset of Renshaw inhibition (cf. p. 91).

Dead time. An important feature of this control system is evident in Fig. 15-9: the delay resulting from impulse conduction in the afferent and efferent nerves, the *dead time* of the system. The dead time limits the speed of regulation. Evidently nature has minimized the dead time of the stretch reflex in that the nerve fibers involved (Ia, A α) have the highest conduction velocities found in peripheral nerves.

Closed loop. Fig. 15-9 D shows the step response of the controlled variable with the circuit closed – the *step response of the control system*. The controlled variable (length of muscle L) first changes passively under the influence of the stepwise disturbance. After the dead time (due to afferent and efferent conduction) has elapsed the effect of regulation becomes apparent, bringing the length of the muscle L back (approximately) to the desired level. Three kinds of dynamic behavior are plotted. The dashed curve (1) corresponds to the (here hypothetical) case in which both sensor and controller have *pure P characteristics* (proportional sensor and controller). The controlled variable changes relatively slowly, because of the inertia of muscle contraction induced by an efferent impulse train at constant frequency. Clearly this effect would introduce an extra delay in the regulation process, in addition to the dead time due to nerve conduction. The continuous curve (2) shows the step response of muscle length if the *D (differential) components* of sensor and controller are taken into account. Because the frequency F_α is higher initially, the muscle contracts *more rapidly* and reaches the new steady-state value sooner. The third case in Fig. 15-9 (Curve 3) gives the resulting behavior of the control system if one were to speed up the process still more by further *increasing the gain* of the controller.

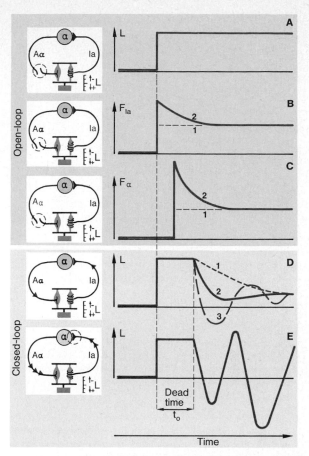

Fig. 15-9 A–E. Step responses in the control system for muscle length. The elements of the stretch reflex corresponding to each response are emphasized (in *red*) in the diagram at the left. **A** Stepwise change in muscle length L by sudden increase in the load on the muscle (disturbance). **B** Discharge rate F_{Ia} of the muscle spindle (sensor plus transducer) in response to the disturbance. **C** Discharge rate F_α of the α-motoneuron (controlled variable, response of the controller) resulting from the disturbance. A, B and C measured in open-loop conditions. In each case Curve 1 shows the behavior of a sensor and controller with response proportional to length (P elements), whereas Curve 2 contains an additional component corresponding to the time derivative of muscle length (rate of length change): proportional-differential sensor and controller (PD elements). **D** Step response of the controlled variable L under closed-loop conditions, with P elements (Curve 1) or PD elements (2, 3) and either low (2) or high (3) gain. **E** Undamped oscillation of an unstable system – e. g., one with excessively high gain

Damped oscillations of the controlled variable occur during the transition to the new steady state.

Comparison of the three possibilities in Fig. 15-9 D demonstrates that the inherent inertia of a control system (due to dead time and the limited speed of operation of the effector) can be partially compensated in the overall system behavior by the *D (differential) components* of the feedback responses and the initial high gain of the controller.

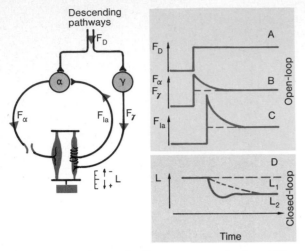

Fig. 15-10 A–D. The stretch reflex as a servomechanism. **A** Time course of the discharge rate F_D in descending pathways at the beginning of a movement (reference signal). **B** Response of α- and γ-motoneurons to change in the descending excitation (reference signal acts on controller). **C** Response of the muscle spindle to the descending activity of γ-neurons (reference signal acts on transducer). B, C measured in open-loop conditions. **D** Step response of the controlled variable to a stepwise change of the reference signal, closed-loop system. Dashed curves (1) based on P elements, solid curves (2) on PD elements

In many control systems the controlled variable even in the steady state oscillates slightly about the set value; the control system is in continual operation. Such an oscillation can also appear in the stretch reflex, and here is known as *physiological tremor*.

Instability of a control system. If the gain of a control system is made too large, the damped oscillation in the step response may give way to *undamped oscillations* (Fig. 16-9 E). In such cases of *instability* the amplitude of the undamped oscillation can be so large that the controlled variable sweeps back and forth between its two extreme values. The net result is that *the degree to which gain can be raised in order to make regulation more effective is limited by the appearance of instability.* An unstable controller is worse than no control at all.

Several states of the stretch reflex, some of them pathological, can be interpreted as instability of the control circuit: the resting tremor of Parkinsonism, the clonic convulsions observed, for example, in strychnine poisoning, and the clonus of hyperreflexia. Undamped or slowly damped oscillations occur here at a frequency determined by the dead time of the control system and the ballistic properties of the affected joint movement.

Operation of a Servomechanism

Having discussed the operation of the muscle-length control circuit as a regulator, which tends to keep length constant, we now consider the system as a *ser-*

vomechanism. As noted above, in this case the difference between input signals measured by the controller arises from a *change in the reference signal;* as a consequence the controlled variable is adjusted to a *new set point.*

Variable reference signal. When a *movement* – i.e., a change in muscle length – is to be made, there must be a *set-point readjustment* in the stretch-reflex control circuit. Nature has provided a *servosystem* to solve this problem [5, 16, 23]. The reference signal, which determines the set point, originates in supraspinal regions of the central nervous system. The step response of the servomechanism is shown in Fig. 15-10. A step change in the reference signal, the impulse frequency F_D in the descending pathways to the motoneurons (Fig. 15-10 A), brings about a corresponding change in the discharge rates of the α- and γ-motoneurons (Fig. 15-10 B) and in the muscle spindles (Fig. 15-10 C), here shown in the open-loop system. The result, in the closed-loop system, is lengthening or shortening of the muscle (Fig. 15-10 D).

As we saw in Fig. 15-8, the set point of the control circuit is changed by a parallel shift of the controller characteristic (transition from Curve 1 to Curve 3 in Figs. 15-7 and 15-8). Now recall that in Fig. 15-8 we found that only the points at which the controller characteristic intersects that of the effector can represent *steady-state* values of the controlled variable. It follows that *shifting* the controller characteristic on supraspinal command brings the system to a *new muscle length L.* Again as can be seen in Fig. 15-8, the control circuit in this new state still functions to keep the (new) muscle length nearly constant (e.g., when load P_1 is replaced by P_2; Points D and E in Fig. 15-8).

Elements affected by the reference signal. A notable feature of the stretch reflex is that the reference signal acts at two points (cf. Figs. 15-6 B, C and 15-10) – at the *controller* (the α-motoneuron) and, by way of the γ-motoneuron, at the site of transduction of the feedback signal (the muscle spindle) [5, 8, 9, 27]. To explain these possibilities, let us consider the supraspinally initiated shortening of the muscle, brought about by the transition of the controller characteristic from Curve 1 to Curve 3 in Figs. 15-7 D and 15-8. This parallel shift can be produced both by a change in the relationship $F_{Ia} = f(L)$ (coding characteristic of the muscle spindle; Fig. 15-7 B) and by a change in the relationship $F_\alpha = f(F_{Ia})$ (input-output characteristic of the α-motoneuron; Fig. 15-7 C). Both of these mechanisms of *set-point adjustment* are used. The action of the γ-innervation of the muscle spindle (Fig. 15-7 B) has been discussed previously (p. 87). The change in the α-motoneuron characteristic is brought about by *synaptic excitation* by way of *descending pathways;* for example, when the level of tonic activity in the reticulospinal tract increases, the membrane potential is shifted in the *depolarizing* direction. The *threshold* for the generation of impulses in the α-motoneuron due to additional synaptic activation by the Ia afferents is thereby *lowered,* which amounts to a leftward shift of the characteristic curve (transition from Curve 1 to Curve 3 in Figs. 15-7 C, D and 15-8).

Simultaneous alteration of gain and reference signal. There has as yet been no systematic attempt to find actual instances of pure parallel shift of the α-motoneuron characteristic, as shown schematically in Fig. 15-7 C. The few experimental results demonstrating supraspinal influence of the α-motoneuron characteristic indicate that its slope is changed along with its position. In terms of control theory, this means that the descending activity has changed the *set point* and the *gain* of the α-motoneuron at the same time.

Analogous effects have been observed in the *muscle spindle;* some of the input from the γ-fibers causes not a pure parallel shift of the characteristic (as shown in Fig. 15-7 B) but rather a combined shift and slope (gain) change. In particular, the marked increase in the *dynamic* response of the Ia fibers when some of the γ-efferents are activated is interpretable as an increase in the amplification factor of the muscle spindle. The chief result of this increase is modification of the initial transient in the step response of the control system (Fig. 15-9 D).

Concatenation of Segmental and Supraspinal Control Circuits

The control-system concept is not limited to the regulation of length of a single muscle. Movement at a hinge joint, for example, involves flexor and extensor muscles, which *reciprocally* inhibit one another (antagonist inhibition; pp. 73 and 87). Thus the two stretch-reflex control circuits of antagonistic muscles are doubly *coupled* – there is a mechanical coupling in that the contraction of one muscle amounts to a disturbance for the other, and the antagonist inhibition exerts a reciprocal influence on the gain of each circuit. Control systems coupled in this way can be considered as a single system governing *position of a joint* [8].

At the supraspinal level several such joint-position control systems are *intermeshed* in a complex way, and together govern the performance of a coordinated movement [8]. This coordination involves a variety of *feedback signals* directly to these supraspinal CNS regions [16, 27] – from muscle spindles and from receptors in joints, ligaments, the skin and the vestibular organ. Several such *superordinate* supraspinal control circuits have been identified. Although it is not yet possible to give a complete description of these circuits, our understanding of supraspinal motor systems has also been furthered considerably by application of the control-system concept [16].

15.3   References

Textbooks and Handbooks

1. BAYLISS, L. E.: Living Control Systems. New York: Plenum Press 1966
2. BURNS, B.: The Uncertain Nervous System. London: English Universities Press 1968
3. DESMEDT, M. E. (Ed.): Cerebral Motor Control in Man: Long Loop Mechanisms. Progr. Clin. Neurophysiol. 4, Basel: Karger 1978
4. GARNER, V. R.: Uncertainty and Structure as Psychological Concepts. New York: John Wiley 1962
5. GRANIT, R.: The Basis of Motor Control. London–New York: Academic Press 1970
6. GRODINS, F. S.: Control Theory and Biological Systems. New York: Columbia University Press 1963
7. HOMMA, S. (Ed.): Understanding the Stretch Reflex. Progr. Brain Res. 44, 1976
8. HOUK, J.: Principles of system theory as applied to physiology. In: Medical Physiology, 14th Ed., Vol. 1, p. 225 (MOUNTCASTLE, V. B., Ed.). St. Louis–Toronto–London: The Mosby Company 1980
9. MATTHEWS, P. B. C.: Mammalian Muscle Receptors and their Central Actions. London: Arnold 1972
10. MILSUM, J. H.: Biological Control Systems Analysis. New York–San Francisco–Toronto–London: McGraw-Hill 1966
11. MOUNTCASTLE, V. B. (Ed.): Medical Physiology, 14th Ed., Vol. 1, St. Louis, Toronto, London: The Mosby Company 1980
12. SHANNON, C. E., WEAVER, W.: The Mathematical Theory of Communication. Urbana: The University of Illinois Press 1949
13. SMITH, J. M.: Mathematical Ideas in Biology. Cambridge–New York: Cambridge University Press 1968
14. TALBOTT, R. E., HUMPHREY, D. R. (Eds.): Posture and Movement. New York: Raven Press 1979
15. WIENER, N.: Cybernetics. Paris, New York: Freymann 1948

Research Reports and Reviews

16. HOUK, J. C.: On the significance of various command signals during voluntary control. Brain Res. *40,* 49 (1972)
17. HOUK, J. C., SINGER, J. J., GOLDMAN, M. R.: An evaluation of length and force feedback to soleus muscles of decerebrate cats. J. Neurophysiol. *33,* 784 (1970)
18. JOHNSON, K. O., DARIAN-SMITH, I., LA MOTTE, C.: Peripheral neural determinants of temperature discrimination in man: A correlative study of responses to cooling skin. J. Neurophysiol. *36,* 347 (1973)
19. KRUGER, L., KENTON, B.: Quantitative neural and psychophysical data for cutaneous mechanoreceptor function. Brain Res. *49,* 1 (1973)
20. LA MOTTE, R. H., MOUNTCASTLE, V. B.: Capacities of humans and monkeys to discriminate between vibratory stimuli of different frequency and amplitude: a correlation between neural events and psychophysical measurements. J. Neurophysiol. *38,* 539 (1975)
21. MARSDEN, C. D., MERTON, P. A., MORTON, H. B.: Servoaction in the human thumb. J. Physiol. *257,* 1 (1976)
22. MATTHEWS, P. B. C., STEIN, R. B.: The regularity of primary and secondary muscle spindle afferent discharges. J. Physiol. (Lond.) *202,* 59 (1968)
23. MERTON, P. A.: How we control the contraction of our muscles. Sci. Amer. *226,* 30 (1972)
24. MOUNTCASTLE, V. B., LA MOTTE, R. H., CARLI, G.: Detection thresholds for stimuli in humans and monkeys: comparison with threshold events in mechanoreceptive afferent nerve fibers innervating the monkey's hand. J. Neurophysiol. *35,* 122 (1972)

25. NEILSON, P.: Interaction between voluntary contraction and tonic stretch reflex transmission in normal and spastic patients. J. Neurol. Neurosurg. Psychiat. *6*, 853 (1972)

26. NICHOLS, T. R., HOUK, J. C.: Improvement in linearity and regulation of stiffness that results from actions of stretch reflex. J. Neurophysiol. *39*, 119 (1976)

27. PHILLIPS, C. G.: Motor apparatus of the baboon's hand. Proc. roy. Soc. B *173*, 141 (1969)

28. STEIN, R. B.: The information capacity of nerve cells using a frequency code. Biophys. J. *7*, 797 (1967)

29. WALLØE, L.: On the transmission of information through sensory neurons. Biophys. J. *10*, 745 (1970)

30. WERNER, G., MOUNTCASTLE, V. B.: Neural activity in mechanoreceptive cutaneous afferents: stimulus-response relations. Weber functions and information transmission. J. Neurophysiol. *28*, 359 (1965)

31. ZIMMERMANN, M.: Mechanoreceptors of the glabrous skin and tactile acuity. In: Studies in Neurophysiology presented to A. K. McIntyre (PORTER, R., Ed.), p. 267. Cambridge: Cambridge University Press 1978

32. ZOTTERMAN, Y. (Ed.): Sensory Functions of the Skin in Primates. Oxford–New York–Toronto–Sydney–Paris–Frankfurt: Pergamon Press 1976

Part III
Blood, Circulation and Respiration

16 Functions of the Blood

Ch. WEISS

16.1 Basic Concepts

Blood is an opaque red fluid consisting of the pale yellow *plasma* (called serum when the fibrin is removed) and the cells suspended in it – the red corpuscles *(erythrocytes),* the white corpuscles *(leukocytes)* and the platelets *(thrombocytes).*

Functions of the Blood

Transport. Blood is primarily a medium by which substances are conveyed within the body. It transports the respiratory gases oxygen and carbon dioxide both in physical solution and in chemically bound form – O_2 from the lungs to the respiring tissues and CO_2 from the tissues to the lungs. It moves nutrients from the places where they are absorbed or stored to the sites of consumption. The metabolites produced there are transferred to the excretory organs or the places where they can be further utilized. Blood serves as a vehicle for the hormones, vitamins and enzymes produced by the body itself, taking them up at the sites of production or storage and carrying them – distributed throughout the intravascular space – to their target organs. Thanks to the high heat capacity of water, its chief component, blood distributes the heat produced by metabolism and disperses it into the environment by way of the lungs and respiratory passages and the exposed body surface.

Homeostasis. As the blood circulates through the body its composition and physical properties are continually monitored by certain organs and, if necessary, corrected so as to ensure constancy of the *internal milieu.* This condition of homeostasis – approximate constancy in the concentration of dissolved substances, in temperature and in pH – is a basic requirement for the normal function of all cells.

Prevention of hemorrhage. Another important function of the blood lies in its capacity to counteract bleeding by the closing of small injured vessels and by coagulation (cf. p.345).

Defense against foreign agents. The body is capable of making foreign bodies and pathogenic organisms harmless; this ability is associated primarily with phagocytic and antibody-forming blood cells (cf. pp.350ff.).

Blood Volume

Blood accounts for about 6–8% of the weight of the body. In an adult this corresponds to a blood volume of 4–6 liters. The way this volume is measured is explained on p.454, and its distribution among the different parts of the vascular system is described on p.406.

Hematocrit

Definition and normal levels. *The fraction of the blood volume made up of erythrocytes is called the hematocrit.* In a healthy adult man it is 44–46 vol. %, and in a woman 41–43 vol. % (ml cells/dl blood). A healthy person exhibits appreciable and maintained departures from this value only when adapted to high altitudes. The newborn hematocrit is about 10% higher, and that of small children is about 10% lower.

To **determine hematocrit** (by Wintrobe's method) the blood, having been prevented from clotting, is centrifuged for 10 minutes at about 1000 g (g = relative acceleration due to gravity) in standard hematocrit-tubes of small diameter. The blood cells, having higher specific gravity than the plasma, sink to the bottom; because the leucocytes are lighter than the erythrocytes, they form a thin whitish layer between the sedimented erythrocytes and the plasma. Because of the special flow properties of the erythrocytes, the hematocrit values of the various organs differ, and there are differences among the venous, arterial and capillary values. The average whole-body hematocrit can be derived by multiplying by 0.9 the hematocrit obtained for cubital-vein blood with the Wintrobe method.

Hematocrit and viscosity of blood. Taking the viscosity of water as 1, the mean **relative blood viscosity** of healthy adults is 4.5 (3.5–5.4), and that of the blood plasma is 2.2 (1.9–2.6). The internal friction of the blood, its viscosity, increases more than proportionally as the hematocrit increases (cf. Fig.18-3, p.399).

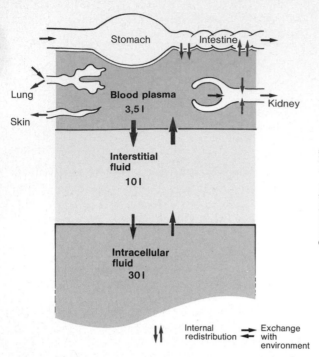

Fig. 16-1. Diagram of the fluid compartments in the body. The volumes are indicated in round figures, for a person weighing 70 kg. After [8]

Because resistance to flow rises linearly with viscosity, any pathological increase in hematocrit puts a greater load on the heart and can result in inadequate circulation through certain organs.

16.2 Blood Plasma

Human **plasma** is 90–91% water (by weight, mg/dg); 6.5–8% of its weight is due to protein, and the remaining 2% to substances of low molecular weight. The specific gravity of plasma is 1.025–1.029; its pH varies slightly (7.37–7.43) about a mean of 7.40 (arterial blood).

Fig. 16-1 is a diagram of the three great fluid compartments in the body, the **blood-vascular-system,** the **interstitial space** (the spaces between cells) and the **intracellular space.** The interstitial fluid constitutes the environment of the mass of cells in the body. By way of the large surface of the capillary walls (highly permeable to water and electrolytes) it exchanges substances with the plasma. Because the exchange of water and small molecules between plasma and interstitial space is very rapid, the range within which the composition of the interstitial fluid can vary is small despite the considerable variations in uptake

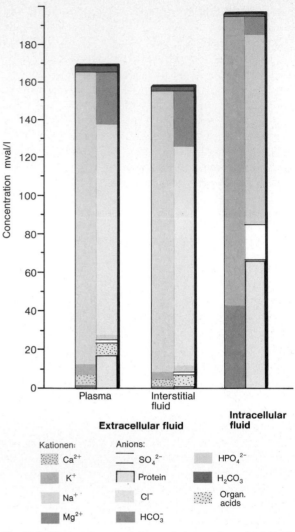

Fig. 16-2. Electrolyte composition of plasma, interstitial fluid, and intracellular fluid. After [8]

and release of substances by the cells. For example, experiments with heavy water (deuterium-labelled, D_2O) have shown that over 70% of the plasma fluid is exchanged with the interstitial fluid in one minute.

There are appreciable *concentration differences between plasma and interstitial space* only with respect to the proteins, for these molecules are so large that they cannot pass readily through the capillary membrane.

Plasma Electrolytes

Electrolyte concentrations. Table 16-1 and Fig. 16-2 summarize the ionic composition of plasma. Among the substances in the group called simply "organic acids" are lactic acid, the amino acids, citric acid and pyruvic acid.

It is preferable to give concentration not as w/v ratio (g/dl or mg/dl) but rather in terms of **molarity** (mol/liter) and **normality** or equivalent concentration (eq/liter = mol/valence · liter). In Table 16-4, however, where groups and mixtures of substances varying in composition are listed, w/v ratios are used. When it is necessary to allow for limitations on the volume of a solution in which the dissolved particles require a great deal of space, **molality** (mol/kg solvent) is often used as a measure of concentration.

Osmotic pressure. The concentration of dissolved substances in the plasma can be expressed by the *osmotic pressure*. That of normal plasma is about 7.3 atm (5 600 mm Hg = 745 kPa), which corresponds to a freezing-point depression of $-0.54°$ C. Solutions with the same osmotic pressure as plasma are called *isotonic,* and by the same convention *hypertonic* solutions have higher, and *hypotonic* solutions lower osmotic pressure. Plasma is isotonic with a barely 1/3 molal solution of a nonelectrolyte. 96% of the osmotic pressure of blood is due to the presence of inorganic electrolytes, mainly sodium chloride. The molecular weight of NaCl is low, so that there are many molecules per unit weight.

Constancy of the internal milieu, or **homeostasis,** depends critically on regulation of the osmotic pressure of the plasma. Any departure from the normal extracellular osmotic pressure (plasma and interstitial fluid) causes a redistribution of water between the cells and their surroundings. *Hypotonicity* of the extracellular fluid causes influx of water into the cells and hence swelling *(cellular edema).* Great increases in volume can destroy the cell membrane (cf. osmotic hemolysis of erythrocytes, p. 341).

Hypertonicity, on the other hand, causes the cells to lose water and shrink, so that the normal tissue turgor is lost. In both cases the ability of the cell to function is more or less severely impaired.

Functions of the plasma electrolytes. Isotonicity of the suspension medium is one of the fundamental requirements for the maintenance of function in isolated, surviving tissue. In itself, however, it does not suffice to preserve cell function; the various ions must be present in suitable proportions. Table 16-2 gives the composition of some "balanced" saline solutions which have proved useful as suspension media for living tissue in vitro. Although the different actions of the various ionic species have long been known, the mechanisms underlying these effects are not understood in all details.

Table 16-1. Average concentrations of electrolytes and non-electrolytes in human plasma. From [20]

	mg/dl	meq/l	mmol/kg plasma water
Electrolytes			
Cations:			
Sodium	328	143	153
Potassium	18	5	5
Calcium	10	5	3
Magnesium	2	2	1
Total		155	
Anions:			
Chloride	365	103	110
Bicarbonate	61	27	28
Phosphate	4	2	1
Sulfate	2	1	1
Organic acids		6	
Protein	7 000 to 8 000	16	1
Total		155	
Non-electrolytes			
Glucose	90–100	5	5
Urea	40	7	7

Table 16-2. Composition of some commonly used suspension media. The numbers indicate the concentration (meq/l) of each ion

Ringer				Tyrode	
Amphibians		Mammals		Mammals	
Na^+	115	Na^+	146	Na^+	149.4
K^+	1	K^+	4	K^+	2.7
Ca^{++}	2	Ca^{++}	5.4	Ca^{++}	3.6
Cl^-	106	Cl^-	155.4	Mg^{++}	2.1
HCO_3^-	12			Cl^-	145.1
				HCO_3^-	12.0
				HPO_4^-	0.7
				Glucose	0.1%

Plasma Proteins

General properties and functions. The high relative viscosity of plasma, 1.9–2.6 (water = 1), is almost entirely due to its protein content, *6.5–8 g/dl.* Because of the high molecular weight of proteins, the molal concentration, as Table 16-1 shows, is considerably less impressive – only about 2 mmol/kg. The protein fraction of plasma is a mixture of many individually identifiable proteins. Their **molecular weights** range from 44 000 to 1 300 000, and their **molecular diameters** are between 1 and 100 nm. Particles of this order of magnitude are classified as colloids (Fig. 16-3). The

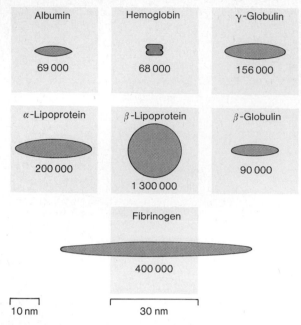

Fig. 16-3. Molecular weights and shapes (schematic) of some plasma proteins and of hemoglobin. After [19]

plasma proteins function in a number of different ways.

1. Nutrition. The approximately 3 liters of plasma in an adult's body carry about 200 g of protein in solution, a convenient reserve supply. In general the cells of the body take up not proteins but rather their components, the amino acids; however, certain cells – especially those of the reticuloendothelial system (RES) – can take in whole plasma proteins and break them down by means of intracellular enzymes. The amino acids thus produced diffuse into the blood and are immediately available to other cells for the synthesis of new protein. The turnover of plasma protein can become so rapid that the entire daily requirement of protein may be injected parenterally (i.e., bypassing the gastrointestinal system) in the form of plasma proteins.

2. Transport. Many small molecules (cf. p. 338) are bound to specific plasma proteins during transport from the intestine or storage organs to the places where they are needed. The large surface area of these proteins, with numerous hydrophilic and lipophilic attachment sites, makes them especially suitable to serve as vehicles. By binding of their lipophilic groups to water-insoluble fat-like substances they can hold these substances in solution. Their ability to bind a large number of low-molecular-weight substances during their transport in the bloodstream also assists in maintaining a constant osmotic pressure.

3. Unspecific carrier function. All the plasma proteins bind blood cations in a non-diffusible form. For example, about 2/3 of the calcium present in plasma is unspecifically bound to proteins. This bound calcium is in equilibrium with the physiologically effective, ionized calcium freely dissolved in the blood.

4. Production of colloid osmotic pressure. The contribution of the proteins to the total osmotic pressure of the plasma is very small, because of their low molecular concentration. Nevertheless, the colloid osmotic (oncotic) pressure plays an important role in *regulating the distribution of water between plasma and interstitial fluid*. Because the capillary membranes are essentially freely permeable to small molecules, the concentration of these molecules – and thus the osmotic pressure associated with them – is approximately the same in the two fluids. But the plasma-protein molecules are so large that they encounter a relatively large resistance in passing through the capillary wall (for example, isotope-labelled albumin leaves the bloodstream with a half-time of about 14 hours). This effect, combined with the removal of protein by uptake into cells and transport through the lymph, brings about a protein concentration gradient between plasma and interstitial fluid that provides a colloid osmotic pressure difference of about 22 mm Hg (3 kPa).

Any change in the osmotically effective concentration of plasma protein disturbs the exchange of substances and the distribution of water between blood and interstitial fluid. Because albumin (cf. p. 336) represents the largest fraction of the plasma protein (a relatively small molecule, its molal concentration is about 6 times higher than that of all the other plasma proteins), changes in albumin concentration have an especially pronounced effect on colloid osmotic pressure. Reduction of the plasma albumin concentration often leads to retention of water in the interstitial space *(interstitial edema)*.

5. Buffer function. Because the plasma proteins are able to form salts by combining with acids and bases, they contribute to maintenance of a constant pH (cf. p. 502).

6. Protection against loss of blood. The coagulability of blood, which interferes with bleeding, is based in part on the fibrinogen content of the plasma (cf. p. 337). The process involves a chain of reactions in which a number of blood proteins that act as enzymes cooperate, terminated by the conversion of dissolved fibrinogen into the fibrin meshwork of which the clot is composed (cf. p. 348).

Fractionation of plasma proteins. Qualitative and quantitative analyses of the plasma proteins are carried out routinely (Fig. 16-4). Protein electrophoresis is an important diagnostic aid, for many diseases involve characteristic changes in the plasma-protein spectrum.

Electrophoresis is the migration of electrically charged particles, dissolved or suspended in a fluid, along a voltage gradient. Protein molecules are built up of single amino acids joined together by peptide bonds. The electrolytic nature of these molecules is derived from the ionization of amino ($-NH_2$) and carboxyl ($-COOH$) groups; especially when these are present in side chains, they are electrically charged in accordance with the pH of the solvent ($-NH_3^+$ or $-COO^-$).

The **electrophoretic mobility** of a protein is basically a function of the applied voltage, the size and shape of the molecule, and its electric charge, which depends on the difference between its isoelectric point (IP) and the pH of the solution. As can be seen in Table 16-3, the IPs of the different plasma proteins are below pH 7 by varying amounts. In neutral or alkaline solutions, then, the proteins will migrate in the same direction, toward the anode, but with different velocities (Fig. 16-4).
In another method of fractionation, which allows simultaneous determination of molecular weight, the **ultracentrifuge** (Svedberg) is used to generate accelerational forces from 100000 to

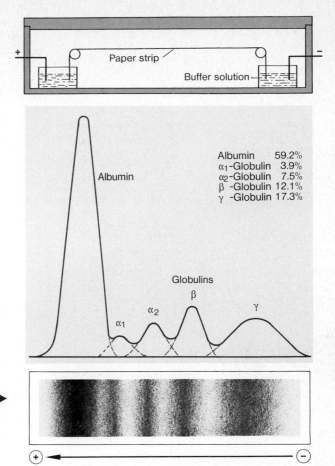

Fig. 16-4. Electropherogram of human serum. The stained bands on the paper strip (bottom) correspond to peaks in the photometric curve, which represent the indicated percentages of the various protein fractions. *Top:* diagram of the apparatus for paper electrophoresis

Albumin 59.2%
α_1-Globulin 3.9%
α_2-Globulin 7.5%
β -Globulin 12.1%
γ -Globulin 17.3%

Table 16-3. Protein fractions in human plasma. MW, molecular weight; IP, isoelectric point. From [9, 18, 26, 27]

Protein fraction		Mean concentration		MW (× 1000)	IP	Physiological significance
Electrophoretic	Immunoelectrophoretic	mg/dl	μmol/l			
Albumin	Prealbumin	30	4.9	61	4.7	Limited binding of thyroxin; colloid
	Albumin	4000	579.0	69	4.9	osmotic pressure, vehicle function; reserve protein
α_1-globulins	Acid α_1-glycoprotein	80	18.2	44	2.7	Product of tissue degeneration?
	α_1-lipoprotein	350	17.5	200	5.1	Lipid transport (esp. phospholipids)
α_2-globulins	Ceruloplasmin	30	1.9	160	4.4	Oxidase activity
	α_2-macroglobulin	250	3.1	820	5.4	Plasmin and proteinase inhibition
	α_2-haptoglobulin	100	11.8	85	4.1	Binds hemoglobin to prevent loss in urine
β-globulins	Transferrin	300	33.3	90	5.8	Iron transport
	β-lipoprotein	550	0.3 to 1.8	3000 to 20000	–	Lipid transport (esp. cholesterol)
	Fibrinogen	400	11.8	340	5.8	Blood clotting
γ-globulins	γ-globulins	1200	76.9	156	5.8	Immunoglobulins: Antibodies against bacterial antigens and foreign protein "Natural" antibodies (e.g., isohemagglutinins)
	γA-globulin	240	16.0	150	7.3	
	γM-globulin	125	1.3	960		
	γE-globulin	0.03	0.002	190	–	Antibodies

750000 times the earth's gravity. For a given centrifugal force, the rate of sedimentation depends on the specific weight and the shape of the molecule (Fig. 16-3) and on the density of the suspension medium. In **density-gradient centrifugation** the protein components of a mixture can be especially well separated, for each becomes concentrated at a particular level in the tube.

A still more refined separation of plasma proteins can be achieved with a combination of electrophoresis and immunoprecipitation. In this procedure, **immunoelectrophoresis,** electrophoretically separated protein fractions are allowed to diffuse within a gel into a drop of antibody-containing serum. When the protein antigen encounters the serum antibody precipitation occurs, and is evident as a whitish zone of turbidity in the gel. In this way it has been shown that electrophoretically uniform protein fractions can consist of several immunologically distinguishable proteins (cf. Table 16-3). More than 30 proteins have been identified in human plasma.

Properties and functions of individual fractions. Because electrophoresis is the analytical procedure most commonly used, discussion will be restricted to the components distinguishable by this method. Fig. 16-3 shows diagrammatically the size relationships and the shapes of the most important plasma proteins.

Plasma albumin. About 60% of the total plasma protein is albumin (3.5–4.5 g/dl). With a molecular weight of 69000, it is one of the smallest proteins in the plasma. Because of its relatively high concentration and the small size of the molecule, it is responsible for almost 80% of the colloid osmotic pressure of the plasma. The many small molecules have a very large total surface area, so that they are especially well suited to act as carriers, binding a number of substances for transport in the bloodstream. Among the substances bound by albumin are bilirubin, urobilin, fatty acids, bile-acid salts and a few extraneous substances such as penicillin, sulfonamides and mercury. A single albumin molecule, for example, can bind 25–50 molecules of bilirubin (MS 500) at a time. In many pathological states the amount of albumin is reduced.

Plasma globulins. The term "globulin" designates a group of electrophoretically separable components. In order of diminishing mobility in the electric field, these are called α_1-, α_2-, β- and γ- globulins (Fig. 16-4). Even these subfractions, however, do not represent individual proteins. With other procedures, such as immunoelectrophoresis, each can be further separated (Table 16-3).

Together with the subgroup of α_1-**globulins** migrate a number of conjugated proteins, with carbohydrate prosthetic groups predominantly in the form of hexoses and hexosamines; these are called *glycoproteins.* About 2/3 of the glucose in the plasma is bound as

glycoprotein. This bound glucose is not detected by clinical tests for blood sugar in deproteinated plasma. It can be measured only after it is released from the protein by acid hydrolysis, when its concentration is found to be 80–165 mg $\cdot$ dl^{-1}. This subfraction also includes another group of carbohydrate-containing proteins, the *mucoproteins,* with incorporated mucopolysaccharides.

In the α_2-**globulin** fraction are the haptoglobins, which chemically are classified as mucoproteins, and the copper-containing *ceruloplasmin.* The latter has 8 atoms of copper per molecule, which are responsible for the oxidase activity of the protein. About 90% of the total plasma copper is bound to ceruloplasmin. However, the copper transported in the bloodstream to the cells of the body is bound to albumin rather than to ceruloplasmin. Other proteins that migrate with the α_2 group are *thyroxin-binding protein,* vitamin-B$_{12}$-binding globulin *(transcobalamin), bilirubin-binding globulin,* and cortisol-binding globulin *(transcortin).*

The β-**globulins** include the most important carrier proteins for lipids and polysaccharides. The *lipoproteins* are of great functional significance in that they can hold non-water-soluble fats and lipoids in solution and act as a vehicle for their transport in the blood. About 75% of all fats and lipoids in the plasma are bound as lipoproteins. Small amounts of lipoproteins are also found in the α_1-fraction, but the majority migrate with the β-globulins. Of these, the most important is β_1-lipoprotein, a molecule of which can comprise as much as 77% lipid. Analysis of the lipoprotein mixture in the plasma by means of *ultracentrifugation and electrophoresis* (the electrophoretic mobility of the lipoproteins is due to their protein component) has become a useful tool in diagnosis of the various forms of hyperlipoproteinemia (cf. textbooks of biochemistry). Apart from the lipoproteins, the fraction comprises a group of metal-binding proteins; one of these, *transferrin,* serves as a carrier of copper and, most importantly, of iron. This metalloprotein binds 2 (ferric) iron atoms per molecule, and is the vehicle for iron transport in the blood.

The heterogeneous group of γ-**globulins** includes the proteins with the lowest electrophoretic mobility; their isoelectric points, accordingly, are nearer the neutral point than those of the other plasma proteins (cf. Table 16-3). Among the γ-globulins are most of the protective and defensive substances of the blood, many of which have enzymatic activity. Because the demand for proteins with such special functions varies, there are wide fluctuations in the quantity and composition of the γ-globulin fraction; in almost all diseases, particularly the inflammatory ones, the amount of γ-globulins increases. The total amount of plasma protein in general remains approximately the same, however, because the increase in γ-globulins is accompanied by a roughly equal decrease in albumin; the so-called *albumin-globulin ratio* is reduced. The erythrocyte-agglutinating substances anti-A and anti-B are also γ-globulins.

Fibrinogen appears as a narrow separate band, between the β- and γ-globulin fractions. Fibrinogen is the dissolved precursor of fibrin, which precipitates out of solution to form a blood clot (cf. p.348). Fibrinogen is an elongated molecule with an axial ratio (length: width) of 17 : 1. The high viscosity of fibrinogen solutions results from the tendency of these molecules to aggregate in a string-of-beads formation.

Characteristic changes in the fibrinogen fraction appear only in a few rare diseases, so that there is little diagnostic value in electrophoretic demonstrations of altered fibrinogen concentration. Moreover, the mobility of this elongated molecule in paper electrophoresis is more dependent on the kind of paper used than is that of the other plasma proteins. For these reasons, serum rather than plasma is usually used in clinical paper electrophoresis of blood proteins; the typical electropherogram shown in Fig. 16-4 thus has no fibrinogen band.

Synthesis and turnover of plasma proteins. A human on a normal diet synthesizes about 17 g albumin and 5 g globulin in 24 hours. The half-life of albumin in the human is 10–15 days, and that of globulin is about 5 days. That is, when these times have elapsed 50% of the protein present on the first day has been replaced by newly synthesized protein.

Transported Plasma Components

As has been shown in the preceding sections, the inorganic electrolytes and the proteins transported by the plasma critically affect, by their very presence, its most important functional properties. In this sense the *inorganic electrolytes and the proteins are functional elements of the plasma.*

There is another group of plasma components which are simply transported and have little effect – within the physiological range of concentrations – on the characteristic physiocochemical properties of the plasma. For this heterogeneous group of substances the plasma is first and foremost a means of transport. Among them are (a) *nutrients, vitamins and trace elements,* (b) *products of intermediary metabolism,* (c) *hormones and enzymes,* and (d) *substances to be excreted.*

Transported nutrients, vitamins and trace elements. The largest fraction, by weight, of the nutrients transported in the plasma is made up of **lipids** (all ether-soluble substances: fats, lipoids and

Table 16-4. Nonprotein nitrogen and lipids (mg/dl) in human plasma. From [26]

Substance	Mean	Range
Urea N	14	10–17
Amino-acid N	5.0	3–7
Uric-acid N	1.7	1.0–2.3
Creatinine	0.5	0.4–0.5
Ammonia N	0.2	0.1–0.2
Total N. P. N.	25	22–30
Fats, neutral fat		0–450
Fatty acids		200–450
Steroids, cholesterol		120–350
Free cholesterol		40–70
Bile acids		0.2–3
Bile salts		5–12
Phospholipids, total		150–250
Lecithin		100–200
Cephalin		0–30
Sphingomyelin		10–30
Total ether-soluble material		380–680

steroids). The concentration of these substances, however, fluctuates widely (Table 16-4).

After a very fatty meal the lipid content can rise to such an extent (up to 2000 mg/dl) that the plasma looks milky white **(lipemia).** About 80% of the fatty acids are bound to globulin as glycerides, phospholipids and cholesterol esters (lipoproteins); most of the non-esterified fatty acids form albumin complexes. In contrast to the plasma lipids, the concentration of which depends on the momentary metabolic state, the concentration of **glucose,** the most important carbohydrate, stays relatively constant at 80–120 mg/dl despite differences in uptake and widely varying rates of utilization. Another group of transported nutrients, the amino acids, are present in the plasma in an intermediate concentration, about 4 mg/dl. These are derived primarily from the proteins in food.

All the **vitamins** (cf. p.579) and the essential nutrients with the character of vitamins (e. g., choline) are continually present in the plasma. But their concentration varies, not only because of differences in the amounts present in food or synthesized by the intestinal flora. The concentration of some vitamins depends on the presence of specific factors that facilitate absorption; for example, absorption of vitamin B_{12} is affected by Castle's "intrinsic factor." Whereas many vitamins are transported in free solution in the plasma, others – especially the fat-soluble vitamins and a few water-soluble ones such as vitamin B_{12} – are bound to proteins.

One of the more important **trace elements** (elements indispensable as components of structural molecules as well as of hormones and the like) is *iron.* It is absorbed from the intestine at a rate that depends not on supply but on the body's demands. Iron is absorbed as a protein complex *(ferritin).*

Most of the other metals among the trace elements are found in the serum as metalloproteins; 90% of the copper, for example, is bound to the protein *ceruloplasmin* (cf. p.337). Cobalt is an essential component of vitamin B_{12} *(cobalamin).* Practically all the iodine takes the form of a complex with the so-called *thyroxin-binding protein* (cf. p.337).

Transported products of intermediary metabolism. Among the intermediary products of metabolism, **lactic acid** is present in the greatest quantities. Its concentration rises in oxygen deficiency and during hard muscular work. Another organic acid that is always present is **pyruvic acid,** a key substance in energy metabolism because of its involvement in the metabolism of both amino acids and carbohydrates.

Transported hormones and enzymes. More than 50 different substances in this category have so far been identified in the plasma, on the basis of their action or their chemical constitution. Many of them are proteins, polypeptides, amines, amides or steroids.

Transported substances to be excreted. The substances in this group are not utilized further, but are end products of metabolism which must be eliminated from the body. The most important of these are *carbon dioxide, urea, uric acid, creatinine, bilirubin* and *ammonia.* All of these except carbon dioxide contain nitrogen and are excreted by the kidneys. When kidney function is impaired, their plasma concentration rises. They are measured as an aid to the diagnosis of kidney diseases, by Kjeldahl's method for determining nitrogen content of plasma after precipitation of the proteins. The value for **nonprotein nitrogen** (N. P. N.) thus obtained corresponds, for practical purposes, to the nitrogen in the above-mentioned waste products. But about 1/7 of the N. P. N. is incorporated in the plasma amino acids, which are not waste products. In Table 16-4 the most important components of the N. P. N. of normal plasma are summarized.

16.3 Erythrocytes

Number, Shape and Size

Of the cellular components, which make up about 44 vol. % of the blood, the red corpuscles are the most numerous; *men average 5.1 million, and women 4.6 million, per μl blood.*[1] Apart from their water content, the mass of the erythrocytes is chiefly composed of hemoglobin. 34% of their wet weight, and 90% of the dry weight, is attributable to this protein (cf. p. 489).

Erythrocyte diameter (Price-Jones curve). Human erythrocytes are flat disks, indented in the middle on both sides. These non-nucleated cells have diameters that form a normal distribution (the Price-Jones curve) with a mean of 7.5 μm **(normocyte)** in a healthy adult (Fig. 16-6). The biconcave shape of the normo-

---

[1] Values for Central Europe; for North America (after WIN-TROBE) 5.4 and 4.8 million/μl respectively

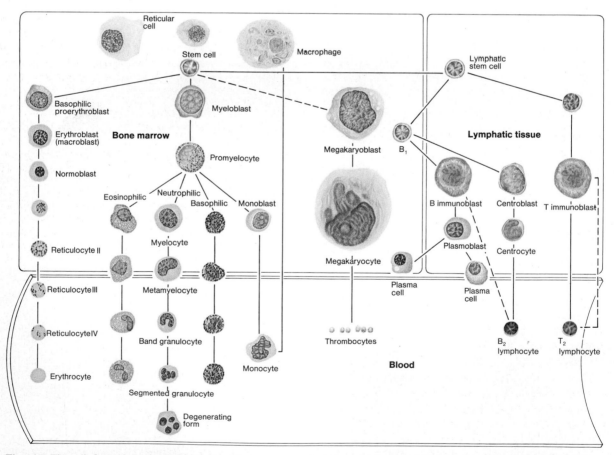

Fig. 16-5. The cells found in peripheral blood and their precursors in the germinal centers, the bone marrow and lymphatic system. After [2]

cyte results in an increase in surface area, as compared with a sphere. The total surface area of the erythrocytes of an adult man is about 3 800 m². The main function of the erythrocyte, gas transport (cf. p.492), is facilitated by this characteristic shape, for the diffusion area is large and the diffusion distance small. Moreover, it is easier for cells so shaped to be reversibly deformed in order to pass through narrow, curved capillaries. The *plasticity of the erythrocyte* is less in older cells. It is also reduced in pathological forms of erythrocytes, such as *spherocytes* and *sickle cells*; the loss of plasticity is one reason why such cells are retained in the meshwork of the spleen and subsequently destroyed there.

Principle of erythrocyte counting. A measured quantity of capillary blood is diluted 100- or 200-fold with isotonic saline solution. The cells in a specified volume of this mixture are counted by microscopic examination, and the dilution factor is applied to determine the cell count in the original blood.

In recent years it has become increasingly common to use more precise, non-microscopic procedures. The erythrocyte concentration in a diluted suspension is determined from the degree of scatter of transmitted light, or from the changes in electrical conductance observed during passage of the cells through a thin tube.

When **impairment of the erythropoietic system** causes a shift of the Price-Jones curve to the right – i.e., a significant increase in the number of erythrocytes over 8 µm in diameter – the condition is termed *macrocytosis*. In pernicious anemia some of the erythrocytes *(megalocytes)* can have diameters of over 12 µm. A leftward shift of the Price-Jones curve (a significant increase in the number of erythrocytes with diameters < 6 µm) is called *microcytosis*. The diameter of these short-lived dwarf forms can be as little as 2.2 µm. When the Price-Jones curve is flattened, as a result of the simultaneous increase in both macro- and microcytes, a state of anisocytosis exists. *Poikilocytosis,* in which there is abnormal variation in erythrocyte shape, can accompany pernicious anemia and thalassemia. Among the characteristically altered cells are rounded spherocytes (hemolytic icterus) and sickle cells (sickle-cell anemia).

Production, Life Span and Destruction

Erythropoiesis. In adults, erythrocytes are produced in the red marrow of the flat bones, by conversion of a nucleated stem cell through several stages (Fig. 16-5). Once formed, an erythrocyte circulates in the blood for 100–120 days. Then it is phagocytized by cells of the reticuloendothelial system in the liver, spleen and bone marrow. But as is evident in the gradual disappearance of the "black and blue" marks caused by intracutaneous bleeding, any tissue is capable of degrading blood corpuscles. About 0.8% of the 25 × 10^{12} erythrocytes of an adult are renewed in 24 hours. This implies an *erythropoiesis rate of 160 × 10^6 erythrocytes per minute.* After loss of blood, and when the erythrocyte life span is pathologically shortened, the erythropoiesis rate can increase severalfold. The ef-

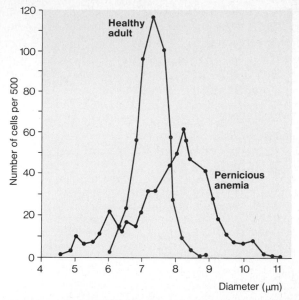

Fig. 16-6. Price-Jones curves. Frequency distribution of erythrocyte diameter in a healthy person (*red* line) and in a patient with pernicious anemia (*black* line). After [22]

fective stimulus that triggers erythropoiesis is a fall in the O_2 partial pressure in respiring tissue (an imbalance between O_2 supply and demand). Under such conditions there is an increased plasma concentration of a substance called **erythropoietin,** which accelerates erythropoiesis. The chemical structure of erythropoietin has not yet been completely clarified; it is probably a glycoprotein with a molecular weight of ca. 33000. The kidneys play a central role in the synthesis of erythropoietin; bilateral nephrectomy results in a marked lowering of the concentration of erythropoietin in the blood. Small amounts of erythropoietin are evidently produced by the liver and the submandibular gland. However, no erythropoietin can be extracted from the kidney. Therefore it is thought that the kidneys release an enzyme, the *renal erythropoietic factor,* into the blood; this factor cleaves a plasma globulin to produce the glycoprotein molecule erythropoietin. Erythropoetin stimulates differentiation and accelerates the proliferation of the committed erythropoietic stem cells in the bone marrow (Fig. 16-5, p.338) and in addition increases the rate of hemoglobin synthesis in the erythroblasts.

Reticulocytes. Counts of the reticulocytes in the blood (Fig. 16-5) can give information about erythropoiesis that is useful in diagnosis and therapy. Reticulocytes are the stage immediately preceding the mature erythrocyte. Whereas the latter has no intracellular structures visible by light microscopy, vital staining of the reticulocytes (staining of the living cells with, e.g., brilliant cresyl blue) reveals granular or filamentous structures. These young blood cells can be found in bone marrow and in the circulating blood. Under normal conditions they account for 5–10% of the erythrocytes in healthy blood. Any acceleration of erythropoiesis increases this percentage, and any retardation decreases it. When the rate of erythrocyte degradation rises, the proportion of reticulocytes can increase to over 50%. In cases of excessively rapid erythropoiesis, even normoblasts can occasionally appear in the blood.

Anemia means, literally, bloodlessness. In clinical usage, the term refers primarily to the diminished ability of the blood to transport oxygen, because of the lack of hemoglobin. In this state, there can be a reduction in the number of erythrocytes as compared with the norm and/or in the hemoglobin content of the individual erythrocytes. The term "anemia" implies nothing about the causes of the hemoglobin deficiency.

The most common form of anemia is *iron-deficiency anemia.* This can be produced by a diet with inadequate iron content (especially common among infants), by diminished iron absorption from the digestive tract (for example, in the so-called malabsorption syndrome), or by chronic loss of blood due, for example, to ulcers, carcinomas and polyps and diverticuli in the gastrointestinal tract, esophageal varicosities, hook-worm infestation (common in the tropics), and heavy menstrual bleeding.

Another group of anemias is termed *megaloblastic anemia;* the most important common characteristic of these anemias is the presence of abnormally large erythrocytes (megalocytes) and their immature precursors (megaloblasts) in the blood and bone marrow. Production of these giant cells is caused by a deficiency of the erythrocyte-maturation substances vitamin B_{12} and/or folic acid, due to inadequacies in either diet or absorption (e.g., in pernicious anemia). When these substances are lacking, cell division is delayed although the rate of growth hardly changes, so that the cells develop to an abnormally large size. Megalocytes have a shorter life span than normal erythrocytes and this, together with the delayed maturation of erythrocytes, leads to anemia.

Pathological states in which the rate of hemolysis increases, because the erythrocytes have become more vulnerable to degradation, can give rise to *hemolytic anemia* if the production of erythrocytes cannot keep pace with the accelerated destruction. Examples of this condition include the hereditary form of spherocytosis and the (also hereditary) diseases sickle-cell anemia and thalassemia. The anemia that accompanies malaria, accelerated hemolysis due to autoimmune responses and erythroblastosis fetalis (anemia caused by incompatibility of rhesus factors) are also in this category.

Cases of *aplastic anemia* and *pancytopenia* are characterized by diminished cytogenesis in the bone marrow, even though all the materials necessary for the production of blood cells are present. In the aplastic anemias only the erythrocytes are affected, whereas in the pancytopenias all the blood cells produced in the bone marrow are reduced in number. Among the aplastic anemias are both hereditary (Diamond-Blackfan, Fanconi) and acquired, idiopathic forms. The inhibition of cell production in the pancytopenias can be caused by bone-marrow damage due to ionizing radiation (X rays or exposure to radioactive elements), cell toxins (cytostatics, benzene etc.), or tumor metastases, which take the place of normal tissue.

Metabolism and Membrane Properties

The metabolic activity of the mature, anuclear erythrocyte is specialized for its oxygen-transporting function and its intermediary role in the transport of carbon dioxide. Erythrocyte metabolism is thus unlike that in the other cells of the body. One of its prime tasks is to maintain the cell's ability to bind oxygen reversibly, not least by providing a means for reduction of the heme ion. The ferrous iron it contains is continually changed to the ferric state by spontaneous oxidation, and must be returned to the ferrous form before it can again combine with oxygen.

Whereas the nucleated precursors of the erythrocytes contain the familiar enzymes for the oxidative release of energy and protein synthesis, the mature erythrocyte must rely on glycolysis, with glucose as the chief substrate. The main energy source, as in other cells, is ATP; it is required in particular for the active transport of ions through the erythrocyte membrane and thus serves to maintain the intracellular ion-concentration gradient. When ATP is derived from glycolysis, reducing substances such as NADH (reduced nicotinamide-adenine dinucleotide) and NADPH (reduced nicotinamide-adenine dinucleotide phosphate, derived from the pentose-phosphate cycle) are produced as well. NADH is required for the above-mentioned reduction of **methemoglobin** to hemoglobin, which can bind oxygen; NADPH is involved in the reduction of the glutathione in the erythrocyte. Glutathione, which is readily oxidizable, protects a number of important enzymes with SH groups in the cell (especially those associated with the hemoglobin molecule and the cell membrane) from inactivation by oxidation.

The **erythrocyte membrane** is a flexible molecular mosaic composed of protein, lipo- and glycoproteins and, probably, regions of pure lipoid. The membrane is about 10 nm thick; it is about a million times more permeable to anions than to cations. Substances that can pass through the membrane do so in several ways, depending on their chemical properties: by diffusion or hydrodynamically, moving as a solution through water-filled membrane pores, or – if they are lipid-soluble – by penetrating the lipoid areas. Certain substances can be bound in readily reversible form to carrier molecules in the membrane, and are thus channelled through the membrane either passively or by way of so-called active transport (cf. p. 657).

Special Physicochemical Properties

Deformability. The shape of a normal erythrocyte can easily be changed by external forces. As a result, the cells can pass through capillaries with inside diameter smaller than the mean diameter of a free erythrocyte (7.5 μm). Because of this deformability, the relative viscosity of the blood in small-bore vessels is effectively lower than in vessels of diameter well above 7.5 μm. The plasticity of the erythrocyte is associated with the presence of Type A hemoglobin (cf. p. 490); in certain hereditary hemoglobinopathies the cells are much more rigid and circulation is impeded.

Osmotic properties. The concentration of protein in the erythrocyte is higher than in plasma, and that of small molecules is lower. The osmotic effect of the higher internal protein concentration is to a great extent compensated by the lower concentration of small molecules, so that the intracellular osmotic pressure is only slightly higher than that of the plasma, and just suffices for the normal turgor of the erythrocyte. (Na^+ and K^+ are actively transported through the membrane, Na^+ out of the cell and K^+ into it; cf. Fig. 16-2). In principle, the erythrocyte membrane is permeable to small molecules, to different degrees depending on the ion concerned. Because of this permeability, inhibition of the active transport of ions results in a reduction of their transmembrane concentration gradient, so that the continued high intracellular protein concentration is no longer compensated, and the osmotic pressure increases.

Therefore water flows into the erythrocyte, until the membrane bursts and hemoglobin emerges into the plasma – a process called (colloid) **osmotic hemolysis.** When the extracellular fluid is only slightly hypotonic, the erythrocytes swell and approach a spherical shape (spherocytes). In a hypertonic medium the cells lose water and become *crenated* (cf. Fig. 16-7).

Systematic study of the **osmotic resistance** of erythrocytes suspended in media of progressively reduced osmotic pressure has demonstrated that in some diseases, certain forms of anemia in particular, osmotic resistance is changed. The curve in Fig. 16-8 shows that 50% of the erythrocytes of a healthy person are hemolyzed when the tonicity of the medium reaches 0.43 g/dl NaCl.

Osmotic hemolysis also occurs when erythrocytes are suspended in an isosmotic solution of substances, such as urea, to which the membrane is highly permeable. **Urea** becomes uniformly distributed within the erythrocyte and in the suspension medium. Because the erythrocyte membrane prevents the larger molecules from leaving the cell, the intracellular osmotic pressure rises above that of the medium, in proportion to the influx of urea. Water enters the cell and causes mechanical disruption of the membrane. Finally, **lipid solvents** such as chloroform, ether and the like can make leaks in the membrane by dissolving out its lipid components, which also leads to hemolysis. The hemolytic effect of soaps, saponins and synthetic detergents results from reduction of the surface tension between the aqueous and lipid phases of the membrane. The lipids are emulsified and drawn out of the membrane, leaving holes through which the cell contents emerge.

Sedimentation rate of blood corpuscles. The specific weight of erythrocytes (1.096) is higher than that of plasma (1.027), so that in an anticoagulated blood sample they slowly sink toward the bottom. The *erythrocyte sedimentation rate* (ESR) of a healthy man is 3–6 mm in the first hour; the value for women is 8–10 mm. Sedimentation is more rapid in certain pathological states (particularly inflammation and increased tissue breakdown due to tumors), chiefly

because of the greater tendency for the red cells to gather into clumps. The frictional resistance of such an *aggregate* is less than the total resistance of its indi-

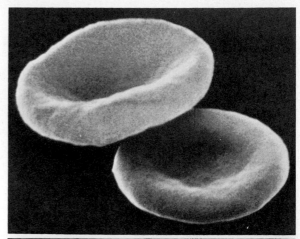

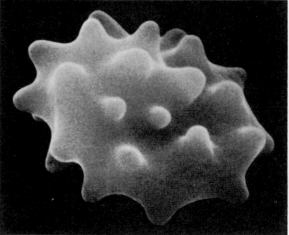

Fig. 16-7. *Above:* biconcave discoid shape of normal erythrocytes. *Below:* crenated erythrocyte, the result of exposure to hypertonic saline solution. After [5]

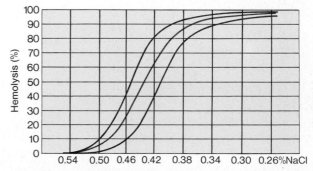

Fig. 16-8. Osmotic resistance of erythrocytes in a blood sample diluted 1:40 with solutions of the indicated salinity. Normal curve with range of deviation. Ordinate: photometrically determined degree of hemolysis as % of total hemolysis. Abscissa: salinity of NaCl solution in % (g/dl). After [13]

vidual elements because of the smaller surface-to-volume ratio, so that the aggregates sink more rapidly.

A marked reduction of cell concentration (lowered hematocrit) reduces the viscosity of the blood and thus accelerates sedimentation; increase in the hematocrit has the reverse effect. Change of erythrocyte shape, as occurs in sickle-cell anemia, and extreme nonuniformity of shape (*poikilocytosis,* as in pernicious anemia) interfere with aggregation and thus reduce the ESR.

The effects of these physical factors, however, are less pronounced than those of changes in the composition of the plasma proteins. Erythrocytes from a patient with accelerated ESR as a rule sink at the normal rate when introduced into plasma of the same blood type from a healthy person. Conversely, erythrocytes from the healthy subject sink more rapidly in the patient's plasma. ESR is retarded by increase in the plasma albumin concentration, and accelerated by increase in the concentration of fibrinogen, haptoglobin, ceruloplasmin, and lipoproteins and *paraproteins* immunoglobulins produced in abnormally large numbers in certain illnesses; cf. textbooks of biochemistry and immunology). The effects of each of these plasma components are additive. Plasma proteins that accelerate sedimentation are called agglomerins. The observation that albumin and globulin have opposite effects on ESR explains the earlier finding that shift of the albumin-globulin ratio in favor of globulin is associated with an increased sedimentation rate.

Measurement of ESR is most commonly done by Westergren's method. 1.6 ml of blood are withdrawn from the cubital vein with a 2-ml syringe containing 0.4 ml 3.8% sodium citrate solution to prevent clotting. A 2.5-mm (i. d.) tube calibrated in mm is filled with this mixture to the zero mark and fixed in a vertical position. After some time, the height of the erythrocyte-free supernatant is read off (readings at one hour and two hours are customary).

16.4 Leukocytes

Properties Common to All Leukocytes

Leukocyte number. Leukocytes, or white (colorless) corpuscles, are nucleated cells lacking hemoglobin. The blood of a healthy person contains *4000–10000 per* μl. This category includes a variety of cell types, which are classified according to morphology and function and to their site of production (Fig. 16-5). Whereas the number of erythrocytes in healthy blood is relatively constant, that of leukocytes varies widely with the time of day and the functional state of the organism. When there are more than 10000 leukocytes per μl the condition is called **leukocytosis;** in **leukopenia** there are less than 4000 per μl. Leukocytosis is most commonly associated with inflammatory diseases and – in its severest form – with leukemia.

Leukocyte counts are made by microscopic examination, on the same principle as used for erythrocytes. Because there are considerably fewer white than red corpuscles, the sample is diluted only 1 : 10 in the calibrated pipette, with 0.3% acetic acid to which methylene blue has been added. The acetic acid destroys the erythrocytes, and the leukocyte nuclei, which are not destroyed, are stained blue. 0.1 μl of the resulting suspension is placed in a standard chamber for counting, and the number of leukocytes in 1 μl blood is computed from the chamber volume and the dilution factor.

Emigration. All leukocytes are capable of ameboid movement, which permits them to emigrate through the walls of blood vessels (this process is also called *diapedesis).* They are attracted *(chemotaxis)* by bacterial toxins, the products of decomposition of bacteria or body cells, and antigen-antibody complexes; they can surround foreign bodies and take them into the cytoplasm *(phagocytosis).* Each type of leukocyte contains certain enzymes; among them are proteases, peptidases, diastases, lipases and deoxyribonucleases. Most of the leukocytes (> 50%) are to be found in the extravascular, interstitial space; the remainder (> 30%) are in the bone marrow. Evidently the blood is primarily a transport medium for these cells (with the exception of the basophilic granulocytes; cf. p.343), carrying them from the sites of production in bone marrow and lymphatic tissue to the places where their action is required.

The three types of leukocytes, in order of their numbers in the bloodstream, are as follows (Fig.16-5, Table 16-5): *granulocytes, lymphocytes* and *monocytes.*

Granulocytes

Granulocytes are so called because of the granules revealed in their cytoplasm by the customary fixation and staining procedures. The various types are produced in the bone marrow (and hence may be called the *myelocytic series).* The diameters of cells observed in a dry-smear preparation range from 10 to 17 μm. *About 60% (50–70%) of the leukocytes in the blood are granulocytes.* The time a granulocyte spends in the bloodstream can be very brief and amounts at most to two days (the life span of these cells). According to the staining properties of the granules, the granulocytes are classified as *neutrophils, eosinophils* and *ba-*

sophils. The proportions of these three types can be seen in Table 16-5.

Neutrophilic granulocytes. The great majority of granulocytes (93–96%) are neutrophils, with about 4150 cells per µl blood. These are also called polymorphonuclear leukocytes. Because of their high rate of emigration into the mucosa, they circulate in the blood only briefly, 6–8 hours on the average. With the onset of acute infections their numbers increase rapidly. The neutrophils can obtain energy by glycolysis, so that they can live even in tissues that are deficient in oxygen, inflamed, edematous or inadequately perfused by blood. Neutrophils can phagocytize bacteria and tissue debris and decompose them by means of their *lysosomal enzymes* (e.g., proteases, peptidases, oxidases, deoxyribonucleases and lipases). **Pus** is largely composed of neutrophils or remnants of these cells. The lysosomal enzymes released during neutrophil degradation cause softening of the surrounding tissue (*abscess* formation).

The neutrophils are the most important functional elements in the unspecific defense system of the blood (cf. p.354). They can be employed for sex determination in humans, for in a genetically female person at least 7 out of 500 neutrophil nuclei exhibit sex-specific lobules, so-called **drumsticks** ("heads" 1.5–2 µm in diameter, attached to a segment of the nucleus by fine chromatin bridges; cf. Fig. 16-9). Such clues to the sex of a patient are useful, for example, in deciding on therapy for malformation of the primary reproductive organs, as in hermaphroditism.

Eosinophilic granulocytes. 2–4% of the leukocytes in the blood are eosinophils (100–350 cells per µl). The blood eosinophil count follows a marked 24-hour periodicity; their numbers are about 20% lower than the 24-h average in the late afternoon and early morning, and about 30% higher at midnight. These fluctuations are associated with the secretion of glucocorticoids by the adrenal cortex. A rise in the blood corticoid level results in a decrease in the number of blood eosinophils, and vice versa. The cells are capable of phagocytosis. They contain large, oval, acidophilic granules made up of amino acids, proteins and lipids. Increase in eosinophil number beyond the range of the daily fluctuation is called **eosinophilia.** This is especially likely to accompany allergic responses, worm infestations and the so-called autoimmune diseases, in which the body elaborates antibodies against its own cells.

Basophilic granulocytes. 0.5–1% (about 50 cells per µl) of the leukocytes in the blood are basophils. Their mean circulation time is 12 h. Their diameter in a dry

Table 16-5. Leukocyte count (cells/µl) in healthy blood. After [26]

	Mean	Range
Granulocytes		
Neutrophils	4150	712– 7588
Eosinophils	165	0– 397
Basophils	44	0– 112
Lymphocytes	2185	1029– 2341
Monocytes	456	66– 846
Leukocytes	7000	2800–11200

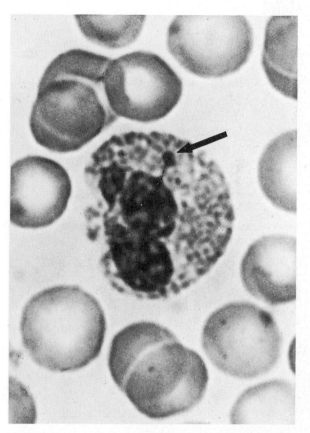

Fig. 16-9. Sex-specific nuclear lobule (drumstick) in a granulocyte of a genetically female person

smear is 7–11 µm. The granules in the cytoplasm of these cells are relatively large, stain deeply with basic dyes, and contain heparin and histamine in salt-like compounds. Recent studies have shown that after absorption of food fats the number of basophils in the peripheral blood is increased. By *releasing heparin* they activate serum lipolysis via the so-called **clearing factor;** heparin may be the prosthetic group of the serum lipase. This enzyme (or enzyme complex) cleaves the ester bonds of the triglycerides bound to polypeptides in the chylomicrons of the blood. As a result, the plasma opalescence due to its fat content is diminished and the content of free fatty acid is increased.

In the surface of the blood basophils are γE-specific receptors to which γE-globulins are attached; these in turn can bind antigen – for example, in cases of **hay fever,** when exposed to pollen. The formation of this immunocomplex at the surface of the basophils causes release of *histamine* from the granules, which gives rise to allergic symptoms such as vascular dilatation, reddening of the skin, an itchy rash and in some cases bronchial spasm.

Lymphocytes

25–40% of the blood leukocytes (1 000–3 600 cells per μm*) in adults are lymphocytes,* and as many as 50% in small children. An increase beyond this range (to over 4 000 cells/μl in adults and a proportional increase in Children) is called *lymphocytosis;* a decrease to less than the mean number is called *lymphopenia.* Lymphocytes are produced by a number of organs: the lymph nodes, tonsils, Peyer's patches, appendix, adenoids, spleen, thymus gland and bone marrow.

By addition of the plant protein *phytohemagglutinin* to cultures of blood lymphocytes it can be demonstrated that these cells, previously thought to be relatively highly differentiated and inactive, are capable of considerable enlargement, mitotic division, and increased synthesis of RNA, DNA, proteins and enzymes. Evidently these changes, triggered in situ by antigens, have a specific defensive function in making available more immunoglobulins.

Monocytes

A second group of leukocytes with agranular cytoplasm contains the monocytes, cells with diameters of 12–20 μm as seen in a dry smear. *These make up 4–8%* (on average, 450 cells per μl) *of the blood leukocytes.* The monocytes do not come from the reticuloendothelial system, as had once been thought, but from the bone marrow; they emerge into the bloodstream while still relatively immature. Monocytes have a higher content of unspecific esterase than any other leukocyte, and *exceed the phagocytic capacity of all other blood cells.* From the blood the monocytes migrate into the surrounding tissue, where they grow in size and in the number of lysosomes and mitochondria they contain. Now, as mature cells, they become stationary and are called *histiocytes* or *tissue macrophages.* In the vicinity of inflammation they can multiply by cell division. Histiocytes form isolating walls around foreign bodies that are invulnerable or highly resistant to enzymatic destruction. These cells are always present in large numbers in the lymph nodes, the alveolar walls, and the sinuses of liver, spleen and bone marrow.

During **infectious diseases** the proportions of the various types of leukocytes change in characteristic ways. Acute bacterial infections induce a neutrophilic leukocytosis accompanied by a decline in the numbers of lymphocytes and eosinophils. As the battle against the infection proceeds it enters a phase of monocytosis – a sign that the bacteria are being overcome. The final phase is a clean-up operation, in which lymphocytes and eosinophils participate. Chronic infections are accompanied by lymphocytosis.

In the tables used clinically to survey the various forms of leukocytes in the blood, those with less segmented nuclei are customarily shown on the left side. Therefore when these forms become relatively more numerous one can speak of a *"leftward shift".* It was once thought that the greater the number of lobules in the granulocyte nucleus, the older the cell; recent autoradiographic studies have shown that there is no such correlation. Evidently the degree of segmentation is predetermined. In a number of diseases (e. g., pernicious anemia), however, granulocytes with an unusually large number of lobes are produced.

To determine the **numbers of leukocytes of the different types,** a capillary-blood smear on a microscope slide is left to dry in air and stained with standard mixtures of acid and basic dyes (e. g., that of Giemsa). When examined microscopically at high magnification, the individual types can be distinguished on the basis of stain affinity and structure. At least 100 leukocytes are included in the sample, and the proportion of each type is given as a percentage.

A pathological leukocyte deficiency, *leukopenia* or – in the most severe form – *agranulocytosis,* results in collapse of the body's defense against bacterial infection. In leukopenia the neutrophils are most markedly affected. The deficiency can be caused by a lowered rate of cell production or a more rapid disappearance of the cells from the blood. As in the case of erythrocyte production, physical (ionizing radiation) or chemical (benzene, cytostatics, etc.) agents can retard multiplication of the leukocyte stem cells and their maturation in the bone marrow. The most severe acute infections (e. g., sepsis and miliary tuberculosis) and diseases involving enlargement of the spleen (splenomegaly) induce leukopenia.

In **leukemia,** on the other hand, there is an uncontrolled (cancer-like) proliferation of leukocytes. The cells produced in excessive numbers are usually not completely differentiated and are incapable of performing their physiological functions – especially in defense against bacterial infections. The causes of human leukemia are still unknown. On the basis of the origin of the leukemic cells, a distinction is made between *lymphogenous* and *myelogenous* leukemia. In the former the overabundant cells are lymphocytes, and in the latter they belong to the myelocytic series (Fig. 16-5, p. 338).

16.5   Thrombocytes

By the method (of Fonio) ordinarily used in the clinical determination of the blood thrombocyte count, healthy adults are found to have 150 000–300 000 platelets per μl blood. These non-nucleated cells, flat and irregularly circular in outline, have longest diameters of 1–4 μm and are 0.5–0.75 μm thick. They are produced in the bone marrow (cf. Fig. 16-5) by the shedding of cytoplasmic buds of megakaryocytes. The platelets circulate in the blood for 5–11 days, and finally are destroyed in the liver, lungs or spleen. When viewed in the light microscope, the platelet exhibits a zone of unstructured protoplasm (the *hyalomere*) just inside the outer membrane. In the central part of the cell (the **granulomere**) granules are embedded in the cytoplasm. These differ in morphology and in chemical composition; three types are distinguished. These are the α granules, which contain a lipoprotein (**platelet factor 3**), β granules, which probably contain the enzymes involved in platelet metabolism, and γ granules, tubules and vesicles containing phagocytized material. Thrombocytes contain appreciable amounts of serotonin and histamine, as well as enzymes involved in glycolysis, the pentose phosphate cycle, the citric acid cycle, and the respiratory chain. ATPase is also present, and the ATP content is large. In addition to their role in arresting blood flow and in coagulation (see below), they participate in the unspecific defense system of the organism (cf. p. 354) by virtue of their ability to phagocytize abiotic foreign matter, viruses and immune bodies.

When the number of platelets falls below 50000–30000 per μl blood there is an increased tendency toward bleeding and, usually, small punctate hemorrhages in which blood effuses from capillaries into all tissues of the body *(thrombocytopenic purpura)*.

16.6   Hemostasis and Coagulation

Basic Considerations

Mechanisms of hemostasis. When a healthy person is injured in such a way that some small blood vessels are opened, bleeding stops after 1–3 minutes. This initial **primary hemostasis** is brought about chiefly by vasoconstriction and the mechanical blockage of small vessels by a plug of thrombocytes. Platelets adhere to connective-tissue fibers at the edges of the wound, and as a result of this contact the platelet membrane becomes more permeable; vasoconstricting substances – serotonin and catecholamines – as well as ATP and ADP are released. (A phospholipid, platelet factor 3, is also released; its role in coagulation is discussed below.) By the action of the vasoconstrictors the lumen of the injured vessels becomes smaller (a functional ischemia is induced), and it is

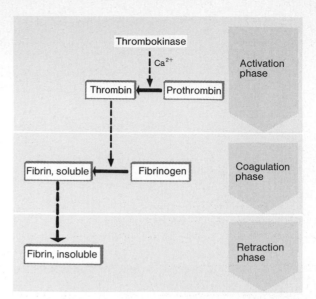

Fig. 16-10. Classical scheme of blood coagulation, after MORAWITZ

obstructed by the mass of platelets caught on the collagen fibers. The release of ADP causes further aggregation of the platelets and thus accelerates the plugging of the leak. The aggregation of platelets under the influence of ADP is reversible.

Irreversible thrombocyte aggregation is brought about by thrombin a little later, in the course of **secondary hemostasis.** During this coagulation phase prothrombin is converted to thrombin by **tissue thrombokinase.** Once the thrombocyte plug has been formed the vessels in the injured region no longer constrict so strongly, and the plug might be washed out and bleeding resumed if it were not for the secondary hemostatic processes. These events (Figs. 16-11 and 16-12) ensure that the damaged vessels are firmly closed off by clots.

Principle of coagulation. The main steps in the clotting of blood have been known for some time. As early as 1915 Morawitz described the basic sequence, and his description is still valid (Fig. 16-10). Outside the body blood clots in a few minutes. The first change, from a fluid to a gelatinous mass, is brought about by conversion of the **fibrinogen** dissolved in the plasma into the fibrous material **fibrin.** Within a few hours the fibrin retracts and squeezes out a clear fluid, the *serum* (fibrinogen-free plasma); the firm, compact red clot that remains is composed of a fibrillar mesh with blood cells in its interstices.

The plasma protein *prothrombin* is converted to *thrombin* by *thromboplastin* (produced during breakdown of the platelets) in the presence of *ionic calcium*. Thrombin brings about the conversion of dissolved

Table 16-6. Blood-clotting factors; a, activated stages. After [9, 12, 18, 21, 27]

Factor	Name, synonym	Site of production	Found in	Properties, function	Deficiency syndrome Name	Cause
I[a]	Fibrinogen	Liver	Plasma	Soluble protein, precursor of fibrin	Afibrino-genemia	Hereditary (recessive, congenital)
II	Prothrombin	Liver	Plasma	α_2-globulin, precursor of thrombin	Hypoprothrom-binemia	Liver damage, vitamin-K deficiency
(III)	Thromboplastin	Precursors in plasma, tissues, thrombo-cytes	Transitory clotting activity of blood	End product of complex reactions of many plasma clotting factors with phospholipids from tissue (extrinsic thromboplastin) and platelets (intrinsic thromboplastin); catalyzes the conversion of F.II to F.II a	–	–
IV	Ca^{++}	–	Plasma	Necessary for activation or conversion of most clotting factors	Unknown in humans	
V	Proaccelerin, accelerator globulin	Mainly liver	Plasma	Soluble globulin, accelerates conversion of F.II to F.II a, activated by thrombin and Ca^{++}	Parahemo-philia, hypoproacceler-inemia	Hereditary (congenital), dystrophy of liver
(VI)	Deleted: activated Factor V.					
VII	Proconvertin	Liver	Serum	β-globulin, accelerates thrombin formation by activating F.X. in presence of Ca^{++}	Hypoprocon-vertinemia	Hereditary (dominant, congenital), vitamin-K deficiency
VIII	Antihemophilic globulin, AHG	Mainly liver (kidney, spleen)	Plasma	β_2-globulin, in early stage of clotting crucial for production of intrinsic thromboplastin, activated by F.IX a and Ca^{++}	Hemophilia A (classical hemophilia	Abnormal gene on X chromo-some, hereditary (congenital)
IX	Christmas factor	Liver	Serum	Contact-sensitive protease, function like F.VIII, effective in presence of F.XI a and Ca^{++}	Hemophilia B	Hereditary (congenital)
X	Stuart-Prower factor	Liver	Serum	Accelerator of F.III, activated by F.VII, Ca^{++} and F.VIII a in turn	Factor X deficiency	Hereditary (congenital)
XI	Plasma thromboplastin antecedent, PTA	–	Serum	Soluble globulin, contact-sensitive protease, activated in early stage of clotting by F.XII a	PTA deficiency	Hereditary (congenital)
XII	Hageman factor	–	Serum	Acid glycoprotein, protease, contact-sensitive (i.e., activated by contact with wettable surfaces)	Hageman syndrome	Hereditary (congenital)
XIII	Fibrin-stabilizing factor, FSF	–	Serum	Transpeptidase, in presence of Ca^{++} stabilizes fibrin by polymerization, activated by thrombin	Factor XIII deficiency	Hereditary (congenital)

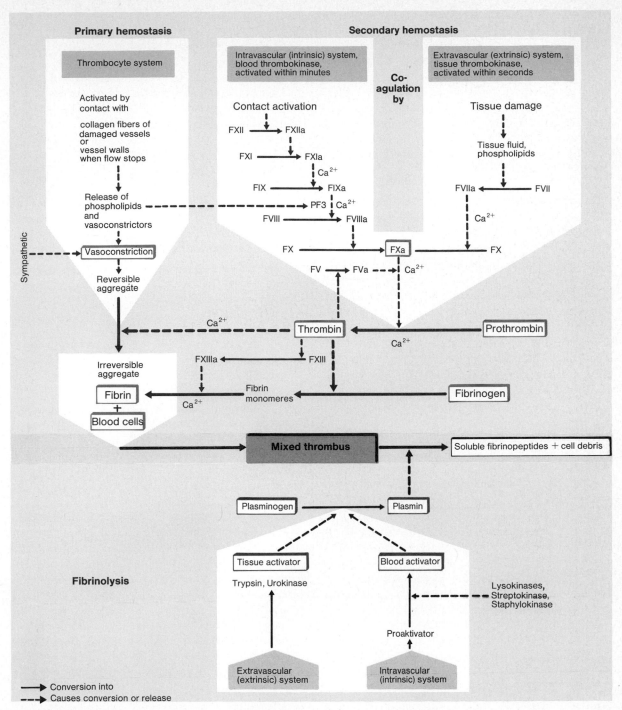

Fig. 16-11. Diagram of blood clotting and fibrinolysis. For data on clotting factors see Table 16-6 (Pf3 = platelet factor 3). After [3, 10, 18, 21, 27]

fibrinogen to fibrin, the supporting element in the clot. Since these interactions were first established, many other clotting factors have been discovered; the chief effect of their absence is impairment of thromboplastin or thrombin formation. We now have a fairly comprehensive understanding of the causes of the various clotting abnormalities (Table 16-6).

Clotting Factors and the Process of Coagulation

Thromboplastin. Although this term refers to the enzymatic activity of the blood in the conversion of prothrombin, it denotes not a single specifiable enzyme, but rather a series of complex reactions. (The term "thrombokinase" is sometimes used as synonymous with "thromboplastin activity.") Depending on the origin of a lipid factor which interacts with plasma factors to form thromboplastin, a distinction is made between *tissue* and *plasma thromboplastin*. Because in the former the activating lipid factor is derived not from the blood but from injured cells in the vessels and from other tissues, the events leading to its production are called the *extrinsic system*. In the *intrinsic system* the activating lipid factor is released from damaged blood cells, chiefly thrombocytes (Fig. 16-11).

Thrombin production. Thromboplastin has a proteolytic action on the plasma protein **prothrombin** (m. w. 66,800; electrophoretically part of the α_2-globulin fraction). In the presence of Ca^{++} prothrombin is converted to **thrombin.** A healthy person has 10–15 mg prothrombin per 100 ml plasma. *Vitamin K* is required for its production in the liver; thus vitamin-K deficiency (for example, when enteral fat absorption is impaired) interferes with blood clotting. The half life of prothrombin in the plasma is 1.5–3 days. Thrombin (m. w. 35000) is a peptidase particularly effective in the splitting of arginyl bonds; it causes partial proteolysis of the fibrinogen molecule.

Fibrin production. The first step is splitting apart of the two subunits of the dimer **fibrinogen** (m. w. 340000); each subunit consists of three polypeptide chains (α, β, γ). **Thrombin** then breaks four arginylglycine bonds, one in each of the two α and the two β chains, to release two amino-peptides, A and B. Both of these are thought to act as vasoconstrictors. The fibrin monomers that remain after fibrinopeptides have been removed are initially brought into parallel alignment with one another by electrostatic forces, forming so-called fibrin polymers. This **polymerization** requires the presence of both the plasma factor fibrinopeptide A and calcium. The gel that results can be liquefied again by the addition of reagents (such as *urea*) that break hydrogen bridges. The fibrin-stabilizing Factor XIII, activated by thrombin in the presence of Ca^{++}, is required for the establishment of covalent bonds between the fibrin monomers; these bonds give the fibrin fibrils their definitive physicochemical properties. However, the mechanical structure of the fibrin network has not yet taken its final form in this stage, for the three-dimensional mesh in which many cells and platelets are trapped is still relatively open.

Retraction. During degeneration of the thrombocytes, a factor called **thrombosthenin** is released which, by an incompletely understood mechanism,

causes the fibrin fibrils to move closer together and shorten by folding. This *retraction* of the fibrin makes the clot more compact. It is thought that the relatively large quantities of ATP metabolically produced in the platelets provide the energy for this process. After retraction the clot is firm, pulling the edges of the wound together so as to facilitate closing of the gap by connective-tissue cells.

From the diagram of blood clotting in Fig. 16-11 it is evident that quite a number of substances are required in addition to the factors just mentioned. Some of these act as enzymes, while others are incorporated into the complexes formed during coagulation. The entire process can be regarded as a cascade of intermeshed events, in which each step provides (by synthesis or activation) the substances required for the next.

Fibrinolysis

Significance of fibrinolysis. The dissolution of a clot is a cascade process similar to clot formation (Fig. 16-12). It is now thought that there is a continuous conversion of small amounts of fibrinogen to fibrin. To maintain equilibrium, this fibrin formation is compensated by a continual process that is almost its mirror image, fibrinolysis. Only when the clotting system is additionally stimulated by injury does fibrin production dominate at the site of the injury, so that localized coagulation becomes apparent.

Activation of fibrinolysis. One of the plasma globulins is **plasminogen** (profibrinolysin). Like prothrombin, this substance can be converted to an active form, **plasmin** (fibrinolysin), by tissue or blood factors (fibrinokinases) in ways analogous to the extrinsic and intrinsic systems of coagulation. Plasmin, a protease related chemically to trypsin, disintegrates the clot by virtue of its affinity to fibrin. It splits soluble peptides off from the fibrin by hydrolysis, and these are further decomposed by peptidases. Because plasmin has a similar action on other elements involved in clotting – fibrinogen, Factor V, Factor VIII, Factor XII and prothrombin – it not only dissolves clots but also diminishes the ability of the blood to coagulate.

The **plasminogen activators** derived from tissue (most conspicuously, the myometrium of the uterus), the *tissue fibrinokinases,* can convert plasminogen directly to plasmin (Figs. 16-11 and 16-12). The **activators from blood,** by contrast, are effective only under the influence of so-called *proactivators* **(profibrinokinases).** The most important proactivators are *lysokinases,* which are released from blood cells by traumatic or inflammatory damage to tissues. *Urokinase,*

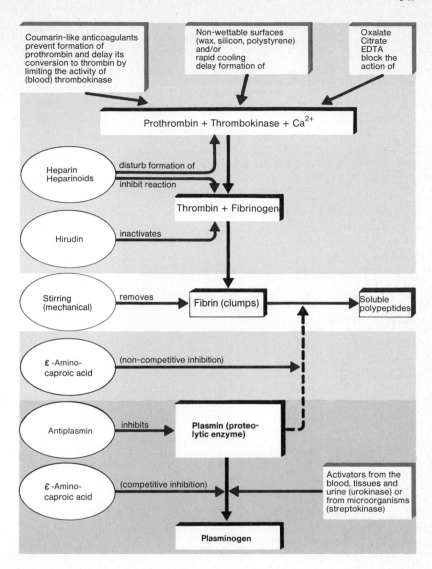

Fig. 16-12. Mode of action of some anticoagulants and fibrinolytics. After [3]

a highly active lysokinase, is found in the urine. It is not known whether it serves to prevent the formation of or to dissolve clots in the urinary tract, or whether it is simply being excreted. A therapeutically important extrinsic lysokinase, *streptokinase,* is produced from hemolytic streptococci and used in the treatment of thromboses.

The proteolytic action of plasmin is inhibited by the antiproteolytic effect of a plasma albumin, **antiplasmin.** There is therefore a gradient of fibrinolytic activity within the clot. In the interior, where plasminogen is adsorbed to fibrin, the plasmin concentration is high and the antiplasmin concentration low, for the latter diffuses slowly from the flowing blood into the clot. When fibrinolysis is to be slowed for therapeutic purposes protease inhibitors such as ε-aminocaproic acid are used; their action can be seen in the diagram of Fig. 16-12.

Disturbance and Inhibition of Coagulation, Tests of Clotting Activity

Clotting defects. In view of the many functions of the thrombocytes in the coagulation process, abnormalities would be expected in cases of **thrombocytopenia** (too few platelets in the blood) and **thrombasthenia** (the production of functionally inadequate platelets). As has been mentioned, when the blood contains < 50000 platelets per µl there are petechial (pinpoint) hemorrhages from the capillaries into all organs, bleeding time is increased, and clot retraction is delayed and incomplete.

In **thrombasthenia,** a rare condition, the symptoms are similar although the platelet count is normal. Thrombopenic tendencies are classified as of known origin (following damage to the bone marrow by, for example, ionizing radiation, mitotic poisons, or neoplastic or chronic inflammatory processes) or as idiopathic thrombocytopenias of unknown origin.

Severe forms of inflammatory and degenerative **liver disease** can restrict the synthesis of prothrombin and Factors VII, IX and X so greatly that clotting defects appear. Clotting is also impaired when there is **vitamin-K deficiency** without liver damage.

An "internal" deficiency of this fat-soluble vitamin, which is present in vegetables and can be synthesized by intestinal bacteria, occurs when enteral fat absorption is inadequate, particularly because of the diminished secretion of bile. The mode of action of vitamin K is not yet entirely understood, but it is known to be necessary for the normal production of prothrombin and Factors VII, IX and X.

The sex-linked (overt in males, carried by females), recessive hereditary disease **hemophilia** is associated in the great majority of cases with a **lack of Factor VIII** (also called *antihemophilic globulin),* though occasionally it is *Factor IX* that is lacking. The two forms are indistinguishable in symptomatology, mode of inheritance, and pathology as revealed by the prothrombin-consumption test and coagulation time. A third and even rarer form of hemophilia results from a deficiency of *Factor XI.* Again, the clinical symptoms are indistinguishable from those of the other forms, though they are usually less well-defined. This disease is also inherited as a recessive trait but affects both sexes.

Because Factors IX and XI are relatively stable and remain effective for long periods even in stored blood, hemophilias involving deficiency of these factors can be treated with stored plasma or blood. Factor VIII is labile, however, so that until the relatively expensive lyophilized Factor-VIII concentrates became available classical hemophilia could be treated only by transfusion of fresh blood or plasma.

Prevention of coagulation (Fig. 16-12). **Cooling** retards extravascular coagulation, though it does not prevent it. Coagulation of blood samples can also be retarded by the use of cannulas and storage containers coated with silicon or paraffin. These **unwettable surfaces** do not induce aggregation and the subsequent degradation of thrombocytes as rough surfaces do. Therefore the build-up of (blood) thrombokinase activity is considerably delayed under these conditions. Extravascular clotting can also be prevented by adding substances that remove from solution the ionic calcium required at many stages in the coagulation process, by *binding calcium in relatively insoluble or weakly dissociated compounds.* Suitable additives include sodium, potassium or ammonium oxalate, sodium citrate, and the chelating agent EDTA (ethylenediamine-tetraacetic acid). Sodium citrate is most commonly used, because it is nontoxic in small amounts, so that inadvertent injection while a sample is being drawn is not dangerous.

Heparin inhibits coagulation both in vivo and in vitro. This anticoagulant is a mixture of polysulfonated mucopolysaccharide esters that occurs naturally in the tissues of liver, lung, heart and muscle, as well as in the mast cells of tissue and the basophilic granulocytes of the blood. It has an antithrombic action when conjoined with a plasma protein called "heparin complement" or "heparin cofactor", to form antithrombin II.

Because heparin must be administered parenterally, and is broken down and excreted so rapidly that it acts for only 4–6 hours, **coumarin derivatives** are preferred for long-term anticoagulant therapy. These drugs can be given orally; they act as *vitamin-K antagonists,* preventing the vitamin from binding with its apoenzyme in the liver. This effect can be overcome by increasing the concentration of vitamin K (competitive inhibition).

Other anticoagulants. Plasma contains an albumin-like protein, called **antithrombin III,** which converts thrombin to inactive metathrombin and thus lowers the thrombin content of the flowing blood. Because fibrinogen (and fibrin) can bind large quantities of thrombin by adsorption, fibrinogen in combination with other substances that inhibit clotting is called **antithrombin I.** Another naturally occurring anticoagulant is **hiru-**din, an antithrombin in the saliva of the medicinal leech. Certain snake toxins inhibit clotting by way of their antithromboplastin activity. The saliva of blood-sucking insects also acts as an anticoagulant; the antithrombin **tabanin** has been isolated from the salivary gland of a biting fly *(Tabanus).*

Tests of clotting activity. For measurement of **recalcification time,** blood anticoagulated with sodium citrate is put into a test tube with a glass bead, and the tube is left to rotate slowly, in a slanted position, in a water-bath at $37\,°C$. After the temperature has equilibrated an excess of calcium chloride is added and the time until clot formation (indicated when the bead rotates with the tube) is measured. The normal range is 80–130 s.

The **prothrombin time (Quick test)** is the most common method of estimating the effectiveness of coumarin therapy. A preparation containing in excess all the factors required for clotting except those to be studied is added to oxalated or citrated plasma and the clotting time is observed. Differences from the normal time (about 14 s) can result from a reduced prothrombin concentration or from differences in the activity of the (thromboplastin) factors that were not added to the plasma.

16.7   The Role of the Blood in Defense

Basic Considerations

Classification of defense mechanisms. There are various ways in which the organism can defend itself against potentially injurious substances. 1. Unspecific mechanisms involve cells **(unspecific cellular defense)** and dissolved substances **(unspecific humoral defense).** 2. Specific mechanisms are based on highly specialized chemical reactions **(immune responses).** When presented with a particular noxious agent **(antigen),** the organism elaborates a specific defense substance **(antibody).** The antibody becomes bound to the antigen *(antigen-antibody reaction,* to form an *antigen-antibody complex),* which as a result loses its noxious properties. (For example, enzymes that act as antigens are inactivated in antigen-antibody complexes.) The antibody may be an immunoglobulin in the plasma **(specific humoral defense)** or a specialized lymphocyte **(specific cellular defense).** The *unspecific system* is capable of rendering foreign bodies harmless even though they have not been previously encountered, whereas the *specific system* becomes effective (immunity is acquired) only after the initial contact with the foreign body.

Antigens are potentially harmful substances (disease pathogens, protein from another species, inert substances) which, when they invade the body, trigger the formation of specific antibodies to neutralize them. An antigen is composed of an unspecific, large **carrier molecule** (polysaccharide, protein, lipid; m.w.

> 10000) and the structural components *(determinants)* exposed on the surface of the molecule that are responsible for its serological specificity. Determinants separated from the macromolecular carrier are called **haptens.** A hapten is capable of reacting with the appropriate (homologous) antibody, but cannot trigger the synthesis of new antibodies.

Antibodies are specific products of the response of the (animal or human) organism to invasion by antigens; they are found in the serum of the immunized organism. Exposure of the organism to the antigen causes the ribosomes of the cells of the immune system to synthesize antibody molecules. These have antigen-binding sites so shaped that the three-dimensional antigenic determinant (hapten) fits into it (lock and key). Antibodies are γ globulins of the glycoprotein type. As a group they are called **immunoglobulins (Ig);** they are classified on the basis of molecular weight (Table 16-3). All antibodies are capable of reacting specifically with a corresponding antigenic determinant, to form an antigen-antibody complex.

Precipitable antigen-antibody complexes. If an antigen molecule bears more than one determinant group *(hapten)* with the same antigenic properties, introduction of the specific antibody to the solution can result in molecular aggregates so large that they precipitate out. For diagnostic purposes, *precipitability* is used to determine the type of antigen and the specificity of the antibody (by, for example, the agar diffusion method or immunoelectrophoresis).

Agglutination in the antigen-antibody reaction. When antibodies and large particles (blood corpuscles, bacteria) bearing antigens on their surfaces are in suspension together, they may react to form large clumps. This process of agglutination can be visible to the naked eye. Agglutination can be used to determine blood group and to identify species of bacteria; it is part of the process by which antibodies inactivate bacterial proteins (e.g., the tuberculosis bacterium) and hormones in blood and urine (e.g., growth hormone).
The agglutinating antibodies are classified as *complete or incomplete,* depending on whether they are capable by themselves of causing agglutination. Whereas suitable complete antibodies cause visible agglutination of, for example, erythrocytes, incomplete antibodies react with the antigen bound to the erythrocytes but do not form bridges to other particles. Because they occupy the specific antigen attachment sites and thus can prevent complete antibodies that arrive later from binding with these sites, they are also called *blocking antibodies.*
But even erythrocytes with antigenic groups occupied by incomplete antibodies agglutinate when antibodies against human immunoglobulin are added to the suspension. The latter antibodies can bind at two places to the incomplete antibodies attached to the erythrocytes, thus forming a bridge between cells and causing agglutination (Fig. 16-13).
This reaction is employed in the *antiglobulin (Coombs) test.* One application of this test is in the field of blood transfusion, to demonstrate *isoantibodies* that are not otherwise identifiable. (Isoantibodies react with an antigen found on cells and in the body fluids of other individuals of the same species, but not in the individual itself.)

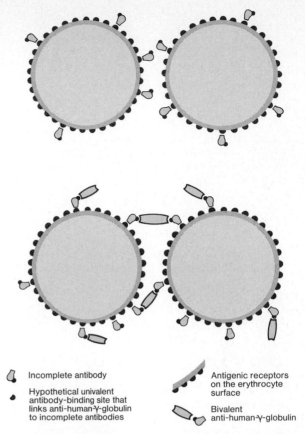

Incomplete antibody	Antigenic receptors on the erythrocyte surface
Hypothetical univalent antibody-binding site that links anti-human-γ-globulin to incomplete antibodies	Bivalent anti-human-γ-globulin

Fig. 16-13. Demonstration of incomplete or non-agglutinating antibodies, by addition of anti-human γ-globulin. After [12]

Many of the biological effects that accompany an antigen-antibody reaction require the participation of a group of nine plasma factors together called **complement** (C1–C9). The various components of complement react in a specific sequence, in which some are bound to the antigen-antibody complex (both agglutinating antibodies and some precipitating antibodies). The presence of complement is required especially for the hemolytic, bacteriolytic and cytotoxic effects of antibodies. The individual steps in activation of the nine complement factors are associated with particular biological effects (Table 16-7).

(*Immune adherence* denotes the tendency of, for example, bacteria and primate erythrocytes to aggregate. In *opsonization* the surfaces of bacteria are covered by a plasma component, an antibody, so as to reduce the electrical surface charge of the cell and thus make it more susceptible to *agglutination* and *phagocytosis.*)
The complement factors are not all synthesized in the same place. One factor (C1) is formed in the intestinal epithelia, another (C2) is probably elaborated by macrophages, and a third (C3) comes from the liver. Humans are subject to hereditary deficiency in individual factors.
In vitro the effect of complement can be suppressed by adding reagents that form complexes with Ca^{++} or Mg^{++} (such as citrate or EDTA) and by heating. **Complement inhibitors** occur

Table 16-7. Some important biological effects of successive stages of complement activation. After [25]

Antigen-antibody complex plus:	
Cl C4 C2 C3	Immune adherence Immune opsonization including Immune phagocytosis
C5	
C6 C7	Chemotaxis
C8 C9	Cytolysis (immune hemolysis) Immune bactericide (cytotoxin)

naturally in the blood; their function has not yet been fully explained. In hereditary angioneurotic edema one of these inhibitors is lacking.

Specific Defense Mechanisms

The **lymphocytes** play a central role in development of the organism's capacity to protect itself. Within the specific system a distinction is made between cellular and humoral antibodies; the latter are released into the blood by plasma cells.

Cell-mediated immune response. The lymphatic stem cells in the bone marrow give rise to immunologically uncommitted lymphocytes, which are carried in the bloodstream to the sites where they become differentiated (Fig. 16-5). Those that remain in the thymus and proliferate there become, by an unknown process, immunologically competent **T lymphocytes** (T for thymus). These again circulate with the blood; they constitute the majority of blood lymphocytes. At the first contact with an antigen some of the T lymphocytes proliferate. Some of the new daughter cells find the antigen and destroy it. This process involves an antigen-antibody reaction that takes place at the surface of the *cytotoxic effector T cells,* where receptor proteins (which can be thought of as fixed immunoglobulins) are embedded in the membrane. This interaction requires the cooperation of T-helper cells (see below).

Another group of daughter cells from the germinal centers comprises the so-called *memory T cells.* These long-lived cells circulate in the blood and, having once been exposed to an antigen, recognize it the second time even though years may have elapsed. At the second antigen contact the "memory cells" trigger a secondary response in which they proliferate more vigorously than in the primary response (initial contact) and soon give rise to a large number of effector T

cells ("killer cells"). *Suppressor T cells,* a subgroup of effector T cells, can suppress antibody formation by B lymphocytes as well as the effector mechanisms of other effector T cells. Although the secondary part of the cellular immune response just described takes place relatively rapidly, reaching a peak after about 48 h, it is called a **delayed immune response** by comparison with the still more rapid development of the humoral secondary response. The delayed immune responses include many of the so-called contact allergies (e. g., reactions occurring in certain people when the skin is exposed to particular synthetic products, to leather tanned with chromium salts, and to jewelry containing nickel), which are manifested by reddening of the skin, blistering and discharge.

Humoral immune response. Other immunologically uncommitted cells produced by the bone marrow acquire immunological competence at other sites – the bursa of Fabricius in birds, and in mammals at sites as yet unknown (perhaps the lymph-node aggregations in the small intestine, the appendix and the tonsils). These are called **B lymphocytes** (B for bursa). Then they reenter the bloodstream and are carried to the spleen, lymph nodes and other lymphatic organs, where they remain. These constitute only a small fraction of the lymphocytes in the blood. When they are first exposed to an antigen (primary response or *sensitization*) those B lymphocytes sensitive to that particular antigen proliferate. Some of the daughter cells leave the germinal centers as *"memory cells";* others settle, for example, in the medulla of a lymph node and there are converted to plasma cells. These plasma cells and their precursors produce antibodies and release them into their surroundings – that is, into the plasma *(humoral antibodies).* In some way not yet understood, antibody production by the B cells is assisted by T "helper" cells (Fig. 16-14).

The secondary response of the humoral immune system, like that of the cellular system, is more rapid and intense than the primary response. When the plasma cells are exposed to antigen for the second time there is an exponential rise in the concentration of the appropriate immunoglobulin in the blood. Because the *humoral immune response is more rapid than the cellular response,* the former is also called the **immediate immune response.** This category includes many kinds of hypersensitivity – for example, that to medicines and pollen *(hay fever),* as well as the allergic form of *bronchial asthma* and the *transfusion reactions* of a recipient to blood of a group other than his own.

In comparison with the various forms of lymphocytes and with the plasma cells to which they give rise, the contribution of other blood cells to the specific defense system is relatively slight. But studies with marked antibodies have shown that eo-

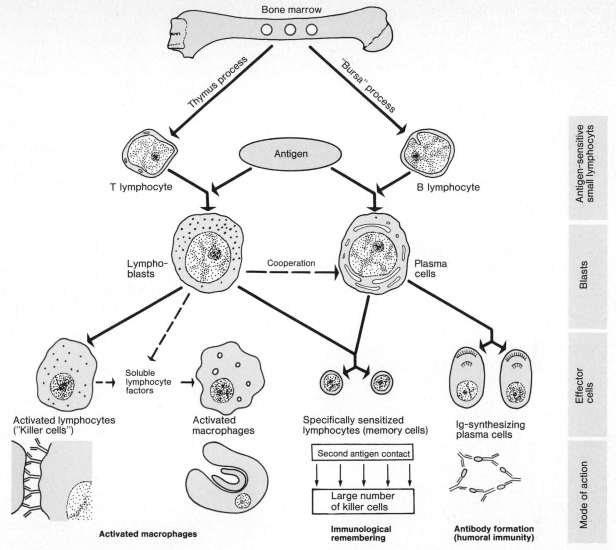

Fig. 16-14. Diagram of the production of T and B lymphocytes and their involvement in the cellular and humoral defense systems of the blood. After [16]

sinophilic granulocytes are capable of phagocytizing antigen-antibody complexes and decomposing them intracellularly. Certain antibodies adhere to the membranes of **basophilic granulocytes** and **thrombocytes** and when again exposed to the antigen form membrane-bound antigen-antibody complexes. These alter the permeability of the cell membrane, with various consequences; in the case of basophils, histamine and heparin are released from the cell. An *immunoglobulin E* has been shown to act as an antibody with affinity for the basophil membrane.

Allergy and immunity. When the defense system of an organism is capable of rendering a foreign substance harmless without any pathological reaction, the organism is immune to that substance. After repeated exposure to a foreign substance the antigen-antibody reaction may lead to pathological symptoms of hypersensitivity (anaphylaxis), such as increased capil-

lary permeability, increased blood flow through skin and mucous membranes, the formation of itchy swellings, more voluminous secretion from exocrine glands and bronchial spasms. This condition is termed an **allergy.** In cases of **immunological paralysis** or tolerance, exposure to a substance that acts as an antigen in other humans fails to elicit the production of antibodies. If the substance is a noxious one, such a person is entirely unprotected.

Immunological tolerance is dangerous, but it can be a useful therapeutic tool; for example, rejection of the foreign protein in a transplant can be prevented or delayed by inactivating appropriate parts of the defense system (by selective inhibition or removal of lymphocytes, by administration of antimetabolites or by the use of ionizing radiation). Immunological tolerance can be induced by exposure to excessively large doses of an antigen, because very large quantities of antigen can suppress a normal immune response.

Vaccination is a method of *"active" immunization,* which takes advantage of the increased defensive potential that can be established before renewed exposure to an antigen. It amounts to induction of the primary response under controlled conditions, by exposing the organism to harmless quantities of an antigen or antigen producer (living but attenuated or dead bacteria or viruses). If an involuntary subsequent exposure to the same antigen should occur (often years after the vaccination), specific antibodies are already present. Even more importantly, the cellular and humoral defensive responses develop much more rapidly than at the time of first exposure. In *"passive" immunization* the patient is injected with specific antibodies against the antigen concerned.

Unspecific Defense

Unspecific humoral mechanisms. The unspecific humoral defense capacity of the blood is based on the presence of so-called "natural" antibodies; this term was applied because it was at first thought that they were formed with no previous exposure of the organism to an antigen. Now it is becoming ever more widely accepted that, strictly speaking, there are no natural antibodies – that the apparently "natural" antibodies actually result from previous contact with bacterial antigens from the obligate intestinal flora (gram-negative microorganisms have been found to be most sensitive to the "natural" antibodies).

In many tissues and body fluids, the growth and multiplication of bacteria and viruses is inhibited by a basic protein with enzyme properties and a mucolytic action, called **lysozyme.** High concentrations of this substance are found in the granules of the polymorphonuclear leukocytes and in the macrophages of lung tissue. When these cells disintegrate the enzyme is released into the extracellular fluid. The intestinal and nasal mucus and the conjunctival secretion also contain lysozyme. Presumably it restricts multiplication of the saprophytic microorganisms living there.
Properdin, a proteinaceous factor present in normal plasma, was thought to be able to destroy a number of bacteria and viruses. First regarded as chemically uniform, this factor has since been separated into several antibodies of the γM type (with the properties described) and a distinguishable protein (m. w. 230000) of unknown function.
Many animal cells, after taking in living or dead viruses, produce a soluble protein (m. w. ca. 20000–30000) called **interferon.** This protein conveys a not very specific resistance to virus infections. It is synthesized and released rapidly (within hours), so that even before the concentration of specific antibody in the body has begun to increase, a certain degree of protection against viral multiplication is provided. The way interferon acts is not entirely understood; one function is probably to make the cell ribosomes less readily available for viral protein synthesis.

Unspecific cellular mechanisms. The element in the blood most extensively involved in this system is the leukocyte, with its capacity for **phagocytosis.** Foreign material can be phagocytized by the granulocytes, the monocytes, the thrombocytes, and – in contrast to earlier views – the lymphocytes. The phagocytic activity of the monocytes is the greatest; they, like the granulocytes, are particularly rich in lysosomal enzymes, which break down the ingested material. It may be that some of the products of this decomposition, when released from the granulocytes and monocytes into their surroundings, act as antigens (via the enzyme components of the leukocytes); by triggering the formation of antibodies these would constitute a link between the unspecific and specific systems.

16.8   Human Blood Groups

Agglutination. When blood samples from two people are mixed on a microscope slide, in most (not all) cases the erythrocytes clump together, a phenomenon known as agglutination. This process is often combined with *hemolysis.* The same thing would occur in the circulatory system following blood transfusion, if the two types of blood were *incompatible.* The consequences of such a mixture would be blockage of the capillaries by agglutinated erythrocytes, damage to the tubules in the kidney by hemolysis, and other difficulties such as anaphylaxis – which in some cases could be lethal.
The **cause of agglutination** is an antigen-antibody reaction. The erythrocyte cell membrane comprises a number of specific polysaccharide-amino acid complexes that function as antigens. These are called **agglutinogens** (synonyms: *hemagglutinogens, agglutinable substances).* The specific antibodies that react with these agglutinogens on the erythrocyte membrane are dissolved in the plasma. They are part of the γ-globulin fraction, and are called **agglutinins** (or *isohemagglutinins*). In the antigen-antibody reaction the antibody molecule, which has two binding sites, is thought to form a bridge between two erythrocytes, each of which is also bound to other antibodies, so that a clump is produced. It is evident that the blood must normally contain only agglutinins that do not interact with its own erythrocytes; otherwise self-agglutination would occur.
The blood of each person is characterized by a particular set of specific erythrocyte agglutinogens. Of the many erythrocyte antigens that have so far been identified, there are about 30 reasonably common ones (that is, not limited to just a few tribes) that trig-

ger fairly vigorous responses. The 9 most important systems, their agglutinogens and the phenomena accompanying the antigen-antibody reaction are summarized in Table 16-8. Today about 400 characteristic features of the erythrocyte membrane are known. In the classified groups alone, there are almost 300 million possible combinations. If one takes into account the unclassified groups as well, the possible combinations number more than 500 billion. Fortunately, the antigen properties of most of the group characteristics are so weak that they can be neglected for purposes of blood transfusion. The **ABO and RH systems** are of the greatest significance in clinical practice.

ABO System

Blood groups in the ABO system. Landsteiner's discovery, in 1901, of the ABO groups marked the beginning of systematic study of blood groups. In the **ABO system** *human erythrocytes* are described in terms of four different antigenic properties. Three of the groups, *A, B and AB,* are characterized by the presence of the antigens so designated, and thus by the absence of the corresponding antibodies. The erythrocytes in group O have neither A nor B antigens (though there is evidence of an antigenic property H), and the plasma contains both anti-A and anti-B antibodies. Anti-A_2 (see below) and anti-H antibodies are not uncommon but are of very little clinical significance. The blood group of an individual is thus defined by the antigenic properties of his erythrocytes. The blood of a newborn child, as a rule, contains no antibodies of the ABO system; during the first year of life antibodies (isoagglutinins, anti-A, anti-B, and anti-AB) are produced against those antigens *not* carried by the child's own erythrocytes. Among the agents that might trigger this antibody production are substances ingested with food or produced by intestinal bacteria.

Inheritance of blood-group characteristics. Two of the three **alleles A, B, O** (properties localized in the genes) are found in the diploid chromosome complement of each individual; together, they determine the blood-group phenotype (the antigenic properties of the erythrocytes). Table 16-9 lists the phenotype associated with each of the possible combinations of genes. It is evident that the alleles A and B are *dominant,* so that O is expressed as a phenotype only when homozygotic. The principle of *codominance* applies to A and B; each is expressed if present, with no interaction between the two. Knowing the way blood groups are inherited, one can draw conclusions about the parents from the phenotype of a child. For legal pur-

Table 16-8. Some important blood-group-specific antibodies. After [26]

Blood-group system	Antibody	Hemolytic transfusion reaction	Erythro-blastosis fetalis
ABO	Anti-A	yes	yes
	Anti-B	yes	rare
	Anti-A_1	very rare	no
	Anti-H	no	no
Rh	Anti-C	yes	rare
	Anti-c	yes	yes
	Anti-C^W	yes	rare
	Anti-D	yes	yes
	Anti-E	yes	yes
	Anti-e	rare	very rare
MNSs	Anti-M, $-$N, $-$S, $-$s	very rare	very rare
P	Anti-P	very rare	no
Lutheran	Anti-Lu^b	yes	very rare
Kell	Anti-K	yes	yes
Lewis	Anti-Le^a	yes	no
	Anti-($Le^a + Le^b$)	yes	no
Duffy	Anti-Fy^a	yes	very rare
Kidd	Anti-Jk^a	yes	rare

Table 16-9. Antigens and antibodies of the blood groups in the ABO system

Group name (phenotype)	Genotype	Agglutinogens (on the erythrocytes)	Agglutinins (in serum)
O	OO	Neither A nor B	Anti-A (α) Anti-B (β)
A	OA or AA	A	Anti-B (β)
B	OB or BB	B	Anti-A (α)
AB	AB	A and B	$-$

poses it has been accepted that a man with blood group AB cannot be the father of a child with blood group O, although use of this criterion alone involves a 10% chance of error. Paternity can be excluded with greater certainty, the greater the number of blood-group factors considered. Today about 99% certainty is achievable.

Blood group A can be subdivided into the *subgroups A_1 and A_2.* The chief difference between the two is that A_1 erythrocytes in contact with anti-A serum agglutinate considerably more extensively and rapidly than do A_2 corpuscles. About 80% of the people in group A have Type A_1 erythrocytes, while the remaining 20% have A_2. This distinction is of no practical significance to transfusion, because antigen-antibody reactions between A_1 and A_2 blood are rare and not very strong.

Geographical distribution of blood groups. More than 40% of Central Europeans are in blood group A, barely 40% in group O, 10% or more in group B and about 6% in group AB. Among the native inhabitants of North America, 90% are of group O. Group B includes more than 20% of the population of central Asia. From the presence and the proportions of the various blood groups in different parts of the world, anthropologists can draw certain conclusions about the origin and mixing of populations.

Rh System

Serum taken from rabbits previously immunized to the erythrocytes of rhesus monkeys (by injection of rhesus erythrocytes) agglutinates the blood of most Europeans; it is **Rh-positive.** Red blood cells that do not agglutinate are, accordingly, called **Rh-negative.** After receiving a transfusion of Rh-positive blood, an Rh-negative recipient gradually, over a period of months, produces agglutinins against the Rh-positive erythrocytes.

Rh properties of the erythrocytes. The response of an erythrocyte to the Rh test is determined by several antigens *(partial antigens)* located in different regions of the red-cell surface. The most important of these are called C, D, E, c and e. Of these, *agglutinogen D has the strongest antigenic effect.* Blood containing D erythrocytes is therefore, for the sake of simplicity, called **Rh-positive** (Rh + or Rh), and those lacking the D property are called **Rh-negative** (Rh − or rh). In Europe 85% of the population are in the Rh + group, and 15% are Rh −.

One **difference between the Rh and the ABO systems** that is of practical significance is that the agglutinins of the ABO system are always present after the first few months of life, whereas agglutinins of the Rh system do not appear unless the carrier has been exposed to Rh antigens *(sensitization).* It follows that the first transfusion of unmatched blood does not result in an overt reaction; antigen-antibody reactions appear only when Rh-incompatible blood is given repeatedly.

Another difference between the two systems lies in the fact that most of the antibodies of the Rh system are *incomplete antibodies* which, in contrast to the complete ABO agglutinins, are small enough to pass the placental barrier.

Rh incompatibility and pregnancy. During pregnancy, and especially as its end is approaching, small quantities of erythrocytes can move from the blood of an Rh + fetus to that of an Rh − mother, and there trigger the production of agglutinins against Rh corpuscles. Because the agglutinin concentration in the mother's blood rises relatively slowly, over a period of months, the first pregnancy is completed without serious difficulties. But if the mother should again become pregnant with an Rh + child, her agglutinin level can become so high that the diaplacental movement of agglutinins destroys the child's red cells so extensively as to cause severe injury or intrauterine death *(erythroblastosis fetalis).* Antibody formation in the Rh-mother can be reduced or eliminated by so-called **anti-D prophylaxis.** When an anti-D γ-globulin is administered immediately after a woman gives birth, the Rh + erythrocytes that have invaded her circulatory system are destroyed and her immunological apparatus is not stimulated to produce antibodies. Differences between mother and fetus with respect to other blood-group characteristics, especially those of the ABO system, can also result in antigen-antibody reactions, but the symptoms of these are usually very mild.

Blood Transfusion

Blood-group tests. At present, only blood compatible in the ABO characteristics is considered acceptable for transfusion. As far as the Rh system is concerned, a match with respect to the D antigen is ordinarily considered sufficient; that is, the blood is identified as Rh-positive (D) or Rh-negative (no D). Commercially available test sera are used for identification. These are mixed with a drop of blood on a microscope slide; in case of a mismatch there is agglutination, and many small clumps of corpuscles appear, whereas the red cells in compatible blood remain uniformly distributed. To minimize the possibility of error due to the wrong choice of serum, misinterpretation of the result, or the rare occurrence of incompatibility due to other group characteristics, the blood is **cross-matched** prior to transfusion; erythrocytes from the donor are combined with defibrinated plasma (serum) of the receiver on a slide at 37 °C. This procedure, to determine whether the recipient's serum contains antibodies against antigens of the donor erythrocytes, is called the *major test*. If there is no agglutination, the reverse test (the *minor test*) follows; by suspending recipient erythrocytes in donor serum, again at 37 °C, donor antibodies against antigens on the recipient erythrocytes are detected. Transfusion is permissible only if both tests are clearly negative.

The question of the "universal donor." Although persons of *group O* were formerly called "universal donors" and their blood was given to recipients of other groups, such transfusions are no longer considered acceptable. It is true that the A and B antigenic activity of group-O erythrocytes is absent or negligible, so that practically any desired quantity of O erythrocytes can be transferred to recipients of other groups without causing a reaction. But because group-O plasma contains agglutinins against A and B erythrocytes, only a limited amount of plasma can be transfused without reaction. When larger volumes are transfused the donor agglutinins are not sufficiently diluted by the recipient's plasma, and the recipient's erythrocytes are extensively agglutinated.

I am grateful to Dr. G. Gronow of Kiel for valuable help and criticism.

16.9   References

Textbooks and Handbooks

1. BAYLISS, L. E.: The Rheology of Blood. In Handbook of Physiology Section 2, Circulation Vol. I, Amer. Physiol. Soc. Washington 1962
2. BEGEMANN, H., RASTETTER, J.: Atlas der klinischen Hämatologie. 3. Auflage, Berlin–Heidelberg–New York: Springer 1978
3. BELL, G., DAVIDSON, J. N., SCARBOROUGH, H.: Textbook of Physiology and Biochemistry. Edinburgh, London: Livingstone 1965
4. BESSIS, M.: Living Blood Cells and their Ultrastructure. Berlin–Heidelberg–New York: Springer 1973
5. BESSIS, M.: Corpuscles. Atlas of Red Blood Cells. Berlin–Heidelberg–New York: Springer 1974
6. BROBECK, J. R. (Ed.): Best & Taylor's Physiological Basis of Medical Practice, 10th Ed. Baltimore: Williams and Wilkins 1979
7. FOWLER, N. O.: Plasma Substitutes. In Handbook of Physiology Section 2, Circulation Vol. I. Amer. Physiol. Soc. Washington 1962
8. GAMBLE, J. L.: Chemical Anatomy, Physiology and Pathology of Extracellular Fluid, 6th Ed. Cambridge Mass.: Harvard University Press 1954
9. GANONG, W. F.: Review of Medical Physiology. Lange Med. Publ., Los Altos, Calif. 1979
10. GUYTON, A. C.: Textbook of Medical Physiology, 5th Ed. Philadelphia. London: Saunders 1966
11. Hämatologische Tafeln Sandoz. 2. Aufl. (1972)
12. HUMPHREY, J. H., WHITE, R. G.: Immunology for Students of Medicine. Oxford 1930. 3rd Ed.
13. KEIDEL, W. (Hrsg.): Kurzgefaßtes Lehrbuch der Physiologie, Stuttgart: Thieme 1973
14. KLEIHAUER, E. (Hrsg.): Hämatologie. Berlin–Heidelberg–New York: Springer 1978
15. LAWSON, H. C.: The Volume of Blood – A Critical Examination of Methods for its Measurement. In Handbook of Physiology Section 2, Circulation Vol. I, Amer. Physiol. Soc. Washington 1962
16. ROITT, J. M. (Ed.): Essential Immunology. 5th Printing. Oxford: Blackwell Scientific Publications 1971
17. SJÖSTRAND, T.: Blood Volume. In Handbook of Physiology Section 2, Circulation Vol. I, Amer. Physiol. Soc. Washington 1962
18. WINTROBE, M. M. (Ed.): Clinical Hematology, 6th Ed. Philadelphia, Lea & Febiger 1968

Reviews and Research Reports

19. COHN, E. J.: Chemical, physiological and immunological properties and clinical uses of blood derivatives. Experientia (Basel) 3, 125 (1947)
20. GERLACH, E., MOSER, K., DEUTSCH, E., WILLMANNS, W. (Eds.): Erythrocytes, Thrombocytes, Leukocytes: Recent Advances in Membrane and Metabolic Research. Stuttgart: Thieme 1973
21. JAENECKE, J. (Hrsg.): Antikoagulantien- und Fibrinolysetherapie. Stuttgart: Thieme 1971
22. PRICE-JONES, C.: The variation in the sizes of red blood cells. Brit. med. J. 1910 II, 1418
23. SCHERER, R.: Zum Mechanismus der beschleunigten Blutkörperchensenkung. Verlag Chemie GmbH, Medizin in unserer Zeit 2, 34–41, 1977
24. WHITTACKER, S. R. F., WINTON, F. R.: The apparent viscosity of blood flowing in the isolated hindlimb of the dog, and its variation with corpuscular concentration. J. Physiol. (Lond.) 78, 339 (1933)
25. BRANDIS, H. (Hrsg.): Einführung in die Immunologie, Stuttgart, Fischer 1975
26. Documenta Geigy: Wissenschaftliche Tabellen, 7. Aufl. Basel: J. R. Geigy AG 1968
27. KABOTH, W., BEGEMANN, H.: Blut. In Physiologie des Menschen (Hrsg. GAUER, KRAMER, JUNG), Band 5. München–Berlin–Wien: Urban & Schwarzenberg 1971

17 Function of the Heart

H. ANTONI

17.1 Structure and General Functional Aspects

The blood can perform its many-faceted role only if it circulates continually through the body. The pump that drives the blood through the vessels is the heart. It can be considered as two hollow organs – the right half and the left half (Fig. 17-1) – with muscular walls. Each half comprises an atrium and a ventricle. The right half receives oxygen-depleted blood from the entire body and sends it to the lungs, where it is charged with oxygen. The oxygenated blood is returned to the left half of the heart and thence distributed to the organs of the body. The right heart, then, pumps out only deoxygenated blood, and the left half only oxygenated blood.

Subdivisions of the circulatory system. The movement of the blood from the right to the left heart, by way of the lungs, is called the **pulmonary circulation.** Its distribution to, and return from, all the rest of the body is the **systemic circulation.** Strictly speaking, of course, the two constitute a single pathway of blood movement, with the propulsive force provided at two points by the two halves of the heart (cf. Fig. 17-1).

The discovery of the closed circulation of blood is attributed to the English physician WILLIAM HARVEY (1578–1657), who refuted the established doctrine of his time with reasoning of exemplary clarity in his famous treatise, published in 1628, "De motu cordis et sanguinis in animalibus." Until that time the prevailing view was that of GALEN (120–201 A.D.), who held that the blood was formed in the liver from food components, sent to the heart by way of the vena cava, and from there passed through the veins to the organs where it was used up.

Systole and diastole. The pumping action of the heart is based on a rhythmic sequence of relaxation *(diastole)* and contraction *(systole)* of the ventricles. During diastole the ventricles fill with blood, and during systole they expel it into the large arteries (aorta and pulmonary artery). Backflow out of the arteries is prevented by the valves at their openings. Before entering the ventricle, the blood passes from the large veins (venae cavae and pulmonary veins) into the associated atrium. The systole of each atrium precedes that of

its ventricle, so that the atria act as booster pumps to help fill the ventricles.

Arteries and veins. The distinction between these two kinds of vessels is based on the direction of blood flow within them, rather than on the state of the blood itself. Veins carry the blood to the heart, and arteries

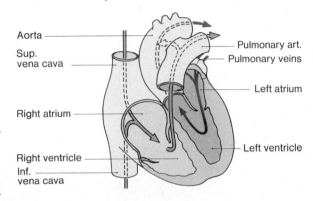

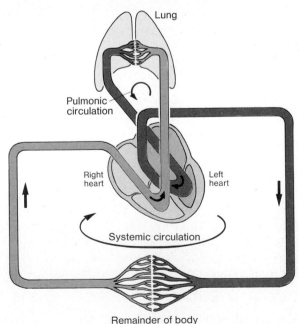

Fig. 17-1. *Top:* Frontal view of the opened heart and the large vessels. The direction of blood flow is indicated by the arrows. *Bottom:* Schematic diagram of the connections of the two halves of the heart with the pulmonary and systemic circulations

carry it away. In the systemic circulation the arteries carry oxygenated blood, and in the pulmonary circulation the oxygenated blood is carried by the veins. When the term "arterial blood" is used to denote oxygenation, the reference is thus to the systemic circulation.

Fetal heart. The functional subdivision of the heart into a right, pulmonary half and a left, systemic half develops during birth. In the heart of the fetus the two atria communicate with one another by way of the foramen ovale, and there is a short-circuit between the aorta and pulmonary artery, by way of a wide passage, the **ductus arteriosus** (Botallo's duct; cf. Fig. 17-2). In the fetus, then, atria and ventricles act as a single hollow organ. At this stage the lung is collapsed and nonfunctional, and little blood circulates through it. The fetal blood becomes oxygenated in the placenta.

Changes at birth. When the lungs expand at birth and begin to function in respiration, their resistance to blood flow decreases. As a result, the pressure in the left atrium exceeds that in the right. The valve at the foramen ovale folds over the opening and closes it off temporarily; there is also a progressive constriction of the ductus arteriosus. The **parallel** arrangement of the two halves of the heart in the fetus is converted to a **serial** arrangement (Fig. 17-2 A and B). This reorganization of the circulatory pattern during birth causes the work load of the right heart to be considerably less than that of the left. Because the resistance to flow in the vascular bed of the lung is only about one-eighth that in the systemic circulation, the right ventricle needs to exert less force to propel the blood through the pulmonary circuit. This difference in work load brings about an accelerated growth of the more heavily loaded left ventricle, which eventually develops a mass of muscle almost three times that of the right ventricle. The heart of an adult accounts for about 0.5% of the total body weight.

Functional range of variation. Because the demands made on the circulating blood are quite different at different times, the heart must be able to adjust its activity over a wide range. For example, the volume of blood expelled by one ventricle per minute *(cardiac minute volume)* is about 5 liters when a person is at rest, and rises to almost 30 liters during hard physical work. Optimal adaptation is achieved only when all the partial functions of the heart – time course of excitation, contractility, valve action, its own blood supply, and so on – change together in an orderly way. Even slight departures from the norm can severely impair cardiac activity.

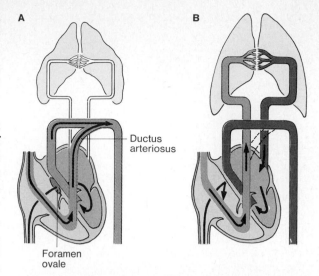

Fig. 17-2. **A** Fetal heart before birth. The two halves are in parallel, with the lung on a side circuit. **B** After birth the two halves are in series. This conversion involves expansion of the circuit through the lungs and closure of two shunt passages – the foramen ovale between right and left atrium, and the ductus arteriosus between aorta and pulmonary artery

17.2 Basic Processes of Excitation and Excitation-Contraction Coupling

The functional elements of the heart are the cardiac muscle fibers. The term *myocardial fiber* is applied to a chain of myocardial cells arranged end-to-end and enclosed in a common sarcolemmal envelope (the basement membrane). There are two types of myocardial fibers, identifiable by morphological and functional criteria:
1. the fibers of the **working myocardium** of atria and ventricles, which make up the main mass of the heart and do the mechanical work of pumping,
2. the fibers of the **pacemaker and conducting system,** which are specialized to generate excitatory impulses and send them to the working cells.

Origin and Spread of Excitation

Myocardial fibers, like nerve or skeletal muscle fibers, are excitable structures – that is, they have a *resting potential,* respond to suprathreshold stimuli by generating *action potentials,* and are capable of propagating action potentials without decrement. The cell boundaries, which can be seen in the microscope as the *intercalated discs,* offer no obstacle to the conduction of excitation. The musculature of the atria and ventricles behaves functionally as a *syncytium.* Excitation arising anywhere in the atria or ventricles

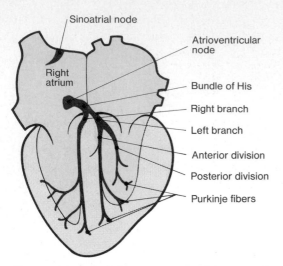

Sinoatrial node

Right
atrium

Atrioventricular
node

Bundle of His

Right branch

Left branch

Anterior division

Posterior division

Purkinje fibers

Fig. 17-3. Diagram of the arrangement of the pacemaker and conducting system as seen in frontal section

thus spreads out over all the unexcited fibers, until the very last cell is brought into play. This property provides one explanation of the **all-or-none response of the heart**; that is, when stimulated the heart either responds with excitation of all its fibers or gives no response, if the stimulus does not reach the suprathreshold level in any cell. In a nerve or skeletal muscle, by contrast, each cell responds individually, so that only those fibers exposed to suprathreshold excitation discharge conducted impulses.

Autorhythmicity. The rhythmic pulsation of the heart is maintained by excitatory signals generated within the heart itself. Under suitable conditions, therefore, a heart removed from the body will continue to beat at a constant frequency. This property is called *automaticity* or *autorhythmicity*. Ordinarily, the spontaneous rhythmic triggering of excitation is performed exclusively by the specialized cells of the pacemaker and conducting system. The various elements in this system are diagrammed in Fig. 17-3.

Geometry of propagation. Normally the heartbeat is initiated in the sinoatrial (SA) node, in the wall of the right atrium at the opening of the superior vena cava. When the body is at rest, the SA node drives the heart at a rate of about 70 impulses/min. From the SA node the excitation first spreads over the **working myocardium of both atria.** The only pathway available for conduction to the ventricles is shown in red in Fig. 17-3. All the rest of the atrioventricular boundary consists of inexcitable connective tissue. As the excitation propagates through the conducting system it is briefly delayed in the **atrioventricular (AV) node.** Propagation velocity is high (ca. 2 m/s) through the

remainder of the system – the **bundle of His,** the left and right **bundle branches** and their terminal network, the **Purkinje fibers** – so that the different ventricular regions are excited in rapid succession. From the subendocardial endings of the Purkinje fibers, excitation spreads at a speed of ca. 1 m/s over the **ventricular musculature.**

Hierarchy of pacemaker activity. The autorhythmicity of the heart is not entirely dependent on the operation of the SA node; as mentioned above, the other parts of the pacemaker/conduction system are also spontaneously excitable. But the intrinsic rhythm of these cells becomes considerably slower, the further away from the SA node. Under normal conditions, therefore, these cells are always triggered into action by the more rapid build-up of excitation in the higher centers, before they have a chance to trigger themselves. The SA node is the leading **primary pacemaker** of the heart, because it has the highest discharge rate.

Escape rhythms. If for any reason the SA node should fail to initiate the heartbeat, or if the excitation is not conducted to the atria (sinoatrial block), the AV node can substitute as a **secondary** pacemaker (the *AV rhythm* has a frequency of 40–60/min). If there should be a complete interruption of conduction from the atria to the ventricles **(complete heart block),** a **tertiary** center in the ventricular conducting system can take over as pacemaker for ventricular contraction. With respect to pacemaker activity, the SA node can be termed the **nomotopic** (in the normal place) center and the remainder of the system, the **heterotopic** (in an abnormal place) centers.

In the case of complete heart block, atria and ventricles beat entirely independently of one another, the atria at the frequency of the SA node and the ventricles at the considerably lower frequency of a tertiary center (30–40/min). When there is a sudden onset of total heart block several seconds can elapse before the ventricular automaticity "wakes up." In this pre-automatic pause an insufficient supply of blood to the brain may cause unconsciousness and convulsions **(Adams-Stokes syncope).** If the ventricular pacemakers fail altogether, the ventricular arrest leads to irreversible brain damage and eventually to death.

Artificial pacemakers. Even in the absence of autorhythmicity, the working myocardium remains excitable for a time. It is therefore possible to keep the blood in circulation by artificial **electrical stimulation** of the ventricles. If necessary, the electrical impulses can be applied through the intact wall of the chest. When attacks of Adams-Stokes disease are frequent, and in cases of complete heart block with very low-frequency ventricular automaticity, electrical stimulation can sometimes be continued for years. The stimuli are generated by subcutaneously implanted battery-driven miniature pacemakers and conducted to the heart by wire electrodes.

Bundle-branch block. When conduction along the bundle branches is interrupted the result is an incomplete heart block, as long as at least one branch or subdivision of a branch remains functional. In this case the excitation spreads out from the terminals of the intact conduction system and eventually covers the whole ventricular myocardium; the time required for complete excitation, of course, is considerably longer than normal.

Characteristics of the Elementary Process of Excitation

The **action potential** of the cardiac muscle cells, like that of neurons or skeletal muscle fibers, begins with a rapid reversal of the membrane potential, from the resting potential (ca. − 90 mV) to the *initial peak* (ca. + 30 mV). This rapid phase of depolarization, lasting only 1–2 ms, is followed by a special feature of the myocardium, a prolonged *plateau*. This is terminated by *repolarization* to the resting potential. The action potential of the cardiac musculature lasts ca. 200–400 ms – more than 100 times as long as that of a skeletal-muscle or nerve fiber. The functional consequences, as we shall see, are considerable.

Ionic mechanisms. The action potential is generated by a complicated interplay of membrane-potential changes, changes in ionic conductivity, and ion currents. The fundamentals of the ionic theory of excitation have been discussed in detail elsewhere (cf. Chapter 1); here we shall give only a short recapitulation, with reference to the specific peculiarities of cardiac muscle [8, 17]. The *resting potential* of the myocardium is primarily a K^+ *potential*. As in the neuron, the rapid upstroke phase of the action potential is brought about by a brief pronounced *increase in Na^+ conductance g_{Na}*, which results in a massive Na^+ *influx* (cf. Fig. 17-4). This initial Na^+ influx, however, as in the neuron, is very rapidly inactivated. Hence, further mechanisms are required for the considerable delay in repolarization of the cardiac muscle tissue. These are

(i) an *increase in Ca^{++} conductance (g_{Ca})*, with delayed onset and slow decline, which causes a depolarizing influx of calcium (*slow inward current* [22, 36, 37]), and (ii) a *decrease in K^+ conductance (g_K)* with depolarization, which reduces the repolarizing K^+ outward current [32, 40].

Repolarization of the myocardium results from a *gradual decrease* in g_{Ca} and an increase in g_K due to the more *negative membrane potential*. The decrease in g_{Ca} diminishes the slow inward current, and the increase in g_K enhances the K^+ outward current. When the membrane is at its resting potential, the depolarizing and repolarizing currents are in balance.

The *mechanism underlying the slow inward current* and that of the fast Na^+ inward current differ in several ways, among them the time course, potential-dependence and susceptibility to blocking agents. The so-called fast Na^+ channel is blocked by tetrodotoxin, while the slow Ca^{++} channel is blocked by Mn^{++} and organic Ca^{++} antagonists (e.g., verapamil). The threshold for activation of the Na^+ channel is ca. − 60 mV, and that of the Ca^{++} channel is ca. − 30 mV. Depolarization of the membrane to about − 40 mV inactivates the fast Na^+ channel.

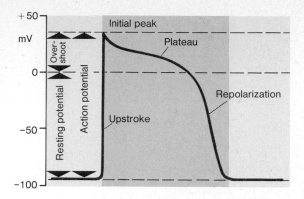

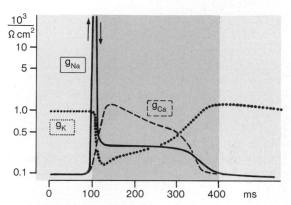

Fig. 17-4. *Top:* General form of the action potential of a cardiac muscle cell. *Bottom:* Diagram of the changes in Na^+, Ca^{++} and K^+ conductance that underlie the action potential

Under these conditions, more intense stimuli can elicit so-called *Ca^{++} action potentials*, which have a slower upstroke phase and are propagated at low speed (slow response [27, 35]).

Refractory period. Cardiac musculature shares with other excitable tissues the property of reduced responsiveness to stimuli during particular phases of the excitatory process. The terms **absolute** and **relative refractory period** are used for phases of abolished and diminished responsiveness, respectively. Fig. 17-5 shows how these are related to the action potential. During the absolute refractory period the cell is inexcitable, and during the subsequent relative refractory period excitability gradually recovers. Thus a new action potential can be elicited sooner, the stronger the stimulus. Action potentials generated very early in the relative refractory period do not rise as sharply as normal action potentials, and have a lower amplitude and a shorter duration (Fig. 17-5).

The chief **cause of refractory behavior** is the inactivation of the initial Na^+ influx during prolonged depolarization (cf. [1]). Not until the membrane has repolarized to ca. − 40 mV does this system begin to recover. The duration of the refractory period is therefore, as a rule, closely related to the duration of the action potential. When the action potential is shortened or lengthened, the refractory period changes accordingly. But drugs that act as

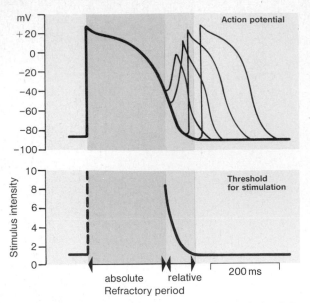

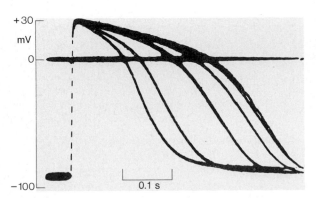

Fig. 17-5. The absolute and relative refractory periods of the myocardial action potential. Threshold during the latter is indicated in multiples of the minimal threshold intensity. During the absolute refractory period – from the action-potential upstroke to about the end of the plateau – the threshold is infinitely high

Fig. 17-6. Superimposed action potentials of a single fiber in an isolated ventricular trabecula obtained during an operation on a human heart. The record shows shortening of the action potential duration as stimulus frequency is raised in steps from 24/min to 162/min. From TRAUTWEIN et al.: Circul. Res. *10*, 306 (1962)

local anesthetics, inhibiting the initial Na$^+$ influx or retarding its recovery after inactivation, can prolong the refractory period without affecting action-potential duration.

Functional significance of the refractory period. The prolonged refractory period protects the musculature of the heart from too-rapid reexcitation, which could impair its function as a pump. At the same time, it prevents recycling of excitation in the muscular network of the heart, which would interfere with the rhythmic alternation of contraction and relaxation. Because

the refractory period of the excited myocardial cells is normally longer than the time taken for spread of excitation over the atria or ventricles, a wave of excitation originating at the SA node or a heterotopic center can cover the heart only once and must then die out, for it encounters refractory tissue everywhere. *Reentry* thus does not normally occur.

Frequency-dependence of action-potential duration. An action potential triggered immediately following the relative refractory period of the preceding impulse is normal, as Fig. 17-5 shows, in upstroke rate and amplitude. Its duration, however, is distinctly less than that of the preceding action potential. In fact there is a close relationship between the duration of an action potential and the interval that preceded it, and thus between duration and repetition rate. This effect is illustrated in Fig. 17-6 by an original recording from a fiber in human ventricular myocardium.

The main cause of this phenomenon is an increase in g_K, which outlasts the repolarization phase of the action potential and returns only gradually to the basal level (Fig. 17-4). When the interval between action potentials is short, the increased K$^+$ conductance accelerates repolarization of the next action potential.

The elementary events in impulse formation. The working myocardium of atria and ventricles is not automatically active; action potentials are generated by spread of excitation. The response is triggered by current loops, whereby current flowing from excited parts of the fiber cable passes through unexcited parts and there lowers the membrane potential from the resting level. When this depolarization has reached a critical threshold level the action potential begins (cf. [1]). In all cardiac muscle cells capable of autorhythmicity, by contrast, depolarization toward the threshold occurs spontaneously. This elementary process of excitation can be observed directly by intracellular recording from a pacemaker cell. As shown in Fig. 17-7, the repolarization phase of such an action potential is followed – beginning at the *maximal diastolic potential* – by a *slow depolarization* which triggers a new action potential when the threshold is reached. The **slow diastolic depolarization** *(pacemaker potential, prepotential)* is a local excitatory event, not propagated as the action potential is.

Actual and potential pacemakers. Normally only a few cells in the SA node are in fact responsible for timing the contraction of the heart (*actual* pacemakers). All the other fibers in the specialized tissue are excited in the same way as the working musculature, by conducted activity. That is, these *potential* pacemakers are rapidly depolarized by currents from activated sites before their intrinsic slow diastolic depolarization reaches threshold. Comparison of the two processes, as illustrated in Fig. 17-7, shows how a potential pacemaker can take over the leading role when the actual pacemaker ceases to function. Because the slow diastolic depolarization of the potential pacemaker, by definition, takes longer to reach threshold, its discharge rate is lower. In the working myocardium there is no automatic depolarization; the upstroke of the action potential triggered by the imposed current rises sharply from the resting-potential baseline (Fig. 17-7, bottom).

Mechanism of the pacemaker potential. On the basis of the data available at present, the origin of the slow diastolic depolarization of autorhythmic tissue is as follows [26]. During the repolarization phase of the action potential the K^+ conductance of the membrane rises above the resting level. As a result, the membrane potential approaches the theoretical K^+ equilibrium potential E_K, and reaches the maximal diastolic potential (Fig. 17-7). While the K^+ conductance then slowly returns to the resting level, the membrane potential shifts away from E_K and reaches the threshold for generation of a new action potential. In the last analysis, the slow diastolic depolarization is based on influx of Na^+ or Ca^{++}. Only when the conductance of the membrane for these ions is not negligibly small can a decreased K^+ efflux lead to depolarization. In the non-automatic working myocardium the Na^+ and Ca^{++} conductances are so low in resting conditions that changes in K^+ conductance have no appreciable effect.

Ectopic pacemakers. The capacity for spontaneous excitation is more a primitive than a highly specialized function of myocardial tissue. In the early embryonic stage all the cells in the heart primordium are spontaneously active. As differentiation proceeds, the fibers of the prospective atrial and ventricular myocardium give up their autorhythmicity and develop a stable, high resting potential. But the stability of the resting potential can be lost in various pathological states associated with an increase in Na^+ conductance. Then the affected fibers can exhibit diastolic depolarizations like those of natural pacemaker cells, and under certain circumstances can interfere with the rhythm of the heartbeat. A center of autorhythmicity apart from the regular pacemaker tissue is called an *ectopic center* or *ectopic focus* [42].

Types of action potential. The action potentials in different parts of an individual heart differ in characteristic ways. A few typical forms are shown in Fig. 17-8, where the sequence (top to bottom) and time shift (left to right) correspond to their position in the excitatory cycle of the heart. In the various parts of the pacemaker and conduction system the slope of the slow diastolic depolarization becomes distinctly less steep with increasing distance from the SA node. Moreover, both upstroke rate and amplitude of the potentials in the SA and AV nodes are conspicuously less than in the remainder of the system. The duration of the plateau in the atrial myocardium is less than in the musculature of the ventricle, and the refractory periods are correspondingly related. Because of the greatly prolonged action potential in their terminals,

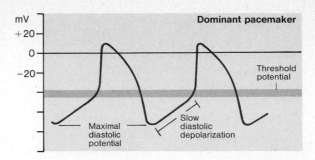

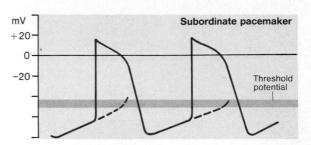

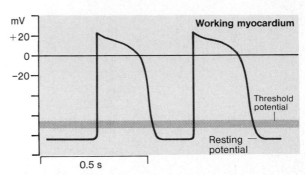

Fig. 17-7. General form of the process of excitation in automatic tissue, compared with that in the non-automatic working myocardium

the Purkinje fibers act as a "frequency filter" between the atria and the ventricular muscles, protecting the ventricles from abnormally high atrial discharge rates.

Relationships between Excitation and Contraction: Excitation-Contraction Coupling

As in the case of skeletal muscle (Chapter 2), it is the action potential that gives rise to contraction of the myocardial cell. However, there is a characteristic difference between the two types of muscle with respect to the temporal relation between action potential and contraction. Whereas the action potential of skeletal muscle lasts only a few milliseconds, and contraction does not begin until the excitatory process is nearly over, in the myocardium the two events overlap considerably in time (cf. Fig. 17-9, top). The myocardial action potential ends only when the mus-

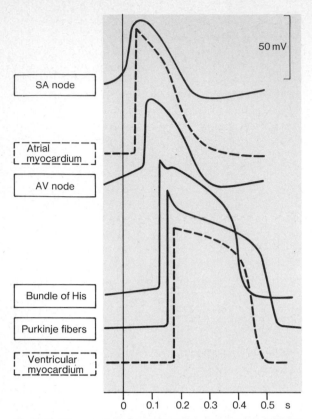

Fig. 17-8. Characteristic forms of action potential in different regions of the heart. The continuous lines represent potentials in the pacemaker and conducting system. The shift along the time scale corresponds to the arrival time in each region, as the excitatory wave spreads through the heart. After [11]

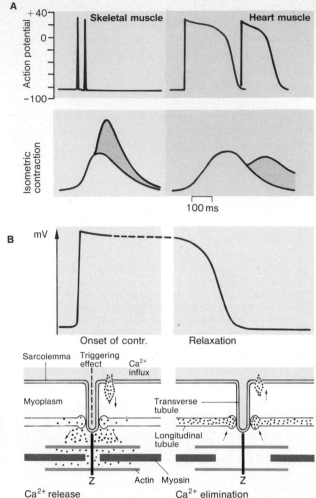

Fig. 17-9. *Top:* Temporal relation between action potential and contraction in skeletal and cardiac muscle. *Bottom:* Diagram of the interplay of excitation, Ca^{++} movement and activation of the contractile apparatus. Events at the onset of contraction shown on the left, those during relaxation on the *right*

culature has begun to relax again. Because a new contraction must be initiated by new excitation, which can occur only after the absolute refractory period of the preceding excitation has elapsed, cardiac muscle – unlike skeletal muscle – is incapable of responding to a rapid sequence of action potentials with superposition of single contractions or with a tetanus (cf. p. 39).

The **"non-tetanizability"** of the myocardium is a property that seems entirely appropriate to the pump function of the heart; a tetanic contraction of the heart that outlasted the blood-ejection phase would interfere with refilling. On the other hand, the superposition property of skeletal muscle enables the force of contraction to be varied with action-potential frequency; myocardial contractions cannot be graded in this way. Moreover, because the myocardium is a functional syncytium the force of contraction cannot be graded by recruitment of a variable number of motor units (cf. p. 43), as is possible with skeletal muscle. Myocardial contraction is an all-or-none event, in which all fibers participate at each occurrence. In compensation for these physiological disadvantages, the opportunity for influencing contraction by way of the excitatory processes or by direct interference with the excitation-contraction coupling is considerably greater in cardiac muscle.

The mechanism of excitation-contraction coupling in the myocardium. The myocardial fibers of man and other mammals in principle comprise the same structural elements as are involved in the electromechanical coupling processes in skeletal muscle (cf. [2] and Fig. 17-9, bottom). The **transverse tubular system (T system)** is clearly a feature of the myocardium, particularly in the ventricles, where it also has connections in the longitudinal direction. By contrast, the **longitudinal system** of tubules, which functions as an intracellular Ca^{++} reservoir, is less well developed than in skeletal muscle. Both the structural peculiarities of the myocardium and its functional behavior offer evidence of a close interaction between the intracellular Ca^{++} stores and the medium external to the fibers. A key event in contraction is the **influx of calcium** during the action potential. This Ca^{++} current does not only serve to prolong the action potential (as mentioned above), and thus the refractory period; because of the associated displacement of Ca^{++} from the extracellular space to the interior of the cell, it also helps to control the force of contraction. Most of the inflowing Ca^{++}, however, is evidently used not for direct activation of the contractile apparatus, but to replenish the Ca^{++} stores for the following contractions.

If one experimentally shortens the duration of a single action potential by applying an anodal current pulse, so that the Ca^{++} influx is prematurely interrupted, the corresponding contraction is attenuated only slightly, whereas the following contraction, elicited by a normal action potential, is considerably reduced. When an action potential is artificially prolonged the reverse effect is observed – that is, an enhancement of the next contraction. If the action potential is shortened or lengthened for several beats, an equilibrium is attained after 5 to 7 beats, with a level of contraction that may be considerably decreased or increased, respectively [20].

The action potential, then, affects contraction in at least two important ways. It has
(i) a **triggering action,** eliciting the contraction by liberation of Ca^{++}, primarily from intracellular depots, and
(ii) a **replenishing action,** renewing the supply of Ca^{++} to a degree closely correlated with the duration of the action potential, in preparation for subsequent contractions.

Mechanisms by which contraction is influenced. A number of influences on the force of myocardial contraction are exerted indirectly, by way of a change in **duration of the action potential** (e.g., force reduction by increase of extracellular K^+ concentration or by acetylcholine in the atrial myocardium, and the enhancement of contractile force by cooling). An increase in the number of action potentials per unit time acts in the same direction as an increase in action-potential duration *(frequency inotropism,* increased contractile force due to *paired pulse stimulation, postextrasystolic potentiation).* The so-called **staircase phenomenon,** a stepwise increase in the amplitude of contraction following temporary arrest, is also associated with the replenishment of intracellular Ca^{++} [12, 34].
In view of all these effects, it comes as no surprise that **changes in the extracellular Ca^{++} concentration** rapidly affect the force of cardiac contraction. Complete

excitation-contraction uncoupling can be achieved by the experimental withdrawal of extracellular Ca^{++}; the action potential of the myocardium remains almost unchanged, but it is no longer accompanied by a mechanical response.

From all that has been said one would expect that Ca^{++} withdrawal would *shorten* the action potential. The reason this does not happen is that the slow channel allows Na^+ to pass as well as Ca^{++}. When the normal extracellular concentration of Ca^{++} is present, Na^+ accounts for only a small fraction of the slow influx, but when the Ca^{++} is depleted the slow inward current is based mainly on Na^+.

Chemical agents can produce an effect similar to that of extracellular Ca^{++} withdrawal by blocking Ca^{++} influx during the action potential; such agents include bivalent cations ($Ni^{++}, Co^{++}, Mn^{++}$) and certain organic compounds, so-called *Ca^{++} antagonists* (verapamil, nifedipine [28, 29]).
Conversely, the contraction amplitude can be increased both by raising the extracellular Ca^{++} concentration and by administration of agents that enhance Ca^{++} influx during the action potential *(adrenalin* or *noradrenalin).* In clinical practice the force exerted by the heart can be increased by the so-called **cardiac glycosides** (digitalis, strophanthin); the mechanism underlying this effect is not entirely known.

By immersing an isolated atrium preparation in a solution containing radioactively labelled Ca^{++}, an increase in the intracellular Ca^{++} fraction (which is continually exchanging with the extracellular Ca^{++}) in response to cardiac glycosides can be demonstrated, in the absence of an increased flow of Ca^{++} across the membrane. One mechanism that has been proposed is an interaction of the drug with Ca^{++}-binding structures in the cell. In toxic concentrations cardiac glycosides inhibit the transport ATPase of the cell membrane (the Na^+ pump) and thus cause an increase in the intracellular Na^+ combined with a loss of K^+. Whether this effect is also involved in the therapeutic action of the cardiac glycosides remains debatable.

Autonomic Innervation; the Basic Actions of Autonomic Transmitters

The cardiac centers in medulla and pons (cf. p.435) exert a direct influence on the activity of the heart, by way of **sympathetic and parasympathetic nerves.** This influence governs the rate of beat (**chronotropic** action), the systolic contractile force (**inotropic** action), and the velocity of atrioventricular conduction (**dromotropic** action). These actions of the autonomic nerves are mediated in the heart, as in all other organs, by chemical transmitters – **acetylcholine** in the parasympathetic system, and **noradrenalin** in the sympathetic.

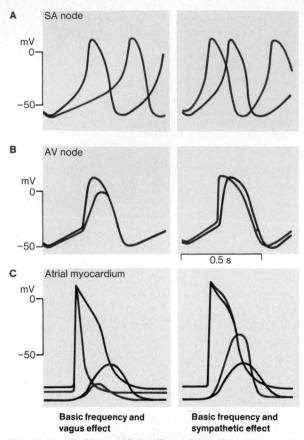

Fig. 17-10 A–C. Characteristic effects of the efferent autonomic cardiac nerves or their transmitter substances on the action potentials of SA node (**A**), AV node (**B**) and atrial myocardium (**C**). The isometric contraction of the atrial myocardium is also shown. The action of the sympathetic system on the ventricular myocardium is like that on the atrium. By contrast, the vagus has little or no effect on the musculature of the ventricle

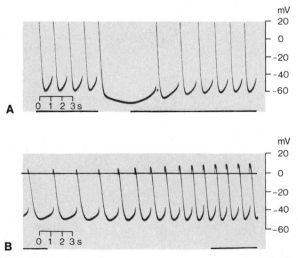

Fig. 17–11 A, B. Influence of vagus (**A**) and sympathetic (**B**) fibers on pacemaker activity in the primary center of the frog heart. The duration of nerve stimulation (20 Hz) is shown by the break in the line below the time scale. From HUTTER, O. F. and W. TRAUTWEIN: J. gen. Physiol. *39,* 715 (1956)

Parasympathetic innervation. The parasympathetic nerves supplying the heart branch off from the **vagus nerves** on both sides in the cervical region. These *preganglionic cardiac fibers* on the right side pass primarily to the right atrium and are concentrated at the SA node. The AV node is reached chiefly by cardiac fibers from the left vagus nerve. Accordingly, the predominant effect of stimulation of the **right** vagus is on *heart rate,* and that of **left**-vagus stimulation is on *atrioventricular conduction.* The parasympathetic innervation of the ventricles is sparse, and its significance is in dispute.

Sympathetic innervation. The sympathetic nerve supply, unlike the parasympathetic, is nearly uniformly distributed to all parts of the heart. The preganglionic elements of the sympathetic cardiac nerves come from the lateral horns of the upper thoracic segments of the spinal cord, and make synaptic connections in the cervical and upper thoracic ganglia of the sympathetic trunk, in particular the stellate ganglion. The postganglionic fibers pass to the heart in several *cardiac nerves.* Sympathetic influences on the heart can also be exerted by catecholamines released from the adrenal medulla into the blood.

Chronotropy. Stimulation of the right vagus or direct application of acetylcholine to the SA node causes a *decrease in heart rate* (**negative chronotropy**); in the extreme case cardiac arrest can result. Sympathetic stimulation or application of noradrenalin increases the heart rate (**positive chronotropy**). When vagus and sympathetic nerves are stimulated at the same time, the vagus action usually prevails. Modification of the autorhythmic activity of the SA node by these autonomic inputs occurs primarily by way of a change in the time course of the slow diastolic depolarization (Fig. 17-10 A). Under the influence of the *vagus* diastolic depolarization is retarded, so that it takes longer to reach threshold. In the extreme case, diastolic depolarization is eliminated and the membrane actually becomes hyperpolarized (Fig. 17-11 A). The *sympathetic* fibers act to increase the rate of diastolic depolarization and thus shorten the time to threshold. Fig. 17-11 shows both effects, in original intracellular recordings from the sinus venosus of the frog heart.

Because the positive chronotropic action of the sympathetic nerves extends to the entire conducting system of the heart, when a leading pacemaker center fails the sympathetic input can determine when and to what extent a subordinate center takes over as pacemaker. Moreover, the sympathetic system also has a positive chronotropic action on pacemaker cells when their spontaneous activity has been suppressed by external influences such as increased K^+ or an overdose of drugs that interfere with automaticity. In the same way, however, an ectopic focus of rhythmicity can be stimulated to greater activity, so that the danger of arrhythmia increases.

Vagal and sympathetic tone. The ventricles of most mammals, including humans, are influenced almost exclusively by the sympathetic system. By contrast, the atria can be shown to be subject to the continual antagonistic influence of both vagus and sympathetic nerves; this effect is most clearly evident in the activity of the SA node. It can be observed, for example, by transecting or pharmacologically blocking one of the two sets of nerves; the action of the opponent then dominates. When the vagus input to the dog heart is removed the rate of beating increases, from ca. 100/min. at rest to 150/min or higher; when the sympathetic input is removed it falls to 60/min or less. This maintained activity of the autonomic nerves is called *vagal and sympathetic tone.* Because the rate of the completely denervated heart (the *autonomic rate*) is distinctly higher than the normal resting rate, it can be assumed that under resting conditions vagal tone predominates over sympathetic tone.

Inotropy. Change in heart rate in itself has a considerable effect on the strength of myocardial contraction (cf. p.365). In addition, the autonomic nerves to the heart act directly on mechanical force generation (cf. Fig.7-10). The *vagus* acts to reduce the strength of contraction of the atrial myocardium; at the same time, the rise time of the mechanogram – the time from the initial deflection of the contraction curve to the peak – decreases. This **negative inotropic action** results from a primary shortening of the action potential (cf. Fig.17-10C). *Sympathetic* activity increases the strength of contraction in both atrial and ventricular myocardium **(positive inotropic action)**. The contraction curve rises more steeply, the peak is reached sooner, and relaxation is accelerated. By contrast, the shape of the action potential is hardly changed (Fig.17-10C).

Dromotropy. An influence of the autonomic nerves on the conduction of excitation can normally be demonstrated only in the region of the *AV node* (Fig.17-12). The *sympathetic* fibers accelerate atrioventricular conduction and thus shorten the interval between the atrial and ventricular contractions **(positive dromotropic action)**. The vagus – especially on the left side – retards atrioventricular conduction and in the extreme case can produce a transient complete AV block **(negative dromotropic action)**. These effects of the autonomic transmitter substances are associated with a particular feature of the cells in the AV node; in contrast to those of the atrial myocardium and to the ventricular conducting system, the fibers of the AV node have a relatively low diastolic membrane potential and a low rate of rise of the action potential (Fig.17-8). As Fig.17-10B shows, the vagus

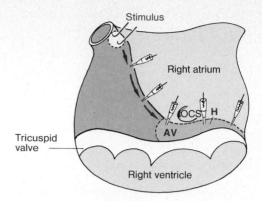

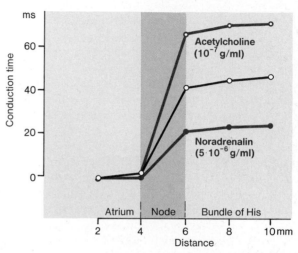

Fig. 17-12. Measurement of conduction times (from stimulus onset to arrival of excitation at the recording electrode) in an isolated preparation from rabbit atrium. AV, atrioventricular node; H, bundle of His, OCS, ostium of coronary sinus. *Below:* Dependence of conduction time on the distance between stimulus site and recording electrode, under control conditions and in the presence of acetylcholine and noradrenalin. The autonomic transmitters affect conduction time only in the region of the AV node; prolongation of conduction time is equivalent to reduction of conduction velocity and vice versa. From B. F. HOFFMAN et al.: Circul. Res. 7, 11 (1959) and our own results

acts to decrease the rate of rise still further, and sympathetic activity increases it. Because the slope of the action-potential upstroke and the velocity of conduction are closely related, such changes in action-potential shape reflect changes in conduction velocity.

Various findings suggest that the rapid initial inward Na^+ current is inactivated by the low resting potential of AV-nodal cells. The sluggish onset of excitation in the AV-nodal fibers is thus brought about by the slow influx of Ca^{++}, which in other cells acts only to determine the duration of the plateau (cf. p.361). The effects of the autonomic transmitters on upstroke slope are probably related to a change in the Ca^{++} influx. In the myocardial fibers with a high resting potential and an action potential that begins with a rapid Na^+ influx, one would thus not expect to find a direct modification of the action-potential upstroke by activity of the autonomic nerves or application of their transmitter substances. On the other hand, vagal activity can cause a slight increase in the resting potential of the atrial myocardium, which secondarily effects an increase in rate of potential rise and in conduction velocity (cf. Fig. 17-10C).

Bathmotropic action. The term "bathmotropy" denotes an influence on *excitability* in the sense of a *lowered or raised threshold*. However, experimental observations of bathmotropic effects of the autonomic transmitters on the heart are not consistent. All that is fairly certain is that sympathetic activity increases excitability when it has been reduced (low resting potential). The notion of a bathmotropic action has introduced more confusion than clarity, and it should be discarded.

Mechanism of autonomic transmitter action. The effects of *vagal stimulation* and of application of the parasympathetic transmitter, **acetylcholine,** are attributable to one fundamental action – an **increase in the K^+ conductance** of the excitable membrane. In general, such an influence is expressed in the tendency of the membrane potential to approach the K^+ equilibrium potential, which is opposed to depolarization. This tendency is evident in both the retardation of the slow diastolic depolarization in the SA node, described above, and in the shortening of the action potential of the atrial myocardium, which in turn weakens the contraction. The reduction of the rate of rise of the action potential in the AV node can also be explained on this basis, in that a stronger outward K^+ current counteracts the slow inward Ca^{++} current.

As far as the **sympathetic** fibers and their transmitters are concerned, they probably act at several points. Studies of the Purkinje fibers have shown that the positive chronotropic action is based on a **change in potential dependence of the K^+ conductance.** It is likely that the mode of action in the SA node is different. On the other hand, the increase in contractile strength (positive inotropic action) is brought about by an **increased Ca^{++} conductance** and the resulting *enhanced slow Ca^{++} influx,* which intensifies the excitation-contraction coupling. The positive dromotropic action on the AV node also, in view of the above considerations, may well be related to enhancement of the slow inward Ca^{++} current [2, 25].

Pharmacological effects. The actions of the autonomic transmitter substances are thought to involve binding of the transmitters to certain molecular configurations on the effector cell (the word "receptor" is used both for these subcellular structures and for sensory cells). The effects of noradrenalin and adrenalin on the heart, described above, are mediated by so-called β receptors (cf. Chapter 6, p. 115). Sympathetic effects can be prevented by β-receptor blocking agents such as dichloroisoproterenol (DCI) and pronethalol (cf. p. 115). In the heart, as in other organs, the deadly-nightshade poison *atropine* acts as an antagonist to the parasympathetic effects of acetylcholine.

Afferent innervation. In addition to the efferent autonomic supply, the innervation of the heart comprises a large number of afferent fibers, divided among the vagus and sympathetic nerves. Most of the *vagus afferents* are myelinated fibers originating in receptors in the atria or the left ventricle. Recordings from single fibers in the atria have revealed two types of mechanoreceptors; the **B receptors** signal passive stretching and the **A receptors,** active tension.

Apart from the myelinated afferent fibers from specialized sensory receptors, the main group of fibers leaving the heart comes from dense subendocardial plexuses of non-myelinated fibers with free endings; these fibers run in the *sympathetic nerves*. It is probably these fibers that mediate the severe, segmentally radiating pains experienced when circulation within the heart itself is impaired (angina pectoris, myocardial infarction).

Effects of the ionic environment. Of all the features of the extracellular solution that can affect the activity of the heart, the K^+ *concentration* is of the greatest practical importance. An *increase* in extracellular K^+ (K_o^+) has two effects on the myocardium: (i) the resting potential is lowered because the gradient K_i^+/K_o^+ is less steep, and (ii) the K^+ conductance of the excitable membrane is increased – as it is by acetylcholine in the atrial myocardium. Doubling of the K^+ concentration, from the normal 4 mmol/l to about 8 mmol/l, results in a slight depolarization accompanied by increased excitability and conduction velocity, and in the suppression of heterotopic centers of rhythmicity. A large increase in K^+ (over 8 mmol/l) reduces excitability and conduction velocity, as well as the duration of the action potential, so that the strength of contraction is diminished and the SA node eventually ceases to function as pacemaker. When the extracellular K^+ concentration is *lowered* to less than 4 mmol/l the stimulating influence on pacemaker activity dominates. The enhanced activity of heterotopic centers can lead to cardiac arrhythmias.

The excitability-reducing action of large extracellular K^+ concentrations is turned to advantage during heart operations, to immobilize the heart briefly for the surgical procedures **(cardioplegic solutions).** While the heart is inactive, circulation is maintained by an extracorporal pump (heart-lung machine). Impairment of cardiac function due to increased blood K^+ during extreme muscular effort or in pathological conditions can be largely compensated by sympathetic activity. When diastolic depolarization has been suppressed in the SA node by K^+ increase, it reappears following administration of adrenalin or noradrenalin. In the K^+-paralyzed working myocardium of atria and ventricles excitability and conduction can be restored by the sympathetic transmitters even though the state of depolarization is maintained [27].

Table 17-1 summarizes the most important physical and chemical influences on excitation and contraction of the heart; only the dominant effects are considered.

Table 17-1. The action of various physical and chemical influences on the electrical and mechanical activity of the heart. + increase; − decrease; 0 no effect.

	Resting potential	Action potential			Conduction velocity	Pacemaker potential (slope)	Strength of contraction
		Amplitude	Duration	Rate of rise			
Heart-rate increase	0	0	−	0	0	+	Staircase +
Heart-rate decrease	0	0	+	0	0	−	−
Temperature increase	0	0	−	0	0(+)	+	−
Temperature decrease	0▶−	0▶−	+	0▶−	−	−	+
pH < 7	0	0	+	−	−	−	−
O₂ deficiency	−	−	−	−	−	+ ▶ −	−
K₀⁺ increase	−	−	−	−	(+)▶−	−	−
K₀⁺ decrease	0▶−	0▶−	+▶−	0	0	+	+
Ca₀⁺⁺ increase	0▶+	0	0▶−	0	0	0	+
Ca₀⁺⁺ decrease	0▶−	0	0▶+	0	0	(+)	−
(Nor)adrenalin	0	0▶+	(+)	in AV node +	in AV node +	+	+
Acetylcholine (in region of atria)	(+)	0	−	in AV node −	in AV node −	−	−

17.3 Electrocardiogram

As excitation spreads over the heart and dies out, an electrical field is produced that can be sensed on the surface of the body. The changes in magnitude and direction of this field in time are reflected in alterations of potential differences measurable between various sites on the body surface. The **electrocardiogram (ECG)** is a representation of such potential differences as a function of time. It is thus an indicator of cardiac *excitation – not contraction!*

Because the directly measured potentials amount in some cases to less than 1 mV, the commercially available ECG recorders incorporate electronic amplifiers. The amplifier inputs include capacitive coupling – high-pass filters with a cutoff frequency near 0.1 Hz (a time constant of 2 s). Therefore d. c. components and very slow changes of the potentials at the metal recording electrodes, which would be distracting, do not appear at the output. All electrocardiographs have a built-in means of monitoring amplitude, in the form of a 1-mV calibration pulse set to cause a deflection of 1 cm.

ECG form and nomenclature. With electrodes attached to the right arm and left leg, the normal ECG looks like the curve shown in Fig. 17-13. There are

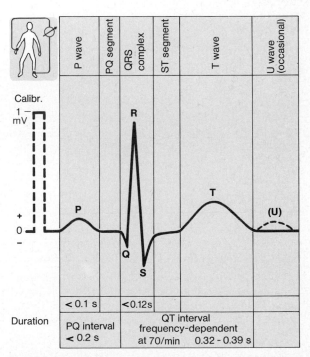

Fig. 17-13. Normal form of the ECG with bipolar recording from the body surface in the direction of the long axis of the heart. The times below the ECG curve are important limiting values for the duration of distinct parts of the curve

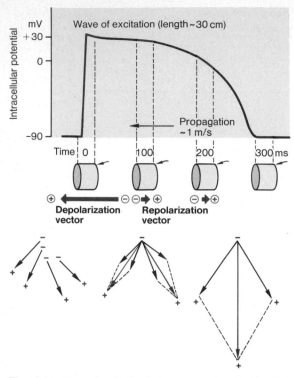

Fig. 17-14. Wave of excitation in the myocardium; intracellular potential plotted as a function of position. The cylinders below the curve symbolize a myocardial segment over which the wave passes (length of free way), in four successive phases of excitation. The front of the wave generates a depolarization vector; during the recovery phase repolarization vectors in the opposite direction are produced. *Below:* The principle of vector addition. 4 single vectors are replaced by 2 resultants and these in turn by one resultant, the so-called integral vector

both positive and negative deflections *(waves),* to which are assigned the letters P to T. The distance between two waves is called a *segment* (the PQ segment, extends from the end of the P wave to the beginning of the QRS complex). An *interval* comprises both waves and segments (e.g., the PQ interval, from the beginning of P to the beginning of QRS). The RR interval, between the peaks of two successive R waves, corresponds to the period of the beat cycle and is the reciprocal of beat rate (60/RR interval (s) = beats/min).

Relation to the cardiac excitation process. Before proceeding to analyze the sources of the ECG curve, let us consider the general significance of its elements. An **atrial part** and a **ventricular part** can be distinguished. The atrial part begins with the **P wave,** the expression of the spread of excitation over the two atria. During the subsequent **PQ segment** the atria as a whole are excited. The dying out of excitation in the atria coincides with the first deflection in the ventricular part of the curve, which extends from the be-

ginning of Q to the end of T. The **QRS complex** is the expression of the spread of excitation over both ventricles, and the **T wave** reflects recovery from excitation in the ventricles. The intervening **ST segment,** analogously to the PQ segment in the atrial part, indicates total excitation of the ventricular myocardium. Occasionally the T wave is followed by a so-called *U wave;* this may correspond to the dying out of excitation in the terminal branches of the conducting system.

The normal ECG. The **PQ interval** is the time elapsed from the onset of atrial excitation to the onset of ventricular excitation, and is normally less than 0.2 s. A longer PQ interval indicates a disturbance in conduction in the region of the AV node or the bundle of His. When the QRS complex extends over more than 0.12 s, a disturbance of the spread of excitation over the ventricles is indicated. The **overall duration of the QT interval** depends on heart rate. When the heart rate increases from 40 to 180/min, for example, the QT duration falls from about 0.5 to 0.2 s. The amplitudes of the individual waves are about as follows: P < 0.25 mV; Q < ¼ of R; R+S > 0.6 mV; T = ⅙ to ⅔ of R.

Origin of the ECG

The following explanation of the origin of the ECG is based on a number of facts which will first be summarized and then, where necessary, explained in more detail.
– The complex electrical field of the excited heart results from the **superposition** of many **elementary field components** arising in individual fibers (for definition of the cardiac muscle fiber cf. p. 359).
– Each excited cardiac muscle fiber acts as a **dipole,** and determines the direction and amplitude of an elementary dipole vector.
– Many single vectors summate at each moment during the excitation process to give an **integral vector.**
– The amplitude of a **voltage measured far from the source** is determined chiefly by the **magnitude** of the integral vector and by the relationship between the **recording and vector directions.**

Excitation wave and length of free way. The ventricular conducting system distributes excitation rapidly to many parts of the ventricles. As a result, each section of the ventricular myocardium supplied by a single Purkinje-fiber ending – so that a wave of excitation continually advances along it – is relatively short (about 1 cm long). This distance is called the **length of free way.** The length of the excitation wave can be

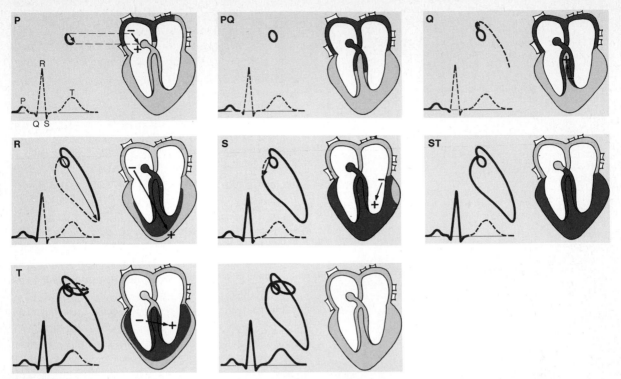

Fig. 17-15. The phases of cardiac excitation associated with particular parts of the ECG. The excited regions are shown in red. The *light red shading* shows where excitation is dying out. The *black arrows* indicate the momentary direction and relative magnitude of the integral vector. The curve between ECG and heart is the envelope of the vector-tip movement in frontal projection (the frontal vectorcardiogram), from the onset of excitation to the time represented by each diagram

computed from the product of conduction velocity (ca. 1 m/s) and duration of excitation (ca. 0.3 s), and amounts to 0.3 m = 30 cm. It follows that at each moment of the excitation cycle only small sections of the excitation wave are actually in existence, as diagrammed in Fig. 17-14.

The myocardial fiber as a dipole. As a wave of excitation passes over a cardiac muscle fiber a *potential gradient* dV/dx is generated along the free path, the magnitude of which depends on the momentary phase of excitation (Fig. 17-14). At the front of the wave there is a steep gradient of 120 mV (corresponding to the amplitude of the action potential) over a distance of only ca. 2 mm ($\doteq$ 600 mV/cm). During the repolarization phase, by contrast, there appear much smaller gradients in the opposite direction. To a first approximation the excited myocardial fiber behaves in the physical sense as a *variable dipole,* the magnitude and direction of which are symbolized by an arrow *(vector).* By definition, the **dipole vector points from minus to plus** – that is, from the excited to the unexcited region; an excited site, as seen from the outside, is effectively electronegative as compared with an unexcited site. We can call the dipole vector at the front of the excitatory wave a **depolarization**

vector, and the vector in the opposite direction at the end of the wave, a **repolarization vector.**

Integral vector. At every moment during the excitatory process, all the individual vectors in the heart summate to an integral vector. The formation of the integral vector can be compared to the construction of the resultant in a force parallelogram, in which two vectors are replaced by a third (cf. Fig. 17-14, bottom). A large fraction of the vectors will neutralize one another, as observed from outside the system, because they exert equal effects in opposite directions. It has been estimated that in the excitation of the heart at times 90% of the individual vectors balance each other out in this way.

Relationship of the integral vector to the excitatory cycle of the heart. In Fig. 17-15, the instantaneous integral vectors for successive phases of cardiac excitation are represented. As excitation spreads over the atria **(P wave)** the predominant direction of spread is from top to bottom; that is, most of the individual depolarization vectors point toward the tip of the heart and thus generate an *integral vector pointing toward the apex.* When the atria are excited as a whole, the potential differences disappear transiently, for all the

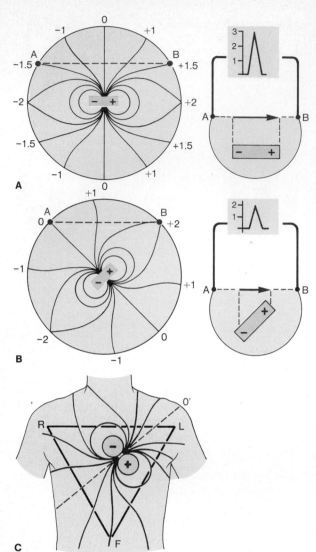

Fig. 17-16 A, B. Bipolar recording in the electrical field of a dipole within a homogeneous medium with a circular boundary. Relative potential of isopotential lines indicated at the edge. Rotation of the dipole (**B**), with the electrodes at the same sites, causes the recorded voltage to fall from 3 to 2 relative units. **C** The electrical field generated by a dipole heart at a particular moment, projected onto the anterior wall of the thorax: RLF, Einthoven's triangle (cf. p. 374; representation according to M.J. HALHUBER, R. GÜNTHER, M. CORESA: ECG Introductory Course, Berlin–Heidelberg–New York, Springer, 1978)

atrial fibers are in the plateau phase of the action potential (cf. Fig. 17-14). The simultaneous onset of the spread of excitation through the ventricular conducting system, because of the small mass of excited cells, produces no appreciable potential difference (**PQ segment**). Only when the excitation moves into the ventricular myocardium do demonstrable potential gradients reappear. Spread of excitation over the ventricles begins on the left side of the ventricular septum and generates an integral vector pointing *toward the*

base of the heart (**Q wave**). Shortly thereafter, spread *toward the apex* predominates (**R wave**). During this phase excitation moves through the ventricular wall from inside to outside. Spread through the ventricles is completed with the excitation of a band at the base of the left ventricle, at which time the integral vector points toward the right and back (**S wave**). While the excitation was spreading over the ventricles (QRS), it died out in the atria. When the ventricles are totally excited (**ST segment**) the potential differences disappear briefly, as they did during atrial excitation (PQ segment) and for the same reasons. During the subsequent ventricular recovery phase (**T wave**) the direction of the integral vector hardly changes; during the entire process of recovery it points *downward to the left*. If repolarization of the ventricles took place in the same sequence as depolarization and at the same rate, the behavior of the integral vector during recovery would be expected to be approximately the opposite of that during the spread of excitation. This is not the case, for the following reasons. First, the process of repolarization is fundamentally slower than that of depolarization. Moreover, the *rates of repolarization are not the same* in the different parts of the ventricles. Repolarization occurs *sooner at the apex than at the base,* and *sooner in the subepicardial than in the subendocardial* layers of the ventricles (Fig. 17-15).

Direction and amplitude of the ECG deflections. It is easy to convince oneself of the relationship between the behavior of the integral vector (Fig. 17-15) and the direction of deflection of the ECG curve (Fig. 17-13). When the integral vector points to the *apex of the heart* the ECG trace is deflected upward (P, R, T), and when it points toward the *base* there is a downward deflection (Q). (The polarity of the ECG trace is established by convention.) In order to understand the basis of this relationship, let us consider the electrical field surrounding a dipole in a homogeneous conducting medium (Fig. 17-16). All points at the same potential lie on the so-called **isopotential lines.** Parts A and B of the figure show that the potential difference (voltage) measurable between points A and B depends fundamentally on the relation of the **lead axis** (the line joining A and B) to the dipole direction. The voltage behaves as the *projection of the integral vector onto the lead axis;* that is, the voltage is greatest when the two directions are the same, and is zero when they are perpendicular to one another. This idea can in principle be applied to the human heart (Fig. 17-16 C), though in this case the situation is considerably more complicated. One reason is that the body is not an electrically homogeneous medium; another is that the heart does not, as in the ideal case, lie at the exact center of a spherical conductor. Because of these factors, the electrical field of the heart is distorted at the surface of the body.

Vector loops and vector cardiography. If one thinks of the integral vectors during one cycle of cardiac excitation as having a common starting point, with their tips connected by a continuous line, the result is a three-dimensional figure, the **vector loop.** Fig. 17-15 illustrates the development of the vector loop in projection onto the frontal plane, during a single cycle. By using the recording technique shown in Fig. 17-17 it is possible to display the vector loop directly on an oscilloscope screen. This recording method is called **vector cardiography.** The principle is illustrated in Fig. 17-17, with an integral vector projected onto the frontal plane taken as an example. One pair of electrodes, arranged horizontally, is connected by way of amplifiers to the vertical plates of the oscilloscope, so as to produce a deflection x of the cathode ray. Another pair, arranged vertically, is connected to the horizontal plates and causes deflection y. The cathode ray is displaced from the middle of the screen as the resultant of these two inputs, so that its position corresponds to the direction and magnitude of the integral vector under study (red arrow). Because the principle is the same for all the other integral vectors, during a cycle of excitation the beam traces out the enveloping curve for all the vector tips – that is, the vector loop. By shifting the electrode pairs into the sagittal and horizontal planes, the projections of the vector loop onto these planes can be drawn. From any two of these projections one can obtain the three-dimensional vector loop (cf. Fig. 17-17, bottom).

Electrode Arrangements

The different curve forms obtained with the arrangement of leads ordinarily used, on extremities and chest wall, are basically projections of the three-dimensional vector loop onto certain lead axes. That is, the vector loop contains just as much information as all these recordings together. For practical purposes, however, the preferred ECG representation is the familiar curve of voltage as a function of time; apart from the less extensive apparatus required for direct recording with paired leads, the changes in excitation that are of practical significance – particularly alterations in the rhythm – are more easily detectable in such records than by the analysis of vector loops. The disadvantage is that several recordings must be compared for an exhaustive evaluation.

A distinction is made between **bipolar** recordings and so-called **"unipolar"** recordings. In the latter, a recording electrode is placed at a defined site on the

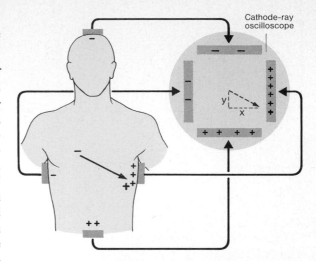

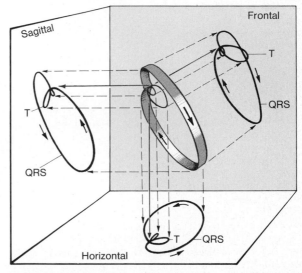

Fig. 17-17. *Upper diagram:* Principle of vector cardiography. Pairs of recording electrodes are connected to the paired deflector plates of an oscilloscope by way of preamplifiers. The potential field of the integral vector is projected onto the plates and deflects the cathode ray away from the center of the screen, to a degree and in a direction corresponding to the integral vector at that moment *(red arrow).* The body plane onto which the loop is projected *(lower diagram)* is determined by electrode position

body surface and the potential with respect to a *reference electrode* is monitored (cf. Fig. 17-18). This electrode can be thought of as positioned at the null point of the dipole, between positive and negative charge. In clinical practice, the following recording arrangements are the most commonly used today.

Limb Leads

Bipolar: Standard Einthoven triangle (leads I, II, III)
Unipolar: Goldberger's augmented limb leads (aVR, aVL, aVF).

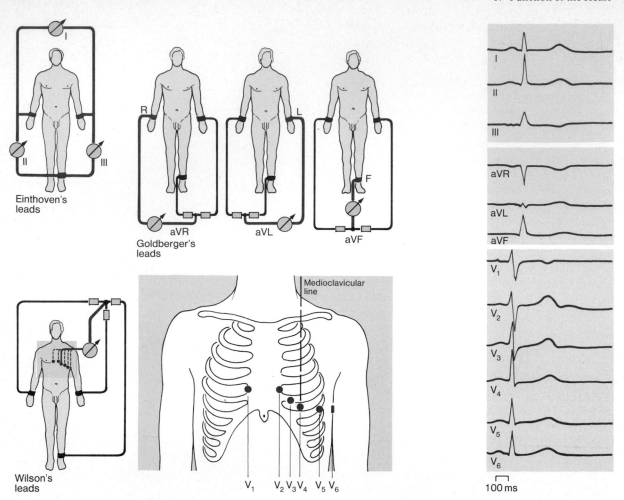

Fig. 17-18. Arrangements of ECG leads in common use. For the so-called unipolar leads (GOLDBERGER, WILSON) the recording electrode is shown in red. For WILSON's precordial leads, the general arrangement is shown at the left and the recording-electrode positions at the right. *Right:* Typical curves recorded from a healthy subject

Chest Leads

Bipolar: So-called small chest triangle of Nehb (D, A, I); not shown in Fig. 17-18

Unipolar: Wilson's precordial leads (V1-V6).

Einthoven's triangle. Because in bipolar recording from the limbs by the method of Einthoven the arms and legs act as extended electrodes, the actual recording sites are at the junction between limbs and trunk. These three points lie approximately on the corners of an equilateral triangle, and the sides of the triangle represent the lead axes. Fig. 17-19 illustrates the way in which the relative amplitudes of the various ECG deflections in the three recordings are derived from the projection of the frontal vector loop onto the associated lead axes. The temporal relationships here are assumed to be those of a normal ECG.

Types of QRS-axis orientation. As Figs. 17-15 and 17-19 show, the frontal vector loop has an elongated shape. The direction of the largest integral vector (the chief vector) during the spread of excitation is rather inappropriately called the **electrical axis** of the heart. When the spread of excitation is normal its direction in frontal projection agrees well with the anatomical long axis of the heart. Therefore limb recordings can be used to infer the **orientation of the heart.** The various categories are based on the **angle α** between the electrical axis and the horizontal. In the **normal range** (shown at the top in Fig. 17-19) the angle to the horizontal varies from $0°$ to $+90°$. Angles above the horizontal are given a negative sign. The general categories of QRS-axis orientation are: **normal range** ($0° < \alpha < +90°$); **right axis deviation** ($+90° < \alpha < +180°$); **left axis deviation** ($-120° < \alpha < 0°$).

For the construction of the electrical axis from the ECG by means of Einthoven's triangle (Fig. 17-19, bottom) two lead pairs suffice, for the third can be derived from the other two. At each instant during the excitatory cycle it holds that: deflection in II = deflection in I + deflection in III (downward deflections having negative sign).

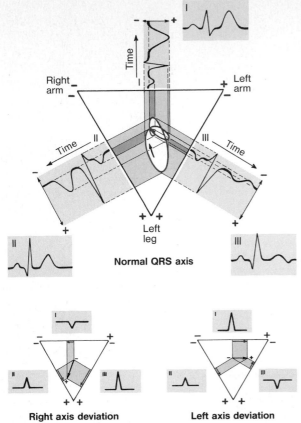

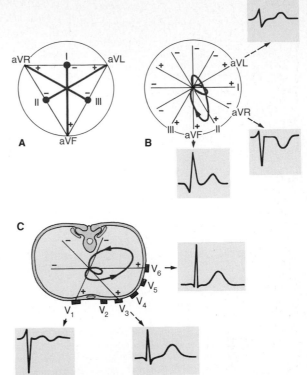

Fig. 17-19. *Top:* The triangle diagram of Einthoven. The recording sites at the extremities are represented as the corners of an equilateral triangle, and the sides of the triangle correspond to the lead axes. The projection of the frontal vector loop on the three axes is shown, and in the gray areas the relative magnitude of the various deflections in each axis is indicated by the customary curves. The curves should include a time calibration for precise analysis of the vector loop. *Bottom:* Direction and relative magnitudes of the maximal deflection in the QRS complex with right and left axis deviation. The deflection is positive when the polarity of the projected vector is as indicated for the leads

Fig. 17-20. A Lead axes onto which the frontal vector loop is projected with GOLDBERGER's unipolar limb leads. **B** Summary of axis orientations with the unipolar (Goldberger) and bipolar (Einthoven) limb leads. Lead aVR is an exception to the usual polarity rule. **C** Cross section through the thorax at the level of the heart, indicating the lead axes onto which the horizontal vector loop is projected with WILSON's precordial leads. Three sample records are shown (V1, V3, V6)

The electrical axis of the heart coincides approximately with the anatomical axis only when the spread of excitation is normal; under abnormal conditions the two axes can be quite different. The main direction of the QRS loop then contains no information about the orientation of the heart, but it is still a useful diagnostic characteristic in combination with other signs that indicate alterations in the process of excitation.

Unipolar limb leads. In Goldberger's method, the voltage measured is that between one extremity – for example, the right arm (lead aVR) – and a reference electrode formed by voltage division between the two other limbs (cf. Fig. 17-18). With aVR recording, the lead axis on which the vector loop is projected is represented by the line bisecting the angle between I and II in the Einthoven triangle (cf. Fig. 17-20A). The axes for aVL and aVF are found in the analogous

way. The terminology derives from a system no longer in widespread use, in which V stands for voltage with respect to a reference electrode and L, R, and F stand for recording electrodes on left arm, right arm and left leg; the "a" in aVR stands for "augmented" (the recorded voltage is greater in this method). In the diagram of Fig. 17-20 B the directions of the bipolar and unipolar limb leads have been shifted, without change in orientation, so that they all intersect the origin of the vector loop. It is evident that each lead line forms an angle of 30° with those on either side. This hexaxial reference system provides all the essential information contained in the frontal vector loop.

Unipolar precordial leads. Whereas the limb leads just described are fundamentally related to the frontal projection of the vector loop, the unipolar precordial leads of Wilson provide information chiefly about the *horizontal* vector projection. A reference electrode is produced by joining the three limb leads, and

A

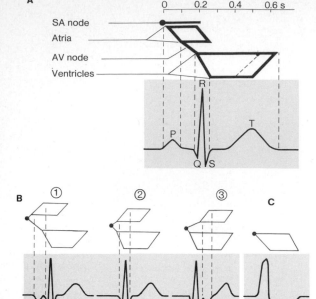

Fig. 17-21. A Diagram of the normal time course of cardiac excitation. The successive stages in the spread of excitation are shown from top to bottom, with the duration of each indicated in the direction of the abscissa. **B** (1–3) Excitation generated at various parts of the AV junctional region, with retrograde excitation of the atria (negative P wave). In (2) atrial excitation coincides with QRS. **C** Excitation originating in the ventricles spreads more slowly and the QRS complex is severely deformed

an exploring electrode records from specific points on the chest at the level of the heart (cf. Fig. 17-18). Fig. 17-20 C illustrates the *lead axes* onto which the vector loop is projected with the recording electrode in different positions. A positive deflection is seen when the instantaneous vector, projected onto the appropriate axis, points toward the recording site. If it points in the opposite direction, the deflection is negative. The *onset of a shift in the negative direction* thus indicates the moment when the vector loop switches from movement toward the recording site to movement in the opposite direction. This moment is of special diagnostic significance (delayed excitation due to a disturbed spread of excitation in certain regions).

Use of the ECG in Diagnosis

The ECG is an extremely useful tool in cardiological practice, for it reveals changes in the excitatory process that cause or result from impairment of the heart's activity. From routine ECG recordings the physician can obtain information of the following basic kinds:

Heart rate. Differentiation between the normal rate (60–90/min at rest), tachycardia (over 90/min) and bradycardia (below 60/min).

Origin of excitation. Decision whether the effective pacemaker is in the SA node or in the atria, in the AV node or in the right or left ventricle.

Abnormal rhythms. Distinction among the various kinds and sources (sinus arrhythmia, supraventricular and ventricular ectopic beats, flutter and fibrillation).

Abnormal conduction. Differentiation on the basis of degree and localization, delay or blockage of conduction (sinoatrial block, AV block, right or left bundle-branch block, fascicular block, or combinations of these). **QRS-axis orientation.** Indication of anatomical position of the heart; pathological types can indicate additional changes in the process of excitation (unilateral hypertrophy, bundle-branch block, etc.).

Extracardial influences. Evidence of autonomic effects, metabolic and endocrine abnormalities, electrolyte changes, poisoning, drug action (digitalis) etc.

Primary cardiac impairment. Indication of inadequate coronary circulation, myocardial O_2 deficiency, inflammation, influences of general pathological states, traumas, innate or acquired cardiac malfunctions, etc.

Myocardial infarction (complete interruption of coronary circulation in a circumscribed area). Evidence regarding localization, extent and progress.

It should, however, be absolutely clear that departures from the normal ECG – except for a few typical modifications of rhythmicity or conduction – as a rule give only tentative indications that a pathological state may exist. Whether an ECG is to be regarded as pathological or not can often by decided only on the basis of the total clinical picture. In no case can one come to a final decision as to the cause of the observed deviations by examination of the ECG alone.

Examples of ECG Abnormality

A few characteristic examples follow, to indicate how disturbances of rhythmicity or conduction can be reflected in the ECG. The recordings, where not otherwise indicated, are from Einthoven's limb lead II (cf. Fig. 17-13).

SA rhythm. As a basis for comparison, we first consider the normal ECG (Fig. 17-21 A), with the pacemaker in the SA node and the QRS complex preceded by a P wave of normal shape. Above the ECG trace in Fig. 17-21 A, the process of excitation is diagrammed in a way that has proved useful in characterizing impairments of rhythmicity or conduction. The successive stages in the spread of excitation are shown from top to bottom, and along the abscissa the duration of excitation (absolute and relative refractory periods) in atria and ventricles is indicated. The trapezoidal form of the diagram for the ventricle reflects the greater duration of excitation in the areas first excited than in those excited last (cf. Fig. 17-15).

Rhythms originating in the AV junction (Fig. 17-21 B). A source of rhythmicity in the AV junctional region (the AV node itself and the immediately adjacent conductile tissue) sends excitation back into the atria (including the SA node) as well as into the ventricles. Because excitation spreads through the atria in a direction opposite to normal, the *P wave is negative*. The QRS complex is unchanged, conduction occurring normally. Depending on the degree to which the retrograde atrial excitation is delayed with respect to the onset of ventricular excitation, the negative P wave can precede the QRS complex (Fig. 17-21 B(1)), disappear in it (2) or follow it (3). These variations are designated, not very precisely, as upper, middle and lower AV junctional rhythms.

Rhythms originating in the ventricles (Fig. 17-21 C). Excitation arising at an ectopic focus in the ventricles spreads over various paths, depending on the source of the excitation and when/where the excitation enters the conducting system. Because myocardial conduction is slower than conduction through the specialized system, the duration of spread through the myocardium is usually considerably extended. The differences in conduction path can cause pronounced deformation of the entire QRS complex.

Extrasystoles. Beats that fall outside the basic rhythm and temporarily change it are called *extrasystoles*. These may be **supraventricular** (SA node, atria, AV node) or **ventricular** in origin. In the simplest case an extrasystole can be *interpolated* halfway between two normal beats, and does not disturb the basic rhythm (Fig. 17-22 A). Interpolated extrasystoles are rare, since the basic rhythm must be so slow that the interval between excited phases is longer than an entire beat. Interpolated extrasystoles always arise from a ventricular focus, for such excitation cannot propagate over the conducting system (which is still refractory from the previous beat) to the atria and thus cannot interfere with the SA rhythm. When the basic heart rate is higher, a ventricular extrasystole is ordinarily followed by a so-called **compensatory pause**. As shown in Fig. 17-22 B, the next regular excitation of the ventricles is prevented because they are still in the absolute refractory period of the extrasystole when the excitatory impulse from the SA node arrives. By the time the next impulse arrives the ventricles have recovered, so that the first postextrasystolic beat occurs in the normal rhythm; the interval between the last normal beat before the extrasystole and the first one after it corresponds exactly to two regular RR intervals. But with supraventricular extrasystoles or ventricular extrasystoles that penetrate back to the SA node, the basic rhythm is shifted (Fig. 17-22 C). The excitation conducted backward to the SA node

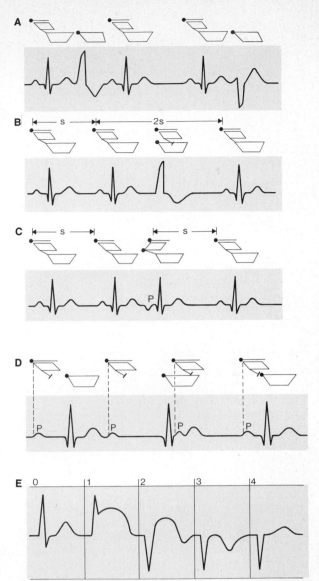

Fig. 17-22 A–E. Examples of typical alterations in the ECG. **A** Interpolated ventricular extrasystoles. The differences in form indicate different ectopic foci within the ventricles. **B** Ventricular extrasystole with fully compensating pause. s, normal SA interval. **C** Supraventricular extrasystole from the region of the AV node, with incompletely compensating pause. **D** Complete (third-degree) AV block. **E** Progressive ECG deformation during myocardial infarction: in this example, WILSON's lead V3 with infarction of the anterior wall of the heart. (0) Normal picture before infarction. (1) Early stage, a few hours after onset. (2) Intermediate stage, after hours to days. (3) After several days to weeks. (4) Final stage, months to years after infarct formation

interrupts the diastolic depolarization that has begun there, and a new cycle is initiated. These events result in an abrupt phase shift of the basic rhythm.

Atrioventricular disturbances of conduction. The ECG observed in cases of *complete AV block* is shown in Fig. 17-22 D. As de-

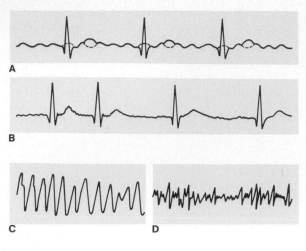

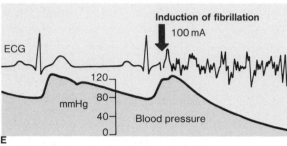

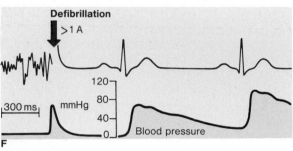

Fig. 17-23 A–F. ECG changes during flutter and fibrillation. **A** Atrial flutter; the flutter waves during the ventricle complexes are dotted. Here conduction to the ventricles occurs after every 4th flutter wave. **B** Complete ventricular arrhythmia due to atrial fibrillation. **C** Ventricular flutter. **D** Ventricular fibrillation. **E** Triggering of ventricular fibrillation by an electrical shock (100 mA) during the vulnerable period. **F** Interruption of ventricular fibrillation by a strong shock (> 1 A)

scribed on p. 360, the atria and ventricles beat independently of one another – the atria at the rate of the SA node, and the ventricles at the lower rate of a tertiary pacemaker. The QRS complex has the normal configuration if the ectopic pacemaker is in the bundle of His, so that excitation spreads over the ventricles in the normal way. *Incomplete AV block* is characterized by interruption of conduction at intervals, so that (for example) every second or third beat initiated by the SA node is conducted to the ventricles (2 : 1 or 3 : 1 block, respectively). In some cases the PR interval increases from beat to beat, until eventually a QRS complex is eliminated and the process begins again *(Wenckebach phenomenon)*. Such disturbances of atrioventricular conduction can readily be produced under experimental conditions (increased K^+, oxygen deficiency etc.) in which the resting potential is lowered.

Changes in ST segment and T wave. Myocardial damage due to oxygen deficiency and other influences in general causes a depression of the single-fiber action-potential plateau, before there is a noticeable decrease in the resting potential. In the ECG such effects are evident during the recovery phase, as a flattened or negative-going T wave or as an elevated or lowered (with respect to the baseline) ST segment. When circulation through a coronary blood vessel is prevented *(infarction),* an area of dead tissue develops; its location can usually be determined only by analysis of several recordings, precordial recordings in particular. It must be kept in mind that ECG alterations due to infarction can change considerably in time (cf. Fig. 17-22 E). The monophasic form of the QRS complex which results from ST elevation, a characteristic of the early stage of infarction, disappears when the infarct has become demarcated from the excitable surrounding tissue by the formation of a boundary zone.

Atrial flutter and fibrillation. These are arrhythmias resulting from an uncoordinated spread of excitation over the atria, so that some atrial regions contract at the same time as others are relaxing *(functional fragmentation).* **Atrial flutter** is reflected in the ECG by so-called flutter waves with a regular sawtooth shape and a frequency of 220–350/min, which take the place of the P wave (Fig. 17-23 A). Because of incomplete AV block due to the refractory period of the ventricular conducting system, normal QRS complexes appear at regular intervals. In the ECG associated with **atrial fibrillation** (Fig. 17-23 B) atrial activity appears only as high-frequency (350–600/min) irregular fluctuations of the baseline. The QRS complexes appear at irregular intervals **(absolute arrhythmia),** but their configuration is normal as long as there is no additional disturbance. There is a continuum of intermediate states between atrial flutter and fibrillation. In general the hemodynamic effects are slight; the patient is frequently quite unaware of the arrhythmia.

Ventricular flutter and fibrillation. When the ventricles are affected by the same sort of disturbance, the consequences are much more severe. Because the electrical activity is uncoordinated, the ventricles do not fill and expel the blood effectively. Circulation is arrested and unconsciousness ensues; unless circulation is restored within minutes death results. The ECG during **ventricular flutter** exhibits high-frequency, large-amplitude waves (Fig. 17-23 C), whereas the fluctuations associated with **ventricular fibrillation** are very irregular, changing rapidly in frequency, shape and amplitude (Fig. 17-23 D). Flutter and fibrillation can be set off by many kinds of heart damage – oxygen deficiency, coronary occlusion (infarction), overstretching, excessive cooling, and overdoses of drugs, anesthetics etc. Ventricular fibrillation is the most common acute cause of death in electrical accidents.

Causes of flutter and fibrillation. The basic problem in cases of flutter and fibrillation is disruption of electrical activity. Two main mechanisms are currently under consideration as causes of this disorganization, (i) abnormalities in the *generation* of excitation, and (ii) abnormalities in its *spread*. In the first case, fibrillation would result when one or more ectopic foci come into action, driving the associated part of the heart at a high rate and thus overcoming the regular pacemaker and conductile activity. In the second case, *reentry* would be responsible for fibrillation. This term denotes a state in which, as a result of shortening of the refractory period or reduced conduction velocity, the wave of excitation spreading through the myocardial network returns to its starting point after excitability has been restored and thus sets off a new wave of excitation over the same or a similar circuit. At present it is generally accepted that both mechanisms are probably involved in fibrillation, *ectopic foci* being primarily responsible for *triggering fibrillation,* and *circus movement or reentry of excitation* for its *persistence*. Between flutter and fibrillation there are gradations in the degree of functional fragmentation – i.e., in the sizes of the independently activated areas.

Vulnerable period. Flutter and fibrillation can be induced by a single suprathreshold electrical shock – either experimentally or accidentally – if it occurs in a particular phase of the *recovery of excitability*. This so-called *vulnerable period* coincides approximately with the rising flank of the T wave in the ECG (cf. Fig. 17-23 E). At this time parts of the heart are still absolutely refractory and others, relatively so. As described on p. 362, when the heart is excited during the relative refractory period the following refractory period is shorter and the conduction time longer – a situation in which reentry becomes possible. A further condition that must be fulfilled for reentrant activity is the existence of a unidirectional block of impulse propagation at a certain site of the pathway. This condition is also favored by stimulation during an inhomogeneous state of recovery. Spontaneous extrasystoles can give rise to fibrillation in the same way as does stimulation, if they occur during the vulnerable period following previous excitation.

Electrical defibrillation. Electrical current can trigger flutter and fibrillation of the heart. But if suitably applied, it can also stop ongoing ventricular flutter or fibrillation. A single brief shock is required, a few amperes in magnitude; when applied through the intact chest wall with large superficial electrodes such a shock usually stops the disorganized contraction instantly (cf. Fig. 17-23 F). Electrical *defibrillation* is the most effective method of abolishing life-threatening ventricular flutter or fibrillation.
The synchronizing effect of this application of current over a large area is probably due to simultaneous excitation of the multiple myocardial zones that are in an excitable state, so that when the reentering excitation reaches them they are refractory and further spread is blocked. For electrical defibrillation to be successful, it is of course crucial that the interruption of blood circulation during the preceding period of fibrillation not cause irreversible damage to organs (the brain can be revived if circulation resumes in 8–10 minutes). This danger can be averted if a minimal circulation is maintained by external heart massage combined with mouth-to-mouth resuscitation (cf. pp. 464f.). Every medical student should be competent in this procedure.

17.4 The Mechanical Action of the Heart

The excitatory events just described are of importance in that they govern the mechanical activity of the heart. Excitation causes the myocardial cells to contract. But for the alternation between contraction and relaxation of the myocardium to propel blood in the appropriate directions, from the venous to the arterial systems, an arrangement of precisely operating valves is required to prevent backward flow. There are two sets of such valves in the heart.

Action of the Heart Valves

There are valves covering the inlets and the outlets of both ventricles. The *atrioventricular valves* (mitral valve on the left, tricuspid on the right) prevent regurgitation of blood into the atria during ventricular systole. The *aortic and pulmonary valves,* at the bases of the large arteries, prevent regurgitation into the ventricles during diastole (cf. Fig. 17-24).
The AV valves are composed of membranous leaflets or cusps that hang into the ventricles to form a sort of funnel. Their free edges are attached to the papillary muscles by fine tendons, which prevent the cusps from being pushed back into the atria during systole. The total surface area of the cusps is considerably greater than that of the opening they cover, so that their margins are pressed together. This arrangement guarantees reliable closure even if the ventricle changes size. The aortic and pulmonary valves are somewhat different in structure; they form three crescent-shaped pockets around the opening of the vessel (hence the term *semilunar valves*). When the valves are closed the cusps touch one another to form a "Mercedes star" (Fig. 17-24). In diastole, the valves close rapidly, keeping regurgitation to a minimum, owing to the currents of blood flowing past and eddying behind them (Bernouilli effect). The edges of the cusps draw closer together, the higher the velocity of flow.

Sequence of Valve Action

Opening and closing of the valves of the heart is brought about basically by pressure changes in the adjacent heart cavities or vessels. The motion of the valves in turn affects the mode of contraction of the myocardium.
Accordingly, in both systole and diastole periods of action can be distinguished, in which the dominant feature is either pressure change with constant vol-

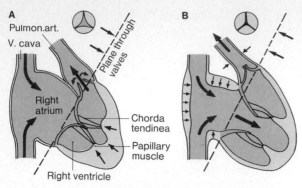

A
Pulmon.art.
V. cava
Plane through valves
Right atrium
Chorda tendinea
Papillary muscle
Right ventricle

B

Fig. 17-24 A, B. Semidiagrammatic longitudinal section through the right half of the heart, to show valve operation and the valve-plane mechanism. **A** Atrial diastole and ventricular systole; tricuspid valve closed, pulmonary valve open. **B** Atrial systole and ventricular diastole; tricuspid valve open, pulmonary valve closed. The insets above show the pulmonary valves as seen from inside the ventricle

ume, or volume change with relatively little change in pressure. During systole there are an **isovolumetric contraction period** and an **ejection period,** and in diastole an **isovolumetric relaxation period** and a **filling period.** In Fig. 17-25 the temporal relations between these phases and certain variables in the cycle are diagrammed, for the left heart.

Isovolumetric contraction period. At the onset of ventricular systole, the rise in intraventricular pressure causes immediate closure of the AV valves. Because the arterial valves also remain closed at first, the ventricular musculature continues to contract about the incompressible contents, so that there is a further sharp increase in pressure (cf. Fig. 17-25). Although the ventricular volume in this phase does not change, the contraction is not entirely isometric because there is a change in shape of the ventricle; it approaches a spherical conformation, and practically all the fibers of the ventricular myocardium – some actively and some passively – change in length. With the heart rate at the normal resting level, the duration of the isovolumetric contraction period in the left ventricle is about 60 ms.

Ejection period. When the intraventricular pressure exceeds the diastolic aortic pressure of ca. 80 mm Hg, the semilunar valves open and blood begins to be expelled. Initially the intraventricular pressure continues to rise, until it reaches a maximum of ca. 130 mm Hg; toward the end of systole it falls again. As the volume curve in Fig. 17-25 shows, under resting conditions the ventricle ejects only about half of the ca. 130 ml blood it contains; this is the **stroke volume** (SV). When the ejection phase is completed, therefore, an end-systolic volume (EV) of ca. 70 ml

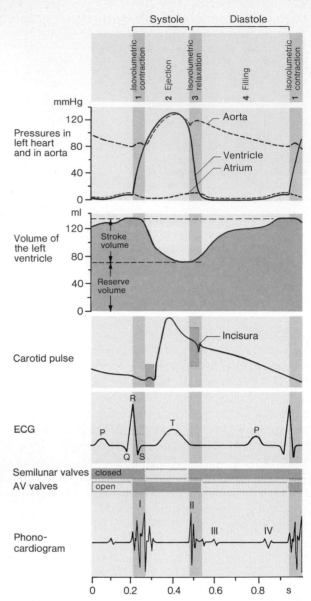

Fig. 17-25. The changes in certain processes and variables during the course of a heartbeat; the 4 periods are marked at the top. Valve action is indicated by a *dark gray bar* to represent the duration of the closed phase. The *red* Roman numerals designate the first to fourth heart sounds

blood remains in the ventricle. Closure of the aortic valve, which marks the end of systole, occurs somewhat later than would be expected from the observed pressure change (cf. Fig. 17-25). This discrepancy can be explained by the inertia of the systolically accelerated blood volume; because of the kinetic energy imparted to it, it continues to flow for a short time, even against the existing pressure gradient.

Isovolumetric relaxation period. Diastole, like systole, begins with a brief period (ca. 50 ms) during which all the valves remain closed. Relaxation during this time is thus isovolumetric. The intraventricular pressure falls rapidly almost to zero. When it is lower than the atrial pressure the AV valves open, and the ventricle begins to fill in preparation for the next systole.

Filling period. During this phase the intraventricular pressure rises only slightly. Volume increases rapidly at first *(rapid filling period)* and then more slowly *(diastasis).* When the heart is beating at the normal rate the ventricle is almost completely filled by the time the atrium contracts, so that atrial systole has but a slight additional effect (the volume is increased by about 8%). But when the heart rate is high diastole is shortened more than systole. Under these conditions contraction of the atrium can make a considerable contribution to ventricular filling.

Comparison with the right heart. The periods just described for the left heart can be shown to be in principle the same in the right heart. But because the vascular resistance is lower in the pulmonary circulation, the pressure the right heart must develop in systole is considerably lower (cf. p. 359). The stroke volumes of the two ventricles are about the same. The periods are not exactly synchronous in the two halves of the heart. Contraction of the right ventricle begins after that of the left and lasts for a shorter time, because the rise in pressure is less. Accordingly, the ejection period begins earlier in the right ventricle than in the left. The end of systole, however, occurs somewhat later in the right ventricle than in the left. These time differences are relatively small (of the order of 10–30 ms) and have practically no effect on the hemodynamics.

Valve malfunction. Anyone who has the opportunity to observe the opening and closing of the valves through a window in an animal heart is surprised at the rapidity and precision of their movement. It follows that when anything interferes with this movement – for example, when inflammation of the valves causes them to open too little **(stenosis)** or not close firmly enough **(insufficiency)** – the activity of the heart is seriously impaired. The parts of the heart affected are burdened with the need to develop greater pressure or move a larger volume, a burden to which the myocardium responds with hypertrophy or dilation. By adjustments of this sort the heart can in some cases compensate for disturbances in valve function over a period of years.

General relationships between wall tension and pressure. The rise in intraventricular pressure in the ejection phase is not, as one might easily suppose, brought about by the exertion of additional force by the ventricle musculature. Rather, it is a physical effect associated with change in size of the heart, which can be explained as follows. The muscular tension in the heart wall F (force per unit cross-sectional area of wall) and the internal pressure P of a hollow sphere of radius r and wall thickness d are related, according to Laplace, as

$$F = P \cdot \frac{r}{2d} \quad \text{or} \quad P = F \cdot \frac{2d}{r} \quad \text{(cf. Fig. 17-26).}$$

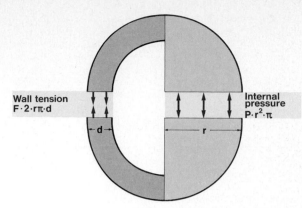

Fig. 17-26. Relationship between the pressure in the cavity of a ventricle considered as a sphere and the tension in its wall. For clarity the two actions are shown separately. The internal pressure P (force per unit area) acts to push the two hemispheres apart, with the total force $P \cdot r^2 \pi$. The tension in the wall acts in the opposite direction. When the thickness of the wall is small as compared with r, the tension is $F \cdot 2r\pi d$, where F is the force per unit area of wall cross section. Laplace's law amounts to setting the two expressions equal to one another

If the ventricle is considered to be a hollow sphere, the radius of which decreases during the ejection phase while the wall thickness increases, it is evident in the above equation that when the force is constant an increase in internal pressure is to be expected. Conversely, under constant-pressure conditions the force acting on a unit area of wall cross section is proportional to the radius and inversely proportional to the wall thickness. This relationship **(Laplace's law)** has important consequences, to which we shall return in various contexts.

Functional Anatomy and Pattern of Ventricular Movement

When the heart is viewed in cross section at the level of the middle of the ventricles, there is a conspicuous difference in the thickness of the wall on the two sides. This difference reflects the adaptation of the heart to the different forces required of the ventricles. This adjustment is not in muscle mass alone; the substructure of each ventricle is characteristic of its function. The wall of the left ventricle is made up primarily of a very powerful *circular musculature:* these fibers form a hollow cylinder on the inside and outside of which are layers of so-called spiral muscles running from base to apex. The wall of the right ventricle consists almost exclusively of such spiral muscles; the circular musculature is relatively poorly developed.

Contraction of the right ventricle. The arrangement of the musculature of the right ventricle in itself indicates its mode of operation. The right ventricle is apposed to the left like a thin-walled, crescent-shaped shell. The wall area of this cavity is therefore large with respect to its volume, so that a slight movement of the wall toward the septum must cause a relatively large change in volume. Because the resistance to flow in the pulmonary circulation is low, no great expenditure of force is necessary to produce the pressure necessary to eject the stroke volume. Moreover, the systolic decrease in right ventricular volume is aided by contraction of the left ventricle, which increases the curvature of the septum.

Contraction of the left ventricle. The powerful circular musculature of the left ventricle is an effective generator of the high pressure required to eject the stroke volume into the systemic circulation. With normal diastolic filling, ejection is brought about primarily by the shortening of these fibers. But if ventricular filling should decrease for any reason, the radius of the ventricle is necessarily reduced and the amount by which the circular fibers can shorten is therefore smaller. The more longitudinally oriented spiral muscles are similarly affected, but to a relatively lesser degree, so that as filling diminishes they take over a growing proportion of the work of ejecting blood. Whereas with normal filling the dominant effect of contraction is reduction of ventricle cross-section, when the end-diastolic volume is small the ventricle tends more to shorten in the longitudinal direction. This effect is of crucial importance in the so-called valve-plane mechanism now to be discussed.

Valve-plane mechanism. Ventricular systole has so far been discussed only from the viewpoint of the ejection of blood from the heart. In considering the valve-plane mechanism, we turn to an effect of systole that is closely related to diastolic filling. During the ejection period the ventricles, in a *single* operation, push blood out into the great arteries and simultaneously suck blood into the atria from the great veins. The suction is produced by a shift of the valve plane (the plane through the boundary between atria and ventricles, in which the valves lie) toward the apex of the heart; the atria, which have already relaxed, are thus stretched. This effect is most pronounced in the right ventricle because of its predominance of spiral muscles, which shorten the ventricle in the longitudinal direction. In the left ventricle the effect is enhanced as end-diastolic volume decreases, for the reasons discussed above. At the end of the ejection period, therefore, the atria are filled to capacity with blood (Fig. 17-24 A). Now, as soon as the ventricle musculature relaxes, the valve plane returns to the starting position; as this movement begins the valves open, so that the plane shifts, so to speak, over the blood that fills the atria (Fig. 17-24 B). In this way a rapid initial filling of the ventricles is guaranteed – a factor of special importance when the heart is beating rapidly, with correspondingly shortened diastole.

One might wonder at this point why shortening of the ventricles in the longitudinal direction pulls the valve plane down rather than the heart apex up, as would happen in an isolated heart mounted on an aortic cannula. There are at least two explanations. In situ the apex cannot be pulled up because there is an incompressible (and thus unstretchable) layer of fluid between the heart and the pericardium, which in turn is anchored to the diaphragm. Moreover, during ventricular systole there is a reactive force on the ventricles in the direction of the apex.

It is not by this valve-plane mechanism alone that blood is made available for diastolic filling of the ventricles. The diastolic relaxation of the ventricles in itself exerts a certain suction, owing to the reversal by passive elastic effects of the deformation imposed during systole. This action is comparable to that of the rubber bulb of an eye-dropper, which snaps back into shape after being pressed. Other forces driving the venous return to the heart will be considered in the discussion of circulation.

External Signals of Heart Activity

For information about how the human heart is functioning, one must usually rely on related phenomena that are externally observable. There are a number of useful signals that can be monitored at the body surface by means of suitably designed equipment, without appreciable inconvenience to the subject. Such methods of study are called **noninvasive procedures.** One example is the ECG, an expression of the electrical activity of the heart that has been discussed. Of the mechanical correlates of heart action, the following are particularly accessible to noninvasive monitoring: the *apex impulse, heart sounds,* and the *arterial and venous pulses.*

Apex impulse. The movement of the heart apex in a thin person can easily be felt with the fingers and sometimes even seen, as a rapid outward (occasionally also inward) bulging in the medioclavicular part of the left fifth intercostal space. This precordial pulsation is not, however, simply due to displacement by the apex. Changes in shape, volume and orientation of the entire heart interact in a complicated way to produce the movement. A recording of the apex impulse (**apex cardiogram**) can give supplementary evidence as to the timing of the periods in the contraction cycle of the left ventricle.

Heart sounds. As the heart beats it transmits to the chest wall oscillations in the audible range (15–400 Hz); these heart sounds can be heard by placing an ear on the chest, or by means of a *stethoscope.* While listening by either means *(auscultation),* one can usually hear two sounds with no difficulty, the first at the onset of systole and the second at the onset of diastole. The **first heart sound** is the longer of the two, a dull noise of complicated structure. It is primarily associated with the sudden contraction of the ventricular myocardium about its incompressible contents when the AV valves close; the resulting vibration of the ventricles and valves is transmitted to the wall of the chest. The shorter, sharper **second heart sound** is caused when the cusps of the semilunar valves strike one another *(valve sound)* and set the columns of blood in the great vessels into vibration. The most favorable sites for auscultation of the second sound are therefore not directly over the heart but somewhat away from it, in the direction of blood flow (i. e., in the second intercostal space, on the right for the aortic valve and on the left for the pulmonary valve). The best auscultation sites for the first sound are directly over the ventricles – in the medioclavicular region of the left fifth intercostal space (left heart) or on the right edge of the sternum (right heart).

Phonocardiography. With suitable microphones and recording apparatus the waves composing the heart sounds can be displayed (Fig. 17-25). The so-called *phonocardiogram* not only provides a permanent record, but offers an opportunity to analyze the temporal relationships of the heart sounds to other events during the cycle. By inserting frequency filters one can distinguish the components of the sounds more clearly and classify pathological sounds.

First sound. There are three main components of this sound. The first is a low-amplitude slow wave associated with deformation of the left ventricle at the beginning of isovolumetric contraction. The following larger wave accompanies the steep rise in intraventricular pressure. The third component consists of two waves, one coinciding with the onset of ejection and the other occurring early in the ejection period.

Second sound. The beginning of the second sound usually coincides with the end of the T wave of the ECG; it signals the *end of the ejection period*. Occasionally the second sound is split into a first component associated with closure of the aortic valve and a second, synchronous with closure of the pulmonary valve.

Third and fourth sounds. The rush of blood into the ventricle early in the filling period causes a third sound, which usually is audible only in children, where sound is conducted more readily to the body surface. At the end of the P wave and before the onset of the Q wave of the ECG a sound can occasionally be recorded which is caused by contraction of the atria. This fourth sound is not detectable by ordinary auscultation.

Murmurs. The abnormal heart sounds called murmurs are produced chiefly by turbulence in the bloodstream. Murmurs have a higher frequency than normal heart sounds (800 Hz), last longer and build up and die away more gradually. Inborn or acquired stenosis or insufficiency of the heart valves frequently cause murmurs; other causes include defects in the atrial or ventricular septa. Murmurs are diagnosed on the basis of the nature of the sound, the time of occurrence (systolic, diastolic) and the site at which the sound is heard most clearly. In cases of *aortic stenosis,* for example, blood is pushed through the narrowed opening of the aorta during the ejection period. The resulting turbulence causes the first sound to be followed by a loud *systolic* murmur of gradually rising and falling intensity that is heard best in the second intercostal space to the right of the sternum. If the murmur were most distinct over the apex of the heart, one would infer *mitral insufficiency*. In this condition the murmur is caused by systolic regurgitation of the blood from the left ventricle into the left atrium, through the defective mitral valve. Systolic murmurs, however, are by no means always a sign of anatomical abnormalities. For example, they can arise from changes in the composition of the blood. *Diastolic* murmurs occur when, for example, arterial valves are insufficient or AV valves are stenosed. Again, the site of best auscultation indicates the location of the defect.

Carotid pulse. The pulsation of blood in the vessels will be discussed here only to the extent that it provides indications of the functional state of the heart. When the stroke volume is ejected from the left ventricle, a pressure wave spreads through the arterial system. Measurement near the heart (common carotid artery) reveals a typical time course of pressure change (Fig. 17-25). The first result of ejection is a sharp rise in pressure, to a distinct peak. During the subsequent falling phase the aortic valves snap shut, causing a sharply delimited deflection, the incisura, in the pressure curve. The time from the base of the rising flank to the incisura corresponds to the **duration of the ejection period** of the left ventricle. In determining the onset of the ejection period, however, it should be kept in mind that the carotid pulse is somewhat delayed with respect to the practically instantaneously transmitted electrical and acoustical phenomena, because it takes some time for the pressure wave to pass from the aorta to the carotid artery. This **central pulse-wave transmission time** can be derived from the interval between the beginning of the second heart sound and the incisura (red-shaded region in Fig. 17-25).

Venous pulse. The veins near the heart are filled with blood to different degrees during the course of a cardiac cycle; these changes can be monitored as externally visible *volume* fluctuations in, for example, the external jugular vein. The recording of this movement (the jugular phlebogram) indicates events in the right heart, the right atrium in particular (cf. [18]).

X-ray examination and echocardiography. One can obtain clues as to the size and shape of the heart simply by tapping on the chest **(percussion)** and noting the distribution of dull-sounding areas. For more precise measurements, and for the sake of documentation, roentgenograms are useful. By placing the patient at a distance of 2 meters from the x-ray source, one can avoid the projection errors that arise at smaller distances due to divergence of the rays. The **roentgenkymogram** is used to represent the movements at the edges of the heart shadow. A metal grating placed

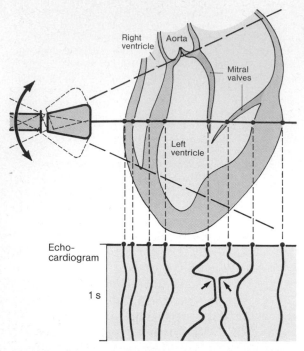

Table 17-2

(A) Physiological pressures (mm Hg) in the heart and the large arteries of a resting adult human

	Highest systolic pressure	End-diastolic pressure	Mean pressure
Right atrium	–	–	5
Right ventricle	25	5	
Pulmonary artery	25	10	
Left atrium	–	–	10
Left ventricle	120	10	
Aorta	120	70	

(B) Coronary blood flow and artery-coronary vein O_2 difference (AVD_{O_2}) of the human heart at rest and under load

	Rest	Work
Coronary blood flow ($ml \cdot g^{-1} \cdot min^{-1}$)	0.8	3.2
AVD_{O_2} ml/ml	0.14	0.16
Coronary venous O_2 content ml/ml	0.06	0.04

Fig. 17-27. Principle of echocardiography. The transducer acts as both sender and receiver in rapid alternation. The distances and movements of the echo-reflecting surfaces are recorded as a function of time. The closing of the mitral valve at the beginning of systole, for example, is a distinct feature *(arrows)*

in front of the roentgen film is shifted by one slit width during a heartbeat. The resulting picture shows a sawtooth contour of the heart that is most distinct in the region of strong pulsation, and thus is a measure of pulsation. Most recently, the principle of echosounding has come into widespread use as a method of studying the heart. In **echocardiography** the reflection of ultrasonic waves at the heart's various surfaces (inner and outer sides of walls, valves, etc.) is recorded (Fig. 17-27). This method provides useful information about the distance between structures within the beam and about changes in these distances – for example, changes in size of the heart, valve movements, and so on. Because experience so far indicates that these controlled doses of ultrasonic waves, unlike x-rays, are harmless to humans, such examinations can be repeated as often as desired.

Invasive Techniques: Intracardial Measurement

The extracardial recordings just described, such as ECG, heart sounds and the like, are clearly of great practical importance. However, they can give only indirect evidence of heart function, and for certain questions this is not enough. In recent years diagnostic techniques have been developed in which *cardiac catheters* are used for intravascular and intracardial measurements. These are flexible tubes of various designs, lengths and

diameters, which are introduced into a peripheral blood vessel and passed into the heart, usually under roentgen control. A transvenous catheter can usually reach the right atrium, the right ventricle and the pulmonary artery with no difficulty. The left heart is reached by retrograde catheterization, through a peripheral artery, or by way of the right atrium after careful perforation of the atrial septum.

Applications of the cardiac catheter. The primary purpose of heart catheterization is to **measure pressure** in the various chambers of the heart and the associated vessels. Pressure curves like those of Fig. 17-25 can be obtained in this way. In Table 17-2 the pressures of greatest practical importance are summarized. A catheter can also be used to obtain *blood samples* from regions of interest, for analysis of – for example – oxygen content. Following injection of a test substance, so-called **indicator-dilution curves** can be constructed; from these the cardiac output can be calculated (cf. p. 453). When contrast material is injected, roentgenograms can be made in rapid sequence to show the heart chambers and vessels in various phases of the beat **(angiocardiography)**. Finally, certain special questions can be answered by using the catheter for intracardial recording of electrical activity **(His-bundle electrocardiography)** or heart sounds **(intracardial phongraphy)**. But the apparatus required for these procedures is so elaborate that they can only be employed by clinical specialists.

17.5   Dynamics of Adjustment to Changing Work Loads

First we shall examine the work the heart must do to maintain adequate circulation under normal conditions. Then we shall turn to the mechanisms that permit the necessary modification of this activity.

A healthy heart is capable of changing its output of blood over a wide range. The **cardiac output** – the amount of blood the right or left ventricle ejects per unit time – can if necessary be increased to more than 5 times the resting level. Because the two ventricles are arranged in series (Fig. 17-1), their outputs must be nearly the same at each beat. For example, if the right ventricle were to discharge only 2% more than the left, within a few minutes pulmonary edema would be imminent as a result of accumulation of blood in the lung. The fact that such complications do not normally arise implies that there is a mechanism for precise adjustment of output. Even when the resistance to flow in the systemic circulation increases – for example, because of extensive vasoconstriction – there is normally no serious congestion; the left ventricle quickly adapts to the changed conditions by contracting more strongly and raising the pressure sufficiently to propel the same volume of blood. Changes in venous return and diastolic filling are also compensated by adjustment of the heart's output. This astonishing adaptability of the heart arises from two basic kinds of mechanism. 1. **Intracardial regulation** is brought about by intrinsic properties of the myocardium, and therefore can be demonstrated in an isolated heart. 2. **Extracardially initiated regulation** operates under the control of the endocrine and autonomic nervous systems.

Pressure-Volume Relations in the Isolated Heart

The mechanical properties of skeletal muscle can be shown to take basically the same form in strips of cardiac muscle. For example, an isolated papillary muscle is elastic and can be stretched; under a constant load it can shorten actively **(isotonic contraction)**; if its length is kept constant, it can actively develop tension **(isometric contraction)**. The contractile properties can be visualized in terms of a **two-component model,** in which the muscle is represented as consisting of two elements in series, one contractile and the other elastic (Fig. 17-28 B). (A third component, in parallel with these, is required to account for certain resting properties, but can be neglected here.) Isometric contraction in the model appears as a shortening of the contractile element, with equivalent stretching of the elastic element.

Elementary forms of contraction. It can safely be assumed that the myocardium in an intact heart behaves in fundamentally the same way as the isolated papillary muscle. But when applying the results of experiments on linear muscles to hollow muscular structures, one must take account of the fact that vol-

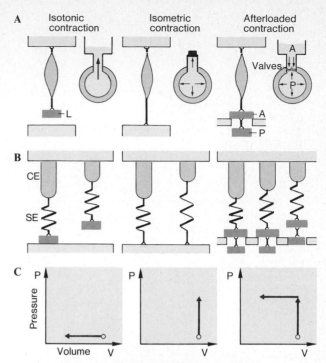

Fig. 17-28 A–C. Elementary forms of myocardial contraction (**A**). Mechanical conditions of contraction of an elongated myocardial preparation (papillary muscle) and a hollow mass of myocardium (cannulated ventricle). **B** Behavior of the two-component model during the various kinds of contraction (CE, contractile element; SE, series elastic element; L, load; P, preload; A, afterload). **C** Pressure-volume diagrams for the three forms of contraction. With the hollow sphere, the preload corresponds to the filling pressure, and the afterload is the pressure of the fluid column on the closed valves

ume varies as the cube of fiber length. Furthermore, for a given tension in the wall the cavity pressure is inversely proportional to the radius of the (approximately spherical) structure, according to Laplace's law discussed above (p. 381). In Fig. 17-28 A the mechanical conditions applying to the three main forms of contraction with which we shall be concerned are compared for linear muscles and hollow muscular spheres. Fig. 17-28 B shows the corresponding behavior of the elastic and contractile elements of the two-component model. By analogy with the length-tension diagrams of skeletal muscle, **pressure-volume diagrams** are constructed for hollow organs (Fig. 17-28 C). An **afterloaded contraction,** the type that corresponds most closely to the natural activity of the heart, begins with an isovolumetric phase, in which the internal pressure rises while the volume remains constant. At the moment when the internal pressure equals the hydrostatic pressure of the column of fluid bearing on the valve, the valve opens and there follows an isotonic decrease in volume.

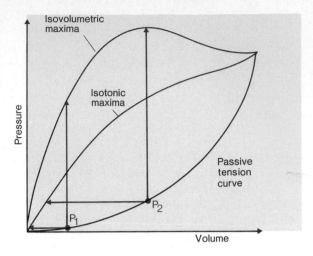

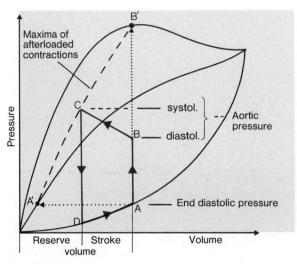

Fig. 17-29. Equilibrium curves and work diagram of the isolated frog heart, according to Frank. *Top:* In a coordinate system with intraventricular pressure on the ordinate and ventricular volume on the abscissa, three equilibrium curves are plotted – the passive tension curve, and the isovolumetric and isotonic maxima. Each point on the passive tension curve (two points are shown as examples) is associated with a particular isovolumetric and isotonic maximum *(arrows). Bottom:* Diagram of a cardiac cycle (work diagram) in the above coordinate system. The continuous curve ABCDA represents the different periods of the heartbeat (see text). All afterloaded contractions beginning at point A must end on the dashed Ac curve joining B' (the isovolumetric maximum for point A) and A' (the isotonic maximum for point A)

Equilibrium curves. The pressure-volume diagrams shown in Fig. 17-28 C refer to a single specified initial condition – a certain volume at a certain end-diastolic pressure. Variation of this pressure can bring about changes in volume which in turn affect the amplitude of the isovolumetric or isotonic contraction. These relationships are summarized in so-called *equilibrium curves* (Fig. 17-29, top). Equilibrium curves represent the boundary conditions within which, *for a particu-*

lar contractile state of the hollow muscle concerned, all pressure and volume changes occur.

Equilibrium curves are obtained experimentally (for example, with an isolated frog heart) in the following way. First the **passive tension curve** is obtained by filling the ventricle under different pressures and measuring the resulting volume. The increasing slope of this curve indicates that the passive extensibility of the heart decreases as its volume increases; that is, progressively greater pressure increments are necessary for a given volume increment. Starting at any point in the passive tension curve, both isovolumetric and isotonic contractions can be elicited, as shown in Fig. 17-29. The maximal pressures and volumes so obtained are plotted and curves – of the **isovolumetric** and **isotonic maxima** – are drawn through these points. As an example, two points on the passive tension curve (P_1 and P_2) and their associated maxima are shown in Fig. 17-29. One can easily see that both the pressure and the ejection maxima vary, depending on the initial degree of filling of the ventricle. As initial volume rises the maxima increase up to a certain point, and from there on decrease (or rise less steeply). This is an important finding. It implies that the heart can exert different pressures or eject different volumes of blood entirely on the basis of the amount of blood received, in the absence of any other influence.

Cause of variation in the maxima. The chief reason for the dependence of the contraction maxima on the initial volume of the ventricle is the arrangement of myofilaments in the sarcomere. The shortening of the contractile element, as discussed in detail for skeletal muscle (pp. 33 f.), results from shifting of the actin filaments past the myosin filaments, like the closing of a telescope. This shifting is brought about by cross bridges between the filaments, which can operate only where the actin and myosin overlap. The degree of overlap is optimal at intermediate levels of prestretching. When the volume is very large contraction becomes impossible, because the actin filaments have been pulled away from the myosin filaments so far that they are mostly or entirely out of reach. When the volume is very small, the actin filaments overlap somewhat with each other in the middle of the sarcomere, which interferes with cross-bridge attachment. Here, again, it should be remembered that the amount of pressure developed depends not only on the contractile strength of the musculature but on the geometry of the ventricle as well. Less force is required to produce a given pressure when the volume is small than when it is large (cf. p. 381).

Work diagram. The lower diagram of Fig. 17-29 shows a normal contraction cycle of the left ventricle as a red curve superimposed on the equilibrium curves of the above pressure-volume diagram. This closed pressure-volume loop is called the *work diagram*. The areas in the pressure-volume diagram (the product of P and V) do in fact have the dimensions of work (pressure-volume work; cf. p. 391). It is no exaggeration to say that the work diagram, originally derived by O. Frank [30] from his experiments on the frog heart, still remains the most important foundation for understanding of cardiac dynamics. Points A to D stand for the sequential periods of the heartbeat. At Point A, on the passive tension curve, systole begins with an *isovolumetric pressure increase*. The segment AB thus corresponds to the isovolumetric contraction period. When the diastolic aortic pressure (B) is reached, the aortic valves open and ejection begins. During this **auxotonic contraction,** volume and pressure change simultaneously. At Point C the ejection of the stroke volume has been completed, and *isovolumetric relaxation* (CD) begins. Finally, when the mitral valve opens, the ventricles begin to fill (DA) in preparation for the next beat.

The normal ventricular systole, by the definition given above, is an **afterloaded contraction** (Fig. 17-28 B). The **preload** is given by the end-diastolic pressure, and the **afterload** by the diastolic aortic pressure. With a large afterload – that is, with high diastolic aortic pressure – the afterloaded contraction would eventually become a purely isovolumetric contraction; the pressure would rise to Point B' before it sufficed to open the valves and allow ejection. At the other extreme, if there were no afterload contraction would be entirely isotonic, with volume reduction until Point A' was reached. Under normal conditions neither occurs. The maxima of all the afterloaded contractions that originate at Point A lie on a line joining the extremes A' and B'; this is the curve of the **afterloaded maxima** – the **Ac curve** for Point A (Fig. 17-29). For each cardiac pressure-volume diagram, then, there is one passive tension curve and one curve for each of the two maxima, isotonic and isovolumetric, but a large number of Ac curves – one for each of the possible starting points A along the passive tension curve.

Autoregulatory Responses to Acute Volume and Pressure Loads

Heart-lung preparation. E. H. STARLING developed a mammalian-heart preparation (Fig. 17-30) that enables variation of aortic pressure and venous return independently over a wide range, so that these factors can be correlated with the end-diastolic size of the ventricles. The heart retains its natural connections to the artificially ventilated lung, but the systemic circulation is replaced by a system of blood-filled tubes incorporating a variable resistance, with provision for pressure measurement at a number of points. The rate of venous return is determined by adjusting the outflow from a reservoir. Because the temperature of the blood is kept constant and the cardiac nerves are

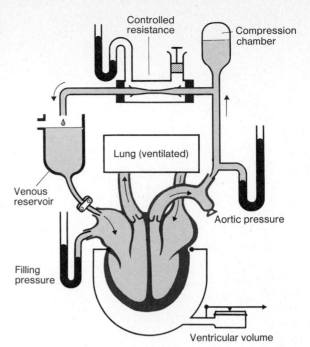

Fig. 17-30. Starling's heart-lung preparation. The pulmonary circulation is kept intact, while a blood-filled measuring system replaces the systemic circulation. The blood is oxygenated in the artificially ventilated lung. A venous reservoir catches the blood expelled from the left ventricle, and can be raised and lowered to change the filling pressure in the right ventricle (and in the left ventricle, because of the low resistance to flow in the lung) by controlled amounts. The resistance to flow can be adjusted by the variable compression of a thin-walled rubber tube when the pressure in the glass tube surrounding it is altered

transected, the heart beats at a constant rate. Let us consider the extent to which a "reduced" heart of this sort can react to imposed loads.

Adaptation to acute volume loads. In the Starling preparation venous return is increased by raising the input reservoir. Fig. 17-31 A shows how the left ventricle responds to such volume loading. Under the initial conditions, with an *end-diastolic volume* of 130 ml, the gray-shaded work diagram applies and the stroke volume is 70 ml. Thus the *end-systolic volume* is about 60 ml. When venous return is increased the end-diastolic volume rises to 180 ml. Now the red-shaded work diagram applies. It is evident that an increase in stroke volume, to around 90 ml, is achieved with no change in the isovolumetric or isotonic maxima or in the diastolic and systolic aortic pressure. The end-systolic volume has also increased. Because the starting point of the diagram is different, it is constructed with reference to another Ac curve (Ac_2). The essential point of this result is that the isolated heart, beating at a constant rate, can of its own accord – by *autoregulation* – compensate for increased diastolic

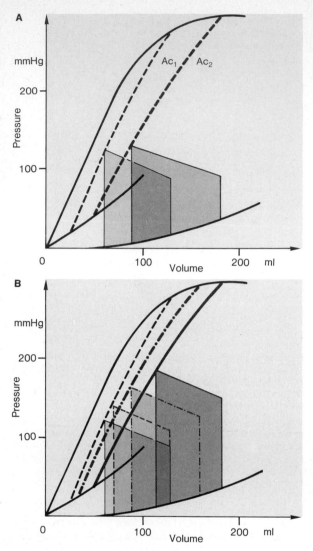

Fig. 17-31 A, B. Pressure-volume diagrams for the left ventricle, to show how the Frank-Starling mechanism provides automatic adaptation to acute volume or pressure loads. **A** Adaptation to an acute volume load due to increased diastolic filling. **B** Stepwise adaptation to acute pressure load due to increase in the peripheral resistance to flow. Further explanation in text

filling by ejecting a greater stroke volume. This kind of adaption is called the Frank-Starling mechanism in honor of its discoverers [30, 39]. In principle it also underlies adaptation to increased pressure loads.

Adaptation to acute pressure loads. If the resistance to flow in the artificial part of the heart-lung preparation is increased, the activity of the heart adjusts in a *stepwise* manner; the result is that the left ventricle, when fully adjusted, ejects the same stroke volume as before against the higher aortic pressure. In the work diagram of the heart this adjustment appears as in Fig. 17-31 B. Because of the higher resistance to outflow of blood, the aortic pressure in diastole does not

return to the original level, so that the left ventricle must exert greater pressure (here 110 rather than 90 mm Hg) in the following systole before ejection can begin (dashed red diagram). This necessarily results in *diminution of the stroke volume.* At the end of systole, therefore, the **systolic reserve volume is greater.** In this arrangement the venous return is held constant, so that there is automatically a *larger end-diastolic volume.* The working range of the left ventricle is therefore shifted along the passive tension curve, to a progressively larger volume with each beat. By this process a new equilibrium state is eventually reached, in which the left ventricle ejects **the original volume under higher pressure** (solid red diagram). Pressure loading is thus also compensated by autoregulation, owing to increased diastolic volume – that is, by way of the Frank-Starling mechanism mentioned above. In contrast to primary volume loading, however, the increased stretching of the fibers results in a more forceful contraction.

Increase in the diastolic aortic pressure also raises the pressure in the coronary arteries (cf. p. 393). The vessels fill with more blood, and the vascular tree expands ("garden hose effect"). This effect in turn contributes to increased prestretching of certain myocardial regions and thus to an increased work capacity of the heart.

Dynamics of the Innervated Heart in situ

The mechanisms by which the *isolated* heart adjusts were long regarded as the basis of cardiac dynamics in general. According to what was called *Starling's Law,* the heart in situ was also supposed to perform more stroke work entirely as a result of increase in its end-diastolic volume, with no change in its contractile state (i.e., in its isovolumetric and isotonic maxima). The current opinion, however, is that this view is not generally valid; at least, it does not apply to the changes in cardiac output correlated with physical exertion. Starling's Law would predict that a fully functional heart is small when the body is at rest, and when a load is imposed enlarges in adaptation to the increased venous return. But just the opposite happens! For example, the heart of a healthy subject doing physical work on a bicycle ergometer can be monitored on a roentgen screen; such experiments show a clear *reduction* in the end-diastolic and end-systolic size of the heart shadow during exercise. This adaptation occurs under the influence of the *sympathetic nervous system,* and results from an increase in the contractile force of the myocardium that is independent of the degree of prestretching. We have encountered this *positive inotropic action* of the sympathetic system in an earlier discussion (p. 367).

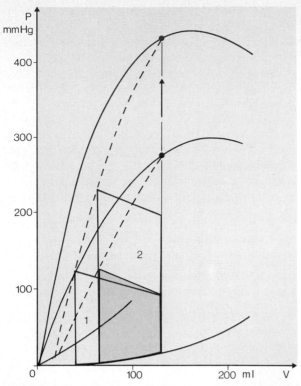

Fig. 17-32. Effect of increased contractility (positive inotropic action) on the work done by the left ventricle. Under sympathetic influence the curve of isovolumetric maxima is shifted to greater pressures (arrow). The slope of the associated Ac curve is thus increased. Now, although its end-diastolic volume remains the same, the ventricle is able either to eject a larger stroke volume (1) or to eject the same stroke volume against a higher pressure (2). When the stroke volume increases the end-diastolic volume decreases – that is, the heart becomes smaller during systole

Enhanced contractility (positive inotropic action) reflected in the work diagram. The adaptation of the heart to physical exertion just described appears in the work diagram of the left ventricle (Fig. 17-32) as an upward shift of the curve of isovolumetric maxima, with a corresponding increase in slope of the afterloaded-contraction line. Study of Fig. 17-32 reveals that this rearrangement enables the ventricles *either to overcome a* **higher pressure** *or to eject a* **larger stroke volume, without increase in the end-diastolic volume.** The increase in stroke volume leaves a *smaller systolic reserve volume,* so that if venous return does not increase the end-diastolic volume must be less – which explains the observed reduction in size of the heart. But even when venous return increases simultaneously, the rise in heart rate caused by sympathetic activity (positive *chronotropic* action) increases the amount of blood propelled through the system and thus prevents excessive filling.

Cardiac reserve. Under the influence of the sympathetic system, then, the heart can increase its output even before the venous return begins to increase. The further possibility, as yet untapped, of increasing output by enlarging end-diastolic volume remains available. The *cardiac reserve* – the ability of the heart to meet unusual demands – thus appears in a new light. In the earlier view the reserve was thought to depend on the extent to which the heart can increase its end-diastolic volume in conditions of exertion as compared with that at rest. By contrast, under the positive inotropic influence of the sympathetic system the reserve is limited by the size of the *end-diastolic volume at rest*. The hearts of trained athletes, for example, are conspicuously large at rest, and in some cases can hold 3 to 4 times the normal stroke volume – as opposed to 2 stroke volumes in an untrained person. The athletic heart (Fig. 17-33), accordingly, has a large reserve. In the old view its reserve would have had to be considered very small.

Influence of heart rate on cardiac dynamics. One of the most conspicuous differences between the isolated heart and the heart in situ is that the rate of beating of the latter varies. The *increase in heart rate* caused by sympathetic activity in fact is the most important mechanism for *increasing the cardiac output* under load. An increase in heart rate not only raises the number of beats per unit time but also changes the temporal relations between systole and diastole in a characteristic way. An example is given by the following table

Beats per min.	Duration of systole (s)	Duration of diastole (s)	Net working time (s/min)
70	0.28	0.58	19.6
150	0.25	0.15	37.5

As can be seen in this example, **shortening of the period** of the cardiac cycle primarily affects the **diastolic phase.** This means that the **net working time** of the ventricles (the sum of all the systole durations in a minute) increases considerably at higher heart rates, and the recovery pauses decrease correspondingly. Adequate *filling of the ventricles* despite even very brief diastole is guaranteed by the facts that most of the inflow occurs at the beginning of diastole, and that sympathetic activity causes a distinct increase in the rate of relaxation (cf. p. 367 and Fig. 17-10C). The sympathetic system also causes the atria to contract more strongly, which accelerates filling of the ventricles. Therefore when the heart rate rises under sympathetic influence, up to a frequency of ca. 150/min there is usually no critical diminution of ventricular filling.

Role of the Frank-Starling mechanism in the intact heart. The dominant influence of the sympathetic system in adjusting cardiac output does not exclude the possibility that under some conditions the heart is governed by other factors. For example, the capacity of the heart to regulate its activity by end-diastolic volume in the sense of the *Frank-Starling mechanism*

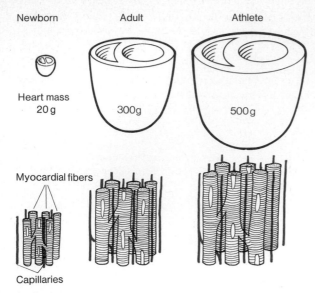

Newborn   Adult   Athlete

Heart mass
20 g   300 g   500 g

Myocardial fibers

Capillaries

Fig. 17-33. Diagram for comparison of natural heart growth and the further development of an athletic heart. The heart enlarges because the individual myocardial cells increase in thickness and length. In the adult there is about one capillary per muscle cell; in the newborn the relative capillary density is lower. From LINZBACH, J.: Klin. Wschr 1951, 621

is brought into play when *changes in filling* occur *without a general increase in activity.* This applies in particular to the *coordination of the output of the two ventricles.* Because the ventricles beat at the same rate, the outputs of the two can be matched only by adjustment of stroke volume. Other examples include changes in the position of the body which affect venous return (greater stroke volume when reclining than when standing), acute increase in the volume of the circulating blood (transfusion), and increase in the resistance to outflow. Moreover, when the sympathetic system is pharmacologically inactivated by β-sympatholytics the autoregulatory mechanisms continue to operate and their effect is more important.

Measures of contractility (maximal rate of pressure increase, ejection fraction). The positive inotropic action of the sympathetic system enables the heart, without increased diastolic filling, to eject a larger stroke volume or to eject the stroke volume against a higher pressure. A similar effect on cardiac dynamics can be obtained by raising the extracellular Ca^{++} *concentration,* by administering *cardiac glycosides,* and as a direct consequence of *increasing heart rate.* A common feature of all these effects is that they enhance cardiac performance independently of the degree of stretching of the myocardium – in other words, they increase its **contractility.** There is no increase in contractility *(positive inotropy)* when the stroke volume or the peak systolic pressure rise en-

tirely as a result of greater diastolic filling, as in the Frank-Starling mechanism.

Changes in myocardial contractility can be detected by examination of the maxima curves in the pressure-volume diagram (Fig. 17-32), as discussed above. But the shape of these curves can be determined only under experimental conditions involving surgery. To obtain data for an analysis of contractility of the heart in situ, especially the human heart, one must draw on other criteria – for example, the **maximal rate of pressure increase (dP/dt max)** in the *isovolumetric contraction period,* which can be measured with cardiac catheters (norms for the human are 1500–2000 mm Hg/s, or 200–333 kPa/s).

The **theoretical justification** for the use of this parameter as a measure of contractility is ultimately based on the finding that influences which increase contractility for a given degree of prestretch of the myocardium enhance not only the maximal isometric force, but also the **maximal possible rate of shortening** (v_{max}) of the contractile element under isotonic conditions. Here v_{max}, by definition, refers to the limiting case of afterloaded contraction, in which the load approaches 0 (cf. p. 387). An increased rate of shortening of the contractile element would naturally stretch the series elastic elements more rapidly and thus increase the rate of the isovolumetric rise in pressure – hence the choice of this parameter to measure contractility [24, 33, 38].
The measure of contractility of the heart during the *ejection period* is the ratio of stroke volume (SV) to end-diastolic volume (EDV). This ratio, called the **ejection fraction,** gives the proportion of the blood in the heart that is expelled during systole; norms for a person at rest range from 0.5 to 0.7 (i.e., 50–70%). The ejection fraction is usually measured by angiocardiography (p. 384), the two volumes being calculated by an approximation from the observed change in size of the image of the contrast material. Recently echocardiography (p. 384) has also been used to determine the ejection fraction.

Adaptation of the Heart to Prolonged Exertion

Hypertrophy. All the adaptive processes considered so far have enabled rapid adjustment of the heart's activity to acute changes in the demands upon it. If the demand for increased effort is repeated or continuous, structural changes occur; the heart enlarges. An example of such *hypertrophy* is the large heart of the trained athlete, mentioned above (p. 389). Typically, enlargement of the heart is greatest (a mass of up to 500 g, the mass of a normal heart being 300 g) in athletes who specialize in long-term performance (long-distance runners, bicycle racers and the like; cf. Fig. 17-33).
As hypertrophy develops in a chronically loaded heart, the number of myocardial cells at first remains constant, while their length and thickness uniformly increase (cf. Fig. 17-33, bottom). During this process the cavities within the heart must necessarily increase in volume. According to Laplace's law (p. 381), the re-

sult is that a greater wall tension is required to produce a given pressure. But because the muscle mass has grown, the force per cross-sectional unit area of muscle is still essentially the same. That is, the athletic heart contains a large volume of blood but does not pay for this advantage, as the acutely stretched heart does, with an unfavorable ratio for the conversion of muscle tension to pressure. When an athlete's training is terminated, the hypertrophy disappears within a few weeks.

Once the mass of the hypertrophied heart reaches the critical level, ca. 500 g, both size and number of the fibers increase. This condition is called **hyperplasia**.

Pathological states. When only parts of the heart are subjected to an increased chronic load, the hypertrophy is limited to the affected region. In general, this occurs only in pathological conditions. Here two forms of adaptation can be distinguished. When increased **pressure** alone is required, the initial hypertrophy is not accompanied by appreciable increase in cavity volume (for example, in hypertrophy of the left ventricle due to aortic stenosis). But if the extra work is required to propel an increased **volume**, hypertrophy and cavity enlargement occur together (for example, hypertrophy and dilatation of the left ventricle due to aortic valve insufficiency). The degree to which the heart can compensate for such defects by changes in myocardial structure, however, is limited. As myocardial fiber radius increases, so do the diffusion paths between the capillaries and the interior of the fibers (Fig. 17-33), which threatens an inadequate O_2 supply. The Ca^{++}-dependent processes in excitation-contraction coupling are also unfavorably affected by marked enlargement of the myocardial cells. For these reasons, when such pathological states are prolonged they may eventually result in heart failure (myocardial insufficiency).

17.6   Energetics of the Heartbeat

In the preceding sections the *work* performed by the heart has been treated in various contexts. Now we turn to certain quantitative aspects of the subject, and consider more closely those processes that serve to provide energy to the heart. First let us look at the debit side of the energy balance sheet.

Cardiac Work and Power

Physical forms of work during the heartbeat. Work is defined as the product of force and distance; the unit of work is the $N \cdot m$ (newton-meter = joule). This formula applies, for example, to the work done by a skeletal muscle when it shortens and lifts a weight for a certain distance (work = weight · distance). Cardiac muscle also, in the last analysis, does its work by shortening of the fibers and development of force. But in this case no weight is lifted; rather, a certain

volume of blood (V) is displaced against a resistance by the application of pressure (P). The **pressure-volume work** thus performed is computed as the product $P \cdot V$. To the pressure-volume work is added the so-called **acceleration work** expended to bring the inert mass (m) of the blood to a relatively high velocity (v). This is computed from the formula for kinetic energy $(\frac{1}{2}m \cdot v^2)$.

Calculation of cardiac work. Because the individual factors that determine cardiac work change continually during the work phase of the cardiac cycle, the time-dependent products $P \cdot V$ and $\frac{1}{2}m \cdot v^2$ ought to be integrated over the duration of the ejection period. Here, however, we shall be content with a simplification that permits satisfactory approximation, taking:

for **P**, the *systolic mean pressure* at the outlet from the ventricle (here 1 mm Hg corresponds to 133 N/m^2 (= 133 Pa));

for **V**, the *stroke volume* (in m^3)

for **m**, the *mass of the accelerated blood* (stroke volume, in kg);

for **v**, the *mean ejection velocity* (in m/s).

The values of these for a single systole are as follows.

Pressure-volume work: $P \cdot V$

Left ventricle P = 100 mm Hg $\doteq$ 100 · 133 N/m^2 V = 70 ml $\doteq$ 70 · 10^{-6} m^3	$P \cdot V = 0.931\ N \cdot m$
Right ventricle P = 15 mm Hg $\doteq$ 15 · 133 N/m^2 V = 70 ml $\doteq$ 70 · 10^{-6} m^3	$P \cdot V = 0.140\ N \cdot m$

Acceleration work: $\frac{1}{2}m \cdot v^2$

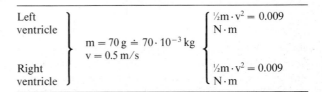

Total work $W = 1.089\ N \cdot m$

The dimension $N \cdot m$ for acceleration work results naturally from $kg \cdot m^2 \cdot s^{-2}$, for $N = kg \cdot m \cdot s^{-2}$ (cf. Chapter 30). In the older literature cardiac work is usually expressed in kilogram-force-meter ($kgf \cdot m$) rather than $N \cdot m$; $1\ N \cdot m = 0.102\ kgf \cdot m$.

The acceleration work performed by the left ventricle is much less than its pressure-volume work, only

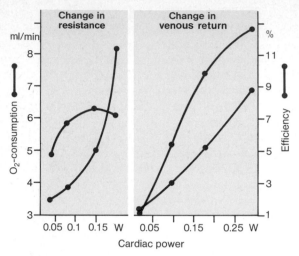

Fig. 17-34. Dependence of oxygen consumption and efficiency of the dog heart on cardiac power, as resistance and venous return are varied. From results obtained with heart-lung preparations by GOLLWITZER-MEIER and KROETZ: Klin. Wschr. *18,* 869 (1939)

about 1%. The work performed by the whole heart per systole is determined chiefly by the size of the stroke volume and the level of aortic pressure. It is of the *order of magnitude of 1 N·m (= 0.1 kgf·m)*.

The **proportion of acceleration work** in the total cardiac work can increase considerably when greater volumes are ejected, so that the velocity of blood flow increases. A decrease in the elastic extensibility of the aorta in old age has the effect of increasing the acceleration work of the heart, for the greater rigidity of the "compression chamber" (cf. p. 387) causes the rate of blood flow in the aorta during diastole to fall to low levels. Then the left ventricle during systole must accelerate not just the stroke volume, but a considerably greater amount of blood. Under such conditions the acceleration work can almost equal the pressure-volume work.

Cardiac power and power-to-weight ratio. Power is work per unit time. If we assume about one systole per second, *cardiac power* is of the order of 1 W (= N·m/s) or 0.1 kgf·m/s. A useful figure of merit for engines in general is the *power-to-weight ratio;* for the heart, given a weight of ca. 3 N, this works out to 0.3 W/N. This is a far poorer performance than is achieved by most engines (the motor of a car, for example, puts out 15–25 W/N). During muscular work, however, cardiac power can be considerably greater, so that the power-to-weight ratio approaches that of mechanical pumps. In any case, this calculation shows that it must be possible to construct artificial pumps that could, under appropriate conditions, replace a living heart and weigh less.

Oxygen and Nutrient Consumption

The energy the heart requires for its mechanical work comes primarily from the oxidative decomposition of nutrients. In this regard cardiac and skeletal muscle

differ fundamentally, for the latter can obtain a large part of the energy needed to meet short-term demands by anaerobic processes; the "oxygen debt" that is built up can be repaid later. The dependence of the heart on oxidative processes is manifest in the large numbers of mitochondria in the myocardial cells; these organelles are the site of the enzymes that catalyze oxidation in the cell.

O_2 consumption and efficiency. The oxygen consumption of a heart in situ is ordinarily found by measuring the difference in O_2 content of the arterial and coronary venous blood (AVD_{O_2}) and multiplying this by the rate of blood flow through the coronary vessels. When the body is at rest the cardiac oxygen consumption so determined is of the order of 0.08–0.1 $ml·g^{-1}·min^{-1}$. A heart with a mass of 300 g thus consumes 24–30 ml O_2/min. This is about 10% of the total resting O_2 consumption of an adult – though the weight of the heart is barely 0.5% of the total body weight. When the body is performing hard work the O_2 consumption of the heart can rise to 4 times the resting level. One would expect the O_2 consumption of the heart to be determined basically by its per-systole contribution to the work of the body as a whole. But this is not the case; for a given amount of cardiac work the heart consumes considerably more oxygen when it is working against high pressure than when it is ejecting a large volume against a correspondingly low pressure. The **efficiency** of the heart – that is, the fraction of the total energy expenditure that is converted to mechanical work – is therefore less when **pressure loading** predominates than when **volume loading** predominates (Fig. 17-34). The efficiency of a fully sufficient heart depends on the prevailing conditions, and lies in the range 15–40% [23].

In cases of *coronary insufficiency,* when the O_2 consumption of the heart tends to exceed the O_2 supplied by the blood, an attempt is made to reduce the resistance to flow in the systemic circulation so as to lower arterial pressure and thus lessen cardiac oxygen consumption. The beneficial action of nitroglycerine in attacks of angina pectoris is an example of such an effect.

Factors that determine consumption. Recent studies indicate that the per-systole oxygen consumption of the heart depends primarily on the myocardial *fiber tension,* and increases with the duration of contraction. The customary reference is the **tension-time index,** the product of mean myocardial fiber tension and systole duration. When the size of the ventricles is constant (Laplace's law, p. 381), the mean systolic aortic pressure can be used instead of fiber tension. Changes in **heart rate** affect O_2 consumption to about the same extent as they change the **net working time** (The product of systole duration and heart rate). As a result, O_2 consumption rises and falls about in proportion to the square root of heart rate. Furthermore, a small fraction (ca. 0.015 ml $g^{-1}min^{-1}$) of the O_2 consumption of the active heart must be maintained when the heart is quiescent to prevent irreversible changes in the structure of the organ (the **basal consumption**).

Nutrient consumption. The kinds and quantities of substances used by the heart to obtain energy can be determined by the same principle as was applied to the measurement of O_2 consumption. That is, the concentration difference between arterial and coronary venous blood is multiplied by the coronary flow rate. Such experiments have shown that the heart – as compared, for example, with skeletal muscle – is a sort of "omnivore" (Fig. 17-35).

An especially noteworthy feature is the large proportion of **free fatty acids** in the substrate, as is the fact that cardiac muscle, unlike skeletal muscle, can metabolize **lactic acid** (lactate). Because during hard muscular work the anaerobic glycolysis within the muscles releases lactic acid into the bloodstream, the heart is automatically provided with a certain amount of supplementary fuel to support the additional work demanded. In breaking down lactic acid the heart does not only obtain energy; at the same time, it contributes toward stabilization of the pH of the blood.

The proportions of the different substrates consumed are primarily determined by supply – that is, by their **arterial concentration.** Because the heart is so remarkably adaptable, using whatever happens to be available, the chief danger of coronary insufficiency lies not in a substrate shortage but in oxygen deficiency.

Energy-rich phosphates. Breakdown of the various substrates results in the formation of **ATP,** the direct source of energy for the contraction process. The ATP content of cardiac muscle is 4–6 µmol/g. This is a small amount in comparison with that required for the work of contraction; the active myocardium *recycles it several times within seconds* – that is, splits it to form ADP and inorganic phosphate and then resynthesizes ATP. Another phosphate found in the myocardium in about the same amount as ATP is **phosphocreatine** (7–8 µmol/g). This is a particularly sensitive indicator of the adequacy of the substrate and of the oxygen supply to the heart, for the metabolic resynthesis of split ATP initially relies on the breakdown of phosphocreatine [31].

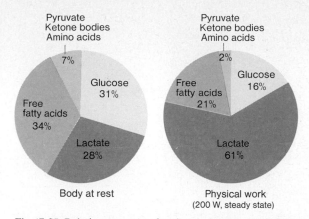

Fig. 17-35. Relative amounts of various substrates in oxidative metabolism of the human heart, with the body at rest and doing hard work. Substrate uptake is expressed as the percentage of total cardiac oxygen consumption that involves the substrate concerned (O_2-extraction quotient). From KEUL et al.: Pflügers Arch. ges. Physiol. *282,* 1 (1965)

The Myocardial Blood Supply

The coronary vessels, which supply the heart, are part of the systemic circulation (cf. Fig. 17-1), but they exhibit special features closely related to the way the heart operates. Therefore it seems appropriate to treat this part of the circulatory system here. In the human heart there are as a rule two coronary arteries, both arising from the base of the aorta. The right coronary artery supplies most of the right ventricle and various parts of the septum and of the posterior wall of the left ventricle; the rest of the heart is supplied by the left coronary artery. Venous drainage is mainly through the coronary sinus; about ⅔ of the total returns by this route to the right atrium, and the remaining ⅓ returns by way of the anterior cardiac veins and the Thebesian veins.

Flow rate through the myocardium. In experiments on animals, blood flow through the heart can be determined directly by electromagnetic flow-meters. With humans one must fall back on indirect methods; some of these involve determination of the uptake or dilution in the heart of nonphysiological gases (NO_2, argon, xenon), the tissue solubility of which is known. Such measurements have shown that flow through the heart of a resting human amounts to ca. 0.8–0.9 ml $g^{-1} \cdot min^{-1}$. The coronary circulation accounts for about 5% of the minute volume. During muscular work circulation through the heart can rise to 4 times the resting level (cf. Table 17-2). The increase in the heart's O_2 consumption during hard work is of the same order of magnitude (cf. p. 392).

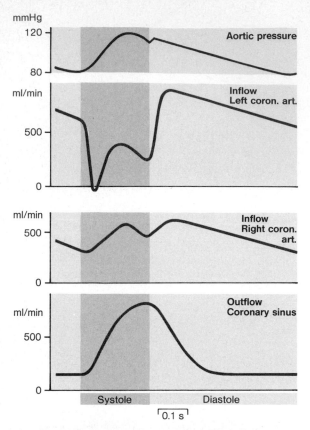

Fig. 17-36. Variations in coronary blood flow in relation to systole, diastole and aortic pressure

Variation in blood flow during the cardiac cycle. The coronary circulation, in contrast to that through other organs, exhibits marked fluctuations of flow rate in the rhythm of systole and diastole. The rhythmic pulsations in *aortic pressure* are partially responsible for these phasic fluctuations; the other main contributing factor is changes in the *interstitial myocardial pressure*. The latter acts to compress the blood vessels in the middle and inner parts of the heart wall. As Fig. 17-36 shows, the result is complete interruption of flow into the *left* coronary artery at the beginning of systole. Not until diastole, when the intramural pressure falls, is there a high rate of influx. In the branching region of the *right* coronary artery the intramural pressure is lower, so that influx basically follows the fluctuations in aortic pressure. During systole, because of the compression of the muscular wall of the heart, there is a surge of blood out of the coronary sinus; during diastole this outflow subsides (Fig. 17-36).

Regulation of coronary flow. Even during normal resting activity the heart withdraws far more oxygen from the blood than do the other organs. Of the 0.2 ml/ml O_2 in the arterial blood, the heart extracts around 0.14

ml/ml (cf. Table 17-2). Therefore when the load on the heart increases and more oxygen is required, it is essentially impossible to increase the rate of extraction. **Increased O_2 requirement** must be met primarily by **increased blood flow,** brought about by dilation of the vessels and hence reduction of the resistance to flow. It is generally agreed that the *strongest stimulus to dilation* of the coronary vessels is O_2 **deficiency.** A 5% decrease in the oxygen content of the blood (ca. 0.01 ml/ml O_2) leads to coronary vasodilation. The additional direct effect of the autonomic cardiac nerves on the coronary vessels is difficult to evaluate because of their other simultaneous influences on cardiac activity. Recent studies, however, indicate that the sympathetic fibers act directly to constrict the vessels, and the parasympathetic fibers to dilate them [21].

Adequacy of coronary supply; coronary reserve. The heart is adequately supplied with blood when the amount of oxygen available corresponds to that consumed. The ratio of the two is taken as a criterion for the adequacy of coronary flow. By cancelling out the factor coronary flow rate, the expression can be reduced to the ratio of arterial O_2 content to AVD_{O_2} (for example, 0.2 ml/ml divided by 0.14 ml/ml = 1.4). A ratio of less than 1.2 indicates a critical restriction of the oxygen supply to the heart *(coronary insufficiency).* Apart from the adequacy under normal conditions, the degree to which flow can be adjusted is of interest; this is the **coronary reserve,** the difference between the maximal amount of O_2 available (with maximal flow rate and maximal extraction, ca. 0.5 ml $O_2 \cdot g^{-1} \cdot min^{-1}$) and the actual O_2 consumption, or the ratio of this difference to the actual consumption. Under resting conditions the reserve of a fully adaptable coronary system, expressed in the latter way, is between 4 and 5; that is, the O_2 reserve available amounts to 4 to 5 times the quantity required by the heart during rest.

Anoxia and resuscitation. Because cardiac metabolism relies so heavily on oxidative reactions to provide energy, it is understandable that a sudden interruption of circulation *(ischemia)* results in extensive loss of function within a few minutes. In an experiment in which the heart is deprived of oxygen while coronary perfusion is maintained *(anoxia),* the changes produced are practically identical; as the contractions grow progressively weaker a marked dilation develops, and after about 6–10 minutes the heart stops beating. The severe impairment of the energy-providing system under these conditions is reflected in the dramatic reduction in the amount of *energy-rich phosphates* (phosphocreatine, ATP). The heart is capable of anaerobic glycolysis to a small degree, producing lactic acid. But lactic-acid breakdown in the myocardium comes to a halt during O_2 deficiency, so that the concentration of this substance in the coronary veins builds up to exceed that in the arteries. If anoxia lasts longer than 30 min, the myocardium undergoes irreversible structural changes in addition to the functional impairment, so that resuscitation is impossible. At normal body temperature, then, a 30-min duration of cardiac anoxia is a critical limit called the **resuscitation limit**. The resuscitation limit of the heart can be extended considerably if the metabolic rate is lowered by cooling. Advantage is taken of this possibility in modern heart surgery. When anoxia affects the entire organism, as in cases of suffocation, the possibility of successful resuscitation is limited by the brain, which is more sensitive than the heart and suffers irreversible damage after anoxia lasting only 8–10 minutes.

Cardiac Insufficiency

Cardiac insufficiency *(heart failure)* in the broadest sense denotes the situation in which the heart *propels less blood than the circulatory system demands*. This can happen even when the body is at rest **(resting insufficiency),** but it many become noticeable only during physical exertion **(active insufficiency).** An inadequate pumping action can result from several conditions not primarily associated with the heart's contractile function (valve defects, pericardial induration, extreme bradycardia etc.). In a narrower sense, cardiac insufficiency denotes *diminished contractility* **(myocardial insufficiency).** This can result when the heart is chronically overworked due to an increase in either pressure or volume (cf. p. 391). Other conditions inducing myocardial insufficiency include oxygen deficit (coronary sclerosis, myocardial infarction), inflammation (myocarditis) and certain poisons (overdose of Ca^{++} antagonists, cobalt salts etc.). The sites at which such influences interfere with the fundamental cellular processes of excitation, excitation-contraction coupling and contraction are extremely varied. It is particularly useful in practice to distinguish two types of myocardial insufficiency, on the basis of metabolism of the energy-rich phosphates – especially phosphocreatine [29, 30]. In the first case, the resynthesis of phosphocreatine is hampered by an inadequate energy supply (oxygen deficiency, metabolic poisons, etc.). The diminished contractility results because *insufficient energy is provided* to the contractile proteins, and is associated with a *reduction in phosphocreatine content*. In the second, enough energy-rich phosphates are available but they are not properly utilized because of *inadequate activation* of the excitation-contraction coupling (overdose of Ca^{++} antagonists, poisoning with local anesthetics, barbiturates, etc.). This form of insufficiency is characterized by *high tissue content of phosphocreatine*. Agents that stimulate excitation-contraction coupling (catecholamines, cardiac glycosides) can restore nearly normal contractility in cases of utilization difficulty. When the energy supply is inadequate, by contrast, such treatment tends to make matters worse; here treatment must be designed to save energy by lightening the workload of the heart.

17.7 References

Textbooks and Review Articles

1. ANTONI, H.: Elementary events in excitation-contraction coupling of the mammalian myocardium. Basic. Res. Cardiol. *72*, 140 (1977)
2. BASSENGE, E., HOLTZ, J., v. RESTORFF, W.: What is the physiological significance of sympathetic coronary innervation? In: MASERI, A., KLASSEN, G.A., LESCH, M. (Eds.): Primary and Secondary Angina Pectoris. New York: Grune & Stratton 1978
3. BERNE, R.M. (Ed.): The heart. In: Handbook of Physiology. Section 2, Vol. I. Amer. Physiol. Soc. Bethesda 1979
4. BERNE, R.M., RUBIO, R.: Coronary Circulation. In: (3)
5. BING, R.: Cardiac metabolism. Physiol. Rev. *45*, 171 (1965)
6. BRADY, J.: Mechanical properties of cardiac fibres. In: (3)
7. BROOKS, C. McC., HOFFMAN, B.F., SUCKLING, E.E., ORIAS, O.: Excitability of the Heart. New York: Grune & Stratton 1955
8. CARMELIET, E., VEREECKE, J.: Electrogenesis of the action potential and automaticity. In: (3)
9. CRANEFIELD, P.F.: The Conduction of the Cardiac Impulse. Mt. Kisco, New York: Futura Publishing Comp. 1975
10. FLECKENSTEIN, A., DÖRING, H.J., JANKE, J., BYON, Y.K.: Basic actions of ions and drugs on myocardial high energy phosphate metabolism and contractility. In: SCHMIER, J., EICHLER, O. (Eds.): Handbook of Experimental Pharmacology. Vol. XIV/3, 345 (1975)
11. HOFFMAN, B.F., CRANEFIELD, P.F.: Electrophysiology of the Heart. New York: McGraw-Hill 1960
12. JOHNSON, E.A.: Force-interval relationship of cardiac muscle. In: (3)
13. MELLO DE, W.C. (Ed.): Electrical Phenomena in the Heart. New York: Academic Press 1972
14. NOBLE, D.: The Initiation of the Heartbeat. Oxford: Clarendon Press 1979
15. PARMLEY, W.W., LAWRENCE, T.: Heart as a pump. In: (3)
16. SCHAEFER, H., HAAS, H.G.: Electrocardiography. In: HAMILTON, W.F., DOW, P. (Eds.): Handbook of Physiology. Vol. I, Circulation. Amer. Physiol. Soc. Washington 1962
17. TRAUTWEIN, W.: Membrane currents in cardiac muscle fibres. Physiol. Rev. *53*, 793 (1973)
18. VASALLE, M.: Cardiac Physiology for the Clinician. New York/San Francisco/London: Academic Press 1976
19. WINEGRAD, S.: Electromechanical coupling in the heart. In: (3)

Research Reports

20. ANTONI, H., JACOB, R., KAUFMANN, R.: Mechanische Reaktionen des Frosch- und Säugetiermyocards bei Veränderung der Aktionspotentialdauer durch konstante Gleichstromimpulse. Pflügers Arch. *306*, 33 (1969)
21. BASSENGE, E., HOLTZ, J., MÜLLER, C., KINADETER, H., KOLIN, A.: Experimental evaluation of coronary artery vasomotion: Possible significance for myocardial ischemia in coronary heart disease. Adv. Clin. Cardiol. *1*, 300 (1980)
22. BEELER, G.W., REUTER, H.: Membrane calcium current in ventricular myocardial fibres. J. Physiol. Lond. *207*, 191 (1970)
23. BRETSCHNEIDER, H.J., HELLIGE, G.: Pathophysiologie der Ventrikelkontraktion – Kontraktilität, Inotropie, Suffizienzgrad und Arbeitsökonomie des Herzens. Verh. Dtsch. Ges. Kreislaufforsch. *42*, 14 (1976)
24. BRUTSAERT, D.L.: The force-velocity-length-time interrelation of cardiac muscle. In: PORTER, R., FITZSIMONS, D.W. (Eds.): The Physiological Basis of Starling's Law of the Heart. Amsterdam: Elsevier 1974
25. CARMELIET, E., VEREECKE, J.: Adrenaline and the plateau phase of the cardiac action potential. Pflügers Arch. *313*, 300 (1969)
26. DUDEL, J., TRAUTWEIN, W.: Der Mechanismus der automatischen rhythmischen Impulsbildung der Herzmuskelfaser. Pflügers Arch. *267*, 553 (1958)
27. ENGSTFELD, G., ANTONI, H., FLECKENSTEIN, A.: Die Restitution der Erregungsfortleitung und Kontraktionskraft des K^+-gelähmten Frosch- und Säugetiermyocards durch Adrenalin. Pflügers Arch. *273*, 145 (1961)

28. FLECKENSTEIN, A.: Neuere Ergebnisse zur Physiologie, Pharmakologie und Pathologie der elektro-mechanischen Kopplungsprozesse im Warmblütermyokard. In: KEIDEL, W.D., PLATTIG, H. (Eds.): Vorträge der Erlanger Physiologentagung 1970. Berlin/Heidelberg/New York: Springer 1971

29. FLECKENSTEIN, A.: Specific pharmacology of calcium in myocardium, cardiac pacemakers, and vascular smooth muscle. Ann. Rev. Pharmacol. Toxicol. *17*, 149 (1977)

30. FRANK, O.: Zur Dynamik des Herzmuskels. Z. Biol. *32*, 370 (1895)

31. GERLACH, E., DEUTICKE, B., DREISBACH, R.H.: Der Nucleotid-Abbau im Herzmuskel bei Sauerstoffmangel und seine mögliche Bedeutung für die Coronardurchblutung. Naturwissenschaften *50*, 228 (1963)

32. HAAS, H.G., KERN, R.: Potassium fluxes in voltage clamped Purkinje fibres. Pflügers Arch. *291*, 69 (1966)

33. JACOB, R., GÜLCH, R., KISSLING, G., RAFF, U.: Muskelphysiologische Grundlagen für die Beurteilung der Leistungsfähigkeit des Herzens. Z. inn. Med. *28*, 1 (1973)

34. KAUFMANN, R., BAYER, R., FÜRNISS, T., KRAUSE, H., TRITTHART, H.: Calcium movement controlling cardiac contractility. J. Molec. Cell. Cardiol. *6*, 543 (1974)

35. KOHLHARDT, M.: Genese, Eigenschaften und funktionelle Bedeutung des Slow-response-Aktionspotentials am Herzen. Z. Kardiol. *69*, 307 (1980)

36. NEW, W., TRAUTWEIN, W.: The ionic nature of slow inward current and its relation to contraction. Pflügers Arch. *334*, 24 (1972)

37. ROUGIER, O., VASSORT, G., GARNIER, D., GARGOUIL, Y.M.: Existence and role of a slow inward current during the frog atrial action potential. Pflügers Arch. *308*, 91 (1969)

38. RUMBERGER, E.: Der Zeitverlauf der Kontraktionsfähigkeit des Herzmuskels nach plötzlichen Entdehnungen während der isometrischen Kontraktion in Abhängigkeit von der Reizfrequenz. Pflügers Arch. *318*, 353 (1970)

39. STARLING, E.H.: Linacre Lecture on the Law of the Heart. London: Longmans, Green & Co. 1918

40. TRAUTWEIN, W.: Elektrophysiologie der Herzmuskelfaser. Ergeb. Physiol. *51*, 131 (1961)

41. WEIDMANN, S.: The diffusion of radiopotassium across intercalated discs of mammalian cardiac muscle. J. Physiol. Lond. *187*, 323 (1966)

42. WEIDMANN, S.: Die ektopische Erregung. Schweiz. med. Wschr. *103*, 258 (1973)

18 Functions of the Vascular System

E. WITZLEB

General structure and function of the vascular system. The **vessels** – arteries, capillaries and veins – together with the **heart** constitute the **cardiovascular system.** This is a *transport system,* within which the medium to be transported (blood) is propelled by a pump (the heart) in a closed circuit through elastic tubes (vessels).

This continual circulation of fluid throughout the body serves, most importantly, as a route for the delivery and removal of substances; it provides all the living cells of the organism with the *materials required* for their normal function (e.g., O_2 and nutrients), and it carries away the *products* of cell metabolism (CO_2 and other metabolites). These substances do not enter and leave the bloodstream directly; their passage is *indirect,* by way of the interstitial (extracellular) fluid. The many other functions of the circulatory system, discussed elsewhere in this book, are summarized on p. 331.

The human **circulatory system** consists of two main sections arranged one after the other (in series):
1. the *systemic circulation,* with the left ventricle as the pump, and
2. the *pulmonary circulation,* with the right ventricle as the pump.

Because of this serial arrangement the amounts ejected by the two ventricles must always (apart from short-term imbalance) be *exactly matched* (Fig. 18-1).

In the **systemic circulation** *the blood is propelled during systole from the left ventricle into the aorta,* which gives rise to numerous *arteries.* The stream of blood is thus divided among many regional vascular beds *in parallel,* each of which supplies a **particular organ** (heart, brain, liver, kidney, musculature, skin, etc.). Each artery undergoes repeated dichotomous branching, so that the total number of vessels increases while the individual vessels become progressively smaller in diameter. The smallest arteries (arterioles) branch to form the *capillary bed,* a very dense network of narrow vessels with extremely thin walls; the total surface area of the capillaries is enormous (ca. 1 000 m² in the entire body). The capillaries are the part of the circulatory system in which the specific functions of the blood circulation occur – the many and varied ex-

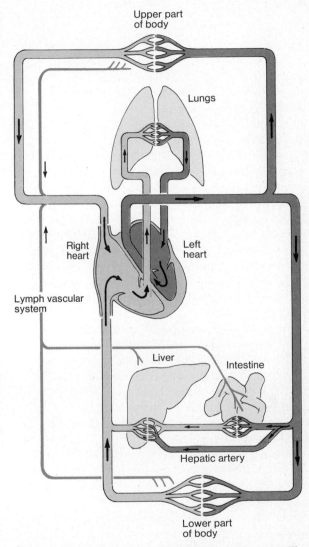

Fig. 18-1. Schematic diagram of the cardiovascular system. The vessels containing O_2-saturated blood are dark red, and those with partially unsaturated blood are light red. The systemic and pulmonary circulations together form a closed circuit. The lymphatic system (grey) is a supplementary transport system

changes, in both directions, between the blood and the cells in the surrounding tissue. The capillaries merge to form *venules,* which in turn join to form the *veins.* As this fusion progresses, there is a steady decrease in number and increase in diameter of the ves-

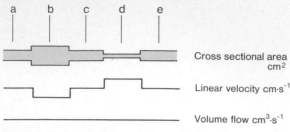

Fig. 18-2. Changes in linear velocity and volume flow in a series of vessels differing in cross-sectional area

sels, so that ultimately only two, the superior and inferior vena cava, remain to pass the blood into the right atrium. One of the vascular subcircuits, the splanchnic circulation, departs somewhat from this general pattern; from the mesenteric and splenic capillary beds, in the intestine and spleen respectively, the blood passes through a second capillary bed in the liver before returning to the heart (Fig. 18-1). This type of sub-circuit is called a portal circulation. In general, however, the **arteries distribute** and the **veins collect** the blood.

In the **pulmonary circulation** the blood passes from the right ventricle through the *pulmonary trunk* into the vascular system of the lungs, which has in principle the same arrangement as the systemic circulation. Four large pulmonary veins carry the blood to the left atrium; it then enters the left ventricle, completing the circuit.

There is a fundamental **functional difference** between the pulmonary and systemic circulations, in that the volume of blood propelled by the heart in a given time through the **systemic circulation** must be distributed to *all organ systems* and tissues, which differ in their basic requirements and in addition vary from time to time in the amount of blood they need, depending on their activity level. These variations are monitored and the blood supply regulated by a number of control mechanisms. The pulmonary circulation, through which the same total amount of blood passes, represents a relatively constant load, serving essentially only for *gas exchange and heat dissipation.* Therefore a less elaborate system is required to monitor and regulate blood flow through the lungs.

The blood vascular system is supplemented by the *lymph vascular system,* within which the fluid and proteins from the **interstitial space** are collected and transported to the blood vessels (Fig. 18-1).

18.1   Fundamentals of Hemodynamics

Blood flow is brought about by pressure differences between the individual vascular regions, so that the blood flows from regions of higher pressure to those where the pressure is lower. The *pressure gradient* provides the force that overcomes the resistance to flow, which depends on the *dimensions* of the vessels and the *viscosity* of the blood [7].

The Physics of Blood Flow

Flow, pressure and resistance. To a rough approximation, the factors that determine flow can be summarized in an equation analogous to Ohm's law:

$$\dot{V} = \frac{\Delta P}{R} \tag{1}$$

That is, the volume flow $\dot{V}$ is equal to the ratio of ΔP, the average pressure difference between the arterial and venous parts (or other parts) of the system, and the resistance R to flow in the region concerned.

The **volume flow** $\dot{V}$, which describes an organ's blood supply, is the amount of blood flowing through a vascular cross section per unit time (ml $\cdot$ s^{-1}). It can be calculated from the linear velocity of flow ($\bar{v}$) through the cross section and the cross-sectional area (A = $\pi \cdot r^2$); that is, $\dot{V} = \bar{v} \cdot A$.

According to the **law of continuity of flow,** the volume flow in a system composed of tubes of different diameters (such as the vascular system) is constant in each segment with a given cross-sectional area, regardless of the size of that area (cf. Fig. 18-2); that is, for two segments (a and b) in series,

$$\dot{V} = \bar{v}_a \cdot A_a = \bar{v}_b \cdot A_b \ldots \tag{2}$$

The consequence is that with equal volume flow in the successive segments, the *linear velocity* of flow in each segment is *inversely proportional* to its cross-sectional area.

The **pressures** in the vascular system, the arterial and venous **blood pressures,** are equivalent to the forces per unit area exerted by the blood on the walls of the vessels. Because of the long history of clinical measurements with mercury manometers, blood pressure is usually expressed in mm Hg, though it is sometimes given in cm H$_2$O (1 mm Hg $\approx$ 13.6 mm H$_2$O $\approx$ 133 Pa; 10 mm H$_2$O $\approx$ 98 Pa. For further conversion factors see p. 689).

The **resistance** R in Equation (1) cannot be measured directly, but can be calculated from the *pressure dif-*

ference between two points in the vascular system and the *volume flow*. For ΔP in mm Hg, resistance (in SI units) is found as follows:

$$R = \frac{\Delta P}{\dot{V}} \cdot 133 \, (Pa \cdot ml^{-1} \cdot s) \qquad (3)$$

Resistance to flow arises from the internal friction between the fluid layers and against the wall of the vessel, which is determined by the dimensions of the vessels, the viscosity of the fluid and the type of flow.

Resistance to flow in systems of tubes. For a system consisting of tubes in *series,* the total resistance (according to KIRCHHOFF's first law) is the sum of all the series resistances; that is,

$$R_{tot} = R_1 + R_2 + \ldots \qquad (4)$$

For tubes in *parallel,* such as the vascular beds of the various organs, KIRCHHOFF's second law applies and it is the conductances that add, so that

$$C_{tot} = C_1 + C_2 + \ldots \qquad (5)$$

or, because C is the reciprocal of resistance,

$$C_{tot} = \frac{1}{R_1} + \frac{1}{R_2} + \ldots$$

According to Equation (3) or (1), then,

$$C = \frac{\dot{V}}{\Delta P} \quad and \quad \dot{V} = \Delta P \cdot C \qquad (6)$$

That is, for a given pressure difference the volume flow increases in proportion to the conductance.

Because resistance is the reciprocal of conductance, the total resistance of vessels in parallel can be found from Equation (5) to be

$$R_{tot} = \frac{1}{\frac{1}{R_1} + \frac{1}{R_2}} \qquad (7)$$

One can see from Equation (7) that the *total resistance of several tubes of equal diameter in parallel* corresponds to the resistance of a single vessel divided by the number of vessels; it is thus considerably smaller than the resistance of each individual vessel.

Viscosity of the blood. *Factors that determine viscosity.* Viscosity (η) is the property of fluids that gives rise to internal forces affecting their flow. Whenever a fluid flows over a stationary surface (and hence when it flows through a tube) the layers within it move at different velocities, so that a shear force arises between the layers – the faster layer tends to drag along, and to be held back by, the slower layer.

η is a temperature-dependent constant for many fluids. According to Newton's viscosity equation, it is given by the ratio of shear force τ (force per unit surface area) and the velocity gradient between adjacent layers γ:

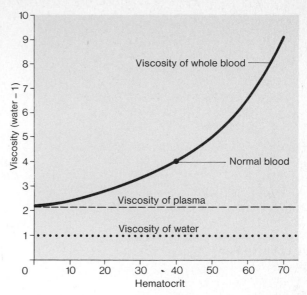

Fig. 18-3. Relative viscosity of the blood as a function of hematocrit

$$\eta = \frac{\tau}{\gamma} \, (Pa \cdot s) \qquad (8)$$

As will become clear below (Hagen-Poiseuille law), not only the *driving pressure* but also the *radius and length of the vessel* affect the forces required to move layers past one another, or to develop and maintain flow.

Viscosity is often given in *relative units,* the viscosity of water at $20\,^\circ$C (10^{-3} Pa $\cdot$ s) being taken as 1.0. *Homogeneous* fluids (for example, water, electrolyte solutions, plasma) have *constant* viscosity, whereas that of *inhomogeneous* (heterogeneous) fluids (for example, blood and all emulsions) *varies,* depending on flow rate and other factors.

The viscosity of blood derives primarily from its *corpuscular components,* and to a lesser extent from the *protein content of the plasma.* In humans, the viscosity of blood is **3–5 relative units,** and that of plasma is **1.9–2.3 relative units.** The values are higher, the larger the cell count and/or the greater the plasma protein content (Fig. 18-3).

Viscosity in blood vessels. An important factor affecting blood flow is that the viscosity of the blood changes in certain parts of the circulatory system owing to various effects, some of which are not entirely understood. Where the velocity of flow (and thus the shear stress) is low, *viscosity increases as flow becomes slower,* reaching more than 1 000 relative units at very

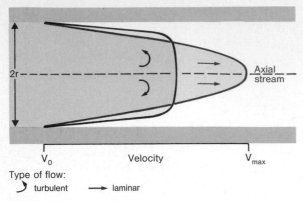

Type of flow:
⤵ turbulent   ⟶ laminar

Fig. 18-4. Velocity profiles associated with laminar (coaxial cylindrical) and turbulent flow. In turbulent flow both axial and mean velocities are lower than in laminar flow

low velocities and shear stresses. Under *physiological conditions* these effects play a role only in the smallest vessels, where the effective viscosity can rise by about tenfold because the shear force is so small. In the other parts of the vascular system, by contrast, the shear forces are so large that the effective viscosity is nearly the same as the viscosity measured in vitro. But under certain *pathological conditions* even greater increases in viscosity can be brought about by a reduced rate of flow. For example, blood flows more slowly in the part of a vessel distal to a constriction (the same effect occurs in the venules, where the cross-sectional area is larger than in the capillaries); moreover, velocity is less when the driving pressure is lowered. In such cases the increased viscosity can reduce the velocity still further, until flow ceases altogether. Lowered flow velocity increases viscosity because of the **reversible aggregation** of the erythrocytes, which form rouleaux (rows like stacks of coins) or clumps at the wall of the vessel.

On the other hand, there is another mechanism which causes the effective viscosity to decrease considerably in tubes with diameters less than 1 mm **(sigma phenomenon** or **Fåhraeus-Lindqvist effect).** Because of this effect, which becomes more pronounced at smaller diameters, the *effective viscosity* of blood in the capillaries is only 50% of that in the large vessels – that is, it is *reduced* to about the viscosity of plasma. The reduction probably results from an alignment of the erythrocytes along the axis of the vessel, so that they advance through the capillary like a "snake" sheathed in plasma. The low-viscosity, cell-free surrounding zone acts as a layer over which the cells slide smoothly, so that the conditions of flow are improved and pressure drops reduced. These effects

counteract, at least partially, the tendency for low flow velocity to increase blood viscosity in small vessels as described above.

Types of Flow

Laminar flow. Under physiological conditions flow is *laminar* or layered in nearly all segments of the vascular system. The fluid moves in *coaxial cylindrical layers,* within which motion of all particles is exclusively *parallel* to the axis of the vessel. The individual fluid layers shift past one another like the parts of a telescope tube, with the layer immediately adjacent to the wall of the vessel held still by adhesion, the second layer moving over it, the third over the second, and so on. The resulting **parabolic velocity profile** has maximal velocity at the axis of the vessel (Fig. 18-4).

The smaller the vessel, the more the central "layers" are slowed by viscous interaction with the stationary wall, because they are closer to it; the mean velocity of flow is therefore low. In larger vessels the more centrally situated layers are further from the wall as the axis of the vessel is approached, the successive fluid cylinders glide more and more rapidly, so that the mean velocity of flow is considerably increased.

A peculiarity of the laminar flow of blood is that the corpuscular elements are forced toward the axis more strongly, the larger they are. The **axial stream** is therefore composed almost entirely of erythrocytes, which move like a fairly *compact cylinder* within a largely cell-free coating of plasma. Their mean velocity of flow is thus greater than that of the plasma.

Turbulent flow. Under certain conditions, laminar flow can give way to *turbulent flow;* the latter is characterized by eddies in which the fluid particles move not only parallel to the vascular axis but also perpendicular to it. This turbulence increases the internal friction appreciably, and the flow profile becomes flattened (Fig. 18-4). Now volume flow is no longer linearly related to the pressure gradient, but is approximately proportional to the square root of the pressure difference. For volume flow to be doubled, the driving pressure must be about quadrupled. Turbulent flow therefore can add considerably to the load on the heart.

The presence or absence of turbulent flow depends on a number of factors, the net effects of which are summarized in the dimensionless **Reynolds' number.** Reynolds' number is directly proportional to the radius of the vessel r (in m), the mean velocity of flow $\bar{v}$ (in $m \cdot s^{-1}$), and the density of the fluid ρ (for blood,

$1\,060$ kg $\cdot$ m^{-3}), and is inversely proportional to the viscosity η (in Pa $\cdot$ s):

$$Re = \frac{r \cdot \bar{v} \cdot \rho}{\eta} \qquad (9)$$

Where REYNOLDS' number exceeds 200, local vortices can be generated near the walls of branching and constricted arteries or of vessels that are sharply bent; when it is between $1\,000$ and $1\,200$ there is a *complete* transition from laminar to turbulent flow. This so-called critical value is far exceeded in the proximal parts of the aorta and pulmonary artery during the ejection period, and there is thus transient turbulence in these places. If the velocity of flow is increased (for example, during muscular exercise) or the blood viscosity reduced (for example, in severe anemia) turbulence can occur in all the large arteries. The noise of this turbulent flow can sometimes be heard even without a stethoscope.

Relations between Volume Flow and Resistance to Flow

Calculation of linear flow velocity. For laminar flow, the relation between mean velocity and tube diameter can be calculated by integration of the velocities of all the concentric fluid cylinders, which results in the following equation:

$$\bar{v} = \frac{\Delta P \cdot r^2}{8 \cdot \eta \cdot l} \qquad (10)$$

Here $\bar{v}$ is the *mean velocity,* ΔP is the *pressure difference,* r is the *radius,* η is the *viscosity* of the fluid, l is the *length* of the vessel and the factor 8 arises from *integration of the velocity profile.*

The Hagen-Poiseuille law. Because the volume flow rate $\dot{V}$ is given by $\bar{v} \cdot \pi \cdot r^2$, one can substitute for $\bar{v}$ in Equation (10) and obtain the *Hagen-Poiseuille equation* for the *volume flow:*

$$\dot{V} = \frac{\pi \cdot r^4}{8 \cdot \eta \cdot l} \Delta P \qquad (11)$$

In terms of *Ohm's law* (Equation (1)), the *resistance to flow* is then

$$R = \frac{8 \cdot \eta \cdot l}{\pi \cdot r^4} \qquad (12)$$

We see that volume flow and resistance to flow are directly and inversely proportional, respectively, to the 4th power of the radius. Therefore both of these variables are much more strongly affected by changes in vessel diameter than by changes in length, pressure difference or viscosity. For example, the volume flow in a vessel through which the flow is initially 1 ml $\cdot$ s^{-1} will rise to 16 ml $\cdot$ s^{-1} when the diameter of the vessel is doubled and to 256 ml $\cdot$ s^{-1} when it is quadrupled, while the resistance to flow falls to $1/16$ or $1/256$, respectively.

Given these relationships, it is clear that *changes in radius* of the vessels constitute the decisive mechanism for effective *regulation of flow rate and pressure,* whether local or large-scale adjustments of the circulatory system are required.

On the basis of the relationships defined by the laws of OHM and HAGEN-POISEUILLE, one can obtain a general picture of the elements of circulatory function. But the usefulness of these laws is limited by the facts that the HAGEN-POISEUILLE law holds only for (i) rigid tubes, (ii) laminar flow, (iii) homogeneous fluids and (iv) wettable walls, and Ohm's law only for constant unidirectional flow (direct current). By contrast, the *vascular system* consists of *elastic tubes,* within which the flow of the *inhomogeneous fluid* blood under special conditions can be *turbulent,* and in large parts of which flow is *pulsatile* because of the rhythmic activity of the heart. A detailed analysis of circulatory hemodynamics therefore requires complicated methods that allow for these and other factors [7, 18, 34].

18.2   Properties of the Vessel Walls

Structure of the Walls

All blood vessels are lined by an **endothelial layer,** adjacent to the lumen, which usually consists of a single layer of flat cells. The endothelium provides the vessel with a smooth inner surface which, as long as it is intact, *prevents blood clotting.*

In addition to the endothelium, all vessels except the true capillaries comprise varying amounts of (i) **elastic fibers,** (ii) **collagen fibers,** and (iii) **smooth muscle fibers.**

The *elastic fibers,* particularly in the *intima,* form a relatively dense network and can easily be stretched to many times their original length. They exert **elastic tension,** which opposes the tendency of the blood pressure to stretch the vessel, without the expenditure of biochemical energy.

In the *media* and *adventitia* the *collagen fibers* form a network that offers a great deal more **resistance to stretch** than do the elastic fibers. They are relatively loosely embedded in the wall of the vessel and occasionally are folded, so that they begin to exert a counterpressure only after the vessel has been distended to some extent.

The spindle-shaped (ca. 4 μm in diameter and 20 μm long) *smooth muscle cells* are interconnected electrically as well as mechanically to the elastin and collagen networks. Their chief function is to provide active tension in the vessel wall (**vascular tone**), and to regulate the size of the lumen as physiological adjustments require. The majority of blood vessels are innervated by the autonomic nervous system.

Transmural Pressure, Vessel Diameter and Wall Tension

Transmural pressure and vessel diameter. The transmural pressure is the *pressure difference* between the *inside* and the *outside* of the vessel wall ($P_t = P_i - P_o$). Because of the elastic properties of the vessels, increases or decreases in transmural pressure cause increases or decreases in stretching and diameter of the vessels.

In most parts of the body the external pressure, that exerted by the surrounding tissue, is not very high, so that the transmural pressure is effectively the same as the intravascular pressure. But under certain conditions the transmural pressure can be considerably altered by local changes in the extramural pressure, the intravascular pressure remaining constant. In this situation, particularly when the easily deformable veins are affected, the resulting cross-sectional changes can affect flow rate and capacity.

Transmural pressure and wall tension. For the elastic walls of hollow structures, the wall tension associated with the external and internal pressures can be described by **Laplace's law.** This formulation states that under equilibrium conditions the stretching (transmural) pressure across the wall of a spherical body, P_t ($N \cdot m^{-2}$) is equal to the product of wall tension T ($N \cdot m^{-1}$) and the sum of the reciprocals of the two orthogonal radii of curvature of the wall r_1 and r_2:

$$P_t = T \cdot \left(\frac{1}{r_1} + \frac{1}{r_2}\right) \tag{13}$$

In a cylinder – as in the nearly cylindrical blood vessels – one of the two radii of curvature is infinitely

large (i.e., $1/r = 0$) and the other is the radius of the cylinder, so that

$$P_t = \frac{T}{r} \tag{14}$$

In this case the cylinder is considered to have an "infinitely thin wall"; the *tangential tension* (T) here is thus

$$T = P_t \cdot r \, (N \cdot m^{-1}) \tag{15}$$

The tension T_h in a wall with finite thickness h and inner radius r_i is

$$T_h = P_t \cdot \frac{r_i}{h} \, (N \cdot m^{-2}) \tag{16}$$

It is evident in these equations that in blood vessels the *wall tensions developed at a given pressure are smaller, the smaller the radius and/or the thicker the wall* (Fig. 18-5).

Table 18-1 lists the *tangential wall tensions* in the different types of vessels, calculated from the average values found for pressure and inside radius. The tension in the capillaries is about 10,000 times smaller than that in the aorta, and about 1 300 times smaller than that in the vena cava. It is because of this *lower wall tension* in vessels of *small radius* that the capillaries, consisting of only a single cell layer, can withstand the stretching force of intravascular pressure without tearing. Another feature of small vessels is that when the radius of the vessel is reduced by contraction of the smooth musculature, the already *low wall tension is further reduced,* not only by the decrease in radius but also by the simultaneous increase in wall thickness. It is understandable, then, that changes in arteriole diameter can be achieved without difficulty by the smooth musculature of the vessels at all naturally occurring pressures.

Table 18-1. Transmural pressures (P) and tangential wall tensions (T) in various vessels. (From data of BURTON [6] and others)

Vessel	Inside radius (m)	Wall thickness (m)	P (Pa)	P (mm Hg)	T ($N \cdot m^{-1}$)
Aorta	$13 \cdot 10^{-3}$	$2 \cdot 10^{-3}$	13 300	100	173
Arteries	$2 \cdot 10^{-3}$	$1 \cdot 10^{-3}$	12 000	90	24
Arterioles	$60 \cdot 10^{-6}$	$30 \cdot 10^{-6}$	8 000	60	0.480
Capillaries	$4 \cdot 10^{-6}$	$1 \cdot 10^{-6}$	4 000	30	0.016
Venules	$10 \cdot 10^{-6}$	$2 \cdot 10^{-6}$	2 660	20	0.027
Veins	$0.5 \cdot 10^{-3}$	$0.5 \cdot 10^{-3}$	2 000	15	1
Vena cava	$16 \cdot 10^{-3}$	$1.5 \cdot 10^{-3}$	1 330	10	21

Pressure-Volume Relationships

Elastic properties. The degree to which the vessels can be **stretched** is determined both by the numbers of elastic and collagen fibers and by the ratio between the two. For example, in comparable parts of the systemic vascular system the *arteries are 6–10 times less distensible* than the veins. In the pulmonary system, by contrast, the arteries are about half as distensible as the veins, which have about the same properties as the veins in the systemic system.

Volume elasticity coefficient E′. The elastic properties of a hollow structure (or of isolated parts of a vessel) can be expressed by the volume elasticity coefficient E′, the ratio of pressure change (ΔP) to volume change (ΔV):

$$E' = \frac{\Delta P}{\Delta V} \ (Pa \cdot ml^{-1}) \tag{17}$$

When the elastic elements can be *easily* stretched E′ is *small,* and conversely.

The distensibility of a vessel is also expressed as

$$Compliance = \frac{\Delta V}{\Delta P} \tag{18}$$

The *overall distensibility* of a system of hollow elastic elements is computed as the *sum* of the distensibilities of the elements.

The relationships between pressure and volume, in single vessels or parts of vessels as well as in the system as a whole, are represented by *pressure-volume diagrams* (cf. Fig. 18-12).

Volume modulus of elasticity K. The elastic properties *per unit volume* – that is, the amount of pressure change required to produce a *relative* volume change – are described by the volume modulus of elasticity K:

$$K = \frac{\Delta P}{\Delta V} \cdot V = E' \cdot V (Pa) \tag{19}$$

The volume modulus of elasticity is related to density ρ and to the propagation velocity c of the pulse wave (cm $\cdot$ s^{-1}; cf. p. 411) as follows:

$$K = \rho \cdot c^2 \quad or \quad c = \sqrt{\frac{K}{\rho}} \tag{20}$$

This relationship allows one to obtain information about the elasticity of the arterial system relatively easily, by measurement of pulse-wave velocity.

Vascular tone. In many vessels there are a limited number of smooth muscle cells that undergo repeated *spontaneous contractions* (cf. pp. 47 f.). This activity

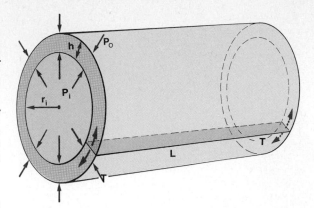

Fig. 18-5. Diagram of the application of Laplace's law to a cylindrical blood vessel. P_i, intravascular pressure; P_o, pressure outside the vessel; r_i, inside radius; h, wall thickness; T, tangential tension in the vessel wall. If a longitudinal cut (L) were made in the vessel wall the edges of the cut would be driven apart with the force T

is *independent of the innervation* of the vessel, so that it proceeds even after denervation of the vascular region. Because of it the walls of the vessels, to different degrees in different regions, have a background tension, the so-called **myogenic basal tone** (Figs. 18-25 and 18-26).

In most vessels under resting conditions this basal tone is *supplemented by contraction* of the smooth musculature of the vessel elicited by *vasoconstrictor impulses* in autonomic nerve fibers; this enhanced tension in the vessel walls is called **resting tone** (Fig. 18-25).

Stress relaxation. When an isolated piece of vessel is suddenly inflated so that its *volume increases,* the intravascular pressure at first rises sharply but then, while the volume remains the same, *declines steadily;* after a few minutes the pressure may be little greater than before the volume change (Fig. 18-6). The reason for this slow decline in pressure is that after the initial elastic distension the tension in the smooth muscle fibers adjusts to the greater stretch, a process called *"stress relaxation"* or *"delayed compliance".* Stress relaxation probably results from a rearrangement of the actin-myosin bonds in the stretched muscle fibers that permits the filaments to slide slowly past one another, so that tension is reduced.

A sudden *volume reduction* has the *opposite* effect (Fig. 18-6). The tension in the smooth muscle fibers, greatly reduced at first, rises over the next few minutes by *"reverse stress relaxation",* and the intravascular pressure rises accordingly.

These reactions are considerably more pronounced in veins than in arteries. Because of this property, together with their larger capacity, the veins can receive

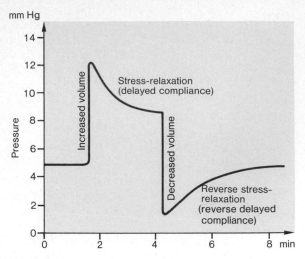

Fig. 18-6. Graph of the pressure changes resulting from step-wise changes in the volume of an isolated segment of vein. (After GUYTON [13])

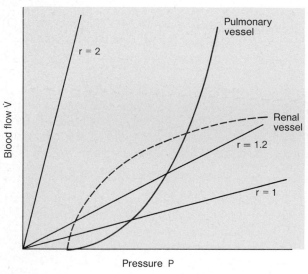

Fig. 18-7. Flow-pressure diagram for various types of vessel. As pressure increases, either passive stretch (pulmonary vessel) or autoregulatory (reactive) contraction (renal vessel) results. Therefore rising pressure produces a greater increase in volume flow in pulmonary-type vessels than in rigid tubes, and a smaller increase in those of the renal type. Below a certain pressure (critical closing pressure) flow through the vessels is arrested. By contrast, the volume flow in rigid tubes *(black lines)* rises linearly, with a slope that increases by factors of 2 and 16 as the radius increases from 1 to 1.2 and 2 μm, respectively

or give up large volumes of blood without maintained changes in intravascular pressure. Stress relaxation and reverse stress relaxation might be an important mechanism for maintenance of *filling pressure* (cf. p. 407) *matched to the needs* of the moment under various conditions (cf. pp. 439 ff.).

Pressure-Volume Flow Relationships in Vessels of Different Types

Passive stretch. Because the vessels are elastic, pressure changes affect volume flow not only directly (by Ohm's Law) but also *indirectly,* by way of changes in lumen diameter due to vessel distensibility.

Volume flow in certain vessels is therefore much *more strongly affected* by pressure increase than would be expected according to the HAGEN-POISEUILLE law for rigid tubes. The blood flow-pressure curves in these cases have continually increasing slope. The **pulmonary vessels** (Fig. 18-7) can be taken as a prototype of the kind of vessel that is distended *passively* by pressure change.

Autoregulatory contraction. In other vessels, however, pressure increases produce progressively *smaller increases in volume flow,* so that the slope of the flow-pressure curve decreases continually (Fig. 18-7). These effects are due to *autoregulatory* (mechanogenic) reactions of the smooth musculature **(Bayliss effect),** which can respond to stretch with an *overshooting* contraction. The autoregulatory contractions are stronger as intravascular pressure increases, so that when pressure rises little or no increase in volume flow is possible. This mechanism *tends to stabilize* the blood supply to a tissue. In certain cases volume flow is uniform over a range of pressures from 120 to 200 mm Hg. The **renal vessels** can be taken as a prototype of this category. This myogenic autoregulation is *independent* of the autonomic innervation and thus is unimpaired by transection of the vasomotor nerves [33].

The relations between pressure and volume flow can be *approximated* by raising ΔP to powers ± 1 in the Hagen-Poiseuille equation. The exponent n is greater than 1 in vessels of the pulmonary type, and smaller than 1 in the renal type. Shape and position of the curves are affected by the state of contraction of the vascular musculature, which depends on neural and metabolic factors, the chemical composition of the blood and so on (cf. pp. 421 ff.).

Critical closing pressure. The flow-pressure curves often do not pass through the origin but rather intersect the abscissa at a positive pressure, the so-called *critical closing pressure* (cf. Fig. 18-7). This pressure *averages 20 mm Hg* during perfusion with blood, but if vascular muscle tone is greatly increased it can rise to 60 mm Hg; it can fall to 1 mm Hg in the absence of tone.

The critical closing pressure is the transmural pressure below which the arterioles *collapse,* because as the radius of the vessel becomes smaller owing to the lower pressure (according to LAPLACE's law) the stretching forces *decrease more* than would correspond to the pressure change. The interruption of flow may well be affected in addition by the *increased viscosity* associated with low rates of flow (cf. p. 400). The critical closing pressure must therefore be subtracted from the measured pressures when the effective arteriovenous pressure difference in the circulatory system is to be determined. It can happen that under pathological conditions the critical closing pressure is so high that circulation in a region is interrupted when excessively high blood pressure is brought down to the normal level.

18.3   Functional Organization of the Vascular System

The Functional Categories of Vessels

With regard to their function, vessels can be classified in 6 categories: 1. (elastic) *"Windkessel" vessels,* 2. *resistance vessels,* 3. *sphincter vessels,* 4. *exchange vessels,* 5. *capacitance vessels* and 6. *shunt vessels* [10].

Windkessel vessels. These are arteries of the *elastic* type, with a relatively large proportion of elastic fibers; among them are the aorta and the pulmonary arteries plus the adjacent parts of the great arteries. In the **aorta** in particular, this large elasticity is responsible for the so-called *Windkessel* (German for "compression chamber") *effect,* by which the phasic systolic inflow of blood is converted to a smoother outflow (for details see p. 410).

The **distal arteries** are constructed of increasing proportions of smooth muscle fibers, and are thus of the muscular type. There is a gradual transition between the two types. In the large arteries the smooth musculature seems to be mainly fibroblastic in function, with a lesser effect on the elastic properties of the vessel wall and practically none on the diameter of the vessel and thus the resistance to flow.

Resistance vessels. The **terminal arteries** and **arterioles,** and to a lesser extent the *capillaries* and *venules,* are resistance vessels. The *greatest resistance to flow* is in the *precapillary* region (terminal arteries and arterioles) – in vessels with relatively small lumens and thick walls having a large muscular component. Changes in the contractile state of the musculature of these vessels cause distinct changes in the diameter of the vessel and thus considerable changes in total *cross-sectional area,* particularly at the level of the numerous arterioles. In view of the effect of cross-sectional area on resistance to flow (cf. p. 401), it is understandable that the activity of the smooth muscles in these vessels is the decisive factor in *regulation of volume flow* within each vascular bed, as well as in the *distribution* of the cardiac output (volume flow

through the overall circulation) among the various organs [10].

The *postcapillary* resistance, by contrast, is determined by the venules (and veins). The ratio between precapillary and postcapillary resistance is significant with regard to the magnitude of the *hydrostatic pressure* in the capillaries and thus also to the conditions of *filtration* and *absorption* (cf. p. 419).

Sphincter vessels. The constriction or dilation of the sphincter vessels, the terminal segments of the precapillary arterioles, determines the *number* of open capillaries and thus the **size of the capillary exchange surface** (cf. Fig. 18-21).

Exchange vessels. These are the **capillaries,** in which the decisive processes of diffusion and filtration occur. The capillaries are *not contractile;* capillary diameter changes passively as a result of pressure changes in the region of the pre- and postcapillary resistance and sphincter vessels.

Capacitance vessels. The main capacitance vessels are the **veins,** which because of their high distensibility can take in or pass on large volumes of blood with no marked effects on the other parameters of the circulation; they can thus act as **blood reservoirs.**

In the closed vascular system, regional changes in capacity are necessarily associated with a **redistribution of the blood volume,** so that changes in the capacity of the veins under the control of the vascular smooth muscles affect the distribution of blood in general and thus, directly or indirectly, influence *overall cardiovascular function.* Moreover, some veins (mainly superficial) at low intravascular pressures are flattened (oval) in cross section, so that a certain extra volume can be accommodated simply by the approach to a cylindrical shape, before the vessel becomes distended at all. This is the major factor contributing to the high **effective** compliance of the veins.

Certain venous regions have anatomical properties that make them particularly capacious storage areas. Chief among these are (i) the **venous vessels of the liver,** (ii) the **large veins in the splanchnic region,** and (iii) the **veins of the subpapillary plexus of the skin;** together, these vessels can hold more than 1 000 ml of blood above their minimal volume. The **pulmonary vessels** too, which are in series with the systemic vessels, can be used for short-term storage or mobilization of fairly large amounts of blood, by alteration of the venous return to the right heart and/or the volume ejected by the left heart (cf. p. 438).

In contrast to other species, *humans have no true blood depot* (such as, for example, the spleen of the

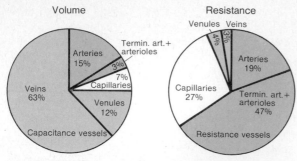

Fig. 18-8. Distribution of blood volume and resistance to flow in the systemic circulation. The "capacitance vessels", with a volume of ca. 75% of the total, account for only about 7% of the resistance; the "resistance vessels", with ca. 66% of the total resistance, contain only about 18% of the volume

Table 18-2. Resistance to flow (R) in the vascular beds of human organs; %CO, percent of cardiac output received by the organ

	%CO	$\dot{V}$ (ml·min^{-1})	$\dot{V}$ (ml·s^{-1})	R (Pa·ml^{-1}·s)
Brain	13	750	13	1025
Coronary vessels	4	250	4	3330
Muscles	21	1200	20	670
Splanchnic region	24	1400	23	580
Kidneys	19	1110	18	740
Skin	9	500	8	1670
Other organs	10	600	10	1330
Total systemic circulation	100	~5800	~96	~140
Pulmonary circulation	100	~5800	~96	~11

Table 18-3. Distribution of blood volume within the circulatory system of a (hypothetical) human[a]

Region	Volume		
	ml	%	%
Heart (diastole)	360	7.2	7.2
Pulmonary circulation			
Arteries	130 ⎫	2.6 ⎫	
Capillaries	110 ⎬ 440	2.2 ⎬	8.8
Veins	200 ⎭	4.0 ⎭	
Systemic circulation			
Aorta and large arteries	300 ⎫	6.0 ⎫ 14	
Small arteries	400	8.0 ⎭	
Capillaries	300 ⎬ 4200	6.0	84.0
Small veins	2300	46.0 ⎫ 64	
Large veins	900 ⎭	18.0 ⎭	
	5000		100.0

[a] 40 years old, weight 75 kg, body surface 1.85 m². (After MIL-NOR [20])

dog), where blood can be stored in special structures and returned to circulation as needed.

Shunt vessels are found in certain tissues in the form of **arteriovenous anastomoses.** When these vessels are open, flow through the capillaries is reduced or entirely interrupted (cf. Fig. 18-21).

Resistances in the Vascular System

Variation in the different vessels. The aorta, the large arteries and the relatively long arterial branches account for about 19% of the total resistance to flow (Fig. 18-8). The contribution of the terminal arteries and arterioles amounts to just under 50%; that is, almost half of the resistance to flow lies in vessels only a few millimeters long. This enormous increase in resistance is due to the relatively small diameter of the terminal arteries and arterioles, which is not fully compensated by the increase in number of parallel passages. The resistance in the capillaries is also considerable, 25% of the total. In the venous region, resistance is highest in the venules (4%), with all the remaining venous vessels contributing only 3%.

Total peripheral resistance. The term total peripheral resistance (TPR) is applied to the overall resistance of the systemic circulation – that is, the resistance of *all the parallel vascular beds* together. With a pressure difference ΔP of ca. 100 mm Hg and a volume flow $\dot{V}$ of ca. 95 ml · s^{-1}, it amounts to about 140 Pa · ml^{-1} · s (Table 18-2). The total peripheral resistance and the *total volume flow* (the cardiac output) together determine the *blood pressure* at any moment.

In the pulmonary vascular system the total resistance, for ΔP of ca. 8 mm Hg and $\dot{V}$ of 95 ml · s^{-1}, is about 11 Pa · ml^{-1} · s.

Because the resistances to flow through each organ system vary (Table 18-2), each receives a different proportion of the cardiac output. *Changes in the resistance* of any of the parallel organ systems, by the processes described on pp. 421ff., in combination with *changes in cardiac output* are the decisive events in *adjustment of volume flow* through the organs to meet their varying demands.

Blood Volume in the Vascular System

Total volume. The magnitude of the intravascular blood volume is an important determinant of the *filling pressure* of the heart during diastole, and thus of the *amount ejected* by the heart.

The **volume of blood** in men is 77 ml/kg body weight, and in women 65 ml/kg (± 10% in both cases); the difference is due chiefly to the larger proportion of fat in the female body. The **total volume** is thus ca. 5.4 liters on the average for men, and 4.5 liters for women.

Considerable *long-term departures* from this average can occur, depending on state of *training* and *climatic and hormonal factors*. For example, the blood volume of some athletes can be greater than 7 000 ml, whereas after a long period of bed rest it can be below normal. In an advanced state of varicosis blood volume can also be increased. *Short-term changes* accompany standing upright and muscular effort.

Distribution of the blood volume. Within the vessels of an adult human (Table 18-3), about 84% of the blood is in the *systemic system,* and the remaining 16% is divided between the *pulmonary system* (barely 9%) and the *heart* (ca. 7%).

The *arteries* in the human systemic circulation contain ca. 18% of the total volume; of this about 3% is in the arterioles (Fig. 18-8). This distribution makes clear that even maximal constriction or dilation of the resistance vessels has practically no effect on the total volume of blood in other parts of the vascular system.

Despite the enormous enlargement in cross section at the level of the *capillaries* these too contain only a relatively small fraction of the total volume, ca. 6%, because they are so short.

The *storage function of the venous system* is reflected in the large proportion of blood it contains – 75% of the regional volume, or 64% of the total volume.

The *resistance vessels,* then, are characterized not only by high resistance to flow but by small capacity, and the *capacitance vessels* by low resistance to flow as well as by large capacity. Only small arteries and veins (0.5–2.0 mm diameter) occupy a special intermediate position; here changes in distension have a marked effect on both capacity and resistance.

Blood volume and mean filling pressure. The mean filling pressure or *static blood pressure* is a measure of the *state of filling* of the vascular system, It corresponds to the pressure that prevails throughout the *entire* cardiovascular system in the absence of heart activity, when the different pressures in the system have equilibrated. The mean filling pressure is ca. 6 mm Hg; it can be affected both by changes in the blood volume and by changes in vascular capacity that result from changes in the state of contraction of the smooth musculature. The mean filling pressure is an important determinant of the *inflow of blood* from the venous system into the *right atrium,* and thus indirectly affects the amount *ejected by the left heart.*

In the "normal" circulation part of the blood volume is *transferred from the venous to the arterial side* by each beat of the heart; the resulting changes in the pressure within the vessels depend on their capacity and distensibility. The pressure in the veins is only

minimally reduced, while that in the arteries undergoes a relatively pronounced *increase* because of the much smaller effective compliance of the arterial system (Fig. 18-10). In this way a dynamic equilibrium is established, in which the regional blood volume depends on the intravascular pressure relative to the distensibility of the vessels concerned.

18.4 The Arterial Part of the Systemic Circulation

As a result of the features just described and the geometry of the vascular system, the various parts of the system exhibit the following distinctive **hemodynamic properties.**

Flow in the Arterial System

Flow pulse. Entry of blood into the ascending aorta because of heart pulsation occurs only during the *ejection period* of the left ventricle. During this so-called *flow pulse* the rate of flow rises sharply after the aortic valves open, reaches a maximum after about the first third of the ejection period, and by the end of the ejection period has returned to zero (Fig. 18-9). From the onset of the *relaxation period* to the closure of the aortic valves there is a brief backflow into the left ventricle. As diastole proceeds the blood in the ascending aorta essentially stands still, until the next ejection period begins.

In the human aorta under resting conditions, with an ejection period lasting 0.25 s and a stroke volume of 70–90 ml, the *peak velocities* far exceed 100 cm $\cdot$ s^{-1} and the *average velocity during the ejection period is ca. 70 cm $\cdot$ s^{-1}*. During fairly long parts of the ejection period Reynolds' number exceeds the critical value; during this time flow in the aorta is *turbulent.* (For measurement techniques see p. 452.)

At increasing distances from the heart the *amplitude* of the flow pulse in the aorta and the large arteries (in contrast to that of the pressure pulse) *decreases continuously*. At the same time, in the thoracic aorta and in the distal arteries, an anterograde *diastolic* flow component develops (Fig. 18-9). The brief retrograde flow at the beginning of the relaxation period can be demonstrated as far away as the femoral (or brachial) artery under resting conditions. But when the cardiac output increases so does the velocity, so that eventually the pulse curve no longer crosses the zero line.

In the region of the *terminal arterial branches* and *arterioles,* there is a progressive transition from pulsatile flow to a more *continuous* flow. However, if the vessels are maximally dilated there can be small fluctua-

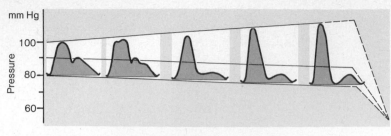

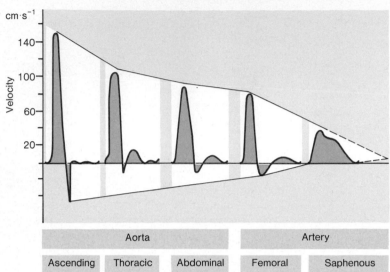

Fig. 18-9. Changes in pressure and flow pulses in the aorta and leg arteries. Note the development of an anterograde flow component during diastole and the rise in systolic pressure at increasing distances from the heart. (After McDonald [18])

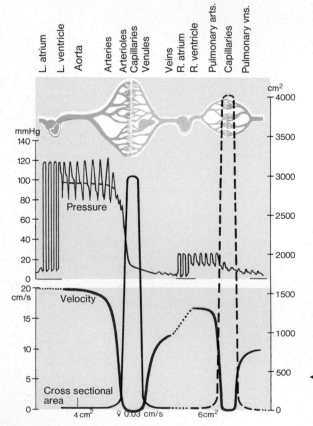

Fig. 18-10. Diagram of the relationships between total cross-sectional area, pressure and mean linear velocity of flow in the cardiovascular system

tions in flow even in the capillaries and the small veins.

Velocity of flow and cross-sectional area. Because flow is discontinuous, especially in the aorta and the great arteries, the *mean flow velocity* here is distinctly lower than that measured during systole. It can be calculated from $\bar{v} = \dot{V}/(\eta \cdot r^2)$. Under resting conditions, with a cardiac output of 96 ml $\cdot$ s^{-1}, the **mean flow velocity** in an aorta with radius 12–13 mm is 21.2 or 18.1 cm $\cdot$ s^{-1}, respectively – that is, about 20 cm $\cdot$ s^{-1} (Fig. 18-10 and Table 18-4). The mean flow velocity can rise to over 100 cm $\cdot$ s^{-1}, however, as a result of increased cardiac output.

Because of the inverse proportionality between mean flow velocity and cross-sectional area, the blood flows **much more slowly** in the distal arteries and especially in the region of the terminal arteries and arterioles; velocity is *lowest in the capillaries,* 0.03 cm $\cdot$ s^{-1} (cf. Fig. 18-10 and Table 18-4). The *transit time* through a capillary of intermediate length (750 µm) is thus ca. *2.5 s.*

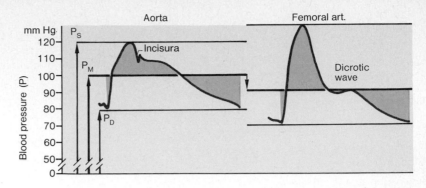

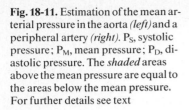

Fig. 18-11. Estimation of the mean arterial pressure in the aorta *(left)* and a peripheral artery *(right)*. P_S, systolic pressure; P_M, mean pressure; P_D, diastolic pressure. The *shaded* areas above the mean pressure are equal to the areas below the mean pressure. For further details see text

Pressures in the Arterial System

Pressure pulse. The inertia of the mass of blood prevents simultaneous acceleration of the entire column of fluid in the vessels by the volume of blood pressed into the aorta during an ejection period. Acceleration extends only to the blood in the basal segment of the ascending aorta; here there is a transient *pressure increase,* the so-called *pressure pulse* (Fig. 18-9). Pressure at first rises sharply together with flow velocity, but then continues to rise more slowly, so that the maximum of the pressure pulse occurs later than that of the flow pulse.

The pressure then falls, but the *end-systolic pressure* reached by the time systole is completed is usually distinctly higher than that at the beginning of the ejection period. The end of systole is marked by a brief, sharp fall in pressure, the so-called **incisura,** brought about by the relaxation of the ventricle and the resulting backflow of blood until the sudden closure of the aortic valve (Fig. 18-11). During the remainder of diastole there is an essentially uniform fall in pressure. Unlike the flow pulse, however, the pressure pulse *does not fall to zero,* because of the *rectifying* effect of the aortic valves, the *elastic* properties of the arteries and the *peripheral resistance;* at the onset of the following systole the pressure is still relatively high (Fig. 18-9 and 18-11).

Systolic, diastolic and mean pressure. The maximum of the pressure-pulse curve during systole is called the systolic blood pressure (P_S), and the minimum during diastole is called the diastolic blood pressure (P_D) (Fig. 18-11). The blood-pressure amplitude (P_S-P_D) is called the *pulse pressure.* The "mean blood pressure" (P_M) or *arterial mean pressure,* which is the driving force for the flow of blood, is defined as the *average in time* of the pressures in a section of vessel; it is determined by integration of the pressure-pulse curve over time. In *peripheral* arteries the mean pressure can be expressed with sufficient accuracy as the arithmetic mean of P_S and P_D, which is equivalent to the diastol-

Table 18-4. Mean flow velocities and mean pressures in the human systemic circulation

	Diameter (mm)	Mean vel. (cm·s⁻¹)	Mean pressure (mm Hg)
Aorta	20–25	20	100
Small arteries		10–15	95
Very small arteries		2	70–80
Arterioles	0.06–0.02	0.2–0.3	35–70
Capillaries			
arterial end			30–35
middle	0.006	0.03	20–25
venous end			15–20
Very small veins		0.5–1.0	10–20
Small to medium veins		1–5	
Large veins	5–10	5–15	15 or less
V. cavae	20–30	10–16	

ic pressure plus half the blood-pressure amplitude ($P_M = P_D + (P_S-P_D)/2$); in *peripheral* arteries it is more nearly equivalent to the diastolic pressure plus one-third of the blood-pressure amplitude ($P_M = P_D + (P_S-P_D)/3$) (for measurement methods cf. pp. 450 ff.).

In the ascending aorta of a young adult the **systolic pressure** is ca. **120 mm Hg** and the **diastolic pressure** is ca. **80 mm Hg.** The **mean arterial pressure** is thus ca. **100 mm Hg.** In the adjacent part of the aorta and in the large arteries the mean pressure decreases only slightly, so that in arteries 3 mm in diameter it is still 95 mm Hg (Table 18-4). Pulse shape and amplitude, however, change conspicuously at increasing distances from the heart. The systolic pressure in the arteries increases progressively, becoming higher than that in the ascending aorta by 20 mm Hg in the femoral artery and by as much as 40 mm Hg in the dorsal artery of the foot (Figs. 18-9 and 18-11). The diastolic pressure, by contrast, decreases slightly, so that there is a distinct increase in pressure amplitude. When pressure measurements in various parts of the arterial system are to be compared, these effects must be kept in mind to avoid misinterpretations.

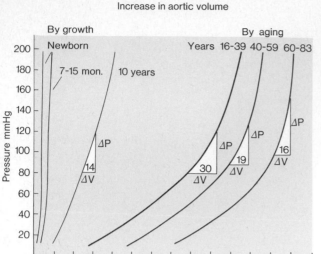

Increase in aortic volume

Fig. 18-12. Pressure-volume curves of the human aorta. During growth the aortic volume increases. Distensibility (compliance) is greatest in the young adult (16–39 years). Further aging is accompanied by expansion of the aorta and reduced compliance. For some of the curves the volume change (ΔV) associated with the normal pressure amplitude (ΔP) for that age is indicated. For further details see text. (After SIMON and MEYER as cited by GAUER[11])

In the *terminal branches* of the arteries and in the *arterioles,* the pressure falls sharply over a distance of a few mm because of the high resistance to flow, reaching 30–35 mm Hg at the end of the arterioles (Fig. 18-10 and Table 18-4). At the same time, the pulsatile pressure fluctuations are much attenuated or disappear altogether.

The changes in the pressure- and flow-pulse curves are due largely to differences in the elastic properties of the various arterial regions, which will now be discussed.

Effects of the Elasticity of Vessels

Volume pulse. The systolic rise in pressure is accompanied by a stretching of the elastic walls of the vessels. The resulting changes in cross-sectional area follow closely the course of the pressure curve, and are called the *cross-sectional* or *volume pulse.*

Windkessel function. As the vessel walls stretch, *kinetic (motion) energy* is changed into *potential (deformation) energy;* at the same time, part of the stroke volume transported into the aorta is *stored* in the stretched segments. In the falling-pressure phase the elastic forces shrink the stretched wall, *emptying* the

store. In this process the potential energy is changed back into kinetic energy and blood is propelled in the direction of least resistance to flow – toward the capillaries, the "drainage channels" of the arterial system (Fig. 18-13). These effects, largely restricted to the elastic vessels (the aorta and arteries of the elastic type), convert the discontinuous systolic flow in the ascending aorta into a *continuous* although not uniform flow in the peripheral arteries. The name *Windkessel* (compression chamber) has been given to these vessels and their function because of the resemblance to the air-filled chambers that similarly affect the velocity and pressure of fluids driven by pistons through systems of pipes.

In a system of *rigid tubes* there would be a much greater rise in pressure during systole, whereas during diastole negative pressures and interruption of flow would occur because of the inertia of the previously accelerated blood. In such a case, at each systole the heart would have to accelerate from zero velocity not just the stroke volume but all the blood in the system. Moreover, a given volume flow could be achieved only by higher flow velocities during systole, which would require a further increase in systolic pressure. Together, the increased mass to be accelerated and the increased flow rate would constitute a considerably greater work load on the heart.

Pressure-volume diagrams. The elastic properties of the Windkessel in humans of different ages are illustrated by the pressure-volume curves in Fig. 18-12. The upward curvature in each case reflects *decreasing distensibility at higher pressures.* On the other hand, until growth is completed distensibility increases as a result of the change in volume (increase in length and diameter); that is, the Windkessel becomes *more compliant* because of the enlargement of the distensible surfaces and the associated (according to Laplace's law) enhanced conversion of pressure into wall tension. As a person grows older the volume contained by the aorta continues to increase, but the distensibility and thus the temporary storage space decrease for anatomical reasons – that is, the Windkessel *hardens* again. As blood pressure increases with age, these effects are enhanced by the shifting of the actual pressures into the steeper ranges of the curves.

The *age-dependent changes* in the PV diagram are probably based on a *passive* expansion under the continual pressure of the blood and on a decreased elasticity in aging tissue; in pathological conditions of high blood pressure these changes are more pronounced. Fig. 18-12 also specifies the *volume change* (of isolated human aortas) associated with the *pulse pressure* for the different age groups. In the "normal" case, the young adult, it amounts to 30 ml, which corresponds to an E′ of 177 Pa · ml^{-1}.

Under the extremely simplified assumption that the end-systolic pressure is uniform in all parts of the arterial system, 40 mm Hg above the diastolic pressure, at the end of systole a volume of 30 ml would be *stored in the aorta.* Estimates indicate that all the other arteries can be stretched only about ⅓ as much as the aorta, so that by extension of the above assumption a further 10 ml would be stored, giving a total storage in the entire arterial system of 40 ml. With a stroke volume of 80 ml, then, 50% of the volume would *flow into the peripheral resistance vessels* during systole, and the remaining 50% would follow during diastole, as the stretched walls of the vessels returned to their original sizes and the blood pressure to its original level.

It follows for the "Windkessel" as a whole that

$$E' = \frac{40\text{mm Hg}}{(30 + 10)\ \text{ml}} = 133\ \text{Pa} \cdot \text{ml}^{-1} \quad (21)$$

That is, **for a volume change of 1 ml in the entire arterial system the pressure changes in the same direction by 1 mm Hg.**

Propagation of the pulse wave. Flow pulse, pressure pulse and volume pulse spread out over the vascular system as a pulse wave, with a particular velocity (Fig. 18-13). In fact the various phenomena do not occur in successive steps, as in the simplified description above, but rather *continuously;* the shifts of blood into and out of storage and thus its movement through various parts of the vascular system occur simultaneously side by side.

Pulse-wave velocity. The rate of propagation of the pulse wave from one site to the next is considerably *higher than the velocity of blood flow.* The pulse wave reaches the arterioles in the feet after 0.2 s, whereas the fluid particles in the ejected blood that gave rise to the wave, with a systolic flow velocity of ca. 70 cm · s^{-1}, by this time have only just arrived in the descending aorta.

The pulse-wave velocity (PWV) depends very much on both the distensibility of the vessels and the ratio of wall thickness to radius; it is higher, the more rigid or the thicker the vessel wall and the smaller the radius. In the *aorta* the PWV is 4–6 m · s^{-1}, whereas in the less elastic *arteries of the muscular type* (such as the radial artery) it is 8–12 m · s^{-1}. As vessel elasticity diminishes with increasing age, the PWV increases. It also increases in cases of high blood pressure, because the increased wall stiffness of the vessels limits the amount by which they can be stretched further. In the more elastic *veins,* by contrast, the PWV is a great deal lower – ca. 1 m · s^{-1} in the vena cava and ca. 2 m · s^{-1} in the large veins of the arm. The pulse-wave velocity therefore reflects the elasticity of the vascular system.

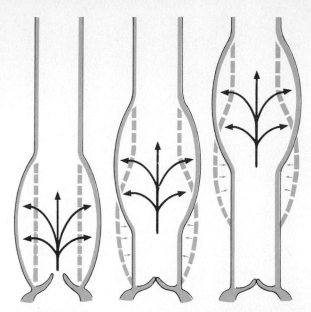

Fig. 18-13. Schematic illustration of "Windkessel function" and the mechanism of pulse-wave propagation. The initial systolic stretching of the aorta next to the heart, so that blood is stored in this region *(left),* is followed by a return to the original dimensions here and a stretching and storage of blood in the next segment *(middle);* this process is repeated in a continual progression along the elastic arteries *(right)*

Wave resistance and reflections of the pulse wave. The changes in form of the pressure waves, including the enhancement of the systolic peak in the peripheral arteries, are based on various mechanisms, the significance of which remains in debate. The most important factors are 1. **wave reflections,** 2. **damping processes** and 3. **frequency-dependent propagation velocities.**

In an elastic system the waves passing over the vessel wall are reflected at all points where the **wave resistance** (Z) increases; this resistance is the ratio of wave pressure ΔP to the wave volume flow $\dot{V}$. Wave resistance is an *impedance,* which in this case is a joint effect of the *inertia* of the fluid and the *elasticity* of the wall; friction is neglected entirely, so that Z must not be confused with frictional resistance.

In the arterial system **positive reflections** appear owing to the increase in wave resistance where vessels divide and to the decreased elasticity in the distal parts of vessels, even in the aorta and the great arteries. But the strongest reflections occur in the *precapillary resistance vessels,* which affect the pulse wave like the closed end of a hose. These reflections are enhanced by vasoconstrictor reactions and attenuated by vasodilation. By *superposition* of the reflected wave on the anterograde wave the systolic pressure wave is enlarged, especially in the peripheral vessels.

The reflected waves, the amplitude of which is only 30–40% of that of the primary waves because of ener-

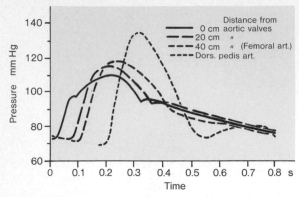

Fig. 18-14. Pulse curves in different parts of the arterial system. The increase in systolic pressure and the dicrotic wave are especially distinct in the dorsal pedis artery. The shift of the curves along the abscissa reflects the time required for spread of the pulse through the arterial system. (After REMINGTON and WOOD, modified by GUYTON [13])

gy loss due to friction, are again reflected but further attenuated at the aortic valves, and so on. In peripheral vessels this multiple reflection produces a distinct diastolic elevation in the descending part of the pulse curve (Figs. 18-11 and 18-14). Because of the high degree of damping, however, it is unlikely that the reflected and re-reflected waves build up actual standing waves in the arterial system.

The **damping** depends on several factors, among them the structure of the wall and the geometry of the vascular system. It is *larger,* the more *compliant* the vessel walls. Increased damping occurs wherever the arteries *divide* or grow narrower (particularly in the region of the resistance vessels). Higher *frequencies* are more strongly damped than lower ones. The early disappearance of the incisura, in the lower end of the abdominal artery (Figs. 18-9 and 18-14), exemplifies this relationship.

The *increase in the systolic peak* in peripheral arteries is reinforced by still another phenomenon; because of the lowered distensibility and the associated increase in pulse-wave velocity at higher pressures (p. 411), the systolic component spreads more rapidly than the diastolic component of the pulse wave, so that the maximum becomes higher and the wavefront steeper. This disparity inevitably changes the shapes of the other parts of the wave as well (cf. Figs. 18-9 and 18-14).

Non-geometrical waves such as the flow- and pressure-pulse curves can be precisely represented by *harmonic (Fourier) analysis.* Here the curves are regarded as the sum of many sinusoidal oscillations at frequencies that are integral multiples of the fundamental frequency. The agreement between recorded and calculated curves increases as the number of computed Fourier series increases; an adequate approximation is achieved with 6–10 Fourier coefficients. In this way the ratio between pulsa-

tile changes in pressure and flow can be used to derive the **impedance of the vascular system** (as done in describing alternating electrical currents) for the entire range of frequencies in the pressure and flow curves. The customary term *resistance to flow* (which, according to Ohm's law for direct currents, is defined as the *ratio of mean pressure difference to mean flow*) denotes only one element in the extremely complex phenomena of frequency-dependent impedance, and thus only approximates the actual situation.

Analysis of Pulse Contour

Pulse qualities. By simple *palpation of the pulse wave* in superficial arteries (for example, the radial artery a little above the wrist) important preliminary information can be obtained about the functional state of the cardiovascular system. The qualities of the pulse so identifiable are as follows:

1. Frequency (frequent or infrequent pulse). In evaluating the frequency of a pulse it should be remembered that the resting rates in children are higher than in adults. After athletic training, people have lower pulse rates than before. Psychological excitation and exercise increase the frequency; in a young adult under maximal load it can rise to 200/min or more.

2. Rhythm (regular or irregular pulse). The pulse rate can fluctuate in the respiratory rhythm, increasing during inspiration and decreasing during expiration. This "respiratory arrhythmia" is physiological and becomes more distinct when breathing is deeper; it occurs more often in younger or "autonomically labile" people. An exact analysis of other forms of arrhythmia (extrasystoles, absolute arrhythmia) can be done only with the ECG.

3. Amplitude (strong or weak pulse). The amplitude of the pulse depends basically on the size of the stroke volume and the amount of blood that flows during diastole. It is also affected by the elasticity of the Windkessel; for a given stroke volume pulse amplitude is small when elasticity is large and vice versa.

4. Sharpness (short or long pulse). The rate of rise of the wave front depends on the speed with which the pressure changes. For a given heart rate, a strong pulse is necessarily accompanied by sharp pressure changes, and a weak pulse by more sluggish pressure changes.

5. Tension (hard or soft pulse). The tension (or hardness) of the pulse is basically determined by the level of the mean arterial pressure, because the amount of pressure required to suppress the pulse wave in the distal parts of the vessel varies with mean pressure. By observation of this quality one can obtain a rough estimate of systolic pressure.

Pulse contour can be more precisely analyzed by relatively simple procedures. The most common clinical method is to place

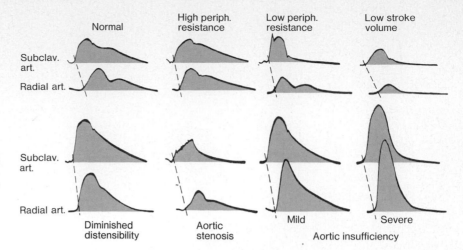

Normal   High periph. resistance   Low periph. resistance   Low stroke volume

Subclav. art.

Radial art.

Subclav. art.

Radial art.

Diminished distensibility   Aortic stenosis   Mild   Severe
Aortic insufficiency

Fig. 18-15. Examples of changes in shape and amplitude of the pulse wave in the radial and sub-clavian arteries accompanying various cardiovascular abnormalities. For details see text. (After WIGGERS [25])

electromechanical transducers on the skin for recording either pressure changes (the **sphygmogram**) or volume changes (the **plethysmogram**) (cf. pp. 452f.).

Pathophysiology. From the shape of the pulse curve one can draw diagnostically useful conclusions about the *hemodynamics* of the arterial system as they are affected by stroke volume, vessel elasticity and peripheral resistance. Fig. 18-15 shows examples of pulse curves from the subclavian and radial arteries. Under *normal conditions* the pulse curve continues to rise during almost the whole of systole. This feature persists with increased *peripheral resistance,* but when peripheral resistance is low an initial peak appears, followed by a lower systolic peak that declines sharply into a relatively flat diastolic slope. When *stroke volume* is small (e. g., after loss of blood) the systolic rise is small, the peak rounded and the diastolic decline slow. Reduced *distensibility* of the aorta (e.g., in arteriosclerosis) produces a rapid and extensive rise; the incisura is high and diastolic decay is gradual. In analogy to the hemodynamic changes, aortic stenosis is accompanied by a sluggish, small systolic rise, whereas with aortic insufficiency the rising phase is steep and the peak high, and in severe forms the incisura is lost. The *time shift* of curves recorded synchronously at two points (cf. the slope of the dashed lines in Fig. 18-15) is an indicator of pulse-wave velocity; velocity is higher the smaller the delay – i.e., the steeper the lines – and vice versa.

18.5   Venous Part of the Systemic Circulation

Pressures and Flow in the Venous System

Pressures in the venous system. Within the venules there is a relatively sharp pressure drop, from 15–20 mm Hg near the capillaries to 12–15 mm Hg in the small veins. In the large extrathoracic veins the pressure amounts to 5–6 mm Hg, and it is still lower at the point where the veins open into the right atrium (cf. Fig. 18-10 and Table 18-4).

Where the *inferior vena cava* passes through the diaphragm the situation is somewhat different, for here the resistance to flow is increased; caudal to the di-

aphragm the pressure is still fairly high, ca. 10 mm Hg, and at the point of passage through it there is a *stepwise* drop to about 4–5 mm Hg.

The pressure in the *right atrium* is identical to the **central venous pressure.** It amounts to 2–4 mm Hg, and under normal conditions exhibits fairly large fluctuations synchronous with respiration and the pulse (cf. p. 439). But because of the subatmospheric pressure in the thorax, −4 to −7 cm H_2O, the *transmural* (effective venous) filling pressure remains positive even when the intravascular pressure is slightly negative [1].

In some parts of the venous system there is a higher resistance to flow, and thus a somewhat *greater pressure gradient,* than in comparable parts of the arerial system. Various factors can account for this situation. For example, some veins under normal conditions are not circular in cross section but more or less *elliptical,* because of "inadequate" filling, and present a correspondingly greater resistance to flow. The veins can also be *compressed* by external pressures at certain points (for example, where the arm veins pass over the first rib) or over whole segments of varying length (for example, by abdominal organs or the intraabdominal pressure).

Venous pulse. The term "venous pulse" refers to the *pressure and volume fluctuations* which appear in veins near the heart due to *retrograde* transmission; these basically reflect the course of pressure change in the right atrium.

The venous pulse is recorded, usually noninvasively, from a recumbent subject with photoelectric devices or sensitive pressure transducers. The following features are characteristic of such measurements. The initial positve wave, the *a-wave,* is elicited by atrial contraction (Fig. 18-16). This is followed after a relatively brief interval by a second positive wave, the *c-wave,* which is caused chiefly by the bulging of the atrioventricular valve into the right atrium during the isovolumetric contraction of the ventricle. The subsequent *sharp fall* (x) is brought about by the shift of the valve plane of the heart toward the apex during the ejection period (p. 417). As the ventricle relaxes the atrioventricular valves at first remain closed, so that there is an initial relatively rapid rise in pressure; when the valves open and blood flows into the ventricle there is a transient pressure drop. This sequence produces a third positive wave, the *v-wave,* fol-

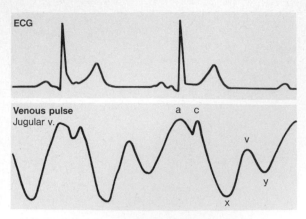

Fig. 18-16. Simultaneous recording of ECG and venous pulse in the jugular vein. For details see text. (After WOOD [26])

lowed by a *depression* (y). As the ventricle continues to fill the pressure rises slowly toward the next a-wave.

Changes in the venous pulse curves can provide useful diagnostic evidence of certain forms of heart disease, such as tricuspid insufficiency.

Velocity of flow in the venous system. In the *venules* and *terminal* veins under normal conditions flow is *continuous,* for the arterial pulsations are not transmitted to the venous side unless the resistance vessels are greatly dilated. In the *main branches* of the veins small flow and pressure *fluctuations* reappear, however, owing to transmission of the pulsation of arteries lying in parallel. In the *great veins,* fluctuations in flow velocity become more pronounced as the right atrium is approached; these are associated with respiration and the heartbeat (cf. pp. 416 f.).

The *mean flow velocity* begins to rise in the venules and vein branches as the total cross-sectional area is progressively reduced, but because the total vein area is larger than that of the arteries at the same level, the blood does not flow as rapidly in the veins as in the arteries. Under resting conditions the mean velocity of flow in the *vena cava* is between 10 and 16 cm $\cdot$ s^{-1}; it can be as high as 50 cm $\cdot$ s^{-1}.

Central Venous Pressure and Venous Return

The central venous pressure, together with the mean filling pressure (p. 407) and the resistance to flow in the vessels, determines the *amount of venous return* to the heart, which under normal conditions critically affects the *stroke volume* [5, 12, 37, 39]. The pressure difference between mean filling pressure and central venous pressure is the pressure gradient for venous return, and under normal conditions it amounts to 2–4 mm Hg. Increases in this gradient (e.g., by increase in blood volume) are accompanied by a larger

venous supply of blood to the heart, whereas increases in resistance to flow reduce venous return.

If the venous return should differ from the output of the right ventricle, adjustment of both quantities begins *automatically.* When the central venous pressure suddenly falls the pressure gradient for venous return is increased, so that venous return becomes greater; at the same time, the stroke volume is reduced because the end-diastolic filling of the heart is less. As a result of the increased venous return accompanying reduced ejection into the arteries, pressure and volume in the right atrium rise. Accordingly, venous return is decreased and stroke volume increases. The effects of sudden increases in central venous pressure are just the reverse. In this way the equilibrium between venous return and cardiac output is restored within 4–6 heartbeats.

In *pathological* states, such as heart failure involving the right heart, central venous pressure can rise to 30 mm Hg, reaching the levels normally prevailing in the capillaries. In these cases the pressure gradient necessary for the blood to flow is maintained by a corresponding increase in pressure in the peripheral veins and capillaries. The central venous pressure is thus determined not only by the supply of venous blood; it is fundamentally affected by the *performance of the right heart.*

Effect of Gravity on the Pressures in the Vascular System

Because the three-dimensional vascular system is within the earth's field of gravity, **hydrostatic pressures** are superimposed on the pressures generated by the heart; the result is an increased pressure proportional to the distance of a vessel below the level of the heart, and a proportional decrease in vessels above the heart.

When a person is *recumbent* the vertical distances within the vascular system, and thus the hydrostatic effects, are negligibly *small* for practical purposes.

Pressures in the erect position. When a person is standing erect the *hydrostatic* pressure in the vessels of the foot (125 cm below the level of the heart) is about 90 mm Hg, so that with a mean *arterial* pressure of 100 mm Hg the total pressure in the arteries of the foot is about 190 mm Hg (Fig. 18-17). In the arteries overlying the brain (ca. 40 cm above the heart) the arterial pressure is reduced by ca. 30 mm Hg, to 70 mm Hg.

The pressure within the *veins* is subject to corresponding hydrostatic effects. Therefore the pressure gradient between arteries and veins, the driving force for the flow of blood, does not vary with height. However, hydrostatic effects cause considerable increases in *transmural* pressure, which are reflected primarily in the state of stretch and thus the capacity of the relatively thin-walled veins. As a result, when a person who has been lying down stands up 400–600 ml of blood accumulates in the leg veins; this amount must of course be withdrawn from other vascular beds, so that these relatively *voluminous shifts of blood* have distinct effects on the function of the circulatory system in general (p. 441).

Hydrostatic indifference level. Because both hydrostatic pressure and the elastic properties of the vessels differ throughout the body, it is not always entirely justified to regard the heart as the reference point for the pressure gradients in the vascular system, or to assume exclusively linear relationships between hydrostatic pressures and arterial or venous pressures.

On the contrary, pressure measurements in the main venous trunk of the human show that the hydrostatic indifference level – the *plane through the vascular system in which pressure does not change with change of position* – is about 5–10 cm beneath the diaphragm [11]. In the thoracic cavity (and thus in the right atrium) and in all the other vessels above this plane, pressure is lower in the erect than in the recumbent position. At the level of the atrium the orthostatic venous pressure is about zero (i. e., equal to the atmospheric pressure), but the subatmospheric intrathoracic pressure counteracts the venous collapse that would be expected in theory, so that the superior vena cava remains open almost as far as the collar bone. In the parts of the body above this level, particularly the region of neck and face, the veins are collapsed, the pressure remaining zero in the entire region. The same is true of the pressures in the arm veins when the arm is raised.

Inside the bony skull, by contrast, the veins are prevented from collapse by their attachment to the tissue. Accordingly, there are "negative" pressures in the venous sinuses of the brain; in the sagittal sinus the pressure is ca. − 10 mm Hg, because of the hydrostatic pressure difference between the top and base of the skull.

Mechanisms to Increase Venous Return

The hydrostatic effects on the vessels below the hydrostatic zero level in the erect human are not the only causes of reduced venous return. Many other factors – for example, exercise and thermal stress – can affect the capacity of the veins. Venous return can be aided or improved by three main mechanisms: 1. the so-called *muscle pump*, 2. the *respiratory pump*, and 3. the *suction effects* of the heart.

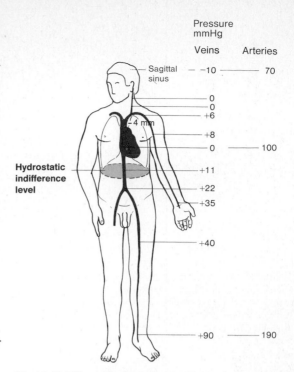

Fig. 18-17. Effect of hydrostatic pressure on the venous and arterial pressures in a quietly standing human

The muscle pump. This "pump" acts by *compression of the veins* within the skeletal musculature when the muscles contract. The blood is squeezed out in the *anterograde* direction, toward the heart, because the venous valves prevent retrograde flow. Each muscle contraction therefore reinforces the normal flow and reduces the volume of blood in the veins of the musculature.

These effects are particularly obvious when the veins are very full, as in the legs of a standing person. At the beginning of each muscle contraction there is a distinct *acceleration* of flow, which had been slowed owing to the increase in cross-sectional area during the standing. The pressure in the veins of the foot, which during quiet standing corresponds to the full hydrostatic pressure of ca. 90 mm Hg, falls to 20–30 mm Hg in the veins emptied by muscle contraction (Fig. 18-18). The *arteriovenous pressure difference,* shifted to a higher level but otherwise unchanged during quiet standing, becomes greater along with the decrease in venous pressure, so that flow through the affected vessel segments is increased. Moreover, the decrease in venous pressure reduces the *capillary filtration pressure,* so that there is less danger of edema (p. 420). The subsequent rise in pressure, as long as the venous valves are intact, results from anterograde filling of the veins from the capillaries rather than from backflow.

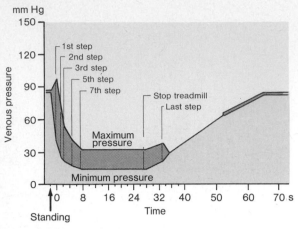

Fig. 18-18. Pressure changes in a dorsal vein of the foot during walking (on a treadmill). When the subject is standing quietly the venous pressure is increased by hydrostatic effects; the pressure drop during walking results from activation of the muscle pump. After a few steps venous pressure stabilizes at a distinctly lower level which is maintained until walking stops. During the subsequent standing period venous pressure returns to the original level. (After POLLACK and WOOD [46])

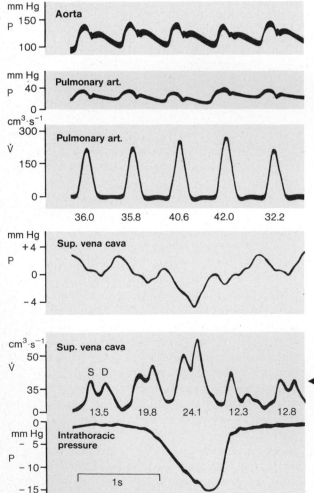

Respiratory pump. During inspiration the progressively reduced intrathoracic pressure causes an increase in the transmural pressure. The associated greater dilation of the intrathoracic vessels results in *decreased resistance to flow* and simultaneously exerts an *effective suction* on the blood in the adjacent vessels. The inspiratory enhancement of venous return is most effective in the region of the *superior vena cava* (Fig. 18-19). On the other hand, depression of the diaphragm during inspiration raises the *intraabdominal pressure,* with the result that the transmural pressures and thus the lumen size – the capacity – of the abdominal vessels decrease. The steeper pressure gradient between intraabdominal and intrathoracic veins *enhances venous influx* into the thorax, whereas a retrograde flow into the lower limbs is prevented by the venous valves. The reverse occurs during *expiration;* the pressure gradient is less steep and flow through the veins from abdomen to thorax is inhibited. The suction-pressure-pump effects on venous flow are considerable – especially when breathing is deep, as during exercise.

As a consequence of the greater filling of the right heart during inspiration, the stroke volume of the *right ventricle* increases by the FRANK-STARLING mechanism (pp. 387 f.). But at the same time the expansion of the lungs enlarges the capacity of the pulmonary vessels, so that venous return to the left heart, and thus the stroke volume of the *left ventricle,* are reduced. During expiration less blood enters the right heart and the stroke volume of the right ventricle decreases, but more blood enters the left heart from the pulmonary vessels and so the stroke volume of the left ventricle increases. That is, the *respiratory excursions bring about phase-shifted changes in the stroke volumes* of the right and left ventricles, by their opposed effects on ventricular filling [29].

With *above-normal pressure* in the lungs, the intrathoracic segments of vessels are compressed, which *inhibits* venous return to the heart. "Valsalva's maneuver" carries this condition to an extreme; the subject takes a deep breath and then strongly contracts the expiratory and abdominal muscles with the glottis closed. The increases in intrathoracic and intraabdominal pressures so produced essentially block venous return; the stroke volume of the right ventricle decreases and the pressure in the

Fig. 18-19. Simultaneous recording of pressure in the aorta, pulmonary artery, and superior vena cava, the intrathoracic pressure, and the volume flow in the pulmonary artery and superior vena cava of a dog with closed thorax. A spontaneous deep inspiration produces a transient pressure drop in the vena cava and flow increase in both vein and artery. Two flow peaks are discernible in the vena cava, associated with the systolic shift of the valve plane of the heart (S) and the early diastolic filling of the ventricle (D). (After BRECHER [5])

peripheral veins rises. On the other hand, blood is pressed out of the pulmonary vessels, so that the stroke volume of the left ventricle and the arterial blood pressure show a transient marked increase, followed by a distinct decline owing to the inadequate venous return.

Suction effects of the heart. In the veins near the heart the velocity of flow is also increased by the heart's own movement. An *initial peak flow* (S in Fig. 18-19) results from the suction exerted when downward displacement of the *valve plane* during the ejection period lowers the pressure in the right atrium and adjacent parts of the venae cavae. A *second flow peak* (D in Fig. 18-19) appears when the blood in the atrium and the venae cavae enters the relaxed ventricle after opening of the *atrioventricular valve.* The two peaks S and D correspond to the x and y valleys in the venous pulse curve (cf. Fig. 18-16).

18.6   Microcirculation

The Terminal Vascular Bed

As the site of exchange between the blood and the interstitial fluid, the *capillaries* are functionally the most important part of the circulatory system. The *venules* also participate in the processes of exchange. Because the venules as well as the arterioles and metarterioles are involved in the regulation of capillary perfusion, the entire network of vessels from arterioles to venules – the so-called *terminal vascular bed (microcirculation)* – must be regarded as a functional unit. The arrangement of this system meets two crucial prerequisites for the various exchange processes, in that within the capillaries the blood makes contact with a very *large surface* for a relatively *long time.*

Size of the capillary exchange surface. Rough estimates of the cross-sectional and surface areas of the capillaries can be obtained as follows. The mean capillary radius is 3 μm, and the mean length is 750 μm. Thus the *cross-sectional area* ($\pi \cdot r^2$) of the average capillary is about 30 μm², and its surface area ($\pi \cdot 2r \cdot l$) is about 14,000 μm². If the part of the venule surface involved in exchange processes is included, the **effective exchange area** amounts to ca. **25,000 μm²** per capillary.

Given a mean flow velocity of ca. 210 mm · s⁻¹ in the aorta and ca. 0.3 mm · s⁻¹ in the capillaries (cf. p. 409) – that is, a ratio of 700:1 – the law of continuity (Equation 2) requires that with an aortic cross-sectional area of 4 cm² the *cross-sectional area of all the perfused capillaries* be 2 800 cm², or *about 3000 cm².*

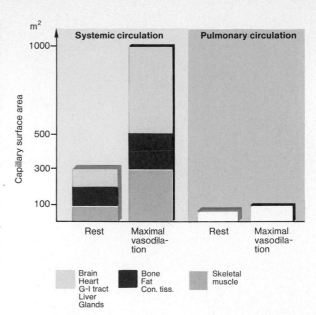

Fig. 18-20. Area of the capillary surface in various organs and in the pulmonary bed, under resting conditions and with maximal vasodilation. (After FOLKOW and NEIL [10])

Under resting conditions, however, blood is actually flowing through only about 25–35% of the capillaries in the body; thus the **cross-sectional area of all capillaries** in the systemic circulation is roughly **11,000 cm²** [10].

Number of capillaries. The above calculations imply that the *total number* of capillaries in the human body is about *40 billion,* so that the **total effective exchange surface** including the venules would be about **1000 m².** Assuming a uniform distribution of the capillaries within the body, this would amount to *600 capillaries per cubic millimeter of tissue, or 1.5 m² of capillary surface per 100 g of tissue.*

Capillary density *varies* considerably, however, in the vascular beds of the different organs. For example, in the myocardium, brain, liver and kidneys there are 2 500–3 000/mm³, in "phasic" units of the skeletal musculature 300–400/mm³, and in "tonic" units approximately 1 000/mm³. Bone, fat and connective tissue also have a relatively low density of capillaries. Another, independent variable is the *ratio of perfused to non-perfused capillaries* under resting conditions; again, the differences are considerable. Therefore the expansion of the exchange-surface area that can be achieved with maximal vasodilation is very different in the different organs. These relationships are summarized in Fig. 18-20; but remember that here, as in the above calculations, some of the numbers are simply rough estimates. Increase in number of "active" (i.e., perfused) capillaries is important in that it *short-*

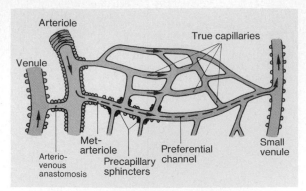

Fig. 18-21. Schematic drawing of the terminal vascular bed. The vessels branching off from the arterioles are metarterioles, which are somewhat larger in diameter than the capillaries and constitute the preferential channel for blood flow. Near their origins the metarteriole walls contain smooth muscle fibers; the smooth muscle fibers found where the capillaries branch off from the metarterioles are the precapillary sphincters. The arteriovenous anastomoses also comprise smooth muscle fibers

ens the diffusion path to the cells and thus improves the blood supply to the tissue.

Structure of the terminal bed. In most cases the "true" capillaries *do not directly join* arterioles to venules (Fig. 18-21). Often they branch off at right angles from **metarterioles,** so-called "preferential channels" with walls containing smooth muscle fibers in diminishing numbers from proximal to distal; these vessels eventually merge with the non-contractile venules. Where the capillaries leave the metarterioles smooth muscle fibers are arranged to form so-called **precapillary sphincters;** other than these, there are *no contractile elements* in the capillaries. The state of contraction of the precapillary sphincters determines the fraction of blood that flows through the true capillaries, whereas the total volume flow through metarterioles and capillaries is set by the state of contraction of the smooth muscle fibers of the arterioles.

The *ratio of metarterioles to true capillaries* varies in the different organs. In skeletal muscle, with its widely fluctuating metabolic requirements, it is 1:8 to 1:10; in the mesenteric circulation, where metabolism is fairly uniform, it is about 1:2 to 1:3. In the human nail bed the capillaries are direct continuations of the metarterioles, giving a ratio of 1:1.

Another special feature is the presence of **arteriovenous anastomoses** (Fig. 18-21), which provide *direct* communication between small arteries and small veins, or arterioles and venules. Their walls are highly muscular. Arteriovenous anastomoses can be found in many tissues, and are especially common in the acral regions of the skin (fingers, toes, earlobes), where they function in thermoregulation (p. 539).

Capillary Exchanges

Ultrastructure of the capillary walls. Three types of capillary can be distinguished on the basis of fine structure: 1. Capillaries with *uninterrupted* membranes. 2. Capillaries with *fenestrated* membranes. 3. Capillaries with *discontinuous* membranes.

The walls of *Type 1* capillaries consist of a continuous layer of endothelial cells having membranes with a large number of minute (4–5 nm) pores. This form is widespread; it is found in both striated and smooth muscle, in adipose and connective tissue, and in the pulmonary circulation. Capillaries of *Type 2* have fenestrations within the cells, up to 0.1 μm in diameter, which are frequently closed by a very thin membrane; such capillaries are found in the glomeruli of the kidneys and in the intestinal mucosa. In *Type 3* the wall is interrupted by relatively large intercellular spaces through which fluid and blood cells can pass. This form is found in the bone marrow, in the sinusoids of the liver and in the spleen.

Exchange by diffusion. In the exchange of fluid and materials between blood and interstitial space, diffusion processes in both directions play by far the greatest role. The *rate of diffusion* here is so high that during a single capillary passage the water in the plasma exchanges 40 times with the water in the interstitium, so that there is a continual mixing of plasma water and interstitial fluid. The numbers of molecules diffusing outward and inward are very nearly the same, so that the volume of plasma in the capillary remains practically constant. The rate of diffusion through the entire capillary surface of the body is about *60 l/min,* or ca. *85,000 l/day.*

Water-soluble substances, such as Na^+, Cl^-, glucose and so on, diffuse entirely through the *water-filled pores.* The permeability to the individual molecules depends on the relative sizes of molecule and pore; small molecules like H_2O and NaCl diffuse more readily than large molecules like glucose or albumins. The relative permeability, with water = 1, is 0.6 for glucose and < 0.0001 for albumin molecules. Because the capillary membrane is so impermeable to albumin, there is a distinct and functionally important difference in the concentration of this substance in plasma and interstitial fluid (see below).

Large molecules unable to pass through the "sieve" of the pores can move through the capillary wall by *pinocytosis* – that is, invagination of the cell membrane to surround the molecule in a vacuole, with the reverse process (emiocytosis) on the other side of the cell.

Lipid-soluble substances such as alcohol, as well as O_2 and CO_2, can *diffuse freely.* Because this diffusion takes place across the entire capillary membrane, the rates of transport of lipid-soluble substances are very much greater than those of water-soluble substances [17].

Exchange by filtration. A second mechanism for exchange between the intravascular and interstitial spaces involves **filtration and reabsorption processes** in the terminal vascular bed. Under normal conditions, according to the classical *theory of Starling,* a **dynamic equilibrium** generally prevails between the amounts of fluid filtered out of the capillaries at their arterial ends and reabsorbed at the venous ends or carried away in the lymph vessels [31, 54].

However, if this *equilibrium is upset* there are (relatively rapid) volume shifts between intravascular and interstitial space; these can crucially affect circulatory function in several ways, particularly in view of the necessity of maintaining an adequate volume of intravascular fluid.

Filtration and reabsorption in the capillaries are basically determined by the **hydrostatic pressure** in the **capillaries** (P_C) and in the **interstitial fluid** (P_{IF}), the **colloid osmotic pressure** in the **plasma** (π_C) and in the **interstitial fluid** (π_{IF}), and a **filtration coefficient** (K). Movement of fluid out of the capillaries into the interstitial space is brought about by P_C and π_{IF}, and that in the reverse direction by π_C and P_{IF}. The filtration coefficient K corresponds to the permeability of the capillary wall to isotonic fluids in ml fluid per mm Hg pressure in 100 g tissue per minute (at 37° C). The volume filtered per minute ($\dot{V}$) can thus be computed as

$$\dot{V} = (P_C + \pi_{IF} - P_{IF} - \pi_C) \cdot K \qquad (22)$$

$\dot{V}$ is positive for filtration, and negative for reabsorption.

The pressure within single capillaries has been measured directly; with 30–35 mm Hg at the beginning of the capillary, and 15–20 mm Hg at the end, the **mean pressure** is about **25 mm Hg.** In relatively large capillary beds the *functional mean capillary pressure* is probably somewhat lower, because of the rhythmic changes in resistance to flow produced by vasomotion in the precapillary vessels (p. 423).

It is impossible to measure the *interstitial-fluid pressure* directly, because the interstitial gaps are at most 1 µm wide. The methodologically unsatisfactory indirect measurements of interstitial pressure give values between +10 mm Hg and −9 mm Hg; pressures near *zero to slightly positive* (+3 mm Hg) are usually regarded as normal [35].

A notable feature of the extracellular space is that regardless of the uncertainty as to absolute pressures, pressure changes within the normal range alter the interstitial fluid volume only slightly; that is, the *distensibility of the interstitial space ($\Delta V / \Delta P$) is low*. But as interstitial pressure increases a point is rather abruptly passed beyond which distensibility becomes decidedly greater; the result is a marked increase in interstitial fluid volume and the onset of *edema* (abnormally large amounts of interstitial fluid). Edema usually does not become noticeable until the interstitial volume becomes about 30% greater than normal.

The *colloid osmotic pressure* of the plasma amounts to about *25 mm Hg;* it is produced by the plasma proteins, present in a concentration of ca. 73 g/l. The capillary walls are not entirely impermeable to protein, as once was thought. Depending on their ultrastructure (see above), the capillaries release varying amounts of protein into the interstitial fluid of the different organs, which are transported away in the lymph vessels. The *average lymph protein concentration* is thus an indicator of *capillary permeability;* in the liver 1 l lymph contains 60 g protein, in the heart 30 g, in the skin 10 g and in the musculature 20 g.

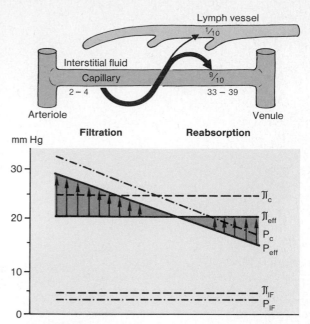

Fig. 18-22. Schematic illustration of the movement of fluid between a blood capillary and the interstitial space in the musculature. P_C, capillary pressure; P_{IF}, pressure in the interstitial space; π_C, π_{IF}, colloid osmotic pressure in the capillary and interstitial space; P_{eff}, effective transmural filtration pressure; π_{eff}, effective colloid osmotic pressure. As a simplification, π_C and π_{IF} are shown as constant over the entire length of the capillary. The whole numbers in the upper drawing indicate the increase in average protein concentration from the arterial to the venous end, and the fractions show the proportions of capillary reabsorption and the transport of interstitial fluid through the lymph vessels under normal conditions

Within a single capillary, protein permeability increases from the arterial to the venous end, for both the surface area and the number of large pores increase in the venous region. This difference is reflected, for example, in the indirectly measured protein concentration in the interstitial fluid of skeletal muscle, which rises from about 3 g/l around the arterial part of the capillaries to just under 40 g/l around the venous part. An acceptable estimate of the *mean protein concentration* of the interstitial fluid of the whole organism is 18–20 g/l; this exerts a *colloid osmotic pressure of* about **4.5 mm Hg** (Fig. 18-22).

Equilibrium between intra- and extravascular fluids. From the data given above it is possible to derive a highly simplified balance for the *movement of fluid* between capillaries and interstitial space.

At the *arterial* end of the capillary there is an outward pressure of 37 mm Hg (P_C = 32.5 mm Hg + π_{IF} = 4.5 mm Hg), which is opposed by an inward pressure of 28 mm Hg (π_C = 25 mm Hg + P_{IF} = 3 mm Hg). The **effective filtration pressure** is thus **9 mm Hg** (Fig. 18-22).

At the *venous* end the outward pressure is 22 mm Hg (P_C = 17.5 mm Hg + P_{IF} = 4.5 mm Hg) while the inward pressure is unchanged, 28 mm Hg; thus the **effective reabsorption pressure** is **6 mm Hg.**

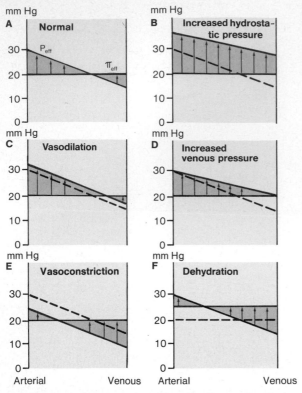

Fig. 18-23 A-F. Diagrams of capillary filtration and reabsorption under various physiological and pathological conditions. Depending on the magnitudes of P_{eff} and π_{eff}, the relative filtration-reabsorption equilibrium in the capillaries is shifted toward increased filtration (**B, C, D**) or increased reabsorption (**E, F**)

Under the simplifying assumption that pressure falls off linearly and the other factors are constant, the net outward pressure under normal conditions is the *mean filtration pressure* of 29.5 mm Hg ($P_C = 25$ mm Hg + $\pi_{IF} = 4.5$ mm Hg), and the net inward pressure is the *mean reabsorption pressure* of 28 mm Hg ($\pi_C = 25$ mm Hg + $P_{IF} = 3$ mm Hg). That is, filtration slightly exceeds reabsorption.

The *effective filtration pressure* causes an average of ca. 0.5% of the volume of plasma flowing through the capillaries to enter the interstitial space in the arterial segment. Because the *effective reabsorption pressure* is slightly less, only ca. 90% of this is reabsorbed in the venous segment, the remaining 10% being removed from the interstitial space in the lymph vessels (Fig. 18-22).

The average **filtration rate of all the capillaries** in the body is thus ca. **14 ml · min^{-1} or 20 l per 24 h,** and the reabsorption rate is ca. **12.5 ml · min^{-1} or 18 l per 24 h;** two liters per day are carried away by the lymph vessels.

This relative equilibrium between filtration and reabsorption in the capillaries must necessarily be upset if

one of the factors involved should change. The *hydrostatic capillary pressure* (P_C) plays a special role in this regard. Increases in P_C shift the filtration-reabsorption conditions in the direction of enhanced filtration, whereas decreases in P_C enhance reabsorption. The level of the hydrostatic pressure in the capillaries is greatly affected by the momentary *precapillary resistance,* which also influences the **number of perfused capillaries** and thus the **area of the exchange surface** in a vascular region. But changes in the postcapillary resistance, which under resting conditions is about ¼ of the precapillary resistance, also affect hydrostatic pressure and thus the filtration-reabsorption ratio in the capillaries. *Vasomotor control* of these processes, for regulation of *intravascular plasma volume* (pp. 431 ff.), is made possible by the innervation of the precapillary vessels and, to a lesser extent, the postcapillary vessels.

These relationships explain the occurence of *enhanced filtration* in conditions so diverse as general hypertension, dilation of the resistance vessels in muscular work, erect posture, increased blood volume owing to transfusion, and isolated pressure increases on the venous side (e. g., in cardiac insufficiency), as well as the reverse effect – *enhanced reabsorption* due to general hypotension, constriction of the resistance vessels, blood loss etc. (cf. Fig. 18-23). Decreases in the *colloid osmotic pressure* of the plasma (for example, in protein deficiency) or an accumulation of *osmotically active substances in the interstitial fluid* also give rise to enhanced filtration, while increases in the colloid osmotic pressure of the plasma enhance reabsorption.

A greater displacement of fluid into the interstitial space can also be due to *increased capillary permeability;* this is induced, for example, by histamine and related substances, kinins etc. released in allergic reactions, inflammation, burns and wounds (cf. p. 446)[45]. Given the many physiological conditions under which strong outward forces increase filtration over the entire length of the capillary, one would expect excessive accumulation of interstitial fluid in the form of **edema** to occur more often than it actually does. The rarity of edema is due in part to the *slight distensibility* of the interstitial space within a relatively large range of pressures, which tends to prevent the accumulation of fluid. On the other hand, as soon as the interstitial fluid begins to increase as a result of inadequate capillary reabsorption it is *more rapidly removed* by the lymphatic system (see below). The associated increased loss of protein reduces the colloid osmotic pressure, which in turn inhibits the accumulation of fluid in the interstitial space and thus contributes to the maintenance of equilibrium between the intravascular and interstitial fluid volumes.

18.7 The Lymphatic System

The lymph vessels constitute a *supplementary drainage system* through which the interstitial fluid is returned to the blood vascular system.

Structure of the lymphatic system. All tissues except the superficial layers of the skin, the CNS and the bones are penetrated by an enormous number of *lymph capillaries* arranged in an extremely fine-meshed network. Unlike the blood capillaries, these are closed at one end. At their open ends the lymph capillaries join to form *larger lymph vessels* which empty into the venous system at a number of points, chiefly by way of the thoracic duct and the right lymphatic duct. The walls of the lymph capillaries are composed of a single-layered endothelium and are easily permeable to electrolyte solutions, sugar, fats and proteins. The walls of the larger lymph vessels have smooth muscle fibers and valves (like those in the veins). At various points along the larger lymph vessels are *lymph nodes,* which act as filters and retain the coarser elements in the lymph.

Composition and amount of lymph. Lymph consists of interstitial fluid. The *average protein content* is 20 g/l, though there are considerable regional differences associated with the differences in permeability of the blood capillaries (60 g/l in the liver, 30–40 g/l in the intestinal tract; cf. p. 419). The lymph vessels are one of the main channels by which *absorbed substances,* particularly fats, are *transported away* from the gastrointestinal tract [54].

Under normal conditions **lymph accumulates** at a rate of ca. **2 l in 24 h,** as the 10% of the capillary filtrate that is not reabsorbed. The **mean velocity of flow** in the lymph vessels, accordingly, is very slow. In those lymph vessels with smooth muscle fibers transport occurs by *rhythmic contractions* of the smooth musculature. Backflow of lymph is prevented by the valves. In the lymph capillaries and vessels of the skeletal musculature propulsion of lymph is also assisted by the so-called *lymphatic pump,* an effect of muscle contraction analogous to that by which blood flow through the veins is facilitated; transient pressure in-

creases in their surroundings compress the lymph vessels and expel the lymph. During muscular work the volume flow of lymph can exceed the resting level by a *factor of 10–15.*

The primary function of the lymphatic system is thus to *remove from the interstitial space* those proteins and other substances that cannot be reabsorbed into the blood capillaries. A second very important function is that of **drainage,** to counteract the accumulation of fluid in the interstitial space when capillary filtration increases (p. 420). When lymph vessels are tied off (during surgery) or blocked (owing to inflammation or other causes) the tissues distal to the obstruction can exhibit marked *regional edema* (so called lymphatic edema).

18.8 Regulation of Regional (Local) Blood Flow

Basic Features of Regional Regulation

The perfusion of organs under resting conditions. The distribution of the cardiac output among the vascular beds of various human organs under resting conditions is summarized in Table 18-5. Because it is technically difficult to measure organ blood flow in humans, these data are only approximate. Comparison between flow rate and O_2 uptake shows that *organs with more active metabolism are perfused more rapidly,* although – as the percentage data for the two variables indicate – there is no fixed relation between perfusion rate and O_2 consumption.

Adjustment of the regional blood supply. Local volume flow is adjusted to functional requirements chiefly by changes in *resistance to flow* accompanying alteration of the vascular cross-sectional area; be-

Table 18-5. Perfusion rate and O_2 uptake in various organs of a human[a] under resting conditions

Vascular region	Blood flow		O_2 uptake		Weight	
	ml/min	% of total	ml/min	% of total	g	% of total
Splanchnic	1400	24	58	25	2800	4.0
Kidneys	1100	19	16	7	300	0.4
Brain	750	13	46	20	1500	2.0
Heart	250	4	27	11	300	0.4
Skeletal muscle	1200	21	70	30	30000	43.0
Skin	500	9	5	2	5000	7.0
Other organs	600	10	12	5	30100	43.2
	5800	100	234	100	70000	100.0

[a] Weight 70 kg, body surface 1.7 m². (After WADE and BISHOP [24])

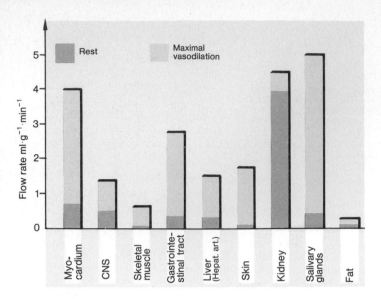

Fig. 18-24. Volume flow in the vascular beds of different organs under resting conditions *(red)* and with maximal vasodilation *(light red).* The data were computed for a normal adult human with a body weight of 70 kg. The volume flow per g tissue also indicates the relative resistance to flow in the individual organ systems. (Modified after MELLANDER and JOHANSSON as cited in [23])

cause resistance varies as the 4th power of the radius, this is a considerably more effective factor than pressure change (cf. p. 401).

The theoretical amount by which flow rate can be increased varies from organ to organ (Fig. 18-24). In organs with widely *fluctuating* functional requirements (skeletal musculature, gastrointestinal tract, liver and skin) blood flow can be changed over the widest range. By contrast, the rate of flow through vital organs such as the brain and kidneys, with requirements that are continually high with relatively *little variation,* is kept nearly constant by special regulatory mechanisms; within limits it is very little affected by even pronounced changes in arterial pressure and cardiac output [4, 16, 22]. (For details of the perfusion of individual organs see pp. 446 ff.)

The reactions by which the vessels adjust their output are based in part on *local mechanisms* [52] and in part on *humoral and neural factors* [44]. The relative effects of these different components on the smooth musculature of the vessels vary in the different organs. Often several factors are involved simultaneously, with a *synergistic* (but sometimes *antagonistic*) action on vascular tone.

In Fig. 18-25, the effects of the most important mechanisms on the vessels in skeletal muscle, skin and the splanchnic system are diagrammed; these will be discussed in the following sections.

Local Regulating Mechanisms

A number of substances which, like O_2, are required for cellular metabolism or are produced as metabolites have a *direct* effect on the state of contraction of the vascular musculature. Various processes are involved, none of which is understood; together they constitute the **metabolic autoregulation of peripheral blood flow.** The very great functional significance of these autoregulatory reactions lies in the *local adjustment of volume flow* in individual vascular beds to the momentary nutritional requirements of the tissue; here the metabolically elicited dilator responses dominate and in some cases completely overcome neurogenic constrictor effects.

O_2 deficiency. *Vasodilation* is elicited by decrease in the O_2 partial pressure of the blood. The changes in regional flow rate associated with altered local metabolism are thought to be based on the fact that *arteriolar O_2 partial pressure decreases when metabolism is accelerated,* and vice versa. This mechanism would require that oxygen diffuse within the arteriole (as has been confirmed in experiments) and that the reaction be related to *changes in the O_2 gradient* along its length.

Metabolites. *Local increases in CO_2 partial pressure and/or H^+ concentration* also cause vasodilation. Of the other metabolites produced in greater amounts during exercise, *lactic acid* exerts a dilator action, not directly but by way of the pH shift it causes. *Pyruvate* is a weak vasodilator, and *ATP, ADP, AMP and adenosine* are strong vasodilators. The actions of these substances on the vessels, however, do not suffice to explain the extreme vasodilation associated with muscular work (Fig. 18-25). Other metabolic products are probably also involved. Further factors that have been proposed as vasomotor agents include changes in the extracellular concentration of osmoti-

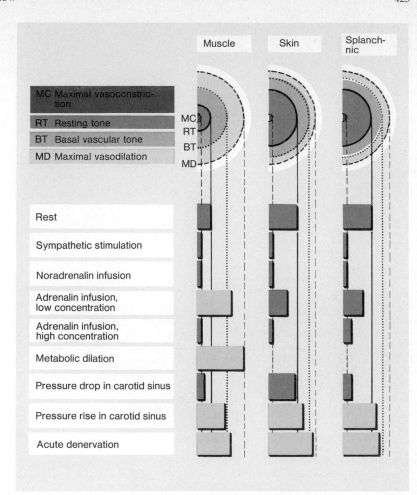

Fig. 18-25. Schematic illustration of the vascular tone in muscle, cutaneous and splanchnic vessels under various physiological and pathological conditions. The proportions of the individual components of vascular tone vary in the different organs, so that a given stimulus elicits quantitatively varying responses

cally effective substances, potassium in particular, owing to their more rapid release from working musculature (cf. p. 516) [50].

Changes in vascular diameter by metabolism-related processes can be elicited *directly by diffusion* of the substances, for the arterioles lie within the active tissue and thus in the immediate vicinity of the capillaries.

Reactive hyperemia. When the blood supply to a muscle is interrupted or restricted experimentally, its restoration is accompanied by an *overshooting* response (reactive hyperemia), the extent of which depends on the *metabolic rate* and the *duration* of the interruption. Reactive hyperemia is probably caused by the same mechanisms as metabolic dilation. When venous blood is experimentally transferred from the working or ischemic musculature into vessels supplying resting musculature, dilation occurs; thus it can be regarded as proven that the eliciting agents are *humoral* in nature.

Myogenic effects. The ability of many vessels to maintain largely *constant volume flow* by smooth-muscle contraction when pressure increases and relaxation when pressure decreases (p. 404), independent of the level of pressure, can be regarded as a form of **myogenic (mechanogenic) autoregulation.** This ability is especially well developed in the renal vessels, but it is also found in those of the brain, heart, liver, intestines and skeletal muscles. No myogenic responses have been observed in the cutaneous circulation [3, 33].

Intrinsic vasomotion. One myogenic effect that does not serve to adjust blood flow to momentary requirements is the rhythmic vasomotion [40] observable in the *arterioles, metarterioles* and *precapillary sphincters.* These contractions of the smooth muscle fibers, and the associated changes in resistance to flow, give rise to *rhythmic fluctuations in the rate of flow* through the parts of the vessels concerned. The frequency and intensity of these processes are variable. The effects are independent of the autonomic innervation, and arise from the tendency of the smooth muscle fibers to *autorhythmicity* (cf. p. 48).

Neural Regulation

The neural vasomotor control mechanism is mediated by the *autonomic nervous system,* predominantly by way of sympathetic fibers, though parasympathet-

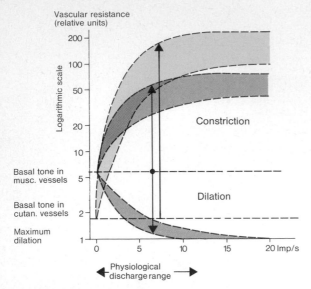

Fig. 18-26. Graph showing the vasomotor effects of efferent impulses on vessels in muscle *(red)* and skin *(black)* of the cat. After transection of the abdominal sympathetic trunk electrical stimulation distal to the cut causes weaker vasoconstriction in the muscle vessels, with their higher basal tone, than in the cutaneous vessels. Vasomotor control of the muscle vessels also involves cholinergic sympathetic dilator fibers. The vasomotor effects of the two systems can be distinguished by appropriate pharmacological blockade; dihydroergotamine blocks the vasoconstrictor action of the adrenergic fibers, and atropine blocks the vasodilator action of the cholinergic fibers. (Modified after CELANDER and FOLKOW as cited in [10])

ic fibers are also involved in some responses. *All the blood vessels except the capillaries are innervated,* but the density and function of the innervation vary widely in different organs and in different parts of the vascular system.

In most *sympathetic* nerves the neuromuscular transmitter substance released by the postganglionic fibers is noradrenalin *(adrenergic fibers).* Cholinergic sympathetic fibers are discussed on p. 425.

Sympathetic adrenergic vasoconstrictor fibers. Efferent nerves in which increased impulse frequency raises the active tension of the vessel musculature are called **vasoconstrictor nerves.** These belong to the sympathetic part of the autonomic nervous system. Details of their site of origin and arrangement in the body are given in Chapter 6.

The small arteries and arterioles of the *skin, skeletal musculature, kidneys* and *splanchnic region* receive a dense innervation, whereas the innervation of those in the *brain* is relatively sparse. The density of innervation of the veins is much lower, on the whole, but otherwise generally corresponds to that of the arteries. Neuromuscular transmission is mediated by *noradrenalin,* which in all cases elicits constriction of the muscles.

The degree of vascular smooth-muscle contraction depends directly on the frequency of the efferent impulses. The **resting tone** of the vessels (p. 403) is maintained by the **continual (tonic) discharge** of 1–3 impulses/s. *Maximal* vasoconstrictor effects are elicited by only ca. *10 imp/s* (Fig. 18-26). Thus increases in impulse frequency produce vasoconstriction, and decreases produce vasodilation; the latter responses are limited by the *basal tone* that prevails when the vasoconstrictor fibers are silent or have been transected (see below). Because of the background discharge of these fibers *"vasomotor tone",* the neurally controlled state of contraction of the vascular muscles, can be varied in both directions to produce *both vasoconstriction and* – without the need for special fibers – *vasodilation.*

In the absence of vasoconstrictor impulses, resistance to flow is determined by the varying levels of **basal tone** in the different vascular regions. Basal tone, and thus resistance, is smaller in the cutaneous than in the muscle vessels (Figs. 18-25 and 18-26). When the constrictor nerve fibers are stimulated the responses of the two regions are fundamentally the same, but *for a given stimulus frequency the cutaneous vessels constrict more strongly* (Fig. 18-26). The *resistance to flow* in the vessels of the skin can thus be varied over a much wider range than that in the muscles by changes in the discharge rate of the vasoconstrictor fibers. This limitation in the muscle vessels is compensated to a great extent by *vasodilator responses* (Fig. 18-26), the mechanism of which is still in debate. The possible causes under discussion include excitation of *sympathetic cholinergic* dilator fibers (see below) and excitation of *β-receptors* in the muscle vessels by catecholamine (p. 425).

The significance of *tonic* activity in the vasoconstrictor nerves (resting tone) with regard to circulatory function is evident, for example, in the fact that when it is eliminated by *spinal anesthesia* or *ganglion-blocking drugs* the resulting vasodilation causes the mean blood pressure to fall to 40–60 mm Hg – a pressure that no longer guarantees an adequate blood supply to the organs (paralytic blood pressure; cf. spinal shock, p. 446).

Surgical transection of the sympathetic nerves *(sympathectomy)* also produces vasodilation in the denervated regions, the vessel diameter thereafter being determined entirely by the *basal tone* (Fig. 18-25). This initially low tone begins to rise a few days after sympathectomy, and after a few weeks can practically regain the pre-operational level even though the fibers have not regenerated. The basal tone itself has increased, probably because of a *hypersensitivity* of the vessel musculature to *catecholamines* and other vasoactive substances which develops after denervation and leads to an increase in the contraction of the muscles.

Sympathetic vasodilator fibers. In various species (among them the dog and cat) there is a special system originating in the cortex (p. 135) which innervates only the *precapillary vessels in the skeletal musculature.* Under resting conditions these fibers exhibit no activity. In contrast to metabolic dilation (p. 422), the vessels that dilate to give increased flow when these fibers are stimulated are probably not the true capillaries, but rather the *arteriovenous anastomoses* and *metarterioles* or even the larger arteries. This system is activated by emotional reactions of alarm, defense, fear or rage (p.135) [28]. If muscular activity should ensue the initial vasodilation in the working musculature is supplemented or replaced by dilator effects of *metabolic origin* (p.448). These sympathetic cholinergic dilator fibers have not as yet been shown to exist in humans, although dilation of the muscle vessels of humans anticipating activity has been observed (cf. pp.442 f.).

Parasympathetic cholinergic vasodilator fibers. The vessels in the *external genitalia* are innervated by parasympathetic cholinergic fibers which are activated during sexual excitation and induce marked vasodilation and correspondingly increased blood flow through the organs. Cholinergic dilator fibers also innervate the *small pial arteries of the brain*. Their functional significance, however, is not yet clear.

Opinions differ as to whether other parts of the circulation are innervated by such fibers. The vasodilation of gland vessels in the *digestive tract* accompanying stimulation of the secretory nerves to the glands is thought to result primarily from the action of *kinins* formed in association with glandular activity (see below). But it cannot be definitely ruled out that specific parasympathetic cholinergic dilator fibers are involved.

Axon reflexes. Mechanical or chemical stimulation of the skin can give rise to local vasodilator responses that are ascribed to so-called *axon reflexes* (for details see p.120).
During *prolonged exposure to cold* the initial vasoconstriction at the tips of the extremities is interrupted by *periodic dilation*. This reaction is also thought by some to be based on (nociceptive) axon reflexes. The warming due to vasodilation prevents damage to tissue in the vicinity of the vessels, which are closely packed for thermoregulatory reasons. The axon reflexes elicited by other stimuli may well also be a mechanism of *defense against local injury*. Axon reflexes are also thought to be involved in the so-called **triple response,** a sequence of reactions to progressively more intense local stimulation such as stroking the skin with a blunt instrument, as follows. 1. *Red reaction,* local reddening in the region of the mechanical stimulus (arteriolar dilation). 2. *Flare,* a brighter red flush in the surrounding area, beginning after ca. 30 s (axon reflex). 3. *Local edema* or wheal formation (damage to capillary walls).

Chemical and Hormonal Effects

Substances acting directly on the vessels. When the glands of the gastrointestinal tract are activated, as when the secretory nerves are stimulated, the vessels in the glands *dilate* [30]. This effect is due primarily to the actions of **kinins** which are formed as follows. The gland cells secrete an *enzyme (kallikrein)* into the extracellular space. This enzyme splits α_2-*globulins (kininogens)* circulating in the plasma, to liberate a

polypeptide (kallidin) which is rapidly converted to *bradykinin*. **Kallidin** and **bradykinin** have a marked vasodilator action and increase the permeability of the capillaries [49]. They continue to act for only a few minutes. They are broken down by *tissue enzymes (kininases)*. These or similar mechanisms may well participate not only in increasing flow through the gastrointestinal tract when the digestive glands are activated, but also in providing more blood to the skin during activity of the sweat glands.

Kinins appear to play a role in inflammatory and allergic circulatory responses as well (cf. p.446). Moreover, the liberation of kinins when tissue is injured could be involved in the sensation of pain.

Histamine is liberated chiefly as a result of *damage to skin and mucosa,* and also in *antigen-antibody reactions;* most of it evidently comes from basophilic granulocytes and mast cells in the damaged region. It elicits local dilation of the arterioles and venules and increases capillary permeability (cf. p.420).

Adrenalin and noradrenalin. The catecholamines adrenalin and noradrenalin are released continuously in small quantities from the adrenal medulla and circulate through the body as **hormones,** with ubiquitous effects on the vascular muscles. Whereas noradrenalin is the chief transmitter substance of the vasomotor fibers, the hormonal effects are due chiefly to adrenalin; the adrenal medulla secretes about 80% adrenalin and only 20% noradrenalin. The effects of the blood-borne catecholamines are not uniform. Adrenalin in particular elicits (i) partly constrictor, partly dilator and (ii) variously intense reactions of the vessel musculature, which has different sensitivities.

Catecholamine receptors. The differential responses of the vessel musculature to circulating catecholamines can be explained by the presence of different "adrenergic receptors", the α *and* β *receptors,* which are particular chemical structures in the membranes of the muscle cells. Excitation of the α receptors elicits *contraction,* and excitation of the β receptors elicits *relaxation* of the smooth muscle fibers. *Noradrenalin* acts primarily on the α receptors, whereas *adrenalin* acts on both. In most (if not all) blood vessels both types of receptor are present, though their proportions and absolute numbers vary in the different parts of the circulatory system. The consequence is that *adrenalin elicits vasoconstriction where α receptors predominate, and vasodilation where β receptors predominate.*

The situation is complicated by the fact that the threshold for excitation of the β receptors is lower than that of the α receptors, whereas when both types are excited simultaneously the effects of the α receptors are dominant. Thus when adrenalin is present in *low* (physiological) concentrations *vasodilation* results, whereas in high concentrations it elicits *vasoconstriction*. A largely *selective excitation of β receptors* can be achieved with the synthetic noradrenalin derivative *isopropyl noradrenalin,* but no analogous substance is known to be produced by the body itself.

A fairly large number of pharmacological substances, so-called *sympatholytics,* block the α or β receptors more or less selectively. *Blocking of the α receptors* eliminates the vasoconstrictor effects of adrenalin, so that when it is injected the blood-pressure increase normally obtained owing to dominance of the α receptors is converted to a blood-pressure decrease mediated by the dilator action of the unaffected β receptors (so-called adrenalin reversal). *β-receptor blockade* has a less striking effect on the vascular responses; its chief therapeutic application is to alter the β-adrenergic effects on heart rate and the contractility of the myocardium.

Angiotensin II (see pp. 431 f.)

Vasopressin (see pp. 433 f.).

18.9 Regulation of the Overall Circulation

Basic Features of General Circulatory Regulation

Blood flow through the body is adjusted to the momentary situation by a combination of regional and higher-level (supraregional) mechanisms, the effects of which are closely interrelated.

The functional state of the circulation is continually monitored by **receptors** at various places in the cardiovascular system. The afferent impulses discharged by these receptors are conducted centrally to structures in the **medulla oblongata.** From these areas, the so-called **vasomotor center** (pp. 435 f.), impulses are sent out both along efferent fibers to the **effectors** in heart and vessels and to other structures in the CNS, some of which participate in circulatory regulation by way of the control of neurohumoral-hormonal mechanisms [9, 15, 38, 41, 42, 51].

The crucial mechanisms in general cardiovascular regulation are those that adjust **total peripheral resistance** and **cardiac output** in such a way as to maintain the *blood-pressure gradient* required for flow through the vascular system. Decreases in the total peripheral resistance as a result of dilation of the resistance vessels are compensated by increases in cardiac output (up to the maximal capacity of the heart in each case),

and vice versa. At the same time, when the vessels in particular organs dilate to meet increased demands, the effect on the total peripheral resistance is at least partially compensated by vasoconstrictor responses in other organs.

There are other important adaptive processes that affect the relationship between **vessel capacity** and **blood volume,** which determines the *static blood pressure.* Fairly large changes in the capacity of the system are elicited by vasomotor reactions of the capacitance vessels [41, 43], whereas the blood volume is affected both by the conditions of *capillary filtration and reabsorption* and by *renal fluid excretion* (in relation to fluid uptake).

The numerous adaptive processes can be classified in three groups, according to the *timing* of their action: 1. *short-term control mechanisms,* 2. *intermediate-term control mechanisms,* and 3. *long-term control mechanisms.*

Short-Term Control Mechanisms

The mechanisms in this category are predominantly **vasomotor adjustments** under **neural** control, which include (i) **baroreceptor (stretch-receptor) reflexes,** (ii) **chemoreceptor reflexes,** and (iii) the **ischemic reflex** of the CNS. The common characteristic of all these is a **rapid** onset of action, within a few seconds. The response is vigorous but if activated continuously, the response within a few days either dies out completely (baroreceptors) or is attenuated (chemoreceptors, CNS ischemic reflex). The neurally mediated vasomotor effects are supplemented by **hormonal** mechanisms involving **adrenalin, noradrenalin** and, with a delayed action, **vasopressin.**

Baroreceptor Reflexes

Locations of the arterial baroreceptors. In the walls of the large thoracic and cervical arteries are numerous so-called **baro- or pressoreceptors,** which are stimulated by the **stretching** of the vessel wall brought about by the transmural pressure. The baroreceptor areas of the greatest functional importance are those in the aortic arch and the carotid sinus (Fig. 18-27).

The sensory innervation of the baroreceptors in the carotid sinus is by way of the carotid-sinus nerve, a branch of the *glossopharyngeal nerve.* The baroreceptors in the aortic arch are innervated by the *left cardiac depressor nerve,* and those at the branch point of the brachiocephalic trunk by the *right cardiac depressor nerve.* Both the nerves to the carotid sinus and those to the aorta also contain fibers of *chemoreceptors* located in the carotid bodies (near the point where the common carotid artery divides) and in the aortic bodies of the aortic arch.

Pressure-discharge characteristic of the arterial baro-receptors. When the vessel wall is stretched by a *maintained* pressure the baroreceptors discharge impulses *continuously,* at a pressure-dependent rate that follows an approximately S-shaped curve, with the steepest (nearly linear) slope at pressures between 80 and 180 mm Hg. The baroreceptors act as *proportional-differential (PD) sensors,* responding to the fluctuation of arterial pressure during the cardiac cycle with *rhythmic discharge patterns* in which impulse frequency changes more the greater the amplitude and/or the rate of pressure change. The frequency in the rising part of the pressure curve is therefore distinctly greater than that in the falling, less steep part (Fig. 18-28); because of this "asymmetry" (i.e., the greater excitation as pressure is increasing) the mean frequency is higher than would be associated with static pressure at the same level. It can be concluded that the baroreceptors convey information not only about the *mean arterial pressure,* but also about the *amplitude* of pressure fluctuation and the *steepness* of pressure rise (and hence the heart rate).

Effects of arterial baroreceptor activity on blood pressure and cardiac function. The afferent impulses from the baroreceptors are conducted to the *cardioinhibito-*

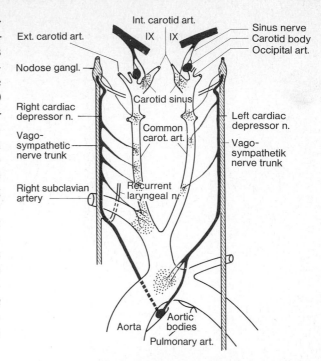

Fig. 18-27. Survey of the locations of baro- and chemoreceptors in the region of the aorta and carotid artery (from studies of dogs and cats). The baroreceptor fields are indicated by dots, and their afferent fibers by the *red* lines. (After MILNOR [20])

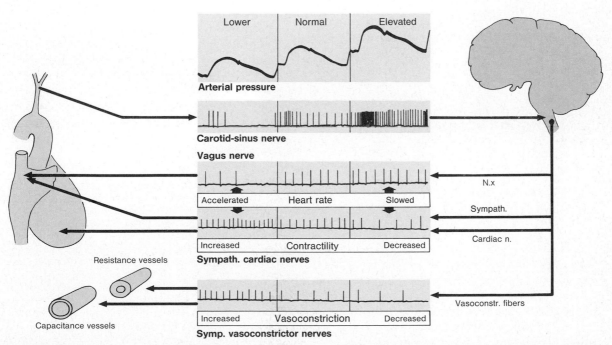

Fig. 18-28. Reflex responses to altered activity of the carotid-sinus baroreceptors. When arterial pressure falls the baroreceptors are less strongly stimulated, and the reflexly enhanced activity of the sympathetic vasoconstrictor and cardiac fibers causes increased peripheral resistance and heart rate, so that the blood pressure rises again. When arterial pressure is elevated the opposite responses occur. For further details see text

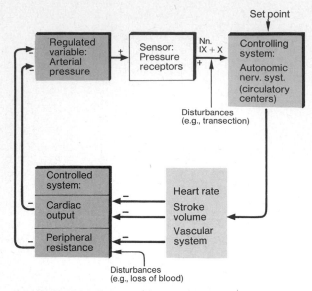

Fig. 18-29. Block diagram of the regulation of blood pressure by the arterial baroreceptors. Facilitatory effects are indicated by + and inhibitory effects by –

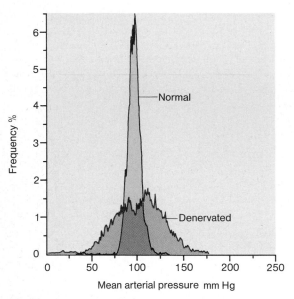

Fig. 18-30. Frequency distribution of mean blood pressure over 24 hours, in a dog with intact baroreceptors (normal) and several weeks after denervation of the baroreceptors (denervated). (After GUYTON [13])

ry and vasomotor centers (p. 435) in the medulla oblongata (and other parts of the CNS), where they cause an **inhibition of sympathetic structures** and an **enhanced excitation of parasympathetic structures.** As a result, the **tonic activity** of the sympathetic vasoconstrictor fibers (the so-called *vasomotor tone*) is reduced, and at the same time *heart rate* and the *contractile force of the myocardium* are inhibited (cf. Fig. 18-28).

Because the baroreceptors are active over a wide range of pressures, these inhibitory influences are in operation even when the blood pressure is "normal". The arterial baroreceptors thus have a continual *depressor* action. When they are further excited by arterial pressure increases, the increased inhibition of the vasomotor center causes further vasodilation, to different degrees in the vascular beds of the different organs. At the level of the resistance vessels this effect results in a **decrease in the total peripheral resistance,** and at the level of the capacitance vessels in an **increased capacity.** Both processes lead to **lowered arterial pressure** either directly or indirectly, by way of reduced central venous pressure and the associated reduction in stroke volume (Fig. 18-28). This effect is further enhanced by the accompanying decreases in heart rate and in myocardial contraction. When the level of baroreceptor excitation is diminished by pressure reduction the opposite reactions ensue, with the result that arterial pressure rises again.

This **homeostatic autoregulatory mechanism** constitutes a complete *control circuit* (Fig. 18-29), whereby the reflex changes in resistance to flow and cardiac output triggered by the arterial baroreceptors in response to acute deviations of arterial pressure tend to *restore the initial conditions.*

The "normalization" of arterial pressure by the adaptive reflexes initiated by arterial baroreceptor activity is quite evident in the distribution of blood pressures measured over 24 hours (Fig. 18-30). With the carotid sinus nerves *intact* there is a *sharp peak* in the region of the *"normal" mean pressure* of 100 mm Hg. When the homeostatic regulatory mechanisms are inactivated by denervation, there is a broad scatter in the measured pressures, both above and below the mean.

The reflex control mechanisms just described are an important element in **circulatory-system regulation,** where arterial pressure is only one of the several variables controlled.

When *chronic hypertension* (high blood pressure) is induced experimentally the arterial baroreceptors **adapt** to the increased pressure within a few days, remaining *fully functional.* Under these conditions the pressure-stabilizing effects fail to reduce the blood pressure, and the autoregulatory mechanism, by maintaining the high pressure, contributes to the development of further pathological changes. Recently an attempt has been made to turn the reflexly elicited effects on blood pressure to therapeutic advantage, by treating patients who have forms of hypertension not susceptible to drugs with pulse-synchronized or maintained stimulation of the sinus nerves by implanted electrodes, in order to reduce blood pressure *(baropacing).*

If the carotid sinus is *compressed* or *struck* from outside the body, the increased excitation of the baroreceptors triggers a drop in blood pressure and heart rate. In older people who have developed arteriosclerosis the blood pressure can fall drastically, with transient cardiac arrest and loss of consciousness *(carot-*

id-sinus syndrome). In most cases the heart resumes beating after 4-6 s, frequently with an initial AV rhythm (p. 360) until the normal sinus rhythm becomes established. But if cardiac activity is suspended for too long, death can result. On the other hand, during attacks of accelerated beating *(paroxysmal tachycardia)* it is possible under some circumstances to normalize the heart rate by applying pressure to the carotid sinus on one or both sides.

Effects of arterial baroreceptor activity on other CNS functions. Increased input from the baroreceptors to the medullary vasomotor centers results in *inhibition* of many other functions of the CNS. For example, respiration becomes more shallow, muscle tone and the activity of the efferent γ-fibers to the muscle spindles decrease, and the monosynaptic reflexes become weaker. The EEG tends to be more synchronized. Waking animals respond to marked stretching of the carotid-sinus region with motor inactivity or even with sleep.

Effects of arterial baroreceptor activity on blood volume. The reflex vasomotion of the pre- and postcapillary vessels influences the *effective hydrostatic capillary pressure* and thus the capillary *filtration-reabsorption equilibrium.* When a rise in arterial pressure causes *increased* baroreceptor activity, the ensuing vasodilation raises the effective capillary pressure and thus capillary *filtration* from the lumen into the interstitial space. Lowered arterial pressure, with correspondingly *reduced* baroreceptor activity, diminishes the effective capillary pressure by vasoconstriction, so that *increased reabsorption* of fluid from the interstitial space results. In **skeletal muscle,** where the total capillary surface is large and the interstitial volume large and variable, these effects can produce relatively rapid and large shifts of fluid between the intravascular and interstitial spaces. When the blood pressure falls, the increase in intravascular volume by mobilization of interstitial fluid begins very quickly. Effects on blood pressure are observable after about 5–10 min, an onset time long enough that this reflex cannot be distinguished from the intermediate-term control mechanisms.

Cardiac Stretch-Receptor Reflexes

Atrial receptors. In both atria there are two functionally important types of **stretch receptors.** The **A receptors** are excited by atrial contraction and the **B receptors** during late ventricular systole, which coincides with the rise of atrial pressure toward the v-wave (Fig. 18-31). Both types are activated by stretch of the atria, the A receptors responding to contraction of the atrial musculature and the B receptors more to pas-

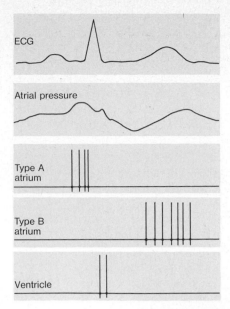

Fig. 18-31. Activity of atrial receptors of Types A and B, and of a ventricular receptor, in relation to the ECG and the pressure fluctuation in the left atrium. (From data of PAINTAL as cited in [10])

sive stretch (increased atrial pressure). The afferent impulses discharged by the atrial receptors are conducted along sensory fibers of the *vagus nerve* to the *medullary circulatory centers* and other CNS structures.

Atrial-receptor influences on blood pressure and cardiac function. When the **B receptors** are excited in isolation, most of the reflex effects are similar to those of arterial baroreceptor excitation – *inhibition of sympathetic and excitation of parasympathetic* structures in the medullary circulatory centers, with corresponding cardiovascular effects (pp. 427 f.). A receptors differ from B receptors in that the latter exert an especially strong vasoconstrictor influence on the *renal vessels* whereas the arterial baroreceptors are more effective on muscle vessels (see above). When the level of B-receptor activity changes, therefore, the predominant effect is likely to be on *renal fluid excretion,* which depends in part on blood flow through the kidneys.

The receptors in the atria (and large veins) also occupy a special position with respect to control of *intravascular volume,* inasmuch as they are optimally situated to monitor the state of filling of the vascular system and the dynamics of ventricle filling, and are very sensitive to these variables. Accordingly, even slight changes in vascular volume affect the state of excitation of these receptors, which also send afferent impulses to *osmoregulatory structures in the hypothalamus* that control vasopressin secretion (pp. 433 f.).

In contrast to the action of the B receptors, that of the **A receptors** is evidently to *increase the activity of the sympathetic system*. Tachycardia, which in experiments frequently (though not regularly) accompanies the extreme increases in atrial pressure brought about by rapid infusion of large amounts of fluid, is thought to be elicited by excitation of the A receptors **(Bainbridge reflex)**. The unreliability of the response could be based on differential activation of A and B receptors depending on the conditions of the experiment. The physiological significance of the Bainbridge reflex is doubtful.

Ventricular receptors. There are also a few **stretch receptors** in the ventricles, the afferent fibers of which (like those of the atrial receptors) run in branches of the *vagus nerve*. These receptors are active, at a low level (Fig. 18-31), only during the period of isovolumetric contraction of the ventricles (just after the R wave in the ECG).

It is thought that under resting conditions the impulses of these receptors maintain the *negative chronotropic action* of the vagus on heart rate, and elicit reflex bradycardia and vasodilation during extreme stretching of the ventricles. But the physiological significance of these effects has not yet been sufficiently well established.

After the intravenous injection of various *pharmacological* substances such as veratrum alkaloids (extracted from hellebore), nicotine, serotonin etc., there is a reflex *decrease in heart rate* and *vasodilation*, with the result that blood pressure falls **(Bezold-Jarisch reflex)** and *apnea* occurs. The cardiac and vascular effects can also be obtained by injecting the substances into the left coronary artery or applying them to the surface of the left ventricle **(coronary chemoreflex)**. The apnea, however, results from the stimulation of pulmonary receptors.

Reflexes Involving Arterial Chemoreceptors

The actions of the chemoreceptors in the carotid and aortic bodies (cf. Fig. 18-27) on the cardiovascular system, unlike those of the baroreceptors, are *not true proprioceptive regulation*, for the adequate stimuli of these receptors are decreased O_2 partial pressure and increased CO_2 partial pressure (or H^+ concentration). The afferent impulses from the chemoreceptors stimulate both the "respiratory centers" (pp. 479 ff.) and the "circulatory centers" in the medulla oblongata, a process which to some extent involves the superposition of antagonistic reflexes [8, 32].

The effects on circulatory function associated with breathing can be kept constant by means of artificial respiration; in such experiments *stimulation of the chemoreceptors causes vasoconstriction and decreased heart rate* by their direct action on the medullary circulatory centers. The increases in peripheral resistance outweigh the reduction in cardiac output, so that the *blood pressure rises*. The same effects appear when blood flow through the carotid and aortic bodies is diminished owing to lowered arterial pressure, and tend (as does reduced excitation of the baroreceptors) to oppose a further fall in pressure.

Under "normal" conditions, however, these effects are modified not only by influences related to respiration but also by possible actions on the vessels themselves. For example, when the respired air is deficient in O_2 the reflexly elicited vasoconstriction is *nullified by local vasodilation* resulting from hypoxia (p. 422), and the *heart rate* (and output) is *increased*.

Ischemic Response of the CNS

The ischemic response involves *excitation of the medullar circulatory centers* such that *vasoconstriction* and the resulting *increased blood pressure* dominate. The response is initiated by inadequate blood supply to the brain, by decrease in arterial pressure, by arterial hypoxia or by impaired perfusion of the brain owing to vascular disorders. The structures in the medulla are evidently stimulated by way of *increased concentrations of H^+ and CO_2* (and perhaps of other metabolites). This could occur either by *direct* effects on the *reticular formation* or by the action of the extracellular $[H^+]$ on *chemosensory areas* on the brainstem surface (as in the regulation of breathing, p. 484). In arterial hypoxia there may well be an additional reflex influence on the response associated with stimulation of the arterial chemoreceptors. The intensity of the responses depends on the degree to which blood supply is impaired. Under extreme conditions, for example, vasoconstriction in the kidneys can restrict perfusion so severely that the production of urine comes to a halt. This can cause a rise in *arterial pressure to 250 mm Hg* or more.

Effects of Adrenalin and Noradrenalin on the Circulatory System

When the sympathetic circulatory centers in the medulla are excited by the events described above, the adrenal medulla, because its innervation is analogous to that of a sympathetic ganglion, releases *increased amounts of adrenalin and noradrenalin*. The rate of release, low under resting conditions, can become 20 times as high in extreme situations.

Adrenalin. Adrenalin *circulating* in the bloodstream in general produces a **decrease in total resistance** by way of its action on β receptors. Because the responses of vessels differ according to the relative numbers of α and β receptors, the **cardiac output is redistributed** (pp. 425 f.). Increased flow through the vessels in skeletal muscle is opposed by decreases in flow through the cutaneous and splanchnic vessels (Fig. 18-25). At the same time, the *cardiac output* increases because of increases in both stroke volume and heart rate. These events bring about little or no increase in mean arterial pressure. Effects of this sort are associated with *exercise or psychological agitation.* Under extreme conditions such as *hemorrhage and intense psychological stress* (anxiety, terror, rage), the adrenalin concentration in the blood can become so high that *vasoconstriction dominates* as a result of excitation of the α receptors (Fig. 18-25). But at this time neuronal vasoconstriction is maximal anyway.

Noradrenalin. The sole effect of noradrenalin *circulating* in the blood in above-threshold concentrations is to **increase the resistance to flow** in the vessels of the systemic circulation (Fig. 18-25). Accordingly, arterial pressure rises, increasing the discharge rate of the arterial baroreceptors (p. 427), so that there is a *reflex* reduction in heart rate. Cardiac output decreases, both for this reason and because the stroke volume is less. But the relatively small proportion of noradrenalin secreted by the adrenal medulla even when it is maximally active is unlikely to be sufficient to enhance directly the similar cardiovascular responses that are elicited neurally.

Intermediate-Term Control Mechanisms

The intermediate-term mechanisms include: 1. *transcapillary volume shifts, 2. stress relaxation of the vessels,* and 3. the *renin-angiotensin mechanism.* These effects require minutes to become apparent and are fully developed only after hours have elapsed.

Transcapillary volume shifts. The filtration-reabsorption conditions in the capillaries are influenced not only by reflex vasomotor responses, which primarily affect the vessels in muscle (p. 448); the capillaries of the entire organism are affected by the pressures in the vascular system (for details see pp. 418 ff.). Increases in arterial and/or venous pressure are as a rule associated with increases in the effective capillary pressure; the resulting *increased filtration* into the interstitial spaces *reduces the intravascular volume.* Because of the relationships between mean filling pressure, venous return and stroke volume (p. 414), the *arterial pressure is thereby reduced.* Primary pressure drops elicit changes just the reverse of those listed above owing to *increased capillary reabsorption,* with a resultant rise in arterial pressure [10, 13].

Vascular stress relaxation. Increases in arterial pressure, which because of the relationship to filling pressure (p. 407) can also be induced by increases in intravascular volume, are attenuated by the *delayed compliance* (p. 403) of the vessels; after initial stretching by the increased pressure the distensibility of the ves-

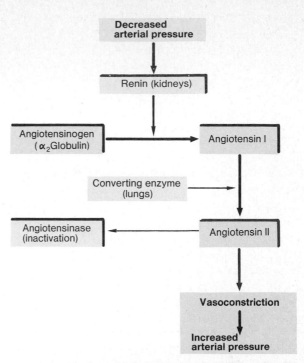

Fig. 18-32. Sequence of reactions in the renin-angiotensin mechanism for blood-pressure regulation

sels slowly becomes greater. When intravascular volume decreases, the opposite responses occur, raising the arterial pressure. These properties, called *"stress relaxation"* and *"reverse stress relaxation",* respectively, are particularly well developed in the capacitance vessels; their effect is to return the pressures in the system to nearly the initial values within 10–60 minutes, even following quite large changes in volume.

Renin-angiotensin mechanism. Renin is an enzyme synthesized and stored in the juxtaglomerular cells of the kidney. When it is released renin splits the *angiotensin* (an α_2 globulin) formed in the liver to produce *angiotensin I* (a decapeptide). A *"converting enzyme"* in the plasma changes the angiotensin I to *angiotensin II* (an octapeptide); this reaction occurs chiefly in the pulmonary circulation. Angiotensin II is broken down to inactive peptides by *angiotensinases* (Fig. 18-32).

Initiation of this sequence of events is closely related to the amount of blood flow through the kidney. **Lowered renal perfusion** in any form – whether due to general hypotension, local vasoconstriction or pathological changes in the renal vessels – causes **increased release of renin** (Fig. 18-32). The same effects appear to result from diminished excitation of the atrial and arterial baroreceptors when the intravascular volume is reduced. Renin release is also thought to be stimulated by changes in *electrolyte concentration,* hyponatremia in particular [27].

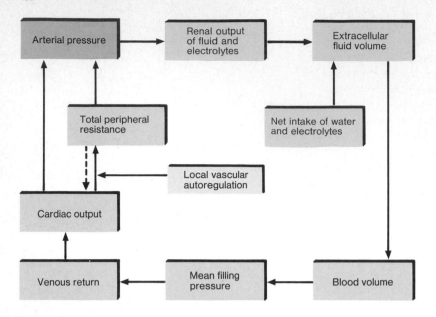

Fig. 18-33. Block diagram of the renal volume-control system for long-term regulation of blood pressure. (Modified after GUYTON)

Angiotensin II elicits very strong *direct vasoconstriction* of arteries and (less strong) of veins, as well as activation of central and peripheral structures in the *sympathetic system*. The consequence is an increase in peripheral resistance and blood pressure. Moreover, angiotensin II is the most important stimulator of the secretion of *aldosterone* from the adrenal cortex.

It takes about 20 minutes for the renin-angiotensin mechanism to become fully effective; its effects then persist, slightly attenuated, for a long time. In cases of *pathologically lowered blood pressure and/or reduced blood volume* the mechanism makes a significant contribution to the normalization of circulatory function. The renin-angiotensin concentration in the blood also appears to participate in control of the *thirst mechanism;* increases in renin-angiotensin concentration enhance the sensation of thirst, and conversely. The thirst experienced after major blood or fluid losses reflects these relationships.

On the other hand, the renin-angiotensin mechanism seems to be involved in producing a certain form of *renal hypertension,* for in this condition the concentration of these substances in the blood is distinctly increased.

Long-Term Control Mechanisms

In the current view, the long-term mechanisms are based primarily on processes that affect the *intravascular fluid volume* in relation to the *capacity* of the vessels. These can be matched in two ways. Capacity can be adjusted to blood volume by the *vasomotor responses* previously discussed (p.428), *stress relaxation* of the vessels (p.431), and the *renin-angiotensin*

mechanism (see above) – all short- or intermediate-term mechanisms. On the other hand, *transcapillary fluid exchange* (p.431) adjusts intravascular volume to capacity; but because the fluid is shifted only from the vessel lumen to the interstitial space (the most important compartments of the extracellular fluid volume) its effects are limited. *Quantitative changes in extracellular fluid volume* can be achieved under normal conditions only by changing the balance between **net fluid intake** (oral fluid consumption minus loss of fluid by all routes except the kidney) and **renal fluid output.** The regulation of extracellular volume is thus crucial not only for *water and electrolyte balance,* but for the *function of the circulatory system* as well. The following mechanisms are involved here: 1. the *renal volume-control system,* 2. the *vasopressin system,* and 3. the *aldosterone system.*

Renal volume-control system. The functions of this system with respect to blood pressure are diagrammed in Fig.18-33. The chief effects are as follows.

An *increase in blood pressure* has four main consequences. 1. Renal fluid output increases. 2. The increased renal fluid output reduces the extracellular fluid volume and hence the blood volume. 3. The reduced blood volume brings about decreased mean filling pressure, as a result of which venous return and cardiac output are diminished. 4. The reduced cardiac output causes the blood pressure to return to the original level.

A *fall in blood pressure* elicits the *reverse* responses. Renal fluid output declines, blood volume enlarges, venous return and cardiac output increase and the blood pressure rises again.

Arterial pressure is affected not only by changes in cardiac output but by the *total peripheral resistance* as well (since $P = \dot{V} \cdot R$). This coupling derives from **autoregulatory responses** (p.404) which alter the resistance to flow in those resistance vessels with autoregulatory properties; the pressure changes triggering this process, which depend on volume flow, are thus *amplified* by factors of 5–10. In this way relatively small chronic increases in extracellular volume, 2–3%, can produce *blood-pressure increases of up to 50%* [13, 14, 36].

The above considerations are not inconsistent with the observation that there is *no appreciable rise* in blood pressure accompanying *acute* changes in blood volume by the rapid infusion of large amounts of fluid. In this case the predicted pressure increases are compensated by the short-term *reflex* control mechanisms; the added fluid volume is excreted by the kidneys before the neural control mechanisms can adapt to the new situation. When the reflex control systems of an animal are suppressed in an experiment, voluminous infusions elicit distinct increases in cardiac output and arterial pressure, which subsequently die away as fluid volume is normalized by a transient increase in renal output. On the other hand, human *hypertension* can in many cases be reduced by administration of diuretics to *decrease extracellular fluid volume*.

Relations between blood pressure and renal fluid output. The effectiveness of blood-pressure regulation by this system depends on the degree to which the amount of fluid excreted by the kidneys changes when blood pressure changes. Fig. 18-34 illustrates the result of experiments in which water and electrolyte input are varied from the normal equilibrium condition (Point A). The sharp rise of the urinary output curve above the "normal" mean pressure of 100 mm Hg (Point A) implies that even *very small increases in arterial pressure* are associated with *considerable increases in renal fluid output*. Urine output appears to rise about by 100% for each mm Hg, so that pressure *increases of 8–10 mm Hg* would increase output by more than eightfold – the *maximal rate* at which the kidneys can produce urine. When blood pressure falls below the "normal" level, fluid output drops sharply until it stops altogether. The significance of these events in blood-pressure control is that when pressure rises the enhanced renal fluid output reduces the extracellular fluid volume and thus the mean filling pressure of the vascular system. The associated reduction in venous return and cardiac output lowers the arterial pressure to the original level. When arterial pressure falls, by contrast, fluid retention increases the extracellular fluid volume and the other parameters also change in the opposite direction, driving the blood pressure back up.

The effect of increased fluid intake. It can also be inferred from Fig. 18-34 that even fairly large changes in

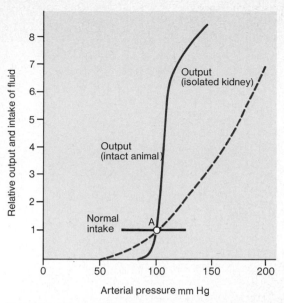

Fig. 18-34. Changes in urinary output with change in mean arterial pressure, as part of the long-term regulation of the circulatory system by the renal volume-control system. (After GUYTON [13])

net fluid intake have a *negligible effect* on mean arterial pressure. If the extra input occurs only once, the raised arterial pressure and increased fluid output soon return to the equilibrium level, whereas if the additional input is maintained a new equilibrium between net intake and output is established, with only a slight increase in mean pressure.

Sensitivity of the control system. Both position and shape of the urine excretion curve can exhibit considerable *individual differences*. Parallel shifts along the abscissa imply a shift of the equilibrium between fluid intake and output (Point A) into a higher or lower range of *arterial pressures*, which are maintained with *equal sensitivity* by alterations of renal fluid output. Such shifts can occur in the course of **vasomotor responses**. Position and shape of the urine excretion curve can also be affected by **hormones** and other factors. *Vasopressin* and *aldosterone* are definitely involved, the former evidently enhancing the sensitivity of this control mechanism. The considerably smaller changes in fluid output when the arterial pressure in isolated kidneys is changed (dashed curve in Fig. 18-34), as compared with the siutation in situ, are probably due at least in part to such effects.

Vasopressin system. Vasopressin (cf. pp.661f.), also called *antidiuretic hormone (ADH)*, in intermediate to high doses causes *vasoconstriction*, especially pronounced in the arterioles. The main effect of the hormone, however is to control the *reabsorption of water* in the distal tubule (for details see p.629).

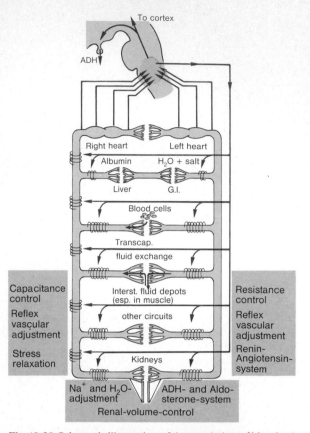

Fig. 18-35. Schematic illustration of the regulation of blood volume. Mutual adjustment of intravascular volume and vessel capacity involves three "lines of defense", mechanisms activated in a specific temporal sequence as follows. 1. Reflex adaptation of the cardiovascular effectors to the available volume of blood. 2. Alteration of the ratio between intravascular and interstitial volumes. 3. Reflex and neurohormonal adjustment of the renal excretion of water and electrolytes. (Modified after Folkow and Neil [10])

As far as its *vascular* action is concerned, vasopressin was previously thought to be ineffective in *physiological concentrations*. Recent experiments on animals have shown that at least when **blood pressure falls** severely fairly large quantities of vasopressin are released from the posterior lobe of the hypophysis; the hormone acts directly to constrict the smooth muscles of the vessels, and by increasing the *total peripheral resistance* contributes to the stabilization or increase of blood pressure. Under normal conditions these effects are masked by the reflex control mechanisms; they can be demonstrated only after denervation of the arterial baroreceptors. In contrast to the reflex effects which dominate initially, the hormonal action on the vessels does not diminish in time. Thus the vascular action of vasopressin can be a significant regulator of the circulation in cases of *chronic malfunction* [21].

Vasopressin plays a special role in fluid-volume control, inasmuch as the *reflexly* elicited changes in vasopressin concentration are involved in the homeostasis of *intravascular volume*. When blood volume increases the associated increase in activity of the atrial receptors inhibits vasopressin release within 10–

20 minutes, so that more fluid is excreted by the kidneys. Decreases in blood volume have the opposite effect; the enhanced vasopressin release restricts renal fluid output. This **volume-control reflex,** which is triggered by **acute** changes in intravascular volume, is also called the **Gauer-Henry reflex.** These effects reinforce the renal volume-control mechanism; indeed, in view of the ability of vasopressin to increase the sensitivity of the renal mechanism, it is difficult to separate the two processes.

Aldosterone system. Aldosterone increases the *tubular reabsorption of* Na^+ (and hence, by osmotic effects, of water) and the *secretion of* K^+ *and* H^+; thus it raises the sodium and extracellular-fluid content of the body. (For further details see pp. 628f. and 634f.). At the same time, aldosterone enhances the *excitability of vascular smooth muscle by constrictor stimuli,* thereby reinforcing the pressor action of angiotensin II.
Angiotensin II, in turn, is the most effective *stimulator of aldosterone secretion*. Whenever the renin-angiotensin mechanism (p. 431) is activated, the aldosterone concentration in the blood rises. Because of this close linkage, the effects of the three substances are frequently lumped as the *renin-angiotensin-aldosterone system*.

The *effects of aldosterone* on the circulatory system begin to appear after hours and are fully developed only after several days. Increased aldosterone production (*hyperaldosteronism* is associated with certain diseases of the adrenal cortex) causes greater retention of water and salt as well as *hypertension,* and hypotension results when aldosterone secretion is diminished.

The action of aldosterone on the *renal volume-control system* is as complex as that of vasopressin, and under normal conditions the effects of the two (to some extent antagonistic) factors cannot yet be precisely analyzed.

It is evident in this description of the many mechanisms regulating the circulation of blood that essentially *none of them acts exclusively on a single parameter.* Nearly all the mechanisms affect, either directly or indirectly and to varying degrees, the cardiac output, the total peripheral resistance, the capacity of the vessels, and the intravascular volume. There are thus three *"lines of defense"* against disturbance of either **arterial pressure** or **blood volume,** characterized by the *timing* (onset and duration) of their actions (Fig. 18-35). Acute disturbance is counteracted at the level of the vessels, chiefly by alteration of vessel capacity, whereas in chronic conditions changes in blood volume dominate. Initially the latter involve modification of water and electrolyte content, followed if necessary, with varying delays, by changes in

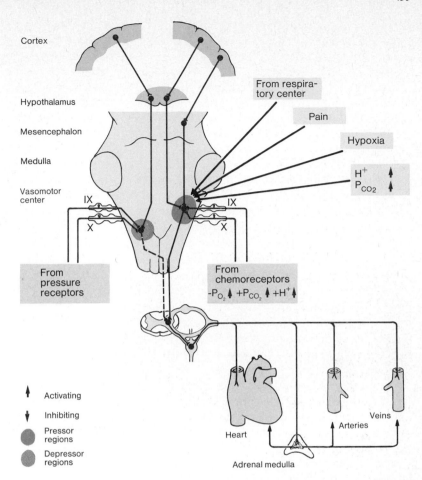

Cortex

Hypothalamus

Mesencephalon

Medulla

Vasomotor
center

IX

X

From respira-
tory center

Pain

Hypoxia

H^+
P_{CO_2}

IX

X

From
pressure
receptors

From
chemoreceptors
$-P_{O_2}$ $+P_{CO_2}$ $+H^+$

↑ Activating

↓ Inhibiting

● Pressor
regions

● Depressor
regions

Heart

Adrenal medulla

Veins

Arteries

Fig. 18-36. Schematic drawing of the most important afferent and efferent connections of the medullary cardio-vascular centers. The efferent fibers that activate circulation come from mostly ipsilateral "pressor regions", whereas the inhibitory fibers from "depressor regions" cross in the medulla and pass to ventrolateral areas of the spinal cord on the contralateral side. (Slightly modified after UVNÄS [23])

the plasma proteins and the cellular elements of the blood.

Central Control of the Circulation

Structures at *all levels of the CNS* participate in the monitoring and regulation of circulatory-system function. Simplifying the situation greatly, we can classify the functions of the different levels in 4 groups [9, 23, 42].

Medullary "centers". In the **reticular formation** of the medulla oblongata and the **bulbar parts of the pons** there are structures, poorly defined anatomically, that together constitute the so-called **medullary** and **rhombencephalic cardiovascular control centers.** Under resting conditions homeostasis of the circulatory system can be maintained by these centers alone, as experiments on decerebrate animals have shown. Basically, this capability is due to the *tonic activity of sympathetic vasoconstrictor fibers* arising in parts of this region, the **vasomotor centers,** which is responsible for the **resting tone** of the vessels (p. 424). This tonic output is continually modulated by afferent im-

pulses from the *cardiovascular receptors* in such a way that increased afferent input reduces tonic activity and results in vasodilation, and decreased afferent input enhances tonic activity and leads to vasoconstriction. In addition, the functional state of the vasomotor center can be influenced by *"unspecific"* afferent impulses and by impulses from the relatively nearby *respiratory centers* and from *higher levels* of the CNS [23, 42, 43]. The medullary control centers also give rise to facilitatory sympathetic and inhibitory parasympathetic (vagal) actions on the *heart* (Fig. 18-36).

Electrical stimulation of these structures elicits a variety of responses. In the *lateral* part of the vasomotor center *pressor* responses (increased blood pressure) are elicited, whereas in the *mediocaudal* parts of the brainstem *depressor* responses are produced (Fig. 18-36). Stimulation of the pressor areas increases the activity of all sympathetic adrenergic effectors; heart rate as well as the force and rate of myocardial contraction increase, the tone of resistance and capacitance vessels rises, and hormones are released from the adrenal medulla in greater amounts. Stimulation of the depressor areas inhibits the activity of the adrenergic sympathetic system.

When the brainstem is transected at about the level of the cuneate nucleus the pressor efferents are cut off;

in the absence of tonic efferent sympathetic activity there is a *sharp fall in blood pressure*. The depressor regions, largely left intact by this operation, suppress the activity of the "spinal" centers (p.437). Spinal control becomes apparent only after the depressor efferents are eliminated by cutting through the medulla caudal to the obex. The relationship of the medullary cardiovascular control center to other neural systems has been pointed out previously (p.429).

Hypothalamic "centers" (cf. pp.133ff.). Stimulation of the *reticular formation* in **mesencephalon** and **diencephalon,** especially in the **hypothalamus,** elicits some facilitatory and some inhibitory cardiovascular responses, which are mediated by the medullary centers (Fig.18-36). By careful positioning and adjustment of the stimulus in the hypothalamus, selective vasoconstriction can be produced in the vascular beds of particular organs – for example, the renal, muscle or splanchnic vessels. Even under resting conditions the hypothalamus appears to exert a maintained influence on both the *tonic activity and the reflex responses of the medullary centers*.

Moreover, the hypothalamus (in particular) participates in certain **general responses** such as the alarm and defense responses, and in **thermoregulation.** Stimulation of the *caudal hypothalamus* activates the sympathetic system in such a way as to increase vasodilation in the skeletal muscles and enhances the adrenergic responses in other effectors (the so-called "ergotropic" zones). As a result, blood pressure, heart rate and cardiac output increase. There is increased blood flow through the muscles, whereas the other vessels undergo distinct vasoconstriction. At the same time other parts of the CNS, including the cerebral cortex, come into play, producing other autonomic responses and signs of *general excitation and greater alertness;* ultimately the phenomena ordinarily accompanying aggression, rage or fear can appear. This pattern of excitation represents an **"alarm state"** in which the organs are prepared to cope, if necessary, with the demands of flight, defense or attack. Conversely, the *rostral hypothalamus* has a *suppressive* effect on cardiovascular function and causes autonomic adaptations that aid recuperation of the organism and are associated with feeding and digestion (so-called "trophotropic" zones).

When the rostral hypothalamus is **warmed** the cutaneous vessels dilate, and when it is **cooled** they constrict; thermoregulation is thus accomplished by modification of the organism's heat loss. Warming of the rostral hypothalamus is also associated with vasoconstriction in the viscera, and cooling with increased muscle tone or shivering.

Cortical influences. Cardiovascular responses can be elicited by stimulation of many parts of the cerebral cortex. The effective sites are concentrated in two regions: 1. in the *neocortex* at the outer convexity of the hemisphere, especially in the vicinity of the motor and premotor areas, and 2. in the *paleocortex,* especially on the medial surfaces of the hemispheres and on the basal surface of the frontal and parietal lobes.

In the **neocortical areas** stimulation elicits predominantly *pressor* responses, usually in combination with *increased* heart rate; *depressor* responses are usually associated with *decreased* heart rate. These cortical effects can be superimposed on the opposite combinations of blood pressure and heart rate associated with the homeostatic reflexes.

When the *motor cortex* is stimulated the resulting pattern of responses can closely resemble the *alarm response* apart from its affective elements. It is notable here that local increases in blood flow through the skeletal musculature can be elicited in areas where stimulation causes contraction of the corresponding muscles. These observations indicate that the motor patterns and the autonomic reactions that accompany them are initiated together in the cortex; that is, they are synchronized by central **"coinnervation"**.

Taken together, these adjustments of the organism are called **anticipatory responses;** in humans, they appear prior to an intended act. They should be regarded as the expression of a *mutual adjustment of autonomically controlled circulatory function and muscle performance under somatomotor control,* which takes place independent of the subsequent actual activity and the adaptive processes it induces. The *"centrogenic"* autonomic impulses are in part mediated by the *hypothalamus,* for when the hypothalamus is selectively eliminated the blood-pressure and heart-rate responses fail to appear. The *mesencephalon* may also act as a relay station for some of these signals. From this region impulses are sent to the medullary cardiovascular control center and other structures in the reticular formation that are involved in activating the sympathetic system. Other vasoconstrictor fibers run directly into the spinal cord near the pyramidal tract. The *dilator system* that originates in the cortex of various species makes synaptic connections in the hypothalamus and mesencephalon; the vasodilator fibers leaving these regions bypass the medullary centers, so that there is no further interruption in the pathway until the lateral horns of the spinal cord are reached.

In the *paleocortical areas,* stimulation of the anterior cingulate gyrus elicits predominantly *depressor* effects, whereas the responses to nearby points on the orbito-insulo-temporal cortex are partly pressor and partly depressor in nature. The paleocortical zones that influence circulation also affect *other autonomically controlled functions* such as gastrointestinal motility and glandular activity.

Spinal influences. After *transection* of the spinal cord between C_6 and Th_1, so that the phrenic nerve and the preganglionic sympathetic fibers remain intact, the first result is a marked *fall in arterial pressure*. The animals survive, however, and after about a week the blood pressure returns to normal. At this stage moderate loss of blood (up to 25% of the total volume) can be compensated as well as in normal animals. These adjustments are mediated by the *cells of origin of the sympathetic fibers* in the lateral-horn gray matter, which develop a certain independence as *"spinal centers"* after the cord has been cut. This is probably less a matter of true reflexes than an excitation of the preganglionic neurones by hypoxia. These mechanisms are probably of no significance in the normal control of circulation, but they could become effective in anoxia (cf. p. 430).

18.10   The Pulmonary Circulation

Hemodynamics of the Pulmonary Circulation

In the **vascular bed of the lungs** the arterial and venous segments are considerably shorter and the diameter of the vessels in general larger than in the corresponding parts of the systemic circulation. The large arteries are relatively thin-walled, whereas the small arteries have strong, muscular walls. There are no typical arterioles – that is, typical resistance vessels [2].

Capillary diameter is about 8 μm; the capillaries anastomose extensively to form a dense network around the alveoli. Their length can thus be expressed only as a so-called *"functional length"*, in terms of their topography with respect to the alveoli. It is *ca. 350 μm*, and the transit time of the blood is about 1 s. The capillary *surface area* under resting conditions is ca. 60 m²; during hard work the non-perfused capillaries can be brought into play, so that the total area rises to ca. 90 m² (Fig. 18-20).

Pressures in the pulmonary vessels. The pressures in the pulmonary circulation of a healthy person are *relatively low*. In the pulmonary artery the **systolic pressure** is ca. **20 mm Hg,** the **diastolic pressure** is ca. **8 mm Hg,** and the **mean pressure** is ca. **13 mm Hg** (Fig. 18-10). The mean pressure in the region of the lung capillaries is ca. 6.5 mm Hg, and in the left atrium it is approximately 5.5 mm Hg. Under normal conditions pressure fluctuations of 3–5 mm Hg are present even in the capillaries of the lung, and these propagate with decreasing amplitude into the lung veins. The *pressure differences* between arteries and capillaries (5 mm Hg) and between capillaries and

right atrium (3 mm Hg) are considerably smaller than in the corresponding parts of the systemic circulation.

Accordingly, the *resistance* in the pulmonary vascular bed is also *small,* barely ¹⁄₁₀ of the overall resistance of the systemic system (p. 406).

Pressure-pulse and volume-pulse curves are nearly identical in shape. The *pulse-wave velocity* (p. 411) in the large pulmonary arteries is only $1–2$ m·s⁻¹, because of their relatively large mechanical compliance.

Flow in the pulmonary vessels. The hemodynamic conditions in the arteries of the lungs are basically the same as in those of the systemic circulation. The pulmonary circuit receives the *total* volume of blood ejected by the right ventricle, and to this is added, in the pulmonary veins, some of the venous blood from the bronchial circulation (at most 2% of the output of the left ventricle).

The *flow pulse* in the pulmonary artery rises and falls less steeply than in the aorta. The stroke volume ejected intermittently from the right ventricle is converted by the elastic properties of the pulmonary arteries into a forward flow even during diastole. In contrast to the attenuation in the systemic circulation, flow remains *pulsatile* with decreasing pulsation amplitude in the *capillaries and veins* of the lung, as far as the left atrium.

The **mean velocity of flow** in the pulmonary artery under resting conditions is ca. 18 cm·s⁻¹. In the capillaries of the pulmonary bed it falls to a level approximating that in the systemic system, and as the total cross-sectional area decreases in the venous segment the rate of flow rises again (Fig. 18-10).

Special Functional Features

Lung perfusion and transmural pressures. Because the intravascular pressures in the lungs are relatively low, *hydrostatic* effects have a much *stronger* influence on flow through the lungs than through the various parts of the systemic circulation. In the apical regions, which in an erect adult are ca. 15 cm above the base of the pulmonary artery, the hydrostatic and arterial pressures are about the same, so that the capillaries are barely (if at all) perfused; at the base of the lung the pressures add, and the vessels are more distended [47]. Lung perfusion thus exhibits *pronounced position-dependent inhomogeneity,* which under some conditions can be reflected in *regional differences in O_2 saturation of the blood*. Despite these differences and the effects of the admixture of blood from the bronchial veins, the O_2 saturation of the mixed blood in the lung veins is 96–98%.

Moreover, the pressures in the pulmonary vessels are affected by the *intrapleural pressure* and the respiration-dependent *fluctuation of intraalveolar (intrapulmonary) pressure* (at most $+3$ to -3 mm Hg). Greater positive pressures, such as can occur during artificial respiration, decrease the transmural pressure and thus cause considerable increases in resistance to flow and reduced blood volume in the lungs (cf. p. 416).

Intrathoracic vessels as blood reservoirs. Because the pulmonary vessels are so distensible, the volume of blood in the lungs can be temporarily increased or decreased by as much as 50% of the mean total volume of 440 ml (Table 18-3) with only slight change in transmural pressure or distensibility. Together with the diastolic volume of the left heart, the volume of the pulmonary circuit constitutes the so-called **central blood volume** (600–650 ml), a *rapidly mobilizable "instantaneous depot"*. When a short-term increase in output of the left ventricle is required, for example, this depot can contribute about 300 ml of blood to meet the additional demand. These effects help to compensate for imbalance between the amounts ejected by the two ventricles, until enhanced venous return can match the stroke volume of the right ventricle to that of the left.

Low-pressure system. On the basis of the distribution of pressure and volume among the various parts of the cardiovascular system, the system can be subdivided in terms of *functional organization* rather than anatomy, into a low-pressure and an arterial (high-pressure) system. The *low-pressure system* comprises the venous parts of the systemic circulation, the right heart, the entire pulmonary circulation, the left atrium and the left ventricle during diastole; the *arterial system* consists of the left ventricle during systole and the arteries of the systemic circulation.

This subdivision reflects not only the distribution of pressure and volume (cf. Table 18-3 and Fig. 18-10), but in particular the largely *identical pressure-volume relationships* in the peripheral veins and the pulmonary circulation, in which regard the right ventricle does not act as a barrier. The mean pressure in the pulmonary arteries is thought to depend chiefly on the output of the right ventricle per unit time, because the changes in tone of the peripheral lung vessels are so slight; the right cardiac output depends on the central venous pressure by virtue of the *Frank-Starling mechanism*.

Changes in blood volume therefore, whatever the absolute pressure may be, cause pressure changes of about the same magnitude in the right atrium, the pulmonary artery and the left atrium, so that these parts

of the system can be regarded as a *functional unit*. The capacity of the vascular system and the state of contraction of the vessel musculature, as well as the blood volume, are taken as (relatively) *static quantities* in this view. When the relation between vessel capacity and blood volume is disrupted, balance is thought to be restored primarily by *volume regulation* involving reflexly elicited changes in vasopressin secretion, which become effective only after a relatively long delay (pp. 433 f.). Short-term equilibration could be achieved by changes in capacity, but in this theory the functional significance of such a mechanism remains debatable.

The *left ventricle* connects the low- and high-pressure systems. During diastole it is part of the low-pressure system, its degree of filling being dependent on the pressure in the pulmonary veins. During systole, on the other hand, the left ventricle functionally belongs to the high-pressure system, in which it is the driving force for blood flow.

Regulatory Mechanisms in the Pulmonary Circuit

Neural control of lung perfusion. The pulmonary vessels are innervated by *sympathetic vasoconstrictor fibers*. Many experiments on animals have indicated that the vessels in the lungs, like those of the systemic circulation, are under the *continual* influence of the autonomic system.

For example, when the baroreceptors in the carotid sinus are stimulated the resistance in the pulmonary vascular bed decreases, whereas stimulation of the chemoreceptors in the carotid body by hypoxia elicits vasoconstriction. The existence of *vasodilator* fibers has also been demonstrated, but their functional significance is not yet clear.

The local control of lung perfusion. When the partial pressure of O_2 *is low* or that of CO_2 *is high* there is a *local vasoconstrictor* response that evidently involves both the small precapillary and the postcapillary vessels of the lung. Local blood flow can thus be adapted to the *regional ventilation,* the perfusion of the more poorly ventilated regions being restricted in favor of those better ventilated. In the human these effects become apparent when the arterial O_2 saturation falls below 80%.

A number of substances such as adrenalin, noradrenalin, histamine etc. also cause constriction of pulmonary vessels, though these effects are frequently masked by the changes in transmural pressure brought about *indirectly* by the action of these substances on the heart and the other vessels.

Afferent innervation and central control of pulmonary circulation. The *baroreceptors* (actually stretch receptors) in the *pulmonary arteries* are situated primarily at the bifurcation of the pulmonary trunk and near the bases of the two arteries. Their function and the reflexes they elicit correspond essentially to those of the baroreceptors in the systemic arteries; that is, increased pressure in the pulmonary arteries causes a reflex pressure drop in the systemic system, and decreased pulmonary pressure raises the systemic pressure.

Under resting conditions the vasomotor influences on the pulmonary vessels are relatively slight; accordingly, the vessels are dilated. But because of the large capacity even small degrees of vasoconstriction bring about relatively large changes in capacity, with corresponding effects on the blood supply to the left heart, although the resistance to flow increases very little.

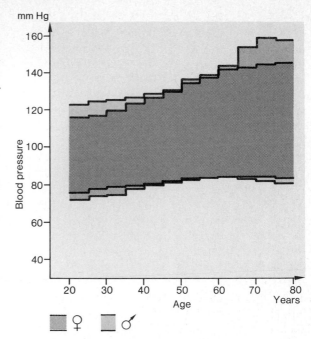

Fig. 18-37. Arterial pressure (systolic, upper line; diastolic, lower line) in men and women at different ages. (From data of MASTER et al. [19])

18.11 Circulatory Adjustments to Physiological and Pathological Circumstances

Human Blood Pressure

The level of an individual's blood pressure depends on *age, sex,* and *genetic and environmental influences,* as well as on other factors, some of which are unknown. When the diagnostically important **resting** or **basal blood pressure** is to be determined, these factors must be taken into account or, where appropriate, eliminated as far as possible.

Norms and age-dependence. Studies of the blood pressures of representative groups of people under approximately resting conditions reveal distinct interindividual differences, with a concentration around an intermediate value and a Gaussian (normal) distribution of higher and lower values. In healthy young adults the peak of the distribution of systolic pressure is 120 mm Hg, and that of diastolic pressure is 80 mm Hg. The great majority of people have systolic pressure between 100 and 150 mm Hg, and diastolic pressure between 60 and 90 mm Hg. With advancing age the systolic pressure increases to a greater extent than the diastolic pressure (Fig. 18-37). These effects are basically due to *loss of elasticity* in the vessels (p. 410). Up to age 50 women have lower blood pressure than men, on the average, whereas above that age the blood pressure of women is slightly higher.

Rhythmic Fluctuations in Blood Pressure

A continual record of blood pressure shows not only the **pulse waves,** which are called **first-order** pressure fluctuations or waves, but also slower rhythmic fluctuations. These **second-order** fluctuations are associated with *respiration.* When a person is breathing at the normal rate the inspiration coincides with the falling phase of pressure and the "wave valley", and expiration coincides with the rising phase and the "wave peak". One cause of these waves is a central coupling of respiration and circulation, but there is also a mechanical effect, in that the pressure and capacity of the pulmonary vessels, and thus the stroke volume of the left ventricle (p. 416), changes during the respiratory cycle. Blood-pressure fluctuations of **third order,** the so-called **Mayer waves,** have a period of 6–20 s or longer, the most common mean duration being 10 s; these are probably caused by fluctuations in *peripheral vascular tone.*

Blood pressure, like heart rate and many other physiological parameters, also exhibits an **endogenous circadian periodicity** that is synchronized with the 24-h rhythm of the environment by external entraining agents, so that pressure is maximal toward 3 p. m. and minimal toward 3 a. m. (pp. 153 f.).

Acute changes. In normal daily life the basal blood pressure is also influenced to varying degrees by environmental, physical or psychological factors; this influence may be direct (e.g., that of physical factors) or indirect, by alteration of autonomic function. The general rule that *increased activity* during arousal is associated with *raised blood pressure* and *decreased activity with lowered pressure* can be broken owing to gravitational or thermal effects on the circulatory system, so as to give an impression of a "paradoxical" blood-pressure response.

A classical example of an *acute* increase in blood pressure associated with a psychogenic alarm response (p. 436) is the so-called **anticipatory hypertension** that can accompany not only examinations or competitions, but also experiences such as a visit to the dentist. In such situations the blood pressure can reach levels corresponding to moderately hard work. Intensive *dreaming* can also be accompanied by considerably increased blood pressure, whereas in *quiet sleep* both systolic and diastolic pressure can fall to 20 mm Hg.

The changes in blood pressure associated with the effects of posture have been discussed together with the changes in other circulatory variables on p. 441; for the effects of *exercise* see pp. 442 f., and for those of *thermal stress* see pp. 443 f.

Food intake is followed by a moderate rise in systolic pressure, whereas diastolic pressure frequently falls slightly.

Pain also usually raises the blood pressure, though if the pain is prolonged blood pressure may fall. The blood-pressure responses to *visceral stimuli* vary; in some cases reflex decreases (e.g., following mechanical stimulation of the pleura) are observed, and in some cases increases occur.

Pathophysiology of blood pressure. When the blood pressure is *above* the normal range a state of **hypertension** exists. According to the recommendations of the World Health Organization (WHO), systolic pressures above 160 mm Hg and diastolic pressures above 95 mm Hg are to be regarded as hypertensive, although in view of the changes with age there can be no rigid boundary line between normotension and hypertension. Indeed, extensive studies of large population samples make it appear better to take the upper limit of normal blood pressure as 140/90 mm Hg in juveniles, 150/100 mm Hg in adults up to 50 years of age, and 160/100 in adults over 50.

Hypertension can be produced by increase of either cardiac output *(cardiac-output hypertension)* or peripheral resistance *(resistance hypertension)* or the two together. It is customary in clinical practice to classify hypertension according to etiology, as 1. **primary or essential hypertension** and 2. **secondary or symptomatic hypertension.**

Primary hypertension (ca. 85% of all cases of hypertension) has no clear cause, and could thus be regarded as a characteristic defined by position within the Gaussian distribution. There are indications that essential hypertension may be genetic in origin and is thus inherited. On the other hand, one of the possible etiological factors that have been proposed is a disturbance of the *distribution of sodium* within the organism, such that it is concentrated in the resistance vessels. Evidence in favor of this

suggestion is that blood pressure can be lowered by dietetic or diuretic measures that decrease the body's sodium content. Another proposal involves *hyperreactivity of the hypothalamic circulatory centers;* in this view the occurrence of hypertension would depend on the personality structure of the individual as well as on environmental factors. This notion is consistent with the observation that most drugs that reduce blood pressure act on the sympathetic nervous system; moreover, there is no doubt that in addition to genetic factors others – constitutional, social and environmental – can be involved in producing hypertension. On the other hand, the absence of any direct evidence of increased sympathetic activity or enhanced reactivity of the vascular system to constrictor stimuli shows clearly that these attempts at etiological interpretation of essential hypertension (and others not mentioned here) are at present only hypotheses. In this connection, finally, it should be mentioned that *frequent acute blood-pressure increases,* regardless of their cause, bring about hypertrophy of the smooth musculature of the resistance vessels; the resulting increase in peripheral resistance favors the development of chronic high blood pressure.

In the remaining 15% of cases hypertension is **secondary** to some other clinical condition. In about 10% the underlying disorder is in the parenchyma or vessels of the kidney *(renal hypertension),* in association with acute glomerular or renovascular disease, chronic reduction of the renal parenchyma, and other kidney diseases. **Endocrine disturbance** (pheochromocytoma, Cushing's syndrome, hyperthyroidism, etc.) is at fault in about 3%, and the remaining cases, with only a few exceptions, are associated with **cardiovascular disease** (sclerosis of the great arteries, aortic-valve insufficiency, aortic-isthmus stenosis and so on).

As a consequence of hypertension *secondary degenerative (arteriosclerotic) changes in the vessels* additionally increase the resistance to flow. The associated restriction in the blood supply can interfere with organ function, particularly in the brain, the heart and the kidneys, or when combined with high pressure can cause vessels to *rupture* (e.g., stroke). Impaired cardiac function on the one hand and increased demands on the other accelerate the development of heart failure *(cardiac insufficiency)* in all forms of hypertension.

Hypotension. Blood pressures below 100 mm Hg constitute hypotension. This condition can result from *decreases in cardiac output or in total peripheral resistance* or both. In most cases, however, reduced cardiac output predominates.

Hypotension, like its opposite, is classified etiologically as 1. **primary (essential)** or 2. **secondary (symptomatic).** Primary hypotension is more commonly found in young people of leptosomatic physique and with signs of constitutional asthenia and enhanced activity of the sympathetic system (tachycardia, cool and moist acral regions). Secondary hypotension appears in association with **endocrine disturbances** (adrenal insufficiency, adrenogenital syndrome, hypothyroidism, hyperparathyroidism, etc.), **cardiovascular disease** (aortic stenosis, mitral stenosis, aortic-arch syndrome, cardiovascular syncope, etc.), **infectious-toxic factors** (infectious diseases, intoxications), and **hypovolemic conditions** (losses of blood or plasma fluid, endocrine disturbances, etc.).

In contrast to hypertension, the *pathological consequences* of hypotension are relatively *slight.* Hypotension is of clinical significance only when inadequate blood flow disrupts organ function, as in assumption of erect posture (see p. 441) or shock (pp. 444 ff.).

Effects of Posture

Passive effects. Chief among the effects to which the circulatory system must adjust at the transition from reclining to standing are the hydrostatic pressure changes and the associated *redistribution of the blood volume* (p. 415). There is a *transient* pooling of 400–600 ml of blood in the capacitance vessels of the legs alone, most of which comes from intrathoracic vessels. As a result there are temporary decreases in *venous return, central venous pressure, stroke volume and systolic blood pressure.*

Active processes of adaptation. The passive effects are largely *compensated* by active adaptation mediated by the baroreceptors in the arterial system and the stretch receptors in the intrathoracic vessels. The location of the baroreceptors – in the aortic arch and carotid sinus – is such that when a person stands up the decrease in hydrostatic pressure here additionally reduces their level of excitation, which in itself initiates reflex compensatory reactions. The reduced excitation in the receptors leads to (i) *vasoconstriction* in the resistance and capacitance vessels, (ii) increased *heart rate,* (iii) a higher rate of *catecholamine* secretion by the adrenal medulla, (iv) activation of the *renin-angiotensin mechanism,* and (v) increased secretion of *vasopressin and aldosterone.*

Vasomotor and cardiac responses. The vasoconstrictor responses to standing involve the *resistance vessels* of the skeletal musculature, the skin, the kidneys and the splanchnic region, in such a way that blood flow through these regions decreases and the total peripheral resistance rises (Fig. 18-38).

The decrease in *brain perfusion* to be expected on physical grounds is largely *compensated* by myogenic and metabolically elicited autoregulatory vasoconstriction. Blood flow through the brain is thus only slightly diminished, reaching the critical level at which signs of *cerebral ischemia* appear only when the mean arterial pressure (in the cerebral vessels) falls below *60 mm Hg.*

Among the *capacitance vessels* it is chiefly those acting as reservoirs (i. e., the veins of the skin and the splanchnic region) that exhibit vasoconstriction.

As a result of the increase in *total peripheral resistance,* the blood pressure returns to about the initial level. The compensatory decreases in *vessel capacity* contribute to maintaining the central venous pressure at a level only slightly lower than before. Because of the increased *heart rate* the decrease in cardiac output is proportionally smaller than that in stroke volume (Fig. 18-38).

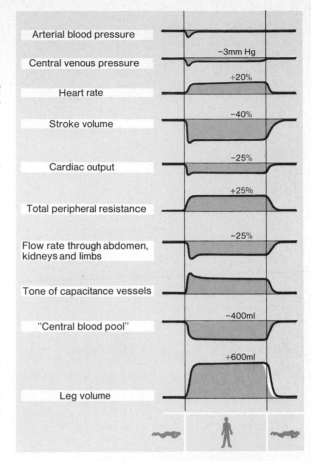

Fig. 18-38. Changes in various cardiovascular parameters at the transitions between the recumbent and erect positions. The numbers represent averages; individual variation can be considerable

Hormonal influences. As the flow of blood through the kidneys is reduced, there is an enhanced release of *renin* with corresponding effects on the formation of *angiotensin* and *aldosterone* secretion (p. 434). The intensified secretion of *vasopressin* additionally reduces renal fluid output, so that the plasma volume increases. These effects, unlike the vasomotor responses, become apparent only after a considerable latency.

The hydrostatic effects on vessels in the lower limbs can be lessened by the *pumping* action of the muscles. Even so, outward filtration predominates, so that during *prolonged* standing the *plasma volume decreases and the interstitial fluid volume in the legs increases.* When a person is walking or running the effects of the muscle pump on venous return and the capillary filtration-reabsorption equilibrium are of course greater because the contractions are repeated continually.

Orthostatic syncope. In some people who frequently, but not necessarily always, have low blood-pressure levels (p. 440), the adaptive mechanisms listed above

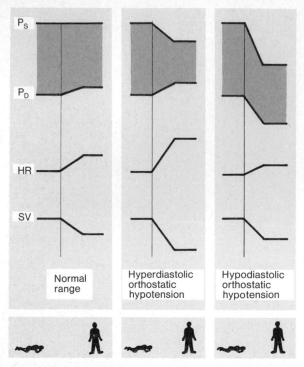

Fig. 18-39. Diagram of the changes in systolic and diastolic pressures (P_S and P_D), heart rate (HR) and stroke volume (SV) when changing from the supine to the standing position

Table 18-6. Organ perfusion and cardiac output when the subject is at rest and when performing different degrees of work. (After WADE and BISHOP [24])

O_2 uptake (ml·min^{-1}·m^{-2})	Rest	Easy work	Hard work	Maximal work
	140	400	1200	2000
Perfusion (ml/min):				
Vascular region:				
Splanchnic	1400	1100	600	300
Kidneys	1100	900	600	250
Brain	750	750	750	750
Heart	250	350	750	1000
Skeletal muscle	1200	4500	12500	22000
Skin	500	1500	1900	600
Other organs	600	400	400	100
Cardiac output	5800	9500	17500	25000

do not suffice for adequate circulatory function; their *blood pressure falls further* below normal when they are erect and the brain is inadequately perfused. Subjective symptoms such as dizziness and impaired vision appear, and the person may even lose consciousness **(orthostatic hypotension** and **orthostatic syncope** or **collapse).** Even entirely healthy people can experience the same difficulties in *warm surroundings,* where orthostatic tolerance is restricted because the

vasodilation required for thermoregulation dominates over the vasoconstriction required for control of blood flow.

When the sympathetic vasoconstrictor fibers are inactivated by *sympatholytic drugs* or surgery *(sympathectomy),* and in rare diseases of the sympathetic system, orthostatic tolerance may disappear altogether. On the other hand, the cardiovascular responses to change of position fail to appear when volume shifts are avoided, as can be done by wearing so-called anti-G suits. These are double-walled pressure suits in which the abdomen and legs are compressed in proportion to the effects of gravity on them. They are used, for example, to compensate the increased gravitational effects on the circulatory system associated with acceleration or deceleration of spacecraft.

Tests of orthostatic response. The regulation of blood flow following change of position is routinely tested by measuring heart rate and blood pressure at certain intervals while the subject is recumbent and erect. It is common in clinical practice to take diastolic pressure as the criterion for evaluating the orthostatic response.

When **circulatory function is normal** the *diastolic pressure* falls by no more than *5 mmHg* after 10 minutes of standing, and the *systolic pressure* departs from the recumbent level by *less than* ± *5%.* The *heart rate,* on the average, is *increased by 20%* and there is a moderate decrease in stroke volume (Fig. 18-39).

In cases of so-called *hyperdiastolic orthostatic hypotension* (80–85% of all cases of impairment) the diastolic pressure rises by more than 5 mm Hg, and at the same time the systolic pressure falls by an even greater amount, so that the *amplitude of the pressure oscillation becomes distinctly smaller.* There are relatively large *increases in heart rate* and decreases in stroke volume. The greater increase in diastolic pressure (which reflects a greater constriction of the resistance vessels) and the tachycardia result from a more pronounced activation of the sympathetic nervous system.

By contrast, in so-called *hypodiastolic orthostatic hypotension* both the systolic and the diastolic pressures decrease, with only slight change in pressure amplitude and little or no increase in heart rate (and moderately reduced stroke volume). In these cases the alterations in pressure and heart rate indicate a relatively low-level activation of the sympathetic system.

Exercise

In healthy young people who are not trained as high-performance athletes the *increase in cardiac output* during muscular effort, which results from increases in heart rate and stroke volume specific to the individual, rarely exceeds 25 l·min^{-1}. Moreover, the fraction of the cardiac output received by the skeletal musculature is *disproportionately increased,* at the cost of most of the other organs [48]. In Table 18-6 the distribution of blood among the different vascular beds of a human exerting himself to different degrees is summarized.

Distribution of the cardiac output. The increased perfusion of working musculature is brought about chiefly by **local metabolic mechanisms,** which take over from those processes responsible for increased perfusion during the anticipation phase (p. 436). The local metabolic control processes overcome the nervous influences during muscular work; in *resting muscles,* however, these fibers are effective in reducing blood flow, and they are even more so in the *splanchnic and renal vessels* (Fig. 18-40). But despite this **collateral vasoconstriction** the decrease in resistance to flow in the vessels of the working musculature is so large that the *total peripheral resistance* is lowered. The *blood volume* in the vessels of the working musculature *does not increase* despite the far greater number of perfused capillaries; because the vessels are compressed by the contractions of the muscles it actually tends to be reduced.

During light to submaximal work *skin perfusion decreases at first* but then increases for purposes of thermoregulation. During maximal exertion, however, the thermoregulatory effect is suppressed temporarily (Table 18-6). *Coronary perfusion* increases in accordance with the work the heart must perform, while *perfusion of the brain* remains constant at all levels of exertion.

Constrictor responses in the *capacitance vessels* of the skin, together with mobilization of blood from the splanchnic and hepatic vessels, provide a *larger supply of blood* to the working musculature. It is notable that when work is prolonged the tone of the cutaneous capacitance vessels remains high even though the rate of perfusion has increased. This situation implies that the resistance vessels of the skin in this phase have taken on a thermoregulatory function, while the capacitance vessels continue to function as regulators of blood flow. The venous return from the working musculature is enhanced by the pumping action of the muscles (p. 415), and the total venous return becomes greater due to the increased suction-pressure-pump effect of respiration (p. 416).

Changes in arterial pressure. Despite the decreased total peripheral resistance, cardiac output increases sufficiently to raise the *mean arterial pressure* further, the greater the load. Pulse pressure is distinctly enlarged, because systolic pressure rises more than diastolic pressure.

When *exercise stops* the blood pressure falls relatively rapidly, owing on one hand to the fact that vasodilation is only gradually reduced until all the metabolites have been removed and the O_2 *debt paid* (p. 551), and on the other to the cessation of the pumping actions of muscles (and respiration) that had been accelerating venous return. Cardiac output, heart rate, O_2 uptake and arteriovenous O_2 difference return to the initial levels the more slowly, the greater the work performed (for further details see pp. 550 ff.).

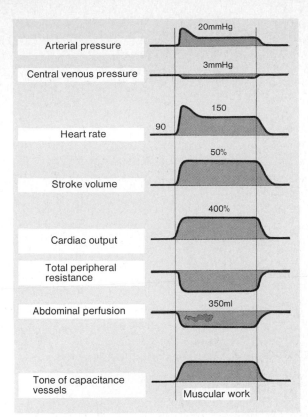

Fig. 18-40. Changes in various cardiovascular parameters when an erect person does muscular work (the curve for abdominal blood flow was obtained from measurements on recumbent subjects). The numbers represent averages; individual variation can be considerable

The effect of training. In trained humans the *heart rate* at rest is lower (down to 40/min) and the *stroke volume* larger than in those without training. The former thus achieve a given cardiac output with a lower heart rate than the latter. The *blood volume* is slightly increased, as are the maximal possible cardiac output and the capacity for O_2 uptake and extraction (for further details see pp. 559 f.).

Thermal Stress

Among the responses of the circulatory system to *thermally effective* ambient temperatures, changes in *cutaneous blood flow* play the leading role (cf. p. 449).

Heat stress. In a warm environment the rate of skin perfusion rises; with a temperature increase from 35° to 45 °C at an intermediate humidity it is approximately doubled. The tone of the *capacitance vessels* in the skin is reduced, and *heart rate* and *cardiac output* increase. The changes in *systolic pressure* are slight and nonuniform, but *diastolic pressure* decreases. All these responses vary widely in degree in different individuals. In some people subjected to ambient temperatures around 44 °C and high humidity (over 85%) cardiac output can rise to 20 l/min and diastolic pressure fall by more than 40 mm Hg – a situation that regularly produces the symptoms of orthostatic hypotension (p. 442) [48].

Cold stress. In a cold environment the *opposite responses* appear; the resistance and capacitance vessels of the skin constrict, and heart rate and cardiac output decline. The blood pressure tends to rise, and intense cold stimuli can elicit very large blood-pressure reactions.

This phenomenon is utilized in diagnosis as a "cold pressure test" (measurement of blood pressure while one hand is dipped in ice-water) of the responsiveness of the sympathetic innervation of the vessels. People with "borderline" hypertension and patients with pheochromocytomas often respond to this treatment with very large increases in blood pressure.

When thermal stimuli are repeated frequently the circulatory responses become weaker, an expression of **adaptation.** A similar effect, **acclimatization,** accompanies prolonged exposure to extreme climates, by mechanisms not as yet completely understood.

Loss of Blood

Decreases in blood volume owing to hemorrhage reduce the **filling pressure** of the vascular system (p. 407). The consequence is *diminished venous return and stroke volume.* The mean arterial pressure hardly changes with blood loss of up to ca. 15 ml/kg body weight, but falls considerably if more blood is lost.

Vasomotor and cardiac responses. Compensation for the above changes is initiated by several agents, among them the *baroreceptors* in the intrathoracic vessels, the atria and the arteries. Because their activity is diminished they exert a smaller inhibitory influence on the vasomotor and cardioinhibitory centers, so that reflex *vasoconstriction* and *increased heart rate* are produced. The vasoconstriction involves primarily the *resistance vessels in the skin, skeletal muscle, viscera and kidneys;* the coronary and cerebral vessels are excluded. In addition, vasoconstriction of the *capacitance vessels* in skin and viscera reduces the capacity of these regions and thus *improves the filling pressure* of the vascular system. The secretion of hormones by the adrenal medulla is accelerated and can contribute to enhancement of the vasoconstrictor responses (pp. 430f.). Independent of these reactions, the capacity of the vascular system is also reduced by the *reverse stress relaxation* of the vessels, and thus is additionally adjusted to the reduced blood volume.

Volume-control responses. Because of the constriction of the resistance vessels and decrease in venous pressure, the *capillary pressure falls,* so that more fluid moves from the interstitial space into the capillaries (pp. 418ff.). In this way the *intravascular volume* is expanded while the *interstitial* (and intracellular) *fluid volumes* shrink. When a human has lost 500 ml of blood, only 15–30 min later 80–100% of the lost plasma has been replaced by interstitial fluid. After greater loss of blood the plasma volume is normalized in 12–72 h, during which time the protein losses not covered by the initial influx of albumin from extracellular regions are compensated by accelerated synthesis. It takes longer (4–6 weeks, cf. p. 339) to replace the corpuscular elements of the blood.

Because perfusion of the kidneys is restricted *urine production* declines, and more Na^+ and nitrogen-containing metabolites are retained in the blood. The concurrent activation of the *renin-angiotensin mechanism* stabilizes the blood pressure. The connection between the sensation of thirst following blood loss and the renin-angiotensin mechanism has been mentioned above (p. 432).

Vasopressin secretion increases as a reflex triggered by the reduced activity of the atrial receptors, and that of *aldosterone* increases owing to the greater concentration of angiotensin. The associated increased retention of salt and water encourages the rapid *restoration of volume equilibrium.*

When cardiac output and blood pressure fall severely, additional functional impairment of the cardiovascular system (and other organs) may ensue and give rise to shock (see below).

Cardiovascular Shock

The term cardiovascular shock comprises all the states in which **inadequate perfusion of tissue** and an associated O_2 deficiency or (less commonly) impairment of O_2 release or utilization cause a persistant *deterioration in the function of vital organs.*

The inadequate tissue perfusion in most cases results because *cardiac output is too small* for the prevailing conditions. There are two fundamental causes of this situation. 1. *Insufficient venous return* can result from (i) diminished blood volume, (ii) reduced vascular tone, or (iii) greatly increased resistance to flow. 2. The *function of the heart* itself may be impaired. Less frequently, inadequate perfusion results from *primary disturbance of the microcirculation.* The different forms of shock can be grouped in a highly simplified way according to their pathogenesis, as follows: 1. *hypovolemic shock,* 2. *cardiogenic shock,* 3. *neurogenic shock,* 4. *septic shock,* 5. *anaphylactic shock.*

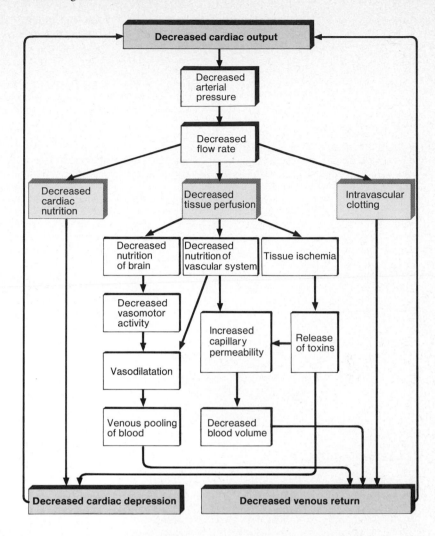

Fig. 18-41. Positive-feedback mechanisms involved in the development of shock. (After GUYTON [13])

The onset and course of shock are critically dependent on whether, and for how long, the *negative-feedback* (homeostatic) mechanisms of the circulatory system suffice to *compensate* for the disturbance, or the extent to which *positive-feedback* mechanisms resulting from the inadequate perfusion set up a *vicious circle* and progressively reduce the ability of the organism to adjust. Fig. 18-41 summarizes the most important events involved in the development of shock.

Hypovolemic shock. Hypovolemia (reduced blood volume) is brought about by loss of either *blood* or *plasma water and electrolytes*. The most common cause of hypovolemic shock is *hemorrhage*, whether external or internal, into body cavities or tissue (for example, by injury to blood vessels, gastrointestinal bleeding, rupture of liver or spleen, the cutting or crushing of tissue, fractures, and intra- or postoperative bleeding). A distinction is made between *hemorrhagic shock* (with blood loss only) and *traumatic shock* (in which damage to tissue secondarily affects the microcirculation and the clotting of the blood). Characteristic features of hypovolemic shock are *hypotensive blood pressure* (at least with respect to the individual's initial pressure), *tachycardia, low cardiac output, cold and pale skin, severe thirst* and *oliguria* (so-called *"cold shock"*). Development of

shock is reflected in the microcirculation by a transition from the reflex constriction of the *precapillary sphincters* to a dilation under metabolic control; the *venules* remain constricted, so that there is **sequestration** of blood in the capillaries. The accompanying increase in hydrostatic pressure causes more fluid to pass through the capillary walls, so that the *intravascular volume is further decreased*. As the process continues the capillary walls are damaged so severely that there is not only a progressive increase in filtration but an actual leakage of blood into the tissue. This shift of the balance in tone of the precapillary sphincters and venules appears to be a decisive factor in the development of **irreversible shock** (see below).

The extremely slow flow in the region of the microcirculation and the resulting increased concentration of CO_2 or products of anaerobic metabolism (lactic acid) in the blood favor aggregation of the erythrocytes (so-called **sludging**). The associated *increase in viscosity* further impedes flow in the affected vessels. Moreover, acidosis weakens the ability of the vessels to respond to circulating catecholamines.

In the region of the *capacitance vessels* loss of tone leads to **venous pooling** and thus to further reduction of the venous return. When the *resistance vessels* lose tone, the peripheral resistance is lowered and the arterial pressure drops still further.

Myocardial function is impaired during shock both by the insufficient coronary perfusion owing to hypotension and tachycardia and by acidosis. In addition, the myocardium is likely to be damaged by toxic substances released by ischemic or necrotic cells in the body. Because the restriction of blood flow through the kidneys is disproportionately large, *renal insufficiency* can develop.

The intense stimulation of the *sympathetic system* by the *ischemic response of the CNS* can give way to paralysis in severe shock, so that decreased heart rate and elimination of the vasoconstrictor influence cause a drastic further *deterioration of cerebral perfusion*.

This incomplete list of positive-feedback mechanisms makes it clear that the disturbances that elicit the shock can also reinforce it and lead to *progressive shock*. In *irreversible shock* the damage is so severe that it cannot be repaired by any therapeutic measures; the result is *death by heart failure*.

Hypovolemic shock by *loss of plasma* can accompany extensive burns or excessive elimination of plasma water and electrolytes through the gastrointestinal tract (e. g., in peritonitis, pancreatitis or intestinal obstruction). When shock follows *burning* the plasma loss greatly increases the viscosity of the blood and thus additionally impedes the microcirculation.

Similarly, *isotonic or hypertonic dehydration* (pp. 647 f.) such as are associated with chronic vomiting, diarrhea, excessive sweating, water deprivation, vasopressin deficiency, etc. can cause hypovolemic shock.

Cardiogenic shock. Cardiogenic shock occurs when the heart is incapable of pumping enough blood. It appears in about 15% of all cases of *cardiac infarction* (necrosis of the myocardium), with a mortality of over 80%. Moreover, cardiac shock can accompany *myocardial insufficiency, ventricular tachycardia, pulmonary embolism* and other illnesses.

The symptomatology corresponds to that of hypovolemic shock, with additional signs of *venous congestion* in the pulmonary and/or systemic circulations as a result of the impaired cardiac function.

Neurogenic shock. *Loss of tone in the resistance and capacitance vessels* leads to neurogenic shock when the capacity of the vessels becomes too great for the volume of blood available. The *mean filling pressure falls,* reducing venous flow and cardiac output. At the same time the *total peripheral resistance is lowered*.

This form of shock most frequently follows high spinal anesthesia in which the efferent sympathetic fibers are blocked *(spinal shock)*. It can also appear during *deep general anesthesia* owing to inactivation of the vasomotor center, or in persistent *cerebral ischemia* as a result of severe damage to the brain.

The category of neurogenic shock also includes the *fainting* induced by standing up in patients with various neurological disorders affecting the sympathetic nervous system or with sympathetic activity suppressed by surgical procedures or drugs (e. g., ganglion-blocking agents).

By contrast, **orthostatic collapse (syncope)** in organically healthy people (cf. pp. 441 f.) – like the fainting associated with *intense emotions* (trauma, fright, pain) – is evidently not due to failure of vasomotor control, but rather to an *excitation of parasympathetic structures* that leads to decreased heart rate and vasodilation in the skeletal musculature. Because of the resulting fall in arterial pressure and reduced cardiac output the flow of blood through the brain becomes inadequate, hence the loss of consciousness *(vasovagal attack)*.

In overheating shock *(heat stroke),* as in neurogenic shock, an imbalance develops between vascular capacity and blood volume, and in most cases it is augmented by *hypovolemia*.

Septic shock. Septic shock is a complication of infection by *gram-negative bacteria* (less commonly by gram-positive bacteria), and is what is generally meant by *"blood poisoning"*. The diversity of pathogenic organisms and sources of infection explains the wide variation in onset and development of septic shock. It is probably elicited by *endotoxins* that are released by the bacteria and injure the cells.

The early stages of septic shock are characterized by *hypotension,* though cardiac output and heart rate are usually raised. There is a conspicuous general vasodilation (so-called *"warm"* or *"red"* shock), with *reduced arteriovenous O_2 difference*. Among the proposed causes of these changes are impaired O_2 transport from the capillaries to the cells owing to increased affinity of the hemoglobin for oxygen, and a primary disruption of oxidative metabolism in the cells.

In more *advanced stages,* when secondary O_2-deficiency symptoms appear, cardiac output falls and a *vicious circle* becomes established as in the other forms of shock, with the primary cell damage progressively exacerbated by increasingly inadequate perfusion of the tissue.

In *anaphylactic shock,* a rapid allergic reaction to an antigen against which the organism has developed antibodies, large amounts of *histamine* are released along with *serotonin, bradykinin* and a so-called *SRS-A* (slow-reacting substance of anaphylaxis). In the initial stages *vasodilation* predominates in the arterioles, venules and veins, and at the same time *capillary permeability* is greatly increased. The hemodynamic alterations correspond largely to those in septic shock.

Other forms of shock. *Intoxication* by medicaments (barbiturates, tranquilizers, etc.) and *endocrine malfunction* (hypophysis, parathyroid, pancreas, adrenal cortex) can be accompanied by states of shock; here a number of factors may be involved, frequently including *hypovolemia* and *acidosis*.

Treatment of shock. The chief forms of therapy are steps to *eliminate the underlying causes* (by operation to stop the bleeding or remove the source of infection and by medication with antibiotics, antihistamines and so on), and *general measures* such as keeping the airways open and administering O_2. In *hypovolemic shock* the cause can be treated directly by *replacement* of the lost volume – by transfusion of blood, plasma or blood substitutes. In the other forms of shock as well (with the exception of cardiogenic shock with venous congestion) it is therapeutically effective to supplement blood volume. Additional measures to *raise blood pressure, improve cardiac force and the flow properties of the blood, eliminate acidosis* and so on may be required, depending on the kind of shock, but cannot be described here.

18.12 Circulation through Special Organs and its Control

Coronary Circulation

Cardiac perfusion. Under *resting conditions* blood flows through the myocardium at a rate of ca. $0.8–0.9 \ ml \cdot g^{-1} \cdot min^{-1}$, which with a heart weight of ca. 300 g amounts to about $250 \ ml \cdot min^{-1}$ or 4% of the cardiac output (Table 18-5). Under *maximal load* coronary flow can increase by a factor of 4–5 – that is, to a maximum of ca. $1250 \ ml \cdot min^{-1}$ (Table 18-6). The rate of perfusion of the heart is affected by changes in *aortic pressure,* by the *heart rate,* by *neural* activity and above all by **metabolic factors.**

The coronary vessels exhibit pronounced *autoregulation.* For details of other features of the coronary circulation see pp. 393 f. and 516.

Cerebral Circulation

Perfusion of the brain. The *average* rate of flow through the brain is 0.5 ml·g^{-1}·min^{-1}; with an adult human brain weight of about 1500 g the total flow is ca. 750 ml/min, or 13% of the cardiac output. Circulation through the gray matter, with its densely packed cells, is considerably greater (0.8–1.1 ml·g^{-1}·min^{-1}) than through the white matter (0.15–0.25 ml·g^{-1}·min^{-1}).

In cases of extreme neuronal activity such as generalized convulsions the overall perfusion rate can rise by as much as 50%. Similar local increases have been observed in particular regions of the brain that are especially active, but the influence of these on the overall blood flow is not very great.

Regulation of cerebral blood flow. Vessel diameter is basically controlled by metabolic factors, especially the *CO_2 partial pressure* in the capillaries and tissues, the *H^+-ion concentration* in the perivascular space and the *O_2 partial pressure.* Increase in the CO_2 partial pressure elicits marked *vasodilation,* with doubled P_{CO_2} approximately doubling blood flow. The CO_2 effects are based on the formation of H^+ by dissociation of carbonic acid. Other substances that increase the H^+ concentration (lactic acid and other metabolites) also increase cerebral blood flow. The cerebral symptoms of *hyperventilation tetany* (dizziness, clouded consciousness, muscle spasms, etc.) result from the opposite effect, a restriction of cerebral blood flow due to hypocapnia. Changes in O_2 partial pressure are somewhat less effective, decrease producing vasodilation and increase slight vasoconstriction. The well developed myogenic autoregulation helps to keep blood flow through the brain constant regardless of the variations in hydrostatic pressure with change of position. Cerebral perfusion is thus controlled largely by local mechanisms, myogenic and metabolic. The autonomic innervation of the cerebral vessels plays a subordinate and not yet entirely understood role.

Hepatic and Portal Circulation

Perfusion. The mesenteric, pancreatic, splenic and hepatic vessels are often called the *"splanchnic circulation"* because of their common innervation by the sympathetic splanchnic nerves. The blood flowing through the liver comes from the hepatic artery and the portal veins, that in the portal veins having previously passed through the capillary bed of the superior mesenteric and splenic arteries in the intestine, pancreas and spleen. The branches of the hepatic artery and portal veins, the interlobular arteries and veins, enter the peripheral parts of the liver through the triangularly thickened part of Glisson's capsule between right and left lobes; here they branch further to form a common system of large-bore capillaries that anastomose with one another, the hepatic sinusoids, which join in the middle of each lobe to form the central vein. The axial central veins fuse into collecting veins and these join as larger branches of the hepatic veins.

The mean pressure of 100 mm Hg in the hepatic artery drops in the vessels of the liver, reaching about 5 mm Hg in the central veins. The pressure in the portal veins, after the blood has passed through the capillaries in the intestines and spleen, is 10–12 mm Hg. Because resistance to flow in the sinusoids is low, the small pressure difference of 5–7 mm Hg between portal and central veins suffices to maintain blood flow here. In this large and highly elastic vascular bed even relatively small pressure changes cause considerable changes in volume. Such pressure changes can occur when flow out of the hepatic veins is impeded and when influx from the intestine is reduced.

Under *resting conditions* blood flow through the liver amounts to ca. 1.0 ml·g^{-1}·min^{-1}, making a total of about 1400 ± 300 ml·min^{-1} or about 25% of the cardiac output. The hepatic artery provides about 25% of this blood, a contribution that can rise to 50% with high O_2 consumption in the liver. The splanchnic vessels contain about 20% of the total blood volume.

About 40% of the oxygen consumed in the liver is supplied by the fully oxygenated blood from the hepatic artery and the rest by the blood from the portal veins – far greater in amount, but deoxygenated to varying degrees by its passage through the intestine, pancreas or spleen.

Regulation of blood flow. The vessels in the *splanchnic region* are innervated by **sympathetic vasoconstrictor nerves.** Constriction of these vessels can send a large fraction of the blood volume into other parts of the vascular system, and conversely – dilation greatly reduces the total peripheral resistance and augments the capacity, so that large amounts of blood can be stored.

Flow through the *mucosa and submucosa* of the intestine, which contain the glands, increases when the glands are active. The release of *bradykinin* (p. 425) is regarded as a possible cause of this increase, although it cannot be ruled out that other factors also participate in the response. In the *muscular layers* increased blood flow is associated with increased motor activi-

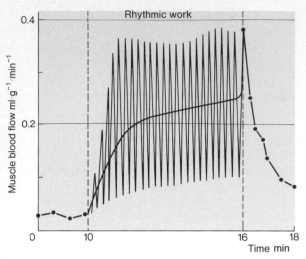

Fig. 18-42. Rhythmic fluctuations in blood flow through the calf musculature of the human leg during intermittent contraction. Flow between the contractions is considerably greater than during contraction. There is a progressive increase in mean volume flow. (After BARCROFT [3])

ty; here the vascular responses are elicited by *metabolic factors.*

The resistance vessels in intestine and liver are capable of extensive **autoregulation,** which during prolonged stimulation overcomes the vasoconstrictor effects after a while. This phenomenon, called *"autoregulatory escape",* is brought about by the enhancement of local metabolic control in the ischemic conditions following vasoconstriction, so that it predominates over the neural vasoconstrictor inputs. Pressure increases in the portal vein and the veins of the liver elicit constriction of the hepatic arterioles by way of retrograde (via the capillaries) activation of *myogenic* autoregulatory responses, so that inflow is inhibited. Because the vascular structures here are so complicated, many hemodynamic questions cannot yet be definitely answered. But the mechanism of *greatest functional importance* is likely to be the *vasomotor alteration of capacity,* by which the liver alone can make available to the rest of the system, on a *short-term* basis, as much as 50% of its normal volume of ca. 700 ml blood.

Renal Circulation

Perfusion of the kidneys. Under *resting conditions* the average blood flow is ca. 4.0 ml·g^{-1}·min^{-1}, so that the kidneys, weighing about 300 g, account for ca. 1 200 ml·min^{-1} or about 20% of the cardiac output. A special feature of the renal circulation is the presence of two capillary beds in series. The *afferent* arteriole feeds into the glomerular bed, which is separat-

ed from the peritubular bed by an *efferent* arteriole with high resistance to flow. Pressure in the *glomerular capillaries* is relatively high, ca. *60 mm Hg,* and that in the *peritubular capillaries* is relatively low, ca. *13 mm Hg.*

Regulation of renal blood flow. The vessels of the kidneys exhibit well-developed **myogenic autoregulation,** which allows the flow rate and capillary pressure in the nephron to be kept largely *constant* for arterial pressures between 80 and 180 mm Hg.

The renal vessels are innervated by sympathetic *constrictor nerves* in which at rest there is little tonic activity. In *the standing human* or after *blood loss* the renal vessels participate in the vasoconstrictor responses that ensure adequate perfusion of the myocardium and brain. Flow through the kidneys also decreases during exercise and exposure to heat, a response that helps to compensate for the vasodilation in muscle and skin, with its effects on arterial pressure.

Circulation in Skeletal Muscle

Perfusion of skeletal muscle. The *resting* blood flow averages $3 \cdot 10^{-2}$ to $4 \cdot 10^{-2}$ ml·g^{-1}·min^{-1}. The entire mass of muscle, ca. 30 kg, thus requires a supply of about 900–1 200 ml·min^{-1}, or 15–20% of the cardiac output. During *maximal work* the rate of perfusion can reach 20–22 l/min with a cardiac output of 25 l, i.e. 80–90% of the cardiac output, and it can be even greater in trained athletes [3].

Regulation of blood flow. The muscle vessels are innervated by both sympathetic *vasoconstrictor* and vasodilator fibers. When these nerves are maximally stimulated flow can be reduced to 25% of the resting level. On the other hand, the increased sympathetic activity in a subject expecting to perform muscular work can increase blood flow through the muscles by a factor of 4 (the complexities of this response are discussed on p. 436).

During *exercise* local *metabolic* control mechanisms dominate. But blood flow is also affected by the *mechanical compression* of the vessels when a working muscle contracts. If contraction is prolonged and is no stronger than half of the maximum possible, the initially abated blood flow increases again until it surpasses the original level. In the *relaxation phase* there is a transient further increase *(reactive hyperemia;* p. 423). During stronger contractions blood flow falls below the starting level by an amount related to the strength of contraction, and can cease altogether. In these cases the reactive hyperemia in the relaxation phase is correspondingly more pronounced.

When the muscle contractions are *rhythmic* blood flow changes analogously, decreasing during contraction and increasing during relaxation, though the mean flow rate is always above the original level (Fig. 18-42). This difference makes it understandable that dynamic muscular work, with a continual alternation between contraction and relaxation, does not tire the muscle as rapidly as maintained static work.

Cutaneous Circulation

Perfusion of the skin. Even in the *neutral range of temperatures* blood flow through the skin under resting conditions exhibits fairly *large regional differences* depending on skin temperature. Flow rates probably range from $3 \cdot 10^{-2}$ to 0.1 $ml \cdot g^{-1} \cdot min^{-1}$, or from 150 to 500 ml/min for a total skin mass of 5000 g.

Regulation of cutaneous blood flow. Cutaneous blood flow is controlled by two different mechanisms, the relative effectiveness of which varies in different regions. In the distal acral parts of the skin (hand, foot, ear) there are many sympathetic *adrenergic vasoconstrictor fibers* which even under thermoneutral resting conditions have a relatively high level of tonic activity. Dilation is thus produced by central inhibition of this activity. By contrast, vasodilation in the proximal parts of the extremities and the skin of the trunk is mainly produced indirectly, by the release of *bradykinin* associated with activation of *cholinergic sudomotor fibers* (pp. 425 and 539 f.). In all parts of the skin, vasoconstriction is based on an increase in the activity of sympathetic adrenergic fibers.

Because of the large *capacity* of the *subpapillary* venous plexus (ca. 1500 ml), venomotor responses can shift fairly large amounts of blood into and out of the skin, so that the cutaneous vessels serve an important function as a **blood depot.**

Thermoregulatory influences. A major function of the blood flowing through the skin is thermoregulation. Under *heat stress* the total blood flow rises to 3 l/min, and it can be still greater under extreme conditions. But the changes in perfusion rate vary considerably with location. They are greatest in the region of the *acral parts of the limbs;* in a finger moved from cold to warm surroundings flow increases from $1 \cdot 10^{-2}$ to 1.0 $ml \cdot g^{-1} \cdot min^{-1}$ have been measured, and sometimes the increase is even greater. The responses of vessels in the proximal parts of the limbs and in the trunk are considerably weaker.

The increased blood flow induced by heat results in part from opening of the many *arteriovenous anastomoses* (cf. Fig. 18-21), through which the greater part of the blood bypasses the capillaries on its way to the veins. The high heat conductance of the tissue makes this form of perfusion an extremely effective mechanism for heat loss through the skin (cf. pp. 539 f.). At the same time the unfavorable effects of non-nutritive increase in flow through the tissue (decrease in P_{CO_2}) are circumvented. Moreover, the low resistance to flow in the arteriovenous anastomoses reduces the loss of energy in this part of the circulation.

Blood flow through the skin during exercise. As part of the general adjustment of the circulation to the conditions of exercise, increased resistance to flow in the cutaneous vessels helps to maintain adequate arterial pressure. When thermal stress is superimposed, the thermoregulatory control mechanisms dominate, so that the fraction of the cardiac output available to the working musculature becomes proportionately smaller. The greater tendency for collapse to occur when work is done in the heat is due to this interaction.

Uterine and Fetal Circulations

Perfusion of the uterus. In the non-pregnant uterus blood flow changes in *parallel to the variations in metabolic activity* of myo- and endometrium during the menstrual cycle.

During *pregnancy* blood flow is considerably increased. In animals 20- to 40-fold increases have been observed, and are thought to be brought about by the local action of hormones (estrogens). Because of the high O_2 consumption and roughly 100-fold increase in mass of the uterus at this time, the *O_2 saturation* of the blood in the intervillous space is *only about 80%* despite the increased blood flow. Shortly before birth perfusion of the uterus decreases, evidently because the arteries are compressed by the increasing tone of the uterine musculature or by the contractions during labor.

Placental circulation. For the **fetus,** the placenta takes over the function of *lungs, gastrointestinal tract and kidneys.* The blood of the mother flows freely through the intervillous spaces, and the fetal blood flows through the capillaries in the chorionic villi, which protrude into the sinus-like intervillous spaces. Here the fetal blood takes up O_2 and gives off CO_2. The higher O_2 capacity of the fetal hemoglobin facilitates the transport of oxygen; however, O_2 and CO_2 exchange occurs less readily through the thicker cell layer of the chorionic villi than through the alveoli of the lung. Water, electrolytes and proteins of low molecular weight can pass the placental barrier in both directions.

Fetal circulation. From the *placenta,* the fetal blood (incompletely saturated with O_2) flows through the umbilical vein in the umbilical cord. *Most* of it passes through the ductus venosus into the inferior vena cava, where it mixes with the deoxygenated blood from

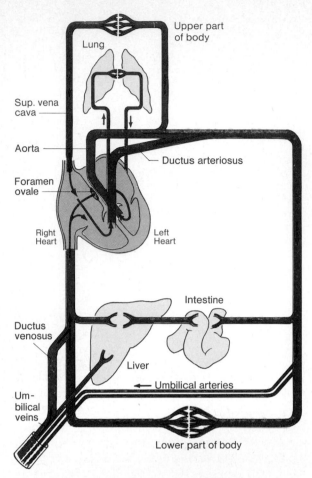

Upper part of body

Lung

Sup. vena cava

Aorta

Ductus arteriosus

Foramen ovale

Right Heart

Left Heart

Intestine

Ductus venosus

Liver

Um- bilical veins

Umbilical arteries

Lower part of body

Fig. 18-43. Blood flow through the fetal circulation. For details see text

the lower part of the body (Fig. 18-43). A *smaller* amount enters the left branch of the portal vein and circulates through the liver and the hepatic veins before entering the inferior vena cava. The mixed blood in the vena cava flows into the right atrium with an O_2 content of 60–65% saturation; almost all of it passes directly from the valvula of the inferior vena cava to the foramen ovale, and through this opening into the left atrium. From the left ventricle it enters the aorta and is distributed in the systemic circulation.

The blood from the superior vena cava primarily enters the pulmonary trunk, by way of the right atrium and right ventricle. Because of the high resistance to flow in the collapsed lung, the pressure in the pulmonary trunk during systole is transiently higher than in the aorta, so that most of the blood flows through the ductus arteriosus into the aorta; only a relatively small amount flows through the capillary bed of the lungs and back to the left atrium by way of the pulmonary veins. The ductus arteriosus opens into the aorta distal to the point where the arteries to the head

and upper limbs branch off, so that these parts of the body are supplied with the more highly oxygenated blood from the left ventricle. From the two umbilical arteries, which branch off from the iliac arteries, some of the blood flows through the umbilical cord to the placenta and the rest circulates through the lower part of the body.

Because the two *atria* communicate by way of the *foramen ovale,* and the *ductus arteriosus* joins the *pulmonary artery and aorta,* the two ventricles are *largely in parallel.* The double ventricle can propel ca. **200–300 ml · kg^{-1} · min^{-1},** of which about 60% flows through the placenta and 40% through the body. At the end of pregnancy the fetal arterial blood pressure is 60–70 mm Hg, and the heart rate is 140/min (120–160/min).

Changes in fetal circulation after birth. At birth the peripheral resistance is raised, when the umbilical arteries are tied off, so that the pressure in the aorta rises. The CO_2 partial pressure in the fetal blood increases when contact with the placenta is lost, which stimulates the respiratory center. The infant's first gasps for breath expand the lungs; as the resistance to flow through the lungs decreases, volume flow increases. Moreover, because the intrathoracic pressure is well below atmospheric pressure more than 100 ml of blood is sucked out of the placenta into the child's circulatory system *(placenta transfusion).* The pressure drop in the pulmonary artery and the rise in the aorta cause a reversal of flow in the ductus arteriosus. When the input of blood from the placenta is cut off the pressure in the right atrium falls, while that in the left atrium increases because of the added influx from the pulmonary veins. As a result, the pressure gradient between right and left atria reverses, so that the valvula of the foramen ovale is pressed against the atrial wall and an initial, functional closure of the foramen ovale is effected. The ductus arteriosus closes by contraction of the sphincter-like muscles. This is a slow process, not completed until several days after birth; the initial continuation of flow through the ductus arteriosus, from the aorta to the pulmonary artery, is important in ensuring adequate perfusion of the lungs. After about 1 week the pattern of circulation in the infant is like that in adults.

Of the *congenital* heart defects, persistent fetal connections in the form of a patent **ductus arteriosus** or **foramen ovale** each account for 15–20%. The associated impairment of circulatory function (when the ductus arteriosus remains open more than 50% of the increased stroke volume of the left ventricle can enter the pulmonary circulation, whereas with a patent foramen ovale the volume ejected by the right ventricle is usually increased) makes surgical correction of the defects essential.

18.13 Measurement of Pressure, Flow and Volume in the Vascular System

Pressure Measurement

Direct methods. Direct (intravascular) measurements of pressure require the introduction of cannulas or catheters into the vessels. In the past pressure was measured predominantly with simple **fluid manometers,** with mercury (for measurement of arterial pressure) or water (for measurement of venous pressure), for example, as the manometric fluids. But the inertia of such manometers severely damps out rapid pressure changes, so that they are suited only for the determination of *mean pressure*.

Membrane manometers can measure more rapid changes in pressure. In principle, these devices consist of a rigid chamber, one wall of which is an elastic membrane. The pressure in the vessel is transmitted across a rigid connection between chamber and cannula, and the displacements of the membrane, which are proportional to pressure, are recorded either *mechanically* (by a lever), *optically* (by a mirror) or *electrically* (by a pressure transducer). Modern membrane manometers, with their small mass and the minimal displacement of their very hard membranes, can monitor accurately pressure changes at 1 000 Hz or more. One kind of **transducer** is a wire or semiconductor crystal that changes its resistance (measured in a *Wheatstone bridge*) when it is stretched (by deformation of the membrane); these are called *strain-gauge manometers*. In another type the membrane is one plate of a *capacitor;* the electrical output represents the changes in capacitance as the pressure changes alter the distance between the plates. Still another possibility is to record the changes in the voltage induced in a coil by displacement of an iron core attached to the membrane.

For reproduction of rapid pressure changes to be *accurate in both amplitude and phase*, the *resonant frequency* of the manometer should be *10 times greater* than the highest frequencies to be recorded. In this case, provided that the measurement chamber and the connecting system are completely filled with suitable fluids and contain no (compressible) gas bubbles, the measurement is not affected by the inertia of the so-called effective mass and the fluid friction within the system. The original small electrical signal is amplified electronically so that the pressure curves can be displayed with a rapidly oscillating mirror galvanometer or a cathode-ray tube.

Indirect methods. The chief tool for the indirect measurement of *arterial pressure* is the *sphygmomanometer* designed by Riva-Rocci. In general the pressure is measured at the upper arm of a sitting or reclining patient. The device consists of an inflatable rubber cuff with a layer of non-distensible fabric on the outer surface. A hand bulb is used to pump air into the cuff and a needle valve to release it, so that the pressure in the cuff can be adjusted and read off from an attached mercury or membrane manometer.

In the **auscultatory method** (of Korotkoff), systolic and diastolic pressures are identified by characteristic sounds, which can be heard by placing a stethoscope distal to the cuff, over the brachial artery inside the elbow (Fig. 18-44). The cuff is first inflated to a pressure higher than the expected systolic pressure, so that the brachial artery is fully compressed and the flow of blood is blocked. Then the pressure is *slowly* reduced by opening of the valve. At the moment when it falls below the *systolic pressure* each pulsation is accompanied by a short, sharp sound (the *sounds of Korotkoff*), produced when the peak blood pressure transiently overcomes the cuff pressure and forces blood to flow through the compressed region. As the cuff pressure decreases further the sounds first be-

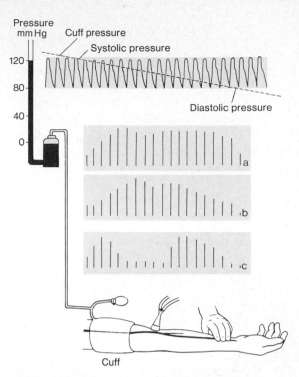

Fig. 18-44. Measurement of human blood pressure by the principle of RIVA-ROCCI. Diagram of the most common acoustic phenomena (sounds of KOROTKOFF) in the auscultatory method. For details see text

come louder and then either remain at a constant level (Fig. 18-44a) or become somewhat more faint (b). In some cases the initial increase in loudness is followed by a transient decrease, the so-called *auscultatory gap* (c), and a second increase. The *diastolic pressure* corresponds to the cuff pressure that has been reached when the sounds *suddenly become muffled and rapidly grow fainter*.

When the sounds finally disappear, at the latest, and probably when they take on a muffled quality, the cuff pressure is below the diastolic pressure. The pressure difference between the two phenomena is only a few mm Hg, so that for practical purposes it does not matter which event is taken as the criterion for diastolic pressure. The sounds of Korotkoff probably result from *turbulent flow* owing to the increased flow velocity through the region under the cuff where the lumen of the artery is smaller. When the cuff pressure is somewhat lower than the systolic level there is brief turbulent flow only at the systolic peak, and as cuff pressure falls this period extends over the duration of systole. On the other hand, at levels somewhat below diastolic pressure the artery is still slightly compressed, so that there is continuous turbulent flow until cuff pressure is so low that the normal laminar flow is restored.

In cases of *increased cardiovascular activity* – for example, during vigorous exercise or in conditions of hyperthyroidism and aortic-valve insufficiency – the sounds frequently persist long after the transition to the quiet-muffled quality, becoming progressively fainter (sometimes until the cuff pressure reaches zero). In these cases the pressure at which sound can no longer be heard is recorded in addition to the systolic and diastolic pressures.

The **palpation method** is useful only for determination of systolic pressure. The same device is used, and by palpation of the radial artery the pressure is determined at which the pulse *just disappears* as cuff pressure is increased and *reappears* as cuff pressure is decreased.

To obtain accurate results with the method of Riva-Rocci and Korotkoff, the cuff must be at the level of the heart, to exclude hydrostatic effects. The width of the cuff should be about half the circumference of the arm; the standard width for adults is 12 cm. For larger arms or for measurements at the thigh wider cuffs are required, and they must be smaller for children. When the cuff is too small higher pressures are needed to compress the artery and the results are incorrectly high, and when it is too broad the measured pressure is too low.

By using *elastic manometers* one can determine the blood pressure from the pressure pulsations transmitted from the artery to the cuff *(oscillometric method)*. At suprasystolic cuff pressures the pressure oscillations are small, resulting from the beating of the pulse against the compressed part of the artery. As soon as it falls below the systolic pressure and permits brief systolic opening of the artery oscillation amplitude increases, reaching a maximum at about the diastolic pressure, when the vessel is opened throughout systole but closed during diastole. At still lower cuff pressures, when the vessels are open all the time, the pulsations rapidly fall to a small amplitude which is then maintained.

With sphygmomanometric methods the blood pressure cannot be monitored continuously. By *automating* the measurement procedure, however, and by detecting the acoustic phenomena with microphones or the flow events with ultrasound detectors, it is possible to sample the pressure repeatedly at arbitrary intervals (the shortest achievable is about 30 s). Thus even this simple procedure can be used to learn something about the changes in blood pressure over relatively long periods of time.

Measurement of venous pressure. For clinical measurements of peripheral venous pressure an *arm vein* situated *precisely* at the level of the right atrium of the reclining subject is usually chosen. The position of the atrium in the thorax is approximately half the sagittal thorax diameter, or 10 cm, above the level of the back. When this condition is met values between 3 and 15 cm H_2O are obtained for the peripheral venous pressure. By placing the patient on his side with the arm hanging down, functional separation of the measurement site from the rest of the venous system is prevented by hydrostatic expansion of the veins, so that after correction for the level-dependent pressure differences conclusions can be drawn about the *central venous pressure*. Pressures measured under these conditions are ca. 4 cm H_2O *above* the pressure in the right atrium (because of the resistance to flow between vein and heart). For exact measurement of central venous pressure a catheter with a miniature manometer at its tip must be introduced into the right atrium, or an electromanometer attached externally.

Venous pressure can be estimated roughly by observing the state of filling of the veins in the neck. The neck veins of a seated person are *not filled when venous pressure is normal*. When the pressure exceeds 15 cm H_2O, the veins in the lower part of the neck stand out clearly, and when it exceeds 20 cm H_2O they are tightly filled. Another indicator of venous pressure is the level, with respect to the heart, at which the veins in the hand or arm collapse or fill as the arm is raised or lowered.

Measurement of Flow

A number of procedures, based on quite different physical principles, can be used to measure volume flow. The most important of those in current use measure the flow through an unopened vessel.

Electromagnetic flow meters. In this method the vessel is placed with its long axis across the field between the poles of an electromagnet; the passage of the electrolyte solution (blood) induces a voltage perpendicular to the lines of force and perpendicular to the direction of blood flow, and this voltage can be picked up by electrodes appropriately arranged outside the vessel. The voltage at each moment is proportional to the *volume flow,* so that pulsatile flow can be monitored in detail. With implanted probes it is possible to make long-term measurements of flow through vessels ranging in size from 1 mm diameter to the aorta.

Ultrasonic flow meters. This procedure is based on the measurement of the transit time of ultrasonic waves. The vessel is enclosed within the two halves of a cylinder with a crystal at each end, on opposite sides. These crystals act alternately as senders and receivers of a sound burst that passes diagonally across the vessel. The transit time downstream is shorter than upstream; from the difference between these electronically determined times the *volume flow* through the vessel can be calculated.

Another ultrasonic procedure can be used to measure the *velocity of flow* in superficial vessels transcutaneously – that is, through the intact skin. The ultrasonic waves are sent diagonally into the vessel from one crystal, and the reflected waves are picked up by a second crystal. As a result of the *Doppler effect,* the frequency of the reflected waves is higher than the sender frequency when the blood corpuscles are moving toward the receiver and vice versa; the difference between sender frequency and the reflected frequency is proportional to the rate of flow of the corpuscles.

With modified apparatus that also permits the diameter of the vessel to be measured, the *volume flow* can be determined.

Thermoelectric methods. Continuous relative measurement of **local volume flow** is possible with procedures based on changes in heat conductivity of tissue associated with blood flow. The system consists of two thermoelectric elements in a bipolar recording arrangement; one of them is kept at a constant temperature slightly above that of the surroundings by an electrical current. From the difference in temperature between the heated and unheated element (at the tissue temperature) the changes in blood flow can be calculated; the difference becomes less with increased volume flow because the heat in the region of the heated element is transported away more rapidly. The recording and heating elements can be mounted in a needle-like *"thermal probe"* to permit measurement of flow through the skin and muscles of humans. In experiments on animals such probes are also used to measure flow through the myocardium, liver and brain.

Venous occlusion plethysmography. In this procedure the **volume increases** in a limb or part of a limb that occur when venous outflow is blocked are used to determine arterial volume flow. The part of the body concerned is enclosed in a rigid chamber with an airtight opening through which the limb enters. Proximal to this chamber a cuff is inflated to a subdiastolic pressure that arrests flow through the veins without reducing inflow through the arteries. The resulting increase in limb volume is recorded. The *arterial influx* is computed from the rate of volume increase in the initial phase. As the veins become increasingly full the venous pressure rises, eventually reaching a level above the cuff pressure and restoring venous flow. At this point a new *volume equilibrium* has been reached from which, if the venous pressure is known, conclusions can be drawn about the distensibility or **compliance** $\Delta V/\Delta P$ of the vascular bed. It is also possible to measure volume changes in a limb relatively simply, by applying to it a transducer that generates an electric current proportional to stretch as the circumference (and thus volume) of the limb increases.

Measurement of human cardiac output. In humans the output of the heart can be measured with *indirect methods* that require no major surgery. These procedures either are based directly on the *Fick principle* or employ the related technique of *indicator dilution*.

According to the **Fick principle,** O_2 uptake in the lung ($\dot{V}_{O_2}$) is related to the arteriovenous O_2 difference (avD_{O_2}) and volume flow through the pulmonary circulation ($\dot{Q}_L$) as follows:

$$\dot{V}_{O_2} = \dot{Q}_L \cdot avD_{O_2} \quad \text{or} \quad \dot{Q}_L = \frac{\dot{V}_{O_2}}{avD_{O_2}} \tag{23}$$

Fig. 18-45 A shows a sample calculation, using values appropriate to resting conditions.

In humans under normal conditions the volume flow through the lung is essentially identical to that through the systemic circulation, so that data obtained in this way also apply to the *cardiac output* of the *left ventricle.* But because the O_2 content of venous blood emerging from the different organs varies, the venous blood must be sampled (by means of catheters) from the pulmonary artery, by which point it has been mixed. Similarly, cardiac output can be measured with CO_2 or foreign gases such as acetylene or nitrous oxide as the indicator.

In the so-called **indicator-dilution techniques** a certain quantity of an indicator *(dye, radioactive substance, cold fluid,* etc.) is introduced into the bloodstream as rapidly as possible, rather than continuously as is the case with O_2 uptake. The concentration of the indicator in "downstream" parts of the circulation is determined as a measure of the volume of blood that has taken up the indicator and transported it to this site. The concentration of the indicator at the measurement site can be analyzed in special cuvettes through which the blood flows or by "punctate" blood samples in rapid succession; it can also be measured without drawing blood by photoelectric recording. The dilution curves so obtained exhibit the following characteristic features (Fig. 18-45 B). The injection occurs at time zero *(injection time, IT);* after a certain *latency (L)* the concentration of indicator at the measurement site begins to rise *(concentration time, CT)* to the *first peak* (C_{max_1}); the *first-peak time FPT* $= L + CT.$ The subsequent *fall in concentration* at first follows an exponential curve, until the *recirculation* of the indicator from the various organs begins and produces further concentration peaks. The time between the first and second peaks is called the *recirculation time (RT).* For calculation of cardiac output the recirculation effects must be eliminated by extrapolation of the descending limb of the curve. In practice that is a simple graphic procedure in which the fall in concentration is represented logarithmically. Extension of the resulting straight line gives the so-called **primary curve,** the curve that would be obtained in the

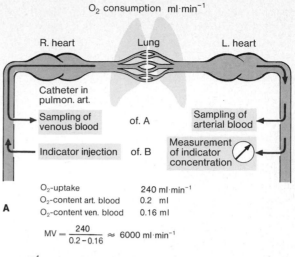

O₂ consumption $ml \cdot min^{-1}$

O_2-uptake	240 $ml \cdot min^{-1}$	
O_2-content art. blood	0.2 ml	
O_2-content ven. blood	0.16 ml	

$$MV = \frac{240}{0.2 - 0.16} \approx 6000 \ ml \cdot min^{-1}$$

A

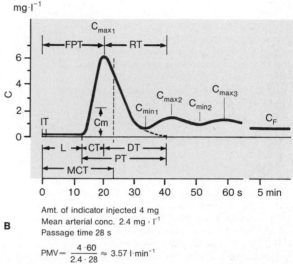

B

Amt. of indicator injected 4 mg
Mean arterial conc. 2.4 mg · l^{-1}
Passage time 28 s

$$PMV = \frac{4 \cdot 60}{2.4 \cdot 28} \approx 3.57 \ l \cdot min^{-1}$$

Fig. 18-45 A, B. Schematic illustrations of cardiac-output measurement by Fick's prinicple (**A**) and by the indicator-dilution method (**B**). In **B** the plasma component of cardiac output (PMV) is computed. Assuming a hematocrit of ca. 45%, the total cardiac output is thus ca. 6 500 ml

absence of recirculation. The distance between the first peak and the point where the straight line intersects the abscissa corresponds to the *dilution time (DT).* The sum of *CT plus DT* is the *passage time (PT).*

The *mean circulation time (MCT)* – the average time taken to transport *all* the indicator particles from the injection site to the measurement site – is obtained by taking the mean of the integrated surface under the primary curve with respect to time, and the *mean concentration* (C_m) is similarly obtained by taking the mean with respect to concentration.

Computation of the unknown volume (V_c) in which the known quantity of indicator (I) is transported from the injection site to the measurement site is done as follows:

$$V_c = \frac{I}{\int_0^\infty C \cdot dt} \tag{24}$$

where the denominator of the fraction is the integral of the *concentration-vs.-time curve,* which corresponds to the area under the **primary curve.** In practice this area is found by planimetry or by summation of many small rectangles with an identical baseline Δt. In this case we have

$$V_c = \frac{I}{\Sigma C \cdot \Delta t} \tag{25}$$

The **cardiac output of plasma** ("plasma minute volume", PMV in Fig. 18-45 B), for intravenous injection of the indicator and measurement of its mean concentration in the arterial blood, can be computed as follows:

$$\dot{V}(ml \cdot min^{-1}) = \frac{I \cdot 60}{C_m \cdot PT} \tag{26}$$

Total cardiac output is obtained from this by taking the *hematocrit* into account. Frequently used indicators are *Evans blue* and *indocyanine green;* the latter is removed from the circulation on its first passage through the liver, so that measurements can be repeated at brief intervals. With the aid of electronic computers the cardiac output can be computed directly from the indicator-dilution curves.

In a modification of the dye dilution method, *thermodilution* is monitored; here the injected indicator is a small amount of plasma or saline at room temperature, and the "concentration change" at the measurement site is actually a change in temperature. Such measurements can be repeated rapidly, because there is no recirculation.

Measurement of circulation time. From the latency (L) and mean circulation time (MCT) on the indicator-dilution curves, the *velocity of flow* between 2 points in the vascular system can be determined fairly accurately. By means of intravascular catheters it is possible to measure **partial circulation times** in nearly all parts of the vascular system. *Norms* for a healthy adult include the following: arm-ear latency 8–12 s, lung-ear latency 3–5 s, arm-lung latency 5–7 s, and arm-ear MCT 14–26 s. The *total circulation time* is the time required for an indicator to return to the site of injection.

In central parts of the circulatory system the local circulation time gives an indication of the cardiac output, in that high velocities of flow are associated with large volumes and conversely. In peripheral parts these relationships are less clear-cut, because the vascular cross-section can change over such a wide range.

For clinical determination of *partial circulation times* it is common to inject intravenously substances that elicit sensations of *smell or taste.* For example, the time for circulation from arm vein to lung capillaries can be measured roughly by injection of ether, which is detected in the expired air by smell; similarly the time from injection of Decholin or saccharin into an arm vein until its arrival at the tongue (10–15 s) is indicated by the bitter or sweet taste. This method of measuring circulation times is problematic, however, in that the time when ether is first noted in the lungs depends on the respiratory cycle, and in both procedures error is introduced by the imprecision of threshold-dependent subjective detection of the indicator.

Measurement of Blood Volume

Indicators can also be used to determine the volume of blood in the system. The dissolved or suspended quantity of indicator I is introduced into the vascular system in a volume V_I of fluid, and after it has become uniformly distributed throughout the blood its final concentration C_F is measured (Fig. 18-45 B). The

volume V_I is usually negligible, so that the *plasma volume* is given by

$$V = \frac{I}{C_F} \quad \left(or\ V + V_I = \frac{I}{C_F}\right) \tag{27}$$

A prerequisite of this method is that the indicator remain in the system long enough to become thoroughly mixed, and that its rate of elimination be taken into account. For precise measurements of *total blood volume* (cell and plasma volumes), an indicator for erythrocytes must be used as well as one for plasma. One can estimate total blood volume from plasma-volume measurements on the basis of the known hematocrit, but this method is less precise.

Among the indicators used to find plasma volume are Evans blue (= T 1824) and radioactive serum albumins; the red corpuscles injected to find erythrocyte volume may be labelled with ^{59}Fe, ^{32}P or ^{51}Cr. For blood-volume norms see p. 331.

18.14   References

Textbooks and Handbooks

1. ALEXANDER, R.S.: The peripheral venous system. In: Handbook of Physiology, Sect. 2: Circulation, Vol. II, p. 1075. Washington: American Physiological Society 1963
2. AVIADO, D.M.: The Lung Circulation. Vols. 1 and 2. New York: Pergamon Press, Inc., 1965
3. BARCROFT, H.: Circulation in skeletal muscle. In: Handbook of Physiology, Sect. 2: Circulation, Vol. II, p. 1353. Washington: American Physiological Society, 1963
4. BAUEREISEN, E. (Ed.): Physiologie des Kreislaufs, Bd. 1 Arteriensystem, Capillarbett und Organkreisläufe, Fetal- und Placentakreislauf. Berlin–Heidelberg–New York: Springer 1971
5. BRECHER, G.A.: Venous return. London: Grune and Stratton 1965
6. BURTON, A.C.: Physiology and Biophysics of the Circulation. Chicago: Year Book Medical Publishers 1965
7. CARO, C.G., PEDLEY, T.J., SCHROTER, R.C., SEED, W.A.: The Mechanics of the Circulation. New York–Toronto: Oxford University Press 1978
8. COMROE, J.H., Jr.: The peripheral chemoreceptors. In: Handbook of Physiology, Sect. 3: Respiration, Vol. I, p. 557. Washington: American Physiological Society 1964
9. FOLKOW, B., HEYMANS, C., NEIL, E.: Integrated aspects of cardiovascular regulation. In: Handbook of Physiology, Sect. 2: Circulation, Vol. III, p. 1787. Washington: American Physiological Society 1963
10. FOLKOW, B., NEIL, E.: Circulation. London–Toronto: Oxford University Press 1971
11. GAUER, O.H.: Kreislauf des Blutes. In: Gauer/Kramer/Jung: Physiologie des Menschen, Bd. 3: Herz und Kreislauf. München–Berlin–Wien: Urban & Schwarzenberg 1972
12. GUYTON, A.C.: Venous return. In: Handbook of Physiology, Sect. 2: Circulation, Vol. II, p. 1099. Washington: American Physiological Society 1963
13. GUYTON, A.C.: Textbook of Medical Physiology. 5th Ed. Philadelphia–London: Saunders 1976
14. GUYTON, A.C., COLEMAN, T.G.: Long-term regulation of the circulation: interrelationships with body fluid volumes. In: Physical Bases of Circulatory Transport Regulation and Exchange. Philadelphia: Saunders 1967
15. HEYMANS, E., NEIL, E.: Reflexogenic Areas of the Cardiovascular System. London: Churchill 1958
16. JOHNSON, P.C.: Peripheral Circulation. New York–Chichester–Brisbane–Toronto: Wiley & Sons 1978
17. LANDIS, E.M., PAPPENHEIMER, J.R.: Exchange of substances through the capillary walls. In: Handbook of Physiology, Sect. 2: Circulation, Vol. II, p. 961. Washington: American Physiological Society 1963

References					455

18. McDonald, D. A.: Blood Flow in Arteries. 2nd Ed. London: Arnold 1974
19. Master, A. M., Garfield, C. I., Walters, M. B.: Normal Blood Pressure and Hypertension. Philadelphia: Lea & Febiger 1952
20. Milnor, W. R., in: Mountcastle, V. B.: Medical Physiology. 13th Ed. Saint Louis: Mosby 1974
21. Share, L.: Blood pressure, blood volume, and the release of vasopressin. In: Greep, R. O., Astwood, E. B. (Eds): Handbook of Physiology. Baltimore: Williams & Wilkins 1974
22. Shepherd, J. T.: Physiology of the Circulation in Human Limbs in Health and Disease. Philadelphia–London: Saunders 1963
23. Uvnäs, B.: Central cardiovascular control. In: Handbook of Physiology I, Neurophysiology II, p.1131. Washington: American Physiological Society 1960
24. Wade, O. L., Bishop, J. M.: Cardiac Output and Regional Blood Flow. Oxford: Blackwell 1962
25. Wiggers, C. J.: Circulatory Dynamics. Philadelphia: Lee & Febiger 1952
26. Wood, P.: Diseases of the Heart and Circulation. 5th Ed. London: Eyre & Spleswode 1968

Research Reports and Reviews

27. Blaine, E. H., Davis, J. O.: Evidence of a renal vascular mechanism in renin release; new observations with graded stimulation by aortic constriction. Circulat. Res. 28, Suppl. 2, 118 (1971)
28. Blair, D. A., Glover, W. E., Greenfield, A. D. M., Roddie, I. C.: Excitation of cholinergic vasodilator nerves to human skeletal muscle during emotional stress. J. Physiol. (Lond.) 148, 633 (1959)
29. Brecher, G. A., Hubay, C. A.: Pulmonary blood flow and venous return during spontaneous respiration. Circulat. Res. 3, 210 (1955)
30. Colman, R. W.: Formation of human plasmakinin. New Engl. J. Med. 291, 509 (1974)
31. Crone, C., Christensen, O.: Transcapillary transport of small solutes and water. In: Guyton, A. C., Young, D. B. (Eds.): Cardiovascular Physiology III Vol. 28, p. 149. Baltimore: University Park Press 1979
32. Daly, M. DeB., Scott, M. J.: The cardiovascular responses to stimulation of the carotid body chemoreceptors in the dog. J. Physiol. (Lond.) 165, 179 (1963)
33. Folkow, B.: Description of the myogenic hypothesis. Circulat. Res. XIV, XV, Suppl. I, 279 (1964)
34. Green, J. F.: Determinants of systemic blood flow. In: Guyton, A.C., Young, D.B. (Eds.): Cardiovascular Physiology III, Vol.18, p.33. Baltomore: University Park Press 1979
35. Guyton, A.: A concept of negative interstitial pressure based on pressures in implanted perforated capsules. Circulat. Res. 12, 399 (1963)

36. Guyton, A.C., Coleman, T.G., Cowley, A.W., Jr., Manning, R.D., Jr., Norman, R.A., Jr., Ferguson, J.D.: A systems analysis approach to understanding long-range arterial blood pressure control and hypertension. Circulat. Res. 35, 159 (1974)
37. Guyton, A.C., Jones, C.E.: Central venous pressure: physiological significance and clinical implications. Amer. Heart J. 86, 432 (1973)
38. Guyton, A.C., Coleman, T.G., Granger, H.J.: Circulation: overall regulation. Ann. Rev. Physiol. 34, 13 (1972)
39. Guyton, A.C., Lindsey, A.W., Abernathy, J.B., Richardson, T.Q.: Venous return at various right atrial pressures and the normal venous return curve. Amer. J. Physiol. 189, 609 (1957)
40. Haddy, F.J.: Vasomotion in systemic arteries, small vessels, and veins determined by direct resistance measurements. Minn. Med. 41, 162 (1958)
41. Hainsworth, R., Linden, R.J.: Reflex control of vascular capacitance. In: Guyton, A.C., Young, D.B. (Eds.): Cardiovascular Physiology III, Vol.18, p.67. Baltimore: University Park Press 1979
42. Korner, P.I.: Integrative neural cardiovascular control. Physiol. Rev. 51, 312 (1971)
43. Longhurst, J.C., Mitchell, J.H.: Reflex control of the circulation by afferents from skeletal muscle. In: Guyton, A.C., Young, D.B. (Eds.): Cardiovascular Physiology III, Vol.18, p.125. Baltimore: University Park Press 1979
44. Lundgren, O., Jodal, M.: Regional blood flow. Ann. Rev. Physiol. 37, 395 (1975)
45. Öberg, B.: Effects of cardiovascular reflexes on net capillary fluid transfer. Acta physiol. scand. 62, Suppl. 229 (1964)
46. Pollack, A.A., Wood, E.H.: Venous pressure in the saphenous vein at the ankle in man during exercise and changes in posture. J. appl. Physiol. 1, 649 (1949)
47. Reed, J.H. Jr., Wood, E.H.: Effect of body position on vertical distribution of pulmonary blood flow. J. appl. Physiol. 28, 303 (1970)
48. Rowell, L.B.: Human cardiovascular adjustments to exercise and thermal stress. Physiol. Rev. 54, 75 (1974)
49. Schachter, M.: Kallikreins and kinins. Physiol. Rev. 49, 509 (1969)
50. Scott, J.B., Rudko, M., Radawski, D., Haddy, F.J.: Role of osmolarity, K^+, H^+, Mg^{++}, and O_2 in local blood flow regulation. Amer. J. Physiol. 218, 338 (1970)
51. Smith, O.A.: Reflex and central mechanisms involved in the control of the heart and circulation. Ann. Rev. Physiol. 36, 93 (1974)
52. Stainsby, W.N.: Local control of regional blood flow. Ann. Rev. Physiol. 35, 151 (1973)
53. Witzleb, E.: Venous tone and regulation of the circulation. In: Les concepts de Claude Bernard sur le milieu intérieur. Paris: Masson 1967
54. Zweifach, B.W., Silberberg, A.: The interstitiallymphatic flow system. In: Guyton, A.C., Young, D.B. (Eds.): Cardiovascular Physiology III, Vol.18, p.215. Baltimore: University Park Press 1979

19 Pulmonary Respiration

G. Thews

Subprocesses in the transport of gases. As a rule animal cells obtain energy by the oxidative breakdown of nutrients. Therefore they must continually be provided with oxygen. Moreover, if they are to function properly it is equally important that the end products of metabolism continually be removed. Chief among these is carbon dioxide. This exchange of gases between the cells and their surroundings is known as **respiration.**

One of the basic processes of gas exchange in animals is **diffusion.** In this process the molecules move from a place where their concentration is high to a place where it is lower, the work of translocation being supported by the *kinetic energy of the molecules.* The ad-

vantage of this passive exchange is that no energy is drawn from cellular metabolism. The disadvantage is that within an organism the distances over which substances can be distributed by diffusion are relatively short (less than 1 mm).

Where greater distances must be covered in the human body, convective transport processes are required. For example, the gas molecules are transported through the airways by convection (bulk flow) in the course of *ventilation.* Transport of gases through the body in the *bloodstream* is another convective process.

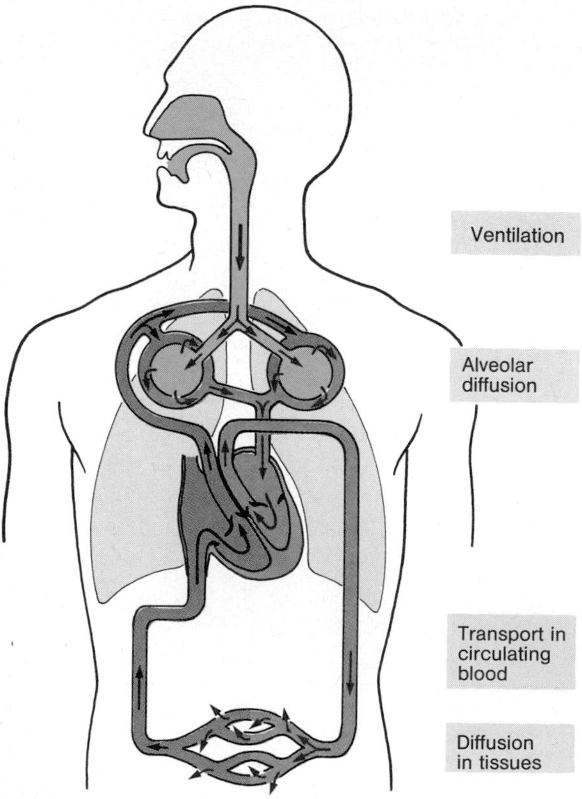

In Fig. 19-1 the four sequential subprocesses of gas transport are depicted, with oxygen as an example. During the movement of oxygen from the outside air to the sites where it is chemically converted by cellular metabolism, the order of events is as follows:

1. *convective transport to the alveoli of the lung, by ventilation,*
2. *diffusion from the alveoli into the blood in the lung capillaries,*
3. *convective transport to the tissue capillaries by the circulating blood,*
4. *diffusion from the tissue capillaries into the surrounding cells.*

The removal of the carbon dioxide formed in the cells as a gaseous end product of oxidative metabolism is brought about by the four subprocesses, in the reverse order.

Subprocesses 1 and 2 together consitute **pulmonary (external) respiration.** Subprocess 3 is called **blood gas transport,** and Subprocess 4 is called **tissue** *(internal)* **respiration.**

19.1 Breathing Movements

Respiratory Excursions of the Thorax

The ventilation of the alveoli necessary for gas exchange is brought about by a rhythmic alternation of **inspiration** (breathing in) and **expiration** (breathing

Ventilation

Alveolar diffusion

Transport in circulating blood

Diffusion in tissues

Fig. 19-1. The route of oxygen transport in the human (*red arrows*)

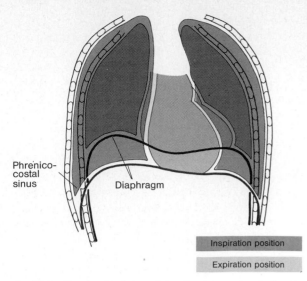

Phrenico-
costal
sinus   Diaphragm

Inspiration position

Expiration position

Fig. 19-2. Changes in shape of the thoracic cavity during the transition from the expiratory position *(black)* to that following inspiration *(red)*

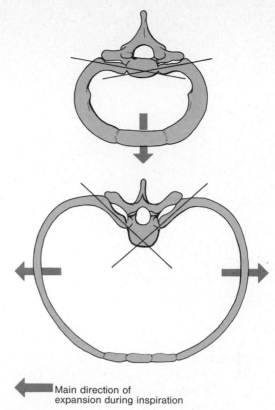

Main direction of
expansion during inspiration

Fig. 19-3. Alignment of the axes of rotation *(red)* of the 1st and 6th ribs. The *arrows* show the main direction in which the thorax at each level expands during inspiration

out). Each inspiration pulls fresh air, rich in oxygen, into the alveolar space, and each expiration expels oxygen-poor air charged with carbon dioxide into the surroundings. The air movements during inspiration and expiration result from the alternating expansion and diminution of the thoracic cavity.

Two events cause expansion of the thoracic volume: 1. **elevation of the ribs** and 2. **flattening of the diaphragm** (Fig. 19-2).

Rib movements. The ribs are connected to the *vertebral body* and the *transverse process* by flexible joints. The line between the two joints forms an axis about which the ribs can rotate. When the ribs are raised by contraction of the inspiratory muscles both the lateral and the anteroposterior diameters of the thorax increase (Fig. 19-3).

The axis of rotation of the upper ribs lies almost *transverse,* whereas that of the lower ribs tends more toward the *sagittal* (Fig. 19-3). The consequence is that during inspiration the upper part of the thorax expands primarily toward the front, and the lower part toward the sides [21]. Moreover, elevation of the lower ribs has a greater effect on the thoracic volume, so that the lower parts of the lungs are considerably better ventilated than the apices.

There is a simple **test of expandability** of the thorax, by measurement of chest circumference in the maximal-inspiration and maximal-expiration positions. The tape measure should be placed just under the armpits, while the subject holds his arms out to the sides. The difference between the inspiratory and expiratory circumferences should be at least 7–10 cm in a young, healthy man, and about 5–8 cm in a woman.

Movement of the diaphragm. The diaphragm forms the lower boundary of the thoracic cavity. It consists of a central tendon and the muscle fibers radiating out from it on all sides and attached at their other ends to the inferior thoracic aperture. Normally the diaphragm is dome-shaped, curving up into the thoracic cavity. In the expiration position it lies against the inner wall of the thorax over about three ribs (Fig. 19-2).

During inspiration the muscles of the diaphragm contract and *flatten* it, pulling the sheet of muscle away from the inner thoracic wall and opening the *phrenicocostal sinus.* The parts of the lung in this region are especially well ventilated.

This movement of the lower boundary of the lungs can be demonstrated by **percussion** of the chest. Taps below the boundary sound dull because the sound is damped by the viscera; taps over the air-filled lung tissue are more resonant. In this way one can determine the *position of the lung boundaries during maximal inspiration and maximal expiration*. The shift of the boundary so determined in a young, healthy man should amount to at least three intercostal spaces.

Types of respiration. Depending on whether the thoracic expansion during normal breathing results

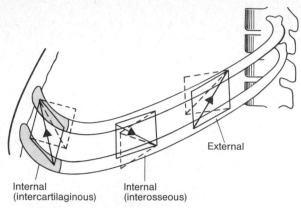

Fig. 19-4. Orientation of fibers in the intercostal musculature. The *red arrows* indicate the direction in which they pull during inspiration (external and intercartilaginous internal fibers) or expiration (interosseous internal fibers), and the dashed lines and quadrangles show the resulting positions

chiefly from elevation of the ribs or more from depression of the diaphragm, the respiration is of the **costal (thoracic) type** or the **abdominal type.** In thoracic respiration the work of breathing is done primarily by the intercostal musculature, the diaphragm tending to follow passively the pressure changes within the thorax. In abdominal respiration the stronger contraction of the diaphragm muscle displaces the abdominal viscera to a greater extent, so that during inspiration the abdomen bulges outward.

It was once thought that women by nature had costal respiration and men, abdominal respiration. It has since been shown that the type of breathing depends more on *age* (the mobility of the thorax decreases with age) and *clothing* (cinched waists restrict abdominal movement), and varies with *type of work* (manual laborers mainly use abdominal breathing). In the last months of *pregnancy* abdominal respiration is naturally restricted, and is supplemented by costal respiration. With regard to the mechanics of respiration and blood circulation, abdominal respiration can be considered the more effective of the two, because it allows the lungs to be more thoroughly ventilated and facilitates the return of venous blood from the abdomen to the heart. For this reason abdominal breathing predominates among such people as manual laborers, mountain climbers and singers.

Function of the Respiratory Muscles

Regular respiratory muscles. During quiet breathing the intercostal musculature and the diaphragm normally suffice to change the shape of the thoracic cavity [8, 9]. The **inspiratory muscles** of the rib cage are the *external intercostals* and the *intercartilaginous* parts of the *internal intercostals* (the anterior fibers, which extend between the cartilaginous ends of the ribs). The fibers of both these elements are oriented in such a

way that the insertion on the lower rib is further from the center of rotation than the point of origin of the fiber on the upper rib. When the fiber contracts the *moment of torque* is greater for the lower rib, so that it is raised toward the rib above it. In this way all the inspiratory muscles cooperate to elevate the thorax.

The most effective of the inspiratory muscles in continual operation, however, is the *diaphragm,* innervated by the phrenic nerve (from C_3–C_5). During expiration the contractile tension in the diaphragm decreases, but even in this phase a certain muscle tone is retained. This tone is eliminated only after transection of the phrenic nerve; when this happens on one side the pressure of the viscera and the pull exerted by the lung cause the diaphragm on this side to bulge far up into the thoracic cavity. In this situation the lower parts of the lung are largely immobilized.

The **expiratory muscles** under normal conditions comprise only the *internal intercostals.* Their fibers are oriented in such a way that when they contract the upper rib is drawn down toward the lower, and the thorax as a whole is depressed (Fig. 19-4). The expiratory musculature need not be as extensive as that for inspiration, because there are additional forces that aid expiration (pp. 459, 467).

Accessory muscles of respiration. When more respiratory work must be done – particularly when breathing is difficult and the subjective feeling of shortness of breath *(dyspnea)* develops – accessory muscles can supplement the muscles regularly used for breathing.

The **accessory inspiratory muscles** include all those that are attached to the pectoral girdle, the head or the spine and can lift the ribs. Foremost among these are the *major and minor pectorals,* the *scalenes,* the *sternocleidomastoids,* and parts of the *serratus* muscles (Fig. 19-5). In order for these to be employed in respiration, their points of origin must be fixed by other muscles or stabilized in some other way. A typical example is the behavior of a breathless person (perhaps during an asthmatic attack) who braces his arms against a firm object to immobilize his shoulders, so that the accessory muscles attached there can come into play. Often the head is bent backward as well, so that the scalenes and sternocleidomastoids can elevate the ribs more effectively.

The main **accessory expiratory muscles** are the *abdominal muscles* that pull the ribs down and compress the abdomen, forcing the viscera and the diaphragm upward.

Transmission of Thorax Motion to the Lung

Pleural pressure. The lung is closely apposed to the inner wall of the thorax over its entire surface, and remains so during the respiratory excursions of the wall even though there are no structures connecting the two. This is possible because the *capillary gap between the visceral pleura and the parietal pleura is filled with* *fluid* that cannot expand. The two sheets of pleura are thus held close together, although they can slip sideways with respect to one another. This capacity for transverse motion is necessary in order that the complex changes in shape of the thoracic cavity (for example, when the phrenicocostal sinus opens) can be transmitted to the lungs without distorting them. In cases of *pleurisy* the membranes become inflamed; if as a consequence they fuse together respiration in this region is hampered considerably.

There is a certain amount of **tensile stress** in the surface of the lung, because of the stretching of the elastic parenchyma elements and the surface tension of the alveoli (p. 467); this force, if not opposed, would reduce the lung volume (Fig. 19-6). The tensile stress can be demonstrated by inserting a fluid-filled cannula inside the chest wall in such a way that its tip lies in the interpleural space, and connecting the cannula to a manometer. The pressure reading on the manometer is then 3–5 cm H_2O (0.3–0.5 kPa) below atmospheric pressure at the end of expiration, and 6–8 cm H_2O (0.6–0.8 kPa) below it at the end of inspiration. The *pressure difference between the interpleural space and the outside of the body* is, as a rule, called simply the *pleural pressure* for convenience. Only the fact that the term actually denotes a pressure difference makes it understandable that the pleural pressure is expressed as a negative quantity.

The measurement of pleural pressure changes. Because direct measurement of pleural pressure (Fig. 19-6) involves the risk of damaging the lung, a less hazardous, indirect method is usually employed for humans. Instead of the pressure changes in the interpleural space, the changes in **esophageal pressure** are measured [49]. The two pressures are approximately the same, because (i) the esophagus, though outside the lung, is within the thorax and (ii) the wall of the esophagus is flexible and thus transmits the pressure changes faithfully. In practice a thin catheter with a balloon 10 cm long at its end is introduced into the esophagus. When the balloon is lying in the thoracic part of the esophagus, a manometer attached to the catheter registers with sufficient accuracy the interpleural pressure changes associated with respiration.

Pneumothorax. The close contact between the surface of the lung and the inner surface of the chest wall is maintained only as long as there is no opening into the interpleural space. If the chest wall or the lung is injured so as to let air into the space the lung *collapses* – its elastic and surface tensions pull it together toward the hilus. *Filling of the space between the pleurae with air is called pneumothorax* [9, 13, 18, 20]. The collapsed lung, having lost contact with the thorax wall, can follow the respiratory movements only incompletely or not at all, so that effective exchange of gases is impossible. If the pneumothorax is restricted to one side the blood can become sufficiently oxygenated and cleared of CO_2 in the other half of the lung, provided that no great physical exertion is required. In time, the air within the interpleural space is resorbed; as this happens the lung expands until it again fills the whole thoracic cavity. Bilateral pneumothorax, however, is lethal unless ventilation is artificially maintained.

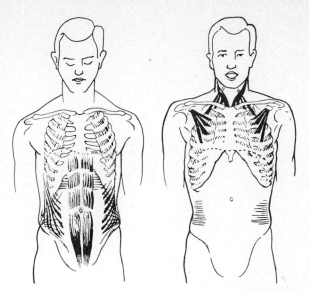

Fig. 19-5. Accessory respiratory musculature. *Left:* accessory muscles for expiration; *right:* important accessory muscles for inspiration. After [4]

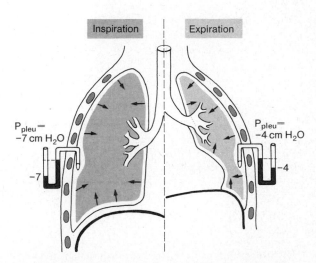

Fig. 19-6. Pleural pressures during breathing. The elastic forces in the lung (which pull in the direction of the *red arrows*) cause the pressure in the interpleural space to be "negative" with respect to the outside of the body; this can be demonstrated by an appropriately positioned manometer

Unilateral pneumothorax is sometimes induced for *therapeutic* purposes, to improve the conditions for healing of tuberculosis by placing one lung at rest. Because the process of healing usually takes a fairly long time, the artificial pneumothorax must be kept up by repeated injections of air to replace what has been resorbed.

Because the lung collapses when the thorax is opened, it used to be impossible to perform **operations on the lung** or the heart. Now procedures are available by which collapse can easily be prevented [10]. The airways of the patient are connected with a *respirator* by way of an airtight *tracheal tube*. The rhythmic pressure changes produced by the machine can be adjusted such that the lung becomes fully expanded in the inspiration phase.

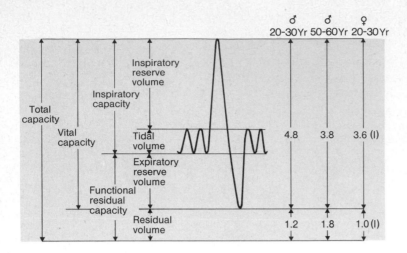

Fig. 19-7. Lung volumes and capacities. The numerical values of vital capacity and residual volume *(right)* vary with age and sex

The lung of the newborn. The fetal lung and that of the newborn before the first breath contain no air at all. This fact is helpful in forensic medicine, as it enables one to determine whether death occurred before or after the first breath. The excised lung is placed in water; if it contains no air it sinks, but if air has entered the alveoli, it floats.

The pleural pressure relationships in the newborn differ from those in an adult. A few minutes after the first breath is drawn, the pleural pressure at the end of inspiration is − 10 cm H_2O (− 1 kPa) [3]. At the end of expiration, however, the pressure difference between the interpleural space and the outside air is zero, so that opening of the thorax does not lead to collapse of the lung. Only gradually does the lung develop a state of greater tensile stress at the end of expiration.

19.2   Ventilation

Lung Volumes and Capacities

The **ventilation** of the lungs depends on the depth of each breath **(tidal volume)** and the number of breaths per unit time **(respiratory frequency).** Both of these can vary over a wide range, depending on the body's requirements.

Subdivisions of lung volume. The tidal volume at rest is small compared with the total volume of gas in the lung. That is, both at inspiration and at expiration a considerable volume of air can be moved in addition to the normal tidal volume. But even the deepest breathing cannot expel all the air from the lungs; a certain amount of air always remains in the alveoli and the airways leading to them. For quantitative evaluation of these relationships the lung volume has been subdivided into a number of components, as follows [7, 9]; here the term *capacity* refers to sets of two or more components (Fig. 19-7):

1. *Tidal volume:* the volume exchanged in normal inspiration or expiration.
2. *Inspiratory reserve volume:* the volume that can still be inhaled at the end of a normal inspiration.
3. *Expiratory reserve volume:* the volume that can still be exhaled at the end of a normal expiration.
4. *Residual volume:* the volume remaining in the lungs after maximal expiration.
5. *Vital capacity:* the greatest volume that can be exhaled after maximal inspiration; the sum of 1, 2 and 3.
6. *Inspiratory capacity:* the greatest volume that can be inhaled after normal expiration; the sum of 1 and 2.
7. *Functional residual capacity:* the volume remaining in the lung after normal expiration; the sum of 3 and 4.
8. *Total capacity:* the volume in the lung after maximal inspiration; the sum of 4 and 5.

The only components in this list that are of much practical significance, apart from the *tidal volume,* are the *vital capacity* and the *functional residual capacity.*

Vital capacity. The vital capacity (VC) is a measure of the *expansibility of lungs and thorax.* It is not, despite the name, a "vital" quantity, because even when extreme demands are made on respiration breathing is never as deep as is potentially achievable.

It is not practical to give a single "norm" for vital capacity, for it depends on a number of parameters such as *age, sex, size and position of the body,* and *state of training.*

As Fig. 19-8 shows, vital capacity decreases with age, especially after the 40th year [14], owing to loss of lung elasticity and increasing restriction of thoracic mobility. The average VC of women is about 25% smaller than that of men. That height should play a role is obvious, for the thorax is in proportion to

Ventilation

the rest of the body. An empirical rule for the young man is as follows[41]:

$$VC(l) = 2.5 \times height(m) \quad (1)$$

A man 180 cm tall would thus have a vital capacity of 4.5 liters. Body position is significant in that the vital capacity of people standing erect is somewhat greater than that of those lying down, because in the upright position there is less blood in the lungs. Most indications of VC refer to recumbent subjects. Finally, vital capacity depends on the state of training. Athletes trained for endurance sports have a considerably greater vital capacity than untrained people. Especially large VCs (up to 8 liters) are found in swimmers and rowers, whose accessory respiratory muscles (major and minor pectorals) are particularly well developed. The chief significance of vital capacity is in the area of diagnosis (p. 471).

Functional residual capacity. The physiological significance of the functional residual capacity (FRC) lies in *equalization of the inspiratory and expiratory O_2 or CO_2 concentrations in the alveolar space.* If the fresh air should move directly into the alveoli, without mixing with gas already in the lungs, the concentrations of gases in the alveoli would increase and decrease in alternation, according to the phase of respiration. Instead, it is mixed with the gas in the lungs – the FRC is several times the volume of the newly inhaled air – and therefore the fluctuations in composition of the alveolar gas mixture are relatively slight. The magnitude of the FRC, the sum of residual volume and expiratory reserve volume, depends on various parameters. On the average the FRC of young men is 2.4 liters, and in older men it is 3.4 liters [10]. The FRC of women is less than that of men by about 25%.

Measurement of Lung Volumes and Volumes Respired

The volumes of air inhaled and exhaled can be recorded directly by means of a **spirometer** or a **pneumotachograph.** By contrast, residual volume and functional residual capacity can be measured only indirectly.

Spirometry. Spirometers are devices that can hold varying volumes of gas at constant pressure (Fig. 19-10). The *bell gasometer* is the most common type; this is a cylinder inverted into a tank of water so as to trap a certain volume of gas, which is thus isolated from the outside air. The weight of the bell is balanced out by a counterweight. A wide tube with a mouthpiece provides communication between the enclosed space and the airways of the subject. During expiration the volume within the spirometer increases and the bell rises, and during inspiration it sinks; these movements can be read off from a calibrated scale or recorded with a writing lever on a kymograph drum **(spirogram).**

Pneumotachography. When respiration is to be recorded over a longer period, a so-called *open spirometric system* offers considerable advantages. Here what is monitored is not the volume itself but the *flow rate* (Fig. 19-9). This is done with a *pneumota-*

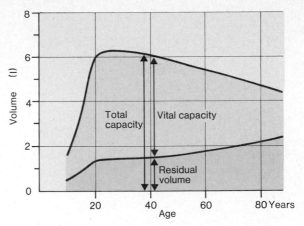

Fig. 19-8. Age-dependence of total capacity, vital capacity and residual volume in people of average height. After[14]

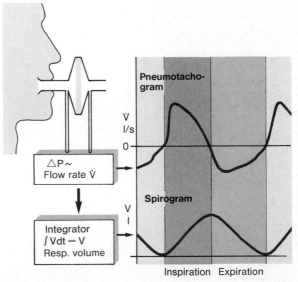

Fig. 19-9. Principle of operation of the pneumotachograph. The pressure difference across a resistance part of the flow path near the mouthpiece is proportional to volume flow $\dot{V}$ (pneumotachogram). Integration of $\dot{V}$ over time gives the ventilated volume (spirogram)

chograph, a device consisting basically of a large-diameter tube incorporating a small resistance to flow. When the respired air flows through the tube a small pressure difference is created between the beginning and the end of the passage, and this can be measured with two pressure transducers. *The pressure difference is directly proportional to the volume flow* – that is, to the amount of air passing a cross section of the tube per unit time. The record of volume flow is called the **pneumotachogram.** From such a curve of volume displaced per unit time, dV/dt, the required volume V can be derived by integration, because

$$V = \int \frac{dV}{dt} \, dt.$$ In most pneumotachographs this integration is

done electronically, so that the curve of respired volume (spirogram) can be recorded directly along with the pneumotachogram.

Measurement of functional residual capacity (FRC). Because the FRC is the volume remaining in the lung at the end of each ex-

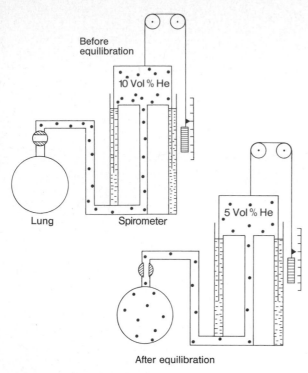

Before
equilibration

10 Vol % He

5 Vol % He

Lung   Spirometer

After equilibration

Fig. 19-10. Principle of the helium-dilution method of measuring functional residual capacity. Initial condition *above:* helium *(red dots)* is restricted to the spirometer system, at a concentration of 10 vol.%. Final situation after He dilution *(below):* helium has become uniformly distributed in the lung (residual capacity) and spirometer, reducing its concentration to 5 vol.%. After [10]

piration, it can be determined only by indirect methods. In principle the technique is to introduce a foreign gas (helium) into the lung *(dilution method)* or to drive the nitrogen already present out of the lung by breathing pure oxygen *(washout method).* In either case, the volume can be determined from the final concentration of the gas [10].

The **helium-dilution method** is illustrated in Fig. 19-10. A closed spirometer system is filled with, say, 3 liters of a gaseous mixture containing 2.7 l O_2 and 0.3 l He. The initial He concentration is thus $F_{He_1} = 0.1$ ml He/ml mixture (F stands for fraction). At the end of a normal expiration the subject is connected to the system, so that during the following breaths the He molecules become uniformly distributed throughout the lung volume V_{FRC} and the spirometer volume V_{Sp}. (Helium diffuses so slowly through tissue that for practical purposes none of it is lost through the alveoli into the blood). When the system is fully equilibrated, which requires only a few minutes, a specially designed device is used to measure the final helium concentration; in our example we assume $F_{He_2} = 0.05$ ml He/ml. The FRC is computed on the basis of the fact that the amount of helium must be the same after mixing as it was initially – in each case, the product of volume V and concentration F:

$$V_{Sp} F_{He_1} = (V_{Sp} + V_{FRC}) F_{He_2} \tag{2}$$

Solving this equation for V_{FRC}, with the above data substituted for the variables, we have:

$$V_{FRC} = \frac{V_{Sp} (F_{He_1} - F_{He_2})}{F_{He_2}} = \frac{3 (0.1 - 0.05)}{0.05} = 3 \text{ liters} \tag{3}$$

In the **nitrogen-washout method** the subject inhales pure oxygen for several minutes following a normal expiration. The air exhaled during this time is collected in a spirometer. All the nitrogen molecules previously in the lungs are transferred to the spirometer during this process. From the expired volume, the initial N_2 concentration in the lung and the N_2 concentration in the spirometer at the end of the test, V_{FRC} can be computed by an equation analogous to Equation 3.

For the practical application of either method certain correction factors must be taken into account [10]. Moreover, both methods suffer from the disadvantage that patients in whom different regions of the lungs are unevenly ventilated require a very long time for full dilution or washout. For this reason it has currently become common to determine FRC by means of the **body plethysmograph** (p. 469).

Anatomical and Functional Dead Space

Anatomical dead space. This term is applied to the volume of the conducting airways – the *trachea,* the *bronchi,* and the *bronchioles* up to the point where they open into the alveoli. These spaces are "dead" only in the sense that they offer no opportunity for the exchange of gases. In other respects the dead space serves important auxiliary functions in respiration; these structures support ventilation and assist in cleaning, moistening and warming the inspired air [33].

Role in ventilation. At each breath there is an *inspiratory dilation of the glottis and bronchi.* At the glottis, through which the inspired air flows at the highest velocity, expansion during inspiration is a very effective way to reduce the resistance to flow. If the muscles that open the glottis *(posterior cricoarytenoids)* are paralyzed, the result is shortness of breath. Moreover, swelling of the mucosa in this region *(glottal edema)* can make breathing very difficult and under some conditions can cause suffocation.

The inspiratory dilation of the bronchi is brought about by relaxation of the smooth bronchial musculature, under the influence of the **sympathetic** system. When the bronchi are dilated the resistance to flow is reduced, so that bronchial dilation facilitates inspiration. During the expiratory phase, by contrast, the bronchi constrict after most of the volume of gas to be expelled from the parts of the lung they serve has passed through. Thus bronchoconstriction assists the expiration. Bronchial diameter is reduced by contraction of the smooth musculature under the influence of the **parasympathetic** system. If the autonomic nervous system should malfunction in such a way as to cause the smooth bronchial muscles to contract too soon or too strongly, expiration can be considerably impeded. The difficulty in breathing encountered by people in the attack stages of *bronchial asthma* results, for example, from increased resistance to the expiratory flow.

Cleaning. The inspired air is partly cleaned as it passes through the nose, where small particles, dust and bacteria are caught on the mucous surfaces. For this reason, those who chronically breathe through the mouth are more susceptible to infections of the respiratory tract. The conducting airways are specially equipped to clean the air by their respiratory epithelium; the *rhythmic movement of the cilia* transports mucus and small adhering particles toward the throat. Larger objects that enter the airways trigger coughing when they touch the walls, and the forced expulsion of air drives them out.

Moistening. The expired gas mixture is *100% saturated with water vapor.* The air begins to be moistened early in inspiration, acquiring most of the water vapor while still in the nose and throat. Saturation is completed in the lower airways.

Warming. A further function of the nose and throat and the conducting airways is to warm the inspired air. Inspiration takes long enough that the air comes very close to body temperature by the time it reaches the lungs. As a rule, therefore, the expired gas mixture has a *temperature of 37° C.*

Measurement of the dead-space volume [5, 39]. The *expiratory tidal volume* (V_E) is made up of two components; one part of the expired volume comes from the *dead space* (V_D) and the other from the *alveolar space* (V_{EA}):

$$V_E = V_D + V_{EA} \tag{4}$$

For tests of pulmonary function it is important to measure these two volume components separately. As in the determination of functional residual capacity, an indirect procedure is used. It is based on the fact that the amounts of the respiratory gases (O_2 and CO_2) in the two components differ. In the air from the dead space the gas concentrations established by the previously inhaled fresh air (F_I) still prevail. That from the alveolar space contains gases at the concentrations prevailing there (F_A). Expressing the quantity of gas as the product of volume V and concentration F, it holds for any respired gas that

$$
\begin{array}{lll}
\textit{Amount expired} & = & \textit{Amount from} + \textit{Amount from} \\
 & & \textit{dead space} \quad\; \textit{alveoli} \\
V_E \cdot F_E & = & V_D \cdot F_I \quad\; + V_{EA} \cdot F_A \quad (5)
\end{array}
$$

(V_E = volume expired, V_D = volume of dead space, V_{EA} = alveolar portion of expired volume; gas concentrations: F_E = expiratory, F_A = alveolar.)

V_{EA} can be replaced by $V_E - V_D$, by Eq. (4):

$$V_E \cdot F_E = V_D \cdot F_I + (V_E - V_D) \cdot F_A \tag{6}$$

which can be rearranged to give

$$\frac{V_D}{V_E} = \frac{F_E - F_A}{F_I - F_A} \tag{7}$$

This relation, called the Bohr equation, is valid for all respiratory gases; in the case of CO_2, however, it can

be further simplified, for the concentration of this gas in the inspired air, $F_{I_{CO_2}}$, is nearly zero:

$$\frac{V_D}{V_E} = \frac{F_{A_{CO_2}} - F_{E_{CO_2}}}{F_{A_{CO_2}}} \tag{8}$$

The relation of dead space to expired volume can be derived from Eq. (7) or Eq. (8), because all the concentrations on the right side can be found by gas analysis. (With regard to the difficulties that arise in measuring alveolar concentrations, see p. 474). For example, say that measurements have shown $F_{A_{CO_2}} = 0.056$ and $F_{E_{CO_2}} = 0.04$ ml CO_2/ml mixture. It follows that $V_D/V_E = 0.3$; that is, the dead space accounts for 30% of the expired volume.

Physiological dead space. The term physiological or *functional dead space* refers to all those parts of the respiratory tract in which there is no exchange of gas. The physiological dead space differs from the anatomical in that it includes not only the conducting airways but also those alveolar spaces which, though ventilated, are not perfused by blood. Such alveoli, in which gas exchange is impossible despite ventilation, are few in healthy lungs. Therefore in a healthy person the volumes of the anatomical and the physiological dead spaces are practically identical. The situation is different in certain cases of *impaired pulmonary function,* in which both ventilation and blood flow are very unevenly distributed throughout the lung. In these cases the physiological dead space can be considerably larger than the anatomical dead space.

Alveolar Ventilation

Minute volume. The minute volume, the volume of gas breathed in or our in a minute, is by definition the product of the **tidal volume** and the **respiratory frequency.** As a rule the volume exhaled is somewhat smaller than that inhaled, because less CO_2 is given off than O_2 is taken in *(respiratory quotient < 1;* cf. p. 473). To be precise, therefore, one must distinguish between the inspired and the expired minute volume. It has been agreed that as a general rule calculations of ventilation should be based on the expiration phase, as indicated by the subscript E. Thus for the (expiratory) minute volume $\dot{V}_E$ it holds that

$$\dot{V}_E = V_E \cdot f \tag{9}$$

(The dot over the symbol for a quantity means "quantity per unit time"; V_E is the expiratory tidal volume, and f is the respiratory frequency.)

The respiratory frequency of the adult under resting conditions averages 14 breaths per minute, though there is considerable variation (10–18/min). Higher respiration rates are found in children (20–30/min), infants (30–40/min) and newborns (40–50/min) [3, 9].

By Eq.(9), therefore, an adult at rest has a *minute volume of 7 l/min,* if the tidal volume is taken as 0.5 l and the respiration rate as 14/min. During exercise the minute volume rises along with the increased O_2 requirement, and in conditions of extreme exertion it can reach 120 l/min. Although minute volume is of some use as a measure of ventilation, it is by no means a critical determinant of the effectiveness of breathing. The decisive factor is the fraction of the minute volume that enters the alveoli and there participates in gas exchange.

Alveolar ventilation and dead-space ventilation. The part of the minute volume $\dot{V}_E$ that actually ventilates the alveoli is called the *alveolar ventilation* $\dot{V}_A$. The remainder is the *dead-space ventilation* $\dot{V}_D$:

$$\dot{V}_E = \dot{V}_A + \dot{V}_D \qquad (10)$$

Each of the ventilation terms is the product of the corresponding volume and the respiratory frequency ($\dot{V} = V \cdot f$). The volumes that make up the total ventilation of the resting, healthy adult are as follows. The tidal volume V_E comprises the alveolar volume V_{EA} (70%) and the dead-space volume V_D (30%). Thus for $V_E = 500$ ml, $V_{EA} = 350$ ml and $V_D = 150$ ml. Taking the respiratory frequency as 14/min, with a *total ventilation* of 7 l/min the *alveolar ventilation is 5 l/min* and the *dead-space ventilation is 2 l/min.*

The alveolar ventilation determines the effectiveness of ventilation as a whole. It, above all else, determines the concentrations of the gases that can be maintained in the alveolar space. The tidal volume tells us very little about the effectiveness of ventilation. For example, if a normal $\dot{V}_E$ of 7 l/min were to be achieved by shallow, rapid breathing ($V_E = 0.2$ liters and f = 35/min), then the dead space (which is encountered first) would be almost the only part of the lung ventilated; hardly any of the fresh air would be pulled in as far as the alveoli. This form of breathing, which sometimes occurs during *circulatory shock,* therefore represents a state of acute danger. Because the absolute magnitude of the dead-space volume is constant, whenever breathing becomes deeper the alveolar ventilation is increased.

Artificial Respiration

Respiratory failure. Interruption of breathing, for whatever reason, creates a potentially lethal situation.

The moment at which arrest of respiration and circulation occurs is called the onset of **clinical death.** From this moment on, 4–6 min are required, as a rule, for the lack of O_2 and accumulation of CO_2 to damage irreversibly the cells in vital organs, so that **biological death** ensues. If during this brief time certain life-saving measures are taken, resuscitation is possible.

Disruption of respiratory function can have a variety of causes, among them obstruction of the airways, injury to the thorax, severe impairment of gas exchange and damage to the respiratory centers resulting from poisoning and brain injury. After sudden respiratory arrest, the circulatory system continues to function for some time; the pulse can still be felt at the carotid artery after 3–5 min. On the other hand, if cardiac arrest is the first to occur, breathing ceases after only 30–60 s.

Immediate measures to normalize breathing. Whenever respiratory activity is suddenly restricted or stopped, steps must be taken to assist ventilation. The term **resuscitation** denotes all the measures that can be applied to restore respiratory and circulatory function when clinical death is imminent or has occurred. The restoration of respiratory function is accomplished by establishing and maintaining the airway and by artificial respiration.

Maintaining the airway. An unconscious person lacks the protective reflexes that normally serve to keep the airways free (p.463). In this situation, if there should be vomiting or bleeding in the nose/throat region the conducting airways (trachea and bronchi) can become obstructed. But even without these complications the airways of an unconscious person lying on his back can be closed by the tongue if the lower jaw drops back.

The first step in resuscitation must therefore be rapid clearing of the mouth and throat. It is equally important to ensure that the tongue does not block the airway, by tilting the head back and at the same time pulling the jaw forward.

Oral ventilation techniques. For artificial respiration without mechanical devices various procedures were once recommended for manually expanding and compressing the thorax. All these manual methods are far inferior to the very old, recently rediscovered method in which the rescuer breathes air directly into the patient [10], by way of the mouth or nose (Fig. 19-11).

In **mouth-to-nose respiration** the head of the patient is tilted backward by placing one hand on the forehead at the hairline. The other hand is used to pull the lower jaw upward and at the same time ensure that the mouth is closed, with the thumb pressing on the lips. After a deep inspiration the operator places his open mouth firmly over the patient's nose. During the subsequent *insufflation* (blowing of air into the patient) the elevation of the thorax must be observed. Then the operator removes his mouth from the patient's face, whereupon the air escapes passively because of the weight of the thorax and the elasticity of the lungs. The operator should check that the thorax has returned to its expiratory level.

In **mouth-to-mouth respiration** the starting position is the same, with one hand at the patient's hairline and the other under the chin. The operator places his mouth over that of the patient and seals the nose with his cheek. Alternatively, he can press the nostrils shut with the thumb and forefinger of the hand on the forehead. Again, the movements of the chest must be observed during insufflation and the escape of air that follows.

In both procedures respiration begins with *5–10 insufflations in rapid succession,* to eliminate the O_2 deficit and CO_2 excess in the tissues as soon as possible. From then on insufflation should be at *intervals of about 5 s.* Under these conditions the O_2 saturation (p. 493) of the patient's arterial blood is practically always over 90%.

One of the great advantages of oral resuscitation is that it can be combined with **extrathoracic cardiac massage,** so that respiratory and circulatory arrest can be treated simultaneously. Cardiac massage, which is permissible only when it has definitely been established that the heart is not beating, is done by rhythmic compression of the thorax to drive the blood out of the heart, into the pulmonary and systemic circulations. Pressure is applied to the sternum with the heel of the hand *70–90 times per minute,* each time depressing the sternum toward the spine by about 4–5 cm.

Artificial respiration with mechanical assistance [10]. There is a simple device that, if it is rapidly obtainable, can be used to assist respiration. It consists of a **mask** placed in an airtight manner over the patient's face, a *valve* and a *bag* that is rhythmically compressed and released by hand. If an O_2 cylinder is available it can be attached to the device so as to raise the proportion of O_2 in the inspired air.

In the method of gas anesthesia generally used today, a **respiratory** supplies air by way of a *tracheal tube* (p. 459). The machine can be controlled so that inspiration is caused by expansion of the lungs under pressure, the subsequent expiration occurring passively. It is also possible to control breathing by a rhythmic alternation between pressures above and below atmospheric pressure, so that the average pressure is that of the atmosphere. Because subatmospheric pressure within the thorax facilitates venous return to the heart (p. 416), respiration by alternating pressure is the preferable procedure.

The use of respiratory pumps or manually operable bags is always required during operations in which *muscle relaxants* (p. 58) have been used to eliminate reflex muscle tension. These drugs inactivate the respiratory musculature as well, so that the lungs could not be ventilated without artificial assistance.

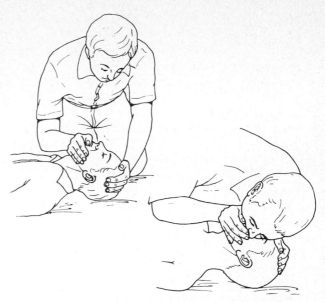

Fig. 19-11. Mouth-to-nose resuscitation

When a patient is chronically unable to breathe (as, for example, in spinal infantile paralysis) ventilation can be maintained by means of a **tank respirator** *("iron lung").* The body of the recumbent patient is enclosed in a chamber with the head outside. During inspiration the pressure in the tank is reduced, so that the intrathoracic pressure is greater than that outside the body. Therefore in this phase the venous return to the heart is not facilitated as it is normally.

19.3   Mechanical Factors in Breathing

The term *"respiratory mechanics"* is usually used in a very special sense, to denote the *analysis and representation of the* **pressure-volume** or the **pressure-flow relationships** during respiratory excursions. These relationships provide information about the resistances in the system and their changes under pathological conditions [9, 10, 22, 36, 54]. For this reason respiratory mechanics are important in the diagnosis of pulmonary function.

Elasticity of Lung and Thorax

Static volume-pressure curves [2, 49, 58]. The contractile force of the respiratory musculature must overcome both *elastic and viscous resistances* during ventilation. When breathing is very slow the effect of the viscous resistance (pp. 468 ff.) is slight, so that the relationship between lung volume and the associated effective pressure is determined almost entirely by the

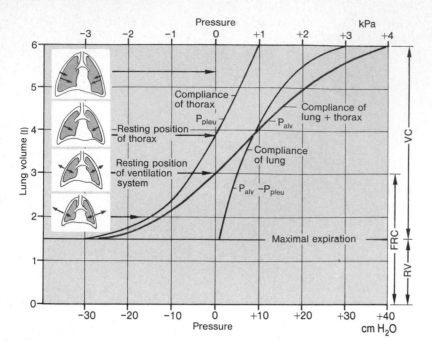

Fig. 19-12. Static volume-pressure curves of the entire breathing apparatus *(red),* the lung and the thorax, modified from [49]. P_{pleu}, pleural pressure; P_{alv}, alveolar pressure; VC, vital capacity; RV, residual volume, FRC, functional residual capacity. Pressures are related to passive variations in lung volume with respiratory musculature relaxed. The inset drawings show the elastic forces acting at the thorax and the lung surface for different volumes

elastic properties of lung and thorax. In order to measure this *"static" volume-pressure curve* one must eliminate the action of the respiratory muscles, so that the elastic forces alone are operating. The subject must be trained to *relax his respiratory musculature* briefly, or *muscle relaxants* (p.58) must be used to inactivate it, with the subject in a respirator.

The static volume-pressure curve of the *entire ventilatory system* – lung and thorax together – can be constructed as follows. The subject inhales a certain volume of air from a spirometer (with nose closed). Then the connection to the spirometer is closed, and the subject relaxes his respiratory musculature as completely as possible. The pressure exerted in the alveoli by the elastic forces in lung and thorax can now be measured by a gauge at the subject's mouth if he keeps his glottis open *(relaxation pressure method).* *The pressure difference between the alveoli and the ambient air* is called the **alveolar pressure** P_{alv}. A typical curve of the alveolar pressures corresponding to various lung volumes, measured in this way, is shown in Fig. 19-12 (red curve). The relaxation curve of lung and thorax is S-shaped, the nearly linear part covering most of the range of normal respiratory excursions. In this range, therefore, the ventilatory system offers an approximately *constant elastic resistance* to the inspiratory movement.

The contribution of the *elastic tension of the thorax,* including the supporting apparatus, the musculature and the abdominal viscera, is determined by the pressure difference between the interpleural space and the ambient air. As mentioned on p.459, this pressure difference is referred to by the abbreviated term **pleu-**

ral pressure P_{pleu}. If in the procedure described above the pleural pressures (or the esophageal pressures; cf. p.459) are recorded simultaneously for each volume, the *relaxation curve for the thorax alone* can be constructed. As shown in Fig.19-12, the slope of this curve increases as pressure (and lung volume) increase.

The contribution of the *elastic tension of the lung* depends on the *difference between the alveolar and the pleural pressures,* $P_{alv} - P_{pleu}$. The relationship between the lung volumes and the quantity $P_{alv} - P_{pleu}$ determines the *relaxation curve for the lung alone,* which characterizes the elastic properties of the lung. The slope of this curve decreases at higher pressures (larger lung volumes).

Comparison of the three curves in Fig.19-12 shows the effect of the *elastic forces* when the lung is filled to different degrees. The entire ventilatory system is in an elastic *resting state* ($P_{alv} = O$) when, at the end of a normal expiration, the lung volume corresponds to the *functional residual capacity* (FRC). In this case the tendencies of the thorax to expand and of the lung to contract are in balance. When the volume increases owing to inspiration the elastic inward pull of the lung is enhanced, and at the same time the outward pull generated by the forces in the thorax decreases. At about 55% of vital capacity the *thorax* has reached its *resting position* ($P_{pleu} = O$), so that any further increase in volume reverses the direction in which the elastic forces act.

Compliance [9, 10, 36]. A measure of the elastic properties of the breathing apparatus (or of its two elements) is the slope of the associated relaxation curve, which is called *compliance*. The *compliance of lung and thorax* is found by the following equation:

$$C_{Th+L} = \frac{\Delta V}{\Delta P_{alv}} \tag{11}$$

Similar definitions apply to the compliance of the thorax

$$C_{Th} = \frac{\Delta V}{\Delta P_{pleu}} \tag{12}$$

and the compliance of the lung

$$C_L = \frac{\Delta V}{\Delta (P_{alv} - P_{pleu})} \tag{13}$$

These three equations are related as follows:

$$\frac{1}{C_{Th+L}} = \frac{1}{C_{Th}} + \frac{1}{C_L} \tag{14}$$

Because compliance in each case is the *reciprocal of the elastic resistance to extension,* it follows from Eq. 14 that the elastic resistance of the entire respiratory system is the sum of those of thorax and lung.

As Fig. 19-12 shows, the relaxation curve of the ventilatory system (lung + thorax) rises most steeply in the range of normal respiratory excursions – that is, compliance is greatest in this range. Here the compliances found for healthy adults are as follows:

$$C_{Th+L} = 0.1 \, l/cm \, H_2O = 1 \, l/kPa$$
$$C_{Th} = 0.2 \, l/cm \, H_2O = 2 \, l/kPa$$
$$C_L = 0.2 \, l/cm \, H_2O = 2 \, l/kPa$$

Any alteration of these values, in particular a *decrease under pathological conditions,* is of diagnostic interest. However, compliance is difficult to measure because the respiratory musculature must be inactive. For this reason it is not uncommon to rely on determination of C_L alone, which can be done by a simpler procedure as follows. A certain volume of air is inhaled and the resulting position of the thorax is fixed by the respiratory musculature; now, with the glottis open, the pressure in the alveoli is equal to the atmospheric pressure. In this case $P_{alv} = 0$, and Eq. (13) takes the form

$$C_L = -\frac{\Delta V}{\Delta P_{pleu}} \tag{15}$$

Thus it suffices to measure the *change in pleural pressure* (or, more simply, in esophageal pressure) and to substitute these values for the corresponding terms in Eq. (15). The *static compliance of the lung* thus obtained depends not only on its elastic properties but also on the *volume* of the lung in each case. The smaller the initial volume the less the volume changes, other conditions being equal. Children 9 to 12 years old have a 2 to 3 times smaller compliance than adults. For diagnostic purposes, therefore, it is necessary to express compliance with respect to the initial volume – as a rule, that is, to the *functional residual capacity* (FRC). The quantity so defined,

$$C_{L_{spec}} = -\frac{1}{FRC} \cdot \frac{\Delta V}{\Delta P_{pleu}} \tag{16}$$

is called the *specific compliance of the lung.*

Surface tension [9, 22]. The tendency of the lung to become smaller when stretched is brought about first by the *tension in the elastic fibers of the lung parenchyma.* A second factor, of equal importance, is the *surface tension of the alveoli.*

At every interface between air and water intermolecular forces of cohesion tend to *reduce the surface area.* Each of the many alveoli has a tendency to become smaller because of its surface tension and in this way contributes to the retraction tendency of the lung as a whole.

On closer examination, however, this concept proves to need further elaboration. When the surface tension calculated on the assumption that there is an aqueous layer on the alveoli is compared with that actually measured, the result is surprising; *the surface tension of the alveoli in the lung is only about one-tenth of that theoretically expected for an aqueous interface.* It follows that the fluid layer on the alveolar wall must contain substances that reduce surface tension. Substances with this property are known to exist elsewhere (detergents, for example). They consist of molecules with a strong attraction for one another but little attraction for other molecules in the fluid. Therefore they accumulate at the surface, and in so doing lower the surface tension. They are thus also called **surface-active substances** or **surfactants.**

The alveolar fluid layer, which evidently contains such surfactants, exhibits still another peculiarity. In stretched alveoli the surface tension is high (0.04–0.05 N/m), and in smaller alveoli it is considerably lower (0.002–0.005 N/m). An explanation of this fact is that the surfactant molecules move closer together as an alveolus becomes smaller, so that there are more of them per unit area. Without this effect the surface tension of the smaller alveoli would be so great that they would collapse.

It has been possible to wash the pulmonary surfactants out of lung tissue and identify them chemically. The alveolar fluid film contains a mixture of *proteins* and *lipoids,* of which **lecithin derivatives** probably contribute most to the specific surface activity. They are formed in the alveolar epithelia.

If anything interferes with the production or the efficacy of the surfactants, many alveoli collapse. Therefore it is possible for

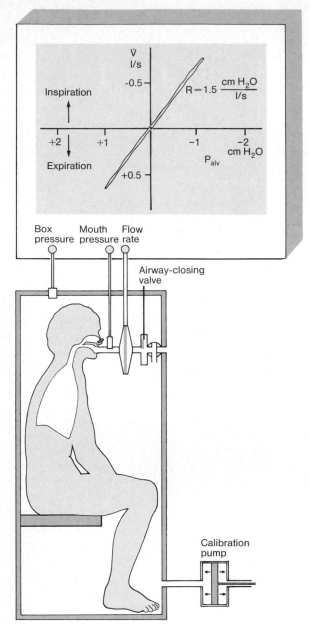

Fig. 19-13. Body plethysmograph (simplified diagram). $\dot{V}$, volume flow; P_{alv}, alveolar pressure

large parts of the lung to become deflated, a condition known as **atelectasis.** In the *newborn*, surface-active substances are necessary for the initial expansion of the lungs. A pathological condition can exist in which the alveolar surface in the newborn lung is covered with *fibrin precipitates (hyaline membranes)* which make the surfactants less effective. Then the lung expands only partially, and a severe disturbance of gas exchange results [3].

In summary, we may say:
1. The elastic forces tending to collapse the lung arise in part from the surface tension of the alveoli.
2. Surface-active substances (surfactants) in the fluid layer over the alveolar walls reduce surface ten-

sion, so that little force is required to stretch the lung during inspiration.
3. The alveoli are protected from collapse in that as their surface area becomes smaller the surfactant molecules come closer together and thus decrease the surface tension.

Nonelastic Resistances

The *nonelastic (viscous) resistances* that must be overcome during both inspiration and expiration comprise the following elements: 1. *the resistance to flow in the airways,* 2. *the nonelastic tissue resistances,* and 3. *the inertial resistances,* which are so small that they may be neglected.

Airway resistance [9, 10, 15, 54]. The flow of inhaled and exhaled gases through the conducting airways is brought about by the pressure difference between the mouth and the alveoli. This *pressure difference, simply called alveolar pressure,* is thus the "driving force" for movement of the respired gases. Flow in the airways is partially *laminar*. But eddies are formed in some places, in particular the branch points of the bronchi and sites of pathological constriction, so that flow there becomes *turbulent*. Laminar air flow, like the laminar flow of liquids, is described by the **Hagen-Poiseuille law,** according to which the volume flow $\dot{V}$ is proportional to the driving pressure difference ΔP. For flow in the airways, therefore, it holds that

$$\dot{V} = \frac{\Delta P}{R} = \frac{P_{alv}}{R} \tag{17}$$

R is the *resistance to flow,* which depends on the cross-sectional area and length of the tube and on the viscosity of the gas. Although the relationships in turbulent flow are different, Eq. (17) is used to express the overall resistance to flow during respiration:

$$R = \frac{\Delta P}{\dot{V}} = \frac{P_{alv}}{\dot{V}} \tag{18}$$

R is usually called the **airway resistance.** To find it, one must measure the pressure difference between mouth and alveoli (in cm H_2O or kPa) and the simultaneous flow rate (in l/s; p. 461). The airway resistance normally found during quiet breathing through the mouth is in the range $R = 1\text{--}2$ cm $H_2O \cdot s \cdot l^{-1}$ ($0.1\text{--}0.2$ kPa $\cdot s \cdot l^{-1}$).

Tissue resistance. There is a second resistance, in addition to the airway resistance, that must be overcome during inspiration and expiration. This is the viscous resistance associated with friction in the tissues and their nonelastic deformation in the thorax and abdomen:

nonelastic resistance = airway resistance + tissue resistance

The latter, however, is relatively small. Normally 80–90% of the pulmonary resistance is contributed by the airways, and only 10–20% by tissue friction.

Measurement of resistance [10, 22, 36]. *To measure resistance one must continually monitor the alveolar pressure.* An indirect procedure employing the body plethysmograph is used. The **body plethysmograph** (Fig. 19-13) basically consists of an airtight chamber shaped like a telephone booth within which a person can sit comfortably. When the subject's respiratory movements bring about pressure changes in the lung, the pressure in the closed chamber must change proportionally in the opposite direction. Having calibrated the system one can proceed to measure the change in alveolar pressure by way of the change in chamber pressure. The flow $\dot{V}$ can be measured at the same time with a pneumotachograph (p.461). The ratio of the two, according to Eq. (18), is the desired *resistance;* it is convenient to plot this as a continuous curve with a two-dimensional pen-writer.

The body plethysmograph can also be used to determine the *functional residual capacity* V_{FRC} (pp.460f.). In this case the mouthpiece is closed off briefly, so that the pulmonary space is separated from the outside air. As the subject makes an effort to breathe in, the changes in mouth pressure and in lung volume are measured; V_{FRC} can then be computed by the *Boyle-Mariott law* [32, 39].

Pressure-Volume Relations in the Breathing Cycle

Pleural and alveolar pressure changes [9, 29]. During a breathing cycle the pleural and alveolar pressures change in a regular way. The relationships between the two are indicated by the following considerations. When the thorax is briefly *at rest,* as it is at the transition from inspiration to expiration, the only force exerted on the pleural space is the elastic recoil force of the lung, which causes a "negative" pressure. We shall call this negative pleural pressure during rest $P_{pleu(stat)}$. The alveolar pressure $P_{alv(stat)}$, however, is zero in the resting thorax because the alveoli are in communication with the mouth, so that the pressure can equilibrate. The situation is approximately the same during very slow movements of the thorax.

The more complex situation during *normal respiratory movements* is illustrated in Fig. 19-14. In this schematic drawing the alveolar space is represented by a large bubble. The black arrows indicate the directions of movement and the red arrows, the directions in which the tensile forces act. During inspiration (left) the airway resistance R prevents the air from flowing

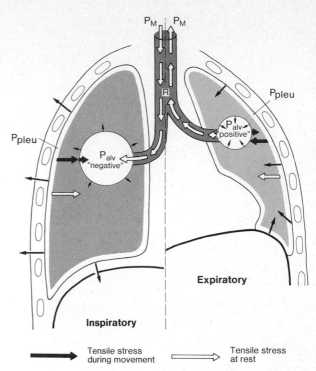

Fig. 19-14. Diagram to explain the changes in pleural (P_{pleu}) and alveolar (P_{alv}) pressures during inspiration *(left)* and expiration *(right)*. P_M, mouth pressure; R, airway resistance

rapidly enough into the enlarged alveolar space. Therefore the pressure in the alveoli must fall, becoming negative with respect to the outside pressure. This decrease in alveolar pressure affects the pleural space in such a way as to make the pleural pressure still more "negative". The movement-dependent pleural pressure $P_{pleu(dyn)}$ is thus the sum of the static pleural pressure $P_{pleu(stat)}$ and the momentary alveolar pressure P_{alv}:

$$P_{pleu(dyn)} = P_{pleu(stat)} + P_{alv} \qquad (19)$$

During expiration (Fig. 19-14, right) the situation is reversed. P_{alv} becomes positive and reduces the negativity of $P_{pleu(stat)}$.

The resulting **pressure changes during a respiratory cycle** are graphed in Fig. 19-15, which is simplified by showing the same duration for inspiration as for expiration. If only the elastic resistance of the lung were to be overcome during respiration, the alveolar pressure P_{alv} would remain zero over the entire cycle and the pleural pressure would follow the dashed curve $P_{pleu(stat)}$. But because of the additional viscous resistances P_{alv} becomes negative in the inspiration phase and positive in the expiration phase. By adding this curve to that for $P_{pleu(stat)}$ one obtains the dynamic pleural pressure $P_{pleu(dyn)}$. It is evident here that in or-

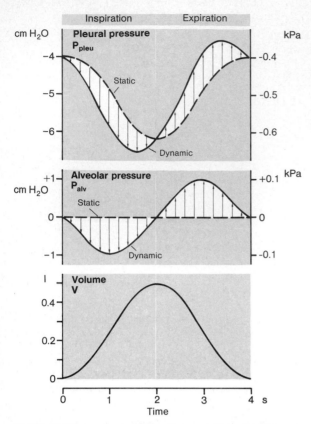

Fig. 19-15. Time course of pleural pressure P_{pleu}, alveolar pressure P_{alv}, and respired volume V during a breathing cycle. The dashed lines show the pressures that would be found if respiration encountered only elastic resistances. Because viscous resistances are also present, P_{pleu} and P_{alv} become more negative during inspiration and more positive during expiration *(red arrows)*

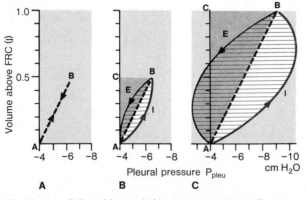

Fig. 19-16 A–C. Breathing cycle in a pressure-volume diagram, modified after [32]. **A** Idealized breathing (as it would occur against purely elastic resistances). **B** Normal breathing at rest. **C** Deep, rapid breathing. I, inspiration; E, expiration. The respiratory work is divided as follows: *red areas,* inspiratory work against the elastic resistances; *hatched,* inspiratory and expiratory work against the viscous resistances; *dark gray,* the fraction of the work of expiration that must be done by the expiratory muscles

der to overcome the viscous resistances, $P_{pleu(dyn)}$ must always be somewhat smaller than $P_{pleu(stat)}$ during inspiration and somewhat larger during expiration.

Pressure-volume diagrams [5, 22, 36]. *A plot of the volume of a lung at various pleural pressures is called, for simplicity, the pressure-volume diagram of the lung.* All the factors determining the shape of this curve have been discussed in the preceding sections, so that they need only be summarized briefly with reference to the pressure-volume diagram.

If inspiration encountered *elastic resistances* alone, any change in the volume of the lung would have to be approximately proportional to the associated change in pleural pressure. In the pressure-volume diagram this relationship between the two quantities is represented by a straight line (Fig. 19-16 A). During expiration the same curve would be followed in the opposite direction.

But because of the additional *viscous resistances* the curve for inspiration is concave upward (Fig. 19-16 B). That is, to move a certain volume the pleural pressure must decrease more than the amount given by the proportionality line. Not until inspiration is completed (at Point B) does the inspiration curve coincide with the straight line, because at this time motion has ceased and only the elastic forces are acting. The curve for expiration is bent in the opposite direction owing to the viscous resistances, returning to the starting point (A) at the end of this phase of the cycle. The dynamic pressure-volume diagram thus has the shape of a **loop**.

The loop in Fig. 19-16 B represents *resting respiration;* the shape of the loop for *deeper and more rapid breathing* is somewhat different (Fig. 19-16 C). The deeper breaths are expressed in a doubling of the tidal volume, and the higher rate in a sharper bending of both the inspiratory and the expiratory curve. The greater curvature is explained by the fact that rapid changes in alveolar pressure do not accelerate the air flow fast enough. *At a high respiration rate the nonelastic airway resistance has a greater effect than during resting respiration.*

The loop for a subject with *healthy lungs* can be used to determine lung *compliance.* Because there is no movement at the reversal points A and B, these two points are representative of the static elastic forces in the lung. The slope of the line joining A and B, $\Delta V/\Delta P$, thus gives directly the compliance C_L. In the example of Fig. 19-16, $C_L = 0.2$ l/cm H_2O. This relation does not apply to diseased lungs, in which the resistances are often increased so that the alveoli cannot all fill equally with air in the time available. In this case static conditions have not yet been reached at points A and B. Therefore the compliance in people with lung disease can be determined only by static procedures such as described on p. 467, in which the breath is held.

Construction of a pressure-volume diagram. The arrangement of the apparatus for simultaneous measurement of pressure and volume is shown in Fig. 19-17. The pressure to be represented on the abscissa of the pressure-volume diagram is the **pleural pressure,** which can be measured as the difference between mouth and esophageal pressures. On the ordinate is the **respired volume,** which is measured spirometrically or by means of an integrating pneumotachograph (p. 461). It is convenient to obtain the continuous record of these two variables in the form of electrical signals which are used to control a two-coordinate plotter, so that the loop can be drawn directly.

There is as yet no general convention for the presentation of this curve. Sometimes ordinate and abscissa are exchanged, or the values on the abscissa are in the reverse order. But as long as the diagram is labelled adequately it is equally useful for diagnosis whatever its form.

The work of breathing [31]. The physical work that must be done to overcome the elastic and nonelastic resistances is equivalent to the product **pressure x volume,** which has the same dimension as the product force × distance. If the pressure changes during the work, the product is replaced by an integral, $\int P\,dV$. The advantage of the pressure-volume diagram lies chiefly in the fact that in it the integral value for work can be visualized as an area.

The areas that represent work against the *elastic resistances* are shaded red in Fig. 19-16. Under dynamic conditions there is an additional component of work required during both inspiration and expiration to overcome the *nonelastic resistances*. The corresponding areas are hatched in Fig. 19-16. The nonelastic expiratory component ABEA during quiet breathing (Fig. 19-16 B) is smaller than the previously elastically stored energy ABCA. Therefore expiration can occur purely *passively,* without the help of the expiratory muscles. This is not the case during accelerated breathing (Fig. 19-16 C). Here the work component corresponding to the dark gray area must be supplied by the *expiratory musculature.*

During resting respiration about 2% of the oxygen uptake is required for the contractile work of the respiratory muscles. During exercise, however, the energy requirement of the respiratory musculature rises out of proportion to the increase in minute volume and oxygen uptake achieved. It is understandable, then, that during hard physical labor as much as 20% of the oxygen must be allocated to the work of breathing.

Tests of Respiratory Mechanics

Types of ventilatory defects. Pathological changes in the respiratory apparatus in many cases interfere with the ventilation of the lungs. For diagnostic purposes it is useful to subdivide these forms of ventilatory defects into two groups, the *restrictive type* and the *obstructive type* [10, 12, 13, 16, 18, 36, 41].

Restrictive disturbances include all the conditions in which the *ability of the lung to expand is limited.* This

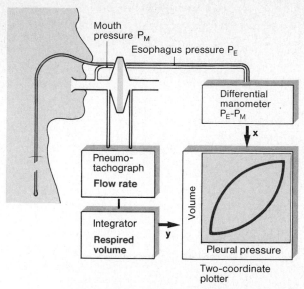

Fig. 19-17. Principle of the arrangement for direct plotting of pressure-volume curves. The difference between mouth pressure and esophageal pressure (pleural pressure) is signalled to the x input of a two-coordinate plotter. A signal representing the respired volume, obtained simultaneously with an integrating pneumotachograph (p. 461), moves the pen in the y direction

occurs, for example, as a result of pathological changes in the lung parenchyma (e.g., in *pulmonary fibrosis*), or of fusion of the pleurae. **Obstructive disturbances** are characterized by *narrowing of the conducting airways* so that the flow *resistance* increases. Such obstruction can be brought about by the accumulation of mucus, swelling of the mucous membranes and bronchial muscle spasms *(bronchial asthma, spastic bronchitis).* Because the patient must breathe out against an increased resistance, in advanced stages the lung often becomes overinflated, with an enlarged residual capacity. A pathological state involving both distension and structural changes (loss of elastic fibers, disappearance of alveolar septa, reduction of the capillary bed) is called *pulmonary emphysema.*

Identification of the type of ventilatory defect. The procedures used to distinguish between restrictive and obstructive disturbances are based on the characteristics of the two. That is, the limitation of lung expansibility in restrictive defects can be demonstrated by the **reduced compliance** (pp. 466 f.). Obstructive defects are characterized by **increased resistance** (p. 468). Fairly elaborate apparatus is required to determine either compliance or resistance, but it is also possible to differentiate roughly the types of ventilatory defects by simpler methods, as follows.

Vital capacity. *A decrease in vital capacity can be taken as a sign of restrictive impairment.* But whereas the

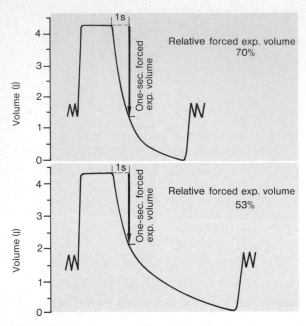

Fig. 19-18. Measurement of the relative forced expiratory volume. After inspiring deeply and holding his breath for a short time, the subject breathes out as rapidly and deeply as possible. The volume exhaled in 1 s is expressed as a percentage of the vital capacity VC. *Above:* healthy subject; *below:* patient with obstructive pulmonary malfunction

compliance C_L reflects only the expansibility of the lung, the vital capacity depends on the degree to which the thorax can expand as well. Thus a reduction in vital capacity can be brought about by either *pulmonary or extrapulmonary restriction.*

Forced expiratory volume (Tiffeneau test). *Obstructive impairment can easily be identified by measuring the volume expelled from the lungs by forced expiration* (Fig. 19-18) in a certain time, usually 1 second. The subject is attached to a closed or open spirometric system (p. 461); after a maximal inspiration he holds his breath briefly and then breathes out as rapidly and deeply as possible. From the recorded expiration curve the volume exhaled in 1 s (FEV_1) can be found. The result is usually expressed as a relative quantity – i.e., as a percentage of the vital capacity. (For example, with an absolute FEV_1 of 3 liters and a vital capacity of 4 liters, the relative FEV_1 is 75%.) People up to age 50 with sound lungs have relative FEV_1 of 70–80%, and this decreases with age to 65–70%. When an obstructive condition is present the increased resistance to flow delays expiration, so that the relative FEV_1 is less than normal.

Maximal volume flow. *A second way of demonstrating obstruction is to measure the maximal expiratory flow.* As in the measurement of forced expiratory volume,

the subject is required to inspire maximally and then make a forced expiration. The volume flow is monitored with a pneumotachograph (p. 461). (The rate of flow can be derived, though less precisely, from the expiration curve of Fig. 19-18, by measuring the change in volume in successive time increments.) The maximal volume flow recorded in this way should be about 10 l/s for healthy lungs. When airway resistance is increased maximal flow becomes considerably less.

There is a limit beyond which expiratory volume flow cannot be raised, no matter how hard one tries. The reason for this limit lies in the *structure of the bronchiole walls,* which have no cartilaginous supporting elements. Flaccid tubes are compressed when the external (pleural) pressure is greater than the pressure in their lumens. *When expiration pressure is very strong, the resistance to flow in the bronchioles increases.* This effect is especially pronounced when the recoil of the elastic fibers of the lung parenchyma that normally keep the bronchial lumen open is diminished. In such a situation (which can occur, for example, in *pulmonary emphysema;* cf. p. 471), the bronchioles can collapse when a great effort is made to exhale.

Maximum breathing capacity. *The greatest volume that can be breathed during a period of maximally forced voluntary hyperventilation is called the maximum breathing capacity.* This measure is of diagnostic interest because mobilization of the respiratory reserves can clearly reveal malfunction. The spirometric measurement is done while the subject performs forced hyperventilation at a rate of 40–60/min. The test should last for only about 10 s, in order to avoid the undesirable consequences of hyperventilation (alkalosis; cf. p. 504). However, the value so obtained is then converted to volume per minute. Norms for the maximum breathing capacity (MBC) vary according to age, sex and dimensions of the body; that for a young man is between about *120 and 170 l/min.* The MBC is reduced by both *restrictive and obstructive impairment.* Therefore, when the MBC is found to be abnormal, further tests (of vital capacity and forced expiratory volume) must be done to distinguish the two conditions.

19.4 Exchange of Gases

Alveolar Gas Concentrations

Calculation of alveolar gas concentration [28]. The gas mixture in those alveoli engaged in gas exchange is usually called the *alveolar air.* Recently, however, a general consensus is being reached to the effect that the term "air" should be reserved for a gas mixture with the composition of the atmosphere. Because the composition of the alveolar content is different (with less O_2 and more CO_2), to be consistent we must speak of an alveolar gas mixture.

The alveolar concentrations of the main gases involved in respiratory exchange, O_2 and CO_2, are determined chiefly by the alveolar ventilation and the amounts of gas exchanged. For calculation of their concentrations in the alveolar space the following relation applies:

exchanged gas = quantity introduced by inspiration − quantity removed by expiration

For **oxygen,** if we again represent the amount of the gas in a mixture by the product of its concentration and the volume of the mixture, we have

$$\dot{V}_{O_2} = F_{I_{O_2}} \cdot \dot{V}_A - F_{A_{O_2}} \cdot \dot{V}_A \qquad (20)$$

($\dot{V}_{O_2}$ = O_2 uptake, $F_{I_{O_2}}$ = inspiratory O_2 concentration, $F_{A_{O_2}}$ = alveolar O_2 concentration, $\dot{V}_A$ = alveolar ventilation.)

When the equation is applied to **carbon dioxide,** the inspiratory CO_2 concentration can be set equal to zero ($F_{I_{CO_2}} \approx 0$), and the sign of the expiratory term is reversed because the direction of change is the opposite:

$$\dot{V}_{CO_2} = F_{A_{CO_2}} \cdot \dot{V}_A \qquad (21)$$

($\dot{V}_{CO_2}$ = CO_2 output, $F_{A_{CO_2}}$ = alveolar CO_2 concentration.)

From Equations (20) and (21) one obtains expressions for the alveolar concentrations:

$$F_{A_{O_2}} = F_{I_{O_2}} - \frac{\dot{V}_{O_2}}{\dot{V}_A}, \quad F_{A_{CO_2}} = \frac{\dot{V}_{CO_2}}{\dot{V}_A} \qquad (22)$$

These equations apply only if all volumes on the right side are measured under identical conditions. *Usually, however, O_2 uptake and CO_2 output are referred to physical standard conditions, whereas respired volumes and ventilation parameters are given for the conditions prevailing within the body.*

Standard conditions and conditions in the body. The volumes respired depend on the momentary **barometric pressure P_B, temperature** T and **water-vapor pressure P_{H_2O}.** For this reason it is necessary to state the conditions under which a particular volume was measured. The conditions particularly to be specified are the following:

1. **STPD conditions** (acronym for *s*tandard *t*emperature and *p*ressure, *d*ry). These are the physical standard conditions, in which volume data are given for T = 273 K, P_B = 760 mm Hg, and P_{H_2O} = 0 mm Hg (dryness) (cf. p. 529).

2. **BTPS conditions** (*b*ody *t*emperature and *p*ressure, *s*aturated). These are the conditions within the lung – that is, T = 273 + 37 = 310 K, P_B varies (the current barometric pressure), and P_{H_2O} = 47 mm Hg (water-vapor saturation at 37 °C.

When the conditions for volume measurement are changed the volumes can be converted to the appropriate form by the **general gas equation:**

$$V \cdot P = M \cdot R \cdot T \qquad (23)$$

where M is the quantity of gas, R is the universal gas constant, and T is the absolute temperature. Applying this equation first to STPD and then to BTPS conditions, we have:

$$V_{STPD} \cdot 760 = M \cdot R \cdot 273;$$
$$V_{BTPS} \cdot (P_B - 47) = M \cdot R \cdot 310 \qquad (24)$$

which gives a volume ratio of

$$\frac{V_{STPD}}{V_{BTPS}} = \frac{273}{310} \cdot \frac{P_B - 47}{760} = \frac{P_B - 47}{863} \qquad (25)$$

This conversion formula should be used when the alveolar concentrations are to be determined by Equations (22):

$$F_{A_{O_2}} = F_{I_{O_2}} - \frac{\dot{V}_{O_2(STPD)}}{\dot{V}_{A(BTPS)}} \cdot \frac{863}{P_B - 47}$$

$$F_{A_{CO_2}} = \frac{\dot{V}_{CO_2(STPD)}}{\dot{V}_{A(BTPS)}} \cdot \frac{863}{P_B - 47} \qquad (26)$$

When the body is at rest O_2 uptake under standard conditions is about $\dot{V}_{O_2(STPD)}$ = 280 ml/min (range of variation: 250–300 ml/min) and the CO_2 output $\dot{V}_{CO_2(STPD)}$ = 230 ml/min (range: 200–250 ml/min). The ratio of CO_2 output to O_2 uptake, called the respiratory quotient, is thus 230/280 = 0.82. For a barometric pressure P_B = 760 mm Hg, the desired values can be obtained from Equations (26), taking $F_{I_{O_2}}$ = 0.209 ml O_2/ml mixture (= 20.9 vol.%) and $\dot{V}_{A(BTPS)}$ = 5000 ml/min:

Alveolar O_2 concentration:
$F_{A_{O_2}}$ = 0.14 ml O_2/ml mixture = 14 vol.% (ml/dl)

Alveolar CO_2 concentration:
$F_{A_{CO_2}}$ = 0.056 ml CO_2/ml mixture = 5.6 vol.% (ml/dl)

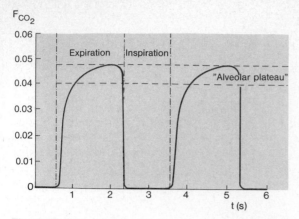

F_{CO_2}

Fig. 19-19. CO_2 concentration during expiration and inspiration, monitored at the subject's mouth by an infrared-absorption plotter. Alveolar plateau: the part of the curve during which the alveolar component of the expired volume passes the detector

The remainder of the alveolar gas mixture is nitrogen plus a very small proportion of noble gases.

Analysis of the alveolar gas mixture [10, 36]. One of the first difficulties one encounters in measuring alveolar gas concentrations is that of obtaining samples of the alveolar gas mixture. During expiration the volume of gas in the dead spaces is at first exhaled, and only after that does the gas from the alveolar spaces begin to appear. But even in this late phase of expiration the composition of the mixture undergoes continual slight change, because gas continues to be exchanged in the alveoli. For this reason devices have been developed by which the final fraction of the expired volume is collected at each breath under mechanical or electronic control.

Once a sample of the alveolar gas mixture has been obtained, the concentrations of the different gases can be determined with a suitable instrument. In **Scholander's procedure** O_2 and CO_2 are chemically absorbed in sequence, and the decrease in volume with each operation is measured directly; the volume that has disappeared is the volume of the gas that has been absorbed.

Rapid-response devices have been designed to give a continuous record of the concentrations of gases in the expired mixture. Devices for CO_2 measurement utilize the special *infrared absorption* of this gas, and those for O_2 employ its special *paramagnetic properties. Mass spectrometers* are also used for the analysis of both gases. The advantage of all these procedures is that with a continuous record the range of gas concentrations in the alveoli can be displayed directly in the form of a curve; it is not necessary to collect a series of samples. As an example, Fig. 19-19 shows the CO_2 concentration during two breathing cycles, as recorded by an infrared plotter. The part of the curve labelled "alveolar plateau" represents the alveolar part of the expired volume.

Alveolar Partial Pressures

Partial pressures in the atmosphere. *According to Dalton's law, each gas in a mixture exerts a partial pressure P_{gas} proportional to its share of the total volume – that is, to its concentration F_{gas}.* When this law is applied to respired gases it should be remembered that in addition to O_2, CO_2, N_2 and noble gases both the atmosphere and the alveolar gas mixture contain water vapor, at a certain partial pressure P_{H_2O}. Because gas concentrations are given for a "dry" gas mixture, in formulating Dalton's law the total pressure (barometric pressure P_B) must be reduced by an amount corresponding to the water-vapor pressure P_{H_2O}:

$$P_{gas} = F_{gas} \cdot (P_B - P_{H_2O}) \tag{27}$$

Dry air contains 20.9 vol.% oxygen ($F_{O_2} = 0.209$), 0.03 vol.% carbon dioxide ($F_{CO_2} = 0.0003$) and 79.1 vol.% nitrogen, including a small amount of noble gases ($F_{N_2} = 0.791$). These values can be substituted in Eq. (27) to obtain the partial pressure of each of the gases. For intermediate atmospheric and water-vapor pressures, the partial pressure of O_2 is in the region of $P_{O_2} = 150$ mm Hg (20 kPa); that of CO_2 is negligible for practical purposes, $P_{CO_2} = 0.2$ mm Hg (27 Pa).

Partial pressures in the alveolar gas mixture. When Eq. (27) is used to determine partial pressures in the alveoli one must keep in mind that here the water-vapor pressure is 47 mm Hg, corresponding to 100% saturation at 37 °C. The formulas are thus as follows:

$$P_{A_{O_2}} = F_{A_{O_2}} \cdot (P_B - 47)$$

$$P_{A_{CO_2}} = F_{A_{CO_2}} \cdot (P_B - 47) \tag{28}$$

Substituting Equations (28) in Equations (26), we obtain

$$P_{A_{O_2}} = P_{I_{O_2}} - \frac{\dot{V}_{O_2(STPD)}}{\dot{V}_{A(BTPS)}} \cdot 863 \; (mm\,Hg)$$

$$P_{A_{CO_2}} = \frac{\dot{V}_{CO_2(STPD)}}{\dot{V}_{A(BTPS)}} \cdot 863 \; (mm\,Hg) \tag{29}$$

These formulas enable one to compute the alveolar O_2 partial pressure $P_{A_{O_2}}$ and the alveolar CO_2 partial pressure $P_{A_{CO_2}}$ if the terms on the right side are known. In resting respiration ($\dot{V}_{O_2(STPD)} = 280$ ml/min, $\dot{V}_{CO_2(STPD)} = 230$ ml/min, $\dot{V}_{A(BTPS)} = 5000$ ml/min) with an inspiratory O_2 partial pressure $P_{I_{O_2}} = 150$ mm Hg, the values in the alveoli are

$$P_{A_{O_2}} = 100 \; mm\,Hg \; (13.3\,kPa);$$

$$P_{A_{CO_2}} = 40 \; mm\,Hg \; (5.3\,kPa).$$

These data are norms for the healthy adult at sea level. Note, however, that they represent the means of temporal changes and spatial distributions. There are slight fluctuations in the alveolar partial pressures in time, because the flow of fresh air into the alveolar space is discontinuous. Small local variations arise because ventilation and blood flow are not quite the same in the different parts of the lung (p. 478).

For given exchange rates of O_2 and CO_2 ($\dot{V}_{O_2}$ and $\dot{V}_{CO_2}$), according to Eq. (29) the alveolar partial pressures depend chiefly on the *alveolar ventilation* $\dot{V}_A$. Increase in alveolar ventilation *(hyperventilation)* results in a rise in $P_{A_{O_2}}$ and a fall in $P_{A_{CO_2}}$, and decreased alveolar ventilation *(hypoventilation)* has the opposite effect. This relationship between alveolar partial pressure and alveolar ventilation is quantitatively illustrated in Fig. 19-20.

Influence of the ventilation-perfusion ratio [34, 37, 60]. The respiratory gases exchanged in the alveoli must be transported to and from that region in the blood. Therefore O_2 uptake ($\dot{V}_{O_2}$) and CO_2 output ($\dot{V}_{CO_2}$) are coupled with the rate of lung perfusion. To the extent that the venous and arterial gas concentrations can be regarded as constant, **lung perfusion $\dot{Q}$** is proportional to $\dot{V}_{O_2}$ and $\dot{V}_{CO_2}$. Thus Equations (29) can also be interpreted as follows: *The alveolar O_2 and CO_2 partial pressures depend on the ratio of alveolar ventilation to lung perfusion $\dot{V}_A/\dot{Q}$.* In a person at rest with healthy lungs $\dot{V}_A/\dot{Q}$ = 0.9–1.0. Under pathological conditions the ventilation-perfusion ratio can change sufficiently to affect the alveolar partial pressures; when $\dot{V}_A/\dot{Q}$ increases the alveolar O_2 partial pressure rises and the CO_2 partial pressure falls, whereas a decrease in $\dot{V}_A/\dot{Q}$ has the opposite results.

Altered states of ventilation. The pattern of ventilation can change for a wide variety of reasons. Heavier breathing can be produced at will, and can also occur during work as an adaptation to the organism's metabolic requirements or in pathological conditions. Respiration can also be reduced voluntarily or by regulatory mechanisms or pathological factors. A number of terms have been coined in the past to denote such changes, but they were not systematically distinguished from one another. Recently an attempt has been made to develop a more precise terminology, in which the alveolar partial pressures are taken as the criterion. These definitions are as follows:

1. *Normoventilation:* normal ventilation, in which an alveolar CO_2 partial pressure of about 40 mm Hg (5.3 kPa) is maintained.
2. *Hyperventilation:* increased alveolar ventilation beyond the actual metabolic needs ($P_{A_{CO_2}}$ < 40 mm Hg).

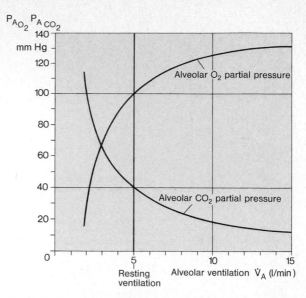

Fig. 19-20. Dependence of alveolar gas pressures ($P_{A_{O_2}}$ and $P_{A_{CO_2}}$) on alveolar ventilation ($\dot{V}_A$), at sea level under resting conditions (O_2 uptake, 280 ml/min; CO_2 output, 230 ml/min). The *straight red line* indicates the levels of $P_{A_{O_2}}$ and $P_{A_{CO_2}}$ in the case of normal ventilation

3. *Hypoventilation:* alveolar ventilation decreased below the actual metabolic needs ($P_{A_{CO_2}}$ > 40 mm Hg).
4. *Increased ventilation:* any increase in ventilation above the resting level (e. g., during work), regardless of the alveolar partial pressure.
5. *Eupnea:* normal comfortable respiration at rest.
6. *Hyperpnea:* increase in the depth of breathing with or without increase in respiratory frequency.
7. *Tachypnea:* increase in respiratory frequency.
8. *Bradypnea:* decrease in respiratory frequency.
9. *Apnea:* cessation of breathing, chiefly due to the absence of the physiological stimulus to respiration (decrease in arterial CO_2 partial pressure; cf. p. 483).
10. *Dyspnea:* Unpleasant subjective feeling of difficult or labored breathing (shortness of breath).
11. *Orthopnea:* marked dyspnea due to congestion of blood in the lung capillaries as a result of left-heart insufficiency, which is most severe when the patient is lying down and thus forces him to remain erect.
12. *Asphyxia:* cessation or suppression of breathing chiefly due to paralysis of the respiratory centers, with considerably restricted gas exchange (hypoxia and hypercapnia).

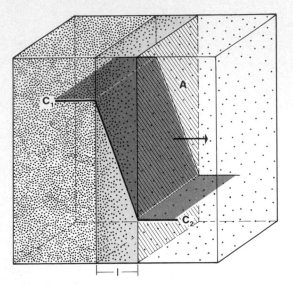

Fig. 19-21. Diagram illustrating the quantities that determine diffusion. Two spaces are separated by a flat layer with thickness l and area A. C_1, high concentration of particles in the left space; C_2, low concentration of particles in the right space; *red area,* concentration gradient in the diffusion layer. The flux is calculated by Eq. (30)

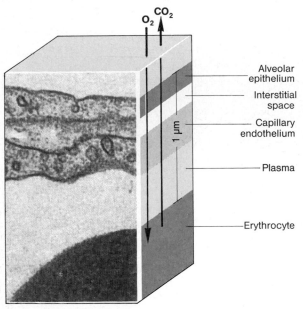

Alveolar epithelium

Interstitial space

Capillary endothelium

Plasma

Erythrocyte

Fig. 19-22. Media through which the respiratory gases must pass during exchange in the lung

Diffusion of Respiratory Gases

The rules governing diffusion. In the pulmonary alveoli the partial pressure of oxygen is kept high (100 mm Hg), whereas the O_2 partial pressure of the venous blood entering the capillaries of the lung is considerably lower (40 mm Hg). For CO_2 there is a partial-pressure gradient in the reverse direction

(46 mm Hg at the beginning of the lung capillaries, 40 mm Hg in the alveoli). These partial-pressure differences are the "driving forces" for the diffusion of O_2 and CO_2, and thus for pulmonary gas exchange.

The basic quantitative description of the diffusion process is given by **Fick's first law of diffusion,** which is illustrated in Fig. 19-21. Consider a substance diffusing through a flat layer of a medium with area A and thickness l; the concentration of the substance is high (C_1) on one side of the layer and low (C_2) on the other. The particles migrate through the layer in the direction of the arrow. Now, Fick's law states that the *flux* $\dot{m}$ (the amount of substance passing through A per unit time) is *directly proportional to the concentration difference* ($C_1 - C_2$):

$$\dot{m} = D\frac{A}{l}(C_1 - C_2) = D\frac{A}{l}\Delta C \qquad (30)$$

It is evident in Eq. (30) that more particles move through the layer, the *larger its area* A and the *smaller its thickness* l. The proportionality factor D is a constant dependent on the diffusion medium and the nature of the diffusing particles; it is called the **diffusion coefficient.**

When a dissolved gas diffuses through a fluid layer the concentrations C can be replaced by the corresponding partial pressures P, for the two quantities are proportional to one another.

$$\dot{m} = K\frac{A}{l}(P_1 - P_2) = K\frac{A}{l}\Delta P \qquad (31)$$

K, which has a different numerical value and different dimensions than D, is distinguished from it by being called **Krogh's diffusion coefficient** or the **diffusion conductivity** [59, 60]. K for CO_2 is 20–25 times as large as for O_2; that is, other conditions being equal 20–25 times as much CO_2 as O_2 diffuses through a given layer. This is the reason why adequate diffusion of CO_2 in the lung is guaranteed despite the small difference in CO_2 partial pressures.

Diffusion paths in the lung. According to Eq. (31), effective exchange by diffusion demands a large exchange area A and a small diffusion path l. Both these prerequisites are ideally met in the lung. The total *surface area of the alveoli* has been estimated to be 50–80 m^2 [61]. The structure of the lung tissue provides excellent conditions for *diffusion* in that the blood in the lung capillaries is separated from the space inside the alveoli by only a thin sheet of tissue. This arrangement is particularly striking when viewed in an electron micrograph (Fig. 19-22). In the direction in which oxygen diffuses it passes through the following sequence of media: the alveolar epithelium, the interstitial space between the basement membranes, the capillary endothelium, the blood plasma, the erythrocyte membrane and the interior of the erythrocyte. The entire diffusion path extends over a distance of the order of only 1 μm.

As can be seen in Fig. 19-22, the longest diffusion path and thus the greatest diffusion resistance is that within the erythrocyte. Here, however, the diffusion of O_2 as a gas is facilitated by other transport processes. As soon as an O_2 molecule enters the erythrocyte it attaches to hemoglobin (Hb), thus converting it to oxyhemoglobin (HbO_2; pp. 493 f.). The HbO_2 molecules themselves can diffuse toward the center of the erythrocyte (facilitated diffusion; cf. p. 655). Moreover, it is thought that when the erythrocytes are deformed as they pass through the lung capillaries there is an additional transport of O_2 by convection of the erythrocyte contents.

The CO_2 molecules diffuse over the same path in the opposite direction, from erythrocyte to alveolar space. They can do this, however, only after they have been released from their chemical bonds (pp. 497 f.).

Diffusing capacity of the lung [9, 17, 23, 28, 32, 45, 56, 57, 59, 60]. During its passage through the lung capillaries, an individual erythrocyte is in diffusion contact with the alveolar space for a relatively brief time, only about 0.3 s. This **contact time** is sufficient, however, to equalize almost entirely the gas partial pressures in the blood and in the alveoli. (For a definition of the gas partial pressures in the blood see pp. 492 f.). Fig. 19-23 illustrates this process; the O_2 partial pressure in the capillary blood approaches the alveolar partial pressure rapidly at first, and then at a progressively slower rate. This time course of partial-pressure change results from Fick's law of diffusion. The initially large difference in O_2 partial pressure between alveolus and capillary becomes steadily smaller during transit, so that the rate of diffusion must steadily decrease. The blood, which enters the capillary with an O_2 partial pressure of 40 mm Hg, leaves it with an O_2 partial pressure of 100 mm Hg. Similarly, during the contact time the blood CO_2 partial pressure approaches the alveolar pressure. The CO_2 partial pressure, 46 mm Hg at the beginning of the capillary, falls to 40 mm Hg as CO_2 diffuses away. We may say, then, that *in the lung of a healthy person the partial pressures in the blood become practically identical to those in the alveoli.*

A measure of the extent to which diffusion can occur in the whole human lung is obtainable from Fick's law of diffusion (Eq. 31). The derivation is based on the fact that the amount of oxygen that diffuses through the entire lung must be identical to the O_2 uptake $\dot{V}_{O_2}$. The factors K, A and l, which cannot be

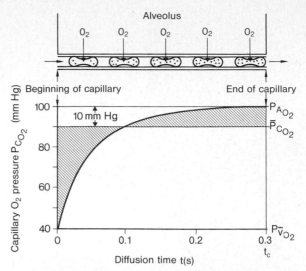

Fig. 19-23. Increase in the O_2 partial pressure in erythrocytes during passage through a lung capillary. *Above:* O_2 uptake of the erythrocytes (indicated by red dots). *Below:* the corresponding curve of capillary O_2 partial pressure $P_{c_{O_2}}$ as a function of diffusion time t. $P_{A_{O_2}}$, alveolar O_2 partial pressure; $P_{\bar{v}_{O_2}}$, mixed venous O_2 partial pressure; $\overline{P}_{c_{O_2}}$, O_2 partial pressure averaged over the duration of diffusion contact; t_c, contact time

measured for each individual, are lumped in a new constant $D_L = K \cdot A/l$. Thus we have

$$\dot{V}_{O_2} = D_L \cdot \overline{\Delta P}_{O_2}; \quad D_L = \frac{\dot{V}_{O_2}}{\Delta P_{O_2}} \tag{32}$$

The quantity D_L is called the **diffusing capacity** of the lung for oxygen. In this case $\overline{\Delta P}_{O_2}$ is the mean O_2 partial-pressure difference between the alveolar space and the blood in the lung capillaries. Because the O_2 partial pressure rises as the blood flows through the capillary, the pressure must be averaged over its entire length (Fig. 19-23).

To obtain a value for the O_2 diffusing capacity, one must measure oxygen uptake $\dot{V}_{O_2}$ and the mean O_2 partial-pressure difference $\overline{\Delta P}_{O_2}$. Whereas the measurement of $\dot{V}_{O_2}$ with an open or closed spirometric system presents no difficulties, a considerable amount of measurement is required to determine $\overline{\Delta P}_{O_2}$.

For a healthy adult at rest the oxygen uptake $\dot{V}_{O_2}$ is found to be ca. 300 ml/min, and the mean O_2 partial-pressure difference $\overline{\Delta P}_{O_2}$ is ca. 10 mm Hg (1.33 kPa). According to Eq. (32), then, *the normal O_2 diffusing capacity D_L is 30 ml · min^{-1} · $mm\ Hg^{-1}$ (230 ml · min^{-1} · kPa^{-1}).* Under pathological conditions D_L can be considerably smaller – a sign of increased diffusion resistance in the lung, which can be brought about by reduction of the exchange area A or extension of the diffusion path l. D_L in itself is not a measure of the extent to which the O_2 partial pressure in the blood approximates that in the alveoli. As with

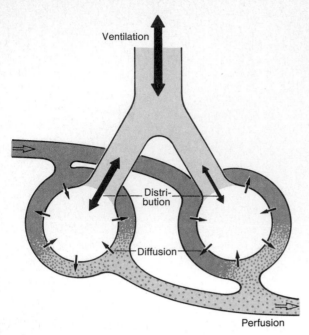

Ventilation

Distri-
bution

Diffusion

Perfusion

Fig. 19-24. Diagram to show the factors determining gas exchange in the lung. After [10]

alveolar ventilation, the diffusing capacity must be expressed with reference to pulmonary perfusion $\dot{Q}$. *The ratio $D_L/\dot{Q}$ is thus the critical determinant of the effectiveness of alveolar gas exchange;* a decrease in $D_L/\dot{Q}$ indicates **impaired diffusion.**

Net Gas Exchange in Normal and Pathological Conditions

Factors influencing gas exchange. We have encountered three factors that determine the degree to which the blood in the lung will be charged with oxygen and relieved of CO_2: 1. the **alveolar ventilation** $\dot{V}_A$, 2. the **pulmonary perfusion** $\dot{Q}$, and 3. the **diffusing capacity** D_L. We have also seen that these quantities do not independently influence the effect of respiration; rather, their ratios – $\dot{V}_A/\dot{Q}$ and $D_L/\dot{Q}$ – are decisive [34, 60].

Now we consider still another factor. Even in healthy people, but particularly in those with lung disease, there is a nonuniform **distribution** of ventilation, perfusion and diffusion in the various parts of the lung [9, 10, 28, 38, 60]. This nonuniform distribution makes the exchange of gases less complete; that is, it causes a reduction in the O_2 partial pressure of the systemic arterial blood and, to a lesser extent, a rise in CO_2 partial pressure. The situation is illustrated in Fig. 19-24, where the lung is represented as consisting of two regions. The difference in ventilation of the two regions is indicated by the different arrows in the airways.

The blood from the well ventilated region, where gas exchange is more thorough, is continually mixed with the blood from the other region; the net result is a somewhat lower O_2 partial pressure and a higher CO_2 partial pressure in the blood emerging from this inhomogeneous lung than would be the case with a uniformly ventilated lung. The gas-exchange parameters can be summarized in the following mnemonic: *The effect of respiration is determined by the factors ventilation, perfusion, diffusion and distribution.*

In **lung diseases** any of the factors listed above can be involved. Usually, however, alteration of one factor predominates and is specified in the diagnosis. Accordingly, the following disturbances of pulmonary function are distinguished [10, 38, 60]:
1. *Alveolar hypoventilation:* decrease in $\dot{V}_A/\dot{Q}$.
2. *Diffusion impairment:* decrease in $D_L/\dot{Q}$.
3. *Ventilation-perfusion nonuniformity:* inhomogeneous distribution of $\dot{V}_A/\dot{Q}$.
4. *Diffusion-perfusion nonuniformity:* inhomogeneous distribution of $D_L/\dot{Q}$.

There is a fifth kind of malfunction which also results in abnormal blood gas concentrations but which can originate outside the lung. Even in healthy people a small fraction of the circulating blood does not participate in gas exchange, for it enters the systemic arteries without having passed through ventilated parts of the lung. This is called *shunted blood.* The normal *anatomical shunts* are the *bronchial veins* and the small cardiac veins (the *Thebesian veins*) that empty into the left ventricle. The perfused but not ventilated alveoli are *functional shunts.* In all these cases the blood from the systemic veins bypasses the gas-exchange regions and returns unchanged into the arteries. Although in a healthy person the shunted blood flow amounts to only about 2% of the total cardiac output, the result is a decrease in arterial O_2 partial pressure by 5–10 mm Hg as compared with the mean end-capillary O_2 partial pressure in the lungs. In the presence of congenital heart disease (e.g., *defects of the ventricular septum*) *or vascular malformations (e.g., patent ductus arteriosus*) considerably larger fractions of the blood volume can be shunted, producing *hypoxia* (lowered O_2 partial pressure) and *hypercapnia* (elevated CO_2 partial pressure). To the above list we must therefore add:
5. *Increase in venous-arterial shunts*

Mean values of arterial partial pressures. *The net effect of breathing is reflected in the partial pressures of O_2 and CO_2 in the systemic arteries.* The two together provide a criterion by which overall pulmonary function can be judged. Therefore "norms" must be established for each, but as is very often the case with biological parameters, they can vary over quite an appreciable range. Moreover, blood gas pressures *depend systematically on age.* The arterial O_2 partial pressure in healthy young people averages about 95 mm Hg (12.6 kPa), but by age 40 it has fallen to ca. 80 mm Hg (10.6 kPa) and in 70-year-olds it is ca. 70 mm Hg (9.3 kPa) [36, 53]. This decrease can probably be ascribed to the increasing inhomogeneities of the lung with advancing age. The arterial CO_2 partial pressure, about 40 mm Hg (4.3 kPa) in the young, changes relatively little with age.

Measurement of arterial blood gases [35, 50]. The method most commonly used to measure the **partial pressure of oxygen** is *polarography* (Fig. 19-25 left). A measurement electrode (platinum or gold) and a reference electrode, both submerged in an electrolyte, are polarized by a voltage source. O_2 molecules that contact the surface of the noble metal are reduced there. The associated movement of charge in the closed electrical circuit can be measured with an ammeter; if a voltage of 0,6 V is supplied the current is directly proportional to the number of O_2 molecules that diffuse to the electrode surface and thus is proportional to the O_2 partial pressure in the solution. In the customary arrangement the electrolyte containing the electrodes is separated from the blood sample to be analyzed by a membrane permeable to oxygen. The entire measuring apparatus can be made so small that only a few drops of arterial blood are enough for the measurement of O_2. This blood is usually obtained from the earlobe, in which a maximal perfusion has been brought about; care must be taken to exclude all air as the blood is transferred to the measurement chamber.

The arterial CO_2 partial pressure can also be measured with very small samples of blood (Fig. 19-25 right). Here the arrangement of the electrode is that used to *measure pH* (p. 501); again, the sample is separated from the fluid around the electrode by a membrane through which gas but not ions can pass. The pH of the electrolyte ($NaHCO_3$) can therefore be affected only by changes in the CO_2 partial pressure of the blood, and after appropriate calibration the electrical signal from the meter is a measure of the CO_2 partial pressure of the blood. Another means of measuring the CO_2 partial pressure in small blood samples is provided by the *Astrup procedure* (p. 506).

If the **concentrations of gases** in the blood are required rather than their partial pressures, procedures are used in which the gases are first liberated from the blood and then analyzed manometrically or volumetrically. The most common technique employs the *Van Slyke manometric apparatus,* which originally required fairly large blood samples (0.5–2 ml), obtainable only by puncture of an artery. The procedure has since been modified so that the O_2 and CO_2 concentrations in smaller samples can be determined.

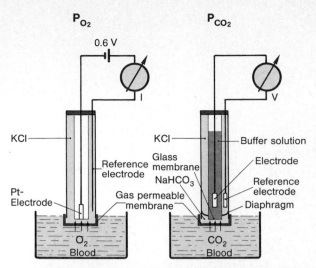

Fig. 19-25. Simplified diagram of the apparatus for measuring P_{O_2} and P_{CO_2} in the blood. P_{O_2} *(left):* In a closed circuit a voltage of 0.6 V is applied between a platinum electrode and a reference electrode; a gas-permeable membrane (red) separates this system from the blood sample. O_2 molecules that diffuse through the membrane are reduced at the surface of the platinum. The associated current I is proportional to the O_2 partial pressure in the blood. P_{CO_2} *(right):* Across a glass membrane permeable to H^+ a pH-dependent voltage is built up, which is displayed by the meter V. This device is separated from the blood sample by a gas-permeable membrane *(red)*. CO_2 molecules that diffuse through the latter membrane change the pH of the solution below the glass membrane. Thus the recorded voltage varies according to the P_{CO_2} in the blood

19.5 The Control of Respiration

The complex mechanisms by which respiration is regulated can best be understood if one begins by examining the goal of all these processes. Control of breathing can be defined very generally as the adjustment of external respiration to meet the needs of the organism as a whole. But this definition is not very helpful until we specify what the organism's needs are with regard to respiration.

It is of first importance that respiratory function be matched to the current *metabolic situation of the organism.* During physical work, for example, the rates of O_2 uptake and CO_2 elimination may have to be increased to several times the resting rates. This acceleration must be achieved by increasing the ventilation of the lungs. Moreover, under all circumstances the *arterial O_2 partial pressure* must be kept high enough to ensure an adequate rate of diffusion of oxygen into the tissues (cf. Chapter 21). At the same time, the *arterial CO_2 partial pressure* must be as required for regulation of the acid-base status (cf. Chapter 20).

An increase in minute volume, such as occurs during hard work, can be brought about by *deeper* or *more rapid breathing.* A further aspect of control, then, is to achieve the most economically favorable balance of these two parameters. Finally, the *form* of breathing can be modified by certain reflexes (swallowing, coughing, sneezing) and specific human activities (speaking, singing) – all of which must be done in such a way that the chemical milieu of the arterial blood is kept reasonably constant. In view of the diverse demands, often made in combination, it is understandable that a complex **control mechanism** with multiple sensors is required for optimal adjustment of breathing [9, 27, 44, 46, 47].

Respiratory Centers

Location of the centers. The *medulla oblongata* was long thought to be the seat of the respiratory center. More than 100 years ago, when the first attempts were

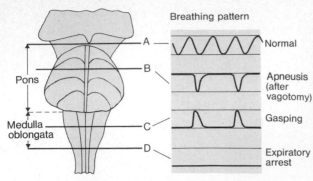

Fig. 19-26. The results of transection of the brainstem (ventral aspect) at different levels

made to examine its location and function more closely, research proceeded from the notion that the automaticity of breathing movements must originate in a narrowly circumscribed nuclear region ("noeud vital"). Subsequently, however, the rhythmic sequence of inspiration and expiration proved to arise from the interplay of various groups of cells. Important information was obtained from experiments on animals (dog, cat, rabbit) in which nervous tissue was *transected* or *stimulated* electrically, and neuronal *activity was recorded*[9, 27, 40].

Transection experiments. These classical studies, in which the brainstem was cut at different levels, provided the first (though rough) indications of the site of the "respiratory center". The picture so derived was as follows (Fig. 19-26):
1. A cut *above the pons* (A) leaves breathing unchanged. A cut that *separates the medulla from the spinal cord* (D) causes complete respiratory arrest. Therefore the coordinated alternation between inspiration and expiration is maintained by a "center" in the lower brainstem. The ability of this region to activate the respiratory musculature rhythmically is retained when all known afferent inputs to the "center" are eliminated.
2. When one makes a cut just below the *upper third of the pons* (B) and simultaneously transects the two *vagal nerves,* one observes maintained inspiration occasionally interrupted by expiratory movements. This form of breathing is called **apneusis.** Evidently a cut at this level blocks the inhibitory influences that the upper pons normally exerts on the cells that activate inspiration.
3. When the brainstem is cut *below the pons* (C) rhythmic breathing continues, but the rhythm is not at all even. Sometimes it gives way to **gasping,** a form of breathing in which long expiratory pauses are interrupted by short inspirations. It is evident, then, that *rhythmic breathing can be sustained by the medulla oblongata alone.* Stabilization and coordination of this rhythm, however, require the cooperation of structures in the middle and upper parts of the pons. It was once thought that this function resided in a "pneumotactic" and an "apneustic" center. This view is no longer tenable, and the misleading terms should therefore be discarded.

Stimulation experiments. Attempts were made to learn more about the locations of the "inspiratory and expiratory centers" by electrical stimulation of parts of the brainstem. For various reasons, however, the results of these experiments are not easy to interpret. One objection to this approach is that when respiration is affected by stimulation one cannot be sure that the decisive centers themselves have been stimulated; the effect could have been produced by stimulation of the afferent or efferent pathways.

Recording experiments. More recently, recording of neuronal activity within the brainstem has contributed to our understanding of the central control of respiration. Intracellular or extracellular **microelectrodes** are inserted into the brainstem so as to pick up the discharge of single neurons, and the record is examined for evidence of correlation with the simultaneously recorded breathing movements. By systematically probing the candidate regions of the CNS in this way, one can localize those groups of cells that are active chiefly during inspiration or expiration.

The results of these experiments in simplified form can be outlined as follows:

1. **Inspiratory neurons,** which discharge shortly before and during the inspiration phase, are found bilaterally in two circumscribed areas of the medulla oblongata (Fig. 19-27). The more lateral of the two coincides with the *rostral part of the nucleus ambiguus.* The second, medial region is smaller and lies immediately adjacent to the *solitary tract.* Because the inspiratory neurons are concentrated in these regions, the two together can, for the sake of brevity, be called the "inspiration center".

2. **Expiratory neurons,** which discharge during expiration and in the expiratory pause, are found in a region *caudal to the inspiratory zone, accompanying the nucleus ambiguus.* This area (again by simplification) can be called the "expiration center".

3. The medial inspiratory region (along the solitary tract) has been found to contain not only the so-called R_α *neurons,* active during inspiration, but a second group of cells, the R_β *neurons.* The latter are activated together with the R_α neurons but also fire during the silent period of R_α. They are particularly active when the lungs are maximally stretched. Therefore the R_β neurons are thought to act as inhibitors of the R_α neurons.

Origin of the central respiratory rhythm. *As the above experimental results show, the rhythmic sequence of inspiration and expiration is brought about by the alternating discharge of impulse volleys by the inspiratory and expiratory neurons* (Fig. 19-27). During the phase in which the inspiratory cells are activated the expiratory cells do not discharge, and conversely. It is therefore plausible that the two groups of cells are recipro-

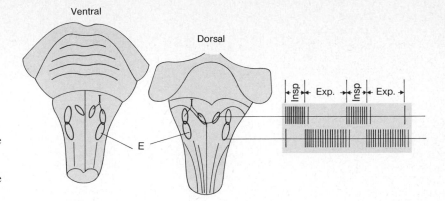

Fig. 19-27. Positions of the inspiratory (I) and expiratory (E) centers in the medulla oblongata. The discharge patterns of the respiratory neurons at these sites are shown in relation to the breathing cycle. Modified after [27]

cally inhibitory. But such a mechanism in itself cannot explain how the rhythmic alternation between expiration and inspiration arises; in addition, one must have some idea how the neural activity is limited in time – that is, what terminates each volley of impulses. Only when one volley stops can the other, previously inhibited group of cells become active. This *limiting mechanism* has been the subject of several theories, some of which regard cellular properties as responsible and others, the inhibitory influences of other cells. One of these theories is based on the notion that when the inspiratory R_α cells discharge the R_β cells are also activated by way of collaterals. If the latter should in turn inhibit the R_α cells, temporal summation of this input could bring R_α discharge to a halt. That is, the alternation of inspiration and expiration could be brought about by central feedback inhibition. The basic circuitry required in this concept is summarized in Fig. 19-28. However, many findings suggest that the neuronal circuitry underlying central rhythmogenesis is considerably more complicated than appears in this simple diagram [27].

Mechanical Control of Respiration

Hering-Breuer reflex [40, 55]. The centrally controlled respiratory rhythm can be modified by peripheral influences, as shown by the following observations. When the *lungs are inflated inspiration is reflexly inhibited* and expiration is thus initiated. Conversely, fairly large *decreases in lung volume* initiate *deeper inspiration*. Evidently the state of stretch of the lung at each moment is signalled to the respiratory centers, which elicit an appropriate countermovement. This sequence of events is named for its discoverers – *the Hering-Breuer-reflex*.

This reflex arc begins at the **stretch receptors in the lung parenchyma.** Such receptors are to be found in

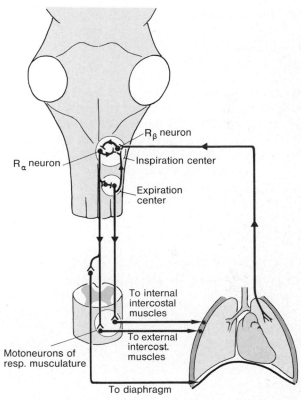

Fig. 19-28. Circuitry of the neuronal control system for inspiration and expiration, with feedback from the pulmonary stretch receptors

the *trachea,* the *bronchi* and the *bronchioles.* Some of these signal the degree of stretch by firing a train of impulses with very little adaptation, while others are excited only when the amount of stretch increases or decreases. In this way both the state of stretch of the lung and changes in that state can be monitored continually. *The afferent pathways of the lung-stretch reflex run in the vagus nerve.* Therefore bilateral transec-

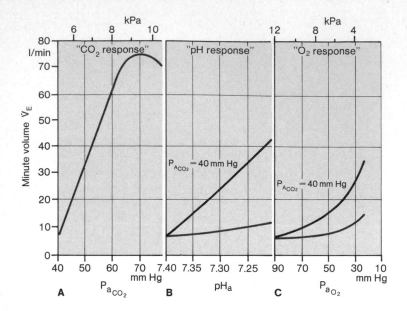

Fig. 19-29 A–C. Minute volume ($\dot{V}_E$) as a function of the arterial CO_2 and O_2 partial pressures ($P_{a_{CO_2}}$, $P_{a_{O_2}}$) and arterial pH (pH_a). *Red curves:* Ventilation response ordinarily observed; *black curves:* response obtained when CO_2 pressure is kept constant ($P_{A_{CO_2}}$ = 40 mm Hg). From data in [27]

tion of the vagus eliminates the Hering-Breuer reflex. Following *vagotomy* breathing is slowed and inspiration is deeper. With the vagus intact inhibition of the inspiratory R_α neurons and activation of the associated R_β neurons can be shown to accompany stretching of the lungs. We may assume, therefore, that the afferent vagus impulses inhibit inspiratory activity by way of the interposed R_β neurons (Fig. 19-28). The *efferent limb* of the arc comprises the motor nerves to the respiratory musculature.

The *physiological significance* of the Hering-Breuer reflex is that it limits the respiratory excursions. In so doing, it helps to adjust the depth of breathing to the prevailing conditions in such a way that the respiratory work is done economically. Moreover, the Hering-Breuer reflex serves in the extreme case to prevent overstretching of the lungs.

Reflexes of the intercostal musculature. The intrinsic control of breathing movements also involves spinal reflexes originating in the respiratory muscles. Like other striated muscles, the muscles used in breathing contain *muscle spindles* that function as *stretch receptors*. When either inspiration or expiration encounters difficulty the corresponding muscle spindles are stimulated, and the resulting *proprioceptive reflex* causes enhanced contraction of the muscle. This property of the intercostal musculature tends to match the mechanics of breathing to the momentary resistance in the lungs. Moreover, it is highly likely that the afferent impulses from the muscle spindles are also conducted to the respiratory centers, forming a longer reflex arc that can similarly modify the activity of the respiratory muscles.

Chemical Control of Respiration

The arterial levels of *CO_2 partial pressure, O_2 partial pressure* and *H^+ concentration* are critically determined by respiratory function, but all three can in turn affect the ventilation of the lungs. This interaction amounts to a **control circuit** that tends to maintain constancy of the three controlled variables – the partial pressures of CO_2 and O_2 and the pH of the blood [24, 27]. *The chemical control of respiration thus contributes to homeostasis and ensures that breathing is adjusted to the organism's metabolic state.*

The effect of CO_2 on breathing. *An increase in the arterial CO_2 partial pressure (hypercapnia) causes an increase in minute volume.* As a rule both the tidal volume and the respiration rate are increased.
The quantitative relationship between the arterial CO_2 partial pressure $P_{a_{CO_2}}$ and the associated minute volume $\dot{V}_E$ is called the **CO_2 response curve.** This curve (Fig. 19-29 A) shows the extent to which ventilation depends on the CO_2 partial pressure. When $P_{a_{CO_2}}$ rises from 40 to 60 mm Hg, $\dot{V}_E$ increases from 7 to about 65 l/min. A $P_{a_{CO_2}}$ increase of this magnitude can occur, for example, when one breathes a gas mixture containing large amounts of CO_2; it is accompanied by a feeling of breathlessness *(dyspnea)*. Fig. 19-29 A shows further that the amount by which ventilation can be increased in this way is limited. Accumulation of CO_2 in the blood can raise the minute volume to at most 75 l/min – far less than the minute volumes achieved during extremely hard work (120 l/min). If the arterial CO_2 partial pressure exceeds 70 mm Hg ventilation declines again, because at such high con-

centrations CO_2 inhibits the respiratory centers. Interruption or reduction of breathing due to such inhibition of the central driving mechanism is called *asphyxia*.

After prolonged, intense forced respiration *(hyperventilation)* some subjects stop breathing temporarily. Because more CO_2 is blown off during hyperventilation, and the arterial CO_2 partial pressure falls correspondingly, this pause in breathing is generally regarded as due to the absence of the physiological "CO_2 stimulus" to respiration. Cessation of breathing under these conditions is commonly called apnea. But many subjects do not exhibit complete apnea following hyperventilation; their breathing is only reduced somewhat. From this observation one may conclude that there is a basic central drive of respiration that persists even without the "CO_2 stimulus" [27].

The effects of CO_2 may be summarized as follows. As an end product of oxidative metabolism, CO_2 affects the minute volume by way of its partial pressure in the arterial blood. The result is an optimal adjustment of the minute volume to the momentary rate of metabolism. As imbalances between respiration and metabolism occur the equilibrium is restored by the CO_2 control system. But the effect of CO_2 alone does not explain the increased ventilation during exercise.

The effect of H^+ on breathing. *When the arterial pH falls below the normal value of 7.4, respiration is increased.* When pH rises above the norm breathing is reduced, but to a lesser extent. Because pH and CO_2 partial pressure are coupled (cf. CO_2 equilibration curve, p. 502) the question arises whether pH and P_{CO_2} in the arterial blood are identical *"respiratory drives"*. The answer is that they clearly are not, for when arterial pH falls owing to altered CO_2 content the effect on respiration is considerably greater than when the same reduction in pH is caused by nonvolatile acids. Quantitative studies have shown that about 60% of the ventilatory CO_2 response is associated directly with CO_2 and about 40% is due to the H^+ alteration [27].

The dependence of minute volume $\dot{V}_E$ on the pH of arterial blood (pH_a) is illustrated in Fig. 19-29 B. The red curve represents the **pH response** observed when pH is reduced by an increase in the blood content of nonvolatile acids (metabolic acidosis; cf. p. 504). In this case a reduction by 0.1 pH unit causes ventilation to increase by about 2 l/min. This relatively modest increase results from the *interaction between the two "respiratory drives" pH and CO_2 partial pressure*. A change in pH alone would have a much greater effect on ventilation; the black curve, for example, was obtained by keeping the CO_2 partial pressure constant ($P_{a_{CO_2}}$ = 40 mm Hg). Normally, however, the increased ventilation induced by pH sends CO_2 out of the lungs at a greater rate, so that $P_{a_{CO_2}}$ falls. Thus when the

blood pH is reduced the CO_2 respiratory drive diminishes. The pH response curve is the resultant of the increasing (from left to right) pH drive and the simultaneously decreasing CO_2 drive.

The effect of O_2 deficiency on breathing. *When the O_2 partial pressure in the arterial blood falls (hypoxia) ventilation is increased.* Arterial hypoxia can occur in people at great altitudes, where, because the atmospheric pressure is lower, the inspiratory O_2 partial pressure is reduced. But it can also be the consequence of pulmonary malfunction (e. g., diffusion impairment).

Fig. 19-29 C shows the relation between *minute volume $\dot{V}_E$ and the arterial O_2 partial pressure $P_{a_{O_2}}$*. The black curve applies to the case in which CO_2 partial pressure is kept constant ($P_{a_{CO_2}}$ = 40 mm Hg); that is, it represents the response to the O_2 drive in isolation. In reality, however, there is an *interaction with the CO_2 drive*. Increased ventilation caused by O_2 deficiency reduces the arterial CO_2 partial pressure, so that its effectiveness in driving respiration diminishes. The **O_2 response** (red curve) under natural conditions thus exhibits a relatively slight increase in ventilation as O_2 partial pressure falls. In practice oxygen regulates breathing effectively only when its arterial partial pressure is less than 50–60 mm Hg – that is, when a state of considerable hypoxia exists.

Although the arterial O_2 partial pressure has little influence on breathing under normal conditions, it can become quite significant in **pathological states.** Its effect is especially marked when the CO_2 sensitivity of regulation is reduced by *drugs* or eliminated altogether as in *barbiturate poisoning*. Similarly, in *chronic hypercapnia* sensitivity to the P_{CO_2} and H^+ stimuli is reduced. It is for this reason that in patients with severe *pulmonary malfunction* breathing is basically stimulated by arterial **hypoxia** and not by the simultaneous **hypercapnia.** In none of these cases is the inhalation of pure oxygen an appropriate treatment. Indeed, it could cause a potentially *lethal apnea,* because the respiratory drive most effective under these conditions is eliminated.

Peripheral chemoreceptors [9, 11, 24, 27]. As we have seen, it is possible for breathing to be influenced chemically by the P_{CO_2}, the pH, and the P_{O_2} of the arterial blood. The gases and the hydrogen ions in some cases can affect the central nervous system directly, and they can also cause peripheral receptors to discharge impulses that are conducted to the respiratory centers. Such receptors, called *chemoreceptors* because they convert chemical stimuli into a train of action potentials, are found in the paraganglia of the carotid sinus and aortic arch.

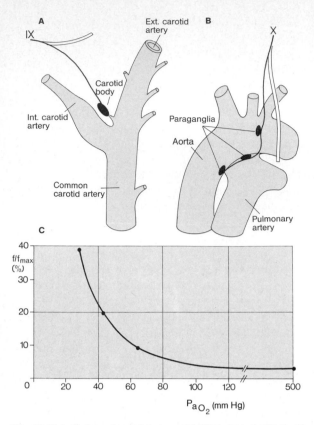

Fig. 19-30 A–C. Locations of the carotid (**A**) and aortic (**B**) bodies, and their afferent pathways. (**C**) Relation between the frequency of chemoreceptor discharge and the arterial O_2 partial pressure. As the carotid sinus of the cat is perfused in isolation with blood at different O_2 partial pressures ($P_{a_{O_2}}$) and constant $P_{a_{CO_2}} = 33$ mm Hg and pH = 7.33, the afferent impulses in the sinus nerve are recorded. (Ordinate: summed activity as % of the maximal activity: f/f_{max}.) From data in [48]

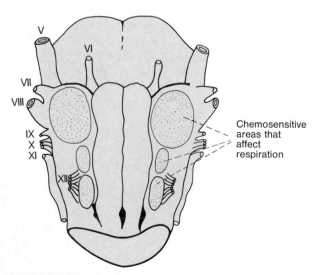

Fig. 19-31. Ventral aspect of the medulla oblongata (cat), showing the chemosensitive areas in the respiration control system. After [51]

The paraganglion at the point where the common carotid artery divides into the internal and external carotids is called the **carotid body** (Fig. 19-30 A). This structure is supplied with blood by small arteries and innervated by a branch of the *glossopharyngeal nerve*. The **paraganglia of the aortic arch,** sometimes called the *aortic bodies,* are also supplied with blood by small side arteries. The nerve impulses from the aortic bodies are conducted to the respiratory centers by fibers of the *vagus nerve* (Fig. 19-30 B).

The chemoreceptors in all these paraganglia are *activated* – that is, increase their discharge rate – when the O_2 partial pressure decreases, the CO_2 partial pressure increases or the pH rises. This relation can be demonstrated by recording the afferent action potentials in animals as the blood parameters are altered (Fig. 19-30 C). Such experiments are convenietly done by perfusing the arteries that supply the paraganglia with blood in which P_{O_2}, P_{CO_2} and pH have been set to the desired levels. Another approach is to denervate the chemoreceptors or block their activity with cold, so as to establish their share in the overall chemical control of breathing.

These experiments have shown that the O_2 *effects are mediated entirely by the peripheral chemoreceptors.* The chemoreceptor activity associated with normal arterial O_2 partial pressures is enhanced when P_{O_2} falls and suppressed when P_{O_2} rises. Denervation of the chemoreceptive paraganglia eliminates the effect of these changes on breathing. By contrast, *both CO_2 and pH act chiefly at central sites.* It is true that the level of chemoreceptor activity is also affected by arterial P_{CO_2} and pH, but the influence of these signals on the respiratory centers is relatively limited.

Central chemosensitivity. CO_2 and pH affect breathing chiefly by way of their action on *chemosensitive structures in the brainstem.* There is a gradation between the effects on ventilation produced by changes in arterial P_{CO_2} and those in arterial pH (Fig. 19-29). This graded effectiveness does not imply that there are two different kinds of specific receptor mechanisms in the brainstem, one for CO_2 and another for H^+. It could be that the receptors are sensitive only to H^+ ions, the effect of CO_2 being exerted by way of H^+-ion formation. The graded difference in the influence of arterial P_{CO_2} and pH would then be interpretable as a consequence of *different resistances to the transport of CO_2 and H^+.* In fact, CO_2 diffuses very rapidly from the blood into the brain tissue, whereas biological membranes are a considerable impediment to the diffusion of H^+ ions. Many experiments support the theory that the central chemosensitivity in the respiratory control system is dependent upon H^+ exclusively [51, 52].

At present it is thought that the **H$^+$ concentration of the extracellular fluid** in the brainstem is the decisive factor in the central respiratory drive. This fluid probably has a composition like that of *cerebrospinal fluid*. Respiration would thus have to be affected by way of the CSF as well. When the ventricles of the brain were perfused with artificial CSF of varying composition, it could indeed be shown that breathing changed in correlation with the pH of the fluid. In addition, H$^+$ sensitive fields on the surface of the brainstem could be located more precisely [51, 52]. As Fig. 19-31 shows, there are *three such fields on the ventral surface of the medulla* (near the roots of the vagus and hypoglossal nerves); application of acids to these fields can elicit increased ventilation.

Other Respiratory Drives

Respiratory drive during exercise. Working muscle requires more oxygen than resting muscle, and this increased demand must be met by increasing the transport of oxygen via respiration and circulation. During strenuous exercise, O$_2$ uptake can be raised from about 300 ml/min at rest to as much as 4 l/min – an effect achievable only by considerably increased ventilation. Within the range of metabolic rates encountered during sustained performance of work, *ventilation rises roughly linearly with O$_2$ uptake* (Fig. 19-32). Only during extreme, short-term exertion does ventilation increase disproportionately. Let us consider the mechanisms responsible for this very accurate matching of breathing to the varying consumption of O$_2$ and release of CO$_2$ during work.

When work is begun the P$_{CO_2}$ of the blood rises and its pH falls. But these changes in blood chemistry occur too slowly and are too small to explain, by themselves, the ensuing increase in ventilation. It must be that additional neural factors come into play.

There are many indications that **central coinnervation** of the respiratory centers operates during exercise, especially in the *initial phase*. The data imply that impulses from the motor centers are conducted not only to the working musculature but to the respiratory centers as well, activating the respiratory neurons there. In the subsequent **steady state,** in which breathing and circulation are adjusted to the intensity of work, several factors probably determine the magnitude of ventilation. In addition to the central coinnervation and the chemical respiratory drives, a **neural feedback** from the mechano- and chemoreceptors in the working musculature can affect breathing. In the *recovery phase,* finally, **blood parameters** are the main factors determining the rate at which ventilation returns to the resting level [27].

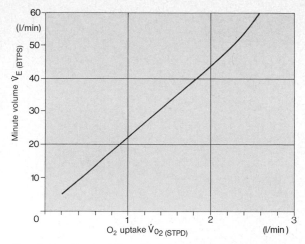

Fig. 19-32. Minute volume $\dot{V}_{E\,(BTPS)}$ as a function of O$_2$ uptake $\dot{V}_{O_2\,(STPD)}$ at rest and during physical work

Unspecific respiratory drives. There are factors that can alter ventilation but are not primarily involved in the control of respiration; these are usually called *unspecific respiratory drives*. Among them are the drives associated with temperature change. Strong **hot and cold stimuli** to the skin can increase the activity of the respiratory centers (e.g. it is possible to stimulate breathing in the newborn by alternating hot and cold baths). Moreover, it has been shown that changes in **body temperature** affect breathing. Both an increase *(fever)* and a slight decrease *(mild hypothermia)* in body temperature enhance ventilation. *Deep hypothermia* (extreme cooling), however, causes central inhibition of breathing. Another unspecific respiratory drive is **pain** (painful stimuli activate breathing in the newborn). The afferent signals from **baroreceptors** in the circulatory system (pp. 426 f.) also affect the respiratory centers; a rise in pressure in the arterial system thus inhibits inspiratory and expiratory neurons, so that both the depth and the rate of breathing are reduced. Various **hormones** can also drive respiration. For example, increased ventilation is observed when *adrenalin* enters the blood (during exercise or mental excitement) and when the *progesterone* level is elevated (in pregnancy).

The various specific and nonspecific respiratory drives are summarized diagrammatically in Fig. 19-33.

Pathological forms of breathing [19, 27]. Even healthy people exhibit a type of *periodic breathing* called **Cheyne-Stokes breathing** while sleeping in the high mountains (Fig. 19-34). After a few deep breaths there is a pause *(apnea),* followed by renewed *deep breathing,* and so on. This pattern is caused by the decreased

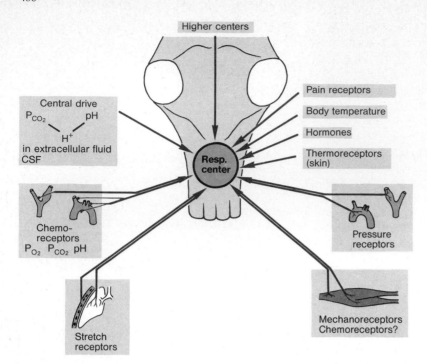

Fig. 19-33. Survey of the central respiratory drives and the peripheral receptors that can modulate breathing

partial pressure of oxygen in the inspired air at high altitudes in combination with the alteration of central respiratory activity during sleep. During inspiratory O_2 deficiency the shape of the CO_2-response curve is different from that shown in Fig. 19-29 A; at very low CO_2 partial pressures the curve is quite flat, but it suddenly rises sharply at somewhat higher partial pressures of CO_2. The deep breaths of Cheyne-Stokes breathing expel so much CO_2 that P_{CO_2} falls into the range where the CO_2-response curve is flat and the CO_2 drive is practically eliminated. The result is apnea. While breathing is stopped, CO_2 accumulates in the blood until P_{CO_2} is once again in the range where the CO_2 response curve rises steeply, and hyperventilation begins again. Under pathological conditions Cheyne-Stokes breathing can result from *poisoning* – for example, when toxic substances ordinarily excreted are retained due to kidney failure *(uremia)*.

Biot's breathing (Fig. 19-34) is a similar form of periodic breathing, brought about by conditions including *brain damage and elevated CSF pressure*. It is probably the result of injury to the respiratory centers. Under these conditions **gasping** (p. 480) can also be observed, as in *infants born prematurely*. When the pH of the blood is lowered by fixed acids *(metabolic acidosis)* – a symptom, for example, of *diabetes mellitus* – a special form of hyperventilation characterized by very deep breaths results. This so-called **Kussmaul breathing** (air hunger) can compensate, at least in part, for the metabolic acidosis (cf. pp. 504).

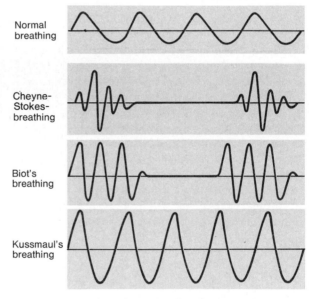

Fig. 19-34. Pathological patterns of breathing

Table 19-1. Summary of data characterizing the respiratory function of a healthy young man (body surface $1.7\,m^2$) at rest. Variations from this norm and contributing factors are noted in the text

Lung volumes and capacities		Functional tests	
Total capacity	6 l	Rel. forced expiratory volume	75%
Vital capacity	4.5 l	Maximal expiratory flow	10 l/s
Funct. residual capacity	2.4 l	Maximum breathing capacity	150 l/min
Residual volume	1.2 l	**Perfusion ratios**	
Tidal volume	0.5 l	Alveolar ventilation/perfusion	0.9
Dead-space volume	0.15 l	Shunt perfusion/total perfusion	0.02

Ventilation		Gas exchange	
Respiratory frequency	$14\,min^{-1}$	O_2 uptake	280 ml/min
Minute volume	7 l/min	CO_2 output	230 ml/min
Alveolar ventilation	5 l/min	Respiratory quotient	0.82
Dead-space ventilation	2 l/min	O_2 diffusing capacity	$30\,ml \cdot min^{-1} \cdot mm\,Hg^{-1}$
			$(230\,ml \cdot min^{-1} \cdot kPa^{-1})$
		Contact time	0.3 s

Respiratory mechanics		Concentrations and partial pressures		
			O_2	CO_2
Pleural pressures:		Inspiratory concentration	0.209	0.0003
end of expiration	-4 cm H_2O (-0.4 kPa)	Alveolar concentration	0.140	0.056
end of inspiration	-6.5 cm H_2O (-0.65 kPa)	Inspiratory partial pressure	150 mm Hg	0.2 mm Hg
Compliance of lung	0.2 l/cm H_2O (2 l/kPa)		(20 kPa)	(27 Pa)
Compliance of thorax	0.2 l/cm H_2O (2 l/kPa)	Alveolar partial pressure	100 mm Hg	40 mm Hg
Compliance of lung			(13.3 kPa)	(5.3 kPa)
plus thorax	0.1 l/cm H_2O (1 l/kPa)	Arterial partial pressure	95 mm Hg	40 mm Hg
Resistance	1.5 cm $H_2O \cdot s \cdot l^{-1}$		(12.6 kPa)	(5.3 kPa)
	$(0.15\,kPa \cdot s \cdot l^{-1})$			

19.6 References

Textbooks and Handbooks

1. ALTMAN, P.L., DITTMER, D.S.: Biological Handbooks: Respiration and circulation. Bethesda: Fed. Amer. Soc. experim. Biol. 1971
2. AGOSTONI, E., MEAD, J.: Statics of the respiratory system. In: Fenn, W.O., Rahn, H. (Eds.): Handbook of Physiology, Sect. 3: Respiration, Vol. I. Washington: Amer. Physiol. Soc. 1964
3. BARTELS, H., RIEGEL, K., WENNER, J., WULF, H.: Perinatale Atmung. Berlin–Heidelberg–New York: Springer 1972
4. BENNINGHOFF, A., GOERTTLER, K.: Lehrbuch der Anatomie des Menschen. München–Berlin–Wien: Urban u. Schwarzenberg 1968
5. BOUHUYS, A.: Respiratory dead space. In: Fenn, W.O., Rahn, H. (Eds.): Handbook of Physiology, Sect. 3: Respiration, Vol. I. Washington: Amer. Physiol. Soc. 1964
6. BOUHUYS, A.: The physiology of breathing. New York–San Francisco–London: Grune and Stratton 1977
7. BRISCOE, W.A.: Lung volumes. In: FENN, W.O., RAHN, H. (Eds.): Handbook of Physiology, Sect. 3: Respiration, Vol. II. Washington: Amer. Physiol. Soc. 1964
8. CAMPBELL, E.J.M.: The respiratory muscles and the mechanics of breathing. Chicago: Year Book Publishers 1959
9. COMROE, J.J.: Physiology of respiration. Chicago: Year Book Medical Publishers 1974
10. COMROE, J.H., FORSTER, R.E., DUBOIS, A.B., BRISCOE, W.A., CARLSEN, E.: The lung: Clinical physiology and pulmonary function tests. Chicago: Year Book Medical Publishers, 1962
11. COMROE, J.H.: The peripheral chemoreceptors. In: FENN, W.O., RAHN, H. (Eds.): Handbook of Physiology, Sect, 3: Respiration, Vol. I Washington: Amer. Physiol. Soc. 1964
12. COTES, J.E.: Lung function: Assessment and application to medicine. Oxford: Blackwell 1968
13. CROFTON, J., DOUGLAS, A.: Respiratory diseases. Philadelphia: Lippincott Comp. 1975
14. DEJOURS, P.: Respiration. New York: Oxford Univ. Press 1966
15. DUBOIS, A.B.: Resistance of breathing. In: FENN, W.O., RAHN, H. (Eds.): Handbook of Physiology, Sect. 3: Respiration, Vol. I Washington: Amer. Physiol. Soc. 1964
16. DUBOIS, A.B.: Obstructions of the airway and restrictions of the lung expansion. In: FENN, W.O., RAHN, H. (Eds.): Handbook of Physiology, Sect. 3: Respiration, Vol. II Washington: Amer. Physiol. Soc. 1965
17. FORSTER, R.E.: Diffusion of gases. In: FENN, W.O., RAHN, H. (Eds.): Handbook of Physiology, Sect. 3: Respiration, Vol. I Washington: Amer. Physiol. Soc. 1964
18. FRIEND, J.A.R., FLOOK, V.: Clinical respiratory physiology. New York: Mac Millan Publ. Co. Inc. 1979
19. GUYTON, A.C.: Textbook of medical physiology. Philadelphia–London–Toronto: Saunders 1976
20. GUYTON, A.C., WIDDICOMBE, J.G. (Eds.): Respiratory Physiology II. Intern. Rev. Physiol., Vol. 14 Baltimore–London–Tokyo: University Park Press 1977
21. HAYEK, H.v.: Die menschliche Lunge. Berlin–Heidelberg–New York: Springer 1970
22. HILDEBRANDT, J.: Anatomy and physics of respiration. In: RUCH, T.C., PATTON, H.D. (Eds.): Physiology and biophysics. Philadelphia–London–Toronto: Saunders 1974
23. HILLS, B.A.: Gas transfer in the lung. Cambridge: University Press 1974
24. HORNBEIN, T.F., SØRENSEN, S.C.: The chemical regulation of ventilation. In: Ruch, T.C., Patton, H.D. (Eds.): Physiology and biophysics Philadelphia–London–Toronto: Saunders 1974
25. JACQUEZ, J.A.: Respiratory physiology. Maidenhead: MacGraw Hill 1979
26. KAO, F.F.: An introduction to respiratory physiology. Amsterdam: Excerpta Medica 1972
27. KOEPCHEN, H.P.: Atmungsregulation. In: GAUER, O.H., KRAMER,

K., JUNG, R. (Hrsg.): Physiologie des Menschen Bd.6: Atmung. München–Berlin–Wien: Urban und Schwarzenberg 1975

28. LENFANT, C.: Gas transport and gas exchange. In: RUCH, T.C., PATTON, H.D. (Eds.): Physiology and biophysics. Philadelphia–London–Toronto: Saunders 1974

29. MEAD, J., AGOSTONI, E.: Dynamics of breathing. In: FENN, W.O., RAHN, H. (Eds.): Handbook of Physiology, Sect. 3: Respiration, Vol. I Washington: Amer. Physiol. Soc. 1964

30. NUNN, J.F.: Applied respiratory physiology, with special reference to anaesthesia. London: Butterworth 1969

31. OTIS, A.B.: The work of breathing. In: FENN, W.O., RAHN, H. (Eds.): Handbook of Physiology, Sect. 3: Respiration, Vol. I. Washington: Amer. Physiol. Soc. 1964

32. PIIPER, J.: Physiologie der Atmung. In: GAUER, O.H., KRAMER, K., JUNG, R. (Hrsg.): Physiologie des Menschen, Bd.6: Atmung. München–Berlin–Wien: Urban und Schwarzenberg 1975

33. PROCTOR, D.F.: Physiology of the upper airway. In: FENN, W.O., RAHN, H. (Eds.): Handbook of Physiology, Sect. 3: Respiration, Vol. I, Washington: Amer. Physiol. Soc. 1964

34. RAHN, H., FAHRI, L.E.: Ventilation, perfusion, and gas exchange – the $\dot{V}_A/\dot{Q}$ concept. In: FENN, W.O., RAHN, H. (Eds.): Handbook of Physiology, Sect. 3: Respiration, Vol. I. Washington: Amer. Physiol. Soc. 1964

35. SEVERINGHAUS, J.W.: Blood gas concentrations. In: FENN, W.O., RAHN, H. (Eds.): Handbook of Physiology, Sect. 3: Respiration, Vol. II Washington: Amer. Physiol. Soc. 1965

36. ULMER, W.T., REICHEL, G., NOLTE, D.: Die Lungenfunktion. Physiologie und Pathophysiologie. Stuttgart: Thieme 1976

37. WEST, J.B.: Ventilation, blood flow and gas exchange. Oxford: Blackwell 1966

38. WEST, J.B.: Regional differences in the lung. New York–San Francisco–London: Academic Press 1977

39. WEST, J.B.: Respiratory Physiology – the essentials. Baltimore: Williams Wilkens 1979

40. YOUNG, A.C.: Neural control of respiration. In: RUCH, T.C., PATTON, H.D. (Eds.): Physiology and biophysics. Philadelphia–London–Toronto: Saunders 1974

Research Reports and Reviews

41. DE BALDWIN, E.F., COURNAND, A., RICHARDS, D.W., Jr.: Pulmonary insufficiency. I. Physiological classification, clinical methods of analysis standard values in normal subjects. Medicine (Baltimore) 27, 243 (1948)

42. BARTELS, H., DEJOURS, P., KELLOG, R.H., MEAD, J.: Glossary on respiration and gas exchange. J. appl. Physiol. 34, 549 (1973)

43. BISCOE, T.J.: Carotid body: Structure and function. Physiol. Rev. 51, 427 (1971)

44. CUNNINGHAM, D.I.C., LLOYD, B.D. (Eds.): The regulation of human respiration. Philadelphia: Davis 1963

45. FORSTER, R.E.: Exchange of gases between alveolar air and pulmonary capillary blood: pulmonary diffusing capacity. Physiol. Rev. 37, 391 (1957)

46. GRODINS, F.S., YAMASHIRO, S.M.: Respiratory function of the lung and its control. New York: Mac Millan Publ. Co. Inc. 1978

47. GUZ, A.: Regulation of respiration. Ann. Rev. Physiol. 37, 303 (1975)

48. HORNBEIN, T.F.: The relation between stimulus of chemoreceptors and their response. In: TORRANCE, R.W. (Ed.): Arterial Chemoreceptors. Oxford: Oxford University Press 1968

49. KNOWLES, J.H., HONG, S.K., RAHN, H.: Possible errors using esophageal balloon in determination of pressure-volume characteristics of the lung and thoracic cage. J. appl. Physiol. 14, 525 (1959)

50. KREUZER, E., HERZOG, H.V. (Eds.): Oxygen pressure recording in gases, fluids and tissues. Progress in respiration research 3. Basel–New York: Karger 1969

51. LOESCHCKE, H.H.: Respiratory chemosensitivity in the medulla oblongata. Acta neurobiol. exp. 33, 97–112 (1973)

52. LOESCHCKE, H.H.: Central nervous chemoreceptors. In: GUYTON, A.C., WIDDICOMBE (Eds.): MTP International Review of Science: Physiology, Vol. 3. Baltimore: University Park Press 1974

53. LOEW, P.G., THEWS, G.: Die Altersabhängigkeit des arteriellen Sauerstoffdruckes bei der berufstätigen Bevölkerung. Klin. Wschr. 40, 1093 (1962)

54. MEAD, J.: Respiration: Pulmonary mechanics. Ann. Rev. Physiol. 35, 169 (1973)

55. MITCHELL, R.A., BERGER, A.J.: Neural regulation of respiration. Amer. Rev. Respir. Dis. 111, 206 (1975)

56. MOCHIZUKI, M.: Graphical analysis of oxygenation and co-combination rates of the red cells in the lung Tokyo: Hirokawa 1975

57. PIIPER, J., SCHEID, P.: Respiration: Alveolar gas exchange. Ann. Rev. Physiol. 33, 131 (1971)

58. RAHN, H., OTIS, A.B., CHADWICK, L.E., FENN, W.O.: The pressure-volume diagram of the thorax and lung. Amer. J. Physiol. 146, 161 (1946)

59. THEWS, G.: Gaseous diffusion in the lungs and tissues. In: REEVE, E.B., GUYTON, A.C. (Eds.): Physical bases of circulatory transport: Regulation and exchange Philadelphia–London: Saunders 1967

60. THEWS, G.: Der Einfluß von Ventilation, Perfusion, Diffusion und Distribution auf den pulmonalen Gasaustausch. Akadem. Wiss. Lit. Mainz; Wiesbaden: Steiner 1979

61. WEIBEL, E.R.: Morphological basis of alveolar capillary gas exchange. Physiol. Rev. 53, 419 (1973)

20 Blood Gas Transport and Acid-Base Balance

G. THEWS

20.1 The Structure and Properties of Hemoglobin

Structure of the Hemoglobin Molecule

One of the most important tasks of the blood is to transport the oxygen absorbed in the lungs to the organs and tissues, and to remove the carbon dioxide formed there and carry it to the lungs. This operation depends fundamentally on the erythrocytes. They contain the red blood pigment *hemoglobin,* which is capable of combining with oxygen in the lung capillaries and releasing it again in the tissue capillaries. In addition, hemoglobin can bind some of the carbon dioxide produced in tissue metabolism and set it free in the lungs. For these reasons hemoglobin occupies a central position in the chain of events by which respiratory gases are transported [1, 7, 10, 15, 18, 19, 20, 21, 38, 39]. Many of the properties of hemoglobin reside in its chemical structure; so that these properties may be better understood, we shall outline the basic structural features here.

Hemoglobin is a chromoprotein. The molecule consists of four *polypeptide chains,* each containing a pigment component called *heme.* The **molecular weight** is about 64,500, so that each of the four subunits has a molecular weight of 16,000 [24, 25].

Pigment components. The four identical heme groups in a hemoglobin molecule can be described as *protoporphyrins with central bivalent iron ions.* Each protoporphyrin framework consists of *four pyrrole rings* linked by *methene bridges* and bearing characteristic side chains (Fig. 20-1). The crucial functional component is the iron ion in the center; the incorporation of this ion by two ionic and two dative bonds converts the protoporphyrin to **heme.** The entire heme structure lies in a plane. When oxygen is transported by hemoglobin the O_2 molecule is reversibly bound to the heme without change in valence of the iron ion; the **hemoglobin** (Hb) thus becomes **oxyhemoglobin** (HbO_2). To indicate that this binding occurs without change of valence, the reaction is called *oxygenation* (rather than oxidation), and the reverse process is *de-*

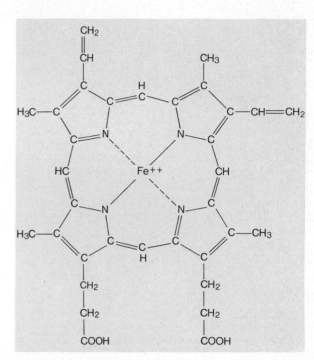

Fig. 20-1. Chemical structure of heme

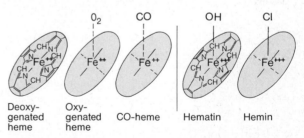

Deoxy-genated heme   Oxy-genated heme   CO-heme   Hematin   Hemin

Fig. 20-2. Characteristic compounds formed by heme (with bivalent iron) and oxidized heme (with trivalent iron). The protoporphyrin rings lie in one plane (cf. red disks in Fig. 20-3)

oxygenation. Hemoglobin is called *deoxyhemoglobin* when one wishes to emphasize its oxygen-free state.

Apart from the oxygenation of the heme group, genuine oxidation can occur; the result is conversion of the bivalent iron to the trivalent state (Fig. 20-2). The oxidized pigment component is called hematin (met-

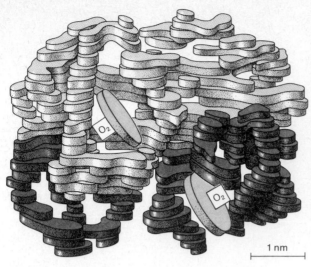

Fig. 20-3. Model of the hemoglobin molecule. After PERUTZ

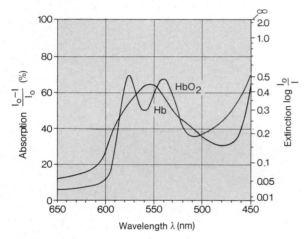

Fig. 20-4. Absorption spectra of oxyhemoglobin (HbO₂) and deoxyhemoglobin (Hb). Left ordinate: absorption; right ordinate: extinction

heme), and the whole molecule is **methemoglobin.** Human blood normally contains only a very small percentage of methemoglobin, but the amount can be increased by certain toxins and in some diseases. Such a condition is dangerous because oxidized hemoglobin is not available for releasing O_2 to the tissues.

Protein component. The great majority of the ca. 10,000 atoms in a hemoglobin molecule make up its protein component. This is composed of *four* individual *polypeptide chains,* each of which comprises more than 140 amino acid residues. The sequence of these amino acids has been determined by chemical analysis, and in recent years the spatial arrangement of the chains within the molecule has also been quite well

elucidated by three-dimensional X-ray diffraction analysis [36, 37].

Fig. 20-3 shows the model of a hemoglobin molecule derived from such studies. Two symmetrically arranged "white" chains interlock with two similarly symmetrical "black" chains in such a way that the whole is roughly spherical. The heme groups, shown as red disks, occupy niches near the surface. In adult hemoglobin **(HbA)** the white subunits (each with 141 amino acids) are called α *chains* and the black subunits (each with 146 amino acids), β *chains*. The hemoglobin of the human fetus **(HbF)** differs from the adult form in having two polypeptides with an amino-acid arrangement different from that of the β chains, the so-called γ chains. Soon after birth the HbF is replaced by HbA.

Light Absorption by Hemoglobin

Light absorption and color. The color of a dissolved substance that does not itself emit light rays depends on its ability to absorb a specific fraction of the incident light. As a rule absorption occurs only in a certain region of wavelengths characteristic of the substance; light at other wavelengths is transmitted with almost no attenuation. The proportions of the different wavelengths in the emerging light determine the color of the dissolved substance.

The red color of a hemoglobin solution – and thus the red color of blood – results from the relatively strong absorption of short-wavelength light by this substance; a considerable amount of the light in the blue part of the spectrum is absorbed, whereas most of the red (long-wavelength) light is transmitted.

By examining the light transmitted by a solution of *oxygenated* hemoglobin with a spectroscope, one can detect not only an attenuation in the blue region *(Soret's band)* but also two characteristic dark stripes *(absorption bands)* in the yellow and yellow-green regions. The maxima of these bands are at the wavelengths $\lambda = 577$ nm and $\lambda = 541$ nm (1 nm $= 10^{-9}$ m) [15].

Deoxyhemoglobin absorbs light somewhat more strongly than oxyhemoglobin at long wavelengths and somewhat less strongly at short wavelengths. Therefore venous blood appears darker, with a bluish-red color. In addition, the spectroscope reveals a single, wider absorption band in the yellow-green region, with a maximum at $\lambda = 555$ nm.

Spectrophotometry. For quantitative analysis of the absorption properties of colored solutions, a spectrophotometer is used. From a prism spectrum or a grating spectrum light of a very narrow range of wavelengths is selected, and this so-called *monochromatic* light is passed through the solution to be analyzed. In passage it is attenuated to a degree depending on the solution and the wavelength. A photocell is used to find the ratio between the intensity of the entering light (I_o) and that of the emerging light (I). The ratio I/I_o is called the **transmittance,** and the ratio $(I_o-I)/I_o$ is the **absorption.** By repeating the measurement with the different wavelengths in succession, one obtains the complete *absorption spectrum* of the solution.

Absorption spectra. Fig. 20-4 shows the absorption spectra of oxyhemoglobin and deoxyhemoglobin. Wavelength regions in which the spectroscope reveals dark absorption bands appear as hills in the absorption spectrum. Two absorption maxima can be discerned in the spectrum of oxyhemoglobin, while that of hemoglobin has a single maximum in an intermediate position. The wavelengths associated with these maxima are those given above for the absorption bands, as can be verified in the diagram.

The points of intersection of the two absorption curves, the so-called *isosbestic points,* correspond to the wavelengths at which solutions of the two substances at equal concentrations absorb equal amounts of light. The absorption of hemoglobin at these wavelengths is independent of its degree of oxygenation. If one wants to determine the *concentration* of hemoglobin without previous chemical alteration (see below), one must use monochromatic light at the wavelength of an isosbestic point. On the other hand, if one wants to determine the O_2 saturation of hemoglobin by photometry one selects a range of wavelengths in which the difference between the absorption of oxyhemoglobin and that of deoxyhemoglobin is particularly great. According to Fig. 20-4, suitable wavelengths for this purpose would include, e. g., 600, 577 and 470 nm.

Lambert-Beer law. Another commonly used measure of absorption is **extinction** (cf. right ordinate in Fig. 20-24), defined as

$$E = \log \frac{I_o}{I} \qquad (1)$$

Here again I_o is the intensity of the light entering the color solution and I is that of the emerging light. The advantage of this measure is that extinction E is directly proportional to the concentration c of a dissolved pigment

$$E = \log \frac{I_o}{I} = \varepsilon cd \qquad (2)$$

where d is the thickness of the layer of solution, and ε is a constant for each substance, called the *extinction coefficient.* The statement of this linear dependence of extinction on concentration and thickness is the *Lambert-Beer law.* It holds only when the light passing through the solution is monochromatic.

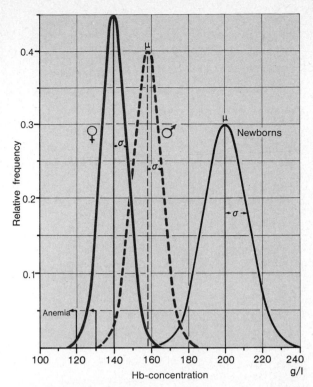

Fig. 20-5. Frequency distributions of hemoglobin concentrations in different populations: male adults (σ), female adults (φ) and newborns. Ordinate: relative frequency; abscissa: hemoglobin concentration; μ, means; σ, standard deviation (σ is the distance from the mean of a Gaussian distribution at which the slope of the curve is steepest; it is a measure of the breadth of the distribution)

Hemoglobin Concentration in Blood; Mean Corpuscular Hemoglobin

Norms [27, 42]. *The average hemoglobin concentration in human blood is 158 g/l (15.8 g/dl) for men and 140 g/l (14 g/dl) for women.* As with almost all biological parameters, there is a certain amount of variation even among healthy individuals. The normal range is found by obtaining the **frequency distribution** of the values in a large number of people (Fig. 20-5).

The concentration of hemoglobin changes systematically with age. The blood of the *newborn* contains an average of 200 g/l, though the individual variation can be considerable (Fig. 20-5). During the *first year of life* the hemoglobin concentration falls to ca. 115 g/l; thereafter it rises slowly to the adult level.

The hemoglobin concentration is relatively high not only in the *fetus* but also in the blood of people who have spent considerable time at *high altitudes* (p. 567). In both cases this modification ensures an adequate supply of oxygen to the organs despite the low O_2 partial pressure.

When the hemoglobin concentration of the blood is below normal, the condition is called **anemia.** As a rule anemia is considered to exist when the hemoglobin concentration is less than 130 g/l in a man, or 120 g/l in a woman.

Measurement of hemoglobin concentration. A number of different techniques can be used, as follows: 1. *Analysis of the amount of bound O_2* (1 g Hb binds at most 1.36 ml O_2); 2. *determination of the iron content* of the blood (Hb contains 0.34% iron), 3. *colorimetry* (comparison of blood color with a standard), or 4. *extinction measurement (spectrophotometry).* The first two require fairly elaborate apparatus, and colorimetry is not very accurate, so that spectrophotometry is the method of choice for the routine determination of hemoglobin concentration.

Spectrophotometric analysis. The principle of this procedure is to determine Hb concentration by measuring the extinction of a blood sample with monochromatic light. But because dilute Hb is unstable, and because its extinction varies with oxygenation, it must first be *converted into a stable pigment.*

The blood is drawn into a capillary pipette and diluted with a solution containing potassium ferricyanide K_3 [Fe(CN)$_6$], potassium cyanide KCN, and sodium bicarbonate NaHCO$_3$. These chemicals cause hemolysis and convert the hemoglobin into **cyanmethemoglobin** HbCN (with trivalent iron), which is stable for weeks. In a photometer the solution is irradiated with monochromatic light at the wavelength 546 nm and the *extinction E* is measured. According to the *Lambert-Beer law* (Eq. 2), the concentration c can be found directly from E if the extinction coefficient ε and the layer thickness d are known. However, it is more convenient to calibrate the extinction scale with a standard solution. The cyanmethemoglobin method is now considered to be the most accurate method for routine Hb-concentration measurement [32].

Mean corpuscular hemoglobin. An important diagnostic criterion for evaluating erythropoiesis and differentiating among forms of anemia is the **amount of hemoglobin in the individual erythrocyte.** *The average absolute hemoglobin content of single erythrocytes is called the mean corpuscular hemoglobin (MCH).* It is found by dividing the hemoglobin concentration by the number of erythrocytes in the same volume of blood.

Taking the norms for healthy men as an example, for a liter of blood one would divide 158 g Hb by 5.1 million $\times$ 10^6 erythrocytes (1 l = 10^6 μl). The MCH would then be

$$MCH = \frac{158 \text{ g}}{5.1 \cdot 10^{12}} = 31 \cdot (10^{-12} \text{ g}) = 31 \text{ pg}$$

When the norms for women are substituted the result is the same:

$$MCH = \frac{140 \text{ g}}{4.6 \cdot 10^{12}} = 31 \cdot (10^{-12} \text{ g}) = 31 \text{ pg}*$$

Erythrocytes containing the normal amount of hemoglobin (26–36 pg) are called **normochromic.** When the MCH is abnormally low they are **hypochromic,** and they are **hyperchromic** when it is high. The same terms are used to denote the different forms of anemia. For example, hemoglobin formation can be reduced owing to *iron deficiency,* so that each erythrocyte contains less hemoglobin and a condition of *hypochromic anemia* exists. In other forms of anemia the production of erythrocytes by the bone marrow is inadequate. In these conditions – as, for example, in *pernicious anemia* – the misshapen erythrocytes contain a great deal of Hb; this is a case of *hyperchromic anemia.* Following massive *blood loss* the MCH is at first unchanged (normochromic anemia), but in the days that follow there is an overproduction of erythrocytes, so that the hemoglobin content of each is low (hypochromic anemia).

Relationships between the erythrocyte parameters. For the diagnostic evaluation of erythrocyte function it is necessary, as a rule, to measure three quantities: the *red cell count* RCC (μl^{-1}), the *hemoglobin concentration of the blood* [Hb] (g/l) and the *hematocrit* HCT. From these, three other characteristic parameters can be derived: the *mean corpuscular hemoglobin* MCH, the *mean corpuscular hemoglobin concentration* MCHC, and the *mean corpuscular volume* MCV. The relationships underlying these calculations are reflected directly in the definitions of the parameters and are summarized in the following diagram:

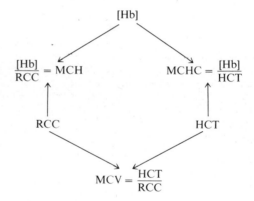

Given, for example, that RCC = 5 · 10^6/μl, [Hb] = 150 g/l and HCT = 0.45, the other parameters are as follows: MCH = 30 pg, MCHC = 333 g/l, and MCV = 0.09 · 10^{-6} μl = 90 fl (femtoliters) = 90 μm^3 (the conversion among units is given in Chapter 30).

20.2 The O_2-Transport Function of the Blood

Physical Solubility of Gases

Partial pressures of gases in liquids. Gases can be taken into almost all liquids – that is, *physically dissolved* – in certain amounts. The amount of gas dis-

---

* Values for Central Europe; for North America (after Wintrobe) MCH = 29 pg

solved depends on its partial pressure. If the liquid is equilibrated with a gas, by bringing the two media into contact over the greatest possible area until thermodynamic equilibrium has been reached, the gas in the liquid can be said to have the same partial pressure as in the gas phase. When we refer to the "partial pressure" of a dissolved gas we are using the term in this sense.

Concentration of dissolved gases. The partial pressure of a gas, P_{gas}, is one of the factors upon which the concentration of the gas dissolved in a liquid depends. A second factor determining the uptake of the gas is its particular solubility properties, which are characterized by the *Bunsen coefficient* (solubility coefficient) α. This coefficient indicates how many ml of a gas are physically dissolved in a ml of liquid at a partial pressure of 1 atm (1 atm = 760 mm Hg = 101 kPa). These two factors are combined in the **Henry-Dalton law,** according to which the concentration of the dissolved gas is

$$[gas] = \frac{\alpha}{760} P_{gas} \qquad (3)$$

The factor 760 is in the denominator because in the units of α the pressure is 1 atmosphere, whereas the partial pressure P_{gas} is ordinarily given in mm Hg.

The numerical value of the *Bunsen coefficient* depends on the nature of the dissolved gas, on the properties of the solvent and on the temperature. Table 20-1 presents some characteristic values of α for solution of the atmospheric gases in water and blood. When α is known for a particular case, the concentrations of the gases in physical solution can be calculated for the given partial pressures by the *Henry-Dalton law* (Eq. 3). In arterial blood, for example, with P_{O_2} = 95 mm Hg and P_{CO_2} = 40 mm Hg, one finds an O$_2$ concentration of 0.003 ml O$_2$/ml blood and a CO$_2$ concentration of 0.026 ml CO$_2$/ml blood. Thus the far greater Bunsen coefficient of CO$_2$ more than compensates for its lower partial pressure, so that 9 times as much CO$_2$ as O$_2$ is present in physical solution.

Although the volumes of O$_2$ and CO$_2$ physically dissolved in the blood are relatively small, this state is extremely significant in the biology of the organism. Before the gases can combine with any other chemical, they must migrate to their partners in the reaction in dissolved form. That is, *each molecule of O$_2$ or CO$_2$ that diffuses into or out of the tissues is at some time in physical solution.*

The Binding of Oxygen to Hemoglobin

Oxygen capacity of the blood. Most of the oxygen transported in the blood is *chemically bound to hemoglobin.* If we wish to know the **maximal amount of**

Table 20-1. The Bunsen solubility coefficient α (ml gas $\cdot$ ml solvent^{-1} $\cdot$ atm^{-1}) for O$_2$, CO$_2$ and N$_2$ in water and blood

	α_{O_2}	α_{CO_2}	α_{N_2}
Water 20 °C	0.031	0.88	0.016
Water 37 °C	0.024	0.57	0.012
Blood 37 °C	0.024	0.49	0.012

O$_2$ that can be bound by Hb we must bear in mind its tetrameric molecular structure (cf. Fig. 20-3), as expressed by the following reaction formula:

$$Hb + 4 O_2 \rightleftarrows Hb(O_2)_4 \qquad (4)$$

That is, 1 mol of hemoglobin is capable of binding at most 4 mol of O$_2$. Taking into account the volume of a mol of ideal gas (22.4 liters), this would mean that 64,500 g Hb bind 4 × 22.4 liters of O$_2$, or 1 g Hb binds 1.39 ml O$_2$. Blood-gas analysis gives a somewhat smaller value (1.34–1.36 ml O$_2$/g Hb); this discrepancy is ascribed to the presence of a small fraction of the hemoglobin in an inactive form [35]. A general rule of thumb is that *1 g Hb in vivo binds 1.34 ml O$_2$* (**Hüfner's number**).

Knowing the Hb concentration, we can use Hüfner's number to compute the *oxygen capacity* of the blood as follows: [O$_2$]$_{max}$ = 1.34 (ml O$_2$/g Hb) × 150 (g Hb/l blood) = 0.20 (l O$_2$/l blood). This concentration, however, is achieved only when the blood is equilibrated with an oxygen-rich gas mixture (P_{O_2} > 300 mm Hg), so that the equilibrium of the reaction in Eq. (4) is shifted far to the right. At the smaller O$_2$ partial pressures that determine the equilibrium in vivo, only part of the hemoglobin is converted to oxyhemoglobin.

O$_2$ dissociation curve [1, 8, 12, 15, 18, 19, 20, 21, 38, 40, 41]. The reaction of oxygen with hemoglobin (Eq. 4) follows the law of mass action. That is, the concentration of the O$_2$ in physical solution, which according to the Henry-Dalton law is proportional to the O$_2$ partial pressure, determines the relative amounts of hemoglobin and oxyhemoglobin. The percentage of the total Hb concentration that is in the form of oxyhemoglobin under any particular conditions is called the *oxygen saturation* (S$_{O_2}$) of the red pigment. We can express this definition, using the simplified symbol HbO$_2$ for oxyhemoglobin, as follows:

$$S_{O_2} = \frac{[HbO_2]}{[Hb] + [HbO_2]} \qquad (5)$$

S$_{O_2}$ is thus 0% when all the hemoglobin is deoxygenated; if all the hemoglobin has been converted to oxyhemoglobin the oxygen saturation is 100%.

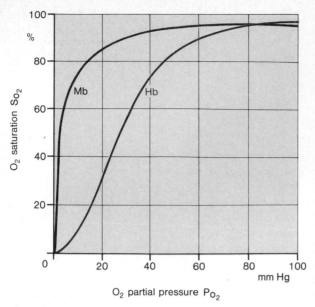

Fig. 20-6. O_2 dissociation curves of hemoglobin Hb (pH = 7.4; T = 37 °C) and myoglobin Mb

According to the law of mass action the O_2 saturation of hemoglobin depends on the prevailing O_2 partial pressure. This relationship is represented graphically by the O_2 *dissociation curve.* As Fig. 20-6 shows, the O_2 dissociation curve of hemoglobin is characteristically S-shaped. Its position, which depends on various parameters (see below), can most simply be characterized by the so-called **half-saturation pressure** P_{50} – the O_2 partial pressure corresponding to 50% oxygen saturation (i. e., that at which 50% of the hemoglobin is oxygenated). For arterial blood under normal conditions (pH = 7.4, temperature = 37 °C) P_{50} is about 26 mm Hg (3.46 kPa) [13, 40].

Interpretation of the O_2 dissociation curve. The origin of the sigmoid shape of the curve is not yet entirely clear. If only one O_2 molecule were to react with each pigment molecule, reaction kinetics would predict a *hyperbolic dissociation curve* [15]. This condition is realized, for example, in the comparable reaction of oxygen with the *red muscle pigment* **myoglobin** (Mb) [1]. The structure of myoglobin is like that of one of the four subunits of hemoglobin. Its molecular weight is thus related to that of hemoglobin as 1:4. Myoglobin has only one pigment component and, accordingly, can bind with only one O_2 molecule:

$$Mb + O_2 \rightleftharpoons MbO_2 \qquad (6)$$

Fig. 20-6 shows the hyperbolic dissociation curve that describes this reaction.

The plausible notion that the sigmoid shape of the curve for hemoglobin results from the *fourfold* combination with O_2 led to the formulation of the *intermediate-compound hypothesis* (ADAIR). This proposes that combination with the 4 O_2 molecules occurs in steps, each stage of the reaction affecting the equilibrium of the next stage [12]. Although ADAIR's proposal does in principle explain the shape of the O_2 dissociation curve,

an alternative interpretation is possible. That is, the special form of the curve would also be understandable if hemoglobin were present in *two O_2-dependent states,* interconvertible either by change of conformation or by combining with or splitting off some substance of low molecular weight. If these two states had different O_2-binding equilibria, the shape of the curve could thereby be explained [15, 21].

Biological significance of the O_2 dissociation curve. The special shape of the oxygen dissociation curve has important consequences for the transport of O_2 in the blood. During **oxygen uptake** in the lungs the O_2 partial pressure of the blood, P_{O_2}, closely approaches that of the alveoli (cf. p. 477). In the arterial blood of a young subject P_{O_2} averages 95 mm Hg (12.6 kPa). It is evident in Fig. 20-6 that at this partial pressure the hemoglobin is about 97% saturated with oxygen. In old age, and even more in cases of pulmonary malfunction, the arterial O_2 partial pressure can be considerably lower. But because the dissociation curve is so flat on the right, the oxygen saturation is reduced very little. For example, even when P_{O_2} has fallen to 60 mm Hg (8.0 kPa) the arterial O_2 saturation is still 90%. *The flattening of the O_2 dissociation curve in the high-pressure range effectively prevents severe desaturation of the arterial blood.*

On the other hand, the steep slope in the middle of the curve offers an extraordinary advantage when it comes to the **release of oxygen** into the tissues. Here it is important that enough oxygen should be released to meet local requirements without major fluctuations in the O_2 partial pressure of the blood. When the body is at rest the P_{O_2} at the venous end of the capillaries averages 40 mm Hg (5.3 kPa), which corresponds to about 73% saturation. A drop in venous O_2 partial pressure of only 5 mm Hg (0.7 kPa) owing to increased O_2 consumption reduces the O_2 saturation by 7%, so that this amount of oxygen becomes immediately available.

Arteriovenous O_2 difference. The amount of chemically bound oxygen in the blood depends on the existing O_2 saturation S_{O_2}. The concentration of O_2 (l O_2/l blood) can be derived from the saturation on the basis of Hüfner's number, as follows:

$$O_2 = 1.34 \cdot [Hb] \cdot S_{O_2} \cdot 10^{-5} \qquad (7)$$

where S_{O_2} is given in % and [Hb] in g/l. Substituting the numbers found above for arterial O_2 saturation (S_{O_2} = 97%) and venous O_2 saturation (S_{O_2} = 73%), we find that the concentration of chemically bound oxygen is about 0.20 in arterial blood and 0.15 in venous blood. *The arteriovenous difference in O_2 concentration avD_{O_2} is thus 0.05 (Table 20-2). That is, normally*

Table 20-2. Blood-gas data and pH for arterial and venous blood of healthy young persons at rest

	P$_{O_2}$		S$_{O_2}$	[O$_2$]	P$_{CO_2}$		[CO$_2$]	pH
	(mm Hg)	(kPa)	%	(l O$_2$/l blood)	(mm Hg)	(kPa)	(l CO$_2$/l blood)	
Arterial blood	95	12.6	97	0.20	40	5.3	0.50	7.40
Venous blood	40	5.3	73	0.15	46	6.1	0.54	7.37
Arteriovenous difference				0.05			0.04	

only 25% of the total oxygen capacity of the blood is utilized during passage through the tissue capillaries. Of course, the blood becomes desaturated to very different degrees in the various organs (cf. Fig. 21-2, p. 512), so that the venous entries in Table 20-2 are the means of fairly wide ranges. During strenuous exercise the arteriovenous O$_2$ concentration difference can be greater than 0.1.

Factors Affecting the O$_2$ Dissociation Curve

Although the shape of the O$_2$ dissociation curve results chiefly from the reaction properties of hemoglobin, other factors can modify the O$_2$ affinity in the blood [21, 23, 31]. As a rule these effects amount to shifting the O$_2$ dissociation curve while increasing or decreasing its slope, without departure from the characteristic sigmoid shape. The factors having such an influence are temperature, pH or CO$_2$ partial pressure, and certain parameters that become relevant under pathological conditions.

The effect of temperature. As in most chemical processes, the equilibrium of the oxygen-hemoglobin reaction depends on the temperature. This dependence affects the dissociation curve in such a way that it rises steeply at low temperatures and progressively less steeply as the temperature increases (Fig. 20-7 A). In warm-blooded animals this effect has to be taken into consideration only in the case of hypothermia or fever.

The effects of pH and P$_{CO_2}$. The H$^+$ concentration in the blood has a considerable effect on the shape of the O$_2$ dissociation curve, as shown in Fig. 20-7 B (where the pH is given as a measure of the H$^+$ concentration). *As pH decreases (i.e., the blood becomes more acid), the affinity of oxygen for hemoglobin is reduced;* the O$_2$ dissociation curve becomes flatter. The pH values indicated in Fig. 20-7 B all refer to the plasma. As far as causal relationships are concerned it would doubtless be more informative to show how the dissociation curve is affected by the pH inside the erythrocytes. But this pH is so difficult to determine that in general the plasma pH is taken as the parame-

ter. The pH dependence of the O$_2$ dissociation curve shown in Fig. 20-7 B is known as the **Bohr effect.**

The pH of the blood at any moment is closely related to the CO$_2$ partial pressure (P$_{CO_2}$). An increase in CO$_2$ partial pressure is accompanied by a decrease in pH. If P$_{CO_2}$ is chosen as the parameter rather than pH, the group of curves shown in Fig. 20-7 C results. *As the CO$_2$ partial pressure increases the affinity of oxygen for hemoglobin is reduced;* the O$_2$ dissociation curve becomes flatter. The term *Bohr effect* is also applied to this modification of the dissociation curve, although precise quantitative analysis reveals that the influence of CO$_2$ on the dissociation curve cannot be ascribed entirely to the associated pH change. There is evidently an additional "specific CO$_2$ effect" [21].

Significance of the Bohr effect. The Bohr effect has certain physiological consequences for both *O$_2$ uptake in the lungs* and *O$_2$ release in the tissues,* though their extent should not be overestimated. First consider the situation in the lungs. Here O$_2$ uptake is coupled with the release of CO$_2$, so that the dissociation curve shifts to the left as the hemoglobin becomes more saturated with O$_2$. These simultaneous changes are indicated by the red curve in Fig. 20-7 C, which is sometimes called the *"effective O$_2$ dissociation curve"*. From the point corresponding to venous blood v (P$_{O_2}$ = 40 mm Hg, P$_{CO_2}$ = 46 mm Hg) oxygenation proceeds to the point of arterial saturation a (P$_{O_2}$ = 95 mm Hg, P$_{CO_2}$ = 40 mm Hg), accompanied by a steady increase in the O$_2$ affinity of the hemoglobin. The transport of O$_2$ occurs by diffusion (pp. 476 f.), but the increased affinity results in a slight increase in the rate of diffusion. Thus the Bohr effect facilitates the uptake of oxygen in the lungs.

The importance of the Bohr effect is somewhat greater when it comes to the transfer of O$_2$ from the capillary blood into the tissues. Because of the simultaneous movement of CO$_2$ into the blood, the O$_2$ dissociation curve shifts to the right. The red "effective O$_2$ dissociation curve" in Fig. 20-7 C is now followed from a to v. As its O$_2$ affinity declines the hemoglobin becomes additionally deoxygenated, so that the O$_2$ diffuses away into the tissues at a higher capillary O$_2$ partial pressure. *Again the Bohr effect assists the exchange of oxygen.*

Pathophysiological factors. In certain pathological states the O$_2$-transport conditions in the blood can be altered. For example, a number of diseases (certain forms of anemia in particular) bring about shifts of the O$_2$ dissociation curve to the right or, less commonly, to the left. The causes of such shifts are not yet completely understood. However, it is known that certain organic phosphate compounds, the intra-

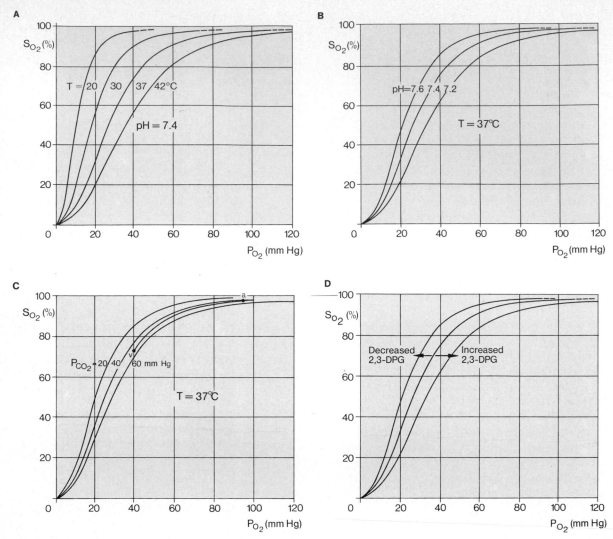

Fig. 20-7 A–D. Dependence of the O_2 dissociation curve of the blood on various parameters [13, 40]. **A** temperature-dependence; **B** pH-dependence (Bohr effect), **C** dependence on CO_2 partial pressure; **D** dependence on intraerythrocytic concentra-tion of 2,3-diphosphoglycerate (2,3-DPG). The *red* "effective O_2 dissociation curve" between the points a (arterial blood) and v (venous blood) determines gas exchange under resting conditions

erythrocytic concentrations of which can change in pathological states, have marked effects on the O_2 dissociation curve [23]. Chief among these is **2,3-di-phosphoglycerate (2,3-DPG)** (Fig. 20-7 D). Moreover, the concentration of the cations in the erythrocyte can influence the O_2-binding properties of hemoglobin. The effects of pathological pH levels also deserve mention. High pH *(alkalosis)* facilitates O_2 uptake in the lungs by way of the Bohr effect, but makes it more difficult for O_2 to be released in the tissues, whereas low pH *(acidosis)* has the opposite effects. Finally, extensive leftward shifts of the O_2 binding curve result from *CO poisoning (cf. p. 497).*

Fetal O_2 dissociation curve [28, 33]. In the placenta, as in the rest of the body, gas exchange occurs by diffu-sion. Here, however, special attention must be paid to the differences in the O_2 affinity of the maternal and fetal blood. *The O_2 dissociation curve of fetal blood* is somewhat *steeper* than that of maternal blood when the two are tested *under identical conditions*. But *in vivo* this difference is almost entirely compensated by the *lower pH* of fetal blood (Bohr effect). Thus the dif-ference in O_2 affinity of the blood of mother and fetus has essentially no facilitatory effect on gas exchange in the placenta. The favorable aspects of the situation become clear only when one takes into account the different *hemoglobin concentrations* of maternal and fetal blood.

Fig. 20-8 shows the O_2 dissociation curves of maternal and fetal blood at the time of birth, for the average placental pH values. To allow for the difference in maternal and fetal hemoglobin concentration (120 g/l and 180 g/l, respectively), the variable on the ordinate is not O$_2$ saturation but O$_2$ concentration. The deoxygenation of the mother's blood and the oxygenation of the blood of the fetus follow the curves in the direction of the arrows between the points a and v or v′ and a′. It is evident that at a given O$_2$ partial pressure the fetal blood can bind considerably more oxygen than that of the mother. For example, at P$_{O_2}$ = 25 mm Hg (3.3 kPa) the O$_2$ concentration in the mother's blood is 0.08 while that in the fetal blood is 0.11.

The Bohr effect has a special significance for gas exchange in the placenta. During the period of diffusion contact the O$_2$ affinity of the maternal blood decreases as a result of CO$_2$ exchange, and at the same time the tendency of the fetal blood to bind oxygen increases. This *double influence of the Bohr effect*, not reflected in Fig. 20-8, causes an increase in the rate of O$_2$ exchange.

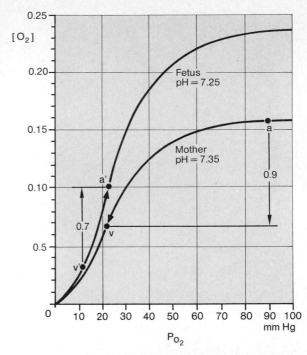

Fig. 20-8. O$_2$ concentrations [O$_2$] as a function of O$_2$ partial pressure P$_{O_2}$, for maternal and fetal blood at the time of birth. During gas exchange in the placenta the O$_2$ concentration in the mother's blood falls from a (arterial) to v (venous), whereas in the blood of the fetus it rises from v′ (blood in the umbilical artery) to a′ (blood in the umbilical vein)

Hemoglobin-Carbon Monoxide Binding

The affinity of carbon monoxide (CO) for hemoglobin is significantly greater than that of oxygen. Even at exceedingly low partial pressures, CO gas is capable of converting hemoglobin into CO-hemoglobin

$$Hb + CO \rightleftharpoons HbCO \qquad (8)$$

The equilibrium of this reaction lies well to the right, so that the CO dissociation curve rises very steeply. In principle this situation could have two causes: the velocity constant of association could be extremely large, or the velocity constant of dissociation could be extremely small (i. e., the backward reaction could be very slow). The effect would be the same in either case, but as we know it is the second of the two possibilities that accounts for the steep CO dissociation curve. *CO is released from combination with Hb about 200 times more slowly than O$_2$*[12].

It is because of this strong affinity for hemoglobin that carbon monoxide is so *poisonous*. This colorless and odorless gas is produced by incomplete combustion of organic material; it is sometimes a component of domestic gas supplies, and is one of the waste products of combustion engines. Even in low concentrations CO can displace O$_2$ from hemoglobin and make it unavailable for the transport of oxygen. With a CO concentration of only 7 · 10^{-4} in the inspired air, 50% of the hemoglobin is blocked. Normally 1% of the hemoglobin in the blood is HbCO; smokers have been found to have 3%, and even as much as 10% after a deep inhalation. In the blood of taxi drivers up to 20% HbCO has been measured. The danger of CO exposure in street traffic is strikingly revealed by the fact that at some intersections where the traffic is heavy the concentration of CO in the air has been found to be 3 · 10^{-4}. This is the concentration at which underground miners are supposed to put on their breathing equipment.

There is another effect, apart from the blocking of Hb, that is responsible for the toxicity of CO gas. When part of the Hb has been converted to HbCO, the hemoglobin that remains unblocked has an *O$_2$ dissociation curve shifted to the left* [11]. As a result, the O$_2$ partial pressures in the tissue capillaries fall even further.

In cases of severe CO poisoning, detectable by the cherry-red color of the blood, immediate artificial respiration (with pure oxygen if possible) can save the victim's life. This procedure increases the O$_2$ partial pressure in the blood so that the O$_2$ can displace CO from hemoglobin. Massive blood transfusion is also helpful, for it supplies the patient with unblocked Hb that can be used for O$_2$ transport.

20.3   The CO$_2$-Transport Function of the Blood

Forms of CO$_2$ Transport

Carbon dioxide (CO$_2$), formed in the cells of the body as an end product of oxidative metabolism, is carried by the blood to the lungs and there given off to the outside air. Like oxygen, carbon dioxide can be transported in *physical solution* in the blood as well as in *chemically bound* form. The process of chemical binding of CO$_2$ is somewhat more complicated than that of O$_2$, for the same process that serves for *CO$_2$ transport* must also maintain the *acid-base balance* in the blood and thus in the organism as a whole.

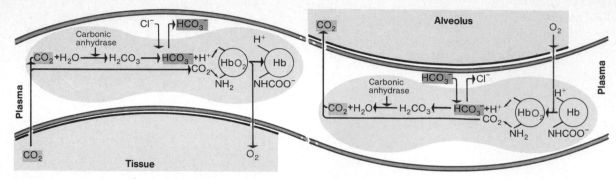

Fig. 20-9. Chemical reactions in plasma and in erythrocyte during gas exchange in tissues *(left)* and lungs *(right)*

CO₂ binding [10, 12, 22, 29, 34]. The arterial blood enters the tissue capillaries with a CO_2 partial pressure of 40 mm Hg (5.3 kPa). In the cells surrounding the capillaries the partial pressure is high, because CO_2 is constantly being produced; thus the physically dissolved CO_2 molecules diffuse down the partial pressure gradient into the capillary. A small fraction remains physically dissolved in the capillary blood, but most of the CO_2 undergoes a further chemical conversion (Fig. 20-9). The first step in this process is **hydration** to carbonic acid:

$$CO_2 + H_2O \rightleftharpoons H_2CO_3 \qquad (9)$$

This reaction proceeds slowly in the plasma, but in the erythrocyte the reaction rate is about 10,000 times as great. This acceleration is brought about by the enzyme **carbonic anhydrase** [12, 34]. Because this enzyme is restricted to the cells, practically all of the CO_2 molecules involved in the chemical conversion must enter the erythrocyte.

The next step is **dissociation** of the weak acid H_2CO_3 into bicarbonate and hydrogen ions:

$$H_2CO_3 \rightleftharpoons HCO_3^- + H^+ \qquad (10)$$

The progressive increase in HCO_3^- concentration inside the erythrocyte creates a diffusion gradient toward the surrounding plasma. However, the HCO_3^- ions can follow this gradient only if their movement does not appreciably disturb the electrical charge equilibrium. For each HCO_3^- ion that leaves the erythrocyte a cation would have to leave as well or an anion would have to enter in exchange. The first of these possibilities cannot be realized, for the erythrocyte membrane is essentially impermeable to cations. Small anions, however, can pass through the membrane with relative ease. Therefore the HCO_3^- ions that leave the erythrocyte are exchanged for Cl^- ions. This exchange is called *Hamburger's shift* or the **chloride shift.**

As CO_2 enters the erythrocyte and HCO_3^- ions are formed, there is a continual production of H^+ ions. But there is no great change in pH, owing particularly to the properties of hemoglobin. First, the red pigment has amphoteric properties and thus a large *buffer capacity*. Second, as it gives off O_2, hemoglobin becomes *"less acid"* and can take on additional H^+ ions (cf. pp. 502 f.):

$$HbO_2^- \rightarrow \overset{\uparrow}{O_2} + Hb^- \rightarrow HHb \leftarrow H^+ \qquad (11)$$

Another way in which CO_2 can be bound is by direct combination with the protein component of the hemoglobin. The reaction takes place at the amino groups, which form a *carbamino compound* with CO_2:

$$Hb \cdot NH_2 + CO_2 \rightleftharpoons Hb \cdot NH \cdot COO^- + H^+ \qquad (12)$$

The product of the reaction is called **carbaminohemoglobin,** sometimes abbreviated to *carbhemoglobin*.

These chemical reactions and their interdependence are summarized in Fig. 20-9. The left half illustrates the reactions accompanying the uptake of CO_2 in the tissue capillaries, and on the right are the events during CO_2 release in the lungs, in which all the reactions take place in the reverse direction.

Proportions of the exchanged CO₂ bound in each form. The blood enters the tissue capillaries with a CO_2 partial pressure of 40 mm Hg and, having acquired more CO_2 in transit, leaves them with an average CO_2 partial pressure of 46 mm Hg. In the process, about 2 mmol CO_2 are taken up per liter of blood. Of this amount of CO_2 about 10% remains in physical solution, 10% forms carbamino hemoglobin, 35% is carried in the erythrocyte as bicarbonate, and the remaining 45% is in the form of HCO_3^- dissolved in the plasma. As the blood passes through the lungs, CO_2 is released from these four transport forms in the same proportions. In Fig. 20-10 this distribution is shown schematically. The amounts of CO_2 in each form are also shown for arterial and venous blood, in each case as mmol CO_2 in one liter of blood composed of 0.55 l plasma and 0.45 l erythrocytes. From these figures the concentrations can be derived; for example, for HCO_3^- in the plasma of the arterial blood 13.2 mmol/0.55 l = 24 mmol/l.

CO₂ Dissociation Curves

P_{CO_2}-dependence of CO_2 concentration. The amount of carbon dioxide bound chemically in the blood is critically dependent on the prevailing CO_2 partial pressure, which is determined by the production of CO_2 in the tissues and its release through the lungs. This relationship between concentration and partial pressure can be represented by a diagram entirely analogous to the O_2 dissociation curve. Fig. 20-11 shows the **CO₂ dissociation curves** for oxygenated and deoxygenated blood. The differential binding of CO_2 in these two conditions results from the fact that oxyhemoglobin has a more acid quality than deoxyhemoglobin, and can remove fewer H^+ ions from solution. Accordingly, the dissociation of carbonic acid necessary for continued uptake of CO_2 occurs to a greater extent, the smaller the fraction of oxygenated hemoglobin. Moreover, deoxyhemoglobin binds CO_2 in the carbamino form on a larger scale than does oxyhemoglobin [12]. The dependence of CO_2 binding on degree of hemoglobin oxygenation is known as the **Christiansen-Douglas-Haldane effect** or, more briefly, as the *Haldane effect*.

The CO_2 dissociation curve differs from that for O_2 in one crucial point. Whereas the O_2 dissociation curve approaches a maximum asymptotically, CO_2 binding exhibits *no saturation*. As the CO_2 partial pressure rises the amount of bound CO_2 continues to increase, for there is no practical limit to bicarbonate formation. It is for this reason that the ordinate of the CO_2 curve is scaled not in % saturation but in concentration units.

Now we ask the degree to which the different binding mechanisms participate in the overall binding of CO_2. Fig. 20-12 represents the dissociation curves for the various components. In each graph the lowest line gives the concentrations of physically dissolved CO_2 and undissociated H_2CO_3 at different CO_2 partial pressures. The middle curve is derived by adding the concentrations of the CO_2 bound in the carbamate form. When those of the CO_2 bound as bicarbonate are added to this curve, the overall dissociation curve shown in red is obtained. Comparison of Fig. 20-12 A and 20-12 B reveals that *the Christiansen-Douglas-Haldane effect is partly due to the different degree of carbamino binding to oxygenated and to deoxygenated hemoglobin.*

Physiological significance of the Christiansen-Douglas-Haldane effect. When considering the uptake of CO_2 in the tissues and its release in the lungs, we must keep in mind that these processes are simultaneous with O_2 exchange. The changes in the O_2 saturation of hemoglobin influence the CO_2 binding of the blood and thus affect CO_2 exchange.

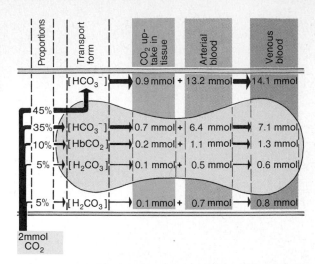

Fig. 20-10. Proportions of CO_2 bound in different forms as it is taken into the capillary blood from the tissues. All data (in mmol) refer to one liter of blood containing 0.55 l plasma and 0.45 l erythrocytes

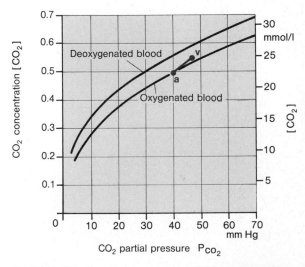

Fig. 20-11. CO_2 dissociation curves for oxygenated and deoxygenated blood. The *red* "effective CO_2 dissociation curve" between the points a (arterial blood) and v (venous blood) is the determinant of gas exchange

When the arterial blood enters the tissue capillaries it is essentially fully oxygenated (point a in Fig. 20-11). With the loss of O_2 to the tissues during passage through the capillaries, the ability of the blood to bind CO_2 increases. The uptake of CO_2 in the tissue capillaries is thus enhanced by the Christiansen-Douglas-Haldane effect.

In the lungs the reverse exchange process occurs. Because of the O_2 uptake that occurs here, the CO_2-binding capacity of the blood is reduced and the release of CO_2 by diffusion is facilitated. During exchange in the lung capillaries the red curve in

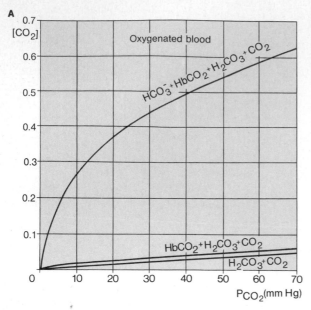

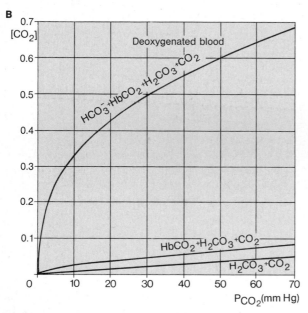

Fig. 20-12 A, B. CO_2 dissociation curves of oxygenated blood **(A)** and deoxygenated blood **(B)**, for the different forms of binding

Fig. 20-11 is followed in the direction from v to a. This curve, the descriptor of CO_2 exchange in both the lungs and the tissues, can be called the *effective CO_2 dissociation curve*. For both processes – the uptake of CO_2 in the tissues and its release in the lungs – it is equally valid to state that *the exchange of CO_2 by diffusion is assisted by the Christiansen-Douglas-Haldane effect.*

20.4   The Acid-Base Status of the Blood

The Blood pH

Acids and bases. According to the definition of Brønstedt, *acids* are substances which in solution give off hydrogen ions **(proton donors),** and *bases* are substances that bind hydrogen ions **(proton acceptors).** This definition is particularly useful in the realm of biology. From it, it follows that in the *dissociation reaction*

$$HA \rightleftharpoons H^+ + A^- \qquad (13)$$

HA is an *acid* (reaction proceeding from left to right), whereas under certain conditions (with the reaction proceeding in the opposite direction) the anion A^- is by definition a *base,* as it binds hydrogen ions. A^- here is called the *conjugate base.* There is a balance between dissociation and association which obeys the *law of mass action.* With a strong acid such as HCl, the balance is shifted far toward the right side of Eq. (13). On the other hand, if HA is a weak acid dissociation may be incomplete, depending on the equilibrium constant (Fig. 20-13).

Definition of pH. The acidity or alkalinity of a fluid depends on its concentration of free hydrogen ions; this is characterized by the pH. *pH is defined as the negative logarithm to the base ten of the molar H^+ concentration:*

$$pH = -\log[H^+] \qquad (14)$$

Thus a pH of 7, which identifies a neutral reaction, corresponds to a H^+ concentration $[H^+] = 10^{-7}$ mol/l. As pH decreases the acidity of the solution increases.

The definition of pH was initially introduced as a technical convenience, but in biological systems it has a special significance. The *electrochemical potential* of ions is proportional not to their concentration but to its logarithm. For this reason it can be assumed that the responses of the sensors or receptors in human and animal bodies that are involved in regulation of acid-base status are proportional to pH rather than to concentration.

pH measurement. The pH of a solution can be determined with *indicators* or by *electrometry.* Most of the pH indicators are very weak acids or bases that dissociate at a characteristic pH, and in so doing change color. For continuously graded and precise measurement of pH, the most widely used procedure is electrometry with a *glass electrode.* Such an electrode usually has a spherically expanded end made of a special glass through which H^+ ions can pass. The space inside this membrane is filled with a buffer solution. When the electrode is dipped into a solution a potential difference builds up according to the Nernst equation (p. 6), to a level dependent on the pH of the external solution. This potential difference is recorded by nonpolarizable electrodes. Today such meters commonly take the form of an easily operable system in which measurement and reference electrodes are housed in a single jacket. After amplification of the voltage signal it is displayed by a pointer or a plotter. Before the measurement is done the instrument must be calibrated with *standard buffer solutions.*

The pH of human arterial blood (37 °C) ranges from 7.37 to 7.43 and averages 7.40. These values, to be precise, are those of the *plasma,* for when the glass electrode is immersed in the blood sample it contacts only the plasma; the intraerythrocytic pH does not enter into the measurement. The pH within the erythrocyte is difficult to measure, but it has been found to differ from that of plasma, amounting to about 7.28–7.29 [26]. As a rule, the term "blood pH" always refers to the pH of plasma.

Human blood is thus weakly alkaline. Despite the continually fluctuating release of acid metabolic products into the blood, its pH is kept *extremely constant.* This constancy is an important prerequisite for maintenance of controlled metabolic processes in the cells of the body, because the activities of all the enzymes involved in metabolism are pH-dependent. Pathological changes in pH affect the different enzymes to different degrees, so that the interplay of metabolic reactions can be disrupted. Several factors participate in regulation of the acid-base balance (i.e., in keeping the blood pH constant). They are the *buffer properties of the blood, pulmonary gas exchange, and the excretory mechanisms in the kidneys* [2, 3, 5, 6, 9, 14, 16, 17, 26, 40].

The Buffer Properties of the Blood

Characteristics of buffer systems. First recall that the dissociation of a weak acid HA into hydrogen ions H^+ and the conjugate base A^- follows the **law of mass action.** Representing the molar concentrations of the partners in the reaction by square brackets, we have

$$\frac{[H^+][H^-]}{[HA]} = K' \qquad (15)$$

K' is the equilibrium constant (dissociation constant); the "prime" signifies that the constant takes account of the special conditions in the solution, such as the ionic strength. If the concentration of H^+ ions in such a system is increased, the concentration of undissociated acid must rise simultaneously in order that the equilibrium condition of the mass-action law be fulfilled. In other words, dissociation is to some extent reduced, and in the process the added free H^+ ions are partly eliminated. The pH change is therefore smaller than would correspond to the amount of H^+ ions added. Conversely, a decrease in H^+ concentration produces but a small pH change. *This attenuation of the effect of added H^+ or OH^- ions is called buffering.*

For a quantitative evaluation of the buffering effect it is convenient to rearrange Eq. (15) and take the logarithm of all its terms:

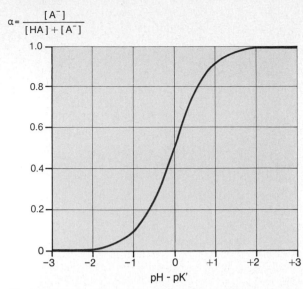

$$\alpha = \frac{[A^-]}{[HA]+[A^-]}$$

Fig. 20-13. Dependence of the degree of dissociation of a weak acid on pH. pK', negative logarithm of the equilibrium constant K'. Such a buffer curve is obtained by adding successive aliquots of H^+ or OH^- to the solution and measuring the pH after each addition

$$-\log[H^+] = -\log K' - \log\frac{[HA]}{[A^-]} \qquad (16)$$

$$pH = pK' + \log\frac{[A^-]}{[HA]} \qquad (17)$$

When the law of mass action is expressed in this form for a buffer system it is known as the **Henderson-Hasselbalch equation.** Here $pK' = -\log K'$, like K' itself, is a constant characteristic of the system. For Eq. (17) one can also write

$$pH = pK' + \log\frac{\alpha}{1-\alpha}, \text{ where } \alpha = \frac{[A^-]}{[HA]+[A^-]} \quad (18)$$

The *degree of dissociation α* introduced here indicates the base concentration $[A^-]$ in relation to the total concentration of acid and base $[HA] + [A^-]$. This relationship between the degree of dissociation α and the pH of the buffer solution is graphed in Fig. 20-13. The curve shows that the degree of dissociation can be changed only over a limited range of pH, from 2 pH units below pK' to 2 units above it. Only in this range does the system have buffering properties.

The buffer capacity of a system consisting of a weak acid and its conjugate base is described by the **buffer value,** the relationship between the amount of H^+ or OH^- ions added and the resulting change in pH. For a given addition of H^+ or OH^- the change in pH is smallest in the steepest part of the buffer curve (Fig. 20-13).

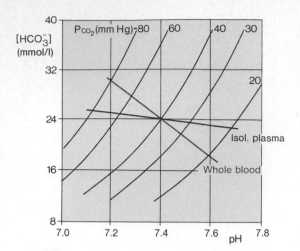

Fig. 20-14. CO_2 equilibration curves of isolated plasma and whole blood. Ordinate: bicarbonate concentration of the plasma; abscissa: pH. Reference curves for constant CO_2 partial pressure are also plotted. Because there is ion exchange between plasma and erythrocytes in whole blood the buffer function of hemoglobin is added to that of plasma, which increases the slope of the CO_2 equilibration curve

Thus the buffer capacity of a system is greatest at pH = pK'. *The buffer value is thus determined both by the concentration of the buffer system and by the difference between the prevailing pH and the pK' of the system.*

Bicarbonate buffer system. Of the several buffer systems in the blood, we shall first consider the bicarbonate system. Carbonic acid, formed by the hydration of CO_2, is a relatively weak acid, and bicarbonate is its conjugate base

$$CO_2 + H_2O \rightleftharpoons H_2CO_3 \rightleftharpoons H^+ + HCO_3^- \qquad (19)$$

The Henderson-Hasselbalch equation for the overall reaction is

$$pH = pK' + \log \frac{[HCO_3^-]}{[CO_2]} \qquad (20)$$

Here $[CO_2]$ can be replaced by the CO_2 partial pressure P_{CO_2}:

$$pH = pK' + \log \frac{[HCO_3^-]}{0.03 \cdot P_{CO_2}} \qquad (21)$$

The factor 0.03 has the units $mmol \cdot l^{-1} \cdot mm\ Hg^{-1}$, so that it applies only when $[HCO_3^-]$ is given in mmol/l and P_{CO_2} in mm Hg.
pK' (at the ionic strength of plasma) is 6.1. Therefore it at first appears that the buffer action of the system cannot be very great, pK' being quite far from the pH

of the blood (7.4). Nevertheless the bicarbonate system accounts for a great deal of the blood's buffer capacity, for its effectiveness is considerably increased by the respiratory interactions. The mechanisms maintaining an arterial CO_2 partial pressure of 40 mm Hg in themselves bring about a high concentration of HCO_3^- in the plasma, 24 mmol/l. That is, the control of CO_2 partial pressure by the respiratory system ensures *high concentrations of the buffer components.* An additional favorable circumstance is that in this "open" system ventilation can be modified so as to vary the CO_2 partial pressure and thus regulate the pH of the blood.

Phosphate buffer system. In the buffer system formed by the inorganic phosphates in the blood, *the monobasic phosphate ($H_2PO_4^-$) acts as the acid and the dibasic phosphate (HPO_4^{--}) as the conjugate base.* The pK' of this system is 6.8, relatively close to the blood pH. But the concentrations of phosphates in the blood are so low that their buffer effect is small.

Protein buffer system. The buffer properties of the blood proteins reside in the ionizable groups of the amino acids of which they are composed. The few carboxyl and amino groups at the ends of the peptide chains are essentially negligible in this regard, particularly because these groups have pK' far from the physiological pH. *The ionizable side groups are considerably more important in buffering the blood, the most effective being the imidazole ring of histidine.*
Proteins that act as buffers include both the **plasma proteins,** *albumin* in particular, and the intraerythrocytic **hemoglobin.** Hemoglobin accounts for most of the protein buffer capacity, because it is present in high concentration and contains a relatively large amount of histidine.

The contribution of Hb becomes especially obvious when one compares the pH change in plasma with that in whole blood, for a given CO_2 partial-pressure change. It is helpful to display the result of this comparison as an *HCO_3^--pH diagram,* in which are plotted the curves of constant CO_2 partial pressure according to the Henderson-Hasselbalch equation (Eq. 21). When the interdependence of the three characteristic quantities, plasma HCO_3^-, pH and P_{CO_2}, is examined by varying the CO_2 partial pressure in **separated plasma** and in **whole blood,** in which the plasma exchanges ions with the erythrocytes, the correspondingly labelled *CO_2-equilibration lines* of Fig. 20-14 are found. The steeper slope of the whole-blood line reflects the great contribution of hemoglobin to the buffer capacity of the blood; the steeper the buffer line, the smaller the pH change resulting from a given increase or decrease in CO_2 partial pressure.

Hemoglobin is also of particular significance in buffering the blood because its acidity changes with oxygenation and deoxygenation. This dependence is il-

$$\frac{P_i^- \text{ (mmol)}}{Hb \text{ (mmol)}}$$

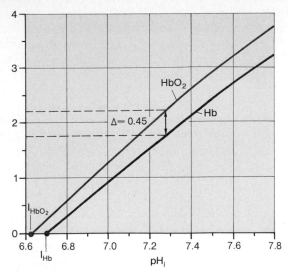

Fig. 20-15. Buffer curves of the nondiffusible systems in the erythrocyte (predominantly Hb, with small contributions from ATP and 2,3-DPG), for oxygenated (HbO_2) and deoxygenated (Hb) hemoglobin, modified from [26]. Ordinate: mmol nondiffusible buffer anions P_i^- per mmol hemoglobin; abscissa: intraerythrocytic pH; I_{HbO_2} and I_{Hb}: isoelectric points. Because of the shift of the curve through complete deoxygenation 0.45 mmol H^+ can be tied up per mmol Hb without change in pH_i

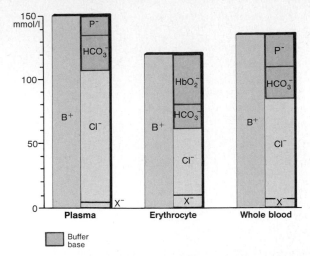

Fig. 20-16. Ion concentrations in plasma, erythrocytes, and whole blood. Buffer base: anions in the buffer systems *(dark red)* (phosphate ions not shown because of their low concentration); P^-, protein anions; X^-, anions of all the nonbuffering strong acids except Cl^-; B^+ sum of all cations

lustrated in Fig. 20-15, where buffer curves (titration curves) are plotted for the nondiffusible buffer systems of the erythrocyte with the hemoglobin in the oxygenated and deoxygenated states. *In the physiological pH range oxyhemoglobin is evidently more strongly acid than deoxyhemoglobin.* The basic cause of this difference lies in the influence of the iron-bound oxygen on the binding of H^+ to the neighboring imidazole groups of histidine. Because of this effect, when O_2 is given off in the tissues the hemoglobin becomes better able to tie up the H^+ ions produced by the simultaneous uptake of CO_2. The same supplementary buffer effect operates when O_2 is taken up in the lungs. We can confirm, then, that *O_2 exchange enhances the buffer action of hemoglobin.*

Buffer base. The buffer properties of the blood are determined by the combined effects of all the anionic groups of weak acids, the most important of which are bicarbonate and proteinate. All of these anions with buffer effects are called *buffer bases* [14].

Fig. 20-16 summarizes the arterial ion concentrations in human plasma, erythrocytes and whole blood. The height of the various columns is proportional to concentration. The anions are arranged such that the buffer bases are at the top *(dark red);* below this are the

anions of the strong acids, which have no buffer property, with all the non-chloride anions (such as SO_4^{--} and organic anions) lumped together as X^-. The graph shows that the buffer bases in plasma are represented chiefly by HCO_3^- ions, whereas in erythrocytes the protein ions predominate. In whole blood more than ⅓ of all the anions are available for buffering.

The concentration of **buffer bases** in arterial blood is about *48 mmol/l.* A point of special importance is that the total buffer base does not change when the CO_2 partial pressure varies. This constancy is revealed by the following considerations. When the CO_2 partial pressure rises, for example, equivalent amounts of H^+ and HCO_3^- are formed. The protons so produced are almost entirely caught up by proteinate, which is thus converted into the undissociated form. Therefore the proteinate concentration is reduced to the same extent that the bicarbonate concentration increases. Because of the P_{CO_2}-independence of total buffer base this parameter provides a suitable measure of those changes in acid-base status that result from increase or decrease of the *"fixed" (nonvolatile) acids* in the blood.

Departures from the normal buffer-base concentration (48 mmol/l) are called **base excess BE.** By this definition, then, the BE of blood in healthy persons is zero. A pathological rise in buffer-base concentration is indicated by a positive BE, and a decrease by a negative BE. Because the term *"negative base excess"* is contradictory, **base deficit** is a preferable designation for the latter case.

pH-Regulating Mechanisms

Contribution of respiration. One of the functions of respiration is to eliminate the CO_2 produced in large quantities as an end product of metabolism. When the body is at rest 230 ml CO_2 are blown off per minute, or about 15,000 mmol/day. At the same time, release of the "volatile" carbonic acid anhydride relieves the blood of a nearly equivalent amount of H^+. Respiration thus makes a crucial contribution to the maintenance of a stable acid-base status.

The *control of breathing* is of particular importance in compensating for disturbance of the acid-base balance. For example, when abnormal metabolic processes cause the acidity of the blood to rise, the increased H^+ concentration acts as an additional respiratory drive that leads to increased ventilation *(hyperventilation)*. CO_2 molecules derived from the reaction $HCO_3^- + H^+ \rightarrow H_2CO_3 \rightarrow H_2O + CO_2$ are breathed out in greater amounts, and the pH returns to normal. An increase in bases elicits *hypoventilation;* the CO_2 partial pressure and thus the concentration of H^+ ions rise, so that the original pH increase is at least partially negated.

Contribution of the kidneys. The kidneys are involved, along with the lungs, in regulating the acid-base balance. Their role consists in excreting the *"fixed" (nonvolatile) acids,* chiefly sulfuric acid. The fixed acids normally provide *40–60 mmol H^+/day,* which must be eliminated by way of the kidneys. If the amount of fixed acid should rise, a healthy kidney is capable of increasing considerably its rate of H^+ excretion and bringing the falling pH of the blood back to normal. Similarly, an increase in pH reduces the renal excretion of H^+ and thus compensates for the acid-base imbalance.

The excretion of H^+ ions occurs in the renal tubules, by a process in which tubular filtrate, tubule cell and capillary blood interact. Ultimately the H^+ ions are bound to HPO_4^{--} and NH_3 in the tubule urine; only a small fraction is eliminated in the urine as free H^+ ions. On the other hand, chemical conversions and exchange processes return HCO_3^- ions to the blood. For this reason the chemical reactions involved here are called the **base-retention mechanism** of the kidney (cf. Chapter 27).

Acidoses and alkaloses [3, 5, 6, 9, 14, 40]. When pathological conditions bring about an accumulation of large amounts of acids or bases in the blood, the regulatory mechanisms described above – buffering in the blood, respiration and renal function – do not suffice to keep the blood pH constant. Depending on the direction of the pH shift, these disturbances of acid-base balance are divided into two categories. An abnormally low blood pH (pH < 7.37) is called **acidosis,** and abnormally high pH (pH > 7.43) is called **al-**

kalosis. Each of these categories is further subdivided according to the origin of the pH change. Pulmonary malfunction can cause the CO_2 partial pressure in the blood to rise, and hyperventilation can lower it; in either case it is a respiratory abnormality that causes the pH change. Such a condition is called **respiratory acidosis** or **alkalosis.** Nonvolatile acids, on the other hand, can accumulate in the blood owing to metabolic disturbances (e. g., diabetes mellitus) or be removed from it when bases are added or HCl lost (vomiting). These states are called *metabolic acidosis* or *alkalosis.* Because renal malfunction can also alter the blood pH, the term **nonrespiratory acidosis** or **alkalosis** is used to cover both renal and metabolic disturbances.

Respiratory and nonrespiratory disturbances of the acid-base balance can be distinguished by way of CO_2 partial pressure (P_{CO_2}) and base excess (BE). The sign of respiratory disturbance is elevated or lowered P_{CO_2} without primary change in the buffer-base concentration (BE = 0). It is characteristic of nonrespiratory disturbance that P_{CO_2} is normal at first, whereas BE departs from the norm. When the fixed acids in the blood increase (metabolic acidosis) they use up some of the buffer base (BE becomes negative), and when the amount of fixed acids is diminished (metabolic alkalosis) the buffer-base concentration rises (BE is positive).

These distinguishing characteristics are diagrammed in Fig. 20-17. In a coordinate system with base excess on the ordinate and pH on the abscissa, curves of equal CO_2 partial pressure are plotted. The norms for pH, base excess BE and CO_2 partial pressure P_{CO_2} are delimited by red lines. Thus all the points to the left of the vertical white band characterize *acidosis,* and those to the right are characteristic of *alkalosis.* The red bands are labelled according to the type of acid-base disturbance, as defined above. By finding the point on the diagram that corresponds to the measured BE and pH in any particular case, one can diagnose the direction and the origin of the disturbance. For example, if the arterial blood is found to have BE = 0 mmol/l and P_{CO_2} = 60 mm Hg, it is a case of respiratory acidosis, whereas a finding of BE = −15 mmol/l and P_{CO_2} = 40 mm Hg implies metabolic or, better, nonrespiratory acidosis.

Compensation of primary acid-base disturbances. The disturbances of acid-base balance considered so far are, as a rule, only primary alterations that can be compensated either immediately or with a certain delay. That is, the primary displacement of the pH toward the acid or alkaline side is reversed by compensatory mechanisms, so that the normal range is regained or at least approached. The mechanisms that act in this sense have been discussed above. *A primary nonrespiratory disturbance can be compensated by an appropriate change in ventilation of the lungs. In cases of primary respiratory disturbance, the kidney can compensate by changing its HCO_3^- retention or H^+ excretion.*

These possibilities, again, are best illustrated by the diagram of Fig. 20-17. First let us consider *primary nonrespiratory acidosis* (arrow 1a). As the fixed acids accumulate in the blood the buffer-base concentration is reduced and the pH at first falls. The fall in pH acts as a respiratory drive to elicit hyperventilation, as a result of which the CO_2 partial pressure drops. This development is represented in the graph by arrow 1b. Once the P_{CO_2} decrease has returned the pH to the normal range, we can consider the primary nonrespiratory acidosis to be *fully compensated.* But if P_{CO_2} does not drop sufficiently to restore normal pH, the acid-base status is described as *partially or incompletely compensated* nonrespiratory acidosis. In *primary nonrespiratory alkalosis* (arrow 2a) the increase in buffer base is compensated by a P_{CO_2} increase caused by hypoventilation. The degree to which ventilation can be reduced, however, is limited by the body's oxygen requirement, so that this compensation is usually incomplete. In *primary respiratory acidosis* (arrow 3a), such as can be caused by pulmonary malfunction, the CO_2 partial pressure is elevated. In this case the base-retention mechanism of the kidney comes into play, with a certain latency. The buffer-base concentration in the blood rises and the pH is returned to the normal range (arrow 3b). In just the same way *primary respiratory alkalosis* (arrow 4a), which is characterized by low CO_2 partial pressure, is compensated by a decrease in the buffer-base concentration (arrow 4b) which shifts the pH back toward the normal range.

Evaluation of acid-base status. The analysis and diagnosis of the acid-base status of the blood is a problem of considerable clinical significance. Such evaluation requires the measurement of those parameters that enable one to make the decisions **acidosis-vs.-alkalosis** and **respiratory-vs.-nonrespiratory,** which in turn enable decisions as to suitable therapy [5, 6, 9, 14]. To this end, the following characteristics of the *arterial blood* must be determined:

1. pH: The pH reading indicates whether the H^+ concentration of the blood is in the normal range (pH 7.37–7.43) or shifted to the acid or alkaline side. However, normal pH does not necessarily imply that the acid-base balance is entirely undisturbed. A pathological state of primary acidosis or alkalosis could be masked by compensation.

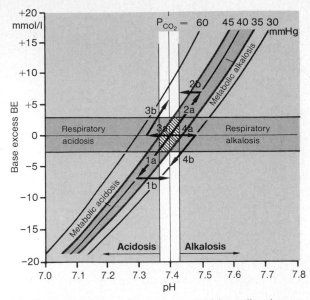

Fig. 20-17. Definitions of the primary acid-base disturbances and ways in which they can be compensated. The normal ranges of base excess BE, pH and CO_2 partial pressure P_{CO_2} are delimited by red lines. *Red cross-hatched field:* range of physiological acid-base balance. Arrow labels: a, primary acid-base disturbances; b, secondary compensations

2. P_{CO_2}: The presence of elevated or lowered CO_2 partial pressure indicates a primary respiratory disturbance (normal range of P_{CO_2}: 35–45 mm Hg).

3. Base excess: The BE reveals whether or not there is a primary nonrespiratory disturbance of the acid-base balance. An increase or decrease in the concentration of fixed acids in the blood is directly reflected in the BE (normal range of BE: -2.5 to $+2.5$ mmol/l).

4. Standard bicarbonate: Another parameter sometimes used to characterize a nonrespiratory disturbance is standard bicarbonate. This is the bicarbonate concentration of the blood plasma when a CO_2 partial pressure of 40 mm Hg has been established by equilibration at 37 °C and the hemoglobin is completely saturated with oxygen. Because this parameter (norm 24 mmol/l) does not take into consideration the part of the buffer function due to proteins, it is relatively uninformative.

Analytical procedures. A method of proven value for the analysis of acid-base status is that of **Astrup,** in which CO_2 partial pressure and acid-base status are determined in one operation [14]. First the blood to be tested is *equilibrated with two gas mixtures* of known composition and different CO_2 partial pressures, and the pH of each sample is measured. The two sets of paired pH-P_{CO_2} data so obtained are entered in a diagram like that of Fig. 20-18. The line joining the two points (A and B) reflects the acid-base status of the blood sample. Now, if the actual pH in the arterial

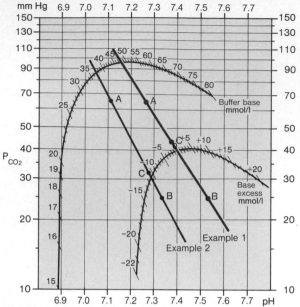

Fig. 20-18. Diagram for determination of the CO_2 partial pressure and the acid-base status of the blood by Astrup's procedure [14]. A and B, points found by measuring the pH of blood previously equilibrated with gas mixtures of known P_{CO_2}. C is the point on the straight line joining A and B that corresponds to the actual measured pH; it gives the actual P_{CO_2}. BE can be read off at the intersection point between the A–B line and the base-excess scale. Example 1, *red line:* $P_{CO_2} = 44$ mm Hg, pH = 7.37, BE = 0 mmol/l; diagnosis, normal acid-base status. Example 2, *black line:* $P_{CO_2} = 32$ mm Hg, pH = 7.28, BE = –11 mmol/l; diagnosis, partially compensated nonrespiratory acidosis

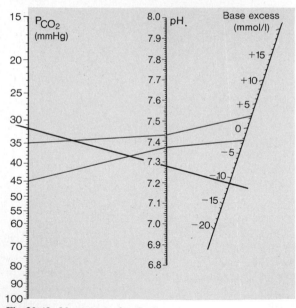

Fig. 20-19. Nomogram for finding the base excess BE from measured data for CO_2 partial pressure P_{CO_2} and pH. The line joining the points for P_{CO_2} and pH intersects the right-hand scale at a point corresponding to the BE of the blood. *Red lines:* limits of the normal range of acid-base status. *Black straight line:* from the measured values $P_{CO_2} = 32$ mm Hg, pH = 7.28 one finds BE = –11 mmol/l; the diagnosis is partially compensated nonrespiratory acidosis. After [40]

blood of the subject is measured, the *actual CO_2 partial pressure* associated with it can be found by reference to that line (Point C). At the points of intersection between the line and the appropriately labelled scales one can read off the concentration of *buffer base* and the *base excess*. For example, the red line in Fig. 20-18 characterizes a normal acid-base balance, whereas the black line implies a nonrespiratory acidosis (BE = –11 mmol/l) that is partially compensated by lowered CO_2 partial pressure ($P_{CO_2} = 32$ mm Hg, black Point C).

Because it has recently become possible to measure the CO_2 partial pressure in small blood samples directly with P_{CO_2} *electrodes* (p. 479), the acid-base status can now be evaluated even without previous equilibration [40]. The reason is that the measured actual values of P_{CO_2} and pH determine the base excess BE, the third quantity required for diagnosis. BE can conveniently be found from the two other parameters by means of the nomogram shown in Fig. 20-19.

When the points on the P_{CO_2} and pH scales corresponding to the measured values are joined by a straight line, the extension of the line intersects the BE scale at a point corresponding to the required BE. For the example in Fig. 20-19, it follows directly from the measured $P_{CO_2} = 32$ mm Hg and pH = 7.28 that BE = –11 mmol/l. The diagnosis (as in the example of Fig. 20-18) would therefore be partially compensated nonrespiratory acidosis.

20.5 References

Textbooks and Handbooks

1. ANTONINI, E., BRUNORI, M.: Hemoglobin and myoglobin in their reactions with ligands. Amsterdam: North Holland 1971
2. DAVENPORT, H. W.: The ABC of the acid-base chemistry. Chicago: University of Chicago Press 1969
3. FRISELL, W. R.: Acid-base chemistry in medicine. New York: Macmillan Comp. 1968
4. GUYTON, A. C.: Textbook of medical physiology. Philadelphia–London–Toronto: Saunders 1976
5. HILLS, A. G.: Acid-base balance: chemistry, physiology, pathophysiology. Baltimore: Williams and Wilkins 1973
6. KILDEBERG, P.: Clinical acid-base physiology. Baltimore: Williams and Wilkins 1968
7. LEHMANN, H., HUNTSMAN, R. G.: Man's hemoglobin. Philadelphia: Lippincott Comp. 1974
8. LENFANT, C.: Gas transport and gas exchange. In: RUCH, T.C., PATTON, H. D. (Eds.) Physiology and biophysics. Philadelphia–London–Toronto: Saunders 1974
9. MASORO, E.J., SIEGEL, P. D.: Acid-base regulation: Its physiology and pathophysiology. Philadelphia–London–Toronto: Saunders 1971
10. PIIPER, J.: Physiologie der Atmung. In: GAUER, O.H., KRAMER, K., JUNG, R. (Hrsg.): Physiologie des Menschen Bd. 6: Atmung. München–Berlin–Wien: Urban und Schwarzenberg 1975

11. Root, W.S.: Carbon monoxide. In: Handbook of Physiol., Sect.3: Respiration, Vol.II. Washington: Amer. Physiol. Soc. 1965

12. Roughton, F.J.W.: Transport of oxygen and carbon dioxide. In: Handbook of Physiology, Sect.3: Respiration, Vol.I. Washington: Amer. Physiol. Soc. 1964

13. Severinghaus, J.W.: Blood gas concentrations. In: Handbook of Physiology, Sect.3: Respiration, Vol.II. Washington: Amer. Physiol. Soc. 1965

14. Siggaard-Andersen, O.: The acid-base status of the blood. Kopenhagen: Munksgaard 1974

15. Weissbluth, M.: Hemoglobin: Cooperativity and electronic properties. Berlin–Heidelberg–New York: Springer 1974

16. Winters, R.W., Engel, K., Dell, R.B.: Acid-base physiology in medicine. A self-instruction program. Westlake, Ohio: The London Co. 1967

17. Woodbury, J.W.: Body acid-base state and its regulation. In: Ruch, T.C., Patton, H.D. (Eds.): Physiology and biophysics. Philadelphia–London–Toronto: Saunders 1974

Research Reports and Reviews

18. Adamson, J.W., Finch, C.A.: Hemoglobin function, oxygen affinity, and erythropoietin. Ann. Rev. Physiol. 37, 351 (1975)

19. Baldwin, J.M.: Structure and function of haemoglobin. Prog. Biophys. Molec. Biol. 29, 225 (1975)

20. Bartels, H., Baumann, R.: Respiratory function of hemoglobin. In: Guyton, A.C., Widdicombe, J.G. (Eds.): Respiratory Physiology II. Intern. Rev. Physiol., Vol. 14. Baltimore–London–Tokyo: University Park Press 1977

21. Bauer, C.: On the respiratory function of haemoglobin. Rev. Physiol. Biochem. Pharmacol. 70, 1 (1974)

22. Bauer, C., Gros, G., Bartels, H. (Eds.): Biophysics and physiology of carbon dioxide. Berlin–Heidelberg–New York: Springer 1980

23. Benesch, R.E., Benesch, R., Yu, C.I.: The oxygenation of hemoglobin in the presence of 2,3-diphosphoglycerate: Effect of temperature, pH, ionic strength and hemoglobin concentration. Biochemistry, 8, 2567 (1969)

24. Braunitzer, G.: The molecular weight of human haemoglobin. Bibl. haemat. (Basel) 18, 59 (1964)

25. Braunitzer, G., Hilse, K., Rudloff, V., Hilschmann, N.: The hemoglobins. Adv. Protein Chem. 19, 1 (1964)

26. Brodda, K.: Zur Theorie des Säure-Basen-Haushaltes von menschlichem Blut. Akadem. Wiss. Lit. Mainz; Wiesbaden: Steiner 1975

27. Dittmer (Ed.): Blood and other body fluids. Washington: Fed. Amer. Soc. exp. Biol. 1961

28. Fischer, W.M., Vogel, H.R., Thews, G.: O_2 and CO_2 exchange in the human placenta. In: Lübbers, D.-W., Luft, U.C., Thews, G., Witzleb, E.: Oxygen transport in blood and tissue. Stuttgart: Thieme 1968

29. Forster, R.E.: CO_2: Chemical, biochemical, and physiological aspects. Physiologist 13, 398 (1970)

30. Grote, J., Reneau, D., Thews, G. (Eds.): Oxygen transport to tissue II. New York: Plenum Press 1976

31. Kilmartin, J.V., Rossi-Bernardi, L.: Interactions of hemoglobin with hydrogen ions, carbon dioxide, and organic phosphates. Physiol. Rev. 53, 836 (1973)

32. King, E.J., Gilchrist, M.: Determination of haemoglobin by a cyanhaematin method. Lancet II, 201 (1947)

33. Longo, L.D., Bartels, H. (Eds.): Respiratory gas exchange and blood flow in the placenta. Bethesda: DHEW Publication No (NIH) 73–361, 1972

34. Maren, T.H.: Carbonic anhydrase: Chemistry, physiology, and inhibition. Physiol. Rev. 47, 595 (1967)

35. Merlet-Bénichou, E., Sinet, M., Blayo, M.C., Gaudebout, C.: Oxygen-combining capacity in dog. In vitro and in vivo determination. Respir. Physiol. 21, 87 (1974)

36. Perutz, M.F.: The hemoglobin molecule. Proc. Roy. Soc., B, 173, 113 (1969)

37. Perutz, M.F.: Stereochemistry of cooperative effects in haemoglobin. Nature 219, 902 (1970)

38. Riggs, A.: Functional properties of hemoglobins. Physiol. Rev. 45, 619 (1965)

39. Roughton, F.J.W., Kendrew, J.C. (Eds.): Haemoglobin. London: Butterworths Scientific Publications 1949

40. Thews, G. (Ed.): Nomogramme zum Säure-Basen-Status des Blutes und zum Atemgastransport. Berlin–Heidelberg–New York: Springer 1971

41. Wagner, P.D.: The oxyhemoglobin dissociation curve and pulmonary gas exchange: Semin. Hematol. 11, 405 (1974)

42. Wintrobe, M.M. (Ed.): Clinical Hematology. Philadelphia: Lea and Febiger 1968

21 Tissue Respiration

J. GROTE

21.1 Metabolism and Oxygen Requirements of the Tissues

Cellular Metabolism and Energy Conversion

The term *tissue respiration* denotes the *exchange of respiratory gases within an aggregation of cells in the course of the biological oxidation of nutrients*. The **oxygen** received by the cells from the capillary blood is consumed in oxidative metabolism, and at the same time the metabolic end product **carbon dioxide** is released into the capillary blood [8]. Here "tissue respiration" is used in a broader sense than in many biochemistry textbooks, where tissue respiration is defined as the oxidative breakdown of nutrients with the participation of molecular oxygen. Because O_2 deficiency in the tissues limits these reactions more effectively than inadequate removal of CO_2, we shall concentrate on questions related to the supply of oxygen to the tissues.

Aerobic and anaerobic mechanisms. Each living cell in the body needs a certain amount of energy in order to maintain its structure and functional capacities and to carry out its functions. This energy, under normal conditions, is acquired primarily by the **oxidative decomposition of nutrients.** For energy to be obtained by aerobic metabolism both a *substrate* – carbohydrates, proteins and fats – and *molecular oxygen* must be present in the cell in adequate concentrations.

Under anaerobic conditions the energy required by the tissues can be obtained only by **glycolysis.** This metabolic pathway is less economic than the oxidative breakdown of glucose because the end product, lactate, still has a high energy content. To make available a given amount of energy an individual cell under anaerobic conditions must metabolize ca. 15 times as much glucose as it needs when oxygen is available.

According to BURTON and KREBS [14], the *oxidative breakdown* of 1 mol glucose under conditions approximately like those within cells (T = 25 °C, pH = 7.0, P_{O_2} = ca. 150 mm Hg = ca. 20 kPa, P_{CO_2} = ca. 40 mm Hg = ca. 5.3 kPa) provides free energy amounting to ca. 689 kcal = 2883 kJ. The amount of energy obtained from the *anaerobic breakdown* of glucose by glycolysis is only 50 kcal = 208 kJ. Despite its relatively low yield of energy, anaerobic glucose metabolism plays an important role in many tissues – for example, the renal medulla, cartilage, retinal cells, erythrocytes and the working musculature.

Biological Oxidation in the Mitochondria

The *biological oxidation* of nutrients takes place in the *mitochondria*. These cell components have been found to contain not only the enzymes of the citrate cycle, the respiratory chain and oxidative phosphorylation, but also those by which fatty acids and various amino acids are broken down [4]. (The various metabolic pathways of biological oxidation in the mitochondria are illustrated schematically in Fig. 21-1.)

Pyruvate, fatty acids and *amino acids* are transported from the cytoplasm through the mitochondrial membrane system into the **matrix space** of the mitochondria. There they are decomposed in specific metabolic pathways into substances that enter the *citrate cycle*. Pyruvate, which is formed chiefly as an end product of anaerobic glycolysis in the cytoplasm, is converted by oxidative decarboxylation in the matrix space to acetyl-CoA, most of which is broken down in the citrate cycle under normal conditions. Whereas the first steps in glucose breakdown (glycolysis) take place in the cytoplasm, the oxidative decomposition of fatty acids is entirely confined to the matrix space. The fatty-acid molecules are oxidized by a series of reactions called β oxidation; the resulting acetyl-CoA enters the citrate cycle or is used for the synthesis of fatty acids. The carbohydrate compounds produced in the matrix space by amino-acid metabolism can be fed into the citrate cycle at various points (acetyl-CoA, α-ketoglutarate, succinyl-CoA, fumarate, oxalacetate).

The $NADH_2$ molecules formed in the citrate cycle by three dehydrogenation reactions, as well as the *succinate* produced in the citrate cycle, diffuse from the matrix space to the inner membrane of the mitochondrion, in which the enzymes of the respiratory chain and oxidative phosphorylation are embedded. There $NADH_2$ is oxidized by a respiratory-chain enzyme complex that includes flavin mononucleotide (FMN) as a coenzyme, whereas the hydrogen is removed from succinate by a respiratory-chain enzyme com-

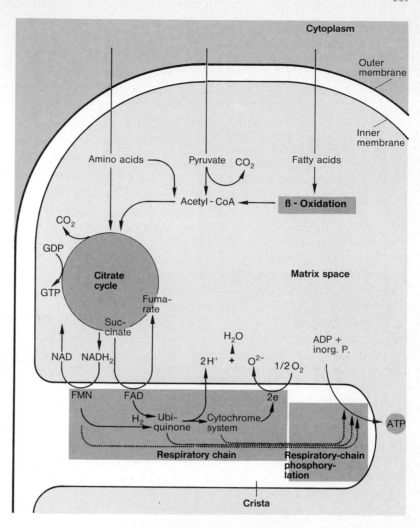

Fig. 21-1. Schematic drawing to show the most important metabolic reactions involved in biological oxidation within the mitochondrion

plex with flavin adenine dinucleotide (FAD) as a coenzyme. Both of the flavoprotein complexes transfer the hydrogen to ubiquinone, which is then oxidized under the influence of a cytochrome complex. As a result, 2 hydrogen ions and 2 electrons are produced for each hydrogen molecule. The electrons are transported by way of specific cytochromes in the respiratory chain to cytochrome oxidase, which transfers them to molecular oxygen. The reduced oxygen combines with the free hydrogen ions to form water. The energy released during the transport of hydrogen and electrons in the respiratory chain is used in part for the simultaneous synthesis of ATP at the inner membrane **(respiratory-chain phosphorylation).** For each oxidized $NADH_2$ molecule 3 molecules of ATP are produced, and for each oxidized $FADH_2$ molecule 2 molecules of ATP are produced. In the first case the ratio of ATP production to oxygen consumption (the P/O ratio) is 3; that is, 1 gram atom of oxygen is consumed in the formation of 3 moles of ATP. In the second case the P/O ratio is 2.

The consequences of inadequate O_2 supply. When pathological conditions restrict the supply of O_2 some of the energy required by the tissues can be provided, for a short time, by the limited energy reserves stored in the form of ATP and creatine phosphate, and by anaerobic glycolysis. There are two basic reasons why these energy sources are inadequate and can be utilized only briefly. First, in this situation the *glucose requirement* of the cells is increased to such an extent that it can rarely be fully met for prolonged periods. Second, the large amounts of *lactate* so produced cannot be removed from the cells rapidly enough for disposal elsewhere – for example, by decomposition in the liver, kidney or myocardium or by the synthesis of glycogen. In severe O_2 deficiency the lactate concentration in tissues and blood rises steadily, resulting in a *nonrespiratory acidosis* that causes pronounced changes in cellular metabolism as soon as the intracellular pH falls below the optimal range for function of the enzyme systems.

Table 21-1. Mean values of perfusion rate ($\dot{Q}$), difference in O_2 concentrations in arterial and venous blood (avD_{O_2}), and O_2 consumption ($\dot{V}_{O_2}$) in various human organs at 37 °C

Organ	Blood flow, $\dot{Q}$ $ml \cdot g \cdot min^{-1}$	Arterioven. diff., avD_{O_2}	O_2 cons., $\dot{V}_{O_2}$ $ml \cdot g^{-1} \cdot min^{-1}$	Refs.
Blood	–	–	$0.6 \cdot 10^{-4}$–$1 \cdot 10^{-4}$	[21]
Skeletal muscle				[1, 3, 8, 25]
at rest	$2 \cdot 10^{-2}$–$4 \cdot 10^{-2}$	$10 \cdot 10^{-2}$–$15 \cdot 10^{-2}$	$2.5 \cdot 10^{-3}$–$5 \cdot 10^{-3}$	
during hard work	up to 0.5		up to ca. $10 \cdot 10^{-2}$	
Spleen	1.0	$1 \cdot 10^{-2}$	$1 \cdot 10^{-2}$	[1, 3, 8, 35]
Brain	0.5–0.6	$6 \cdot 10^{-2}$–$7 \cdot 10^{-2}$	$3.5 \cdot 10^{-2}$	[1, 3, 6, 8, 27]
cortex	0.8–1.1		$8 \cdot 10^{-2}$–$10 \cdot 10^{-2}$	
white matter	0.15–0.25	$4 \cdot 10^{-2}$–$6 \cdot 10^{-2}$	$1 \cdot 10^{-2}$	
Liver	1.0 (25% hep. art.)	$4 \cdot 10^{-2}$–$5 \cdot 10^{-2}$ (portal v. – hep. v.) $8 \cdot 10^{-2}$–$10 \cdot 10^{-2}$ (hep. art. – hep. v.)	$5 \cdot 10^{-2}$–$6 \cdot 10^{-2}$	[1, 3, 8, 17, 29]
Kidney	4.0	$1.5 \cdot 10^{-2}$–$2 \cdot 10^{-2}$	$5.5 \cdot 10^{-2}$–$6.5 \cdot 10^{-2}$	[1, 3, 8, 16, 22]
cortex	4.0–5.0	$2 \cdot 10^{-2}$–$2.5 \cdot 10^{-2}$	$9 \cdot 10^{-2}$–$10 \cdot 10^{-2}$	
outer medulla	1.2	$5 \cdot 10^{-2}$	$6 \cdot 10^{-2}$–$6.5 \cdot 10^{-2}$	
inner medulla	0.25	$1 \cdot 10^{-2}$–$2 \cdot 10^{-2}$	$0.3 \cdot 10^{-2}$–$0.5 \cdot 10^{-2}$	
Heart				[1, 3, 8, 12, 13, 18, 33]
at rest	0,8–0.9	$10 \cdot 10^{-2}$–$15 \cdot 10^{-2}$	$7 \cdot 10^{-2}$–$10 \cdot 10^{-2}$	
strenuous exercise	up to 4.0	up to ca. $17 \cdot 10^{-2}$	up to ca. $40 \cdot 10^{-2}$	

Tissue Oxygen Requirements

O_2 consumption under resting conditions. *The amount of O_2 required by a tissue depends on the functional state of its component cells.* When the body is at rest and at the normal temperature, the O_2 consumption of various organs and parts of organs is as summarized in Table 21–1. The rate of oxygen consumption ($\dot{V}_{O_2}$) in an organ, normally given in ml per 1 g or 100 g fresh weight per minute, is found by the *Fick principle* from the *blood flow* ($\dot{Q}$) through the organ and the *difference in O_2 concentration* between the arterial blood entering it and the venous blood leaving it (avD_{O_2}), according to the equation

$$\dot{V}_{O_2} = avD_{O_2} \cdot \dot{Q} \qquad (1)$$

Under resting conditions O_2 consumption is relatively high in the myocardial tissue, in the gray matter of the brain (e.g., the cerebral cortex), *in the liver and in the renal cortex;* the rate of O_2 consumption is lower in the skeletal musculature, the spleen and the white matter of the brain (Table 21–1).

Regional differences in O_2 consumption within an organ. It is possible to measure *blood flow through circumscribed areas of tissue* in many organs by monitoring the *clearance of inert gases* such as ^{85}Kr, ^{133}Xe and H_2. Therefore if a blood sample can be drawn from a vein draining the region in question, the O_2 consump-

tion in that region can be determined. But as can be seen in Table 21–1, attempts to establish *regional O_2 consumption* have been successful in only a few organs. Studies of the oxygen supply to the brain tissue of various mammals have indicated an O_2 consumption in the *cerebral cortex* of between ca. $8 \cdot 10^{-2}$ and $0.1 \; ml \cdot g^{-1} \cdot min^{-1}$. From the data on O_2 consumption measured directly for the whole brain and the cerebral cortex, one finds that the mean O_2 consumption of the *white matter of the brain* is ca. $1 \cdot 10^{-2} \; ml \cdot g^{-1} \cdot min^{-1}$. It is to be expected that the O_2 consumption within an organ varies not only by region but also among the individual cells within a region. For example, when the *local O_2 consumption* in superficial cell layers of the cerebral cortex was studied with platinum microelectrodes, it was found that under light anesthesia the O_2 consumption within small areas varied between ca. $4 \cdot 10^{-2}$ and $0.12 \; ml \cdot g^{-1} \cdot min^{-1}$. Autoradiographic studies of local blood flow (with iodine-^{14}C-antipyrine) and local glucose consumption (with ^{14}C-2-deoxyglucose) in the cerebral cortex indicated that these parameters also differ considerably in adjacent regions [30, 31]. Comparable differences in the O_2 requirement of individual parts of organs have been found in the kidney. The mean O_2 consumption of the *renal cortex* is ca. 20 times as large as that of the *inner medulla* of the kidney. Because the O_2 requirement of kidney tissue is determined primarily by the extent of active Na^+ reabsorption from the tubule lumen into the tissue, the large differences in regional O_2 consumption are ascribable particularly to the differential reabsorption activity of the cortex and medulla.

O_2 consumption when activity is increased. Whenever higher performance of an organ is called for, its rate of energy conversion rises and its cells require more O_2. During exercise the O_2 consumption of the *myocardial tissue* increases to 3 or 4 times the resting level, whereas that of working groups of *skeletal muscles* can increase by more than 20-to-50-fold. The O_2 requirement of *renal tissue* rises with the rate of Na^+ reabsorption.

In the majority of organs, when the tissue O_2 partial pressure is above a critical level (p.513) the rate of O_2 uptake into the tissue is independent of the rate of blood flow through it. The kidney is an exception. There is a critical perfusion rate above which the formation of ultrafiltrate begins; in this filtration range increased blood flow is accompanied by an increase in the O_2 consumption of the renal tissue. This special situation arises because the change in blood flow causes the rate of glomerular filtration (and thus of Na^+ reabsorption) to change in the same direction.

The influence of temperature on O_2 consumption. O_2 consumption in the tissues is extremely dependent on temperature. If the temperature of the body falls, energy conversion is restricted and most of the organs thus require less oxygen. As long as temperature regulation is maintained, however, those organs involved in the regulatory mechanisms are more active and consume more O_2. Among these is the skeletal musculature (enhanced muscle tone, shivering; cf. p. 532). Elevated body temperature causes a general increase in tissue O_2 requirements. In the range between 20° and 40 °C, according to van't Hoff's rule, any 10° change in body temperature will change tissue O_2 consumption in the same direction by the factor $Q_{10} = 2$ to 3. When surgical operations require that the circulation of blood, and thus the supply of O_2 and nutrients to the organs, be interrupted for a time, *hypothermia* (lowered body temperature) is very often induced. In order to achieve a reduction in the O_2 requirement of all the organs, the patient is so deeply anesthetized that the thermoregulatory mechanisms are restricted or eliminated.

21.2 Tissue Oxygen Supply

Tissue Oxygen Reserves

The amount of O_2 available to the cells for tissue respiration is determined by the magnitude of the *convective O_2 transport* with the blood and the extent of *O_2 diffusion* between the capillary blood and the tissues. Because most tissues have no O_2 stores apart from that in physical solution, a reduction in the O_2

supply leads to O_2 deficiency and diminished oxidative metabolism as soon as the momentary O_2 requirements are not completely met.

O_2-storage function of myoglobin. The *musculature* is an exception to the above rule. It contains the pigment *myoglobin (Mb),* which can bind O_2 reversibly and thus serves to store it. However, the concentration of myoglobin in human muscle tissue is low, so that the amount of stored O_2 is not enough to carry the tissues through a long period of severe O_2 deficiency.

The limitations of the O_2 reserve bound to the myoglobin are especially well illustrated by the cardiac musculature. The mean myoglobin content of the myocardium is 4 mg per g tissue. Because 1 g myoglobin binds at most ca. 1.34 ml oxygen, under physiological conditions about $0.5 \cdot 10^{-2}$ ml O_2 is stored in 1 g of myocardial tissue. If the supply of O_2 to the myocardium should be cut off completely, this amount of O_2 could sustain normal oxidative metabolism in the cells for only ca. 3–4 s.

The role of myoglobin in muscle tissue O_2 supply. Myoglobin functions as a **short-term O_2 store.** In the **myocardium** the oxygen bound to this pigment ensures a supply of O_2 to those parts of the muscle in which blood flow is reduced or completely blocked for a brief time during systole. As soon as the O_2 partial pressure in the muscle cells falls below ca. 10–15 mm Hg (1.3–2.0 kPa), myoglobin gives off O_2 in amounts indicated by its O_2 dissociation curve (p. 494) [18].
In the skeletal musculature the O_2 released by the myoglobin when hard muscular work is begun can cover part of the increased demand for O_2 during the transition period until the adjustment of blood flow again delivers the amount required. The oxygen released by myoglobin accounts for part of the **O_2 debt** that can be incurred by each skeletal muscle fiber.

O_2 Availability and Utilization

O_2 availability to the organs. The amount of O_2 carried by the blood to a given organ per unit time is the product of **arterial O_2 concentration** and the **rate of blood flow:**

$$O_2 \text{ availability} = C_{a_{O_2}} \cdot \dot{Q} \qquad (2)$$

This relationship implies that differences in the availability of oxygen to the various organs are entirely ascribable to differences in blood flow through the organs. Any change in blood flow, as a result of changes in vascular resistance or mean arterial pressure, results directly in a change in the amount of oxygen available to the tissue.
The average supply of O_2 to individual organs under physiological conditions can be found directly from

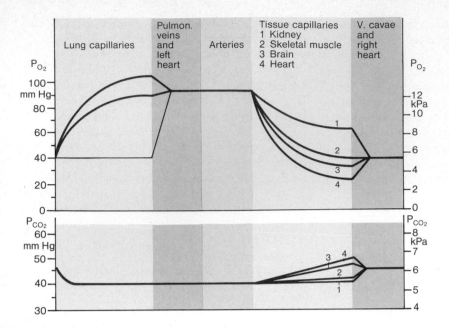

Fig. 21-2. O_2 partial pressure (P_{O_2}) and CO_2 partial pressure (P_{CO_2}) of the blood in the successive segments of the circulatory system under resting conditions. Modified from [34]

the O_2 concentration of the arterial blood (pp. 494 f.) and the values for blood flow given in Table 21-1. The O_2 availability is found to be particularly large for the renal cortex, the spleen and the gray matter of the brain, and small in the cases of resting skeletal musculature, renal medulla and the white matter of the brain.

O_2 utilization coefficient in different organs. The **O_2 utilization coefficient** of an organ is the **ratio of its O_2 consumption to the O_2 availability.** It is found by combining Eq. (1) and Eq. (2) as follows:

$$O_2 \text{ utilization coefficient} = (\text{avD}_{O_2} \cdot \dot{Q}) / (C_{a_{O_2}} \cdot \dot{Q}) = \text{avD}_{O_2}/C_{a_{O_2}} \qquad (3)$$

Because tissues vary in their oxygen requirements, the utilization parameter must also vary. Under normal conditions the cerebral cortex, myocardium and resting skeletal musculature consume ca. 40–60% of the O_2 available in a given time; the accompanying O_2 utilization coefficients are found to be between 0.4 and 0.6. The normal value for the whole body is 0.3. The O_2 utilization coefficient can increase considerably in conditions of greater activity. Maximal values, as great as 0.9 in the extreme case, are found when hard work is being performed, in the working skeletal musculature and in the myocardium. Under pathological conditions, reduction of the arterial O_2 concentration or diminished blood flow can markedly increase the O_2 utilization of an organ. A particularly small fraction of the available O_2 is utilized in the kidney and the spleen. Because of the large amounts of blood that flow through these organs in support of

their normal functions, both the kidney and the spleen have a very large O_2 availability although they require only moderate to slight amounts of oxygen.

Respiratory Gas Exchange in the Tissues

Free and facilitated diffusion. The exchange of respiratory gases between the capillary blood and the cells of a tissue, like gas exchange in the lungs, occurs by **diffusion** (p. 476). The **O_2 molecules** brought to the tissues in the blood move along the O_2 partial-pressure gradient, from the erythrocytes and the plasma into the surrounding tissue. At the same time, the carbon dioxide formed during oxidative metabolism diffuses from the tissue cells with high CO_2 partial pressure into the blood, where the CO_2 partial pressure is lower. Thus the **partial pressure of O_2** and CO_2 in the blood is a factor of particular significance in tissue gas exchange. The mean partial pressures of both respiratory gases in the different parts of the circulatory system of a human at rest are diagrammed in Fig. 21-2.
The release of O_2 from the blood to the tissues can be affected by the *diffusion of the oxygenated hemoglobin* within the erythrocytes, which accelerates the transport of the O_2 molecules to the surface of the blood cell [23]. This effect is described by the term facilitated O_2 diffusion. In muscle tissue the *diffusion of oxygenated myoglobin* has a comparable effect on O_2 transport.
Another factor that may additionally increase the velocity of respiratory gas transport is *convection* of the cytoplasm within the erythrocytes or tissue cells as well as of the plasma and the interstitial fluid.

Both the release of O_2 from blood to tissues and the transport of CO_2 in the opposite direction are determined not only by the *partial-pressure gradient* between the capillary blood and the cells, but also by the size of the *exchange area,* the length of the *diffusion path,* and the magnitude of the *diffusion resistance* of the various structures through which the molecules pass. Under conditions of constant partial pressure or concentration gradient, the effect of these factors on the amount of gas exchanged per unit time is described by **Fick's first law of diffusion** (p. 476).

Models of gas exchange in the tissues. The law of diffusion can be used to analyze respiratory gas exchange in a tissue and to compute the O_2 and CO_2 partial pressures in the cells. Such theoretical analyses are based on mathematical models that describe the functional and morphological conditions during tissue O_2 or CO_2 diffusion in a simplified way.

Various structural models have been proposed to assist the description of gas exchange in the tissues. The best known and most frequently used of these is **Krogh's tissue cylinder.** As early as 1918 KROGH [24] represented the region of tissue supplied by a single capillary as a cylinder with the capillary as its axis. He based his studies of O_2 diffusion in skeletal muscle on this concept.

Although Krogh's model can describe the conditions for gas exchange accurately only in the case of a mass of tissue within which adjacent capillaries lie in parallel, begin and end in the same plane and carry blood flowing in the same direction, the tissue cylinder proved an extremely useful conceptual model for the study of the exchange of respiratory gases and other substances in the tissues. Since it was proposed, many other models have been developed. An alternative to the tissue cylinder is the so-called *cone model,* which is based on the assumption that the blood in neighboring capillaries flows in opposite directions. Still other models for gas-exchange analyses consider the conditions within a *cube of tissue* delimited by four capillaries arranged in parallel, through which the blood flows in different directions; others describe the process of gas exchange in an area of tissue containing a square-meshed *network* of capillaries.

Significance of capillary density and capillary circulation. In addition to the *partial-pressure gradient* between the capillary blood and the cells, the *capillary density* and the *blood-flow distribution in the microcirculation* are crucial factors influencing respiratory gas exchange in a region of tissue. Both the **exchange area** for the diffusion of gases between blood and tissue and the **diffusion distance** within the tissue are directly dependent on the number of perfused capillaries, their length and the distance between them.

Capillary density varies from organ to organ, and in many cases even within a single organ. The capillary network is particularly dense, offering favorable conditions for gas exchange, in those tissues with high energy turnover.

In the *myocardium,* for example, there is one capillary for each muscle fiber; the mean distance between adjacent capillaries is ca. 25 μm. The mean intercapillary distance in the *cortex of the brain* has been found to be ca. 40 μm, and that in the *skeletal musculature* is ca. 80 μm. The **capillary blood-flow distribution** depends on the contractile activity of the metarterioles and the precapillary sphincters. Elevation or depression of precapillary sphincter tone alters the number of capillaries that are perfused at any given time. Thus, not only the amount of oxygen available to a tissue area, but the conditions for O_2 exchange as well, can be varied by enlargement or reduction of the diffusion area and the diffusion distance.

O_2 Partial Pressures in the Tissues

Critical O_2 partial pressure in the mitochondria. The O_2 partial pressure in the cells of a tissue under physiological conditions is between that of arterial blood and a minimum, which in different organs or parts of organs with high O_2 demand has been found to be about 1 mmHg (133.3 Pa). A prerequisite for normal oxidative metabolism in a cell is a *minimal O_2 partial pressure of ca. 0.1–1 mm Hg* (13.3–133.3 Pa) *in the region of the mitochondria – the* **critical mitochondrial O_2 partial pressure** [15, 32]. If the O_2 partial pressure in the immediate vicinity of the mitochondria falls below this level, the reduced *cytochrome oxidase* can no longer be completely oxidized, the transport of hydrogen and electrons in the *respiratory chain* is curtailed, and as a result energy metabolism can no longer continue at the normal rate. *Thus the most important criterion by which to judge the O_2 supply to an organ is the cellular O_2 partial pressure.*

The development of *polarographic* techniques (p. 479) has made it possible to measure directly, with microelectrodes, the O_2 partial pressure in single cells of a tissue. For the measurement of O_2 partial pressure in cells near the surface very small platinum electrodes are used, which can be set directly on the tissue without disrupting the microcirculation in the area under study. Measurement of the cellular O_2 partial pressure in deeper parts of the tissue can be done with needle electrodes having tip diameters of ca. 0.5–5 μm (Fig. 21.3 B).

Both of these procedures have so far been used chiefly in experiments on animals. But they have been successfully applied to human patients (to easily accessi-

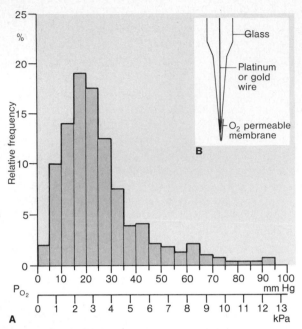

A

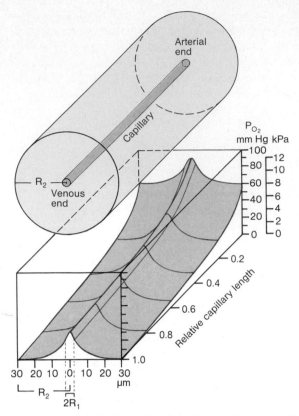

Fig. 21-3 A, B. O_2 partial pressures in the gray matter of the brain cortex. **A** Frequency distribution of the local O_2 partial pressures in the cerebral cortex of the guinea pig during normoventilation. The maximal levels (P_{O_2} = 90–95 mm Hg = 12.0–12.7 kPa) correspond to the O_2 partial pressure of the arterial blood. The minima, in the cells least well provided with oxygen, are 0.5–1 mm Hg (67–133 Pa), and thus are ca. 25 mm Hg (3.3 kPa) below the mean O_2 partial pressure of the venous blood in the cortex (after [28]). **B** Structure of a microelectrode for polarographic measurement of the O_2 partial pressure in tissues

Fig. 21-4. Schematic illustration of the O_2 partial pressure distribution in KROGH's tissue-cylinder model of a capillary in the human cerebral cortex (O_2 consumption = $9 \cdot 10^{-2}$ml · g^{-1} · min^{-1}, blood flow = 0.8 ml · g^{-1} · min^{-1}). The mean O_2 partial pressure of the blood under normal conditions falls from 90 mm Hg (12.0 kPa) at the arterial end of a cortical capillary to ca. 28 mm Hg (3.7 kPa) at the venous end. Within a cross section of the cylinder supplied by the capillary, the mean O_2 partial pressure falls by ca. 26 mm Hg (3.5 kPa) from the capillary to the edge of the cylinder

ble organs in particular), and they have provided important information. For instance, there are a number of examples of muscle disease or disturbance of blood flow through skeletal muscle for which the distribution of O_2 partial pressure in the affected muscle groups has been analyzed in detail. In most cases, however, when one wants to know something about the O_2 supply to a human organ it is necessary to measure directly the most important determining factors – such as the rate of flow, the respiratory gas partial pressures and concentrations, and the pH of the arterial blood – and then to use the results so obtained as the basis for a theoretical analysis of gas exchange within the tissue of interest.

Distribution of O_2 partial pressure in brain tissue. The two tissues for which it is most interesting to know the O_2 partial pressure distribution are the brain and the myocardium, for an inadequate supply of O_2 to either can be a direct cause of death. Within the cylindrical region of the *cerebral cortex* supplied by a capillary, given a tissue O_2 consumption of $9 \cdot 10^{-2}$ ml O_2 · g^{-1} · min^{-1} and a flow of 0.8 ml blood · g^{-1} · min^{-1}, one

obtains the average distribution of O_2 partial pressure illustrated in Fig. 21-4. *During passage through the capillary the O_2 partial pressure of the blood falls from 90 mm Hg (12.0 kPa) to ca. 28 mm Hg (3.7 kPa).* The changes in O_2 partial pressure in the capillary blood conform to the shape of the *effective O_2 dissociation curve* (pp. 495 f.). Perpendicular to this gradient along the capillary is a radial gradient, with an O_2 partial pressure difference of ca. 26 mm Hg (3.5 kPa) between the blood and the peripheral regions of the tissue cylinder. In those cells that are least well supplied with O_2, at the venous end of the cylinder, O_2 partial pressures between 1 and 2 mm Hg (133 and 266 Pa) are to be expected.

The calculated O_2 partial pressures – which are in close agreement with the results of direct measurements on animals under comparable conditions (Fig. 21-3) – indicate that the brain tissue is not at all as well supplied with oxygen as had been thought.

They explain why a decrease in cerebral blood flow very easily produces *O₂ deficiency* in the neurons of the most poorly supplied brain regions. The immediate consequence is an impairment of neuronal function, which in many cases results in partial or complete loss of consciousness.

Distribution of O_2 partial pressure in the myocardium. The cardiac muscle tissue differs from most organs in the **nonstationarity of its O_2 supply.** Both the *perfusion* and the *energy requirement* of the myocardium change in the course of a cardiac cycle. During systole the increased pressure in the tissue reduces the flow of blood through the region supplied by the left coronary artery; in the inner layers of the myocardium of the left ventricle blood flow can be completely interrupted for a short time (p.394). The resulting fluctuations in the *myocardial O_2 availability,* from a *minimum in systole* to a *maximum in diastole,* are accompanied by just the opposite changes in the energy requirements of the individual myocardial cells. These need the *most energy* during the *contraction* phase, and the *least* during the *resting* phase.

Two factors ensure that the myocardium obtains all the energy needed under normal conditions in spite of the restricted O_2 supply during systole. One is that the *myoglobin functions as a short-term O_2 store* (p. 511) which can sustain tissue respiration during this period, and the other is that the myocardium contains *energy reserves* (ATP, creatine phosphate) that can be called upon to meet the momentarily increased demand. During diastole the massive blood flow provides enough O_2 to resaturate the myoglobin completely with oxygen and to replenish the cellular energy stores [18].

The changes in O_2 supply during the course of systole and diastole result in *periodic changes in the O_2 partial pressure of the myocardial cells.* Calculations of the mean O_2 partial pressure in various regions of the left ventricular wall have shown that the O_2 partial pressure fluctuations are especially pronounced in the vicinity of the arterial end of the capillary (Figs. 21-5 and 21-6). In the tissue area supplied by the venous end the variation is smaller, because (i) the O_2 partial pressure changes in the capillary blood of this region are determined by the steep part of the O_2 dissociation curve of the blood (p. 496), and (ii) the myoglobin releases part of its bound oxygen during the contraction phase, especially when the heart is heavily loaded and its O_2 consumption is increased. During the following diastole the cellular O_2 partial pressure returns to the original level in all parts of the myocardium.

During exercise it is more difficult for an adequate supply of O_2 to the heart to be maintained. Its increased activity causes the

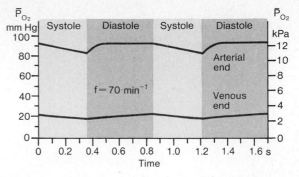

Fig. 21-5. Calculated mean O_2 partial pressures in the tissue supplied by the arterial and venous ends of a capillary in the inner layers of the left ventricular wall of a human under resting conditions. During systole the mean O_2 partial pressures decrease in all parts of the tissue cylinder because capillary perfusion is interrupted, and during diastole they return to their initial levels (after [19])

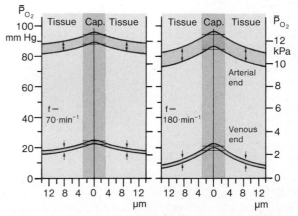

Fig. 21-6. O_2 partial pressure decrease at the arterial (upper pair of curves) and venous (lower pair) ends of the tissue region supplied by a capillary in the inner layers of the left ventricle of a human. Arrows indicate the range over which the mean O_2 partial pressure profile changes as a result of variations in blood flow during a cardiac cycle. The left diagram shows the O_2 partial pressure profiles in a cross section of the cylinder of tissue supplied by the capillary under resting conditions (heart rate 70 min⁻¹; O_2 consumption = 0.1 ml · g⁻¹ · min⁻¹), and the right diagram shows the corresponding profiles during exercise (heart rate 180 min⁻¹, O_2 consumption = 0.21 ml · g⁻¹ · min⁻¹). Because of the interruption of perfusion during systole the O_2 partial pressures in blood and tissue decrease during the contraction phase. In the periphery of the tissue cylinder at the venous end under these working conditions a mean O_2 partial pressure of 7 mm Hg (0.9 kPa) would be expected. The O_2 partial pressures in the parts of the myocardium least well supplied with oxygen are still lower (after [19])

myocardium to use up more oxygen; at the same time with rising heart rate diastole is considerably shortened, so that the degree to which the available oxygen can be matched to the demand is limited. The boundary conditions for very strenuous exercise are reached at heart rates of about 200 min⁻¹. As can be seen in Fig. 21-5, the fluctuation in O_2 partial pressure in the myocardial cells in the inner wall of the left ventricle is significantly more extensive during hard work, with a heart rate of 180 min^{-1}, than under normal conditions. In the parts of the myocardium least well supplied with oxygen, around the venous ends of the capillaries, the O_2 partial pressure would be expected to fall below 1 mm Hg (133 Pa) under these conditions. In fact, the ECG in many such cases exhibits the typical signs of inadequate O_2 supply to the myocardial tissue (depression of ST, flattening or reversal of T; cf. p.378).

21.3 Regulation of O_2 Supply and Effects of O_2 Deficiency

Mechanisms for Matching Supply to Demand

The increased *O_2 requirement* of an organ that is functioning more actively must be met by an increase in and more complete utilization of the amount of oxygen supplied to the tissue. As is evident in Eq. (2), in principle more O_2 can be provided to a tissue by increasing blood flow, the O_2 concentration in the arterial blood, or both. Under physiological conditions, however, the hemoglobin O_2 saturation in arterial blood is already ca. 97%, so that an increase in arterial O_2 concentration by brief hyperventilation is impracticable. Therefore adjustment of the *O_2 availability* in a tissue to a transiently raised O_2 demand must be brought about predominantly by *increased blood flow*.

Regulation of organ perfusion. The amount of blood flowing through an organ is determined primarily by the magnitude of the *cardiac output* and the level of *vascular tone in the vessels preceding the terminal vascular bed*. The neural and hormonal influences and the local chemical mechanisms that modulate organ perfusion are described in detail in Section 19.10. Here we shall consider only a few special aspects of the regulation of O_2 supply in the brain, the myocardium and the skeletal musculature.

In the **brain tissue** the O_2 supply is raised to meet an increased demand chiefly by lowering the tone of the vessel musculature; the factors that elicit this vasodilation are *lowered O_2 partial pressure (hypoxia)* and *elevated CO_2 partial pressure (hypercapnia)* in the intra- and extracellular space, as well as an *increased H^+ concentration* in the perivascular space. Moreover, a comparable change in the tone of the smooth musculature of the cerebral vessels is brought about by the moderate increase in extracellular K^+ concentration and by an increase in the tissue adenosine concentration. But because calcium ions play a central role in setting vascular tone, the reactions just described are attenuated or entirely eliminated if the Ca^{++} concentration in the perivascular space is sub-

normal. An increase in the extracellular Ca^{++} concentration directly elicits vasoconstriction, and a decrease elicits vasodilation [1, 3, 6, 8, 11, 26]. It remains unclear whether additional influences from the chemoreceptors in the arterial system can directly affect the muscular tone of the cerebral vessels.

Increased blood flow through the **myocardium** under an additional load is brought about chiefly by local chemical processes, which are induced especially after *lowering of the tissue O_2 partial pressure (hypoxia)*. The concentration of adenosine, which acts as a vasodilator, rises in the myocardial tissue during O_2 deficiency, and it may be that this is a crucial factor in increasing perfusion. Finally, a large number of *sympathetic β receptors* innervate the myocardium in the region of the coronary vessels, so that the increased perfusion under load can be explained in part by a greater activation of these receptors [1, 3, 8, 10].

The mechanisms underlying increased blood flow through the **skeletal musculature** are still largely unknown. Skeletal muscle is innervated by both *adrenergic sympathetic fibers* – the activity of which, as in many other organs, determines in particular the tone of the smooth musculature of the vessels – and *cholinergic sympathetic fibers* with a vasodilator action. The *activation of these cholinergic sympathetic fibers* is thought to cause the initial increase in perfusion when the muscles begin to work. These fibers have only a slight effect on the parts of the terminal vascular bed in which respiratory gases and other substances are exchanged. As the muscles continue to work, increased perfusion of the true (nutritive) capillaries is presumably maintained by a number of local chemical mechanisms that reduce the basal tone of the vessel musculature, which is not determined by direct neural influences. It is thought that the *rise in K^+ concentration* and in the *osmolarity* of the extracellular fluid play a central role, to which is added the effect of *hypoxia* in the muscle tissue. On the other hand, change in the partial pressure of CO_2 and in the H^+ concentration are only subordinate factors in increasing blood flow through working skeletal muscle [1, 3, 8, 20].

The consequences of prolonged or repeated increases in O_2 demand. When the heart must repeatedly perform extra work under conditions of increased O_2 demand in other organs, the myocardium undergoes *structural changes* and the *weight* of the heart increases. The physiological adaptation found, for example, in athletes trained for endurance sports can result in an increase in the mass of the heart from the normal ca. 200–300 g to a *maximum of ca. 500 g*, owing chiefly to growth of the individual myocardial fibers **(hypertrophy)**. The stimulus that triggers this growth is thought to be *short-term O_2 deficiency in the myocardial tissue*. Myocardial hypertrophy is limited chiefly by the accompanying deterioration of the O_2 supply to the muscle fibers. During growth of the myocardium above a critical heart weight of about 500 g, both the mass of muscle supplied by each capillary and the number of capillaries in the tissue increase, but the precapillary part of the vascular system remains largely unaltered; as a result, the individual myocardial fibers can no longer be adequately supplied with O_2. Whereas the mean radius of a myocardial fiber under normal conditions is ca. 8 μm, at the limiting weight it is ca. 13.5 μm.

Under **pathological conditions** the critical weight can be exceeded, and the resulting O_2 deficiency in many parts of the myocardium causes the destruction of some of the myocardial fibers and a breakdown of the normal structural relationships within the myocardium *(eccentric hypertrophy,* with dilation of the heart cavity).

In addition to the changes in the heart under these conditions, there may be an **elevated O_2 capacity of the blood.** Frequently repeated increases in the O_2 requirements of the organs produce effects similar to those of the lack of oxygen at great altitudes (cf. 25.8) and of disturbances of pulmonary gas exchange – that is, *enhanced erythropoiesis and hemoglobin synthesis.* These processes are triggered by an increase in the production of erythropoietin, primarily in the kidney, which accelerates the formation or maturation of *proerythroblasts.* As the number of erythrocytes increases **(erythrocytosis)** and the hemoglobin concentration rises the O_2 capacity of the blood becomes greater, so that although the partial pressure of oxygen in the arterial blood is unchanged its concentration is higher. However, the *viscosity* of the blood increases with the hematocrit, and the heart must work harder to propel the more viscous blood; thus the degree to which adaptation can be effected by erythropoiesis is severely limited.

The Causes of Inadequate O_2 Supply

Disturbances in either the exchange of respiratory gases in the lung or their transport in the blood can prevent the supply of O_2 from meeting the needs of the tissues – a condition called **tissue hypoxia** (P_{O_2} less than normal) or **tissue anoxia** ($P_{O_2} = 0$ mm Hg). Of the possible causes of inadequate O_2 supply, three predominate: 1. lowered O_2 partial pressure in the arterial blood *(arterial hypoxia),* 2. reduced O_2 capacity of the blood *(anemia),* and 3. restricted blood flow through the organs *(ischemia).*

Arterial hypoxia. When the ventilation-perfusion ratio in the lungs decreases *(alveolar hypoventilation;* cf. p. 475) there is a decrease in the O_2 partial pressure **(hypoxia)** and in the O_2 concentration **(hypoxemia)** of the arterial blood. Because of the simultaneous increase in arterial CO_2 partial pressure **(hypercapnia),** *respiratory acidosis* develops as well. Comparable reductions in arterial O_2 partial pressure and O_2 concentration are observed in people at high altitudes, but here they are accompanied by a reduction of the

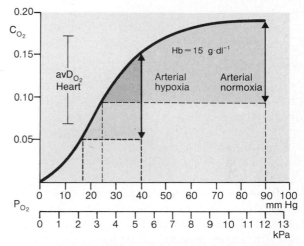

Fig. 21-7. Influence of arterial hypoxia ($P_{O_2} = 40$ mm Hg = 5.3 kPa) on the drop in O_2 partial pressure in the blood during passage through a capillary, for the conditions prevailing in the myocardium when the body is at rest. When the arterial O_2 partial pressure is severely decreased, the changes in O_2 partial pressure in the capillary blood are determined chiefly by the steep part of the O_2 dissociation curve. As a consequence the drop in partial pressure is less than that in normoxia, which can partially compensate for the unfavorable initial conditions for O_2 supply to the tissues (ordinate: O_2 concentration C_{O_2}, ml O_2 per ml blood; abscissa: O_2 partial pressure P_{O_2})

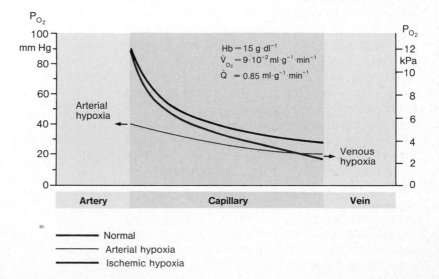

Fig. 21-8. Mean O_2 partial pressure drop in the capillaries of the human cerebral cortex under normal conditions, in ischemic hypoxia (blood flow reduced by 1/3) and in severe arterial hypoxia

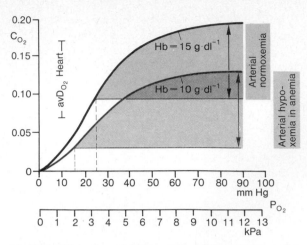

Fig. 21-9. Effect of anemia (Hb = 10 g · dl⁻¹) on the O_2 partial-pressure changes in the capillary blood, under the conditions in the myocardium when the body is at rest (ordinate: O_2 concentration C_{O_2}, ml O_2 per ml blood; abscissa: O_2 partial pressure P_{O_2})

CO_2 partial pressure in the arterial blood **(hypocapnia)** and *respiratory alkalosis* (cf. p. 504).

In severe arterial hypoxia the O_2 supply to the tissues is restricted and only moderate physical exertion is possible. Under these conditions, especially in organs with a high O_2 requirement, the O_2 partial pressure in the capillary blood can fall to very low levels (Fig. 21-7 and 21-8), so that **venous hypoxia** ensues. As can be seen in Fig. 21-7, the changes in O_2 partial pressure accompanying gas exchange in capillary blood within the organs are determined by the steepest part of the effective O_2 dissociation curve in conditions of marked arterial hypoxia. In this part of the curve a given change in O_2 concentration is associated with a smaller change in O_2 partial pressure than in the right-hand part. Therefore, although the arteriovenous O_2 concentration difference is the same as normal, the O_2 partial pressure profile in the capillaries is very flat; this effect partially compensates for the otherwise unfavorable conditions of O_2 supply to the tissues. These relationships are illustrated for the cerebral cortex in Fig. 21-8, under the assumption of an arterial O_2 partial pressure of 40 mm Hg (5.3 kPa). As soon as the O_2 partial pressure gradient between the blood and the tissue no longer suffices to enable an adequate release of oxygen, the O_2 partial pressure in the cells supplied by the venous end of the capillary falls below the critical level for the mitochondria, and energy metabolism is restricted.

Anemic hypoxia. Whenever the O_2 capacity of the blood is diminished as a result of *blood loss* or *inadequate hemoglobin synthesis* **(anemia)** or owing to *methemoglobin formation* or *CO poisoning* **(functional**

anemia), the O_2 concentration in the arterial blood falls. Fig. 21-9 illustrates this situation, with myocardial tissue as an example. Under these conditions, if the amount of O_2 extracted by the tissues is unchanged the O_2 concentration in the blood becomes very low during passage through the capillary. At the venous end, in particular, levels can be reached at which it is impossible for enough O_2 to diffuse to the sites where it is needed **(venous hypoxia).**

Ischemic hypoxia. When *organ perfusion is restricted,* more than the normal amount of O_2 is extracted from the blood as it flows through the capillaries, so that there is a *greater arteriovenous difference in O_2 concentration.* The direct consequence is a more pronounced drop in O_2 partial pressure along the capillary; because the gradient in O_2 partial pressure between blood and tissue is lowered at the same time, the supply of O_2 to the cells may become inadequate (Fig. 21-8).

O_2 Therapy; O_2 Poisoning

The O_2 deficiency conditions just described can in many cases be improved by oxygen therapy, directed toward raising the partial pressure of oxygen in the arterial blood by *increasing the O_2 partial pressure in the inspired air.* The patient breathes a gas mixture with a high proportion of O_2 or pure oxygen **(isobaric O_2 therapy)** or is treated in a pressure chamber at above-atmospheric pressures **(hyperbaric O_2 therapy).** O_2 therapy is of limited value in ischemic and anemic hypoxia, for under these conditions the arterial O_2 concentration can be raised only slightly by increasing the amount of O_2 in physical solution.

O_2 therapy can be used only on a short-term basis, because prolonged exposure to gas mixtures with high O_2 content results in **O_2 poisoning.** Treatment with pure O_2, for example, must be limited to about 4 hours under normal pressure conditions. The marked elevation of the O_2 partial pressure in the cells *(hyperoxia)* affects the activity of many enzymes involved in tissue metabolism. For example, the oxidation of glucose, fructose and pyruvic acid is inhibited in hyperoxia. Typical signs of O_2 poisoning are *dizziness* and *convulsions. Cardiac output decreases* owing to increased vagal tone, and *blood flow through brain and kidneys* is restricted. In the lungs tissue damage is incurred, which can give rise to diffusion impairment and the accumulation of fluid in the interstitial space and in the alveoli *(pulmonary edema)* and to a decrease of surfactant. Newborn infants treated for hours or days with pure oxygen have been found to develop *retinal damage* (retrolental fibroplasia) that impairs vision or causes complete *blindness.*

To prevent O_2 poisoning when prolonged isobaric O_2 therapy of an adult is required, gas mixtures with an O_2 concentration below 0.6 and an O_2 partial pressure less than 450 mm Hg (< 60 kPa) are used. When newborn and young infants are to be treated, the O_2 concentration in the gas mixture may be no greater than 0.4, and its partial pressure no greater than 300 mm Hg (40 kPa).

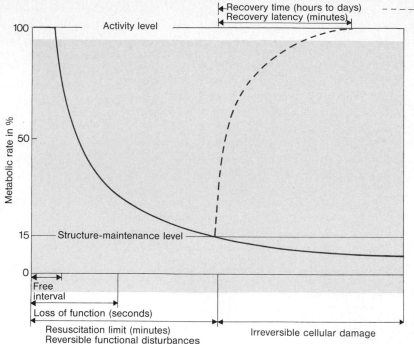

Fig. 21-10. Changes in tissue metabolism after acute ischemic anoxia, diagrammatic. *Below graph:* characteristic time intervals following anoxia within which reversible and irreversible disturbances occur. Dashed curve: return to normal metabolism when normoxia is restored in time. *Above graph:* characteristic time intervals for recovery

Reversible and Irreversible Disturbance in Acute Tissue Anoxia

In all cases of acute tissue anoxia, whether produced by the sudden interruption of the O_2 supply owing to vascular obstruction or by severe arterial hypoxia, a brief *latent period* in which cell function is unimpaired is followed by curtailment of cellular metabolism and thus of cell function [5]. As the energy stores are consumed it eventually becomes impossible for the cells to function even at a reduced level, and complete *loss of function* ensues. As can be seen in Fig. 21-10, cell structure can be maintained for minutes to hours, depending on the amount of energy required, by utilization of the energy reserves, so that the disturbances *initially are reversible* and successful resuscitation is possible. *Irreversible* cellular damage and eventually *cell death* occur when energy metabolism no longer suffices to keep the cell structure intact. In highly differentiated cells such as neurons irreparable damage occurs after about 10 min of maintained anoxia at normal body temperature. In skeletal muscle under comparable conditions and with the normal energy stores in the individual cells, irreversible damage can be detected only after anoxia has lasted for several hours.

Loss of function and resuscitation. The time from onset of tissue anoxia to complete loss of organ function – the *functional limit* – is shorter than the *resuscitation*

limit. That is, there is a period of time following loss of function due to tissue anoxia during which *complete resuscitation of the whole organ remains possible*.

The functional and resuscitation limiting times are particularly short in the brain. Complete interruption of blood flow through the brain causes distinct impairment of function after a latency of only ca. 4 s, and total loss of function, with unconsciousness, after 8–12 s (the *survival time for organ function*). The first changes in the EEG appear after ca. 4–6 s, and after 20–30 s the spontaneous electrical activity of the brain tissue vanishes (flat EEG; cf. p. 152).

Successful resuscitation of the brain after sudden tissue anoxia at 37° C is possible up to about the 8th to 10th minute *(resuscitation limit of the brain)*. When anoxia is very brief organ function returns after a latency of 1 minute (the **recovery latency**). After ischemia has lasted ca. 4 min, the recovery latency is ca. 10 min. Complete recovery of organ function, however, often requires hours or days **(recovery time)**. Even after brain ischemia only 1 min in duration, the recovery time is 15 min. For the *kidney* and *liver*, resuscitation limits of 3–4 h and recovery times of several days have been found. The *heart* can still be resuscitated after hours at rest, but the active heart becomes incapable of resuming its normal circulatory function after only a 3-to-4-min interruption of coronary blood flow. For this reason, an acute interruption of circulation following cardiac arrest can often cause irreversible brain damage and death of the patient within a few minutes even though the heart has been successfully revived, for in the subsequent 4–5 min the damaged heart cannot develop the average arterial pressure necessary for normal perfusion of the brain. The **resuscitation limit of the whole organism** is therefore only about 4 min – considerably shorter than the resuscitation limits of any of the vital organs.

21.4   References

Textbooks and Handbooks

1. BAUEREISEN, E.: Physiologie des Kreislaufs, Bd. 1. Berlin–Heidelberg–New York: Springer 1971
2. JÖBSIS, F. F.: Basic processes in cellular respiration. In: Handbook of Physiology. Sect. 3: Respiration, Vol. I, p. 63. Washington D. C.: American Physiological Society 1964
3. JOHNSON, P. C.: Peripheral Circulation. New York–Chichester–Brisbane–Toronto: Wiley and Sons 1978
4. LEHNINGER, A. L.: Bioenergetics. The Molecular Basis of Biological Energy Transformations. New York–Amsterdam: Benjamin 1965
5. LUFT, U. C.: Aviative physiology – the effects of altitude. In: Handbook of Physiology, Sect. 3: Respiration, Vol. II. p. 1099, Washington D. C.: American Physiological Society 1965
6. PURVES, M. J.: The Physiology of the Cerebral Circulation. Cambridge: University Press 1972
7. ROUGHTON, F. J. W.: Transport of oxygen and carbon dioxide. In: Handbook of Physiology. Sect. 3: Respiration, Vol. I, p. 767. Washington D. C.: American Physiological Society 1964
8. RUCH, T. C., PATTON, H. D.: Physiology and Biophysics, Vol. II: Circulation, Respiration and Fluid Balance. Philadelphia–London–Toronto: Saunders 1974
9. SURGENOR, D. Mac N.: The Red Blood Cell, Vol. I and II, 2nd ed., New York–London: Academic Press 1974

Research Reports and Reviews

10. BASSENGE, E.: Direct autonomic control of the coronary system. Pflügers Arch. *373*, R6 (1978)
11. BETZ, E.: Cerebral blood flow: its measurement and regulation. Physiol. Rev., *52*, 595 (1972)
12. BRETSCHNEIDER, H. J.: Sauerstoffbedarf und -versorgung des Herzmuskels. Verh. dtsch. Ges. Kreisl.-Forsch. *27*, 32 (1961)
13. BRETSCHNEIDER, H. J.: Die hämodynamischen Determinanten des myokardialen Sauerstoffverbrauchs. In: Die therapeutische Anwendung β-sympathikolytischer Stoffe (DENGLER, H. J., Ed.), p. 45. Stuttgart, New York: Schattauer 1972
14. BURTON, R., KREBS, H. A.: The free-energy changes associated with the individual steps of the tricarboxylic acid cycle, glycolysis and alcohol fermentation and with hydrolysis of the pyrophosphate groups of adenosintriphosphate. Biochem. J. *54*, 94 (1953)
15. CHANCE, B., SCHOENER, B., SCHINDLER, F.: The intracellular oxida-

tion-reduction state. In: Oxygen in the Animal Organism (DICKENS, F., NEIL, E., Eds.), p. 367. Oxford: Pergamon Press 1964
16. DEETJEN, P.: Normal and critical oxygen supply of the kidney. In: Oxygen Transport in Blood and Tissue (LÜBBERS, D. W., LUFT, C., THEWS, G., WITZLEB, E., Eds.), p. 212. Stuttgart: Thieme 1968
17. GREENWAY, C. V., STARK, R. D.: Hepatic vascular bed. Physiol. Rev. *51*, 23 (1971)
18. GROTE, J., THEWS, G.: Die Bedingungen für die Sauerstoffversorgung des Herzmuskelgewebes. Pflügers Arch. *276*, 142 (1962)
19. GROTE, J., THEWS, G.: Respiratory gas transport in heart. In: Oxygen Transport to Tissue, Instrumentation, Methods, and Physiology (BICHER, H. I., BRULEY, D. F., Eds.), p. 525. New York: Plenum Press 1973
20. HUDLICKA, O.: Muscle Blood Flow, Its Relation to Muscle Metabolism and Function. Amsterdam: Sweets and Zeitlinger B. V. 1973
21. GREENBAUM, R., NUNN, J. F., PRYS-ROBERTS, C., KELMAN, G. R.: Metabolic changes in whole human blood (in vitro) at 37° C. Respir. Physiol. *2*, 274–282 (1967)
22. KRAMER, K., THURAU, K., DEETJEN, P.: Hämodynamik des Nierenmarks, 1. Mitteilung: Kapilläre Passagezeit, Blutvolumen, Durchblutung, Gewebshämatokrit und O_2-Verbrauch des Nierenmarks in situ. Pflügers Arch. ges. Physiol. *270*, 251 (1960)
23. KREUZER, F.: Facilitated diffusion of oxygen and its possible significance: a review. Respir. Physiol. *9*, 1 (1970)
24. KROGH, A.: The number and distribution of capillaries in muscles with calculations of the oxygen pressure head necessary for supplying the tissue. J. Physiol. (Lond.) *52*, 409 (1918/19)
25. KUNZE, K.: Das Sauerstoffdruckfeld im normalen und pathologisch veränderten Muskel. In: Schriftenreihe Neurologie, Bd. 3. Berlin–Heidelberg–New York: Springer 1969
26. KUSCHINSKY, W., WAHL, M.: Local chemical and neurogenic regulation of cerebral vascular resistance. Physiol. Rev. *58*, 656 (1973)
27. LASSEN, N. A.: Cerebral blood flow and oxygen consumption in man. Physiol. Rev. *39*, 183 (1959)
28. LÜBBERS, D. W.: Local tissue PO_2: its measurement and meaning. In: Oxygen Supply, Theoretical and Practical Aspects of Oxygen Supply and Microcirculation of Tissue (KESSLER, M., BRULEY, D. F., CLARK, L. C., LÜBBERS, D. W., SILVER, I. A., STRAUSS, J., Eds.), p. 151, München–Berlin–Wien: Urban u. Schwarzenburg 1973
29. LUTZ, J., HENNICH, H., BAUEREISEN, E.: Oxygen supply and uptake in the liver and the intestine. Pflügers Arch. *360*, 7 (1975)
30. REIVICH, M., SOKOLOFF, L., KENNEDY, E., DES ROSIERS, M.: An autoradiographic method for the measurement of local glucose metabolism in the brain. In: Brain Work (INGVAR, D. H., LASSEN, N. A., Eds.), p. 377, Kopenhagen: Munksgaard 1975
31. SAKURADO, O., KENNEDY, C., JEHLE, J., BROWN, J. D., CARBIN, G., SOKOLOFF, L.: Measurement of local cerebral blood flow with iodo ^{14}C antipyrine. Am. J. Physiol. *234*, H 59 (1978)
32. STARLINGER, H., LÜBBERS, D. W.: Polarographic measurements of the oxygen pressure performed simultaneously with optical measurements of the redox state of the respiratory chain in suspensions of mitochondria under steady-state conditions at low oxygen tension. Pflügers Arch. *341*, 15 (1973)
33. STRAUER, B. E.: Dynamik, Koronardurchblutung und Sauerstoffverbrauch des normalen und kranken Herzens. Experimentell-pharmakologische Untersuchungen und Katheteruntersuchungen am Patienten. Basel, München, Paris, London, New York, Sydney: S. Karger 1975
34. THEWS, G.: Der Transport der Atemgase. Klin. Wschr. *41*, 120 (1963)
35. VAUPEL, P., WENDLING, P., THOME, H., FISCHER, J.: Atemgaswechsel und Glucoseaufnahme der menschlichen Milz in situ. Klin. Wschr. *55*, 329 (1977)

Part IV

Metabolism, Digestion and Excretion Endocrine Regulation

22 Energy Balance

H.-V. ULMER

22.1 Energy Expenditure

Energy expenditure is characteristic of every living cell; energy-rich nutrients are taken in and chemically converted, and ultimately metabolic end products with a lower energy content are eliminated from the cell (cf. pp. 508 f.). The energy made available by this process is consumed in various ways. It is used, for example, to keep the cell's *structure* (and thus its *functional capacity*) intact, and to fuel *specific cellular activities* (such as the contraction of muscle cells).

The term **anabolism** denotes the metabolic processes by which specific bodily materials are synthesized from the ingested foodstuffs; **catabolism** denotes those by which bodily materials or ingested foodstuffs are broken down, in the course of intermediary metabolism. The metabolism of fats and carbohydrates serves chiefly to sustain physiological functions **(functional metabolism),** whereas that of proteins primarily maintains and modifies the body's structure **(structural metabolism).**

Energy units. Energy metabolism has traditionally been expressed in kilocalories (kcal) per unit time. The International System of Units, however, establishes the joule (J) as the basic unit of energy: 1 joule = 1 watt · second = $2.39 \cdot 10^{-4}$ kcal, 1 kcal = 4.19 kJ (cf. p. 689).

Efficiency. If all cell does external work, the associated energy conversion necessarily produces *heat* (Second Law of Thermodynamics). The efficiency (η) of the active cell, like that of a machine, is the fraction of the energy converted that appears as work, and is always less than 100%:

$$\eta\,(\%) = \frac{\text{external work}}{\text{converted energy}} \cdot 100$$

The efficiency of an isolated muscle is at best 35%; that of the *whole organism during muscular work* rarely exceeds *25%*.

Total energy conversion. The rate of energy conversion by the body as a whole depends on the amounts of energy released (external work, heat) and stored (foodstuff depots, structural modifications) per unit time. That is, the total amount of energy converted is the *sum of external work, lost heat* and *stored energy*.

22.2 Parameters of Metabolism

Metabolic Parameters of Cells

In view of the varied functions of metabolism in a living cell, it is useful to distinguish 3 fundamental *levels of metabolic activity* (Fig. 22-1):

The **active level** is the metabolic rate of an *active cell,* which varies according to the degree of activity at any time. The **readiness level** is the rate at which a momentarily inactive cell must metabolize in order to maintain its *capacity for immediate, unrestricted function.* This category includes, for example, the processes that maintain particular concentration differences of Na^+ and K^+ ions. The **maintenance level** is the minimal energy conversion rate that suffices to *preserve cell structure.* If this absolute requirement is not met, the cell suffers irreversible damage and dies.

It is important to keep this subdivision in mind when evaluating the *effects of disturbed energy metabolism* on a single cell or an isolated organ. Metabolism can be disturbed in a number of ways – for example, by a

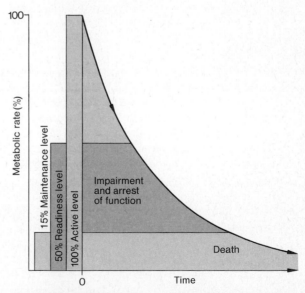

Fig. 22-1. Diagram illustrating active level, readiness level and maintenance level as components of a cell's metabolism, with an approximate indication (in %) of the contribution of each. Modified from [10]

reduction in the oxygen supply or rate of blood flow, and by poisoning.

Fig. 22-1 shows schematically the contribution of each of the three categories to overall cellular metabolism. Here the 100% value represents the active level of metabolic rate of a brain cell.

The **whole organism** is differently affected by metabolic level than an isolated organ. For example, if the metabolism of the respiratory musculature or the myocardium falls to the readiness level, the organs become inactive. As a result, all the cells die, for the organism as a whole cannot survive unless the breathing muscles and heart are in operation.

Interruption of energy supply does not lead to immediate deterioration of cell activity, because certain energy reserves are available (p. 550). However, the time for which cells can sustain full function depends very much on the organ concerned. If the *brain* is affected, complete ischemia (pp. 152 and 519) results in *unconsciousness* after ca. 10 s and in *irreversible damage* after 3–8 minutes; with ischemia of resting skeletal *muscle,* however, metabolism does not fall below the maintenance level until 1–2 hours have elapsed.

Metabolic Parameters of the Whole Organism

Metabolic rate at rest. The metabolic rate of a resting organism cannot be equal to the sum of the readiness levels of all its cells, because some of the organs (for example, the brain, heart, respiratory musculature, liver and kidneys) are *always active.*

The metabolic rate of the body at mental and physical rest is not a precisely defined quantity, for various factors can affect it. To facilitate comparison, conditions have been established under which a basal metabolic rate can be measured.

Basal metabolic rate (BMR). The following four conditions are usually specified for measurement of basal metabolic rate: 1. it is done in the morning, 2. the subject is at rest (lying down), 3. the subject is fasting, and 4. the ambient temperature is neutral.

This *morning resting-fasting metabolic rate under thermoneutral conditions* was once an important clinical tool for the diagnosis of thyroid abnormalities (pp. 673 f.). Now other ways of testing thyroid function are available. Thyroid function may be evaluated, for example, by examination with radioactively labelled iodine or measurement of the thyroid hormone in the blood. Therefore the standard metabolic rate is now relatively rarely used for diagnosis.

The four standard conditions of the BMR measurement reveal the following *factors that can affect human metabolic rate:*

1. Even if the other standard conditions are maintained, metabolic rate is subject to **diurnal fluctuations,** with an increase in the morning and a decline during the night.
2. During *physical* and *mental* **work** the metabolic rate rises, for there is an increase in the number of cells metabolizing at rates above the readiness level. In both cases the main organ affecting metabolic rate is the musculature (cf. the section on metabolic rate during work and Fig. 22-2).
3. The **consumption of nutriments** and the subsequent processes of digestion raise the metabolic rate, particularly after protein has been eaten. This is called the *specific dynamic action* of foodstuffs (p. 573). The increase in metabolic rate after eating can last for 12 hours, or for as long as 18 hours after the consumption of large amounts of *protein.*
4. If the **ambient temperature** deviates from the *neutral range* (thermoneutral zone; cf. p. 533), the metabolic rate increases; downward shifts in temperature effect greater increases than do upward shifts.

The liver and the resting skeletal musculature account for half of the basal metabolic rate (Table 22-1). Because muscle tone decreases during sleep, the metabolic rate of a sleeping or anesthetized person can fall below the basal rate. During starvation, the metabolic rate can be below standard because of a decrease in the metabolism of the liver.

Norms for BMR. Even with strict adherence to the standard conditions, healthy subjects can vary in metabolic rate. Four factors can account for this variation: *age, sex, height, and body weight* (Fig. 22-3).

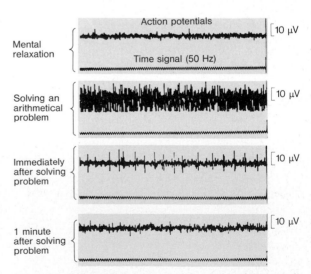

Fig. 22-2. Reflex increase in muscle tone during mental work, as reflected in the muscle action potentials (EMG) recorded from the forearm. Modified from [13]

Table 22-1. The contribution of different organ systems to the basal metabolic rate of a human. From [15]

Organ:	Liver	Muscle	Brain	Heart	Kidneys	Other
Relative contrib.	26%	26%	18%	9%	7%	14%

These variables are taken into account in the **tables of norms** that have been derived from large samples of the population by authors such as BOOTHBY and Du-BOIS, FLEISCH, HARRIS and BENEDICT (see reviews in [1] and [5]) and KESTNER and KNIPPING [8].

Small differences in the norms listed in different tables are based in part on the fact that they were obtained from different populations (North Americans, Swiss, Germans). Averages and "normal" values (p. 563) always depend on the group of subjects tested. As a rule, however, 4.2 kJ/kg·h *(1 kcal/kg·h)* can be taken as a rough estimate of the standard metabolic rate of an adult; for a person weighing 70 kg this would amount to about 7100 kJ/day (1700 kcal/day).

Metabolic rate during work. During *physical* work metabolic rate rises, by an amount dependent on the amount of exertion required. The **"leisure rate"** – the metabolic rate of a very slightly active person – is about **9600 kJ/day** *(2300 kcal/day)* for males. This corresponds to the daily *overall metabolism of a large fraction of the population,* "desk workers" who do not exert themselves physically to any appreciable extent.

The excess energy expenditure above this level formerly was called the **work rate** in the strict sense. The strenuousness of physical work can be estimated by the energy expended; it is convenient to express the degree of occupational work in steps of 2000 kJ (500 kcal). That is, during *light* work the metabolic rate rises by an *excess* of 1 × 2000 kJ per day, during

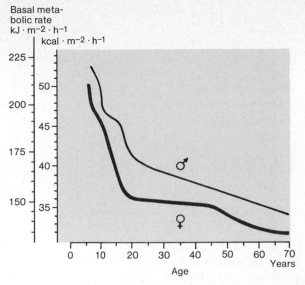

Fig. 22-3. Dependence of the relative BMR on age and sex. The surface area of the body (m²) is a function of height and weight (p. 585). After [11]

moderate work by 2 × 2000 kJ/day, during *moderately heavy* work by 3 × 2000 kJ/day, during *heavy* work by 4 × 2000 kJ/day, and during *extremely heavy* work by 5 × 2000 kJ/day. The *heaviest occupational physical labor* thus requires, on the average, a total metabolic rate as great as **20,000 kJ/day** (20 MJ/day ≈ 4800 kcal/day), which corresponds roughly to *three times the basal metabolic rate.* Because of their lower average body weight and muscle mass, the limit for maximal metabolic rate of *women* is lower, **15,500 kJ/day** (15.5 MJ/day ≈ 3700 kcal/day) (Table 22-2). Each of these values represents a limit that should not be exceeded in the performance of jobs over periods of years.

During *mental work* the metabolic rate also increases, although the brain contributes hardly anything to this

Table 22-2. Metabolic rates under a number of typical conditions (rounded values, in kJ and kcal) and the associated rates of oxygen uptake (cf. indirect measurement of metabolic rate). BMR = Basal metabolic rate

		Metabolic rate		O₂ uptake	
BMR of a person weighing 70 kg	♀ :	6,300 kJ/day	1,500 kcal/day	215	ml/min
	♂ :	7,100 kJ/day	1,700 kcal/day	245	ml/min
BMR plus leisure metabolism	♀ :	8,400 kJ/day	2,000 kcal/day	290	ml/min
	♂ :	9,600 kJ/day	2,300 kcal/day	330	ml/min
Overall metabolic rate of a person doing extremely hard work (maximum permissible for periods of years)	♀ :	15,500 kJ/day	3,700 kcal/day	535	ml/min
	♂ :	20,100 kJ/day	4,800 kcal/day	690	ml/min
BMR per kg body weight		4.2 kJ/hour	1 kcal/hour	3.5 ml/min	
Overall metabolic rate for endurance sports (above-average performance)		4,200 kJ/hour	1,000 kcal/hour	3,500	ml/min

increase. As far as the brain is concerned, concentration on a particular subject amounts simply to shifting the activity from one region to another; even during *sleep* there are no appreciable changes in the metabolic rate of brain tissue. The reason for the increased metabolism during mental work is a reflexly produced *increase in muscle tone* (Fig. 22-2).

22.3   Measurement Techniques

The methods by which metabolic rate is measured can be classified in several ways. Some procedures measure heat loss *directly* and others determine heat production *indirectly,* the devices used may be *open* or *closed* systems which may or may not be *portable,* and they can provide either *continuous* or *discontinuous* monitoring of metabolic rate.

Direct Measurement of Metabolic Rate

This method is based on the direct determination of the *heat loss* of the organism ("direct calorimetry"). As early as 1780, LAVOISIER developed a means of measuring the heat released by living organisms. His "calorimeter" (Fig. 22-4) monitored the amount of heat released directly and continuously, though not under standard conditions. The apparatus required to measure human heat loss directly is massive and elaborate, and therefore it is used only for studying

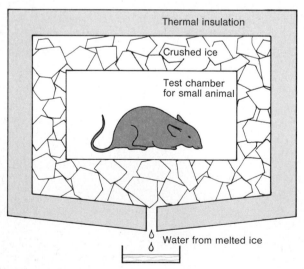

Fig. 22-4. Basic experiment to determine the metabolic rate of a small mammal, designed by LAVOISIER [9]. The water flowing out of the jacket as the ice melts is a direct measure of the heat released by the animal

special problems. Direct measurements of metabolic rate have been particularly useful in one respect: comparison of these results with the foodstuff balance of the organism has provided proof that the *law of conservation of energy holds for living organisms.* Moreover, the results of direct calorimeter experiments can be used to check the validity of indirect procedures.

Indirect Measurement of Metabolic Rate

The indirect measurement of metabolic rate is based on observation of the **amount of oxygen** taken up by the organism. Because oxygen is consumed in every biological oxidation, its rate of consumption reflects the metabolic rate. Attempts have also been made to use the *expired CO_2 volume* as a measure of the amount of heat produced. But because the CO_2-storage capacity of the body is so large, one cannot be sure that the amount of expired CO_2 corresponds closely enough to the amount of CO_2 produced in the same time. The *O_2-storage capacity of the body is small,* so that the amount of oxygen uptake by the lungs is a good measure of the amount consumed by the tissues.

Elements of computation. When the rate of energy expenditure is to be derived from data on oxygen uptake, the following considerations apply. The energy yield by **glucose oxidation** is described by the formula

$$C_6H_{12}O_6 + 6O_2 \rightarrow 6CO_2 + 6H_2O + 2826 \, kJ \qquad (1)$$

The 2826 kJ (675 kcal) in this reaction is the total energy *(enthalpy)* released per mol of glucose; of this amount only part (the *free enthalpy*) can be utilized for cellular function.
Fuel value. Energy yield is frequently expressed with respect to the mass or volume of substrate; 1 mol of glucose has a mass of 180 g, and 6 mol of oxygen have a volume of 6×22.4 liters $= 134.4$ liters. It follows that the complete oxidation of 1 g of glucose yields $2826/180 = 15.7$ kJ. The **fuel value** of glucose is thus 15.7 kJ/g, or 3.75 kcal/g (p. 573).

The *energy equivalent* ("caloric equivalent") expresses the yield of energy with respect to the oxygen consumed, and in the above reaction amounts to 2826 kJ/134.4 liters $= 21.0$ kJ per liter (5.02 kcal/l) O_2. Because the mixture of carbohydrates naturally occurring in food has a somewhat higher energetic value than glucose, the energy equivalent for carbohydrate oxidation is 21.1 kJ per liter O_2 (Table 22-3).
The *Respiratory Quotient* (or Respiratory Exchange

Table 22-3. Respiratory quotients (RQ) and energy equivalents for the oxidation of various foodstuffs

	RQ	kJ/1 O_2	kcal/1 O_2
Carbohydrates	1.00	21.1	5.05
Fats	0.70	19.6	4.69
Proteins	0.81	18.8	4.48

Ratio) is an indicator of the type of foodstuff metabolized; it is defined as

$$RQ = \frac{\dot{V}_{CO_2}}{\dot{V}_{O_2}} = \frac{CO_2 \text{ production}}{O_2 \text{ consumption}}.$$

In the oxidation of glucose just as much carbon dioxide is given off as oxygen is consumed, so that RQ = 1. *An RQ of 1* is thus an *identifying characteristic of* **carbohydrate oxidation.**

Sample calculation: Under resting conditions the oxygen uptake was found to be 280 ml/min (standard volume, STPD; p. 528) and the unusual value 1.00 was found for RQ. The metabolic rate in this situation is thus $0.280 \cdot 21.1 = 5.91$ kJ/min ($\approx$ 1.413 kcal/min) = 8.510 kJ/day ($\approx$ 2034 kcal/day).

Similar relationships apply in the **oxidation of fats.** Because fatty acids contain less oxygen per atom of carbon than do carbohydrates, their oxidation leads to a distinctly lower RQ (0.7). When pure **food protein** is oxidized an RQ of 0.81 is obtained (Table 22-3).

End products of catabolism. These include, among other things, water (ca. 350 ml per day), carbon dioxide (ca. 230 ml per min), carbon monoxide (ca. 0.007 ml per min), urea (ca. 30 g per day) and other nitrogen-containing substances (ca. 6 g per day), and other molecules that are excreted in the urine.

Urea is the typical end product of *protein breakdown;* thus the amount of urea and other nitrogenous substances excreted can be used to determine the rate of protein catabolism. Because the proteins of a mixed diet have an average nitrogen content of 16%, the amount of nitrogen found in the urine must be multiplied by 6.25 to obtain the amount of protein involved in catabolism.

Protein metabolism, which serves chiefly for structural maintenance and growth, is nearly *constant;* protein accounts for about 15% of the total energy in the common Central European diet. The proportions of fat and carbohydrate, by contrast, fluctuate widely, so that differences in RQ are basically due to these foodstuffs. For this reason the *RQ can be used to compute* the portion of the metabolism represented by *fat and carbohydrate break down* and to derive the amount of energy converted when 1 liter of oxygen is consumed (Table 22-4). A change in RQ of 0.1 unit corresponds to a change in the *energy equivalent* of 0.5 kJ

(0.12 kcal) per liter O_2. Table 22-4 can thus be used to obtain indirectly an accurate estimate of metabolic rate.

Sample calculation: Oxygen uptake, as in the preceding example, was 280 ml/min, but the RQ was 0.82 (the average value, with energy equivalent 20.2 kJ/1 O_2). In this case the metabolic rate is $0.280 \cdot 20.2 = 5.66$ kJ/min = 8 150 kJ/day ($\doteq$ 1948 kcal/day). The difference between this result and that in the previous example is 360 kJ/day, or 4%.

Table 22-4. Dependence of the energy equivalent on RQ, neglecting the contribution of protein (15%) to the overall metabolism. The average respiratory quotient is 0.82

RQ	kJ/1 O_2	kcal/1 O_2
1.0	21.1	5.05
0.9	20.6	4.93
0.82	**20.2**	**4.83**
0.8	20.1	4.81
0.7	19.6	4.69

Factors affecting the RQ. The ratio of carbon-dioxide production to oxygen consumption depends on the following three factors:

1. *The kind of foodstuff metabolized.* As has been mentioned, the RQ for the oxidation of carbohydrate is 1.0, for fats 0.7 and for proteins 0.81 (Table 22-3).

2. *Hyperventilation* (p. 475). The extra CO_2 blown off during hyperventilation comes from the large CO_2 stores in tissue and blood, and not from metabolism. Hpyerventilation does not alter oxygen uptake, because the blood and tissues cannot store additional oxygen. In the *transition phase* preceding the establishment of a new, lower CO_2 partial pressure in blood and tissue, the RQ is *distinctly increased,* in some cases to as much as 1.4. Some of the *causes* of hyperventilation are voluntary activity (e.g., blowing up an air mattress), nonrespiratory acidosis (p. 504, RQ up to 1.4), psychological stress (e.g., states of extreme excitation) and artificial respiration with a minute volume above the requirement.

3. *Interconversion of foodstuffs.* When carbohydrates predominate in the diet they are converted to fats. Because fats contain less oxygen than do carbohydrates, a corresponding amount of oxygen is released. Thus with overfeeding of carbohydrates the amount of oxygen uptake through the lungs falls and the *RQ becomes larger.* In extreme cases of *force-feeding,* an RQ of 1.38 has been measured in geese and 1.58 in pigs. During periods of *fasting* and in *diabetics* the RQ can be *lowered* to 0.6. The latter change results from the increased conversion rate of fats and protein that accompanies diminished glucose metabolism (consumption of glycogen reserves or impaired utilization).

When obtaining an indirect estimate of metabolic rate, if one is not certain whether a measured **"respiratory RQ"** corresponds to the catabolic conditions (**"metabolic RQ"**) an average energy equivalent of 20.2 kJ/1 O_2 (4.83 kcal/1 O_2) should be assumed, corresponding to a metabolic RQ of 0.82. As Table 22-4 shows, the energy equivalent does not vary over a particularly wide range as a function of RQ, so that the error introduced by using the mean energy equivalent is at most ± 4%.

Measurement of the Metabolic Rate of Single Organs

The oxygen consumption (and thus the metabolic rate) of single organs can be found by Fick's principle (p.453), from the rate of perfusion of the organ $\dot{Q}$ and the arteriovenous concentration differences of O_2 and CO_2 (in ml/dl):

$$\dot{V}_{O_2}(\text{ml/min}) = \dot{Q}(\text{ml/min}) \cdot (C_{a_{O_2}} - C_{v_{O_2}})/100, \quad (2)$$

$$\dot{V}_{CO_2}(\text{ml/min}) = \dot{Q}(\text{ml/min}) \cdot (C_{v_{CO_2}} - C_{a_{CO_2}})/100. \quad (3)$$

The brain utilizes mainly carbohydrates, so that its RQ is in a range close to 1.0; the RQ of skeletal and cardiac muscle varies considerably, depending on the metabolic situation.

22.4 Measurement of the Oxygen Uptake of the Whole Body

When determining metabolic rate by indirect methods it is necessary to measure the oxygen uptake of the subject per unit time. Both "closed" and "open"

respiration systems are used for this purpose. (See reviews in [2], [5] and [7].)

Closed Systems

The principle of such systems is that the subject inspires gas from an *oxygen-filled* **spirometer** (pp. 461 f.; Fig. 22-5). The expired gas mixture passes through a container in which *carbon dioxide is absorbed* and then returns to the spirometer, so that the circuit is closed. The recorded *spirogram* (Fig. 22-5) has a rising slope; the steeper the slope, the more oxygen is removed from the system per unit time.

Closed systems *must be filled with oxygen,* for if air is used the oxygen is consumed so rapidly that its concentration in the inspired mixture soon falls below 8.5% (the critical threshold, p. 566) with no increase in CO_2 concentration. Oxygen deficiency under these conditions often causes sudden unexpected loss of consciousness, because breathing is stimulated only slightly (pp. 482 f.) and other warning systems usually go unrecognized (p. 565).

Standard volume. Whatever the conditions under which oxygen uptake is measured, the results must be converted to corresponding standard conditions, so that different experiments can be compared regardless of actual temperature and air pressure (p. 473). The **STPD conditions** (standard temperature and pressure, dry) are 0° C, 760 mm Hg, and dryness of air. The conversion factor is usually obtained from tables derived from the following equation:

$$V_o = V \cdot \frac{P_B - P_{H_2O}}{760} \cdot \frac{273}{273 + t}, \quad (4)$$

where V_o is the volume under standard conditions, V is the measured volume, P_B is the barometric pressure, P_{H_2O} is the wa-

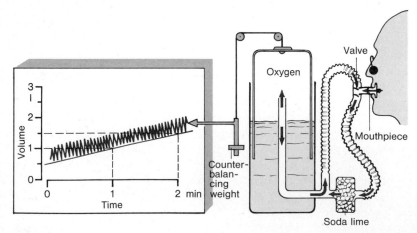

Fig. 22-5. Principle of the *closed system* used to measure oxygen uptake. The subject inspires oxygen from a bell gasometer (p. 461), by way of a tube with mouthpiece and valve. CO_2 is removed from the expired air by adsorption on soda lime before the air returns to the bell. During the experiment the nose is clamped shut. The movements of the bell, in the respiratory rhythm, are recorded on uniformly moving paper by a writing system (pulleys, weight and lever). This record is a *spirogram*. By drawing in a line tangent to the lower reversal points of the curve and determining its slope (liters per unit time) one obtains a direct measure of oxygen uptake (0.5 l/min in this example)

ter-vapor pressure in the spirometer, and t is the temperature of the measured gas volume in $°C$.

Open Systems

In **open respiration systems** the airways for inspiration and expiration are separate. Usually fresh air is inspired, and the expiratory airway is equipped to measure both the *volume of the expired air* and its O_2 and CO_2 *concentrations*. Since the concentrations in the inspired air are known, the amount of oxygen removed from the air and the amount of CO_2 added to it can be calculated.

Douglas bag. The Douglas-bag procedure [12] is one of the classical methods for measuring oxygen uptake. It involves *discontinuous* measurement with a *portable* device that can be attached to a freely moving subject [3]. In studies of the physiology of work the bag is worn like a backpack. The subject inspires fresh air by way of a *valve* with a *mouthpiece;* the nose is closed by a *clamp.* All the expired air is collected in the *air-tight bag* by way of a system of valves and tubes, and the collection time is measured precisely. At the end of this period the bag is kneaded to mix the various components of the expired air thoroughly, and a sample is taken for analysis of oxygen and carbon-dioxide content. The total volume of air breathed is determined by emptying the sack into a gasmeter.

Calculations in the Douglas-bag procedure. The differences between inspired and expired amounts of O_2 as well as those for CO_2 are a direct measure of O_2 uptake and CO_2 output, respectively.
In calculating **CO_2 output** one can ignore the amount of CO_2 inspired, because the atmospheric CO_2 concentration is only 0.03 ml/dl. Thus the amount of CO_2 released in the lungs is identical to that in the expired air:

$$\dot{V}_{CO_2} = \dot{V}_E \cdot F_{E_{CO_2}}. \tag{5}$$

Here $\dot{V}_{CO_2}$ is the amount of CO_2 released per unit time, $\dot{V}_E$ is the expiratory minute volume and $F_{E_{CO_2}}$ is the fraction of CO_2 in the expired air mixture (e.g., 0.04 = 4 ml/dl or vol%).
For precise calculation of **oxygen uptake** the amount of oxygen inspired must be known as well as that expired:

$$\Delta\dot{V}_{O_2} = \dot{V}_I \cdot F_{I_{O_2}} - \dot{V}_E \cdot F_{E_{O_2}}. \tag{6}$$

The amount expired is that in the Douglas bag, and can be calculated in the same way as $\dot{V}_{CO_2}$. The O_2 fraction in the inspired air is known in the case of fresh air ($F_{I_{O_2}} = 0.2095 = 20.95$ ml/dl), but $\dot{V}_I$ is not.
Only if RQ = 1 can one assume that the expiratory and inspiratory minute volumes (adjusted to standard conditions) are identical. With an RQ below 1.0 less air is expired than is inspired. But if RQ is known, either of the minute volumes can be

obtained from the other. Though we shall not describe the derivation here, these considerations allow calculation of oxygen uptake with the Douglas-bag method by the following equation:

$$\Delta\dot{V}_{O_2} = \dot{V}_E(1.265 \cdot \Delta F_{O_2} - 0.265 \cdot F_{E_{CO_2}}). \tag{7}$$

$\dot{V}_E$ can be obtained from the amount of expired air collected in the Douglas bag during the specified time, $F_{E_{CO_2}}$ is the fraction of that air consisting of CO_2, and ΔF_{O_2} is the difference between the oxygen fraction in the inspired air and that in the expired gas mixture. Finally, the result must be adjusted for *STPD conditions*.

Other procedures. Instead of a Douglas bag, the subject can carry a gasmeter on his back, specially adapted so that as the flow rate is measured a sample of the expired gas mixture can be collected in a small accessory vessel. This sample must be *representative* of all the components of the mixture expired (an *aliquot portion*). Because their proportions may change during an expiration, it is necessary that a specific fraction of the airstream be redirected continuously (Fig. 22-6); in this way a certain percentage of each component in the expired gas mixture (e.g., 1%) is collected.
For the *continuous* measurement of oxygen uptake larger, permanently installed apparatus must be used. The respiratory minute volume is usually recorded continuously with a *pneumotachograph* (p.461). The gas concentrations are determined not with discontinuous chemical absorption procedures, but with *gas analyzers* that monitor the output continuously by mechanisms based on certain physical properties of oxygen and carbon dioxide (p.474). The further calculations are similar to those in the Douglas-bag method.

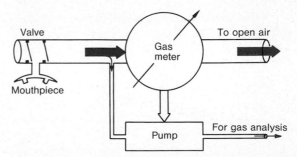

Fig. 22-6. Principle by which an aliquot of expired air is collected in an *open* respiration system. The subject inspires fresh air through a mouthpiece with a two-way valve; the nose is closed with a clamp. The expired air is measured with a gasmeter (or a pneumotachograph), which controls a suction pump in such a way that a small sample of the expired gas, proportional to the rate of flow, is withdrawn and collected. This special arrangement provides a *representative* gas sample, which contains all the components of the expired air in the correct proportions (an *aliquot*)

22.5 Diagnostic Significance of Energy Expenditure

Physiological and clinical aspects of work. Increases and decreases in the physical performance of which a person is capable are associated with changes in the maximal energy metabolism achievable. The *maximal oxygen uptake* at the end of a period of exhausting work is thus a well-established criterion of physical performance (p.563). On the other hand, if it is desired to have a measure of the *strain* of the body by work or sport, energy metabolism is monitored during the activity. Norms have been found for population samples engaged in work of various sorts (for reviews see [3] and [6]), so that it is possible to *classify* them according to the difficulty of the work as discussed on p.525.

Clinical diagnosis. In **shock** (critical drop in blood pressure caused, for example, by severe blood loss) the metabolic rate falls below the basal level, caused by an insufficient blood flow through peripheral regions (cf. pp. 444f.). An *oxygen debt* is built up (p.551); many cells begin to metabolize at a rate lower than is necessary to keep them in functional condition. When peripheral blood flow increases as the state of shock wears off, the metabolic rate rises as well, so that by monitoring the changes in metabolic rate one can evaluate the state of shock.

Thyroid malfunction is also reflected in metabolism, such that when the activity of the gland is abnormally high *(hyperthyroidism)* the basal metabolic rate increases and when it is abnormally low *(hypothyroidism)* it decreases (the clinical picture is described on pp.672f.). In extreme cases the metabolic rate can vary by more than $+100\%$ or -40% from the norm. But BMR is now very rarely used to diagnose thyroid-gland diseases, for simpler and more informative procedures are available (p.674); it is occasionally employed for the long-term monitoring of thyroid function.

22.6 References

Textbooks and Handbooks

1. ALTMANN, P. L., DITTMER, D. S. (Eds.): Biology Data Book, Vol. III. Fed. Amer. Soc. exper. Biol., Bethesda, Maryland 1974
2. ANDREW, B. L.: Experimental Physiology. Edinburgh–London: E. & S. Livingstone Ltd. 1969
3. ÅSTRAND, P.-O., RODAHL, K.: Textbook of Work Physiology. New York: McGraw-Hill 1977
4. BENEDICT, F. G.: Methoden zur Bestimmung des Gaswechsels bei Tieren und Menschen. In: ABDERHALDEN, G. (Ed.): Handbuch der biologischen Arbeitsmethoden. Abtlg. IV, Teil 10: Gasstoffwechsel und Calorimetrie, p.415. Berlin–Wien: Urban & Schwarzenberg 1926
5. CONSOLAZIO, C. F., JOHNSON, R. E., PECORA, L. J.: Physiological Measurements of Metabolic Functions in Man. New York–Toronto–London: McGraw-Hill 1963
6. DURNIN, J. V. G. A., PASSMORE, P.: Energy, Work and Leisure. Heinemann Educational Books Ltd., London 1967
7. FALLS, H. B.: Exercise Physiology. New York–London: Academic Press 1968
8. KESTNER, O., KNIPPING, H. W.: Die Ernährung des Menschen. Berlin: Springer 1924
9. LAVOISIER, A. L., LAPLACE, P. S.: Abhandlung über die Wärme. (First published 1780) In: ROSENTHAL, L. (Ed.): Zwei Abhandlungen über die Wärme, p.3. Leipzig: Wilhelm Engelmann 1892
10. SCHNEIDER, M.: Einführung in die Physiologie des Menschen. (16th Ed.) Berlin–Heidelberg–New York: Springer 1971

Research Reports and Reviews

11. BOOTHBY, W. M., BERKSON, J., DUNN, W. L.: Studies of the energy of metabolism of normal individuals. A standard for basal metabolism, with a nomogram for clinical application. Amer. J. Physiol. *116,* 468 (1936)
12. DOUGLAS, C. G.: A method for determining the total respiratory exchange in man. J. Physiol. (Lond.) *42,* 17 (1911)
13. GÖPFERT, H., BERNSMEIER, A., STUFLER, R.: Über die Steigerung des Energiestoffwechsels und der Muskelinnervation bei geistiger Arbeit. Pflügers Arch. ges. Physiol. *256,* 304 (1953)
14. HARRIS, J. A., BENEDICT, F. G.: A biometry study of basal metabolism in man. Publ. No.279, Carnegie Inst., Washington 1919
15. KINNEY, J. M., LISTER, J., MOORE, F. D.: Relationship of energy expenditure to total exchangeable potassium. Ann. N. Y. Acad. Sci. *110,* 711–722 (1963)

23 Heat Balance and the Regulation of Body Temperature

K. BRÜCK

23.1 Heat Production, Body Temperature and Body Size

Homeothermy, poikilothermy. The **metabolic** processes described in the preceding chapter are associated with the **generation of heat,** in accordance with the laws of thermodynamics. From the metabolic point of view this heat production is a side effect, but when one is concerned with the differences in body temperature and its control within the animal kingdom metabolic heat is of fundamental interest. In one group of animals – that to which humans belong – the temperature of the body is kept at a constant level considerably above that of the surroundings, owing to a **high rate of heat production** governed by **regulatory mechanisms.** These are the **homeothermic organisms.** In a second group (which includes, for example, fish and reptiles), far less heat is produced; the body temperature is only slightly above the ambient temperature, and follows the fluctuations of the latter *(poikilothermic organisms).*

Inasmuch as homeotherms can maintain a uniform temperature, and thus a uniform activity level, independent of the ambient temperature, they are superior in many respect to the poikilotherms. On the other hand, poikilothermy can offer advantages when the availability of food is subject to seasonal changes. For example, when frogs are kept cool they can endure food deprivation for months with no ill effects.

Heat production and body temperature. All chemical reactions in an organism, including the processes of metabolism, are temperature-dependent. The relationship in poikilotherms is just like that pertaining to abiotic chemical processes – that is, the rate of energy conversion increases in proportion to external temperature according to **van't Hoff's rule.** Van't Hoff's rule applies to homeotherms in the same way, but it is masked by other effects. When an intact homeotherm is cooled (starting at a comfortable ambient temperature in the **thermoneutral zone;** cf. p. 534) its rate of energy metabolism and thus heat production rises, preventing a reduction in body temperature. But by pharmacological intervention (e.g., anesthesia) or by

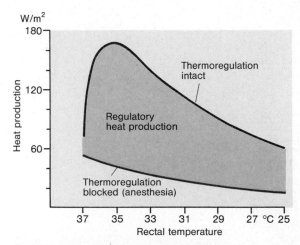

Fig. 23-1. Relationship between body temperature and metabolic rate in homeothermic organisms (from experiments on the dog). *Upper curve:* When thermoregulation is functioning the metabolic rate first rises sharply as temperature falls, passes through a maximum and then falls in accordance with van't Hoff's rule. *Lower curve:* With thermoregulation blocked by deep anesthesia the metabolic rate follows van't Hoff's rule from the onset of cooling. The difference between the two curves corresponds to regulatory thermogenesis. For further discussion see text. After[18]

making lesions at specific sites in the CNS one can eliminate thermoregulation; the curve of heat production vs. temperature then resembles that of a poikilotherm (Fig. 23-1). The component of heat production that can be blocked in this way is called **regulatory thermogenesis.**

Even after blockade of the regulatory component there remains a considerable quantitative difference between the metabolic processes of poikilotherms and those of homeotherms; at a given body temperature the rate of energy conversion per unit body weight in homeotherms is at least three times that in poikilotherms.

The ratio of the reaction rates at temperatures differing by 10 °C is called the Q_{10}. Quantitative evaluation of the falling parts of the curves in Fig. 23-1 shows that *the Q_{10} for the metabolic rate lies between 2 and 3.* Therefore anesthesia combined with lowered body temperature can bring about a quite appreciable **decrease in O_2 consumption** and hence a corresponding **postponement of structural deterioration** (cf. p. 519). This phenomenon is turned to advantage during cardiovascular surgery and transplant operations, when the circulation of blood must be interrupted temporarily (**induced hypothermia** [44]; some-

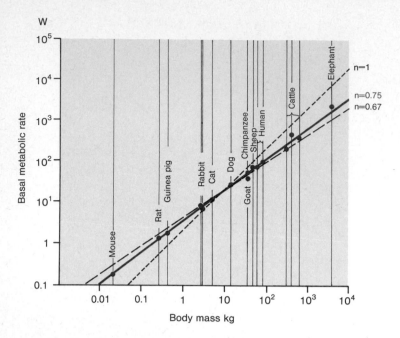

Fig. 23-2. Relationship between metabolic rate and body mass in a double-logarithmic plot. The straight line with a slope of 0.75 most closely fits the experimental data. The line with slope 1 reflects proportionality between metabolic rate and body mass, and that with slope 0.67 reflects proportionality between metabolic rate and surface area. After [9]

times called "artificial hibernation"). Van't Hoff's rule must also be considered when organs are to be kept in storage.

Heat production and body size. The body temperature of most homeothermic mammals is in the range of 36°–39 °C, despite the wide differences in body size within the group – from the mouse, near one end, to the elephant and whale at the other. By contrast, metabolic rate (MR) is a power function of body mass (m):

$$MR = k \cdot m^n \tag{1}$$

This relationship gives a straight line on a double-logarithmic plot:

$$\log MR = k' + n \cdot \log m \tag{2}$$

The exponent n has been found empirically to be about 0.75 (cf. Fig. 23-2). That is, the quantity $MR/m^{0.75}$ is the same for the mouse as for the elephant, although the mouse MR per kg body mass is considerably larger than that of the elephant. This so-called **law of metabolic reduction** [9] reflects the tendency for heat production to be matched to the rate of heat loss to the surroundings. For a given temperature difference between the interior of the body and the surroundings, the loss of heat per unit mass is greater, the greater the surface-to-volume ratio, and the latter decreases with increasing body size. Moreover, the insulating shell of the body (cf. p. 544) is thinner in small animals.

Thermoregulatory thermogenesis. When additional heat is required to keep the body temperature constant, it can be produced in the following ways:

1. By voluntary activity of the locomotor apparatus.
2. By involuntary tonic or rhythmic muscular activity; the latter corresponds to the familiar **shivering** induced by cold. (The tonic activity can be detected by electromyography; cf. pp. 40f.).
3. By the acceleration of metabolic processes not associated with muscle contraction; this form of heat production is called **nonshivering thermogenesis.**

In the adult human *shivering* is the most significant involuntary mechanism of thermogenesis. *Nonshivering thermogenesis* occurs in the newborn (including humans) and in small cold-adapted animals. The so-called **brown adipose tissue,** distinguished by an abundance of mitochondria and a "multilocular" distribution of the fat (numerous small fat droplets surrounded by mitochondria), is a major source of nonshivering thermogenesis. It is found between the shoulder blades, in the armpit and in a few other places [11].

The **thermoregulatory function of the interscapular brown adipose tissue** can readily be demonstrated by local temperature measurement (Fig. 23-3). Whereas the subcutaneous temperature of the back falls during exposure to cold, the temperature in the brown adipose tissue rises. Other studies have shown that **blood flow** through this tissue increases under cold stress. The local rise in temperature in this situation therefore implies thermogenesis in the adipose tissue [21].

Body temperature and thermal balance. If the body temperature is to be kept constant, there must be thermal equilibrium in the steady state; that is, heat production and heat loss must be equal. Fig. 23-4 shows diagrammatically the possible ways in which body

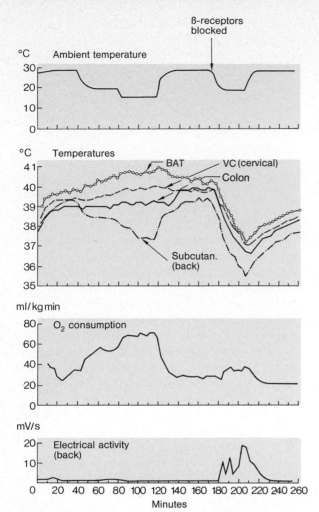

Fig. 23-3. Nonshivering thermogenesis in the newborn guinea pig can be detected by the increase in O₂ uptake while the muscles show no electrical activity. In the *second part* of the experiment nonshivering thermogenesis is inhibited by a β-receptor blocking agent; shivering resulted, as shown by the increase in electrical activity of the musculature. (The threshold for shivering is at a lower body temperature than that for nonshivering heat production.) Note the rise in temperature of the interscapular brown adipose tissue (BAT) and in the vertebral canal (VC) *before* blockade and the parallel fall in all temperatures *after* it. After [25]

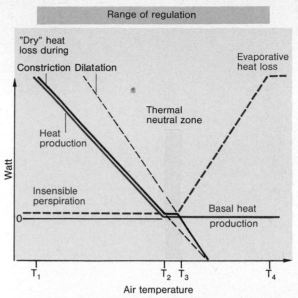

Fig. 23-4. Diagram illustrating thermal balance. In the temperature range T_1–T_4 (zone of normothermy) heat production and loss are equal. Below T_1 more heat is lost than can be produced (hypothermia). Above T_4 the production and influx of heat exceed the capacity for evaporative heat loss (hyperthermia). In the range T_2–T_3 (thermoneutral zone) heat loss can be matched to resting heat production by vasomotor adjustments. For further discussion see text

temperature can be held constant when the ambient temperature changes. These considerations are based on Newton's law of cooling, according to which the heat lost by a body (more precisely, the "dry" heat loss – the total loss minus the loss by evaporation) is proportional to the temperature difference between the body core and the surroundings. For a human subject, then, at an ambient temperature of 37 °C the heat loss would be equal to zero, and at lower temperatures it would increase. But heat loss also depends on the conduction and convection of heat within the body, and thus on the peripheral blood flow. Accor-

dingly, one can plot *two heat-loss curves,* one for peripheral *vasodilation* and another for *vasoconstriction.* The thermogenesis associated with resting metabolism is in equilibrium with heat loss in the range of the graph between T_2 and T_3 if blood flow through the skin is progressively reduced as the temperature falls from T_3 to T_2. Below T_2 the body temperature can be kept constant only if regulatory mechanisms increase thermogenesis in proportion to heat loss. The greatest heat production achievable by such mechanisms in humans corresponds to as much as 3–5 times the basal metabolic rate, and marks the **lower limit of the thermoregulatory range,** T_1 (for absolute values see Fig. 23-15). When this limit is passed **hypothermia** develops and ultimately can result in **cold death.**

At temperatures above T_3, it is conceivable that a diminished metabolic rate could maintain thermal equilibrium. In fact, however, thermal balance is achieved by an *additional heat-loss mechanism,* the evaporation of sweat. T_4 indicates the **upper limit of the regulatory range,** which is fixed by the maximal rate of sweat secretion. Above T_4 **hyperthermia** appears; this ultimately can result in **heat death** (for absolute values see Fig. 23-8). The range of temperatures between T_2 and T_3, within which the body temperature can be kept constant *without either*

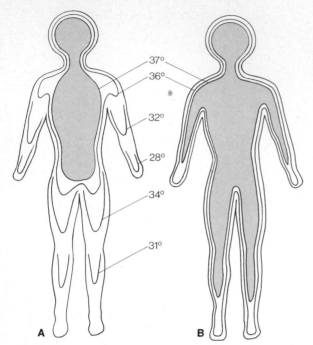

Fig. 23-5 A, B. Temperature isotherms within the human body in cold (*A*) and warm (*B*) surroundings. After [17]

supplementary heat-producing mechanisms or sweat secretion, is called the **thermoneutral zone** (cf. Fig. 23-15).

23.2 The Temperature of the Human Body

Local Temperature Differences (Temperature Gradients)

The heat produced within the body normally (i.e., under equilibrium conditions) is lost to the environment by way of the body surface. In accordance with the physical laws of heat flow, therefore, the temperature of the parts of the body near the surface must be lower than that of the central parts. In the limbs there is a **longitudinal (axial) temperature gradient,** and there is also a **radial temperature gradient** (perpendicular to the surface). The result, owing to the irregular geometry of the body, is a complicated three-dimensional temperature distribution. For example, when a lightly clothed adult is in an ambient temperature of 20 °C, the innermost part of the thigh musculature is at 35 °C, the deep layers of the calf are at 33 °C and the center of the foot is at only 27°–28 °C; the rectal temperature under these conditions is around 37 °C [6]. The fluctuations in body temperature produced by external temperature changes are distinctly greater

near the body surface and at the ends (acral parts) of the extremities. Simplifying the situation somewhat, one can distinguish a **"poikilothermic" shell** from a **"homeothermic" core.** The isotherms in Fig. 23-5 indicate the temperature gradients within the body in cold and warm surroundings. The 37 °C isotherm, which delimits the core, is withdrawn to the interior of the body when the surroundings are cold [17].

Core temperatures of the body. On closer examination we find that the temperature of the core itself is inconstant in both space and time. The core-temperature differences are of the order of 0.2°–1.2 °C; even the brain exhibits a radial temperature gradient of more than 1 °C from center to cortex. As a rule, the highest temperatures are found in the rectum and not, as was long claimed [6], in the liver. In view of this finding it is impossible to express the temperature of the body by a single number. For practical purposes, however, it suffices to find a specific site at which the temperature can be regarded as *representative of the body core,* for one is usually interested in temporal changes in temperature. For clinical measurements it is most important to select an easily accessible site with little spatial variation in temperature, so that slight changes in position of the measuring instrument do not make it difficult to establish a standard.

The preferred measure for clinical purposes is the **rectal temperature,** even though it does not entirely meet the above requirements. When a thermometer is advanced inward from the anus to a depth of 10-15 cm, temperature gradients of as much as 1 °C are observed. This spatial nonuniformity within the rectum derives in part from the communication between the venous plexuses in the rectum and those in the skin of the anal region [6]. For comparative measurements, therefore, it is important to keep to a standard depth of insertion.

The oral temperature (more precisely, the **sublingual temperature**) is usually 0.2°–0.5 °C lower than the rectal temperature. Here, again, there are temperature gradients; the oral temperature is affected by the inspired air and by the temperature of food and drink.

For examinations in the area of sport medicine, the **esophageal temperature** (above the cardia) is often taken, with flexible thermosensors.

The **axillary temperature** can also represent the core temperature, because when the upper arm is held tightly to the thorax the temperature gradients (Fig. 23-5) alter so as to displace the core boundary up to the armpit. However, the parts of the body shell pressed together for this measurement must accumulate a considerable amount of heat before the final temperature is reached. On the order of ½ hour must be allowed for equilibration, if the shell tissues were initially cooled by a low ambient temperature with vasoconstriction – as is especially likely to occur when a fever is building up.

Skin temperature. The shell temperature is usually characterized by the temperature of the skin, which is easily measurable but presents far more problems for standardization than the core temperature. Measurement at a single site is quite inadequate; the temperatures at several places must be averaged. It is common practice to obtain the **mean skin temperature** from measurements at the forehead, chest, abdomen, upper arm, forearm, back of hand, thigh, shin, and dorsum of foot. In calculating the mean these values are weighted in accordance with the body-surface area they represent. The mean skin temperature found in this way for a nude person in a comfortable ambient temperature is about 33°–34 °C. The **"mean body temperature"** can be calculated from the mean skin temperature and the core temperature, with appropriate weighting factors.

Periodic Fluctuations in Core Temperature

The temperature of a human varies in the course of a day, with a minimum toward morning and a maximum (often with two peaks) during the daytime (Fig. 23-6). The amplitude of this diurnal fluctuation averages ca 1 °C. In night-active animals the temperature maximum occurs during the night. The plausible inference that the increased temperature is simply the consequence of increased physical activity has, however, proved false [16].

The 24-h fluctuation in body temperature is but one of many **diurnal rhythms.** Even when all external entraining signals are eliminated (light, temperature, feeding times), body temperature continues to oscillate rhythmically – but no longer with a period of exactly 24 hours. The "free-running" period is between 24 and 25 hours (**"circadian" periodicity;** cf. p. 153). The diurnal oscillation of body temperature is thus based on an endogenous rhythm (the "biological clock"), which is ordinarily synchronized with external signals, the earth's rotation in particular [16]. When one travels across the earth's meridians it takes 1–2 weeks for the temperature rhythm to adjust to the living patterns set by the new local time.

Superimposed on the diurnal temperature changes are rhythms with longer periods. The best known and most conspicuous of these is the temperature rhythm synchronized with the **menstrual cycle** (cf. Fig. 23-6 and pp. 675 f.).

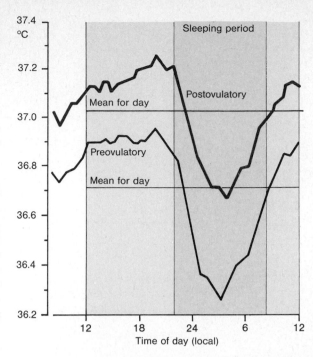

Fig. 23-6. Daily variation in body (rectal) temperature. The *lower curve* was obtained in the first (preovulatory) half of the menstrual cycle, the *upper curve* in the second (postovulatory) half (means of 8 subjects). *Red shading:* sleeping period. After [40]

Body Temperature during Exercise

The core temperature can rise by 2 °C or more during exercise, depending on how vigorous it is and on the measurement site; within a certain range, however, the amount of increase does not depend on the ambient temperature. By contrast, the mean skin temperature falls, because while the muscles are working sweat is secreted and cools the skin (Fig. 23-7). During prolonged, exhausting exercise (marathon running, for instance) rectal temperatures of almost 41 °C have been measured [39]. (These changes in temperature during exercise are discussed in terms of control theory on p. 543.)

23.3 Heat Loss

Under stationary resting conditions, characterized by constant mean body temperature, the *metabolic rate (MR)* must be equal to the rate of heat transfer from the interior to the surface of the body *(internal heat flow H_{int})* and to the rate of heat transfer from the body surface to the surroundings *(external heat flow H_{ext})*:

$$MR = H_{int} = H_{ext} \tag{3}$$

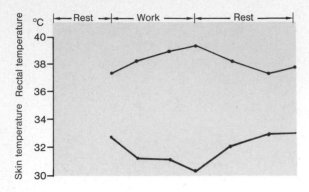

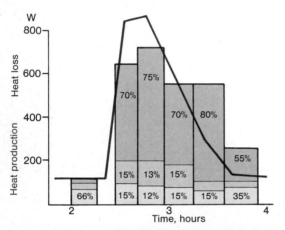

Fig. 23-7. Body temperature, heat production (curve) and heat loss (columns) at rest and during work. The columns are divided as follows: *bottom,* radiative heat loss; *middle,* convective heat loss; *top,* evaporative heat loss; conduction (see text) is neglected. After[29]

Internal Heat Flow

Of the heat produced within the body, less than half flows to the body surface by **conduction** through the tissues; most of it is transferred by **convection,** in the bloodstream. Because of its high heat capacity the blood is particularly well suited for heat transport and thus for maintaining thermal balance within the body. The internal heat flow (in watts), as Eq. 4 indicates, is proportional to the difference between the core temperature T_c and the mean skin temperature $\bar{T}_{sk}$. It is also determined by the **thermal conductance** C, the magnitude of which depends on the rates of blood flow through skin and extremities:

$$H_{int} = C \cdot (T_c - \bar{T}_{sk}) \cdot A \qquad (4)$$

where A is the area of the body surface. In an adult human changes in the rate of blood flow can change the conductance C by a factor of 4 to 7, depending on the thickness of the body shell and of the subcutane-

ous fat [6, 12, 33]. The reciprocal of C, $1/C = I_t$, is called the **thermal resistance** or **thermal insulation.**

The variability in thermal conductance derives in particular from the fact that blood flow through the extremities conforms to the **counter-current principle.** The deep large vessels in the limbs lie in parallel, so that as blood flows outward through the arteries it loses heat to the accompanying veins. This *thermal short circuit* is more effective, the more the axial perfusion of the extremities is limited by vasoconstriction, and the cooler the distal parts of the extremities are. In warm surroundings the *superficial* veins that are not accompanied by parallel arteries open [46], so that a larger fraction of the returning blood flows through them. This additionally reduces the short-circuit effect.

External Heat Flow

For quantitative analysis of external heat flow, and for evaluation of the effects upon it of external factors, it is necessary to consider separately its various components [2, 6, 12]. These are heat transfer by conduction H_k, by convection H_c, by radiation H_r, and by evaporation H_e. The total heat flow is the sum of these components:

$$H_{ext} = H_k + H_c + H_r + H_e \qquad (5)$$

The percentages contributed to the total by these components under resting and working conditions are summarized in Fig. 23-7.

Heat transfer by conduction occurs wherever the body is in contact (standing, sitting or lying down) with a firm substrate. The magnitude of conductive flow is determined by the temperature and the thermal conductance of the supporting material.

From the part of the body surface covered with air, heat is transferred by radiation, convection and evaporation.

Convective heat transfer. If the skin is warmer than the surrounding air, the adjacent layer of air is warmed, rises and is replaced by cooler, denser air. In this process, called **natural convection,** heat is carried away by the laminar current of air produced at the skin surface. The driving force for this flow is the temperature difference between the body and its surroundings. As more movement occurs in the external air the boundary layer within which flow is laminar, 4–8 mm thick at most, becomes thinner; air flow becomes turbulent close to the skin. This **forced convection** considerably increases the rate of heat loss.

Convective heat transfer (in watts) is given by Eq. (6). The determining factors are the difference between the *mean skin temperature* $\bar{T}_{sk}$ and the *ambient air temperature* T_a, the effective surface area A (which is smaller than the geometrical surface area of the body because some surfaces touch one another), and the **convective heat transfer coefficient** h_c, the magnitude of which increases as the square root of wind velocity.

$$H_c = h_c \cdot (\bar{T}_{sk} - T_a) \cdot A \qquad (6)$$

The quantity $I_c = 1/h_c$ is called the thermal resistance or **insulation of the boundary layer.**

Heat transfer by radiation. The loss of heat in the form of long-wavelength infrared radiation from the skin (which does not involve a conducting medium) is described exactly by the **Stefan-Boltzmann equation** (cf. physics textbooks). That is, radiation varies as the fourth power of the absolute temperature. For the small temperature range of interest in biology, radiant heat transfer H_r can be described with sufficient accuracy by the linearized Equation (7):

$$H_r = h_r \cdot (\bar{T}_{sk} - \bar{T}_r) \cdot A \qquad (7)$$

where $\bar{T}_{sk}$ is the mean skin temperature, $\bar{T}_r$ is the **mean radiant temperature** (the temperature of the enclosing surfaces – e.g., walls of the room), A is the effective body-surface area and h_r is the **radiative heat transfer coefficient.** The significance of the temperature of the surrounding surfaces can be illustrated by holding one's palm a short distance away from the face. There is an immediate sensation of warmth, which results from the diminished radiant heat loss. The coefficient h_r takes account of the emissivity ε of the skin, which for the long-wavelength infrared radiation is nearly 1, regardless of pigmentation; that is, the skin emits almost exactly as much radiant energy as a "full radiator", or ideal black body. The emissivity of the surrounding walls must be considered only if they are very close to the body. Radiant heat is **absorbed** in rooms with radiation heaters or in the sunshine when the mean radiant temperature $\bar{T}_r$ (Eq. 7) exceeds $\bar{T}_{sk}$. In the case of *short-wavelength* infrared radiation (emitted by hot radiating bodies such as electrical radiators and the sun), both the emissivity and the absorptance of the skin are considerably smaller than 1 (0.5–0.8) and depend on the skin pigmentation.

Heat transfer by convection and that by radiation are often lumped as **"dry" heat loss.** In this case the value for ambient temperature is the *operative temperature,* a weighted average of the air and radiant temperatures. The heat transfer coefficients for convection and radiation are combined to give the coefficient h_c, the reciprocal of which is the ambient insulation I_a.

Evaporative heat transfer. About 20% of the heat lost by a human under neutral temperature conditions (cf. Fig. 23-7) is accounted for by the evaporation of water that has diffused to the surface of the skin or from the mucous membranes lining the respiratory tract. Evaporative heat transfer from the skin is described by the following equation:

$$H_e = h_e \cdot (\bar{P}_{sk} - P_a) \cdot A \qquad (8)$$

where $\bar{P}_{sk}$ and P_a are the vapor pressures on the skin (the mean pressure) and in the surrounding air, and h_e is the **evaporative heat transfer coefficient.** h_e varies with the curvature of the skin surface, the atmospheric pressure and the wind velocity.

The most important conclusion to be drawn from the above equation is that evaporative heat loss takes place even when the relative humidity of the surroundings is 100%. The only critical requirement is that $\bar{P}_{sk}$ be greater than P_a; this is the case as long as the skin temperature is higher than the ambient temperature and the skin is completely wetted by adequate secretion of sweat.

The water lost by diffusion through skin and mucosa is called **insensible** or extraglandular water loss, as distinct from the **glandular** water loss by way of the sweat glands. Only the latter, which can have a marked effect on the total amount of heat transferred, is under the control of the thermoregulatory system. When the ambient temperature exceeds that of the body heat can be given off only by evaporation. The effectiveness of sweat secretion in thermoregulation is based on the high heat of evaporation of water, 2400 kJ per liter. By evaporating 1 liter of water the human body can lose one-third of the resting heat production of an entire day (cf. water balance, pp. 643 f.).

The effect of clothing. Clothing, in the physiological context, is a form of thermal resistance or **insulation** I_{cl} – a quantity to be added to the thermal resistances of the tissue (I_t) and of the ambient boundary layer (I_a). The effectiveness of clothing is chiefly due to the tiny air spaces trapped in the weave or nap, where no appreciable flow can occur; here heat transfer is entirely by **conduction,** and air is a poor heat conductor.

Environmental Factors and Thermal Comfort

From what has been said so far it is evident that the effect of a person's immediate environment depends on at least **four physical factors: air temperature,** the water-vapor pressure of the air **(humidity), radiation temperature** and **wind velocity.** These determine whether the person feels *"thermally comfortable"* or too warm

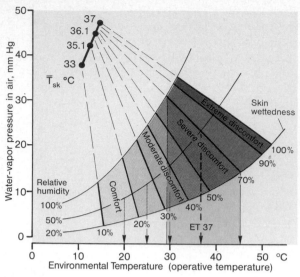

Fig. 23-8. The psychometric diagram represents the relation of ambient temperature (operative temperature: the weighted mean of radiative and air temperature) and humidity to thermal discomfort. This relation holds for conditions of moderate work ("3 met", or three times the resting metabolic rate), light sport clothing and slight relative air movement (0.5 m·s⁻¹). ET, effective temperature; $\bar{T}_{sk}$, mean skin temperature. After [31]

or cold. The condition for comfort is that no thermoregulatory mechanisms must be called into play – neither shivering nor sweat secretion are activated, and blood flows through the periphery of the body at an intermediate rate. This condition corresponds to the previously mentioned **thermoneutral zone** (Fig. 23-4).

The four physical factors are to a certain extent interchangeable with regard to the sensation of comfort and the need for thermoregulation. That is, a sensation of cold produced by low air temperature can be alleviated by an appropriate increase in the radiation temperature. When the atmosphere feels sultry, the sensation can be diminished by reducing the humidity as well as by lowering the temperature. If the radiation temperature is low (cold walls) an increased air temperature is required for comfort. These interactions make it possible to express various combinations of factors by a single number – for example, the **effective temperature.**

According to recent extensive studies [3], the **thermal comfort point** for a lightly clothed (shirt, short underpants, long cotton trousers), seated person is about 25°–26 °C when the humidity is set at 50% and the temperatures of wall and air are the same. The corresponding value for a nude person at 50% R. H. has been found to be 28 °C. In conditions of thermal comfort the mean skin temperature is about 34 °C. As more effort is exerted in physical work the comfortable temperature becomes lower. For example, a

room temperature of ca. 22 °C is preferred for light office work. Curiously, however, during hard work a room temperature such that sweating remains just suppressed is felt to be too cool. Fig. 23-8 is a diagram showing how thermal comfort is related to the humidity and the ambient temperature during light work (3 met; 1 met = the resting metabolic rate). To each degree of discomfort there can be ascribed a *single* temperature, the effective temperature (ET). The numerical value of ET is found by projecting onto the x axis the point at which a discomfort line intersects the curve for 50% relative humidity [31] (an older ET scale was constructed with respect to 100% R. H.). For example, all of the combinations of temperature and humidity within the red field in Fig. 23-8 (e.g., 30 °C at 100% R. H., 45 °C at 20% R. H. and so on) correspond to the ET 37 °C, and this in turn corresponds to a specific degree of discomfort. In the lower temperature ranges the influence of humidity is less (the discomfort lines slope more steeply), because here the contribution of evaporative heat transfer to the total heat loss is slight. As the diagram shows, *discomfort increases with mean skin temperature* and with the *skin wettedness* (the fraction of the total body area that is covered by sweat). When the limiting conditions for maximal skin wettedness (100%) have been exceeded, thermal balance can no longer be maintained. Therefore conditions beyond this limit can be tolerated only briefly; sweat drips off the body, because more is secreted than can evaporate. The discomfort lines plotted in Fig. 23-8 shift, of course, depending on the thermal insulation provided by clothing, on the wind velocity and on the workload. When the work performed rises from 3 met to 6 met, for example, the limit for prolonged tolerance shifts from ET 40 °C to ET 33 °C.

Thermal comfort points in water. When water is the ambient medium, the boundary layer (p. 537) of air is replaced by water – a substance with far greater thermal conductivity and heat capacity. At a given temperature much more heat is withdrawn by convection from a resting body in water than from one in air. When the water is in motion, the resulting turbulent flow at the body surface withdraws heat so rapidly that at an ambient temperature of 10 °C even strenuous physical exertion fails to maintain thermal equilibrium, and **hypothermia** ensues. When the body is completely at rest, a water temperature of 35 °C–36 °C is required for thermal comfort. This lower limit of the thermoneutral zone depends on the thickness of the insulating adipose tissue. In a series of studies on people with different degrees of obesity the lower limit for comfort was found to lie between 31° and 36 °C [42].

23.4 The Regulation of Body Temperature

Biological thermoregulation can usefully be described with the terminology used in systems theory for technical control systems. **Sensors** are required for continuous monitoring of the thermal state of the controlled system. Their outputs are transmitted to a **central controller,** where the thermal information is processed and from which signals are sent out to control the operation of one or more **effectors.** The outputs from the effectors must be such as to counteract temperature changes caused by external or internal disturbances; if this is accomplished, the system is a closed loop with **negative feedback** (Fig. 23-9). Let us now consider the components of the system individually.

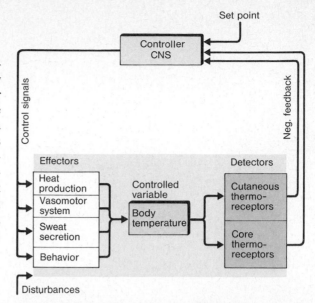

Fig. 23-9. Block diagram of thermoregulation. The system has two groups of detectors, corresponding in the organism to the cutaneous and the internal thermoreceptors

Effector Outputs in Thermoregulation

The effector outputs – **Heat production, tissue insulation and sweat secretion** – are predominantly under *neural control;* only in long-term adaptation do *hormonal processes* play a role. Two neural systems participate in thermoregulation: 1. the *somatomotor* system, and 2. the *sympathetic* system (Fig. 23-10). **Thermoregulatory behavior** such as fanning oneself and adding or removing clothing can also be included in the effector category.

Control of thermogenesis. Shivering (cf. p. 532) is induced and sustained by way of the motor system, the spinal and supraspinal elements of which (the cerebrospinal and reticulospinal tracts) are described in Chapter 5. The so-called **central shivering pathway,** which runs caudad from the posterior hypothalamus (for references see [6]), links the central thermoregulatory areas with the mesencephalic and rhombencephalic nuclei of the motor system. Shivering can also be influenced pharmacologically by the action of curare and other muscle relaxants on the neuromuscular end plate (cf. pp. 57 f.).

Nonshivering thermogenesis (cf. p. 532) is controlled by way of the sympathetic nervous system. When sympathetic activity is suppressed by ganglion-blocking drugs or, more specifically, by drugs that block the adrenergic β-receptors (cf. Fig. 23-3), nonshivering heat production ceases. The noradrenalin released at the nerve endings stimulates the release of free fatty acids from lipid droplets surrounded by mitochondria, as well as the subsequent oxidation of the fatty acids. As for the biochemical mechanism of this form of thermogenesis, see [11, 34].

Control of heat loss. The thermoregulatory effects on **blood flow** differ, depending on the part of the body involved. At least three functionally different regions can be distinguished: 1. the acral areas (fingers, hands, ears, lips, nose), 2. the trunk and proximal parts of the limbs, and 3. the head and forehead [6].

Acral perfusion is controlled by *noradrenergic sympathetic nerves;* an increase in sympathetic tone leads to vasoconstriction and a decrease, to vasodilation. The diameter of the **arteriovenous anastomoses** in the distal parts of the limbs is affected by sympathetic activity in the same way as that of the arterioles. When the arteriovenous anastomoses open, blood flow through the extremities, and thus the **convective transfer of heat,** is markedly increased. Elimination of sympathetic activity produces nearly maximal dilatation of the acral vessels. In the trunk and the proximal parts of the limbs the maximal perfusion rate induced by heat is far greater than that following blocking of the sympathetic system. This fact suggests the existence of specific vasodilator nerves, but the suggestion has not yet been confirmed. The phenomenon is more probably due to the secretion in sweat of **bradykinin** (cf. p. 685), which acts as a **vasodilator.** Vasomotor nerves have little effect on the forehead; exposure to cold elicits no vasoconstriction here. On the other hand, heat elicits both sweat secretion and vasodilation.

The **secretion of sweat** in humans is controlled exclusively by *cholinergic* sympathetic fibers, and can thus be inhibited by atropine. Sweat secretion is triggered

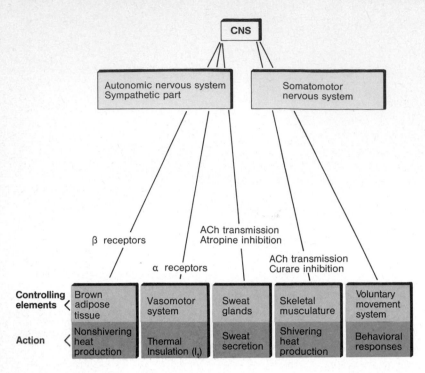

Fig. 23-10. Schematic illustration of the neural control of thermoregulatory effector elements

by acetylcholine, pilocarpine and other parasympathomimetics. Under certain circumstances (extreme psychological tension, for example) cutaneous vasoconstriction in the hands and feet can be associated with the secretion of sweat on the palmar and plantar surfaces. From the viewpoint of thermoregulation this is a paradoxical response – a case of **emotional** rather than **thermal sweating.**

Direct actions of temperature upon effector processes. Blood vessels respond directly to temperature changes; this property, which is independent of neural control, has been demonstrated by experiments on isolated segments of vessels. One peculiar reaction, called **cold vasodilation,** seems to be based to a great extent on this local thermosensitivity of the vessel musculature.

Cold dilation is a commonly observed phenomenon. When one is exposed to intense cold the first result is maximal vasoconstriction, recognizable by the paleness and cold sensation (often combined with pain) in the acral regions. But after a while blood suddenly spurts into the vessels here, reddening and warming the skin. If the exposure to cold is prolonged this sequence is repeated periodically.

Cold dilation has been regarded as a *protective* mechanism to prevent injury due to extended inadequate perfusion of the tissues, **chilblain** and **tissue necroses.** But experience shows that if the cold is sufficient to cause frostbite severe local damage occurs despite the vasodilation; cold dilation has a protective action only in people adapted to cold (cf. p. 546). On the other

hand, it can lethally accelerate the overall cooling of people who have fallen overboard and must float for a long time in cold water [7].

Thermoreception

The **cutaneous cold and warm receptors,** which also mediate the *sensation of temperature* (cf. thermoception, pp. 220 ff.), are one of the receptor groups that act as detectors in the temperature-control circuit (Fig. 23-9). It was proposed long ago that there are also **internal thermoreceptors,** and considerable experimental evidence of their existence has accumulated. For example, local heating or cooling of a narrowly circumscribed part of the anterior hypothalamus elicits both enhanced heat loss and increased thermogenesis. So far, however, it has been impossible to identify these thermosensitive structures morphologically. By electrical recording from single fibers **"warm neurons"** have been identified – nerve cells in which increased activity accompanies local heating, as illustrated in Fig. 23-11. The figure also shows that the increased discharge of these neurons is followed by activation of a mechanism to counteract heating (increased repiratory rate) [38]. In recent years similar thermosensitivity has been found in a few other parts of the central nervous system. In the dog, heating of the **spinal cord** elicits panting [35], vasodilation and inhibition of thermogenesis, whereas cooling produces shivering and vasoconstriction [41, 45]. In the guinea pig a local temperature change in the region of the cervical spinal cord suffices to trigger thermoregulatory responses. The thermosensitive structures in the spinal cord are connected to the posterior hypothalamus by way of ascending pathways in the region of the spinothalamic tract [48]. Additional thermoceptors have been postulated in the musculature, and recently in the abdominal region as well [41].

The distribution of thermoreceptive structures throughout the body may be regarded as a correlate of the body's complicated temperature gradients (p. 534). Such comprehensive sampling would provide the neurophysiological prerequisites for an extremely elaborate control system that takes into account the thermal state of the organism as a whole **(multiple input system).** Primitive control systems, like those in simple domestic air conditioners, usually have only one temperature sensor, at a single position in the system. Only the temperature in the immediate vicinity of this sensor is controlled with approximate accuracy.

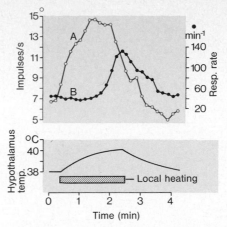

Fig. 23-11. Synchronous recording of the discharge rate of a "warm neuron" in the preoptic region of the hypothalamus (A) and of respiratory rate (B) as the temperature of the hypothalamus is varied by an implanted thermal probe. After [38]

Integrative Processes and Central Nervous Structures for Thermoregulation

The fundamental system-theoretical concepts on which our description of thermoregulation is based demand that there be some element to "process" the thermal information originating at the receptors, and to transform these inputs from the sensors into effector outputs (cf. Figs. 23-9 and 23-10). Because of the many experimental results implicating the hypothalamus, especially the **posterior hypothalamus,** this area has classically been regarded as such an integrative center. Recently neurons have been found in the posterior hypothalamus, the activity (discharge rate) of which is affected by *local thermal stimulation* in both the *preoptic region* and the cervicothoracic part of the *spinal cord* [49, 50].

Information processing in the hypothalamus. The most clear-cut demonstration of the involvement of the hypothalamus in thermoregulation is provided by the **classical transection experiments.** When the brainstem of the cat is cut immediately rostral to the hypothalamus thermoregulation is unimpaired, whereas after transection rostral to the mesencephalon the animals behave like poikilotherms. If the surgery is skilfully done and the ambient temperature suitably controlled, such artificially poikilothermic animals can survive for weeks or months.

Reciprocal connectivity of cold and warm afferents. The most important special feature of biological thermoregulation, as compared with the familiar simple technical systems, is that *two kinds of receptors* in different locations, the cold and the warm receptors, interact antagonistically. By activation of **cutaneous cold receptors,** which are more uniformly distributed

in the skin than warm receptors, effector or controlling processes are triggered (cf. Figs. 23-9 and 23-10) that *protect against cold* – vasoconstriction and thermoregulatory enhancement of heat production. These reactions are *counteracted* by **heat-activated internal thermoreceptors.** This circuitry enables protective mechanisms to be set in motion very rapidly in case of external cooling – long before the core temperature has begun to fall.

In conditions of **heat stress,** such as arise owing to increased thermogenesis during exercise, the **internal warm receptors** are excited and trigger **heat-elimination processes** (vasodilation, sweating). This effect is counteracted by cold-activation of the cutaneous cold receptors. The cutaneous warm receptors cannot be expected to contribute much to heat-loss initiation during exercise, because in this situation the secretion and evaporation of sweat bring the skin temperature below that corresponding to thermoneutrality (cf. Fig. 23-7). But when the body is heated externally, sweat secretion is stimulated by the joint action of cutaneous and internal warm receptors (Fig. 23-12).

A neuronal model of the central controller. Current concepts of the way in which **small groups of neurons** operate (pp. 71 ff.) suggest the following picture of the neuronal correlates of the integrative function of the hypothalamus (Fig. 23-12). Three kinds of neuronal elements are distinguished: 1. *efferent neurons* located in the hypothalamus, the axons of which activate the peripheral controlling elements (Fig. 23-10) either directly or, more probably, by way of a chain of interneurons, 2. *interneurons* within the hypothalamus, and 3. *thermal afferents,* arising in part from the cutaneous thermoreceptors and in part from internal re-

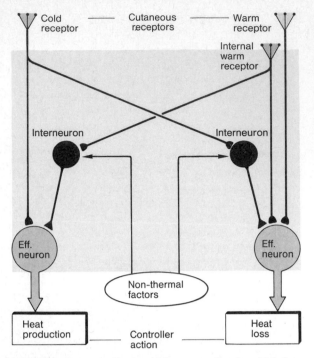

Fig. 23-12. Conceptualization of the connections by which thermal afferents influence the efferent neurons controlling the thermoregulatory effectors. Gray rectangle: integrative part of the hypothalamus. Some of the warm receptors in the body core are in the preoptic region, which is anatomically part of the hypothalamus. The interneurons have an inhibitory action. Such internal cold receptors as may exist are neglected

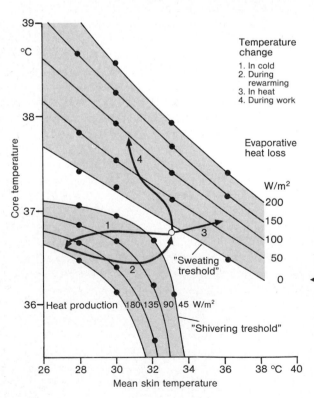

ceptors (e.g., those of the preoptic region). As shown in Fig. 23-12, cutaneous cold receptors directly activate the effectors for thermogenesis; their inhibitory action on the efferents to the heat-loss effectors is exerted by way of interneurons. Activation of the internal warm receptors by increased core temperature excites the efferents to the heat-loss effectors, simultaneously (again by way of interneurons) inhibiting the efferents to the effectors for heat production [1, 6, 26].

Processing of the thermal information. An attempt to represent the **effector outputs** quantitatively as **functions of the surface and core temperatures** gives rise to very complicated nonlinear equations. Shivering (as well as nonshivering thermogenesis) can be represented as *sets of hyperbolas* on a graph with the superficial and internal temperatures as the coordinates (Fig. 23-13) [6, 19, 20, 24, 25]. Sweat secretion is a still more complicated function of the two temperatures [37], but approximates linearity more closely. The processing of the temperature signals is thus *additive* in the case of sweat secretion and *multiplicative* (the equation of a hyperbola is $x \cdot y = k$) in the case of shivering. Cutaneous blood flow obeys an equation like that for sweating [47]. The threshold for vasodilation under heat stress is somewhat lower than the threshold curve for sweating.

The diagram (Fig. 23-13) permits quantitative predictions of numerous thermoregulatory responses. The most important of these will now be examined.

Shivering is induced by cold when the skin temperature alone falls below the normal level (circle), as indicated by Arrow 1 in the diagram. The core temperature can actually rise slightly owing to **overshooting responses to cold,** though more pronounced increases in core temperature (for example, during exercise) would suppress the shivering triggered by cold. If the cold stress is prolonged, as during *swimming in cold water,* the core temperature eventually begins to fall. Subsequent rapid rewarming (by *sunbathing in the dunes,* perhaps) initially increases the skin temperature (Arrow 2) above the shivering threshold, so that shivering stops before the core temperature has recovered. *External heating* at first causes only the skin temperature to rise (Arrow 3); sweating begins while the core temperature is still nearly normal. During *work* (Arrow 4) sweating begins with the *initial sharp rise in internal temperature,* and evaporation then lowers the skin temperature (cf. Fig. 23-7). Therefore if a working person is to secrete sweat at the maximal rate, the internal temperature must rise higher, the lower the ambient (and hence the skin) temperature. Considering the core temperature alone,

Fig. 23-13. Graph illustrating the dependence of shivering and sweating on the mean skin temperature and the core temperature. The circle corresponds to the temperature under thermoneutral conditions. The diagram applies quantitatively only to a particular time of day and a particular state of acclimatization. The set-point shifts described in the text would be represented by shifting the contour lines in the coordinate system. From data and calculations in [19, 20, 25, 37, 43] one would conclude that the thermoregulation system is very inaccurate – that is, that the actual state of the system *departs widely from the set point*. Indeed, the internal temperature was once regarded as the controlled variable, and this discrepancy was extremely difficult to understand; it was thought that during work, as in the case of fever (p. 546), there was a *shift in the set point for body temperature*. But when thermoregulation is considered as a system with multiple inputs and with a weighted mean body temperature as the controlled variable [16, 25], then the **load error** no longer appears so large. In this view there is no need to assume that the set point is shifted during work.

The relative independence of the core temperature from the ambient temperature (for references see [6]) can be explained as follows. When one is working in an erect position the system that regulates circulation shifts the threshold for thermoregulatory vasodilation of the cutaneous vessels to higher body temperatures (Fig. 24-10). As long as vasoconstriction persists in a moderately high ambient temperature, the low conductance (cf. p. 536) brings about a steep temperature gradient with a relatively high internal temperature.

The **load error** that develops under rapid thermal stress is diminished by the so-called **dynamic sensitivity** of the cutaneous thermoreceptors (pp. 220 ff.). Because of this property, when the temperature changes quickly (jumping into cold water) pronounced thermal responses occur, which may soon fade out.

In the region **between the sweating and shivering thresholds** (white area in Fig. 23-13) the temperature is controlled entirely by **vasomotor and behavioral mechanisms**. Whenever possible people try to behave in such a way as to remain in the restricted region of vasomotor control, for sweating and shivering feel uncomfortable.

The Set Point and Its Adjustment

The temperature fluctuations associated with the diurnal and menstrual cycles (p. 535) and the abnormally high temperatures during fever are regarded as shifts of the set point. But when using the term *"set point"* in this connection we become aware that there is a limit to the analogy between biological and technical systems. To the technologist the term is unambiguous; it denotes precisely the value of the controlled variable that the designer intends to maintain with the smallest possible variation; it is set intentionally, and if circumstances require it can be shifted intentionally. In the case of biological systems there is no designer whose "intentions" can be specified, so that the term (if it is not to be discarded as inappropriate to such systems) must be defined indirectly. One can determine the constellation of temperatures at which the individual control processes come into operation (regulatory enhancement of thermogenesis, sweat

secretion and so on). Such analysis provides the threshold curves for shivering and sweat secretion (Fig. 23-13). The "set point" of the system can be thought of as the integrated steady-state **body temperature at which neither the mechanisms for heat elimination nor those for protection against cold are active**. In other words, *the "set point" is a function of the threshold temperatures for the various control processes*.

Let us consider the possible **neurophysiological basis** for the establishment of a threshold curve at a certain level. One might propose that the particular form of a threshold curve is simply the expression of the functional characteristics of the cold and warm receptors involved. At the "normal" temperature both types would be equally active, and they would cancel each other out. With a positive or negative deviation from the set point the resulting predominance of warm or cold signals, respectively, would initiate the appropriate control processes. A "set-point shift" would then be ascribable to a change in the functional characteristics of the thermoreceptors. But long-term cold stress has been found to shift the threshold curves (p. 545) with no associated functional change in the cutaneous thermoreceptors [6]. This finding suggests that functional changes in **nonthermosensitive interneurons** (cf. Fig. 23-12) **cause the threshold shifts**.

This proposal is supported chiefly by the following experimental results [51]. Microinjection of noradrenalin into a hypothalamic area with no thermosensitive properties, which presumably contains the interneurons diagrammed in Fig. 23-12, shifts the threshold for metabolic reactions to higher temperatures. The same effect is obtained by electrical stimulation of a recently demonstrated *catecholaminergic pathway,* which *ascends from the reticular formation of the pons* and ends in the region of these interneurons [26]. Stimulation of this pathway is ineffective in the presence of adrenergic α-blocking agents. According to this concept, *the thresholds for responses to prevent overcooling and overheating are determined by the spontaneous activity of the interneurons, which can be modified by non-thermal factors* (cf. Fig. 23-12). For example, if the level of spontaneous activity of the interneuron on the left in Fig. 23-12 is high, greater activity of the cutaneous cold receptors is required to increase thermogenesis; the threshold for regulatory heat production is at a lower temperature. If the interneuron is inhibited by a non-thermal factor even slight afferent input from the cutaneous cold receptors can suffice to elicit heat production – that is, the threshold has been raised.

A change in threshold can also be produced by changing the **intracerebral Ca^{++}/Na^+ concentration ratio** [36]. It is not yet certain, however, whether changes in the Ca^{++}/Na^+ ratio as large as are required for this effect ever occur under normal physiological conditions.

23.5 Ontogenetic and Adaptive Changes in Thermoregulation

Thermoregulation in the Newborn

The newborn of various mammalian species (ground squirrel, hamster) are incapable of thermoregulatory heat production immediately after birth; their meta-

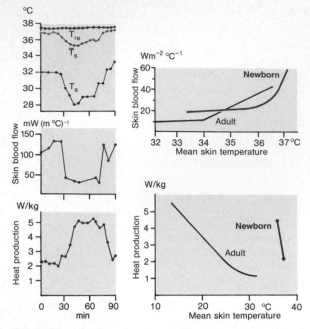

Fig. 23-14. *Left:* Thermoregulatory alterations in skin blood flow (heel: measured as thermal conductivity) and in metabolic rate of a human newborn under cold stress (ambient temperature reduced to 28 °C). It is evident that the thermoregulatory responses appear as soon as the mean skin temperature $\bar{T}_s$ begins to fall. The core temperature T_{re} is kept constant. *Right:* Total peripheral blood flow (measured as *conductance;* cf. p. 536) and heat production as a function of the mean skin temperature. Note that thermoregulatory heat production and vasoconstriction occur at a higher skin temperature in the newborn than in the adult. After [23]

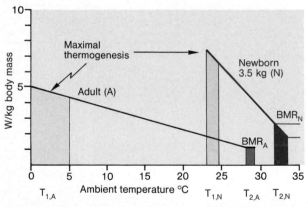

Fig. 23-15. Thermogenesis as a function of the ambient temperature in newborn and adult. The inflection point of each curve marks the lower limit of the thermoneutral zone (T_2), which in the case of the newborn is shifted to a higher temperature because of the relatively low standard metabolic rate (SMR). (SMR = minimal metabolic rate as measured under standard condition specified for neonates, similar to but not identical with BMR conditions employed in adults). As the SMR rises during the first week of life, $T_{2,N}$ shifts to the left. The lower limit of the regulated range (T_1) is determined by the maximal rate of heat production, and is ca. 23 °C in the newborn and 0°–5 °C in the adult. The diagram is based on data from [23]. Evaporative heat loss has been neglected

bolic rates change with temperature like those of poikilothermic organisms (cf. Fig. 23-1). Not until several weeks have passed do the effector mechanisms become capable of responding to a thermal stimulus. In other species (cf. Fig. 23-3), including humans (Fig. 23-14), **all thermoregulatory responses** (enhanced thermogenesis, vasomotor responses, sweat secretion, behavior patterns) **can be triggered immediately after birth,** even in premature infants weighing about 1 000 g at birth [23]. It is widely asserted that neonates and prematures are poikilothermic, certain brain structures responsible for thermoregulation not yet being fully developed. This misapprehension could arise from the fact that newborn infants as a rule rely not on shivering but on nonshivering thermogenesis (p. 532), which cannot be detected without special measuring devices. Their heat production can be raised 100–200% above the resting metabolic rate without shivering (Fig. 23-3). Only under extreme cold stress is this mechanism supplemented by shivering.

The small size of a newborn child is a disadvantage with regard to thermoregulation. The **surface-to-volume ratio** of a **mature newborn** is about three times that of an adult. Moreover, the shell of the body is not very thick and the insulating layer of fat is thin. Therefore even maximal vasoconstriction cannot restrict heat transfer to the extent possible in adults (cf. higher *conductance,* Fig. 23-14). These special problems must be overcome by an increased capacity for heat production – 4 to 5 times as great per unit weight in the mature newborn, and 1 to 10 times in a premature infant weighing 1 000–1 500 g. Immediately after birth the minimal metabolic rate, 1.7 W/kg, is actually below the exponential curve with n = 0.75 shown in Fig. 23-2, but during the first few days and weeks it rises to ca. 2.7 W/kg – a value distinctly above the n = 0.75 curve.

Therefore **if thermal balance is to be maintained at the minimal metabolic rate in the newborn, the ambient temperature must be higher, 32°–34 °C** (Fig. 23-15). Below this temperature thermoregulatory heat production is required to maintain equilibrium, and it does in fact occur – that is, the **lower boundary of the thermoneutral zone** (T_2 in Fig. 23-15) **is shifted to a higher ambient temperature.** The *lower limit of the regulated range* (T_1 in Fig. 23-15) is also shifted to higher temperatures; in the mature newborn it is about 23 °C, and in the nude adult about 0 °C. Within this **restricted control range,** however, the newborn can regulate its body temperature just as accurately as an adult, because the threshold temperatures for vasoconstriction and thermogenesis are adjusted to body size (Fig. 23-14). In prematures T_1 and T_2 (Fig. 23-15) shift upward with decreasing body size, and the two values approach one another. In very small prematures, therefore, thermoregulation becomes ineffective.

Long-Term Adaptation to the Environment

The *regulatory mechanisms* – thermogenesis, vasomotor responses, sweating – are always prepared for action, so that they can begin to operate within seconds or minutes of the onset of thermal stress. Other mechanisms are available for *long-term adaptation* to changes in the climate in which an organism lives.
These processes, also called **physiological adaptation** or **acclimation,** are based on modifications of organs and functional systems that develop only under the pressure of days, weeks or months of continuous or repeated thermal stress [6, 32].

Heat adaptation. The ability of humans to adapt to heat is crucial for life in tropical or desert climates when strenuous physical work is undertaken. The most important modification that occurs during heat adaptation is in the rate of sweat secretion, which can increase by a factor of 3 and for short periods amount to as much as 4 liters per hour. In the course of adaptation, the electrolyte content of the sweat is markedly diminished, so that there is less danger of disturbances due to *loss of electrolytes.*
One fundamental modification – popular opinion to the contrary – is that as heat adaptation progresses one feels thirstier at a given level of water loss through sweating. This is due in part to the lower electrolyte content of the sweat (cf. osmoregulation, pp. 632f.). The increased thirst is necessary to ensure the maintenance of water balance; if the lost water cannot be replenished, potentially lethal hyperthermia can result.
Moreover, the threshold temperatures for the elicitation of vasodilatation and sweating change during heat adaptation – in different directions, surprisingly, depending on whether people are subjected to severe acute or moderate chronic heat exposure. Thus the onset of sweating and peripheral vasodilation is found at about 0.5 °C lower core temperature after four to six days when people are subjected daily to one or two hours of heat stress resulting in maximum sweat secretion. The biological significance of the threshold shift is to be seen in the fact that body temperature for the given heat or work load is lower, so that the body is protected from critical increases in heart rate and peripheral blood flow that could lead to heat syncope. By contrast, in residents and sojourners in areas with tropic climates – that is, in people chronically exposed to moderate heat stress – in-

creased core temperature at rest is found and the onset of sweating and skin vasodilation occurs at about 0.5 °C higher body temperature than in a temperate climate [39a]. This type of heat adaptation is called *tolerance adaptation* (cf. below, tolerance adaptation to cold).

Cold adaptation. Many animal species adapt to cold in a very conspicuous way, increasing their **thermal insulation** by growing fur. Another fundamental modification found in small animals is the development of **nonshivering thermogenesis** and brown adipose tissue (cf. p. 532). Nonshivering thermogenesis can be regarded as an economical mechanism of heat production, because during shivering the rhythmical movements promote air motion around the body and thus increase the rate of convective heat loss (reduction of the boundary layer; cf. p. 536). An adult human exposed to extreme cold for long periods cannot grow a fur coat, nor can he develop appreciable nonshivering thermogenesis. For this reason it is often claimed that adult humans are incapable of any physiological adaptation to cold – that they must rely on "behavioral adaptation" (clothing and heated houses). It is said that human is a "tropical creature" who can survive the temperate or arctic climate only by virtue of his intelligence. But in recent years new light has been shed on this question. During prolonged exposure to cold humans develop **tolerance adaptation.** The shivering threshold and the curves of uniformly intense metabolic thermoregulatory reactions are shifted to lower positions in the temperature coordinate system (Fig. 23-13). This adaptation to cold involves an increase in the load error, so that moderate **hypothermia** can result.

This sort of tolerance adaptation was first noted in Australian aborigines, who can spend the night almost naked without shivering, even though the air temperature is near freezing [32]. This ability is also well developed in the amas – Korean and Japanese women who dive for pearls several hours a day in water at about 10 °C.

Recent studies have shown that the **shivering threshold can be shifted to lower temperatures** in the course of only a few days by repeated 30-to-60-min cold stress [22]. In this process, the threshold for the heat-eliminating mechanisms (sweating, in humans) is unchanged. That is, the white band in Fig. 23-13 becomes wider. This *expansion of the interthreshold zone* makes thermoregulation more economical – at the price, however, of precision [22, 26].

When exposure to cold is prolonged this form of adaptation seems unsuitable. In fact, the Alacaluf Indians of the western Patagonian islands have been found to employ another strategy. These people, who are continually subjected to cold air, rain and snow, have a basal metabolic rate 25–50% higher than normal [32]. A similar phenomenon (**"metabolic adaptation"**) has also been found in Eskimos.

Local adaptation. When the hands of a person who is otherwise warmly dressed are repeatedly exposed to cold, the pain felt in the hands diminishes. This effect is partly due to the fact that cold-vasodilation (cf. p. 540) occurs at higher skin temperature. But there are other events, not yet explained, which help to reduce the painful sensations due to cold [10, 30].

23.6   Pathophysiology of Thermoregulation

Fever

Fever is thought to amount to a **shift of the "set point"** for body temperature. The fever **develops** as a result of increased heat production by shivering combined with maximal vasoconstriction of the peripheral vessels. That is, the body behaves as that of a healthy person does when external cooling has shifted the actual temperature of the body below the normal set point. During recovery from the fever just the reverse occurs; sweat secretion and vasodilation reduce the body temperature exactly as they do in a healthy person who has become too warm. While the fever persists external thermal disturbances are compensated by the appropriate control processes – the thermoregulatory effectors remain fully functional. The temperature, however, is being regulated at an increased level.

It has been proposed that the **pathogenesis of fever** involves the following mechanisms [15]. Certain substances called *pyrogens,* chief among which are lipopolysaccharides of bacterial membranes, stimulate the leukocytes to produce a fever-inducing substance called **leukocyte pyrogen,** which can be extracted from the serum of feverish animals. When this leukocyte pyrogen is injected into the hypothalamus of a cat there is an immediate onset of fever – which does not occur when the same amount of the pyrogen is injected into other parts of the brain [28]. It is thought that the pyrogen acts on integrative elements within the hypothalamus, perhaps on the inhibitory interneurons (Fig. 23-12). In addition, it many change the sensitivity of the central thermoreceptors.

Failure of Thermoregulation at Extreme Temperatures

Hyperthermia. Extreme heat stress, such that the body's capacity for heat loss is exceeded, causes a pathological increase in the temperature of the body.

The subjective sensations produced by this buildup of heat are far more unpleasant than those accompanying fever. In hyperthermia all the effector processes are strained to the utmost, whereas in fever they are not. The **limiting temperature for survival,** however, is the same in both cases – a body temperature of 42 °C. For brief periods people have been known to survive temperatures as high as 43 °C.

In prolonged hyperthermia, with temperatures over 40°–41 °C, the brain suffers severe damage which usually soon leads to death; cerebral edema develops, neurons are destroyed, and the victim exhibits disorientation, delirium and convulsions. This syndrome is popularly referred to as **sunstroke** or **heatstroke,** depending on the circumstances. The brain damage interferes with the central thermoregulatory mechanisms. In particular, sweat secretion ceases, so that the condition is further exacerbated.

These serious disorders should be distinguished from the phenomenon of **heat syncope,** which can occur under relatively mild heat stress and is promoted by prolonged standing. People with orthostatic regulatory malfunction are particularly prone to heat syncope. It is characterized by extreme vasodilation and a sharp drop in blood pressure; it is more a disturbance of the circulatory system than of temperature control (and is thus an example of the interlocking of control circuits) (cf. p. 442).

Hypothermia. When the mechanisms for protection against cold are overloaded – that is, after long exposure to temperatures below T_2 in Fig. 23-4 – hypothermia results. Initially the thermoregulatory processes are operating at full capacity. During this phase, especially at body temperatures around 26°–28 °C, death can occur by myocardial **fibrillation.** If **"induced hypothermia"** is required for therapeutic reasons (cf. p. 531), the thermoregulatory mechanisms must be put out of action by general anesthesia (cf. Fig. 23-1) or by specific inhibiting agents [44].

Hypothermia in this strict sense differs from a reaction found **in the aged.** Some old people can maintain a core temperature of 35 °C or even less without the onset of shivering; the regulatory system has been reset to this low level, and it continues to function normally in other respects. To some extent, this is the counterpart of fever [27].

23.7 References

Textbooks and Handbooks

1. BLIGH, J.: Temperature Regulation in Mammals and Other Vertebrates. Amsterdam–London: North Holland Publ; New York: Elsevier Publ. 1973
2. BURTON, A.C., EDHOLM, O.G.: Man in a Cold Environment. New York–London: Hafner Publ. Co. 1969
3. FANGER, P.O.: Thermal Comfort. Analysis and Applications in Environmental Engineering. New York: McGraw Hill Book Co. 1972
4. FOLK, G.E.: Introduction to Environmental Physiology. Philadelphia: Lee & Febiger 1966
5. HARDY, J.D., GAGGE, P.A., STOLWIJK, J.A.J. (Eds): Physiological and Behavioral Temperature Regulation. Springfield, Ill.: Ch.C. Thomas 1970
6. HENSEL, H., BRÜCK, K., RATHS, P.: Homeothermic organisms. In: Temperature and Life (H. PPRECHT, J. CHRISTOPHERSEN, H. HENSEL, W. LARCHER, Eds.) Berlin–Heidelberg–New York: Springer 1973
7. KEATINGE, W.R.: Survival in Cold Water. Oxford–Edinburgh: Blackwell 1969
8. KERSLAKE, D. MCK.: The Stress of Hot Environments. Cambridge: University Press 1972
9. KLEIBER, M.: The Fire of Life. New York–London: John Wiley & Sons 1961
10. LEBLANC, J.: Man in the Cold. Springfield, Ill.: Ch.C. Thomas 1975
11. LINDBERG, O. (Ed.): Brown Adipose Tissue. New York: Amer. Elsevier Publ. 1970
12. MONTEITH, J.L., MOUNT, L.E. (Eds.): Heat Loss from Animals and Man. London: Butterworths 1974
13. SINCLAIR, J.S. (Ed.): Temperature Regulation and Energy Metabolism in the Newborn. New York–San Francisco–London: Grune & Stratton 1978
14. WHITTOW, G.C.: Comparative Physiology of Thermoregulation, Vol. I–III. New York–London: Academic Press 1971
15. WOLSTENHOLME, G.E.W., BIRCH, J. (Eds.): Pyrogens and Fever. Edinburgh–London: Churchill Livingstone 1971

Research Reports and Reviews

16. ASCHOFF, H.: Circadian rhythm of activity and of body temperature. In: Physiological and Behavioral Temperature Regulation (HARDY, J.D., GAGGE, A.P., STOLWIJK, J.A.J., (Eds.). Springfield, Ill.: Ch.C. Thomas 1970
17. ASCHOFF, J., WEVER, R.: Kern und Schale im Wärmehaushalt des Menschen. Naturwissenschaften 45, 477 (1958)
18. BEHMANN, F.W., BONTKE, E.: Die Regelung der Wärmebildung bei künstlicher Hypothermie. I. Experimentelle Untersuchungen über den Einfluß der Narkosetiefe. Pflügers Arch. ges. Physiol. 206, 408 (1958)
19. BENZINGER, T.H.: Heat regulation: Homeostasis of central temperature in man. Physiol. Rev. 49, 671 (1969)
20. BROWN, A.C., BRENGELMANN, G.L.: The temperature regulation control system. In: see Ref. 5
21. BRÜCK, K.: Non-shivering thermogenesis and brown adipose tissue in relation to age and their integration in the thermoregulatory system. In: see Ref. 11
22. BRÜCK, K.: Cold adaptation in man. In: Depressed Metabolism and Cold Thermogenesis (L. JANSKÝ, X.J. MUSACCHIA, Eds.). Springfield, Ill.: Ch.C. Thomas 1976
23. BRÜCK, K.: Heat production and temperature regulation. In: Perinatal Physiology (U. STAVE, Ed.). New York: Plenum Publ. Corp. 1978
24. BRÜCK, K., SCHWENNICKE, H.P.: Interaction of superficial and hypothalamic thermosensitive structures in the control of non-shivering thermogenesis. In. J. Biometeorol. 15, 156 (1971)
25. BRÜCK, K., WÜNNENBERG, W.: Meshed control of two effector systems: Non-shivering and shivering thermogenesis. In: see Ref. 5
26. BRÜCK, K., ZEISBERGER, E.: Significance and possible central mechanisms of thermoregulatory threshold deviations in thermal adaptation. In: Strategies in Cold: Natural Torpidity and Thermogenesis (J.W. HUDSON, L.C.H. WANG, Eds.). London–New York: Academic Press 1978

27. COOPER, K.E.: Studies of the human central warm receptor. In: see Ref. 5
28. COOPER, K.E., CRANSTON, W.I., HONOUR, A.J.: Observations on the site and mode of action of pyrogens in the rabbit brain. J. Physiol. (Lond.) 191, 325 (1967)
29. DUBOIS, E.F.: The mechanism of heat loss and temperature regulation. Stanford, Calif.: Stanford Univ. Press 1937
30. EAGAN, C.J.: Local vascular adaptations to cold in man. Fed. Proc. 22, 947 (1963)
31. GAGGE, A.P., NISHI, Y.: Physical indices of the thermal environment. ASHRAE J., January 1976, pp. 47–51
32. HAMMEL, H.T.: Terrestrial animals in cold: recent studies of primitive man. In: Handbook of Physiology, Sect. 4: Adaptation to the Environment, p. 413. Washington: Amer. Physiol. Soc. 1964
33. HARDY, J.D.: Physiology of temperature regulation. Physiol. Rev. 41, 521 (1961)
34. HIMMS-HAGEN, J.: Biochemical aspects of nonshivering thermogenesis. In: Strategies in Cold: Natural Torpidity and Thermogenesis (J.W. HUDSON, L.C.H. WANG, Eds.). London–New York: Academic Press 1978
35. JESSEN, C.: Auslösung von Hecheln durch isolierte Wärmung des Rückenmarks am wachen Hund. Pflügers Arch. ges. Physiol. 297, 53 (1967)
36. MYERS, R.D., VEALE, W.L.: The role of sodium and calcium ions in the hypothalamus in the control of body temperature of the unanesthetized cat. J. Physiol. (Lond.) 212, 411 (1971)
37. NADEL, E.R., BULLARD, R.W., STOLWIJK, J.A.J.: Importance of skin temperature in the regulation of sweating. J. appl. Physiol. 31, 80 (1971)
38. NAKAYAMA, T., HAMMEL, H.T., HARDY, J.D., EISENMAN, J.S.: Thermal stimulation of electrical activity of single units of the preoptic region. Amer. J. Physiol. 204, 1122 (1963)
39. PUGH, L.G.C.E., CORBETT, J.L., JOHNSON, R.H.: Rectal temperatures, weight losses and sweat rate in marathon running. J. appl. Physiol. 23, 347 (1967)
39a. RAYNAUD, J., MARTINEAUD, J.P., BHATNAGER, O.P., VIELLEFOND, H., DURAND, J.: Body temperatures during rest and exercise in residents and sojourners in hot climate. Int. J. Biometeor. 20, 309–317, (1976)
40. SCHMIDT, T.H.: Thermoregulatorische Größen in Abhängigkeit von Tageszeit und Menstruationscyclus. Inaugural Dissertation (MPI für Verhaltensforschung). München 1972
41. SIMON, E.: Temperature regulation: the spinal cord as a site of extrahypothalamic thermoregulatory functions. Rev. Physiol. Biochem. Pharmacol. 71, 1 (1974)
42. SMITH, R.M., HANNA, J.M.: Skinfolds and resting heat loss in cold air and water: Temperature equivalence. J. appl. Physiol. 39, 93 (1975)
43. STOLWIJK, J.A.J., HARDY, J.D.: Temperature regulation in man – a theoretical study. Pflügers Arch. ges. Physiol. 291, 129 (1966)
44. THAUER, R., BRENDEL, W.: Hypothermie. Progr. Surg. (Basel) 2, 73 (1962)
45. THAUER, R., SIMON, E.: Spinal cord and temperature regulation. In: Advances in Climatic Physiology (S. ITOH, K. OGATA, H. YOSHIMURA, Eds.) Igaku Shoin Ltd. Tokyo. Berlin–Heidelberg–New York: Springer 1972
46. WEBB-PEPLOE, M.M., SHEPHERD, J.T.: Response of dogs' cutaneous veins to local and central temperature changes. Circulat. Res. 23, 693 (1968)
47. WENGER, C.B., ROBERTS, M.F., NADEL, E.R., STOLWIJK, J.A.J.: Thermoregulatory control of finger blood flow. J. appl. Physiol. 38, 78 (1975)
48. WÜNNENBERG, W., BRÜCK, K.: Studies on the ascending pathways from the thermosensitive region of the spinal cord. Pflügers Arch. ges. Physiol. 321, 233 (1970)
49. WÜNNENBERG, W.: Thermo-integrative function of the hypothalamus. Int. Symposium on Depressed Metabolism and Cold Thermogenesis. Prague 1974. Springfield, Ill.: Ch.C. Thomas 1976
50. WÜNNENBERG, W., HARDY, J.D.: Response of single units of the posterior hypothalamus to thermal stimulation. J. appl. Physiol. 33, 547 (1972)
51. ZEISBERGER, E., BRÜCK, K.: Effects of intrahypothalamically injected noradrenergic and cholinergic agents on thermoregulatory responses. In: The Pharmacology of Thermoregulation. Symp. 5th Congress on Pharmacology. San Francisco 1972 (E. SCHÖNBAUM, P. LOMAX, Eds.), p. 232. Basel: Karger 1973

24 Work Physiology; Environmental Physiology

H.-V. ULMER

24.1 Fundamentals of Work Physiology

The area of applied physiology concerned with work (which includes sports physiology) is closely related to environmental physiology. In recent years the environmental factors with which the organism must cope have become more varied, and work must more often be done unter difficult environmental conditions – in extreme climates, at high altitudes (e.g., air and space travel), and at great depths (in mines or underwater).

The study of work physiology is not concerned solely with the physical work loads encountered during performance of a job or a sport and their effects on man. At one time hard physical labor was a common feature of life, but most present-day workers must perform tasks requiring *pattern recognition, rapid information uptake and processing, and the ability to make plans and decisions* (e.g., on assembly lines, and at testing stations and checkpoints). The work physiologist must devote an ever greater part of his attention to such psychological aspects – even in the area of sport, although here severe to extreme physical exertion usually predominates.

When the work load is too great, whatever its nature, the body is overstrained and health deteriorates. Health is defined by the World Health Organization (WHO) as follows: *a condition of complete physical, mental and social well-being, which cannot be achieved solely by the absence of sickness and weakness.*

Humane working conditions cannot be established without a knowledge of the principles of work physiology. The work physiologist is therefore concerned with the *reciprocal relations between man and his place of work* (including the sports field). Almost all areas of physiology are involved in these relations. Only by this approach can one set up guidelines to *adapt the work environment* or machine to the worker – or, conversely, to *adapt the worker* to the work environment (by aptitude tests or training). In this sense work physiology is a science of optimization, in which human well-being is to be optimized.

In this chapter emphasis is intentionally placed on the physiological *phenomena* associated with work. The physiological *relationships* are discussed in the chapters devoted to the various functional systems involved in work, and the reader should refer to these chapters, if necessary.

Load, Performance and Strain

Terminology. The externally imposed **load** can affect (as stress) different individuals in different ways. The individual's **performance** in dealing with this load is measurable in terms of power, and the resulting **strain** is measurable in terms of various physiological functions (Fig. 24-1). *Psychological* and *physical* loads can be distinguished; in the latter case physical dimensions can usually characterize the load precisely, but psychological loads can often be described only verbally. Some responses to psychological loads are discussed on p. 555.

Factors determining strain. The degree to which physiological functions must be adjusted to deal with a given load depends chiefly on the following two individually variable factors:

Performance capacity. This term denotes the organism's ability to respond to a load and thus achieve a certain performance. Performance capacity depends on one's state of *health and training,* and on *talent* (cf. p. 564). It is also affected, in any particular case, by the environment (e. g., climate, time of day, noise) and one's general psychological condition.

Efficiency (η). Efficiency is defined as the ratio of external (physical) work to total metabolic rate (p. 523). For a given performance, the lower the efficiency is, the greater is the strain.

Types of Performance

Performance can also be *physical* or *psychological,* depending on the nature of the load, though it is often difficult to distinguish the two even on the basis of strain parameters. Physical performance, like physical loads, can be expressed in physical dimensions;

psychological performance – as in artistic creativity or scientific research – is often not measurable.

Physical performance. Dynamic work is done when, in a physical sense, resistances are overcome along a certain distance. In this case (e. g., bicycling and stair or mountain climbing) performance can be given in physical units (1 watt = 1 Joule/s = 1 Nm/s). In *positive* dynamic work the muscles act as a "motor," and in *negative* dynamic work they act as a "brake" (e. g., in descending a mountain). **Static work** is done during *isometric muscle contraction*. Because no distance is traversed this is not work in the physical sense; nevertheless, the body shows *physiological strain responses* to the demand. The performance in this case is measured as the *product* of force and time.

Psychological performance has *mental* and *emotional* components. The **mental** component predominates when the work involves primarily intellectual abilities; examples are problems requiring thought or concentration, and the detection and processing of signals while monitoring objects or events (e. g., checking products or driving a car). Psychological performance in which **emotional** components predominate is associated with distinct reactions of the autonomic nervous system, and tends to find expression in the person's mood (e. g., joy, anger, sadness and hopelessness, nervousness due to unfamiliarity, annoyance by noise).

Combined performance. Sensorimotor performance involves not strenuous muscular effort but rather a degree of dexterity, as in surgical operations or machine assembly. In many activities **environmental influences** cause strain in various organ systems – *noise and vibration* affect workers in heavy industry, vehicle drivers and airport personnel, *heat and cold* act near blast-furnaces and in mines and extreme climates, *pressure* is a factor for divers, pilots and astronauts, and *acceleration* ("g load") can be extreme in aircraft and spacecraft.

Ergometry

Ergometry is a procedure for *determining physical performance capacity*. A specified load (expressed in watts or joules/s) is imposed, while performance and physiological reactions of the subject are monitored. In the simplest case the weight of the body is lifted by **knee bends** or **stepping upward**. The associated *dynamic work* depends on the weight and the distance it is raised; efficiency varies greatly, depending on the way the movement is done, so that it is difficult to compare the physiological strain reactions. **Ergometers** allow efficiency to be kept fairly constant during the performance of work [24, 32]; they take two basic forms, as follows.

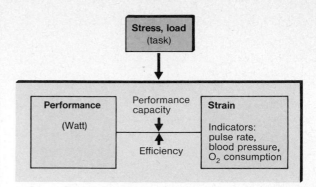

Fig. 24-1. Diagram of the load-strain concept for the case of dynamic work. The load is the assigned task; the strain a person undergoes in performing it depends on his performance capacity and efficiency

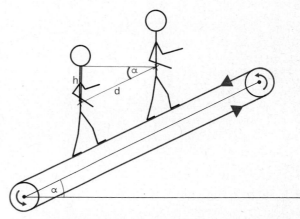

Fig. 24-2. Treadmill ergometer. Depending on the velocity of the belt, the center of gravity of the body, moving over the distance *d* in time *t,* is lowered by the amount *h*. To keep his height *h* constant, a subject must walk "in place" rapidly enough that his body weight *w* is raised by the amount $d \cdot \sin \alpha$. Performance *P* is then given by $P \doteq w \cdot d \cdot \sin \alpha \cdot t^{-1}$

Bicycle ergometers. The wheel of a stationary bicycle, with a specified mass, is rotated against a specified braking force (applied by a friction belt, a dynamo or an eddy-current brake). The higher the frequency of cranking (rotations/min, rpm) and the greater the braking force (f), the greater is the performance achieved. That is, performance (p) is given by: p ≈ rpm · f. Many ergometers display performance automatically; the accuracy of this display should be checked annually.

Treadmill ergometers (Fig. 24-2). When a subject maintains position by walking on an inclined treadmill the center of gravity of the body is continually raised by the same amount that the velocity and slope of the treadmill lower it. These two variables (as in mountain climbing) thus determine the performance. Like the bicycle ergometer, this apparatus permits work with an efficiency of 20–25%.

24.2   Adjustments to Physical Loads

Physical exertion elicits immediate reactions of various organ systems, including the muscular, the cardiovascular and the respiratory system. The extent of this *adjustment,* as a rule, is a direct measure of strain.

Intraindividual and interindividual differences. A given performance can require different physiological adjustments of an individual depending, for example, on the time of day or the ambient temperature; these are *intra*individual differences. There can also be considerable *inter*individual variation within a group of subjects.

Adjustments of the Dynamically Working Musculature

Blood flow through the muscles [3]. Blood flow through an active muscle increases with metabolic rate, by more than a *factor of twenty* during hard work. The increased flow does not appear at the onset of work, but builds up gradually over at least 20 to 30 s; during *light* dynamic work blood flow thereafter is matched to the demand. But during *heavy* dynamic work the demand cannot be matched, and the metabolism of the muscle must be adjusted to the inadequate blood flow.

Muscle metabolism. During *light* work energy is obtained anaerobically only during the brief period in which blood flow increases; thereafter metabolism is entirely *aerobic* (Fig. 24-3), utilizing glucose as well as fatty acids and glycerine [17]. During *heavy* work, by contrast, part of the energy is always obtained *anaerobically.* Anaerobic energy yield (lactic-acid forma-

tion) prevails when blood flow is insufficient, the O_2 saturation of the blood is reduced, or there are bottlenecks in the aerobic pathways (e. g., at the level of pyruvate dehydrogenase [17]). When lactic acid is produced in large amounts muscular fatigue results (pp. 46, 557).

When work begins a certain time is required for the aerobic energy yield of the muscle to increase; this gap is bridged by the briefly available **anaerobic energy reserves** (ATP and creatine phosphate). The amount of energy-rich phosphates stored is small as compared with the glycogen reserves (Table 24-1), but it is indispensable both for this bridging action and to support short-term extremes in performance [3, 17].

Cardiovascular Parameters during Dynamic Work

During dynamic work there are considerable adjustments of the cardiovascular system (pp. 442 f.). Cardiac output and blood flow through the working muscle are enhanced, so that supplies more nearly meet the increased demand and the heat produced is transported away from the working muscle to the point of release.

Heart rate. During light work with constant *performance* the heart rate rises during the first 5–10 min and reaches a *plateau;* this *steady state* is then maintained until the work is completed, even for several hours (Fig. 24-4). The greater the strain, the higher is the plateau. During heavy constant-performance work no such steady state is reached; heart rate rises with fatigue to a maximum that varies among individuals *(fatigue rise).* This different behavior of heart rate during light and heavy work has been demonstrated in experiments lasting as long as 8 hours [51]. Thus *two* forms of work can be distinguished on the basis of heart rate:
1. light, non-fatiguing work – steady state, and
2. heavy, fatiguing work – fatigue rise.

Even after the work session, heart rate varies according to the strain (Fig. 24-4). After light work it returns to the initial level within 3 to 5 min; after heavy work the **recovery time** (time to regain the initial level) is considerably longer, as much as several hours if the work was exhausting. Variations in the demands made by the work can be expressed in terms of the total number of pulse beats above the baseline (the initial pulse rate) during the recovery period (**"recovery pulse sum"** in Fig. 24-4).

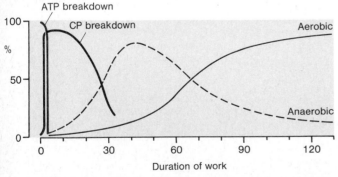

Fig. 24-3. Contribution of various substrates to the total energy yield in the muscle at the beginning of light work. Ordinate: % of the total energy contributed. In the first seconds almost all the energy is provided by adenosine triphosphate (ATP); the next source is creatine phosphate (CP). Whereas anaerobic glycolysis reaches a maximum after about 45 s, the muscle cannot obtain the major fraction of its energy by oxidative reactions until about 2 min have passed. After [17]

Table 24-1. Energy reserves of a person weighing 75 kg, in kJ. From [3]

ATP	4	Glycogen	4,600
CP	15	Fats	300,000

Stroke volume. The stroke volume of the heart rises only by 20–30% at the onset of work and then remains largely *constant*. Only when the strain is maximal does it decline slightly, because the heart rate is then so high that there is not enough time to fill the heart completely at each stroke. Both healthy athletes with their highly developed hearts (athlete's heart, p. 560) *and* non-athletes have a nearly proportional cardiac output and heart rate during work, because of this approximate constancy of the stroke volume.

Blood pressure. During dynamic work the *arterial blood pressure* changes as a function of performance (Fig. 24-5). The *systolic* blood pressure increases nearly in proportion to performance, reaching ca. 220 mm Hg (29 kPa) at 200 watts. The *diastolic* blood pressure changes only slightly, and often decreases. Therefore the *arterial mean pressure* always rises. In the *low-pressure system* (e. g., in the right atrium) there is little increase in blood pressure during work; a distinct rise here is a symptom of cardiac insufficiency.

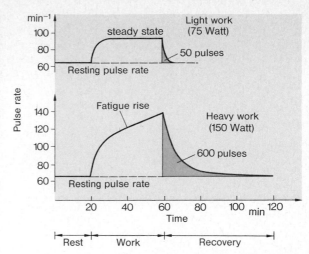

Fig. 24-4. Changes in pulse rate of subjects with average performance capacity during light and heavy dynamic work at constant performance. *Red:* recovery pulse sum. Modified from [52]

Oxygen Uptake and Respiration during Dynamic Work

The oxygen uptake of the organism increases by an amount depending on performance level and efficiency. During *light work* a steady state is reached in which oxygen uptake and consumption are in balance (Fig. 24-6) – but only after 3–5 min have elapsed, during which blood flow and muscle metabolism adjust to the new demand. Until the steady state is reached the muscle depends on the small *oxygen reserve* represented by the myoglobin-bound O_2 and the ability to extract more O_2 from the blood. During *heavy muscular work,* even if performance is constant, there is *no steady state;* as in the case of heart rate (Fig. 24-4), oxygen uptake rises continuously until a maximum is reached [32].

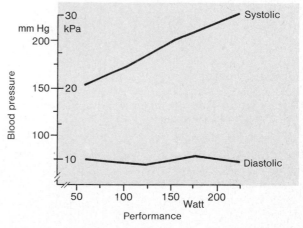

Fig. 24-5. Changes in systolic and diastolic blood pressure as a function of performance. After [14]

Oxygen debt. When work begins the demand for oxygen increases immediately, but blood flow and aerobic metabolism require some time to adjust; thus an oxygen debt is incurred (Fig. 24-6). During *light work* the oxygen debt remains constant after the steady state is reached, but during *heavy work* it builds up until the work ends. Then, particularly during the first few minutes, the rate of oxygen uptake remains above the resting level – the oxygen debt is being *repaid*. But this term is problematic, for the *increased oxygen uptake following work* does not directly reflect processes of replacement in the muscle, but is affected by other factors such as increases in body temperature and the work of breathing, changes in muscle tone and replenishment of the body's oxygen stores [17]. Thus the debt to be repaid is greater than that incurred during the work itself. After *light* work the oxygen debt amounts to as much as 4 l, and after *heavy* work as much as 20 l.

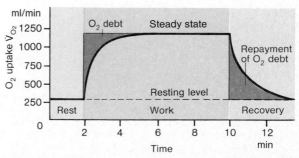

Fig. 24-6. Oxygen uptake during light dynamic work at constant performance

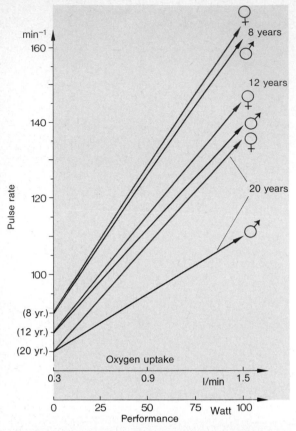

Fig. 24-7. Influence of age and sex on the relationship between pulse rate and oxygen uptake (or performance) during dynamic work. The performance scale applies only to ergometer work at a constant cranking frequency of 60 rpm. From averages given in [29]

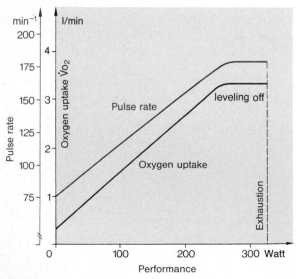

Fig. 24-8. Changes in oxygen uptake and pulse rate as performance rises continuously

Relation between oxygen uptake and heart rate. During dynamic work with a constant efficiency heart rate is *proportional* both to oxygen uptake and to performance. When efficiency varies the close relation between heart rate and oxygen uptake persists, but that between heart rate and performance does not [41]. The proportionality between pulse rate and oxygen uptake can be represented as a straight line (Fig. 24-7), the slope of which varies distinctly among individuals and depends especially on age and sex. For a given increase in oxygen uptake the pulse rate of *children rises more steeply than that of adults, and that of women more steeply than that of men*[29, 32].

The slope of a line on such a plot, the "performance pulse index (PPI)," was once used as a measure of endurance performance capacity [32], but it has since been shown that the PPI does not reflect the increase in performance produced by endurance training [62]. Among subjects at the same level of training the PPI does reflect differences in the capacity for endurance performance, in the sense of an occupational work capacity [51], but it has not proved to be a practicable general test.

The physiological mechanisms underlying the *close relation between heart rate and oxygen uptake* can be explained on the basis of the following hypothesis [32]. *Muscle receptors* other than the muscle spindles send information about the actual *metabolic activity* in the working musculature to the circulatory center. As a result not only local blood flow through the muscle, but the cardiac output as well, can be *adjusted to the momentary demand* over a wide range, cardiac output and heart rate changing in such a way as to maintain proportionality. The postulated muscle receptors have not yet been identified morphologically but there is much functional evidence that they exist.

Oxygen uptake and heart rate during increasing performance. As the intensity of dynamic work increases the heart beats more rapidly and the rate of oxygen uptake rises (Fig. 24-8); the greater the strain on the body, the greater is the increase above the resting level. Thus heart rate and the rate of oxygen uptake together are a *measure of physical strain*. States with considerable strain are reached when one is working hard even with high efficiency (25%), as well as during light work if efficiency is low (cf. p. 549).

When the **frequency of movement** is uniform *efficiency* is about the same regardless of performance. Therefore when performance gradually increases while frequency of movement remains constant *oxygen uptake* rises linearly to a maximum and then *levels off* (Fig. 24-8). In this plateau state the difference between oxygen demand and oxygen supply increases so rapidly that *acute exhaustion* occurs. Pulse rate changes similarly with performance. Once the maximal pulse rate has been reached after 10 to 30 min of heavy work, hardly any additional fatigue rise (Fig. 24-8) can be observed.

Ventilation. During light dynamic work the respiratory minute volume, like the cardiac output, rises in proportion to oxygen uptake. This increase results from an increase in tidal volume and/or respiratory frequency (cf. increased ventilation, p. 475).

The *proportionality* between oxygen uptake and minute volume during light work is thought to be controlled by metabolism-dependent *muscle receptors,* like the control mechanism that adjusts pulse rate. During *heavy* work the increase in minute volume is distinctly *greater than proportional* to the oxygen uptake, because the lactic acid formed in the muscle acts as a supplementary respiratory drive by causing *metabolic acidosis* of the blood.

Blood Parameters during Dynamic Work

During and after dynamic work there are many changes in the blood. Only occasionally do these permit assessment of the degree of physical strain, but they are of special value in laboratory diagnosis.

Blood gas levels. During *light* physical work a healthy person shows only slight changes in *arterial* CO_2 and O_2 partial pressures. *Heavy* work causes a distinct drop in P_{CO_2} with no appreciable changes in P_{O_2}. This situation reflects an *overshooting* increase in ventilation, brought about by a lactate-based acidosis in blood and muscles (Figs. 24-3, 24-9).

The O_2 saturation of *venous mixed blood* falls distinctly as the strain increases; accordingly, the arteriovenous difference (avD_{O_2}, p. 495) rises from ca. 0.05 (resting level) to as much as 0.14 in subjects without training and as much as 0.17 in trained subjects [3]. This increase is based on the improved extraction of oxygen from the blood in the working muscle, and on the restriction of blood flow wherever it is not urgently required (cf. collateral vasoconstriction, p. 443).

Blood cells. During physical work the *hematocrit* rises, as a result both of decreased plasma volume owing to greater capillary filtration and of the release of erythrocytes from their sites of production (with an increased proportion of immature forms). An increase in the number of leukocytes has also been observed (work leukocytosis).

The *leukocyte count* in the blood of long-distance runners increases with duration of the run, by 5000 to 15,000/µl depending on performance capacity (less in those with greater capacity). The increase is due primarily to the neutrophilic granulocytes, so that the *proportions of the different cells* change. Moreover, the *thrombocyte count* rises as a function of the intensity of work. Therefore blood samples should not be taken for the purpose of obtaining cell counts immediately after exercise; at least one hour of physical rest should be allowed.

Acid-base status of the blood. *Light* physical work does not affect the acid-base balance, for all the additional carbonic acid produced is released from the lungs. During *heavy* work metabolic acidosis is pro-

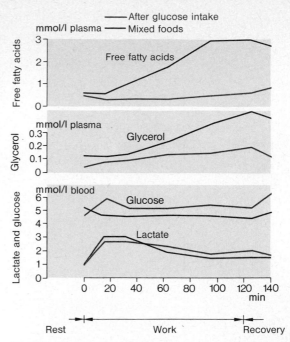

Fig. 24-9. Changes in concentration of lactate, glucose, glycerol and free fatty acids in the arterial blood during 2 hours of ergometer work, immediately preceded by intake of a mixed meal or of 200 g glucose; average pulse rate 150 min^{-1}. There is a distinct inhibition of lipolysis after carbohydrate intake. Modified from [46]

duced in proportion to the rate of lactate production [18], which is compensated partially by respiration (decrease in arterial P_{CO_2}).

Foodstuffs in the blood. The arterial **glucose** level of a healthy person hardly changes during work. Only when strenuous work is prolonged does the arterial glucose concentration decrease, a sign of approaching *exhaustion*. The blood **lactate** concentration, on the other hand, varies widely with the degree of strain [3, 17, 59], depending on the rate of its production in the anaerobically working muscle and the rate of elimination. Lactate is broken down by oxidation in non-working skeletal muscle and in the myocardium; small amounts are converted to glycogen in the liver. Under resting conditions the *arterial lactate concentration* is ca. 1 mmol/l; during hard work lasting about half an hour, or short periods of exhausting work at intervals of one minute, maxima exceeding 15 mmol/l can be reached. During prolonged heavy work the lactate concentration first rises and then declines (Fig. 24-9).

When the diet is rich in carbohydrate the arterial concentrations of the *free fatty acids* and of *glycerol* are little affected by work, for the secretion of insulin brought about by carbohydrate intake inhibits lipolysis [46]. But with an average diet prolonged heavy work is accompanied by fourfold or greater increases in

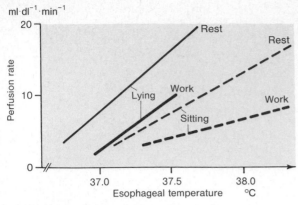

Fig. 24-10. Blood flow through the forearm ($\dot{Q}$) as a measure of skin perfusion at various core temperatures (esophageal temperature). During work (pulse rate 120 to 130 min^{-1}) skin perfusion is less than under equivalent resting conditions despite the increased heat production, and it is less when sitting than when lying down. After [45]

the blood concentrations of free fatty acids and glycerol (Fig. 24-9).

Other substances in the blood. During exercise the blood concentrations of certain *electrolytes* (e.g., potassium) and *organic substances* (e.g., transaminases) rise. These changes are explained by a change in the permeability of the muscle membrane, which allows intracellular components to escape into the bloodstream [18]. The return to the initial concentrations in some cases requires several days.

Thermoregulation during Dynamic Work

Sweating is generally regarded as a sign of hard work. The onset of visible sweating *(sensible perspiration)*, however, depends not only on the level of work but also on the environmental conditions. Sweat secretion begins when the **neutral temperature** (cf. pp. 533 f.) is exceeded, whether because of *increased heat production* during exercise or *insufficient heat loss* owing to high ambient temperature or humidity, improper clothing or the absence of air movement (convection) and finally to heating of the body by excessive thermal radiation (e.g., in a foundry) [3, 26, 32].

As performance increases, other conditions being equal, the secretion of sweat increases about in proportion to the *rectal temperature*. Because of the cooling effect of evaporation the *skin temperature* during sweating is lower than in the case of extraglandular water loss (pp. 537 and 542). After prolonged severe heat exposure the sweat production shows signs of *"fatigue,"* in that the rate of secretion declines. Under normal climatic conditions the average *rate of sweat secretion* during hard physical work or sport activity is about 1 l/h. During hard work *lactic acid* (up to 2 g/l) is contained in the sweat along with electro-

lytes; most of it originates directly in the secreting epithelium, so that its elimination is without effect on the acid-base balance of the body.

Skin perfusion. During exposure to heat while **at rest** blood flow through the skin is increased [26]; in the process, the cardiac output can reach double the initial level. The decrease in tone of the capacitive cutaneous vessels makes very little difference to a *reclining* person, but when *standing* an increased orthostatic intolerance becomes apparent. An abnormally large amount of blood collects in the skin of the lower part of the body, to the detriment of the intrathoracic blood volume; the stroke volume is reduced and both cardiac output and blood pressure fall despite the increased heart rate, and *heat collapse* may result. During physical **work** there is a general vasoconstriction of the cutaneous arterioles; as the intensity of work in the heat increases the rate of skin perfusion rises less rapidly than in moderate temperatures (Fig. 24-10). The degree of *filling* of the capacitive cutaneous vessels in a normal climate is less during work than during rest, but the increased vascular tone responsible for this effect largely disappears when one works in the heat [26]. As a result, intrathoracic filling and thus the stroke volume continue to be diminished, and so do maximal cardiac output and endurance performance capacity.

Hormonal Regulation during Dynamic Work

Two hormonal systems deserve special attention in the context of adjustments to work [8]. **1. The sympathico-adrenergic system** (pp. 679 ff.): During physical work more *adrenalin is released* into the blood, from the adrenal *medulla* in particular; *noradrenalin* is released only in small amounts. Among other actions, adrenalin mobilizes the glycogen and fat depots, stimulates increased production of cyclic AMP and enhances cardiac activity and the clarity of consciousness. The secretion of adrenalin frequently begins before the work load is imposed **(prestart state)** and at the latest coincides with the onset of work. The increase in the rate of adrenalin release is reflected in an increased excretion of *vanillylmandelic acid (VMA)*, a product of catecholamine breakdown, in the urine. **2. The hypophyseal-adrenocortical system:** After work is begun, with a latency of about 2 min, there is an increase in the release of *ACTH* from the adenohypophysis, which stimulates the release of corticosteroids from the *adrenal cortex* (pp. 667 ff.). The significance of the *corticosteroids* with regard to physical work is not well understood; well known is the promoting effect on the mobilization of glycogen.

Adjustments to Static Work

Muscle perfusion. It is characteristic of the physiological events accompanying static work that the blood flow through a muscle becomes inadequate when its contractile force exceeds about *15% of the isometric maximum* [32, 49, 56]. A fundamental cause of the *re-*

duced blood flow is the increased intramuscular pressure, which during powerful isometric contraction is greater than the capillary pressure. Because of the inadequate perfusion energy must be obtained anaerobically, with intramuscular *lactate* production, so that the isometric production of fairly large forces soon results in *fatigue*.

The lactate-based acidosis effects an additional, strong *respiratory drive,* which is further increased when the work requires reflex contraction of the abdominal muscles so that breathing is impaired. During abdominal compression blood is forced out of the intrathoracic and intraabdominal spaces into the remaining *low-pressure system,* one sign of which is swelling of the neck veins. The intrathoracic pressure increase reduces venous return to the heart. For this reason those who are ill or convalescing should avoid work with a large static component (e.g., lifting and carrying heavy loads).

Heart rate. During static work the heart rate rises (Fig. 24-11) even if the abdominal compression is not activated. As in the case of dynamic work, this increase is explained by the action of muscle receptors (p. 552) that strongly stimulate the circulatory center during anaerobic metabolism.

24.3   Responses of the Organism to Non-Physical Loads

Responses to Psychological Loads

The rate of energy metabolism also rises during psychological performance, but the cause is an increase in muscle tone and not an enhanced cerebral metabolism (p. 524). In many cases *autonomic responses* like those associated with physical performance appear – elevated pulse rate and respiratory minute volume, increase in cutaneous blood flow with a decrease in electrical resistance, increased sweating and the release of more adrenalin, with a correspondingly greater excretion of vanillylmandelic acid in the urine.

Although psychophysical work loads are a common feature of present-day life, quantitative study of such situations is difficult. Occasional attempts have been made to evaluate the strain they induce by observation of physiological responses. But such data *by no means* provide insights into psychological and psychophysical performance as reliable as those applicable to purely physical performances.

Certain situations affect primarily the emotions; in responding to such *emotional loads* people show symptoms like those accompanying mental performance – tachycardia, hyperventilation, sweating

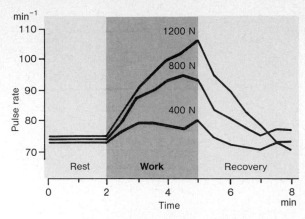

Fig. 24-11. Changes in pulse rate during static work at different intensities (carrying a load). After [49]

(caused, for example, by fear or excitement), and so on. There is marked stimulation of the sympathicoadrenergic system [8], with some variation in the proportions of adrenalin and noradrenalin released. Conditions of extreme anxiety or terror do not only elicit a pronounced *ergotropic reaction* (immediate response) within a few seconds – called the *emergency reaction* by Cannon [38] – but often also stimulate the parasympathetic nervous system. The latter action can result in involuntary defecation and urination in such situations, or even in cardiac arrest.

24.4   Limits of Performance Capacity

On the basis of physiological response criteria (e.g., heart rate; p. 550) one can distinguish physically *fatiguing* work from that which is *not fatiguing*. Psychological performance can rarely be categorized in this way. If the body is not allowed to recover sufficiently from fatiguing work, functional disorders and illness appear; these constitute an "overloading syndrome" (p. 558). The work load the body can bear – that is, a person's performance capacity – is limited by three fundamental factors: the amount of energy available in the muscle, the oxygen supply to the muscle, and the body's capacity for thermoregulation (pp. 539 ff.).

The availability of energy in the muscle. During fatiguing work performance capacity is limited by the various ways the muscle can obtain energy (p. 550), and these depend on the intensity and duration of the work [17, 18]. The basic rule is: *the shorter the duration of work, the greater the achievable performance* (Fig. 24–12) and the smaller the relative aerobic ener-

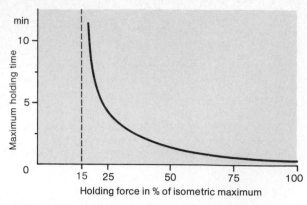

Fig. 24-12. Relation between maximal performance and load duration, taking static work as an example. After [56]

gy yield (Fig. 24-3). It is useful to consider three categories of work duration, though the boundaries must be arbitrarily drawn:

Short-term performance (up to ca. 20 s duration). In this situation the intracellular stores of *ATP* and *creatine phosphate* are critical. These energy-rich phosphates can supply enough energy to support maximal performance during the first 15 to 20 s of work.
Intermediate-term performance. Work at the **short**-duration end of this range (up to ca. 1 min) is fueled mainly by *anaerobic glycolysis,* after the first few seconds. Thus the muscle's capacity for glycolytic metabolism and the tolerance of the resulting lactate-based acidosis are the performance-limiting factors. At the **long**-duration end (up to ca. 6 min) the *aerobic energy yield* makes an increasing contribution, so that performance is limited by *both* the anaerobic and the aerobic metabolic rates.
Long-term or endurance performance (ca. 6 min or more). During prolonged work *aerobic energy metabolism* predominates. Performance capacity is primarily limited by the associated factors – metabolic capacity and the glycogen stores in the muscle cells, and the supply of oxygen and substrates. Therefore blood flow through the musculature is critical in long-term work. Only when work is performed at moderate intensity for hours at a time is its duration limited by depletion of the glycogen reserves.

The supply of oxygen to the muscle. The amount of oxygen available to a muscle depends fundamentally on the rate of blood flow through it [18]. During **dynamic work** employing large groups of muscles (more than ⅓ of the total musculature) performance capacity depends less on local blood flow than on the maximal cardiac output. During **static work** local muscle perfusion becomes inadequate when a force greater than about 15% of the isometric maximum is exerted. The supply of oxygen can also be diminished if the inspired air is oxygen-deficient (at altitude; pp. 565 f.), by gas-exchange disorders and by a lowered hemoglobin concentration in the blood.
When the inspired oxygen fraction is normal (0.2095) oxygen uptake by a healthy person is *not limited by breathing capacity.* Even during exhausting work the

tidal volume is *only about 80% of maximal* [3, 15]. It is evident, therefore, that neither the popular measure "vital capacity" nor any other respiratory parameter actually determines the performance capacity of a healthy subject.

Work in the heat [8, 26]. The diminished performance capacity under hot conditions results from a reduction in the intrathoracic blood volume and not from the pronounced increase in cutaneous blood flow observed at rest (p. 554). The ultimate limiting factor for work in the heat is the *core temperature* of the body. Depending on the simultaneous losses of salt and fluid, and on the intensity of work, various disturbances can occur, so that it is impossible to specify a limiting core temperature. The rectal temperature, however, should not exceed 38 °C during prolonged work in the heat (danger of *heat collapse*). In endurance sports such as *marathon running,* rectal temperatures as high as 41 °C can be tolerated [55], but at higher temperatures there is a considerable risk of *heat stroke* (central nervous collapse).

Specific Performance Limits

Endurance performance limit and maximal capacity. Not uncommonly, a distinction is made between *light,* non-fatiguing work and *heavy* work, which causes fatigue. This distinction is based on the notion that there are *two ranges* of performance capacity, separated by the **endurance performance limit** [14, 32, 52]. Work is considered to be below this limit when it can be performed for *at least 8 hours without muscular fatigue;* during this time, the muscle's metabolism and blood flow are in a steady state. The cardiac and respiratory musculature, for example, do work of this kind. Above the endurance performance limit is the region of **maximal performance capacity.** Performance in this range is *limited in duration* because metabolism and blood flow are not in a steady state; *the longer the working time, the lower the performance maximum,* and vice versa (Fig. 24-12).
The endurance performance limit and thus the *occupational work capacity* [51] varies among individuals. Therefore the question whether work is light or heavy cannot be resolved by any absolute measure of the work load; the actual performance capacity of the individual is decisive. For work in the range above the limit, the degree of fatigue depends on the maximal performance capacity of the individual at that moment. Both the endurance performance capacity and the maximal capacity can be altered by training (p. 559).

Endurance limit for dynamic work. Work below the limit is characterized as follows [52]: **Pulse rate:** constant working pulse rate with no increase due to fatigue (below 130 per min in untrained 20-to-30-year olds), recovery pulse sum less than 100 pulses, recovery time less than 5 min. **Other characteristics:** Constant oxygen uptake (steady state), oxygen debt below ca. 4 liters, no appreciable rise in blood lactate level. In untrained men between 20 and 30 years of age the endurance limit for bicycle-ergometer work is about 100 watts, which corresponds to oxygen uptake of 1.5 l/min. Performance above this level is limited by the factors just described (p. 556).

The occupational work capacity is not identical with endurance thresholds used in sports medicine. Regarding the onset of blood lactate accumulation (OBLA [59]), the *aerobic threshold* corresponds to lactate concentrations of about 2 mmol/l, the *anaerobic threshold* to about 4 mmol/l and the range of *aerobic/anaerobic transition* to 2-4 mmol/l [47, 48].

24.5   Fatigue

Fatigue and Recovery

Fatigue is a state induced by *heavy* work (p. 551) and associated with a *decrease in performance capacity*. It may be **physical** (muscular) or **psychological** (central) [4, 11, 32]. The two forms are combined in hard work, and cannot be strictly distinguished. Hard *physical* work leads primarily to *muscular* fatigue, and strenuous *mental* or *monotonous* work causes *central* fatigue. A sharp distinction should be made between fatigue and the *tiredness* associated with a need for sleep.

Recovery is a process initiated when performance is interrupted, reduced or changed in nature; it correlates with a reduction of fatigue and increase of performance capacity. When these parameters have returned to the initial levels, the recovery process has finished.

Recovery and the timing of pauses. When doing work above the individual endurance limit (p. 556) one must stop occasionally for recovery. Because the recovery processes operate most rapidly at the beginning of such a pause (as shown, for example, in the changes in heart rate; Fig. 24-4), work should be organized on the principle that *many short pauses are better than a few long ones* [32]. Recovery from heavy physical work can occur not only during pauses, but to some extent during periods of easier work (below the endurance limit).

Physical Fatigue

Physical fatigue results from *changes in skeletal muscle* such as depletion of the energy stores and accumulation of lactic acid (the "fatigue substance"), which reduce performance capacity. During the recovery phase following physical work the energy stores are replenished and the lactic acid is eliminated [8, 18].

Fatigue during dynamic work. *Below the endurance limit* the movements of work allow sufficient muscular relaxation time that the energy-rich phosphates used up during contraction can be regenerated and the metabolic end products transported away [32]. The relaxation time corresponds to the required recovery time. Because there is no residuum of fatigue this is called *non-fatiguing work*. During dynamic work *above* the endurance limit there is no opportunity for continual recovery, because the relaxation times amount to less than the required recovery time. Replenishment of the energy stores and removal of the lactic acid are incomplete and a *residuum of fatigue* builds up [32]. The muscle uses up its energy-rich substrates and accumulates metabolic end products, and fatigue increases. The degree of muscular fatigue during dynamic work above the endurance limit can be determined from physiological parameters (e. g., recovery time and recovery pulse sum; p. 551).

Fatigue during static work. Here muscular fatigue is basically caused by inadequate blood flow. If the force of muscle contraction exceeds 15% of the isometric maximum the supply of oxygen no longer matches the demand, and muscular fatigue increases progressively.

Psychological Fatigue

Psychological (central) fatigue causes reduced performance because *central-nervous control* is disturbed [11]. Among the typical symptoms are slower information transmission, deterioration of thought and decision processes, and impaired sensory perception and sensorimotor function. Such fatigue is associated with aversion to work and diminished performance, and occasionally produces a tendency to depression, irrational anxiety or reduced drive, and irritability and emotional lability.

Situations eliciting psychological fatigue include [11] (i) prolonged psychological work demanding close concentration, extreme mental alertness or dexterity, (ii) hard physical labor, (iii) unvaried work under monotonous conditions, (iv) noise, poor lighting and uncomfortable temperatures, (v) conflicts, worries or lack of interest, (vi) illness, pain and malnutrition.
Central fatigue, in contrast to muscular fatigue, can be *relieved instantaneously* [11] under certain conditions – for example, when (i) the fatiguing activity is replaced by another, (ii) the surroundings are changed, (iii) the organism is put into an alarm state by fear or the threat of danger, (iv) interest is reawak-

ened by new information, or (v) a change of affective state (mood) occurs. The fact that such *sudden disappearance* of psychological fatigue is possible implies that neither the accumulation of "fatigue substances" nor the depletion of energy reserves is a critical factor. Rather, psychological fatigue is thought to involve the reticular formation (cf. ARAS, p. 200), the activity of which is affected not only by intense mental activity but also by monotony. Fatigue brought about by monotony can be reduced when the information input is changed, though it cannot prevent fatigue in the long term. For example, during long drives on the highway psychological fatigue is counteracted by listening to a radio.

The occurrence of psychological fatigue during physical work could be caused by afference from the working muscles to the cerebrum, which not only generates the consciousness that the muscles are tiring (or even pain), but also suppresses cortical functions (and hence produces psychological fatigue) [58]. It is conceivable that these receptors are identical to the *muscle receptors* mentioned previously (p. 552).

Overloading and Exhaustion

Overloading is evident when an *overloading syndrome* appears – that is, when over long periods *fatigue is incompletely compensated* by recovery **(chronic damage)** or when maximal short-term load tolerance is exceeded **(acute damage)**, as can happen, for example, when work is performed under the influence of stimulants (cf. p. 562). The overloading syndrome is particularly conspicuous when it affects the structures involved in posture and movement (broken bones, torn muscles and tendons, slipped disks and damage to joint menisci).

Disorders of the posture and movement apparatus. When certain activities place excessive mechanical strain on the posture and movement apparatus for long periods of time, its function is impaired and permanent damage may be incurred – for example, *deformation of the vertebral column* in the drivers of trucks and tractors. A considerable number of joint, ligament and tendon injuries can result from overenthusiastic athletic training and competition.

Exhaustion occurs when physical or psychological performance above the endurance limit is not interrupted *soon enough,* or *long enough* in the case of repeated maximal effort, to allow recovery. Exhaustion necessarily results in the *breaking off of work* if the function of many regulatory systems is impaired.

The term **acute exhaustion** is applied to a sudden decline in performance capacity during fatiguing heavy work. This condition is almost routinely observed during athletic competitions and training, though the participants affected suffer no permanent damage. In *emergency situations* more severe exhaustion can be

incurred, and in this case damage may be permanent. The time required for recovery from exhausting performance is prolonged according to the degree of exhaustion.

If strenuous work is continued for a long time or repeated too frequently, a condition of **chronic exhaustion** can develop. It is accompanied by *prolonged disorders* of regulatory systems (e. g., the adrenal cortex), in some cases so severe as to cause death.

In contrast to earlier views, it is now known that maximal physical performance does not appreciably interfere with the cardiovascular function of a healthy person. During hard physical work the skeletal musculature tires sooner than the myocardium; the "athlete's heart" (p. 560) is an adapted rather than a pathological organ. But if there is preexisting heart disease, such as hardening of the coronary vessels, extreme physical exertion can damage the heart; doping can have the same result (p. 562). Even apparently healthy people run the risk – though the probability is very small indeed – that exhaustion may lead to a lethal collapse, presumably as a result of ventricular fibrillation.

The emergency reaction and the adaptation syndrome are closely related to the autonomic nervous system and the endocrine system. Both systems respond to a wide range of loads in a stereotyped manner. First *adrenalin* and *noradrenalin* are released, and then the increased liberation of *ACTH* stimulates glucocorticoid secretion. The term **emergency reaction** is applied to this situation when it is especially pronounced (CANNON [38]); the state of the organism under these conditions is called **stress** [30], and the stress-eliciting stimuli are called **stressors** (p. 669). Among these are *all severe physical and psychological loads;* they include extremely hard work, cold and heat, inspiratory oxygen deficiency, hypoglycemia, illness, operations, wounds, noise, sudden fright, anxiety, pain and rage. When stressors act repeatedly or for a long time, an **adaptation syndrome** results (SELYE [30]) in which the adrenal cortex is hypertrophied. The increased adrenalin release in stress (p. 680) enables *autonomically protected reserves* [32, 40] to be mobilized (p. 561). The result is a *seeming* enhancement of performance capacity, associated with a risk to health (cf. doping, p. 562).

Psychological stressors in particular are thought to cause functional disturbance if there is inadequate opportunity for recovery; this syndrome is called "autonomic dystonia." Typical symptoms are disturbed sleep, impaired circulatory regulation, sudden outbreaks of sweat, chronic tiredness and generally diminished performance.

Feedback of Performance

It is particularly clear in sporting events that man is capable of arranging his strain according to his physical limits and reserves, and of *adjusting his performance accordingly;* exhaustion usually does not occur until the goal has been reached. The same is true of seasonal work (for example, harvesting) and other jobs done at specific times.

Many jobs involve alternation between heavy and light work, and these can be timed in such a way that the worker rarely becomes exhausted. In the normal case, therefore, people are able to *avoid premature fatigue or exhaustion* and thus to utilize optimally their performance reserves. Observations of this sort have led to the *hypothesis* that man has a mechanism to *control the timing and amount of physical output* [61]. If this were so, exhaustion and overloading would be signs of decompensation of this regulatory mechanism; they would be equivalent to an "emergency brake" that prevents complete collapse by enforcing a recovery period. Decompensation of this sort occurs when the balance between strain and recovery is upset by external influences – for example, by certain kinds of assembly-line work, special motivation (bonuses) or interference with the feedback signals (doping; p.562). The details of operation of this hypothetical system for the feedback control of physical output remain to be explored in future.

24.6   Training and Adaption

In the context of work and sport, *training* is the repeated performance of a specified physical or psychological activity, whether it takes the form of systematic practice sessions or occurs spontaneously in the course of daily life. It results in the activation of *adaptive processes* in the organism, which cause the preservation or enhancement of performance capacity [3, 8, 24, 32, 59].

The training situation can be interpreted in the light of Fig. 24-1 (p. 549); a particular *training quota* is set as load, the act of training is a form of performance, and the state of training is expressed in the *intermediate to long term* adaptation of certain physiological systems. *State of training,* however, is not equivalent to *performance capacity.* Some people who have trained intensively and are thus in a good state of training can perform at a level only slightly above average, whereas others perform well above average with very little training. The reason, of course, is that performance is also determined by *talent.* This term comprises all the factors affecting performance capacity that are *not influenced by training.* Such characteristics are either inborn or acquired and fixed during a child's early development. The performance capacity at any time, then, depends on both training *and* talent.

The improvement in performance achievable by training depends on the *training quota* – the *intensity* and *duration* of practice. As shown diagrammatically in Fig. 24-13, the performance of a person with a constant quota increases considerably when training is first begun. As it proceeds the improvement is less pronounced, until a *performance plateau* is eventually reached (the **performance limit**). When this level has been attained, a further improvement is possible only if the training quota is expanded. The plateau achieved when this expansion has been taken to its limit represents the **performance maximum;** continued training will have no further effect.

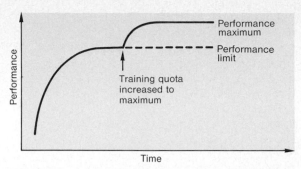

Fig. 24-13. Diagram illustrating the definition of performance limit and performance maximum

This time course obtains in principle for all forms of training. The physiological changes brought about by adaptation during training can be reversed when training stops. In the case of cardiovascular and muscular adaptations, a *rapidly acquired state of training is also rapidly lost* [13]. Acquired central-nervous coordination, however, is more persistent. *Movement patterns* (e.g., writing, piano playing) once learned *are lost very slowly,* even if they are not practiced for years.

Movement-specific training. It is a fundamental principle that one should train that particular sequence of movements for which an increase in performance capacity is desired. Only such movement-specific training ensures *optimal adaptation of all components* essential to a specific performance. To improve dexterity in surgical operations, one must operate, and to improve rowing performance one must row. Other forms of training are useful only as supplements to movement-specific training.

Special Forms of Training

Special forms of training improve performance only in the particular way for which the training was designed. A muscle trained for strength becomes stronger but does not perform better in endurance, and vice versa. Each form of training is applied to achieve a specific result. There are many such special forms [8, 12, 20] of which the following will serve as examples:

Endurance training. This form is characterized by rhythmically repeated movements that do not require maximal force, and is thus the typical form of training for endurance sports such as long-distance running, rowing, swimming and cycling. It takes at least 1 hour, and for some kinds of sport more than 5 hours per day.

In *performing everyday movements* each person reaches a certain, interindividually variable *state of training.* To increase one's performance capacity beyond this level, additional endurance training must last at least 10 minutes per day. The intensity of training during this session should be such as to bring the pulse rate (per min) to more than 170 minus the person's age in years. Less vigorous training has no effect on endurance.

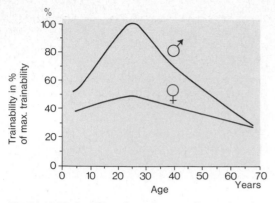

Fig. 24-14. Trainability of muscle strength as a function of age and sex. Maximal trainability of muscle strength in 25-year-old men = 100%. After [13]

Table 24-2. Combinations of strength exerted and duration of contraction required to obtain an optimal effect in *isometric training*. 3–5 of these isometric contractions are required per day. After [13]

% of maximal strength	40–50	60–70	80–90	100
Contraction duration (s)	15–20	6–10	4– 6	2–3

Table 24-3. Comparison of physiological parameters of two 25-year-old, 70-kg men with and without intensive endurance training

Parameter	Untrained	Trained
Pulse rate at rest, recumbent (min^{-1})	80	40
Pulse rate, maximal (min^{-1})	180	180
Stroke volume at rest (ml)	70	140
Stroke volume, maximal (ml)	100	190
Cardiac output at rest (l/min)	5.6	5.6
Cardiac output, maximal (l/min)	18	35
Heart volume (ml)	700	1400
Heart weight (g)	300	500
Respiratory minute volume, maximal (l/min)	100	200
Oxygen uptake, maximal (l/min)	2.8	5.2
Blood volume (l)	5.6	5.9

Endurance training increases the aerobic capacity and the functional capillary density in the musculature, as well as the O$_2$ transport capacity of the cardiovascular system; the latter effect is basically due to an increase in stroke volume and thus in maximal cardiac output. The slight increase in blood volume is of no practical importance. The resting pulse rate falls, whereas the slope of the performance-pulse curve (PPI, p. 552) stays nearly constant.

Interval training. Dynamic muscular work that strains the body almost to its limit is performed at intervals of 0.5–2 min. As soon as the pulse rate in the recovery phase falls below 130 min^{-1}, the next exercise phase is begun; other criteria can also be used. Interval training is particularly effective in increasing the anaerobic capacity of the muscle; beyond this, its effects are similar to those of endurance training.

Strength training [13]. This form of training involves the exertion of considerable muscular strength, by means of relatively

brief maximal performance with a large component of *static, isometric* work. The durations of such training sessions are considerably shorter than those for endurance training. Strength training stimulates the growth of the muscle; the individual muscle fibers become thicker *(hypertrophy)* by a buildup of actomyosin. But there is *no increase* in the number of muscle fibers *(hyperplasia)*.

Isometric training. In this form a maximal load is imposed on single groups of muscles [13]. An optimal effect can be achieved by only a few isometric contractions per day, if they are made with maximal strength (Table 24-2). But if one wanted to train isometrically all the muscle groups involved in a movement pattern, the training program would be complicated indeed, and almost certainly some group participating in a complex movement pattern would be forgotten. To this extent, isometric training is useful only as a supplement to other forms of training. Its particular value lies in rehabilitation, for weak muscle groups can be specifically strengthened.

Degree of Adaptation

In order to evaluate the physiological adaptations achieved by a training program, one must know the *initial condition*. Every healthy person is subject to a *variety of training stimuli in his daily occupations,* and though these are slight their significance should not be underestimated. Their effects become apparent when a person is *immobilized* – for example, by confinement to bed or by a plaster cast. The inactivated musculature *atrophies*. Evidently any reduction in activity causes deterioration of the state of training and thus of performance capacity, and any increase causes improvement. Thus the state of adaptation or training shows not only *inter*individual but also *intra*individual variations, depending on differences in everyday activity.

Endurance training activates many adaptive processes. The number of perfused capillaries per unit volume of muscle increases. The **heart** undergoes typical adaptation, in the course of which it becomes larger *(athlete's heart;* cf. p. 390). This enlargement was once *erroneously* attributed to *cardiac insufficiency,* so that for decades athlete's heart was of concern in sport medicine. It has since been shown that both the increase in heart volume *(dilation)* and the greater thickness of the muscle fibers *(hypertrophy)* are *physiological adaptive processes* and not pathological reactions. Adaptations in **breathing** also occur, for endurance training acts as a sort of respiratory gymnastics; vital capacity and maximal breathing capacity both increase. However, vital capacity is not a measure of physical performance capacity (p. 563). Highly trained participants in endurance sports under exhausting loads have been found to have minute volumes of over 200 l/min (cf. p. 472). Intracellular **enzyme systems** also show adaptations. Table 24-3 summarizes typical adaptive phenomena resulting from intensive endurance training.

Strength training. The *diameter of the muscle fibers,* and thus the strength they can generate, can be about doubled. The improvement is ultimately limited by the progressive lengthening of the diffusion path between the capillaries and the interior of the muscle.

Trainability and age [3, 13, 31]. As an adult grows older his physical performance – muscular strength, for instance – becomes less trainable (Fig. 24-14). But because trainability depends not only on age but also on individual characteristics, there are people in each age class who respond particularly well or poorly to training stimuli. In any case, regular training can clearly counteract and postpone the reduction in performance capacity associated with aging; even though training is begun at an advanced age, it can still enhance performance capacity.

Variability in Performance Capacity

Ranges of performance capacity. Performance capacity can be subdivided into 4 ranges, as diagrammed in Fig. 24-15. The bottom range comprises **automated performances** – ingrained motor patterns that can be voluntarily started and stopped but otherwise proceed automatically. Above these is the range of so-called **physiological readiness,** activities under continual voluntary control which never become so vigorous as to generate a sense of strain or fatigue. The **usual reserves for exertion** above this level are accessible only by the application of will power; fatigue results when these are employed. The fourth range is that of **autonomically protected reserves,** which cannot be utilized even by the strongest voluntary effort and are available to the organism only in *emergencies* (p. 558).

This subdivision is only an approximate representation, for the transitions are continuous and the percentages are rough estimates at best. Nevertheless, the diagram applies in general to the different types of performance.

Rhythmic undulations in performance capacity. Both physical and mental performance vary in diurnal, **circadian rhythms** [2, 7] (pp. 154f.), with a typical pattern despite distinct interindividual differences (e. g., late and early risers). In a large sample of people, the *average* vigilance as a typical factor in performance capacity shows a maximum in the morning, around 9 o'clock (Fig. 24-15, bottom). There is a valley in the curve at about 2 p.m., followed by an afternoon rise which does not go as high as the morning peak. From 7 p.m. on the average vigilance declines uniformly, reaching a *distinct minimum around 3 a.m.* Over the next 6 hours the curve rises steeply to the *morning peak.* Similar curves have been found for widely varying types of work; the undulation is particularly pronounced for assembly-line and observation jobs and practically insignificant for high-intensity activities such as sporting competitions. The problems of shift work are discussed on pp. 154 and 562.

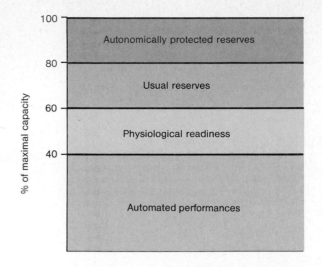

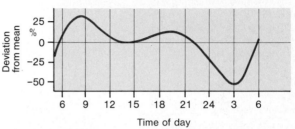

Fig. 24-15. *Top:* Diagram of the 4 ranges of performance, from Graf [40]. *Bottom:* Variation in mean vigilance during the day; ordinate, percent deviation from the 24-h average. After [40]

Menstrual cycle. Contrary to popular assumption, there is no systematic relationship between performance capacity and the menstrual cycle [3]. Studies of athletes have shown that some individuals may vary in performance during the menstrual cycle, but when many individuals are compared the changes in performance capacity are not correlated with any particular phase of the cycle. Maximal sporting performances have been found at each phase. It is thus not advisable, except in a few special cases, to *shift the cycle* in preparation for physically demanding situations.

Maintenance of performance capacity. Several factors are influential in this regard; among them are the proper *adjustment of performance* (pp. 559f.) and timing of *pauses* (p. 557), optimal *nutrition,* and qualitatively and quantitatively adequate *sleep* [19] (pp. 153ff.). Improper diet and disturbed sleep frequently affect both performance and well-being in the highly industrialized countries. Doctors assigned to check on the health of workers and athletes can thus make an important contribution toward keeping performance levels high. The way a person spends his **leisure** and **vacations** also affects his performance capacity. As the work week of large sections of the population is shortened, leaving more time free for other activities, this factor becomes more significant – but it raises complicated questions with many interdisciplinary ramifications, which cannot be discussed further here.

Improvement of performance capacity. A *genuine* increase in performance capacity can be achieved *only by training;* other influences can bring about only *seeming* increases, by mobilizing the autonomically protected reserves (Fig. 24-15). This protection can be overcome, for example, by special motivation, in emergencies or by drugs.

Doping. This term denotes the attempt to raise performance capacity by drugs [3, 8, 27]. Certain substances are thought to *mobilize the autonomically protected reserves;* among them are preparations that imitate the adrenalin effect (artificial emergency reaction) or open the feedback loop controlling performance (pp. 558 f.), so that information about symptoms of exhaustion is inhibited or its processing is disturbed (psychoactive drugs). Doping is therefore associated with large **risks to health** [8, 43, 44]. *Stimulants* have been found to produce severe functional disturbance and permanently impaired health, and even collapse resulting in death. Moreover, it is entirely controversial whether the use of such stimulants in **top-level sport** produces anything like the desired results.

The so-called **anabolics** constitute a special case of doping; these drugs simulate the anabolic effect of male sex hormones, increasing and accelerating the incorporation of protein into the musculature. The risk to health lies in their side effects on hormone balance, and in the possibility of damage to tendons, ligaments and joints by overloading.

Shift Work

The most common form of shift work is the 3-shift system [23]. The day is divided into three *8-hour* working sessions, usually beginning at 6 a.m., 2 p.m. and 10 p.m. [57]. Shift workers experience *desynchronization of the external triggers* (pp. 153 f.), the *terrestrial* triggers remaining constant while some of the *social* triggers vary with the different shifts [2]. Difficulties in adjustment occur especially on the first day after a change of shift; they diminish during the following days as one *becomes accustomed* to the new rhythm. But there is *no true resetting of all rhythms,* even for people on permanent night duty, because many social triggers (in addition to the terrestrial ones) remain in phase with local time – the daily activity of family members, television programs, cultural life and street noise, for example.

Individuals vary in the degree to which they can accommodate to permanent night or shift work, so that it is impossible to design a single ideal shift schedule [57]. Whereas many people can tolerate permanent night work with no great difficulty (e.g., restaurant and newspaper workers, night nurses), others cannot. Individual characteristics must always be taken into account.

Night workers often fail to adjust their *sleeping habits* sufficiently, so that their sleep is *qualitatively* inadequate with regard to the successive stages (pp. 155 f.) as well as *too brief* [19]. In addition, the *daily fluctuating noise level* is a special disturbance that can further increase the sleep deficit. The combination of inade-

quate adjustment to desynchronized external triggers and lack of sleep *endangers health* (e.g., increased susceptibility to functional disorders), and personal well-being and family life deteriorate.

Shift work is often unavoidable – in industry, for instance, or service areas such as hospitals. In such cases work and living conditions should be designed to allow for the shift and night workers' *increased need for recuperation.*

Deficiency of Movement; Physical Therapy

Deficiency of movement results in a loss of physical performance capacity, owing to muscular atrophy, deterioration in the state of endurance training, and the like. Reduced performance capacity, however, is *not equivalent to "illness,"* just as increased performance capacity does not mean that one is "especially healthy." Physical activity does not only enhance performance capacity – it can also impair health (professional diseases, sport injuries). Medical supervision is necessary, particularly for prolonged strenuous work.

The deficiency of movement is frequently presented as a significant epidemiological *risk factor*. In contrast to risk factors such as smoking, high blood pressure, overweight, diabetes mellitus and disturbed fat metabolism, which are recognized as fundamental and which *in themselves* are correlated with a distinct reduction in statistical life expectancy, the *risk associated with deficiency of movement* is a matter of *controversy* [8, 35, 39, 54]. It may be that physical activity has prophylactic value in the presence of a risk factor – for example, certain forms of hypertension and metabolic disorders. In addition to this *prophylactic* role, exercise can also have *therapeutic* value, as in the endurance training of patients with cardiovascular disease and gymnastic training for disorders of the movement apparatus. But exercise should be used as therapy for the ill only when prescribed by a doctor and supervised by professionals.

Whatever its other benefits, physical activity also contributes to a person's general well-being.

24.7 Performance and Aptitude Tests

Tests are instruments for measuring certain personality or behavioral traits [31, 35]. They have a role in work and sports physiology as well as in clinical examination and diagnosis. Some tests are more informative than others, and there are various **criteria** by which the usefulness of a test can be evaluated. The *primary test criteria* include objectivity, reliability and validity; among the *secondary test criteria* are degree of standardization, comparability and economy.

Primary Test Criteria

Objectivity. It is characteristic of an objective test that the results are *independent of the examiner*. Many test procedures are not designed for complete objectivity; therefore they cannot be carried out and interpreted entirely by computer.

Reliability. This criterion refers to the precision with which a personality or behavioral trait is characterized. Reliability has several aspects, and depends on such factors as the nature of the test and the examiner.
Given that the examiner is thoroughly experienced in a test, and that learning by the subject can be ruled out, repeated measurements can reveal the precision with which a result can be **reproduced** (retest reliability). But if the subject can be expected to learn during the test session, so that retesting is likely to produce a different result (for example, in determining intelligence quotient), precision must be evaluated by other means, such as parallel tests.

Validity. The validity of a test is the degree to which it actually measures the personality or behavioral trait that it is designed (or claimed) to measure. Validity, too, has several aspects.
For example, one must verify that a performance test actually measures performance capacity, and that a clinical test measures the particular sign of illness that is of interest. This can be done by critically comparing the results obtained with that given by another procedure *(external criterion)* – that is, a result independent of the test at issue, the significance of which is well established. In developing new test procedures, *validity usually presents the most difficult problem*. It is not sufficient to demonstrate the *plausibility* of a test, for tests that appeared plausible have repeatedly given rise to misinterpretations and thus proved unsatisfactory.
A test with adequately established reliability and validity is at least acceptably **selective**. Selectivity denotes not only the precision with which the trait is characterized, but also the degree to which one can distinguish differences in this trait. A test that differentiates between *sick* and *healthy* with a high degree of certainty would be just as selective as one that permits a differentiation among diabetics according to the severity of their illness. That is, selectivity must always be evaluated with regard to the question at issue.
As an *example,* consider the determination of *vital capacity,* spirometer measurements of which are objective and give reproducible results when repeated – but only on condition that the subject cooperates. Because many athletes trained for endurance have an unusually high vital capacity, it may sound plausible to describe the validity of this test as follows: "The measurement of vital capacity reveals a person's capacity for endurance performance." But opera singers and the players of wind instruments also have above-normal vital capacities, without abnormally great endurance in the sense of sports physiology. Vital capacity can be increased by appropriate respiratory techniques alone – techniques that cannot be expected to improve performance in endurance trials (p. 556). If "vital capacity" were tested by the external criterion "time to run 5000 m" (a typical endurance sport), neither the opera singer nor the trombonist would perform well. A more acceptable expression of the validity of the vital-capacity test is, "The measure 'vital capacity' reveals the maximal volume of a single breath, which is fixed by the respiratory mechanics of the individual." It is thus a test of respiratory mechanics and not of endurance performance capacity (p. 560).

The Problem of the Norm

Diagnosis is often possible only when a representative reference value is available. In practice, it turns out to be much harder than one would think to establish norms for reference (cf. *average weight,* p. 584). It does not suffice to make an arbitrary selection of *"healthy" subjects* and take the *mean* of the data obtained from them as the norm, for the following reasons. 1. The term "healthy" is not sufficiently precisely defined (p. 548). 2. The natural variability is considerable even among healthy people, depending (for example) on biological rhythms, age and sex. 3. Considerable deviations from the "norm" can result from physical activity or advanced training, in the absence of any pathological condition. *Moreover,* deviations from the norm need not be pathological because the conditions normal-healthy and abnormal-ill are often separated by a wide range, "abnormal-healthy," with no sharp demarcation at either end.

Performance Tests

Physiological performance tests are diagnostic procedures for the determination of physical performance capacity [8, 24, 31, 35]; like many diagnostic procedures, they involve a certain *risk* [35]. Whereas ergometric "vita maxima" tests, carried to the point of physical exhaustion, present little risk to the healthy, patients are more vulnerable and should be tested only at the instigation and with the supervision of a physician. There are many kinds of performance tests, and they cannot all be described here. We shall limit ourselves to three that are commonly used to evaluate endurance performance capacity, the test criteria of which are fairly well established.

Maximal oxygen uptake ($\dot{V}_{O_2}$ max). The maximal oxygen uptake is a measure of the *aerobic performance capacity* of the organism. It is monitored during *continuous or stepwise-increasing ergometer work*. Oxygen uptake rises uniformly at first, and then levels off at the transition into the exhaustion state (p. 552). The oxygen uptake in the *plateau region* is a measure of endurance performance capacity (in l/min or, preferably, in ml/min per kg body weight). The average for an adult male weighing 70 kg is ca. 3.0 l/min, or 43 ml $\cdot$ min$^{-1} \cdot$ kg^{-1}. Intensive endurance training can raise the maximal oxygen uptake to about twice this amount.

Physical work capacity (PWC$_{170}$ or W$_{170}$). This test also requires continual or stepwise-increasing work on an ergometer; the critical measure is the performance at the time when the pulse rate reaches 170 min^{-1}. Because the maximal pulse rate decreases with age, the readings for older people are either extrapolated to 170 min^{-1} or expressed with respect to a lower reference rate, such as 130 min^{-1} (i.e., PWC$_{130}$). The result of the test has dimensions of watts. The validity of this test is the same as that of maximal oxygen uptake. Although the PWC test is less reliable than the measurement of maximal oxygen uptake, it is particularly suitable for large-scale studies because it is economical with regard to both time and money. For non-athletes between 20 and 30 years of age the following average values are obtained: for women, 125 watts or 2.2 watts/kg; for men, 200 watts or 3.0 watts/kg. Intensive endurance training can double these figures.

Heart volume. The volume of the heart at rest (cf. *athlete's heart*, p.390) can be observed in *roentgenograms* or by ultrasonic methods. It is *not* a direct measure of performance capacity, but rather indicates the state of adaptation of the heart to endurance training (i.e. state of endurance training), demonstrable even at rest. The results of this test are highly reproducible; the exposure to radiation necessarily involved in repeated measurements should be duly considered. The heart volume of a healthy non-athlete weighing 70 kg is ca. *700–800 ml.* This volume can be nearly doubled by intensive endurance training.

Significance of body weight. The results of performance tests are often expressed with reference to body weight (relative values, p.585). In evaluating a person's physical performance capacity by such test results, however, the demands made upon the subject should be kept in mind. Depending on the question at issue, it is more useful to regard either the *absolute performance capacity* (with no reference to body dimensions) or the *relative performance capacity* (with reference to the weight or the fat content of the body). That is, if the *weight of the subject's own body* is the only load, the performance parameters of different individuals can best be compared if the results are related to body weight. On the other hand, if an *additional weight* is to be transported, the absolute performance capacity is also of importance. For example, when required to carry a heavy (30 kg) pack uphill, a small person with correspondingly slight body weight will certainly perform worse than a tall, heavy person, even though their performance capacities per unit body weight are the same. A relative W_{170} performance capacity of 3 watts/kg corresponds to an absolute value of 150 watts for a person weighing 50 kg, and to 300 watts for a person weighing twice as much. Given an equal relative performance capacity of 3 watts/kg, then, the heavy person has 300 watts available to move a total of 130 kg (i.e., 2.3 watts/kg), whereas the light person has only 150 watts for 80 kg (i.e., 1.9 watts/kg). When the *performance capacity of the skeletal musculature* is to be evaluated, it is reasonable to express the performance-test results with respect to the fat-free body mass (lean body mass, p.585), because this quantity is basically determined by the muscle mass.

Interpretation of Performance Tests

Once the reliability and validity of a test have been established, one can draw precise conclusions from the results – applicable, of course, only to the *performance capacity at the time of the test*. In many cases, however, the *future performance capacity* is of greater interest – for example, in search of **talent** for particular professional occupations or areas of sport. In looking for people qualified for jobs, one must consider two main objects:

1. To find people who are useful *at present*, without instruction or training, for performing particular tasks; in this case the current performance profile should match closely the requirements of the task *(present aptitude, usefulness).*

2. To find people whose talent suggests that training or instruction will make them useful for performing certain tasks, so that a *future* correspondence between performance profile and requirements can be expected *(talented people* with *future aptitude).*

Tests of talent. *Present aptitude (usefulness)* can be evaluated by practical tests in which the subject is observed while performing the task in question for a more or less long period of time, or examined by a battery of tests with subdivisions to explore each of the abilities required for the task. In neither case are prognoses regarding future increases in performance capacity possible.

When an estimate of the *future performance capacity* to be expected *after* instruction or training is desired, it is necessary to use *talent tests*, the results of which are independent of training. Tests that strictly conform to this criterion are extraordinarily rare, and include the examination of certain features of body structure [8, 21] and perhaps of PPI (p.552). Performance in most "talent tests" – including intelligence tests – can be improved by special training.

A special kind of test is the medical examination of workers for the purposes of safety and health; in this case suitability for a task is evaluated in terms of general health, both at the time of hiring and at intervals during employment.

Performance prognosis. Predictions about the development of performance must be based on talent tests. But because tests that measure talent in the strict sense (see above) are so rare, one must try to obtain *indirect* estimates based either on a simultaneous analysis of performance capacity and state of training (or training quota), or on a longitudinal study. That is, test results obtained during the process of training are plotted as a training curve (cf. Fig. 24-13); a plateau in the curve indicates the maximal performance the subject can reach under the prevailing conditions. Interindividual differences in plateau levels for a given training program have a prognostic value. This kind of *talent search* is not new; it corresponds to the old principle of testing by **probation** – a type of selection that always extends over relatively long periods of time.

Confidence levels of prognosis. Estimates of a person's present or future performance capacity should *not be taken too literally*. Performance levels are always based on *many factors,* and one can rarely be certain that a test result reflects all of them. Moreover, nature makes sudden jumps; many a person has proved capable of "excelling himself." It is not advisable to place any more reliance on a performance prognosis than, for example, on a weather prognosis – and the latter are based on decades of experience.

In conclusion, given the widespread tendency in industry and sport to evaluate talent by elaborate test batteries and computer analyses, it should be said that the problem of prognosis lies in the *validity* of the tests and the *interpretation* of the results, and *not in the scale* of the test program.

24.8 High-Altitude Physiology

Four major factors are potentially stressful to a person living at high altitudes [1, 8, 28, 34]: 1. the lower O_2 partial pressure, 2. the increased solar radiation, 3. the cold and 4. the dryness of the inspired air. The most important of these is the O_2 partial pressure.

Oxygen Deficiency

Acute and chronic hypoxia. As altitude increases the atmospheric pressure decreases, whereas the O_2 concentration remains constant up to high altitude. The partial pressure of O_2 falls in proportion to the drop in atmospheric pressure (Table 24-4). The responses of the body to **oxygen deficiency** depend not only on the degree of deficiency but on its duration as well [28]. Depending on the times involved, a distinction is made among **acute hypoxia** (e.g., sudden loss of pressure in an airplane or malfunction of breathing equipment), **rapid-onset hypoxia** (e.g., ascent in a cable car) and **chronic hypoxia** (e.g., a prolonged stay at high altitudes). The influence of the time factor is manifest, for example, in the fact that rapid ascents are tolerated less well than slower ones. Altitude-tolerance also depends on the **manner of the ascent**; one can endure great heights better if one has reached them actively (on foot) than if one has been transported passively (by car or airplane).

Altitude sickness [10, 50]. This term denotes a number of physiological disturbances induced by oxygen deficiency. The general symptoms are a reduction in mental and physical performance, rapid tiring and discomfort.
The *special signs* of oxygen deficiency at altitude are diminished will power, a need for sleep, loss of appetite and apathy (though euphoria can also occur); more severe symptoms include breathlessness, tachycardia, dizziness, vomiting and headache. Depending on the individual's *predisposition* and *situation,* these symptoms can occur separately or in various combinations. Their importance as *warning signals* is often not recognized or is underestimated. *Slowly developing oxygen deficiency is especially dangerous,* particularly for a person at rest, because it can cause unconsciousness before any warning symptoms are apparent.

Effective thresholds. The range of effects of oxygen deficiency can be subdivided into **4 zones** delimited by *effective thresholds* [28] (Fig.24-16). This is of course not a rigid subdivision, for there are various transitional effects and the thresholds can be shifted by *acclimation* (p.567) and *predisposition.*

Table 24-4. Atmospheric pressure, inspiratory O_2 partial pressure (moistened inspired air) and alveolar O_2 partial pressure at different altitudes above sea level. In the last column are the O_2 fractions with which the corresponding partial pressures can be simulated at sea level (100 mm Hg $\approx$ 13.3 kPa)

Altitude	Air pressure	Insp. O_2 partial pressure	Alveol. O_2 partial pressure	Equivalent O_2 fraction
(m)	(mm Hg)	(mm Hg)	(mm Hg)	
0	760	149	105	0.2095
2,000	596	115	76	0.164
3,000	526	100	61	0.145
4,000	462	87	50	0.127
5,000	405	75	42	0.112
6,000	354	64	38	0.098
7,000	308	55	35	0.085
8,000	267	46	32	0.074
10,000	199	32		0.055
14,000	106	12		0.029
19,000	49	0.4		0.014

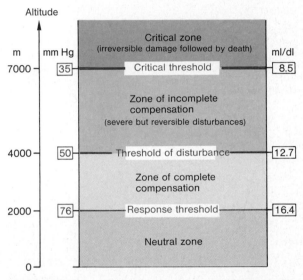

Fig. 24-16. Effects of altitude-related oxygen deficiency. The numbers in *red* give the alveolar O_2 partial pressure at the corresponding altitude, and the *black* numbers give the oxygen content of gas mixtures that would have the same effect at sea level (cf. Table 24-4). The data are rough approximations, for non-acclimatized people (100mm Hg $\approx$ 13.3 kPa). After [28]

Neutral zone. Up to an altitude of 2000 m physiological functions and thus, for example, the maximal rate of dynamic work suffer little or not at all.
Zone of complete compensation. At altitudes between 2000 and 4000 m even at rest a response to the reduced oxygen supply becomes apparent, in the form of a slight increase in pulse rate, cardiac output and respiratory minute volume. During work there is a greater increase in these variables than at sea level, so that both physical and mental performance are detectably impaired.
Zone of incomplete compensation (danger zone). At altitudes between 4000 and 7000 m an unacclimatized person shows var-

ious disorders. When the *threshold of disturbance* (**safety limit**) at 4000 m is passed physical performance is seriously affected, as are responsiveness and the ability to make decisions. Muscle twitches appear, the blood pressure drops and eventually consciousness becomes clouded. These changes are reversible. *Critical zone.* From *7000 m* on up the O_2 partial pressure in the alveolar air is below the **critical threshold,** *30–35 mm Hg* (4.0–4.7 kPa). Potentially lethal central nervous disturbances are accompanied by unconsciousness and convulsions; these can be reversed by a rapid increase in the inspiratory P_{O_2}, if they have lasted only for a short time. In the critical zone, the *duration of oxygen deficiency plays the crucial role.* If hypoxia lasts too long the central nervous control systems fail and death results.

High-altitude intoxication. Depending on the susceptibility of the individual, this condition can appear without any other symptoms at altitudes of 3000 m or more [1, 28]. As in alcohol intoxication, typical signs are euphoria, failure to recognize danger, and conspicuous errors of judgement.
Time of useful consciousness. When there is a *sudden onset* of oxygen deficiency at altitudes above 7000 m (e.g., loss of pressure in an airplane) one has a brief period of grace during which normal function continues (Table 24-5). At the end of this period consciousness becomes impaired, followed by irreversible damages, leading to death [1, 10].

Table 24-5. Time from oxygen cut-off to loss of function (time of useful consciousness) at altitudes above 7000 m. After [28]

Alt. (km)	7	8	9	10	11	12	15
Time (min)	5	3	1.5	1	⅔	½	⅙

Breathing pure oxygen at altitude. Oxygen inhalation shifts the altitude-response thresholds but does not abolish them. When pure oxygen is breathed at an altitude of 14 km the inspiratory P_{O_2} is 106 mm Hg (14.1 kPa). In the dead space at 37 °C the P_{H_2O} accounts for 47 mm Hg (6.3 kPa; p.473), so that about 60 mm Hg (8.0 kPa) remains for the inspiratory P_{O_2}. The alveolar space still contains carbon dioxide at a partial pressure of ca. 30 mm Hg (4.0 kPa, varying according to the degree of hyperventilation; p.475), which reduces the P_{O_2} still further [10]: All that remains is 30 mm Hg (4.0 kPa) – less than the **critical hypoxia threshold.** A person breathing pure oxygen reaches this limit at altitudes between 13 and 14 km, so that to ascend higher pressure suits or pressurized cabins are required [6, 50].

Short-Term Adjustment to High Altitude

Hypoxia at altitude (or in other situations, such as heart malfunction) elicits short-, intermediate- and long-term adaptive reactions [34, 50]. Short-term processes require only a few hours, whereas true acclimation (p.567) to high altitudes requires several days to months.

Circulatory adjustments. At 2000 m or higher the resting **pulse rate** rises, and at 6000 m it reaches about 120 min^{-1}. The increases brought about by exercise are considerably greater than those at sea level. **Stroke volume** changes only slightly; both increases and decreases have been observed. Thus cardiac output is increased slightly at rest but distinctly more so during exercise. The **arterial blood pressure** during exercise does not change appreciably with altitude. But in the **pulmonary artery,** especially at rest, there can be pressure increases associated with pulmonary edema (pulmonary vasoconstriction during hypoxia is described on p.438).

Respiratory adjustments. In *resting* conditions the arterial hypoxia exerts only a slight respiratory drive (p.483); respiratory minute volume at 5000 m is only about 10% above the comparable sea-level value, though at 6500 m it is twice as great. During *exercise* minute volume increases markedly. **Hyperventilation** leads to an increase in respiratory quotient to more than 1.0 (p.527). Despite hyperventilation the amount of oxygen inhaled (expressed as $\dot{V}_{O_2STPD}$) is less, because the minute volume does not increase in proportion to the decrease in P_{O_2}.

Oxygen-transport adjustments. Because the alveolar P_{O_2} falls as altitude increases (Table 24-4), the arterial P_{O_2} also falls. At 2000 m, under resting conditions, the alveolar P_{O_2} is 73 mm Hg (9.7 kPa) and the arterial P_{O_2} is 67 mm Hg (8.9 kPa); nevertheless, the arterial **oxygen saturation** of the hemoglobin is still **93%**. Two additional factors impede *oxygen transport.* First, hyperventilation leads to *respiratory alkalosis,* which causes a leftward shift of the oxygen dissociation curve (pp.495 f.). This shift facilitates oxygen binding in the lung, but makes it more difficult for oxygen to be released in the tissues. Second, during exercise the *alveolar-arterial O_2 partial-pressure difference* AaD_{O_2} (pp.477 f.) in the lung increases as more oxygen is taken up. During exhausting work it can rise to 15 mm Hg (2.0 kPa). Taking the alveolar P_{O_2} at 2000 m as 73 mm Hg (9.7 kPa), any increase in AaD_{O_2} causes a detectable decrease in arterial O_2 saturation because of the shift to the steeper part of the oxygen dissociation curve (p.496). During exhausting work at 2000 m oxygen saturation is less than 90%, which corresponds to an arterial P_{O_2} below 60 mm Hg (8.0 kPa); as a result, maximal performance at 2000 m is reduced by almost 10% (and by ca. 20% at 3500 m).

Adjustments in acid-base balance. The hyperventilation during adjustment to high altitude causes an increased release of carbon dioxide. The CO_2 partial pressure in the blood drops and **respiratory alkalosis** ensues (p.504). At 4000 m the arterial P_{CO_2} is about

30 mm Hg (4.0 kPa); at 6500 m it is only 20 mm Hg (2.7 kPa), and the arterial pH rises above 7.5. *Base excess* (BE) does not change during acute high-altitude stress.

Acclimation to High Altitude

In the intermediate and long term, life at high altitudes brings about adaptations of circulation, respiration, blood and musculature. These changes are basically a *response to arterial hypoxia and respiratory alkalosis*. There are considerable individual differences in the extent and time course of these adaptations, and the adaptive response may go through an overshooting phase (e.g., in erythropoiesis). Months to years are required for complete acclimation. Expeditions have shown, however, that even after a few weeks a remarkable degree of acclimation – and thus of altitude tolerance – can be achieved [1, 42].

The *highest human settlements* are in the Andes, at about 5300 m. This altitude is probably the highest permanently tolerable by man. But regular work at great altitudes is evidently less of a problem than permanent habitation, for mines can be operated at altitudes as high as 6200 m. Presumably the regulation of breathing during work (by muscle receptors; p.552) can produce tolerable physiological conditions despite the altitude, but not the regulation during rest [32]. The inhabitants of villages at great heights have undergone centuries of selection; the acclimation they show can presumably be regarded as the most that adaptation can achieve. In order to learn about the physiological changes accompanying this acclimation, the inhabitants of the city Morococha, 4540 m high in the Andes, were studied [42]. The results are summarized in Table 24-6, in comparison with the findings in lowland dwellers (Lima). In general, the changes during acclimation are as follows:

Cardiovascular acclimation. In the initial stage of acclimation the resting pulse rate rises, but then it falls again and at altitudes up to 5000 m can stabilize below the starting level. Stroke volume does not change appreciably; accordingly, cardiac output at rest varies little and the maximal cardiac output is reduced.

Respiratory acclimation. As acclimation proceeds over weeks, the breathing control system becomes increasingly *sensitive* to arterial oxygen deficiency and elevated P_{CO_2} [50]. This change is evident in that the breath cannot be held as long and the CO_2-response curve changes (leftward shift and steeper slope; p.482). However, people who live permanently at great heights have smaller respiratory responses to inspiratory oxygen deficiency than those at an intermediate stage of adaptation.

Oxygen transport during acclimation. At the beginning of a period at high altitude the number of erythrocytes in the blood sometimes decreases because of

Table 24-6. Various blood, respiration and circulatory parameters of residents at high altitude (Morococha) and the lowlands (Lima); all data in resting conditions. 100 mm Hg ≈ 13.3 kPa [42]

Altitude:	4540 m	0 m
Blood:		
Erythrocytes (million/µl)	6.44	5.11
Reticulocytes (thousand/µl)	46	18
Thrombocytes (thousand/µl)	419	401
Leukocytes (thousand/µl)	7.0	6.7
Hematocrit (%)	60	47
Hemoglobin content (g/dl)	20.1	15.6
Blood volume (ml/kg)	101	80
Plasma volume (ml/kg)	39	42
pH of arterial blood	7.39	7.41
Buffer base (mmol/l)	45.6	49.2
Respiratory minute volume BTPS ($1 \cdot min^{-1} \cdot kg^{-1}$)	0.19	0.13
P_{O_2}, alveolar (mm Hg)	51	104
P_{CO_2}, alveolar (mm Hg)	29.1	38.6
Art. O_2 saturation (%)	81	98
Pulse rate (min^{-1})	72	72
Blood pressure (mm Hg)	93/63	116/79

a higher rate of loss, but after a few days all the signs of *enhanced erythropoiesis* appear (p.339). *Reticulocytes* become more abundant, the red cell count rises, and the hemoglobin concentration is increased, with a slight fall in the mean corpuscular hemoglobin (MCH; p.492) below the normal level of *31 pg/erythrocyte*. The greater the altitude-related oxygen deficiency, the stronger the stimulus to erythropoiesis, though there is no change in the rate of production of other blood cells. Experiments have demonstrated an increase of over 10% in *red cell count* and *hemoglobin concentration* after 2 days at 4500 m. After about 10 days the *rapid* phase of rising RCC and hemoglobin concentration is completed. The following slow increase, lasting months (*maxima:* hemoglobin, 27 g/dl blood; hematocrit, 70%) is terminated by a slight decline to a stable high level (see Table 24-6). Another change in the first 2 days is an increase in the *2,3-DPG content* of the erythrocytes, from ca. 85 µg/ml blood to 140 µg/ml blood, accompanied by a shift of the O_2 dissociation curve to the *right*.

Because the hemoglobin content of the blood is increased, its *O_2-transport capacity* remains about the same up to 5000 m despite the lowered O_2 saturation. 100 ml blood containing 15.5 g hemoglobin binds 20 ml oxygen at 97% saturation; 100 ml blood containing 20 g hemoglobin binds the same amount of oxygen at only 75% saturation (corresponding to ca. 5000 m altitude). But because the elevated hematocrit raises the viscosity of the blood considerably, the microcirculation in the capillaries is impeded (pp.399f.); one result is that during the middle stages of acclimation the maximal cardiac output is less. Therefore during exhausting work the maximal rate of oxygen transport is no greater, even when one returns to sea level after acclimation to high altitude. Such acclimation thus provides no appreciable improvement in endurance performance at sea level. The *leftward* shift of the O_2 dissociation curve resulting from respiratory alkalosis is at first compensated by the increase in 2,3-diphosphoglycerate; after longer adaptation overcompensation leads to a *rightward* shift, which enhances the release of oxygen in the tissues.

Acid-base balance during acclimation. In the course of acclimation increased amounts of bicarbonate are excreted by the kidney. This *renal compensation* of respiratory alkalosis brings the *blood pH* back to normal (pp. 504 f.). Moreover, as the amount of hemoglobin rises so does the buffering capacity of the blood. But the buffering capacity of the tissue decreases because of the compensatory loss of bicarbonate, so that there are *shifts of electrolytes* between the intra- and extracellular spaces [37].

Musculature during acclimation. As acclimation progresses the *capillary density* in the muscles increases; the diffusion paths between the capillaries and the interior of the muscles become shorter. Within the muscle cell various *enzyme systems,* especially those of the mitochondria, adapt to oxygen deficiency so that aerobic metabolism is favored despite the lowered P_{O_2}.

Performance capacity at altitude. The above physiological mechanisms associated with a stay at altitude impair physical as well as mental performance capacity. The compensating processes of adjustment and adaptation have been studied intensively [16, 22, 42]. In summary, it can be stated that (i) the effective thresholds vary considerably, both inter- and intraindividually, and (ii) in most cases the symptoms of dangerous states of oxygen deficiency are small and not fully appreciated, so that a typical consequence is sudden, unexpected unconsciousness.
On the whole, acclimation allows man to live without assistance, for limited periods, at altitudes that would otherwise be lethal. Acclimatized mountain climbers can work for a certain time without oxygen apparatus at altitudes above 8000 m, and in some cases at nearly 8900 m. The limiting altitudes for permanent living are considerably lower (p. 567).

Air and Space Travel

During high-altitude flight one encounters the problems of acute oxygen deficiency discussed above. Moreover, with a pressurized cabin with interior pressure roughly equivalent to an altitude of 2300 m, there are brief pressure changes during take-off and landing that affect chiefly the air-filled cavities in the skull (cf. *barotrauma,* pp. 569 f.). Moreover, as altitude increases one must take precautions against the increased radiation and lower ambient temperature [1, 6, 10].
Still another problem is presented by the *forces of acceleration* in flight [6]. These act on a seated person in the fronto-occipital direction when the velocity of forward flight changes, in various directions when flying through turbulence, and along the long axis of the body when flying in a curve. Forces as great as 10 g (ten times the earth's gravity) have been measured in jet fighters. These (usually brief) changes in acceleration have multiple effects [6, 36]: (i) *air sickness (kinetosis),* (ii) *sensory illusions* with respect to visual and vestibular orientation in space, and (iii) *critical arterial blood-pressure drop* when acceleration in the direction of the body's long axis drives blood into the lower extremities, to the disadvantage of the intrathoracic low-pressure system (cf. orthostatic collapse, p. 446).

Time-zone jumps. Flight across time zones causes discrepancies between the endogenous rhythms and external *triggers* (pp. 153 f., 561) as well as between the phase of the traveller's daily performance cycle and that of the local residents. For example, by reference to Fig. 24-15 we see that with a time-zone jump of 6 hours to the east and a landing at 9 a.m. local time, the traveller is at his *lowest point* on arrival (at 3 a.m. by his "internal clock"). Arriving at 9 a.m. after the same flight in the opposite direction, he finds himself at the afternoon peak of performance (3 p.m. by the "internal clock"). This is why *eastward* flights so often cause greater difficulty in adjustment than do westward flights.
Biological rhythms adjust themselves at different rates (pp. 153 f.). Among those that reset rapidly are the waking/sleeping and performance rhythms; for resynchronization of every 2 hours of time shift about one day is required.

Space flight requires pressurized cabins or suits [6, 50]; without them, blood at 37 °C would boil at altitudes of 19 km or more *(ebullition).* A pressurized cabin also ensures adequate inspiratory oxygen partial pressure (pp. 565 f.) and offers protection from the cold and, though not completely, from the radiation in outer space.
The absence of gravitational attraction **(weightlessness)** produces diverse reactions [6, 36]: (i) *space sickness,* with nausea or vomiting and the feeling of severe illness, especially in the first three days; (ii) *decrease in blood volume* brought about by the regulatory mechanisms that counteract the initial overfilling of the intrathoracic low-pressure system (reversed orthostatism); (iii) *atrophy* of the musculature, especially the postural muscles; (iv) *calcium loss* from the bones and disturbance of electrolyte balance. Finally the movement patterns for food intake, micturition and defecation are considerably impaired. On the whole, however, human adaptability and technology have proved adequate to permit life in outer space for weeks and months – at the price of renewed difficulties in adapting after the *return* to earth.

24.9 Diving

The diver moves through an alien environment; beyond the short time of breath-hold diving, he must provide air for *breathing* and adjust to the increased *pressure*[5, 8, 25, 33]. Immersion in water also makes it harder to maintain *thermal equilibrium,* because heat is lost more rapidly (the heat conductance of water is greater than that of air by a factor of ca. 30, and its heat capacity per unit volume is ca. 4000 times greater). Conditions are thus usually outside the thermoneutral zone. Finally, *orientation* by eyes and ears is distorted [33].

Diving without Equipment

The simplest form of diving, with no equipment at all, is limited to relatively slight depths [33]. Prior **hyperventilation** is dangerous for two reasons: 1. *dizziness* or even convulsions can occur before the dive owing to respiratory alkalosis (p. 504), and 2. the *oxygen reserve can be misestimated* at the end of the dive, because the total respiratory drive (pp. 482 f.) is diminished by the lowered CO_2 partial pressure and the respiratory alkalosis. The oxygen deficiency that develops during diving in itself is only a weak stimulus, so that breathing can be suppressed longer than in a dive without prior hyperventilation – with the risk that the increasing oxygen deficiency will lead to *sudden fainting (black-out)*. Whereas the arterial O_2 saturation does not rise as a result of hyperventilation, the O_2 concentration in the lung can be increased by about 5 ml/dl as the result of a few deep breaths.

Snorkling with face-plate or goggles gives one an opportunity to observe the underwater region without interruption [33]; sunburn on shoulders and neck and overcooling are not uncommon results. The standard snorkel, 30 to 35 cm long, must on no account be extended. Although this enlargement of the dead space would have hardly any effect on respiration, the consequences to the *circulatory system* during a deeper dive are considerable. Because the alveolar pressure corresponds to the atmospheric pressure at the water surface, the additional external pressure of water on the rest of the body causes a *pressure gradient in the low-pressure system* (pp. 438 f.). The thorax would thus become increasingly filled with blood at progressively greater depths, and eventually there could be potentially lethal *overstretching of the pulmonary vessels and heart* [60]. Another danger is associated with entry into *cold-water currents;* particularly in the vagotonic phase after eating, cutaneovisceral reflexes

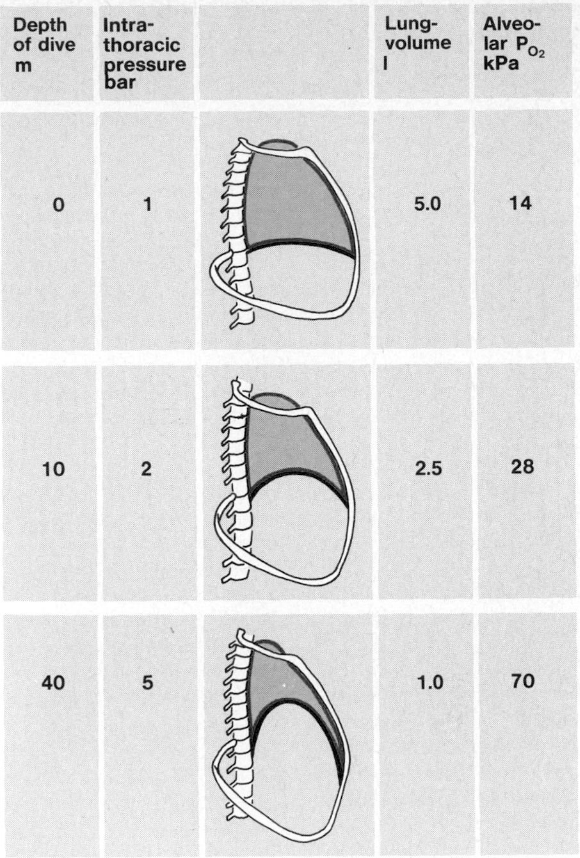

Depth of dive m	Intra-thoracic pressure bar		Lung-volume l	Alveolar P_{O_2} kPa
0	1		5.0	14
10	2		2.5	28
40	5		1.0	70

Fig. 24-17. Lung volumes and partial pressures in breath-hold deep diving. At 0 m the thorax is in the maximal-inspiration position, and at 40 m in the maximal-expiration position (greatest diaphragm displacement). For alveolar P_{O_2} oxygen consumption is neglected; intrathoracic pressure, 1 bar $\doteq$ 100 kPa

(pp. 122 f.) can trigger so-called *vasovagal syncope* with a critical fall in blood pressure.

Deep breath-hold diving requires consideration of the physical gas laws, as follows. 1. *Boyle-Mariotte* law: the product of pressure and volume is constant. 2. *Dalton's* law: the sum of the partial pressures is the total pressure. 3. *Henry-Dalton* law (p. 493): the amount of a gas dissolved is proportional to its partial pressure and solubility coefficient. These laws, of course, are strictly valid only for *ideal* gases, but experience has shown that they are entirely applicable to the problems encountered in deep dives.

Barotrauma *(pressure injury*[33]): The Boyle-Mariotte law holds for all *air-filled cavities* in the body (e.g., lungs, spaces in the skull, hollow teeth or stomach). During descent the rising ambient pressure can lead to disturbances that ultimately injure the tissues. For example, at the beginning of a dive the thorax volume and thus the lung volume decrease with no difficulty, reaching a minimum at a depth of 30–40 m (Fig. 24-17). Because the lung cannot be further compressed at greater depths, the intrathoracic pressure remains constant despite the continually increasing extrathoracic (ambient) pressure with increasing depth. The resulting *pressure difference* causes a considerable *inflow of blood into the thoracic organs* (cf. snorkling); the intrathoracic volume of air is further reduced as the pulmonary vessels and heart are stretched beyond their capacity and eventually suffer damage. – The pressure in the air-filled parts of the skull must be equilibrated with the intrathoracic pressure by way of the nose and throat, either spontaneously or with assistance (cf. Valsalva's test with nose held closed, p. 416). It is difficult or impossible to equalize these pressures if the channels by which the middle ear and paranasal sinuses communicate with the throat are blocked (for example, when the mucous membranes are swollen by a cold). In such cases *pressure equilibration* can be achieved only by an outward bulging of the tympanum (until it bursts) and/or by further filling of the mucous membranes with blood until they swell painfully and tear.

Oxygen shortage following ascent [25]. If a diver holding his breath stays deep underwater as long as he thinks he can resist the need to breathe, he must necessarily become unconscious when he ascends. The ambient pressure increase during the descent has elevated the alveolar P_{O_2} (Fig. 24-17), but this is an illusory advantage, for the reverse process occurs during the ascent. As the diver rises the P_{O_2} in the lungs drops rapidly, soon reaching and passing the *critical hypoxia threshold* of 30–35 mm Hg (4.0–4.7 kPa; p. 565). The drop is especially severe near the surface, for in the last 10 m of the ascent the ambient pressure is halved.

Diving with Equipment

There are three types of breathing apparatus: compressed-air, oxygen and mixed-gas devices [5, 33].

Compressed-air equipment. This includes *portable breathing equipment, hose-and-pump systems, and caissons.* The portable apparatus is used mainly for sport diving, and the others for underwater work. In all cases the pressure of the inspired air is matched to that of the surroundings, and the expired air is released into the water *(open system)*. The actual minute volume (BTPS, p. 473) corresponds roughly to that during equivalent exercise on land, but the minute volume converted to STPD conditions rises considerably with increasing depth underwater (and hence pressure), revealing an increased air requirement. The *work of breathing* (p. 471) is increased because of the greater viscosity of compressed air.

Nitrogen narcosis. The greater the depth and the longer the duration of a dive, the more nitrogen becomes dissolved in the tissues. Under normal atmospheric pressures nitrogen dissolved in the body is inert, but at depths of 40 m or more the concentrations present in the tissues can, depending on the situation and the susceptibility of the diver, cause intoxication symptoms (*euphoria,* but also *anxiety*) accompanied by gross errors in performance and even unconsciousness. Therefore *one should never go below 50 m with compressed-air equipment.*

Decompression. As the ambient pressure falls during the ascent care must be taken to equilibrate the pressures in the body cavities filled with compressed air, if *barotrauma* is to be avoided.

For example, if a diver using such a device rises from 50 m underwater to the surface with glottis closed, the lung is stretched until it tears and air enters the vascular system *(air embolism).* Moreover, *inert gases* (e.g., N_2) stored in the tissues must be gradually removed from storage and breathed out; if decompression is too rapid they form *bubbles* in the blood and tissues, in much the same way as bubbles are formed when a bottle of soda water is opened. The ascent and emergence must be done systematically and slowly, in stages (cf. decompression tables [5, 33]). Only during the time within which the tissue concentrations critical for bubble formation have not yet been reached is it advisable to emerge immediately; this is the case in almost all kinds of breath-hold diving and in all dives no deeper than 10 m. Decompression injury is also observed when a prolonged dive is followed by a rapid ascent above ground (e.g., in an airplane).

Oxygen devices. Self-contained breathing apparatus can also provide pure oxygen. In a *closed system* (the principle of *recirculating* devices) the oxygen-rich exhaled air can be rebreathed if the carbon dioxide it contains is removed by an absorbent material (p. 528). Such apparatus enables *prolonged diving* but is unsuitable for sport, because at depths below about 7 m pure oxygen (P_{O_2} = 172 kPa or 1 292 mm Hg) is toxic to the central nervous system; symptoms of *acute oxygen poisoning* include nausea, convulsions and unconsciousness. Because they are so hazardous, oxygen-recirculation devices are used only for special purposes (by "frogmen", for instance). – When compressed air is breathed, *hyperoxia damage* can be incurred at depths of ca. 74 m or more.

Mixed-gas devices of the closed type can be used at lower depths; here pure oxygen is mixed either with compressed air or with helium. When compressed air is used dives can be deeper than 7 m, whereas the mixture with helium gives protection against nitrogen narcosis. For dives to 70 m or more, however, the mixture must contain less than the normal amount of oxygen in order to avoid hyperoxic injury.

Failure of CO_2 absorption in a closed system produces carbonic-acid poisoning. The highest permissible CO_2 concentration of the air in work areas has been fixed at 0.5 ml/dl; slightly higher concentrations are harmful only in case of chronic exposure. With 1.5 ml CO_2 per dl inspired air the resting respiratory minute volume rises from about 7 to 10 l/min, and with 3 ml/dl a diver can clearly detect the increase. From about 7 ml/dl on, marked shortness of breath is accompanied by signs of severe respiratory acidosis – headache, nausea and other "autonomic symptoms" as well as unconsciousness, convulsions and respiratory paralysis.

Orientation Under Water

Vision. The *light intensity* decreases rapidly with depth under water; even under favorable conditions it is permanently night at 100 m. Without goggles, the cornea/air interface becomes a cornea/water interface, which has different refractive properties. As a result, only objects close to the eye are in focus. *Diving goggles* eliminate this effect, but the multiple refraction of rays incident at a sharp angle causes objects to appear nearer and larger, so that the *field of view is narrower* [33].

Hearing. Sound propagates more rapidly in water than in the air (ca. 1450 m/s instead of 330 m/s). Therefore underwater sound sources appear nearer than they actually are. Moreover, because of the shortened interaural delay (p. 290) *auditory localization* becomes practically impossible [25].

Vestibular system. If the *eardrum* is defective water can enter the middle ear and cause caloric stimulation of the horizontal semicircular canal (pp. 278 f.), which interferes with spatial orientation. A diver who panics in this situation is in danger of his life [33].

Rules for diving. Under water many otherwise innocuous events and situations can present a danger. Two of the 12 most important diving rules [25], in particular, should be taken to heart by all divers, even the unambitious amateur:
1. Never dive alone!
2. Never dive when you have a cold (for fear of barotrauma)!

24.10 References

Textbooks and Handbooks

1. ARMSTRONG, G. (ed.): Aerospace medicine. Baltimore: Williams and Wilkins 1961
2. ASCHOFF, J. (ed.): Circardian clocks. Basel–New York: Karger 1965
3. ÅSTRAND, P.-O., RODAHL, K.: Textbook of work physiology. New York: McGraw-Hill 1977
4. BARTLEY, S. H.: Fatigue (mechanism and management). Springfield (Ill.): Thomas 1965
5. BENNETT, P. B., ELLIOTT, D. H.: The physiology and medicine of diving. London: Baillière Tindall 1975
6. BROWN, J. H. U. (ed.): Physiology of man in space. New York–London: Academic Press 1963
7. COLQUHOUN, W. P., WILLIAM, P. (eds.): Biological rhythms and human performance. London: Academic Press 1971
8. FALLS, H. B.: Exercise physiology. New York–London: Academic Press 1968
9. FOLK, G. E. jr.: Textbook of environmental physiology. (2nd Ed.) Philadelphia: Lea and Febiger 1974
10. GILLIES, J. A. (ed.): A textbook of aviation physiology. Oxford–London–Edinburgh–New York–Paris–Frankfurt: Pergamon Press 1965
11. GRANDJEAN, E.: Physiologische Arbeitsgestaltung. Thun–München: Ott 1979
12. HARRE, D., Autorenkollektiv: Trainingslehre. Berlin: Sportverlag 1971 (English translation in press)
13. HETTINGER, Th.: Physiology of strength. Ed.: THURLWELL, M. H., St. Petersburg (Florida) Springfield (Ill.): Thomas 1961
14. HOLLMANN, W.: Höchst- und Dauerleistungsfähigkeit des Sportlers. München: Barth 1963
15. HOLLMANN, W. (ed.): Zentrale Themen der Sportmedizin. Berlin–Heidelberg–New York: Springer 1977
16. JOKL, E., JOKL, P. (eds.): Exercise and altitude. Basel–New York: Karger 1968
17. KEUL, J., DOLL, E., KEPPLER, D.: Energy metabolism of human muscle. Basel: Karger 1972
18. KEUL, J. (ed.): Limiting factors of physical performance. Stuttgart: Thieme 1973
19. KLEITMANN, N.: Sleep and wakefulness. Chicago: The University of Chicago Press 1963
20. LETZELTER, M.: Trainingsgrundlagen. Reinbek b. Hamburg: Rowohlt 1978
21. MAAS, G. D.: The physique of athletes. Leiden: University Press 1974
22. MARGARIA, R. (ed.): Exercise at altitude. Amsterdam: Excerpta Medica Foundation 1967
23. MAURICE, M.: Shift work. Genf: International Labour Organization (ILO) 1976
24. MELLEROWICZ, H., SMODLAKA, V. N. (eds.): Ergometry – Basics of medical exercise testing. Baltimore–München: Urban & Schwarzenberg 1981
25. MILES, S.: Underwater medicine. London: Staples Press 1969
26. NADEL, E. R.: Problems with temperature regulation during exercise. New York: Academic Press 1977
27. NIJS, P. (Red.): Sports and doping. In: Algemene Pharmazeutische Bond (A. P. B.), ed.: Farmaceutisch Tijdschrift voor Belgie. Vol. 55. Brussel: Algemene Pharmazeutische Bond 1978
28. RUFF, S., STRUGHOLD, H.: Grundriß der Luftfahrtmedizin. München: Barth 1957
29. RUTENFRANZ, J.: Entwicklung und Beurteilung der körperlichen Leistungsfähigkeit bei Kindern und Jugendlichen. Basel–New York: Karger 1964
30. SELYE, H.: The stress of life. New York: McGraw-Hill 1956
31. SHEPHARD, R.J.: Human physiological work capacity. Cambridge–London–New York–Melbourne: Cambridge University Press 1978
32. STEGEMANN, J.: Exercise physiology. Stuttgart–New York: Thieme 1981
33. STRAUSS, R. (ed.): Diving medicine. New York–San Francisco–London: Grune & Stratton 1976
34. WEIHE, W. H. (ed.): The physiological effects of high altitude. Oxford–London–New York–Paris: Pergamon Press 1964
35. ZOHMANN, L. R., Phillips, R. E.: Medical aspects of exercise testing and training. New York: Intercontinental Medical Book Corporation 1973

Research Reports and Reviews

36. BAUMGARTEN, R. J. von, BALDRICH, G., SHILLINGER jr., G. L., HARTH, O., THÜMLER, R.: Vestibular function in the space environment. Acta Astronautica 2, 49 (1975)
37. BÖNING, D.: Wirkungen des akuten Sauerstoffmangels auf die Blutelektrolytkonzentration bei höhenangepaßten und nicht höhenangepaßten Menschen. Pflügers Arch. 314, 217 (1970)
38. CANNON, W. B.: Die Notfallreaktionen des sympathico-adrenalen Systems. Erg. Physiol. 27, 380 (1928)
39. FOX III, S. M.: Physical activity and coronary heart disease. Am. J. Cardiol. 23, 298 (1969)
40. GRAF, O.: Arbeitsablauf und Arbeitsrhythmus. In: LEHMANN, G., ed.: Handbuch der gesamten Arbeitsmedizin. Bd. 1: Arbeitsphysiologie. Berlin–München–Wien: Urban & Schwarzenberg 1961
41. HEINRICH, K. W., ULMER, H.-V., STEGEMANN, J.: Sauerstoffaufnahme, Pulsfrequenz und Ventilation bei Variation von Tretgeschwindigkeit und Tretkraft bei aerober Ergometerarbeit. Pflügers Arch. 298, 191 (1968)
42. HURTADO, A.: Animals in high altitudes: resident man. In: DILL, D. B., Ed.: Handbook of physiology. Sect. 4: Adaptation on the environment. Washington: American Physiological Society 1964
43. JOKL, E.: Notes on doping. In: 16
44. JOKL, E.: Athletes and drugs. In: American Association for Health, Physical Education and Recreation, ed.: Annual safety education review. Washington D.C.: National Education Association 1969
45. JOHNSON, J. M., ROWELL L. B., BRENGELMANN, G. L.: Modification of

the skin blood flow-body temperature relationship by upright exercise. J. Appl. Physiol. *37*, 880 (1974)

46. KEUL, J., HARALAMBIE, G.: Energiestoffwechsel und körperliche Leistung. In: 15

47. KINDERMANN, W., SCHRAMM, M., KEUL, J.: Aerobic performance diagnostics with different experimental settings. Int. J. Sports Med. *1*, 110 (1980)

48. KINDERMANN, W., SIMON, G., KEUL, J.: The significance of the aerobic-anaerobic threshold for determination of work load intensities during endurance training. Eur. J. Appl. Physiol. *42*, 25 (1979)

49. LIND, A.R., McNICOL, G.W.: Cardiovascular responses to holding and carrying weights by hand and by shoulder harness. J. Appl. Physiol. *25*, 261 (1968)

50. LUFT, U.C.: Aviation physiology – The effects of altitude. In: FENN, W.O., RAHN, H., eds.: Handbook of physiology. Sect. 3, Vol. II: Respiration. Washington D.C.: American Physiological Society 1965

51. MÜLLER, E.A.: Occupational work capacity. Ergonomics *5*, 445 (1962)

52. MÜLLER, E.A.: Physical work capacity of man and its diminution by heat stress. In: UNESCO, ed.: Arid Zone Research XXIV: Environmental physiology and psychology in arid conditions. – Proc. LUCKNOW Symp., p.221 Paris: UNESCO 1964

53. MÜLLER, E.A.: Physiological methods of increasing human physical work capacity. Ergonomics *8*, 409 (1965)

54. PAUL, O.: Physical activity and coronary heart disease. Am. J. Cardiol. *23*, 303 (1969)

55. PUGH, L.G., CORBETT, J.L., JOHNSON, R.H.: Rectal temperature, weight loss and sweat rates in Marathon runners. J. Appl. Physiol. *23*, 347 (1967)

56. ROHMERT, W.: Beurteilung statischer Kraftübungen. Zbl. Arb. wiss. *15*, 1 (1960)

57. RUTENFRANZ, J., COLQUHOUN, W.P., KNAUTH, P., GHATA, J.N.: Biomedical and psychosocial aspects of shiftwork. A review. Scand. J. Work environ. Hlth. *3*, 165 (1977)

58. SEYFARTH, H.: The behaviour of motor units in healthy and paretic muscles in man. Acta psych. neurol. (Kbh.) *16*, 261 (1941)

59. SJÖDIN, B., JACOBS, I.: Onset of blood lactate accumulation and Marathon running performance. Int. J. Sports Med. *2*, 23 (1981)

60. STIGLER, R.: Die Kraft unserer Inspirationsmuskulatur. Pflügers Arch. *139*, 234 (1911)

61. ULMER, H.-V.: Perceived exertion as part of a behavioural feedback system for arrangement of strain during exercise. Arh. hig. rada toksikol. *30*, Suppl. Vol.3, 1 143 (1979)

62. ULMER, H.-V., RÖSKE, U., LINK, K.: Die Aussagefähigkeit des LPI nach E.A. Müller bei der Beurteilung der körperlichen Leistungsfähigkeit von Trainierten und Untrainierten. Int. Z. angew. Physiol. *29*, 343 (1971)

25 Nutrition

H.-V. Ulmer

The physiology of nutrition is of great importance in preventive medicine. Once *deficiency symptoms* resulting from inadequate nutrition were the chief concern, but today more attention must be paid to the consequences of overeating. *Overeating* leads to *obesity,* which is often associated with the *"diseases of civilization'* and with a shortened statistical life expectancy. For this reason, obesity is regarded as one of the avoidable epidemiological risk factors in highly industrialized countries.

Eating habits are seldom decided rationally; since early in human's history, the acquisition and consumption of food have been surrounded by tradition and ritual. The socio-cultural aspect of eating manifests itself in many ways – for example, the Holy Communion and fasting rules, the association of special foods with special occasions, the preference in many groups for rotundity as a symbol of wealth and status. It is not surprising that efforts to direct eating habits on the basis of nutritional physiology are often opposed by the "doctrines" of fanatics, sectarians and profit-seekers.

25.1 Foods: Their Composition and Function

Foods consist of the energy-containing foodstuffs plus vitamins, salts, trace elements, spices, crude fiber and water. Food intake is regulated principally by the general sensations *hunger* and *thirst* (cf. pp. 307 ff.).

Foodstuffs

The components of food that provide energy are the **proteins, fats** and **carbohydrates.** Organisms break down these foodstuffs metabolically, producing substances with a lower energy content. The energy thus released per gram is called the **biological fuel value** (p. 573); that of fats is more than twice as great as those of proteins and carbohydrates (Table 25-1, 1 kcal ≈ 4.2 kJ).

As far as the energy they provide is concerned, foodstuffs are equivalent and, according to their fuel

Table 25-1. Biological fuel value of fats, proteins and carbohydrates (in the average mixed Central European diet) as compared with glucose and alcohol (cf. [5])

Fats	37 kJ/g	9.3 kcal/g
Proteins	17 kJ/g	4.1 kcal/g
Carbohydrates	17 kJ/g	4.1 kcal/g
Glucose	16 kJ/g	3.75 kcal/g
Ethyl alcohol	30 kJ/g	7.1 kcal/g

value, *mutually interchangeable* **(isodynamic effect)**. However, foodstuffs are used not only for *functional metabolism* but also for *structural metabolism* (synthesis of secretions or substances of which the body is composed, p. 585); for the latter purpose, certain minimal quantities of proteins, fats and carbohydrates must be made available.

Specific dynamic action. After food has been consumed the metabolic rate increases. This phenomenon is ascribed to a special effect of the particular foodstuff concerned and is called its specific dynamic action. Consumption of a mixed diet raises the metabolic rate by *about 6%.* The increase following *protein ingestion* is much greater than that associated with carbohydrates or fats – basically because for the resynthesis of 1 mol ATP during break down of foodstuffs more protein energy than fat or carbohydrate energy is required [10]. Thus more energy is burned up to supply the body's functional metabolism with a diet consisting entirely of protein than with one based largely on fats or carbohydrates.

There are detailed tables showing the distribution of foodstuffs among various kinds of food; the composition of some of them is summarized in Table 25-2 (after [16]). Because changing methods of animal feeding and agriculture can have a marked effect on the composition of food, one should use recent rables (for example, [9]); also note the *water content* of the food.

Proteins consist of *amino acids* and are required for the synthesis of substances *indispensable for normal structure and function.* It is absolutely necessary that the protein in food contain the **essential amino acids,**

Table 25-2. Water and foodstuff content of some foods (% by weight). The composition of meat and sausage (*) is highly variable and depends on the amount of concealed fat. 1 kJ ≈ 0.24 kcal

Food	kJ/ 100 g	Water (%)	Pro-tein (%)	Fats (%)	Carbo-hydrate (%)
Fruit	250	80	0.7	0.3	15
Vegetables, including legumes	170	85	2.5	0.3	8
Potatoes	290	80	2.1	0.1	18
Potato chips	2400	1.8	5.3	40	50
Nuts	2650	4.5	15	60	18
Meat*	750	70	18	10	0.1
Bread	1050	35	8	1	50
Butter	3000	17	0.6	81	0.7
Cheese	1400	45	23	27	3
Sausage*	1130	60	12	25	0
Milk (3.5% fat)	270	89	3.2	3.5	4.6
Fruit juices	170	85	0.3	0.1	12
Beer (3.6% alcohol)	200	90	0.5	0	4.8

amino acids that the body *cannot synthesize,* or not in adequate amounts. Most of the protein consumed by humans is used in *structural metabolism* – for the synthesis and restructuring of biological materials such as musculature, enzymes and plasma proteins – and thus cannot be replaced by fats or carbohydrates. Proteins are found in both **animal** and **plant** food. Animal protein is obtained chiefly from *meat, fish, milk* and *dairy products,* and *eggs. Bread* and *potatoes* contain appreciable amounts of plant protein, and there are small amounts in almost all kinds of vegetables and fruit (cf. Table 25-2).

Fats are composed primarily of a mixture of different *triglycerides,* triesters of glycerine and fatty acids. A distinction is made between *saturated* and *unsaturated* fatty acids. There are certain unsaturated fatty acids that the body requires and cannot synthesize for itself *(essential fatty acids).*

The fats absorbed are either oxidized to supply *functional metabolism* or deposited in the tissues as an *energy store.* Unlike fat, protein and carbohydrate can be stored in the body only in small amounts; whatever is not used in functional or structural metabolism is converted to fat and stored in that form or is excreted. Because one type of reaction for which the essential fatty acids are required is the synthesis of *phospholipids,* they are a crucial factor in the formation of cell structures, mitochondria in particular. The essential fatty acid most important for humans is **linoleic acid.**

Fats are unavoidable components of *almost all food of animal origin* – in the important protein sources meat, fish, milk, dairy products and eggs. They are also found in plant seeds, such as nuts. Plant fats differ

from most animal fats in their content of unsaturated fatty acids, though these are no longer present in hydrogenated (artificially hardened) plant fats.

The fat in food may be **visible** (pure fats such as oils, lard, butter and the layers of fat in bacon and other meats), but it can also be **concealed** – distributed in droplets too small to be seen with the naked eye, particularly in meat and sausage. Modern methods of feeding animals for market encourage the deposition of *concealed fat,* and as a result the fat content of the average Central European diet is too high. Altogether, it is often difficult for the consumer to achieve an energetically balanced and qualitatively desirable diet.

Food fats and cholesterol. The presence of excessive cholesterol in the blood, above the recommended maximum of 220 mg/dl serum *(hypercholesterolemia)* is under discussion as a *risk factor,* along with obesity [17, 24]. It has been shown statistically that hypercholesterolemia is correlated with an increased incidence of arteriosclerosis, cardiac infarction and stroke – and thus with a decreased life expectancy.

Cholesterol is found only in the animal kingdom. The average amount of cholesterol consumed in food (eggs, milk fat, fat meat) per day is 750 mg. Because the ability of the human intestine to absorb it is limited and the production of cholesterol by the liver (ca. 1 g/day) varies, depending on the amount eaten, the relationships between the intake of cholesterol and its concentration in the blood are complicated [22, 23]. Even complete elimination of cholesterol from the diet lowers the cholesterol level by only 20%; if the average cholesterol intake is reduced from 750 mg/day to half this amount the blood level falls by 7 mg/dl serum, and doubling the intake raises it by 10 mg/dl. Although the details of the interaction are unknown, the fats in diet also may affect the blood cholesterol level. It has been suggested that saturated fatty acids, especially those with a chain length between 12 and 18 carbon atoms, increase blood cholesterol, while polyunsaturated fatty acids reduce it.

Carbohydrates. The basic carbohydrate molecules are the *monosaccharides* (simple sugars); compounds of 2 or more monosaccharides are called *di-, oligo- or polysaccharides.* Most of the carbohydrate in the human diet is in the form of *plant starch* (a polysaccharide). Carbohydrates are stored in the body as *glycogen* (animal starch), particularly in muscle and liver.

Carbohydrates are the chief *sources of energy* for the cells. The energy requirements of the brain are met almost exclusively by glucose; striated muscle, however, can metabolize fatty acids if the carbohydrate supply is inadequate. Glucose serves not only as a fuel; it is also a building block for the synthesis of many important compounds.

The carbohydrates upon which humans depend are almost entirely of *vegetable origin.* In addition to the digestible carbohydrates they contain, fruit, green vegetables, potatoes, grain and legumes have especially large amounts of indigestible carbohydrate such as *cellulose fiber* (crude fiber).

Table 25-3. *Fat-soluble vitamins*. Classification, typical sources and biological functions (for requirements and deficiency symptoms see Table 25-7, p. 579)

Name and synonyms	Typical sources	Typical biological functions
Vitamin A Retinol Axerophthol	Liver and cod-liver oil, milk and dairy products	Essential for all epithelial cells and the growth of the skeleton
Provitamin: Carotenoids	β-carotene in carrots	Vitamin A aldehyde (retinene) is a component of rhodopsin (visual purple)
Vitamin D group (antirachitic vitamins) Vitamin D_2 Calciferol Vitamin D_3 Cholecalciferol Vitamin D_4 Dihydrocalciferol	Liver and cod-liver oil, animal fats and oils	Absorption and metabolism of Ca^{++}, interactions with parathormone, calcification of bones
Vitamin E Tocopherol	Plant oils, wheat sprouts, grain, eggs	Antioxidant (e.g., in the metabolism of the unsaturated fatty acids)
Vitamin K (antihemorrhagic vitamin) Vitamin K_1 Phylloquinone Vitamin K_2 Menaguinone β-phylloquinone	Intestinal bacteria, green plants	Important as "hydrogen transmitter"; essential for normal blood clotting, especially for prothrombin synthesis

Vitamins

The food components called **vitamins** are organic substances *necessary in small quantities for normal function of the body, which the body cannot, or not adequately, synthesize for itself;* their energy content is insignificant. **Antivitamins** are substances that act as antagonists of certain vitamins, by interfering with their absorption or metabolism.

The vitamins are extremely diverse in chemical structure (cf. biochemistry textbooks). They are classified as either **fat-soluble or water-soluble.** When vitamins were first being discovered they were named by letters of the alphabet, but the more recently discovered vitamins are known by chemical names.

Vitamins have *highly specific functions in cellular metabolism.* They are often elements in enzyme systems or have a complex effect on a system, such as that of vitamin C on connective tissue (for further details see Tables 25-3 and 25-4).

Table 25-4. *Water-soluble vitamins*. Classification, typical sources and biological functions (for requirements and deficiency symptoms see Table 25-8, p. 579)

Name and synonyms	Typical sources	Typical biological function
Vitamin B_1 Thiamin Aneurine	Bran, yeast	Component of pyruvate cocarboxylase
Vitamin B_2 Riboflavin Lactoflavin	Grain, milk, liver, yeast	Component of the flavin enzymes (yellow respiratory enzymes)
Vitamin B_6 group Pyridoxine group Tpyridoxol, pyridoxal, pyridoxamine	Grain, meat, liver, yeast	Coenzyme of various enzyme systems (e.g., amino-acid decarboxylase, transaminases, dehydratases, desulfhydrases)
Vitamin B_{12} Cyanocobalamine	Liver, microorganisms	Component of enzymes (methylation, nucleic-acid metabolism)

Other vitamins in the B group:

Biotin (vitamin H)	Intestinal bacteria (also milk, egg yolk, liver, yeast)	Component of enzymes (carboxylases, carboxyl transferases, deamination)
Folic acid group Folic acid (= pteroyl-glutamic acid, tetrahydrofolic acid)	Green leafy vegetables, microorganisms, yeast, liver, milk	Metabolism of one-carbon fragments, purine and methionine synthesis
Niacin Nicotinic acid Niacinamide	Grain, yeast, legumes, meat, liver	Coenzyme of many dehydrogenases (e.g., NADH)
Pantothenic acid	In almost all foods	Component of coenzyme A
Vitamin C Ascorbic acid Antiscorbutic	Fresh fruit and vegetables (esp. rose hips, citrus fruits, blackcurrants, green peppers)	Important for formation of intercellular substances, involved in hydroxylation, incorporation of iron in ferritin

Vitaminoids

Choline	In almost all foods	Fatty-acid transport
Inositol	In almost all animal and plant foods	Building blocks of inositol phosphatides, mitochondrial metabolism, cation transport

Vitamins are found in *food of both plant and animal origin*. The vitamin content of a given food can vary widely, depending on the conditions under which it was produced, stored and prepared for the table. Some vitamins – for example, vitamins A and C – are sensitive to light, heat or pH changes. Certain kinds of food are especially rich in particular vitamins (Tables 25-3 and 25-4; cf. [9] and [16]). Not every vitamin must be obtained from the diet. Vitamin K, for example, is synthesized by the normal intestinal flora; other vitamins are synthesized in the body from certain amino acids or from precursors **(provitamins),** though not always in sufficient amounts. Provitamins are especially important in the vitamin-D group – ergosterol for D_2, 7-dehydrocholesterol for D_3, and 22-dihydroergosterol for D_4.

Fat-soluble vitamins (summarized in Table 25-3). The **vitamins A, D, E and K** are fat-soluble. Vitamin A can be formed in the body from *carotenoids,* provitamins obtained from food. The effective member of the D group, vitamin D_3, is synthesized in the skin from provitamin D_4, in a photochemical reaction involving UV light.
Because of their vitamin-like character the essential fatty acids (p. 574) are occasionally included in this group, as "vitamin F."

Water-soluble vitamins (summarized in Table 25-4). The **vitamins of the B group (B_1, B_2, B_6, B_{12}, biotin,** the **folic acid** group, **niacin** and **niacinamide, pantothenic acid)** and **vitamin C** are water-soluble. **Choline** and **inositol** are counted as vitamins because they are essential components of food, although they serve as structural building blocks rather than as agents in the body chemistry; therefore they are also called **vitaminoids.**

Antivitamins. These are found in various foods – for example, avidin (which binds biotin) in eggwhite and a thiaminase (which decomposes thiamin) in many kinds of raw fish. *Artificial antivitamins* are used for the therapeutic modification of certain biological processes. Coumarin derivatives (antivitamin K), for instance, lower the coagulability of the blood. Isoniazid, an antagonist of pyridoxal phosphate (the active derivative of vitamin B_6), inhibits the growth of the tuberculosis pathogen. Sulfanilamides are effective against bacterial infection because of their antagonistic action on p-aminobenzoic acid, a substance essential for bacterial growth.

Water, Salts, Trace Elements

Water. Most foods contain more than 50% water (Table 25-2). Among the common foods with less than this amount are bread, butter and cheese. To keep accurate track of the body's fluid balance, however, the water produced by metabolic processes must be taken into account as well as that consumed orally. Under resting conditions the body produces ca. 350 ml water per day.

Salts. Salts, like water, serve to maintain the internal milieu (p. 331). One of the major prerequisites for unimpaired cell function is that the ionic composition and the pH of the body fluids be kept constant. The ions of greatest importance are the cations sodium, potassium, calcium and magnesium, and the anions chloride and phosphate (p. 332).

Trace elements. This category includes elements found in extremely small quantities in both the body and its food. They fall into three groups:
1. Elements with a known or suspected physiological function. Among these are **iron** (a component of heme), fluorine, iodine (component of the thyroid hormones), and such components of intracellular enzyme systems as copper, manganese, molybdenum and zinc.
2. Elements with a proved toxic effect. These include antimony, arsenic, lead, cadmium, mercury and thallium. Most of these elements are of particular importance in industrial toxicology.
3. Elements without physiological function that have been shown not to be required – for example, aluminum, boron, silver and tellurium.

Condiments and Crude Fiber

The category of *condiments* includes all the diverse aromatic substances that determine the taste and smell of food. These substances are not necessary for life, but their significance with regard to both *general well-being* and the *secretion of digestive juices* (cf. Chapter 26) should not be underestimated.
Crude fiber (dietary fiber) comprises the indigestible components of food. Chief among these substances are polysaccharides such as cellulose which reinforce the cell walls of plants and cannot be chemically decomposed in the human digestive tract (p. 605). The significance of crude fiber is discussed on p. 583.

Residues

As foods are produced and stored they can acquire, whether by intent or accident, substances not directly necessary to man, which can have toxic effects if they are too abundant.

Medicines. The production of animal food today often involves treatment of the animals with medications for hygiene reasons or to accelerate growth to a marketable size. Because drugs can be stored in liver, fatty tissue and muscle, such residues may affect people who eat these products; for example, allergies, resistance to antibiotics and hormonal disturbances can result.

Metals. In addition to the toxic trace elements, metallic residues include radionuclides such as cesium[137] and strontium[90].

Additives. Most of these are *flavorings, dyes* or *preservatives* introduced during the production of foods. Whatever the benefits of such substances, they should not be used without careful consideration. The carcinogenic action of "butter yellow," for example, was demonstrated only after it had been in use for decades as a food coloring. The number of flavoring and coloring additives is vast; in 1973 a survey in the USA revealed 2764 substances of this sort. It is likely that most of them have no pharmacological effect, but they can cause allergic reactions in susceptible people.

Pesticides. These substances are used to protect plants and stored food. 4 categories are recognized: *insecticides* (against insects), *herbicides* (against weeds), *acaricides* (against mites) and *fungicides* (against fungi). Because some of them have been shown to be noxious to humans, maximal permissible levels for food have been established. Some pesticides (especially those that are fat-soluble) can be stored in the fat of animals; they are slow to leave the body and thus can have long-term effects. The plant products that offer the greatest pesticide threat to humans are fruit, vegetables and flour products; milk fat is the chief animal source.

25.2 Nutritional Requirements; Symptoms of Deficiency and Overdosage

Published figures concerning the required amounts of the individual components of food vary considerably, in part because of the difference between *requirement* and *recommended intake.* Data on nutritional requirements in the strict sense refer to metabolic equilibrium conditions, whereas recommendations as to the desirable intake often allow an extra "safety factor" [5]. The discussion that follows is based on the recommendations of the German Society for Nutrition [8]. Recommendations of other nutritional boards occasionally differ slightly from one another; for an international review see [2] and [15]. – The amounts of particular *nutrients* required by an individual depend on a number of factors – age, sex, physical type, amount of exercise, stress, pregnancy. Because of this wide range of variability, tables of nutritional requirements always represent only *general guidelines.*

Deficiencies arise either because of inadequate *intake* or because the *requirement* has increased. In most deficiency states there is a combined lack of foodstuffs (proteins, fats, carbohydrates) and vitamins, salts or trace elements, as in *starvation* or *inadequate absorption.* But certain typical *deficiency diseases* (Tabl 25-7

and 25-8) result from the predominant lack of a single substance.

Nutritionists were once concerned primarily with the results of particular nutrient deficiencies, but they must now consider problems related to overdosage as well. The consequences of overdosage in general take the form of **obesity, hypervitaminoses** and **water and electrolyte intoxication.**

Foodstuffs

The organism's requirement for the three foodstuffs depends on its energy consumption. In addition, a *minimal amount* of each – protein, fat or carbohydrate – is required for special purposes and cannot be replaced by either of the others (Table 25-5); the remainder can be replaced according to their *isodynamic effect* (p. 573). The disturbances resulting from protein deficiency are particularly severe.

Minimal requirements. Almost all the tissues in the body are continually being broken down and renewed or converted *(structural metabolism).* This is not simply a matter of rearranging a fixed quantity of material; an additional supply is required. One reason is loss of certain substances from the body – for example, when epithelial cells are shed (from the intestinal surfaces and the skin). These losses mainly affect protein balance.

Protein balance. On a diet that supplies enough energy but contains no protein, a person loses 13–17 g protein per day. Even if this amount **(absolute protein minimum)** is added to the diet, the intake and loss of protein are still not in balance, for two reasons: 1. Protein consumption is followed by an increase in the rate of nitrogen excretion (a measure of protein loss), for reasons not yet explained. 2. Depending on the amino-acid composition of the protein in the diet, a variable fraction of it can be converted to body protein. That is, the value of proteins to man differs, according to their content of essential amino acids. The *biological value* of proteins can be expressed by the amount of human body protein that can be replaced by 100 g food protein. The biological value of animal proteins in this sense is 80–100 g – that is, from 100 g of animal protein 80–100 g of body protein can be synthesized. In the case of plant proteins the biological value averages only 60–70 g, because the amino acids essential to man are not present in the right proportions. Concerning the reguirement for essential amino acids, see [2].

For protein balance to be maintained, a mixed diet must include 30–40 g protein per day **(protein-balance minimum).** Normally a state of protein balance exists when the amount of nitrogen ingested equals that excreted (the N_2 content of protein is ca. 16% by weight). It has been shown that although the balance minimum is adequate for survival, it does not suffice for normal physical performance. For the body to be *optimally* supplied with protein a daily intake of *1 g protein per kg body weight* is recommended **(functional protein minimum),** of which at least 30 g should be of animal origin. When physical work is being done, during pregnancy and in severe illness the *daily* requirement is increased to as much as 2 g/kg; that of children and the aged is 1.2–1.5 g/kg.

Table 25-5. Foodstuffs. Recommended daily allowances for adult humans; symptoms of deficiency and overdosage

	Daily allowance	Extra requirement	Depots	Deficiency symptoms	Overdosage symptoms
Proteins	1 g/kg body weight (must contain enough essential amino acids – e. g., at least 30 g animal protein)	Old people and children, 1.2–1.5 g/kg; for heavy work, muscle building, pregnancy and severe illness up to 2 g/kg body weight	Available pool 45 g (muscle 40 g, blood and liver 5 g)	Starvation edema, susceptibility to infection, apathy, muscular atrophy, impaired development of children	Predominance of decay in intestine, gout in predisposed individuals
Carbohydrates	At least 100–150 g (for the brain); alternative: 200 g protein (gluconeogenesis)	During physical work	300–400 g glycogen	Underweight, reduced performance, metabolic disturbances, ketosis	Predominance of fermentation in intestine, adipositas
Fats (a) saturated fatty acids	(a) and (b): 25–35% of energy requirement	During physical work	Extremely variable	Underweight, reduced performance, deficiency symptoms from inadequate absorption of fat-soluble vitamins	Hypercholester- olemia with subsequent sclerosis, adipositas
(b) essential fatty acids	10 g, at least 0.6 g/1000 kJ food intake	During physical work	Extremely variable	Hematuria, changes in skin and mitochondria, metabolic disturbances	Increased tocopherol requirement (vit. E)

Table 25-6. Energy balance for one day; a man doing moderately hard work (toolmaker) is taken as an example. 1 kJ ≈ 0.24 kcal From [7], cf. [5] and [6]

Age: 56 years	
Weight: 77 kg	
Height: 172 cm	
Basal metabolic rate	6,740 kJ
Increments for	
a. Leisure movements	1,670 kJ
b. Work	3,770 kJ
Σ =	12,180 kJ
+ Incomplete absorption (6,5%)	790 kJ
+ Specific dynamic action (6,5%)	790 kJ
Total	13,760 kJ

Minimal requirements of fats and carbohydrates. The minimal fat requirement is determined by the body's need for essential fatty acids and by the fact that fat-soluble vitamins can be absorbed only in the presence of fats. The minimal carbohydrate requirement is basically fixed by the metabolism of the brain, which depends almost entirely on glucose (100–150 g/day).

Foodstuff requirement (Table 25-5). The total amount of protein, fat and carbohydrate required depends on the current rate of energy metabolism (pp. 524 ff.). The requirement is higher when one is working harder, pregnant or suffering certain diseases. In cases of

generally increased muscle tone or cramps it is also considerably higher. Children also require a more energy-containing diet than adults per unit body weight, because of their higher growth rate.

Depot reserves. Carbohydrates and proteins can be reversibly stored in the body to only a limited extent. The protein reserves available on a short-term basis amount to about 45 g, and 300–400 g glycogen is stored. Only the fat depots of the body are a relatively capacious energy reservoir (Table 25-5).

Deficiency symptoms. Among the typical deficiency symptoms are diminished physical and mental performance, susceptibility to various diseases and underweight. Protein deficiency leads, for example, to edema and in children to impaired development (Table 25-5).

Overdosage symptoms. The consequences of eating more than is needed are obesity, diminished physical performance and a reduced life expectancy (Table 25-5).

In drawing up an **energy balance** one must bear in mind that nutrients are not always completely absorbed. Moreover, the specific dynamic effect of foodstuffs must also be taken into account (Table 25-6).

Table 25-7. *Fat-soluble vitamins.* Deficiency symptoms, depots and recommended intake for adult humans

Vita-min	Deficiency symptoms	Depots	Daily allowance
A	*Night blindness,* abnormal keratinization of epithelium, impaired growth	Large amounts in the liver	0.9 mg vitamin A_1, 1.8 mg β-carotene
D	*Rickets,* impaired bone growth and ossification, decalcification	Small amounts in liver, kidneys, intestines, bones, adrenals	2.5 µg; in childhood and pregnancy 10 µg
E	No typical deficiency symptoms ascertained	Several grams in liver, adipose tissue, uterus, testicles, hypophysis, adrenals	12 mg tocopherol; in addition 0.6 mg/g unsaturated fatty acids
K	Delayed blood clotting, spontaneous bleeding	Very small amounts in liver and spleen	None if intestinal flora intact, otherwise ca. 1 mg; as prophylaxis of prematures one dose of ca. 1 mg

Table 25-8. *Water-soluble vitamins.* Deficiency symptoms, depots and recommended intake for adult humans

Vitamin	Deficiency symptoms	Depots	Daily allowance
B_1	*Beri-beri, polyneuritis,* CNS disorders, paralysis, muscular atrophy, cardiac insufficiency	ca. 10 mg; liver, myocardium, brain	1.4–1.6 mg or 0.2 mg/1000 kJ carbohydrate intake; more in alcoholics
B_2	Arrested growth, skin disorders	ca. 10 mg; liver, skeletal muscle	1.8–2.0 mg
B_6	None in adults; convulsions in infants	ca. 100 mg; muscle, liver, brain	1.6–1.8 mg
B_{12}	*Pernicious anemia, funicular myelosis*	1.5–3 mg; especially in liver	5 µg!
Biotin	Dermatitis	ca. 0.4 mg; liver, kidneys	None if intestinal flora intact, otherwise ca. 0.3 mg
Folic acid	*Pernicious anemia*	12–15 mg; liver	0.4 mg; 0.8 mg in pregnancy
Niacin	*Pellagra,* photodermatitis, paresthesia	ca. 150 mg; liver, meat	9–15 mg; replaceable by 60 times as much tryptophan
Panto-thenic acid	Unknown	ca. 50 mg; adrenals, kidneys, liver, brain, heart	8 mg
C	*Scurvy,* connective-tissue disorders, bleeding gums, susceptibility to infection	3.5 g; brain, kidneys, adrenals, pancreas, liver heart	75 mg
Vitaminoids			
Choline	Liver and kidney damage	In every cell	0.5–1 g
Inositol	Unknown	In every cell	ca. 1 g

Vitamins

The daily requirements of humans for various vitamins are summarized in Tables 25-7 and 25-8. *Requirements* are *increased* during and after physical *work* and in many *illnesses*. During exercise the increase in the need for energy is greater than that for vitamins, so that if enough foods are eaten to meet the energy demand the extra vitamins are automatically supplied. In some illnesses loss of appetite is combined with a greater need for vitamins, and vitamin-deficiency symptoms appear; in these cases *prophylactic* vitamin supplements are indicated.

Given an energetically adequate diet, **vitamin deficiencies** can develop if the diet is *not sufficiently varied*. For example, strict *vegetarians* are subject to vitamin B_{12} deficiency. Food can also be deficient in vitamins if it is *incorrectly prepared*. Some vitamins lose potency during storage, canning and cooking; it is thought that decreases in the vitamin content of various foods owing to long storage or associated with the time of year are the cause of *"spring fever."*

A few peculiarities of certain vitamins deserve mention. There are interactions between *niacin* and the essential amino acid *tryptophan*, such that lack of niacin does not produce deficiency symptoms if the diet contains enough tryptophan. More *tocopherol* (vitamin E) is required when the amount of essential fatty acids in the diet increases. Deficiencies in *vitamin K* and *biotin* can result from disturbances of the intestinal flora – for example, after treatment with antibiotics. Finally, the *thiamin* (vitamin B_1) requirement is largely supplied by grain products. Because people are now eating less of these, and tend to prefer refined flours with little thiamin, some flour is now enriched with vitamin B_1 and other B vitamins.

Storage in the body. Fat-soluble vitamins can be stored in large amounts, in some cases (e.g., vitamin D; Table 25-7) a several-months' supply. The same is true of the water-soluble vitamins B_{12} and folic acid

Table 25-9. Vitamins with known overdosage symptoms; daily allowance, toxic doses and symptoms in human

Vita-min	Daily allowance	Toxic dose (per day)	Symptoms of overdosage
A_1	0.9 mg vitamin A_1	120 mg (single dose: 600 mg)	Changes in skin, mucosa and bones; headache, euphoria, anemia
D	2.5 µg	400 µg/kg	Ca^{++} mobilization in bones, increased Ca^{++} level in blood plasma, CNS and kidney disorders
K	0–1 mg	?	Anemia in prematures; sometimes collapse following i. v. injection
B_1	1.4–1.6 mg	?	Sometimes collapse following i. v. injection
Niacin	ca. 150 mg	(3–4 g?)	Gastrointestinal disorders, skin alterations, impaired vision

Table 25-10. Important electrolytes: recommended intake for adult humans, in g/day. After [8]

Na^+	K^+	Ca^{++}	Mg^{++}	Cl^-	P
2–3	2–3	0.7–0.8	0.22–0.26	3–5	0.7–0.8

(Table 25-8). All the other vitamins are stored only in limited quantities, so that the supply must be regularly replenished.

Deficiency symptoms. The classical **vitamin-deficiency diseases** are now rarely encountered in a fully developed form under European conditions. Deficiency states (summarized in Tables 25-7 and 25-8) can result from either *malnutrition* (unbalanced or energy-poor diet) or *malabsorption*. Rickets, a vitamin-D-deficiency disease, is still found today where infants and small children have not received sufficient *vitamin-D prophylaxis*.

Because most of the water-soluble vitamins are stored only in small amounts, *hypovitaminosis* resulting from malnutrition or malabsorption is often associated with symptoms of a *combined* deficiency of several vitamins. Hypovitaminoses nearly always cause *diminished* physical and mental *performance,* which can be alleviated by taking vitamin supplements. But there is *no evidence that excessive vitamin supplements enhance the performance of properly nourished people.*

Overdosage symptoms. On the assumption that vitamins can do no damage, people often take supplements in large amounts. But **hypervitaminosis** is known to occur, although for the vitamins so far recognized as potentially harmful the toxic dose is quite high. Moreover, the intravenous injection of certain vitamins can have undesirable results (e. g., circulatory collapse; cf. Table 25-9).

Many adults, in contrast to growing children and pregnant women, have no actual need for *vitamin D,* because their diet contains enough provitamins. The *recommended intake* includes a safety factor. Today many foods, including special diet preparations, margarine and milk, are enriched with vitamin D, so that adults usually consume it in amounts far exceeding even those required by juveniles. *Niacin* is occasionally administered in doses of 2 g per day with the intention of lowering an excessively high blood-fat level.

Water, Salts, Trace Elements

Water. Human water requirements vary. Conditions that cause sweating (heat, hard work) and excessive salt intake markedly increase the need for water. Depending on the situation, then, the daily adult requirement is set at 21–43 ml/kg body weight. With regard to **water balance,** the following *average data* have been published [16]: A person weighing 70 kg requires at least ca. 1750 ml water per day. Of this amount, ca. 650 ml is obtained by *drinking,* ca. 750 ml is the water contained in *solid food,* and ca. 350 ml is *oxidation water.* If more than this amount is consumed by a healthy person it is excreted by the kidneys, but in people with heart and kidney diseases it may be retained (edema; cf. pp. 420, 637).

Deficiency symptoms. Water loss amounting to 5% of the weight of the body causes a distinct *impairment of performance.* A loss of 10% produces *severe dehydration,* and if 15–20% is lost *death* results [1]. The mean water content of the body is about 60%; thus loss of about ⅓ to ¼ of the total body water is lethal.

Overdosage symptoms. If large amounts of hypotonic solutions are taken into the body, or large amounts of salt are lost, there can be a transient influx of water into the *intracellular space* (pp. 647 f.). The resulting syndrome, called *water intoxication* [13], consists of impaired performance, headache, nausea or convulsions (symptoms of *cerebral edema*).

Salts. The recommended intake of some important electrolytes is shown in Table 25-10. The causes and symptoms of salt and water imbalance are discussed on pp. 632 ff. and 647 f.

More *calcium* is required during *bone growth* (as in pregnant women and children). *Calcium deficiency* is especially likely to occur when food with a high *oxalic acid* content (e.g., cocoa, spinach, rhubarb) is eaten, because a considerable fraction of the calcium in the diet is bound as *insoluble calcium oxalate* and is thus not absorbed. Among the foods that are especially valuable because of their calcium content are milk and dairy products.

The minimal requirement for *sodium chloride* is around 1 g per day; Central Europeans, on the average, consume about ten times this amount. Because it is associated with an increased incidence of high blood pressure, high salt consumption should be avoided.

Trace elements. Of the trace elements with acknowledged physiological function we shall consider here only *iron, fluroine, iodine* and *copper.* Table 25-11 summarizes the recommended intake of these, the amount stored in the body, and the deficiency symptoms. More iron and iodine are required by children and in pregnancy. Overdoses of almost all trace elements cause some disturbance of normal function, and in the case of fluorine the toxic limit is only slightly above the required amount ([2] and Table 25-11). The distribution of trace elements in food is described in [9] and [16].

Iodine deficiency causes an increased incidence of thyroid-gland enlargement in certain parts of the world (endemic goiter), occasionally accompanied by diminished thyroxin production. The occurrence of goiter has been much reduced by the systematic administration of small amounts of iodine (by enrichment of kitchen salt).

Chronic iron deficiency is the reason for the *only deficiency disease common under Central European conditions;* the iron content of food is barely adequate to meet normal requirements [15], because only about 10% of the iron is absorbed as Fe^{++}. Among the symptoms are tiredness, headache, diminished performance and impaired growth of skin and associated structures (hair, nails). Severe deficiency leads to typical *iron-deficiency anemia.* In cases of chronic *blood loss* (for example, menstruation, gastrointestinal bleeding, frequent blood donation) an average Central European diet does not provide enough iron to replace the amount lost. Thus about 40% of all menstruating women have no mobilizable iron reserves, and even slight additional blood loss (e.g., during surgery) or an increased requirement during pregnancy brings on iron-deficiency anemia. In various European countries this kind of anemia has been found in 10–30% of menstruating women.

Table 25-11. Trace elements with known physiological functions: deficiency symptoms, amount stored and recommended intake for adult humans

Trace element	Deficiency symptoms	Amount stored	Daily allowance
Iron	Iron-deficiency anemia	4–5 g, of which 800 mg can be mobilized	Menstruating women 18 mg, otherwise 12 mg as Fe^{++}
Fluorine	Increased incidence of caries	?	1 mg; above 5 mg toxic! (osteosclerosis)
Iodine	Goiter, hypothyroidism	10 mg	150 µg
Copper	Impaired iron absorption, anemia, pigmentation disorders	100–150 mg	2–5 mg

25.3 Utilization of Foodstuffs; Dietetics

Utilization

Only the foodstuffs and other food components actually *absorbed* can be metabolized by the body. Most of the substances contained in the diet must be released by *digestion* before they can be absorbed, and even when digestion proceeds normally not all of the substances (or the products of their decomposition) are absorbed. *Of the fuel value of a mixed Central European diet only 90–95% is utilized,* because some of its components – such as *cellulose,* a typical plant carbohydrate – cannot be broken down in the human upper digestive tract. If the cellulose walls of the plant cells are not destroyed when the food is prepared for digestion (by cooking and chewing, for example) the contents of the cells cannot be absorbed. The percentage absorbed is also reduced in intestinal diseases such as dysentery or cholera and following intestinal resection; however, the transport capacity of the intestinal epithelium is rarely an absorption-limiting factor.

Biological value. The absorbed foodstuffs differ in their value to the organism, depending on their origin (cf. p. 577). This is especially true of proteins, because of their varying content of essential amino acids; *plant proteins have a lower biological value than animal proteins* (p. 577).

Table 25-12. Energy content of diet *(Kostmaß)* and additional energy obtained from alcohol: average values for the population of Germany in 1978, based on inquiries using nutritional protocols. From [9]

	Women		Men	
	Desired	Actual	Desired	Actual
Total energy intake (kJ/day)	9,200	10,790	10,900	13,390
Protein (g/day)	54	79	63	95
Fat (g/day)	58–81	114	68–95	138
Carbohydrate (g/day)	298–352	274	354–417	329
Alcohol intake (from age 15)	$10\,g \approx 300\,kJ$ daily		$27\,g \approx 810\,kJ$ daily	
Fraction of total energy intake	3%		6%	

Balanced Diet

The planning of a balanced diet is a nutritional problem of considerable current importance, and many aspects are still the subject of vigorous debate. The following four *physiological* considerations are fundamental:

1. The **fuel value** of the diet must correspond to the person's energy requirement.
2. The diet must provide at least the **minimal required amounts** of proteins, fats and carbohydrates (Table 25-5).
3. It must also provide at least the **minimal required amounts** of vitamins, salts and trace elements (Tables 25-7, 25-8, 25-10 and 25-11).
4. The **noxious limits** of the various vitamins, salts and trace elements must not be exceeded.

If the energy consumed is not in proportion to that required, the result is under- or overweight. Moreover, nutrition-based disturbances can be produced if the relative amounts of the various foodstuffs are not correct.

In 1875 the German physiologist v. Voit proposed that diet be described in terms of its *Kostmaß* ("diet measure"), which gives its *energy content and relative amounts of foodstuffs* [14]. Voit's *Kostmaß*, derived "from a large number of observations for an average worker," was 118 g protein, 56 g fats, 500 g carbohydrate (in percentages by weight, 18:8:74), with 12,750 kJ/day. At the beginning of this century a large-scale study produced the following *Kostmaß*: 84 g protein, 65 g fats, 453 g carbohydrate (in weight percentages, 14:11:75), with 11,730 kJ/day [11]. It is from these data that the proportions 1:1:4 by weight (15:30:55% in terms of energy) have been derived for the relative quantities of protein, fat and carbohydrate in a desirable diet.

More recent recommendations take into account the practical need for a certain margin (Table 25-12). The recommended daily intake for a healthy adult is as follows [8]: *proteins,* 0.9 g/kg body weight (at least 30 g of which should be of animal origin); *fats,* 25–35% of the total energy requirement (of which at most 15% should be saturated), except for those doing extremely hard labor, who can meet as much as 45% of their energy requirement with fat; *carbohydrate,* the remainder of the energy requirement (ca. 55–65%), as long as it is at least 10%. Experience acquired when nutrition was generally insufficient and poorly balanced, during and after the world wars, and more recent investigations have confirmed that these proportions are appropriate to European situations; they can be regarded as optimal.

However, average *energy requirements* today are generally less than they once were because people do less hard physical work. Taking the German population as an example, about **11,150 kJ/day (2660 kcal/day)** is recommended. The *actual eating habits* of the German population in 1978 are typical of a highly industrialized society: the average diet provides *too much energy* and contains *too much fat and too little carbohydrate* (Table 25-12). In addition, the energy content of the alcohol consumed must be considered; random samples indicate an average consumption of 14 (♀) and 34 (♂) g/day, or 420 and 1020 kJ/day, respectively [9].

Slight **deviations from the recommended proportions** cause no serious disturbances. Fats and carbohydrates are to a great extent exchangeable with regard to their energy content (isodynamic effect; cf. p. 573). In case of **carbohydrate deficiency** glucose can be formed from *glucoplastic amino acids (gluconeogenesis),* if these are present in excess. The first sign of a depressed blood sugar level *(hypoglycemia)* is a strong feeling of hunger and a reduction in physical and mental performance. If the situation persists until the minimal requirement of the brain for sugar is no longer met, unconsciousness and convulsions result *(hypoglycemic shock).* On the other hand, if **more carbohydrate** is consumed than is needed it is *converted to fats* and stored, leading to obesity. Excessive carbohydrate consumption can also cause digestive disturbances owing to the predominance of fermentation processes in the large intestine (p. 600).

A great **reduction in the fat content** of the diet interferes with the absorption of fat-soluble vitamins, with resulting vitamin-deficiency symptoms. Other deficiency symptoms appear when the minimal requirement of essential fatty acids is not met (p. 574). An **increase** in the proportion of fat causes more fat to be stored, and an increased consumption of saturated fatty acids can produce hypercholesterolemia (p. 574), which is regarded as an epidemiological risk factor (p. 584). Conversely, increased consumption of unsaturated fatty acids is thought to lower the blood cholesterol level (p. 574).

When the **protein fraction is reduced** physical and mental performance is impaired, and eventually starvation edema and muscular atrophy result. The defense mechanisms of the body deteriorate and susceptibility to infection increases. When protein is eaten in abundance the metabolic rate rises (specific dynamic action; p. 573), an effect that may be quite desirable in cold climates because of the associated increase in heat production. On the other hand, protein-rich food may lead to digestive disturbances because of the predominance of decay processes in the large intestine. In people with a predisposition to gout protein-rich food increases the likelihood of an attack, because of the large quantities of purine bases it contains.

The **origin of the food** is a significant factor in a balanced diet. Whereas the required amounts of essential amino acids are obtained chiefly from *animal products,* foods of *plant origin* are indispensable sources of the necessary water-soluble vitamins, salts and trace elements. A strictly vegetarian diet always produces symptoms of protein deficiency because of the lack of essential amino acids. Moreover, animal and plant foods have different effects on acid-base balance (pp. 500 ff.); animal products act as weak acids (H^+ donors) and plant products as weak bases (H^+ acceptors). The associated influences on the acid-base status are normally compensated by the kidneys.

Finally, the **preparation** of the food plays a role in a balanced diet. Improper handling can cause deterioration of vitamins (e.g., owing to heat sensitivity; cf. p. 579). The way the diet is spiced and served can exert physiological effects in that digestion is influenced by the *cephalic phase of gastric-juice secretion* (p. 594). In fact, this stimulatory action of spices and drinks (alcohol) can cause overacidity of the stomach contents in susceptible people.

In the German population people over 10 years old, on the average, obtain about 5–8% of their energy requirement in the form of *alcohol.* This corresponds to the total energy input of one month per year, or 14–34 g alcohol per day (see p. 582). But alcohol consumption must be evaluated not only with respect to the energy content of the diet, for it also has a *toxic effect.* Prolonged consumption of more than 80 g of alcohol ($\approx$ 2400 kJ) per day leads to liver damage; toxic effects are observed with consumption of about 160 g/day or more.

Special Diets

In planning a diet, attention must be paid to the subject's *age* and type of *work* as well as to the *therapeutic purpose.* With increasing age, for example, the energy requirement grows less whereas the relative requirement of essential amino acids is augmented.

Low-energy diets. Because **obesity** has attained almost epidemic proportions in Europe and North America, it is worth considering certain aspects of low-energy diets. As in the case of strict fasting – which should be undertaken only under medical supervision – care must be taken that the low-energy diet in the long term provides the minimal required amounts of all nutrients. Diets that achieve this goal can be relatively rich in protein, fat or carbohydrate; the choice must be determined by the various advantages and disadvantages of each.

A **protein-rich, energy-poor diet** has the advantage that the appetite is sufficiently satisfied and the specific dynamic action of protein (p. 573) enhances the metabolic rate. A disadvantage is that protein-rich foods are among the most expensive and usually contain much fat. A **fat-rich, energy-poor diet** is effective in appeasing hunger, but because the content of saturated fatty acids is usually high hypercholesterolemia can result. Moreover, people vary in their digestive tolerance of fatty diets. A **carbohydrate-rich, energy-poor diet** offers the advantage that the stomach is well filled at mealtimes, but the feeling of satiety is short-lived. Furthermore, shortly after carbohydrates of low molecular weight are consumed hypoglycemic undulations often occur, with a renewed feeling of hunger.

In recent years a concerted effort has been made to produce **low-energy foods** with unchanged volume but energetic value reduced by 40–50%. The energetic reduction is achieved by removing the fat, replacing the sugar with sweeteners of lower energy content, and adding water and cellulose-containing products. It remains to be seen how useful these arrangements will be.

Nutrition of the aged. Diets for old people should be planned according to the following guidelines:

1. Their **energy requirement** is lower.
2. Their daily **protein requirement** is increased to 1.2–1.5 g/kg body weight.
3. At most 30% of the energy requirement should take the form of **fats** (ca. 70 g/day). Fats with *unsaturated fatty acids* are preferable.
4. The daily intake of **carbohydrate** should amount to about 300 g, mono- and disaccharides being avoided.
5. An adequate **Ca^{++} intake** must be ensured because of the tendency to osteoporosis (softening of the bones) in the aged. Chief among the calcium-rich foods are milk and dairy products.
6. The **absolute vitamin requirement** is unchanged in old age. But because the energy requirement is less, and thus less food should be eaten, old people may suffer vitamin deficiencies. The preference of many old people for easily digestible foods like mashed potatoes and white bread can also lead to vitamin deficiency.

Crude fiber. Opinions differ as to the significance of crude fiber. The advantages claimed for high-fiber diets are the stimulation of peristalsis and thus more rapid passage through the intestine (pp. 596 f.), and the soft consistency of the feces – both factors that work against constipation and its consequences (p. 601). On the other hand, healthy life has been shown to be possible for long periods on an entirely synthetic diet without fiber. Evidently neither extreme is disadvantageous for the passage of food through the gastrointestinal canal. On the other hand, a diet containing small amounts of crude fiber may well encourage constipation.

Heigth cm
♂ ♀

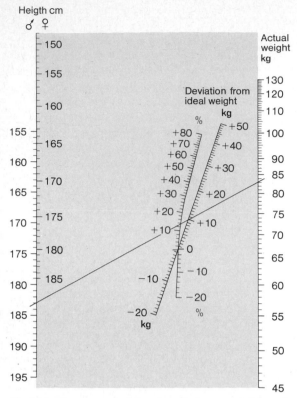

Fig. 25-1. Nomogram to determine whether an adult is under- or overweight (after THEWS). The ideal weight is that given in the MLIC tables for medium frame [16, 27]; the normal range is ± 5% of the ideal weight. The line drawn as an example is for a man 183 cm in height, weighing 83 kg; it shows that he is 10 kg overweight, deviating by 13% from the ideal weight

Artifical feeding. In special cases artificial feeding is done, by way of synthetic oral diets or parenteral (intravenous) infusions:

Balanced synthetic diets (BSD), with all the necessary nutritional components but lacking crude fiber, have been used especially for the first astronauts to avoid defecation in their small space ships. Today this "astronaut's diet" is used with good results before operations on the intestinal tract, in acute intestinal infections or in other cases of illness.

Parenteral infusions are often employed not only to fill the vascular system in case of volume deficit, but also for the nutrition of post-operative patients or those suffering from unconsciousness, injuries or burns. Different types of solutions are used, mostly mixtures of salts, carbohydrates and proteins or sometimes fat emulsions [3]. *Close supervision* of the patients is necessary to achieve a sufficient balance. After severe operations or injuries the *protein demand* for structural metabolism increases to 1.5 g · kg^{-1} per day; patients with severe burns need 2.5 g · kg^{-1} per day. The concentration of such infusion solutions

must be carefully regulated; too-high concentrations lead to impairments of the blood-vessel wall (with the consequence of *thrombosis*).

25.4   Evaluation of Body Weight and Body Surface Area

Obesity as a Risk Factor

The term **risk factor** is used in epidemiology for factors statistically correlated with *shortened life expectancy*, which are closely related to the so-called *"diseases of civilization"* (e.g., cardiac infarction, stroke [17, 23, 24, 29]). One of the risk factors that can be avoided is obesity – a condition that paves the way for high blood pressure and metabolic disorders. The complex relationships between obesity and shortened life expectancy will not be treated here.

Reference weights are a basis for determining the desirable weight in particular cases depending on various references. *Overweight* is a state in which the actual weight exceeds the recommended weight by 10–20%; an excess amounting to more than 20% is interpreted as *obesity* or adiposis. Recommended weights are established with reference to the following:

Ideal weight. This is the weight associated with the *highest statistical life expectancy*. The so-called MLIC norms (ideal-weight norms) are based on studies of over 5 million North Americans by life insurance companies [27]. The ideal weight depends on body size, sex and constitution, and can be found from tables (e.g., in [16]) or by the nomogram in Fig. 25-1.

BROCA index. This method of determining recommended weight (in kg) is to *subtract 100 from the body height (in cm)*. Because of its simplicity the BROCA index is very popular, but it gives a recommended weight higher than the ideal weight. A correction can be made by subtracting 10% of the index weight.

New recommendations [19], based on the BROCA-index without corrections, take account of the fact that only relatively high degrees of overweight correlate with shortened life expectancy.

Body Mass Index. A further way to assess body weight is the Body Mass Index, also called *weight/ height^2* or QUETELET-index:

$$BMI = \frac{\text{body weight (g)}}{\text{body height}^2 \text{ (cm}^2)}$$

Index values higher than 2.4 correlate with a higher incidence of ischemic heart disease (e.g. [29]).

Average weight. Population surveys in which the data are classified according to sex and body height have shown a good correlation between weight and height, and between weight and sex. The average weight of the population as a whole can vary widely depending on nutritional conditions, with conspicuous deviations from the ideal weight during times of starvation or of overnourishment. This average weight or *normal* weight, of course, cannot be used to estimate the weight-correlated risk to the health of individuals within the population.

Somatogram. The relationship between height and size in children is determined by means of so-called somatograms based on age-dependent averages [16, 26].

Composition of the Body

The weight of a person is determined principally by three factors: *water content, fat content* and *muscle mass*. The mean extracellular water content accounts for about 15% of the body's weight; the mean fat content is 16%, and the mean muscle mass is 43%. When the weight of the body changes it is due to changes in one or more of these three compartments. Therefore the relative contribution of each, especially the fat content, can deviate considerably from the average.

When the **water content** of the body increases a state of edema or hydrops develops; the water can be distributed among different spaces. Methods for measuring changes in water content are discussed on pp. 646f. The **fat content** of the human body can vary between ca. 8 and 50%, women having a higher average proportion of fat than men (Table 25-13). The mean percentage of fat also rises with age. A useful method for estimating fat content is to pull up a fold of skin with a pair of *calipers*. The thickness of the fold is measured in four representative parts of the body (the biceps, triceps, subscapular and suprailiac regions). The sum of these four values is closely related to the percentage of fat in the body ([20]; cf. Table 25-13). The total body fat can also be calculated from the specific gravity of the body, the deviations from the specific gravity of water being largely due to the fat content. The **muscle mass** of the body decreases during fasting and increases as a result of special training ("body building" or isometric training; cf. p. 560). Muscle mass can be determined by way of creatine excretion and also by measuring the total body content of potassium radiologically with a "body counter", because most of the body potassium is found in the musculature.

Overweight and obesity. The variability of body composition described above must be kept in mind, if overweight is interpreted as obesity and thus as a risk factor. Especially in people with an above-average state of muscular training, overweight is *not necessari-*

Table 25-13. Change in body fat with age and sex; the contribution of fat to total body weight is given, along with the sum of the skinfold thicknesses measured at 4 representative places (averages from healthy people in the USA). After [20] and [28]

Age (years)	Women		Men	
	% fat	Σmm	% fat	Σmm
25	26	48	13	31
35	31	62	18	36
45	35	70	22	42
55	39	77	26	49

ly a sign of obesity, but of an above-average muscle mass. In these cases measurements of the body fat mass are very useful.

Surface Area of the Body

It is very difficult to measure the area of the body's surface directly. It can be estimated, however, with the approximation formula of DuBois and DuBois: $A = 71.84 \cdot W^{0.425} \cdot H^{0.725}$ (after [16]; A is the surface area in cm², W is the weight of the body in kg, and H is its height in cm). Nomograms simplify the estimation of surface area, but these too give only approximate values.

Wallace's *rule of nine* is used in cases of burn injury, to estimate roughly the area of the body surface affected. The rule divides the surface into percentages as follows: 9% for each arm, 18% for each leg, 36% for the trunk and 9% for head and neck together.

Body surface as a reference value. Many biological parameters depend on the size of the body – for example, basal metabolic rate, resting cardiac output, total blood volume or heart volume. For this reason these parameters are often expressed with respect to the surface area or weight of the body, in which case the adjective *relative* is applied (e.g., relative heart volume). Theoretical considerations indicate that it is more correct to refer to the surface area of the body than to its weight. In practice, however, the weight is most often used because it can be measured far more accurately than the surface area, with simple direct methods, and because it is one of the basic terms in the calculation of surface area.

25.5   References

Textbooks and Handbooks

1. ADOLPH, F. (ed.): Physiology of Man in the Desert. Intersci. Publ., New York–London 1947
2. ALTMANN, P.L., DITTMER, D.S. (eds.): Biology Data Book. vol. III (2nd Ed.) Fed. Amer. Soc. Exper. Biol., Bethesda/Maryland 1974
3. AHNEFELD, F.W., BURRI, C., DICK, W. HALMAGYI, M. (eds.): Parenteral Nutrition. Springer, New York 1976
4. BÄSSLER, K.H., FEKL, W. LANG, K.: Grundbegriffe der Ernährungslehre. Heidelberger Taschenbuch Nr.119, Basistext Medizin Springer, Berlin–Heidelberg–New York 1973
5. BENDER, A.E.: Nutrition and Dietetic Foods. (2nd Ed.) Leonard Hill Books, Aylesbury 1973
6. CONSOLAZIO, C.F., JOHNSON, R.E. PECORA, L.J: Physiological Measurements of Metabolic Functions in Man. McGraw-Hill Book Company, New York–Toronto–London 1963
7. Deutsche Gesellschaft für Ernährung e.V. (ed.): Die wünschenswerte Höhe der Nahrungszufuhr. (12.Ausgabe) Schriftenreihe der "Ernährungsumschau" Umschau-Verlag, Frankfurt/Main 1966
8. Deutsche Gesellschaft für Ernährung e.V. (ed.): Empfehlungen für die Nährstoffzufuhr. (3rd Ed.) Umschau-Verlag, Frankfurt/Main 1975
9. Deutsche Gesellschaft für Ernährung e.V. (ed.): Ernährungsbericht 1980 (including "Material zum Ernährungsbericht") Deutsche Gesellschaft für Ernährung e.V., Frankfurt/Main 1980
10. KREBS, H.A.: The metabolic rate of amino acids. In: MUNRO, H.N., ALLISON, J.B., eds.: Mammalian Protein Metabolism. Vol.1, p.125. Academic Press, New York–London 1964
11. RUBNER, M.: Physiologische Verbrennungswerte, Ausnutzung, Isodynamie, Calorienbedarf, Kostmaße. In: BETHE, A., BERGMANN, G. VON, EMBDEN, G., ELLINGER, A. eds.: Handbuch der normalen und pathologischen Physiologie. Bd.5: Stoffwechsel und Energiebedarf. P.134. Springer, Berlin 1928
12. SCHREY, A.: Die koronare Herzkrankheit. Urban & Schwarzenberg, München–Wien–Baltimore 1978
13. STEGEMANN, J.: Exercise Physiology. Physiologic Bases of Work and Sport. Thieme, Stuttgart–New York 1981
14. VOIT, C.: Physiologie des allgemeinen Stoffwechsels und der Ernährung. In: Hermann, L., ed: Handbuch der Physiologie. Bd.6, Teil II F.C.W. Vogel, Leipzig 1881
15. WHO (World Health Organization, ed.): Handbook on Human Nutritional Requirements. WHO Monograph Ser. No.61. World Health Organization, Geneva 1974
16. Wissenschaftliche Tabellen – Documenta GEIGY. (7th Ed.) Ed.: J.R. Geigy AG, Pharma, Basel. J.R. Geigy AG, Basel 1969

Research Reports and Reviews

17. ASHLEY Jr., F.W., KANNEL, W.B.; Relation of weight change to changes in atherogenic traits: the Framingham study. J. chron. Dis. 27, 103–114 (1974)
18. BROŽEK, J.: Changes of body composition in man during maturity and their nutritional implication. Fed. Proc. 11, 784 (1952)
19. Deutsche Gesellschaft für Ernährung e.V. – Arbeitsgruppe "Übergewicht". Stellungnahme zu den gesundheitlichen Auswirkungen des relativen Körpergewichtes. Ernährungsumschau 27, 322–323 (1980)
20. DURNIN, J.V.G.A., WOMERSLEY, J.: Body fat assessed from total body density and its estimation from skinfold thickness: measurements on 481 men and women aged from 16 to 72 years. Br. J. Nutr. 32, 77 (1974)
21. KANNEL, W.B., LEBAUER, E.J., DAWBER, T.R., McNAMARA, P.M: Relation of body weight in development of coronary heart disease. Circulation 35, 734–744 (1967)
22. KAPLAN, J.A., COX, G.E., TAYLOR, C.B.: Cholesterol metabolism in man. Arch. Pathol. 76, 359–368 (1963)
23. KEYS, A., ANDERSON, J.T., GRANDE, F: Serum cholesterol response to changes in the diet. IV. Particular saturated fatty acids in the diet. Metabolism 14, 776–787 (1965)
24. KEYS, A., ARAVANIS, Ch., BLACKBURN, H., VAN BUCHEM, F.S.P., BUZINA, R., DJORDJEVIC, B.S., FIDANZA, F., KARVONEN, M.J., MENOTTI, A., PUDDU, V., TAYLOR, H.L.: Coronary heart disease: overweight and obesity as risk factors. Ann. Int. Med. 77, 15–27 (1972)
25. KNUSSMANN, R., TOELLER, M., HOLLER, H.D.: Zur Beurteilung des Körpergewichts. Med. Welt (Stuttgart) 23, 529 (1972)
26. KUNZE, D.: Somatogram. Fortschr. Med. 95, 548 (1977)
27. Metropolitan Life Insurance Company (MLIC, ed.): New weight standards for men and women. Statist. Bull. 40, 1–12 (1959)
28. OTT, H.: Normalgewicht und Optimalgewicht. Ernährungsumschau 10, 49 (1963)
29. RABKIN, S.W., MATHEWSON, F.A.L., HSU, P.-H.: Relation of body weight to development of ischemic heart disease in a cohort of young North American men after a 26 year observation period. The Manitoba study. Am J. Cardiol. 39, 452–458 (1977)

26 Functions of the Gastrointestinal Canal

F. WALDECK

The gastrointestinal tract serves primarily to convert food into absorbable particles and to pass them on to the interior of the body. These events are initiated by *mechanical processes* (fragmentation, mixing, transport) and the *secretion of digestive juices*. Numerous *enzymes*, within the digestive juices or on the cells of the intestinal epithelium, act to split proteins, fats and carbohydrates by hydrolysis into constituents small enough to be absorbed **(digestion)**. These end products of digestion, together with water, minerals and vitamins, then pass through the intestinal mucosa, from the lumen of the intestine into the blood and lymph **(absorption).**

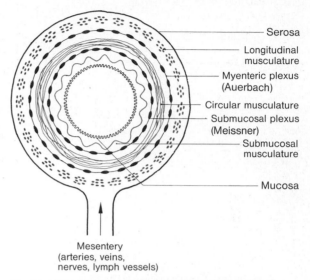

Fig. 26-1. Diagram of the layers in the gastrointestinal wall

Labels: Serosa; Longitudinal musculature; Myenteric plexus (Auerbach); Circular musculature; Submucosal plexus (Meissner); Submucosal musculature; Mucosa; Mesentery (arteries, veins, nerves, lymph vessels)

26.1 Gastrointestinal Motility and Secretion

Basic mechanisms of motility. Throughout the gastrointestinal canal, except for the entrance (buccal cavity, throat, upper esophagus) and exit (external sphincter of the anus), movements are brought about by smooth musculature. The structure of the wall of lower esophagus, stomach, and small and large intestines is in priciple quite uniform; apart from certain local modifications, it consists of three layers of smooth muscle. There is an outer longitudinal muscle layer with a circular layer just inside it; the innermost layer, the submucosa, also contains longitudinal fibers (Fig. 26-1). The inner surface of the gastrointestinal canal is lined with mucous membrane, which varies considerably in the different sections. The outer muscle layer is covered by the serosa, a sheath of connective tissue continuous with the mesentery. Within the mesentery lie the nerves and the blood and lymph vessels that supply the digestive tract.

The two outer muscle layers are separated by the myenteric (Auerbach's) plexus, and the submucosal (Meissner's) plexus separates the circular and submucosal layers. Both plexuses are aggregations of ganglion cells, most of which receive synaptic input from fibers in the vagus nerve, with respect to which they are second-order neurons. The postganglionic sympathetic fibers entering the intestinal wall from the celiac ganglia terminate chiefly on the muscle fibers and vessels. The myenteric plexus primarily influences motility, whereas the submucosal plexus affects both motility and secretion. Both plexuses must be functional – although their sympathetic and parasympathetic inputs are not required – for transport and mixing to occur.

The basic patterns of motility and their effects are illustrated in Fig. 26-2. Oral-aboral **transport** is brought about by *propulsive peristalsis,* a contraction of the circular musculature that progresses as a wave along the tube, usually preceded by a wave of relaxation. The food mass is **mixed** with digestive juices by *non-propulsive peristalsis,* propagated over only short distances, and by *segmentation* and *pendular* movements. Segmentation is the simultaneous contraction of the circular musculature at closely adjacent, alternating points, which gives the intestine the appearance of a string of beads in a roentgenogram. Pendular movements are brought about by contraction of the longitudinal muscle over a certain distance, causing the mucosa to slide over the intestinal contents. Prolonged tonic contraction in specialized regions (sphincters) separates functionally different areas and at the same time ensures unidirectional transport, without reflux.

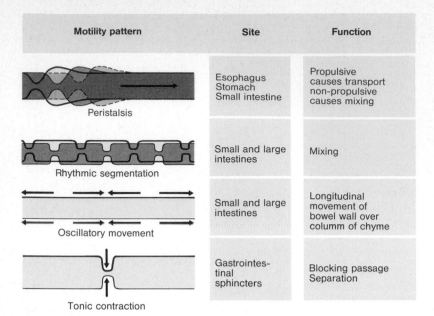

Motility pattern	Site	Function
Peristalsis	Esophagus Stomach Small intestine	Propulsive causes transport non-propulsive causes mixing
Rhythmic segmentation	Small and large intestines	Mixing
Oscillatory movement	Small and large intestines	Longitudinal movement of bowel wall over columm of chyme
Tonic contraction	Gastrointestinal sphincters	Blocking passage Separation

Fig. 26-2. Motility patterns in the gastrointestinal tract (schematic) and their effects

Basic mechanisms of secretion. The digestive juices are produced by active synthesis in secretory cells located in the salivary glands of the mouth, the glands of stomach and intestines, the exocrine part of the pancreas and the liver. The primary secretion consists of enzymes and other substances in an electrolyte-containing solution. During its passage through the ducts of the gland this primary secretion can undergo appreciable changes, especially with regard to electrolyte concentration. The digestive glands are innervated chiefly by the parasympathetic (vagus nerve) and to a lesser extent by the sympathetic system. They are also affected by gastrointestinal hormones. These influences cause considerable variation in the amount and composition of the different digestive juices. The digestive glands produce a total of ca. 6–8 liters of juices per day, essentially all of which is absorbed in the intestine [6].

Gastrointestinal hormones. The gastrointestinal hormones of known structure – *gastrin, secretin* and *cholecystokinin* (pancreozymin) (Table 26-1A) – are all peptides. Each has a broad spectrum of action on both motility and secretion in the gastrointestinal canal [13, 26]. A number of other peptides have been isolated from the mucosa of stomach or intestine; although these have marked effects on the gastrointestinal tract their physiological significance is not yet certain (Table 26-1B). Finally, physiological observations suggest that there are still other, not yet identified gastrointestinal hormones (Table 26-1C). Among the cells producing the gastrointestinal hormones, 9 distinct types have so far been recognized; they are

scattered in the mucosa of stomach and small intestine and in some cases in the pancreas. Recent studies indicate that the total mass of these cells, derived from the neural crest, is greater than that of the hypophysis [26, 31]. Release of the gastrointestinal hormones is triggered predominantly by products of digestion in the stomach and small intestine, but is also mediated to some extent by the vagus nerve.

Mouth and Esophagus

Food placed in the mouth or drawn in by sucking is passed on to the throat, either immediately or after chewing and mixing with saliva, and swallowed.

Mastication. The process of chewing requires coordination of the teeth of the upper and lower jaws, the chewing musculature, the tongue and cheeks and the palate and floor of the mouth. Mastication is normally a reflex action. Without voluntary control, the food is repeatedly pushed between the teeth by the tongue and cheeks, where because of the special arrangement of the mandibular joint it is subjected to both cutting and grinding actions. The forces involved ordinarily amount to 15–30 N. The maximal chewing force is 600 N, sufficient to fragment even very rigid cellulose and connective-tissue membranes. During fragmentation the food is thoroughly mixed with saliva. Finally, the food is formed into a bolus and pushed back into the pharynx when the tongue is pressed against the hard palate.

Table 26-1. Gastrointestinal hormones (A), and presumed gastrointestinal hormones of known structure (B) and of unknown structure (C). For further details see text

	Substance	Composition	Main site of production	Main actions
A.	Gastrin I and II	Protein 17 amino acids m.w. 2117	Gastric antrum and duodenum	Increases gastric secretion, especially HCl; promotes antrum motility, delays stomach emptying (cf. pp. 592, 595)
	Secretin	Protein 27 amino acids; m.w. 3056	Duodenum	Increases secretion and bicarbonate concentration of pancreatic juice and bile (cf. pp. 598, 599); antagonizes gastrin action (cf. p. 592)
	Cholecystokinin (CCK; = pancreozymin)	Protein 33 amino acids; m.w. 3919	Duodenum	Stimulates secretion of an enzyme-rich pancreatic juice, empties gallbladder (cf. pp. 598, 599)
B.	Motilin	Protein 22 amino acids m.w. 2700	Duodenum	Increases gastric motility
	Gastric inhibitory peptide (GIP)	Protein 43 amino acids m.w. 5105	Duodenum	Inhibits secretion and motility of stomach (cf. pp. 592, 596)
	Vaso-intestinal peptide (VIP)	Protein 28 amino acids m.w. 3328	Duodenum	Increases blood flow through gastrointestinal canal
C.	Bulbogastrone	Unknown	Duodenal bulb	Hypothetical gastrin antagonist
	Enterogastrone	Unknown	Duodenum	Inhibits secretion and motility of stomach (cf. p. 592)
	Villikinin	Protein	Duodenum and ileum	Stimulates villi to contract rhythmically (cf. p. 597)

Secretion of saliva. The saliva in the mouth is produced primarily by 3 large paired glands, the parotid (serous), submandibular (serous-mucous) and sublingual (mucous) glands. Whereas the sublingual gland, like the numerous small salivary glands in the oral mucosa, continuously secretes a thin fluid, the parotid and submandibular glands secrete only when stimulated. A total of 0.5–2.0 liters of saliva is produced per day. It is always hypotonic; its most important organic component is the enzyme *α-amylase,* which splits carbohydrate. It also contains mucopolysaccharides and glycoproteins (mucus, traces of blood-group substances), proteins (immunoglobulin A, traces of plasma proteins) and electrolytes (Na^+, K^+, Ca^{++}, I^+, Cl^-, HCO_3^-, $H_2PO_4^-$, F^-, SCN^-) [16].

The **main functions** of saliva can be inferred from its composition. The large amount of water dilutes the food and provides a *solvent* for some of its components. Taste stimuli, for example, can be effective only if the molecules responsible can diffuse to the taste buds in aqueous solution. The α-amylase initiates *carbohydrate digestion* while the food is still in the mouth, and continues it in the stomach. The mucus in the saliva makes the food slippery, so that it can be more easily swallowed. In addition, saliva keeps the buccal cavity moist, *rinses* it clean, and has a disinfecting action owing to the rhodanate ions it contains. The pH and the concentrations of electrolytes in saliva depend very much on the rate of secretion. When little saliva is secreted it is weakly acid, and when secreted in large amounts it is weakly alkaline (pH 5.8–7.8). Fig. 26-3 illustrates the dependence of electrolyte concentration on the rate of parotid saliva secretion. The concentration differences, as compared with the blood plasma, are evidently the result of glandular activity. Animal experiments have shown that the primary secretion, produced in the acini, is changed on its way through the subsequent intercalary and intralobular ducts, by active processes of secretion and reabsorption.

Regulation of saliva secretion. In man the rate of secretion during sleep is much lower than the waking rate. The increase in secretion during food consumption is brought about by *conditioned reflexes* (cf. p. 595) and by a *direct, inherent reflex.* The sight, smell and even thought of food can "make one's mouth water." The reflexes are triggered by excitation of olfactory, gustatory and tactile receptors.

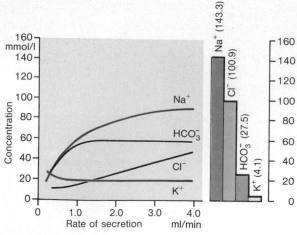

Fig. 26-3. Electrolyte concentrations in the parotid saliva of the dog, as a function of the rate of secretion. For comparison the concentrations in the blood plasma are shown as columns. After[15]

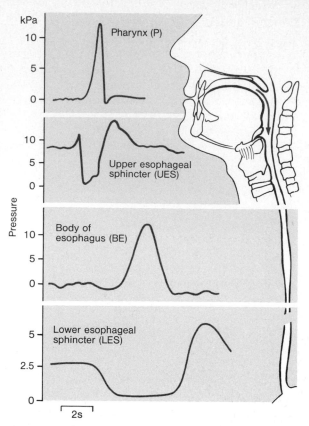

Fig. 26-4. Pressure changes during swallowing, in pharynx and esophagus and at the upper and lower esophageal sphincters. After[3]

Both parasympathetic and sympathetic fibers contribute to the complicated innervation of the salivary glands (for details see textbooks of anatomy). The activation of either increases the rate of secretion of saliva, though the parasympathetic is considerably more effective. After electrical stimulation of the chorda tympani or administration of parasympathomimetics (e.g., pilocarpine), a thin, watery saliva with a low content of organic components is produced. Stimulation of the sympathetic nerve, by contrast, affects only the submaxillary gland, causing a slight elevation of the secretion rate with an increased proportion of organic components [5].

The rate of *blood flow* through the salivary glands depends on the rate of secretion; in animal experiments perfusion can increase by a factor of 5 over the resting rate of 20–40 ml/100 g · min. The rate of O_2 consumption was found to increase linearly with the rate of secretion.

Deglutition. Before food is swallowed, it is formed into a bolus and moved into position. When it touches the palatine arch, the base of the tongue or the posterior wall of the throat it triggers a centrally programmed swallowing reflex. The reflex center in the medulla oblongata is excited by afference in the glossopharyngeal nerve and sends out efferent signals by way of the hypoglossal, trigeminal, glossopharyngeal and vagus nerves, to the muscles of the buccal cavity, throat, larynx and esophagus. The coordinated activity of these muscles propels the bolus into the lower pharynx and thence into the esophagus (buccopharyngeal phase of deglutition). In the process the bolus crosses the respiratory passage (Fig. 26-4), but is pre-

vented from entering it because the nasopharynx is closed off by raising of the soft palate, and the entrance to the trachea is blocked by an upward and forward movement of the larynx, with the glottis closed and covered by the epiglottis. The bolus is prevented from sliding back into the buccal cavity by elevation of the tongue. As these events occur, the upper esophageal sphincter (the region of the cricopharyngeal muscle and the upper part of the esophagus) opens and the bolus enters the cranial part of the esophagus. This marks the beginning of the esophageal phase, in which a contraction of the circular musculature propagates toward the stomach, preceded by a wave of relaxation *(primary peristalsis)*. Whereas the contraction is elicited by neurons that liberate acetylcholine, relaxation is caused neither by acetylcholine nor by sympathetic transmitters (noradrenalin, adrenalin). The effective neurotransmitter has not yet been identified, though dopamine, various peptides and adenosine triphosphate have been proposed as candidates. The notion that ATP mediates relaxation has suggested the name "purinergic system."

The events in swallowing that can be monitored manometrically are illustrated in Fig. 26-4. Relaxation of the *upper esophageal sphincter* begins before the intrapharyngeal pressure rises. As a result, the intraluminal resting pressure of ca. 8 kPa falls to 0, returning to the initial level with a transient overshoot after the bolus has passed. The peristaltic wave in the tubular esophagus is 2–4 cm in length and propagates with a velocity 2–4 cm/s, generating pressures of 8–16 kPa. Even before the wave of contraction reaches the *lower esophageal sphincter,* its intraluminal pressure falls from the normal 2.5 kPa to 0; once the bolus has passed into the stomach the initial pressure is rapidly restored [3, 9].

Esophageal peristalsis is capable of transporting food into the stomach even when the head is lower than the stomach. When the body is upright gravity considerably assists esophageal transport. Esophageal motility during swallowing is controlled by the vagus; when it has been transected cervically primary peristalsis is no longer possible. But if the vagus is intact, a peristaltic sequence of contraction is detectable even when the esophagus is transected at various levels.

Should the bolus stick in the esophagus or the stomach contents regurgitate into it, a proximal sequence of contractions known as *secondary peristalsis* occurs. In appearance and mechanism primary and secondary peristalsis are identical.

Disturbance of deglutition in pharynx and esophagus (dysphagia) can be psychological in origin or result from disrupted innervation, spasms or certain diseases. Reduction in tone of the lower esophageal sphincter can lead to heartburn and inflammation (reflux esophagitis), whereas if tone is increased so that the sphincter does not relax sufficiently (achalasia) food accumulates in the esophagus [9]. In *achalasia* the intramural plexuses in the region of the cardia are lacking. Because these plexuses are also responsible for relaxation (purinergic system?), in their absence spasm of the smooth musculature occurs.

Stomach

The stomach serves as a reservoir, in which the swallowed food is mixed with gastric juice and released, a little at a time, into the duodenum for further digestion and absorption.

Gastric motility. The motor events in the stomach affect filling, mixing and transport. The stomach can receive considerable volumes of food with no appreciable increase in pressure – that is, its passive tension curve is very flat. This property derives in part from the basic plasticity of smooth musculature (cf. p.48) and in part from an alteration in the structure of the stomach wall. In addition, a relaxation mediated by the vagus (receptive relaxation) is thought to accompany food consumption.

Mixing of the food mass with gastric juice is achieved by *peristaltic contractions*. These usually begin near the greater curvature in the upper part of the corpus ("pacemaker"). The waves progress toward the pylorus as annular contractions at 20-s intervals, with a velocity of 10–40 cm/s. In the process, part of the food mass near the wall is pushed aborally. The resulting mixture of food and gastric juice is called *chyme*. Mixing of the usual stomach contents occurs so slowly that the inner layers have a pH < 5 only after 1–2 hours. During this time carbohydrate digestion can proceed by the action of the salivary amylase in the stomach. Most of the peristaltic waves fade out in the antrum. Waves that propagate further become larger as they go, causing especially deep constrictions in the antrum. If the pyloric canal is closed by such strong peristaltic contractions of the antrum, roentgenograms reveal that some of the chyme is repelled so that mixing is *extremely thorough*. Many authors have interpreted these motility phenomena as "frictional" or "grinding" effects.

The release of portions of the stomach contents into the duodenal bulb occurs during vigorous antrum peristalsis. The antrum is nearly closed off from the corpus, and then there is a longitudinal shortening of the pyloric canal (antral "systole"). The time course of stomach emptying after consumption of mixed food is nearly exponential – that is, emptying occurs most rapidly immediately after the meal, and progressively more slowly as time passes. Stomach emptying depends on many factors such as the *total quantity, composition* and *particle size* of the food. Poorly chewed food stays in the stomach longer than soupy, fluid food. After a fatty meal it may take 4 hours or more for the stomach to empty; protein is processed more rapidly and carbohydrate the most rapidly of all [2].

In addition to the movements that follow filling of the stomach, the empty stomach can be observed to give occasional contractions at the basic gastric rate (every 20 s), called "hunger contractions" (although "fasting contractions" is preferable because their role in the sensation of hunger is not clear). Motilin (cf. Table 26-1 B) may contribute to the production of these contractions.

Regulation of gastric motility. The intramural plexuses, the vagus nerve and the gastrointestinal hormones are all involved in regulating gastric motility. The adequate stimulus for motility is stretching of the stomach wall, probably detected and mediated by bipolar ganglion cells in the submucosal plexus (Fig. 26-5). At the top of the hierarchy is the vagus nerve. When the transected vagus is stimulated near the stomach powerful contractions of the antrum result. Total vagotomy is followed by a reduction in

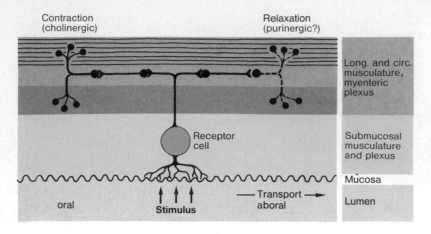

Fig. 26-5. Diagram of the intramural peristaltic reflex. The stimulus excites stretch receptors, which by way of interneurons elicit contraction on the oral side and relaxation aborally. Thus the travelling wave of contraction is preceded by a wave of relaxation

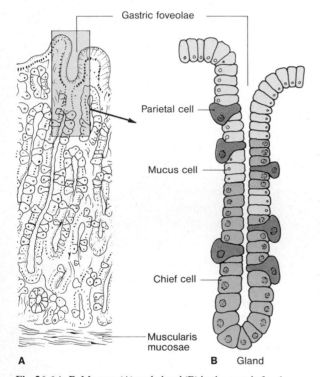

Fig. 26-6 A, B. Mucosa (A) and gland (B) in the gastric fundus

bulb and reactivated when the bulb has emptied. Moreover, it has long been known that the entry of fat and hydrochloric acid into the duodenum inhibits stomach emptying. This effect has been ascribed to the action of a hypothetical substance produced in the duodenum (enterogastrone, Table 26-1 C) and to a reflex. But recently it has been shown that under these conditions secretin, gastric inhibitory peptide (GIP) and cholecystokinin (CCK) are released in the duodenum (Table 26-1). These substances inhibit gastric motility and presumably have the function of the enterogastrone postulated earlier. It has also been shown that gastrin both increases motility in the gastric antrum and delays gastric emptying.

In **vomiting,** the stomach is emptied by way of the esophagus and mouth. The actual **vomiting reflex** is preceded by nausea, copious secretion of saliva, slower and deeper breathing, perspiration and constriction of the cutaneous vessels. The center for the vomiting reflex is in the *reticular formation of the medulla;* dopaminergic neurons in the region of the triggering zone (area postrema) play an important role [36]. Vomiting begins with a deep inspiration, after which the glottis is closed and the contents of the atonic stomach are propelled through the esophagus and into the mouth by powerful contractions of the diaphragm and abdominal musculature. In this phase the esophagus and its sphincters are relaxed.

tone lasting 2–4 weeks, with extensive loss of peristalsis and thus prolonged disturbance of the emptying process. As would be expected, tone and peristalsis can also be inhibited by administration of parasympatholytics such as atropine. Among the gastrointestinal hormones, gastrin enhances antrum motility when injected intravenously, whereas secretin has an antagonistic effect (cf. Table 26-1 A).

In the **regulation of stomach emptying** strong duodenal influences are superimposed on the above factors. Animal experiments have revealed an enterogastric reflex, mediated by the vagus, by which stomach emptying is inhibited after filling of the duodenal

Gastric-juice secretion. The gastric juice is produced in amounts of 2–3 liters per day by cells in the **gastric glands.** These glands vary in fine structure in the different parts of the stomach. The actual digestive juice of the stomach is secreted by the glands of the fundus and corpus (Fig. 26-6). The most important elements of these are the **chief cells,** which produce **pepsinogen,** and the **parietal cells** (oxyntic cells), which produce hydrochloric acid. In the cardiac and pyloric areas mucus is the only exocrine product. The gastric juice obtainable by suction is a mixture of these secretions, and in addition usually contains swallowed saliva and occasionally duodenal contents.

The fasting stomach secretes only small amounts of juice (5–15 ml/h), which has a neutral to alkaline pH and apart from its main component, water, contains only mucus and electrolytes. Whenever food is eaten, the event is accompanied by the production of ca. 600–1200 ml of a pellucid, slightly opalescent juice, with secretion beginning before the meal and ceasing some time thereafter. Because of its high concentration of HCl this gastric juice has a *strongly acid reaction* (pH 0.8–1.5); it is nearly isotonic with blood. Its organic components are the protein-splitting enzyme mixture *pepsin* (endopeptidases), a lipase of lesser significance, *mucin* (gastric mucus) and *intrinsic factor,* necessary for the absorption of vitamin B_{12}. It also contains the cations Na^+, K^+ and Mg^{++} and the anions HPO_4^{--} and SO_4^{--}.

Functions of hydrochloric acid. The HCl in the gastric juice initiates the production of pepsin from its inactive precursor, pepsinogen; the conversion then proceeds autocatalytically. At the same time HCl brings the pH to the optimal level for pepsin action. It also denatures protein and thus acts as a bactericide.

Production of HCl. The site of HCl production is the parietal cells. As Fig. 26-7 shows, mitochondria are particularly abundant in the parietal cells; they are also characterized by secretory canaliculi, invaginations of the cytoplasmic membrane in contact with the lumen (Figs. 26-7, 26-8). At rest the canaliculi are relatively inconspicuous; instead one sees vesicular structures, the so-called tubulovesicles. During secretion the tubulovesicles disappear and the canaliculi become steadily larger. It is thought that during the secretory process the membranes of the tubulovesicles fuse with the cytoplasmic membrane and enlarge its area; the resulting highly convoluted surface forms the secretory canaliculus (Fig. 26-8). In animal experiments the *maximal HCl secretion rate* has been found to be *directly proportional to the number of parietal cells*. Staining of the parietal cells with indicator dyes has shown that the canaliculi are strongly acid (ca. pH 1), whereas the pH of the cell interior is like that of cells in other tissues (pH 7.2). The concentrations of H^+ and Cl^- in the gastric juice are each 150 mmol/l, whereas the plasma contains only 0.00004 mmol/l (H^+) and 105 mmol/l (Cl^-); thus the parietal cells build up a *H^+ concentration gradient of ca. 1:1,000,000.*

Many theories have been developed to interpret these relationships, but so far none has proved satisfactory. Therefore it seems particularly important here to separate the experimentally confirmed facts from the inferences to which they give rise. The confirmed facts are as follows. 1. For 1 H^+ in the gastric juice, 1 HCO_3^- appears in the blood plasma. During the

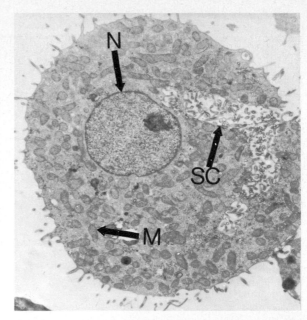

Fig. 26-7. Electron micrograph of an isolated human parietal cell (N, nucleus; M, mitochondrion; SC, secretory canaliculus)

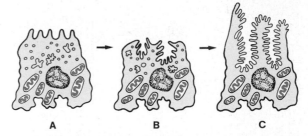

Fig. 26-8 A–C. Semidiagrammatic drawing of a parietal cell in different functional states: **A** resting, **B** submaximally stimulated, **C** maximally stimulated. The membranes of the tubulovesicles and the secretory membrane are drawn in red. After [19]

main phase of HCl production an "alkaline tide" can be observed in the plasma, and even the urine can become alkaline. 2. The formation of H^+ and HCO_3^- requires the participation of carbonic anhydrase; inhibition of this enzyme prevents HCl secretion. 3. The development of the high concentration gradient of H^+ is an active-transport process; the energy required is obtained from intermediary metabolism. Either an inadequate supply of O_2 or glucose or an inhibition of oxidative phosphorylation by dinitrophenol can interrupt HCl secretion. Ca. 1 mol O_2 is required for the production of 2 mol H^+. 4. The distribution of Cl^- is affected by both a concentration gradient between plasma and gastric juice and an electric gradient in the gastric mucosa (the gastric lumen is ca. 40 mV negative with respect to the serosa). For these reasons one must infer the active, energy-consuming transport of Cl^-.

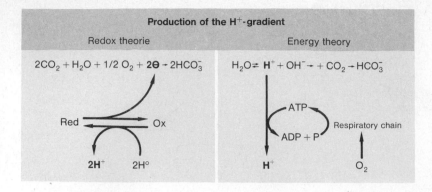

Fig. 26-9. The two most important theories of production of the H$^+$ gradient by the parietal cell

At present there are two theories about the buildup of the H$^+$ gradient (Fig. 26-9). According to the "redox theory" hydrogen is converted to hydrogen ion by removal of an electron. The electron is then transferred to oxygen to produce OH$^-$ ions, which are converted to HCO$_3^-$ ions by the action of carbonic anhydrase. In the "energetic theory," on the other hand, an energy-consuming ion pump is proposed, by which H$^+$ ions accumulate on the luminal side of the secretory membrane. The OH$^-$ ions left behind combine with CO$_2$ as described above to form HCO$_3^-$ ions.

The H$^+$ ions, however produced, must either be freed directly at the secretory cytoplasmic membrane or be transported to it in nonionic form, perhaps along iron-containing enzymes within the cell. Then the H$^+$ ions are released from the cell by the secretory cytoplasmic membrane; this process may be aided by a K$^+$-stimulated ATPase pump and/or an electrogenic mechanism (Rehm effect).

Production and function of macromolecules. Pepsin formation begins with the production of the inactive precursor **pepsinogen** in the chief cells of the gastric glands, and its storage in the form of zymogen granules. These vesicles release their contents as needed, at the cell surface. If the secretion stimulus persists after the stored quantities are exhausted, mew material is synthesized. This is also transported to the outer cell membrane in the form of intracellular vesicles, and is released there. Pepsinogen is activated in the gastric lumen by the splitting off of an inhibitor (a protein complex with m. w. ca. 3200), and converted to pepsin. This process is initiated by HCl and progressively accelerated by the released pepsin *(autocatalysis)*. According to recent electrophoretic and column-chromatographic tests, pepsinogen is a mixture of at least 7 proteases [34]. Five pepsinogens (Group I) are produced in the fundus; they have a pH optimum between pH 1.8 and 2.2 and are destroyed at pH 7.2. The pepsinogens in Group II are produced in the fundus, antrum and duodenum, have a pH optimum around 3.5 and are not destroyed by a pH of 7.2. Group II corresponds to what was formerly called cathepsin. During the secretion of gastric juice small amounts of pepsinogen enter the blood and appear as uropepsinogen in the urine. The blood concentration in these conditions is normally ca. 100 ng/ml [33].

The synthesis of **gastric mucus** (mucin) takes place in the mucus cells of the gastric glands and the mucosal surface. The mucus is released both by the emptying of preformed vesicles at the apical cell membrane and by the shedding of superficial mucus cells. It forms a layer that adheres firmly to the mucosa, the superficial parts of which become detached to form the "soluble mucus" found in samples of gastric juice. Chemically, the mucus consists chiefly of *glycoproteins* containing ca. 80% carbohydrate and characterized by their content of amino sugars, hexoses and sialic acid (usually in the N-acetylated form). The widespread claim that mucin protects the gastric mucosa remains in debate; the terminal N-acetylneuraminic acid is thought to have some significance with regard to this protective function.

The only component of gastric juice of vital importance is **intrinsic factor,** which is secreted by the parietal cells. The presence of this glycoprotein is absolutely necessary for the absorption of vitamin B$_{12}$ (cyanocobalamine). If intrinsic factor is lacking the condition called pernicious anemia results; it is treatable by vitamin B$_{12}$ injection (cf. p. 579).

Regulation of gastric-juice secretion. The secretion of gastric juice is controlled immediately before, during and after eating; there are three phases which overlap in time, the *cephalic, gastric* and *intestinal* phases.

The **cephalic phase** of secretion is initiated by *conditioned reflexes;* the expectation or sight of food causes not only the mouth, but also the stomach to "water." When food is taken into the mouth the excitation of gustatory and olfactory receptors triggers *reflex secretion*. The efferent activity originates in the diencephalon, limbic cortex and hypothalamus and is conveyed to the stomach by the vagus nerves.

These relationships were studied in detail by Pavlov (1889) (Fig. 26-10). He prepared a dog with an esophageal fistula and an isolated pouch of the corpus-fundus part of the stomach, an "accessory stomach" consisting of a pocket of mucosa with vagal and blood supply intact and an opening to the exterior. A variety of experiments on such animals gave the following re-

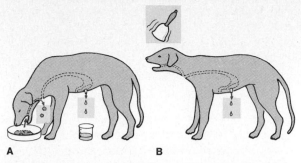

Fig. 26-10 A, B. Pavlov's experiment to demonstrate the central nervous influences on gastric secretion; the dog has esophageal and gastric fistulas. **A** Cephalic secretion phase triggered by food (unconditioned reflex). **B** Learned triggering of secretion by the sound of a bell (conditioned reflex)

sults. 1. A feeding during which the food swallowed falls out of the esophageal fistula (sham feeding) results in marked secretion of juice by "Pavlov's pouch" *(cephalic phase, unconditioned reflex)*. 2. If a bell was rung regularly each feeding time, after a few days the sound of the bell alone caused increased secretion of saliva and gastric juice, which dripped out of their respective fistulas *(cephalic phase, conditioned reflex)*. The study of conditioned reflexes began with these experiments.

Excitation of the vagus nerve causes (by way of synapses in the gastric wall) the release of **acetylcholine,** which stimulates directly the parietal cells and the chief cells. Acetylcholine also causes the release of **gastrin** from the G cells of the antrum. Gastrin is carried to the parietal cells by the bloodstream (Fig. 26-11) and is the strongest known stimulus for HCl secretion. Human gastrin consists of a sequence of 17 amino acids (heptadecapeptide), either unesterified *(gastrin I)* or with a sulfated tyrosine *(gastrin II)* [22, 23]. The two forms are equally effective. The concentration of gastrin in the blood plasma can be measured in vitro by allowing the gastrin in the plasma sample to displace radioactively labelled gastrin from a specific gastrin antibody *(radioimmunoassay)*. That of a fasting subject is 20–50 pg/ml; during digestion it rises to ca. 150 pg/ml plasma [7, 21]. In recent years gastrins have been found with both larger and smaller molecular weights than the heptadecapeptide. The *larger gastrins* have a longer half-life but are relatively ineffective, whereas the *small gastrins* have a short-term action. It has also been shown that an artificially synthesized piece of the molecule – a tri-, tetra- or pentapeptide at the C-terminal end of gastrin I – exhibits the entire action spectrum of the whole molecule. For this reason, the C-terminal pentapeptide is used clinically to stimulate HCl secretion [10]. Vagal excitation also promotes the activity of histidine carboxylase, so that greater amounts of histamine are produced in the mucosa. Within the mucosa histamine is found in the mast cells and in special

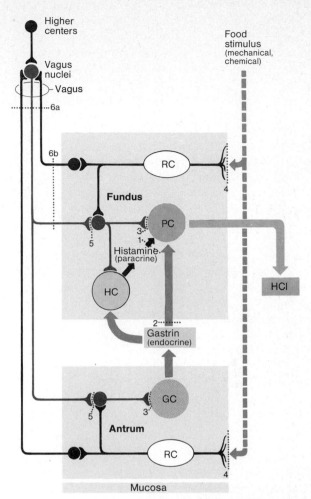

Fig. 26-11. Diagram of the processes regulating the secretion of HCl by the gastric mucosa. The cholinergic neurons are drawn in *red*. PC, parietal cell; GC, gastrin cell; HC, histamine cell; RC, sensory receptor cell. The numbers indicate the possible ways HCl secretion can be inhibited: 1. H2 (histamine) receptor antagonist = cimetidine, 2. gastrin antagonist = secretin, 3. acetylcholine antagonist = pirenzepine (muscarinic receptor), 4. sensory receptor blocking by local anesthetic or low pH, 5. acetylcholine antagonist = hexamethonium (ganglion blocker, nicotinic receptor), 6. vagus transection (a, selective vagotomy; b, selective proximal vagotomy)

histaminocytes [32], the locations of which are correlated with those of the parietal cells. Recent findings indicate that *histamine* plays a central role in the physiology of HCl secretion. It strongly stimulates HCl secretion, and this action can be inhibited only by specific histamine-receptor antagonists. These "H2-receptor antagonists" (e. g., cimetidine) also inhibit the gastric secretion stimulated by gastrin, and to some extent that stimulated by vagal activity [12]. Histamine is therefore thought to act directly, from cell to cell, on the parietal cell (paracrine mechanism) and to be required for secretory activity of the parietal cell.

As indicated in Fig. 26-11, the vagus-mediated secretion of HCl can be inhibited by ganglion blockade (hexamethonium), by parasympatholytics (atropine) and by specifically acting muscarine receptor antagonists (pirenzepine). The HCl secretion elicited by gastrin is inhibited by secretin, atropine and cimetidine. The action of histamine on the parietal cell is antagonized only by cimetidine, an inhibitor of the specific histamine receptors (H2 receptors) [12].

The **gastric phase of secretion,** which can continue for hours, is controlled by the vagus as well as local cholinergic reflexes in the gastric wall, histamine, and the gastrin release triggered by products of digestion. Gastrin release is stimulated by the presence of amino acids, dipeptides or alcohol, as well as by moderate stretching of the antrum. The mechanism is excitation of receptors in the mucosa, which are thought to act on the G cells by way of interneurons (Fig. 26-11). Local application of acetylcholine on the mucosa of the antrum also causes release of gastrin. On the other hand, the release of gastrin can be inhibited by acidifying the antrum to a pH < 3. All these results were obtained with dogs in which gastric pouches had been surgically prepared.

Another kind of gastric pouch can be prepared by the method of Heidenhain, in which part of the corpus-fundus region on the greater curvature is completely separated from the stomach. When the antrum or a similarly prepared pouch in the antrum region is perfused with meat extract, Heidenhain's pouch secretes profusely. In this case there is no neural connection between the two pouches, so that secretion must be stimulated by a hormonal agent. Radioimmunoassay has shown that the enhanced secretion is accompanied by an elevation of the blood gastrin level.

During the **intestinal phase** of secretion there is an initial increase and subsequent reduction of gastric secretion. The *increased secretion* is elicited by the entry of recently consumed, not acidified food. It presumably results from the release of gastrin from the G cells of the duodenum. When acid chyme later enters the duodenum, gastric-juice secretion is inhibited at intraduodenal pH < 4. This inhibition may be mediated by the release of *secretin* from the duodenal mucosa. Although secretin is an antagonist of gastrin, it causes a remarkable increase in pepsinogen secretion. The pronounced *inhibition of gastric-juice secretion* following the movement of fatty chyme into the duodenum is not satisfactorily explained by the secretin mechanism alone. The effect was once ascribed to a hypothetical substance called enterogastrone, but it now appears more likely that other peptides from the duodenal mucosa (gastric inhibitory peptide, cholecystokinin) inhibit gastric-juice secretion; neural influences may also operate here.

Among the other factors that affect gastric-juice secretion, *emotional excitation* predominates. Stress, annoyance and rage cause hypersecretion with increased motility, whereas fear and sadness inhibit both secretion and motility.

Blood flow through the stomach tissues has so far been measured accurately only in animal experiments. In a dog weighing 15 kg the organ is perfused at an overall rate of ca. 50 ml/min. During digestion the rate can rise to ca. 80 ml/min, with most of the increase accounted for by blood flow through the mucosa.

Gastric and duodenal ulcers are among the most common and, because of the danger of bleeding, the most dangerous diseases of the gastrointestinal tract. Development of an ulcer is affected by both aggressive factors (HCl, pepsin and the reflux of digestive enzymes from the duodenum) and protective factors (renewal of the mucosal epithelium, a good blood supply, perhaps mucus). The decisive causative factor in the case of duodenal ulcers is excessive HCl secretion [10, 14]. By contrast, gastric ulcers are usually accompanied by reduced acid secretion and atrophy of the mucosa – that is, the protective factors are apparently weakened. The significance of the aggressive factors is especially clear in the *Zollinger-Ellison* syndrome, the excessive production of gastrin in tumor-like aggregations of G cells, which can lead to gastric and/or duodenal ulcers.

Small Intestine

In the small intestine the acid chyme is mixed with the alkaline secretions of the pancreas, liver and intestinal glands. The enzymes in the pancreatic juice and those of the intestinal epithelial cells, together with the bile, are responsible for most of the digestive process. As digestion proceeds absorption of its products begins – a process almost entirely restricted to the small intestine.

Motility. Movements of the small intestine at first achieve a thorough mixing of the chyme with the pancreatic juice, bile and secretions of the intestinal glands. The *mixing movements* – non-propulsive peristalsis, rhythmic segmentation, pendular movements and contraction of the villi (see below) – cause frequent changes in the areas of contact between mucosa and chyme. **Non-propulsive peristalsis** is most commonly observed in the duodenum and upper jejunum. It always propagates in the aboral direction, usually for only a short distance; the wave of contraction passing along the circular musculature is in general not preceded by a wave of relaxation. **Rhythmic segmentation** also involves the circular musculature (Fig. 26-2), which contracts in regions 1–2 cm wide at intervals of ca. 15–20 cm, causing deep notching of the intestine. When the contracted muscles relax, muscles in the intervening regions contract; this alternation is repeated at a rate as high as 8–10 times a minute, and can persist for several hours. The **pendu-**

lar movements are contractions of regions of the longitudinal musculature, which lead primarily to displacement of the intestinal wall with respect to the contents. The alternation between rhythmic segmentation and pendular movement provides very effective mixing. The *intestinal villi* alternate constantly between contraction and relaxation, during the entire process of digestion, so that they are repeatedly exposed to new chyme. Their rhythmic contractions also help to move lymph along the central chylous vessels (Fig. 26-12) [4, 8]. The **propulsive peristalsis** in the small intestine, usually preceded by a wave of relaxation, takes the form of constrictions varying in depth, propagated over varying distances. The more superficial constrictions propel only the parts of the chyme near the wall. The powerful, deep constrictions observed chiefly toward the end of a digestive phase travel along the whole small intestine, as far as the ileocecal valve, and are clearly propulsive. It has been shown that a series of such peristaltic contractions sweeps the small intestine practically clean. The transfer of a test meal from the small to the large intestine begins 4 hours after ingestion at the earliest, and is completed when a total of 8–10 hours have elapsed.

Regulation of small-intestine motility. These motor events are regulated primarily by way of the *myenteric plexus*. The external sympathetic and parasympathetic innervation is evidently of subordinate importance, for transection of the vagus (vagotomy), for example, has no detectable consequences. The stimulus that elicits and maintains these intestinal movements is stretching of the intestinal wall. The extent to which the submucosal plexus participates in peristalsis is not known, though the plexus is known to contain bipolar ganglion cells, one process of which extends into the mucosa and the other into the myenteric plexus. It may be that stretching of the mucosa is signalled to the myenteric plexus by these cells. The peristalsis in the small intestine is distinctly *polarized;* that is, it always proceeds from oral to aboral (Cannon's law). If a piece of small intestine is cut out and sewed back in the reverse orientation, the "polarization" of this section is retained and chyme accumulates above the site of the operation.

The movements of the villi are controlled by the submucosal plexuses. Moreover, it has been shown that after acid chyme enters the duodenum a factor can be extracted from the intestinal mucosa that elicits and maintains *contraction of the villi* [27]. This substance, called *villikinin,* has no influence on the rest of the intestinal musculature. Stimulation of the vagus enhances contraction of the villi, and the contractions cease following sympathetic stimulation.

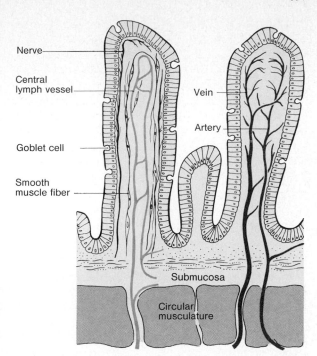

Fig. 26-12. Structure of the intestinal villi, semidiagrammatic

Pancreatic secretion. The exocrine part of the pancreas can be regarded as a sort of abdominal salivary gland; it produces 1.5–2.0 liters of watery fluid per day. The juice secreted during digestion is isotonic with blood plasma, and has a pH of 8–8.5. Its alkalinity results from the high concentration of *bicarbonate,* 125 mmol/l in man during maximal secretion. The juice also contains the cations Na^+, K^+, Ca^{++}, Mg^{++} and the anions Cl^-, SO_3^{--}, and HPO_4^{--}. The bicarbonate content of the pancreatic juice, the bile and the intestinal juice suffices to raise the pH of the acid chyme in the small intestine toward the neutral point or even into the weakly alkaline range. It thus creates a favorable milieu for the pancreatic enzymes, which function optimally at pH 7–8.

The **enzymes of the pancreatic juice** are crucially important in the digestion of **protein, fat** and **carbohydrates** (cf. Tables 26-3, 26-4). They are secreted as inactive precursors, and are normally not activated until they arrive in the intestinal lumen. The most important **protein-splitting** proenzymes are *trypsinogen, chymotrypsinogen, procarboxypeptidase* A and B, and *elastase.* Activation of trypsinogen is initiated when a hexapeptide is split from the C terminal by enterokinase, and proceeds autocatalytically. Trypsin not only catalyzes its own activation, but also activates chymotrypsinogen and the procarboxypeptidases. The pancreatic juice also contains enzymes for the breakdown of **fats** (*pancreatic lipase, phospholipase A, lecithinase*), **carbohydrates** (*pancreatic α-amylase*) and

Table 26-2. Composition of liver and gallbladder bile

	Liver bile		Gallbladder bile
Water	95–98	g/dl	92 g/dl
Bile salts	1.1	g/dl	3 –10 g/dl
Bilirubin	0.2	g/dl	0.5–2 g/dl
Cholesterol	0.1	g/dl	0.3–0.9 g/dl
Fatty acids	0.1	g/dl	0.3–1.2 g/dl
Lecithin	0.04	g/dl	0.1–0.4 g/dl
Na^+	145	mmol/l	130 mmol/l
K^+	5	mmol/l	9 mmol/l
Ca^{++}	2.5	mmol/l	6 mmol/l
Cl^-	100	mmol/l	75 mmol/l
HCO_3^-	28	mmol/l	10 mmol/l

nucleic acids *(nucleases)*. It is not yet clear whether – and if so, how – these enzymes must be activated.

Production of pancreatic juice. The proenzymes are synthesized by the ribosomes of the acinar cells and stored in the form of zymogen granules. When the stored proenzyme is released, an event triggered chiefly by **cholecystokinin** (CCK; = pancreozymin), the vesicles empty their contents into the acini and vigorous synthesis of new proenzyme begins. An electrolyte solution is released into the acini along with the proenzymes. This *primary secretion* undergoes permanent changes in electrolyte composition, primarily in the region of the intralobular duct. By micropuncture of the rabbit pancreas it has been shown that Cl^- is exchanged for HCO_3^- in the intralobular duct, by an active (energy-consuming) process involving carbonic anhydrase which is greatly accelerated by **secretin** [35].

Regulation of pancreatic secretion. Secretion is begun during the cephalic phase, owing to reflex activation of the vagus. Most of the pancreatic juice, however, is produced after the chyme has entered the duodenum and the gastrointestinal hormones secretin and cholecystokinin are released. **Secretin** causes the production of a large volume of juice with a high bicarbonate content and low concentrations of enzymes. The site of secretin action is probably the epithelial cells of the intralobular ducts. In addition to its action on the pancreas, secretin increases the volume and bicarbonate content of the bile. Cholecystokinin (CCK) triggers secretion of a pancreatic juice rich in enzymes, and in higher concentrations also causes emptying of the gall bladder. Once gall has entered the duodenum, further release of CCK is thought to be inhibited.

For the formation of pancreatic juice with a high enzyme content, secretin, CCK and the vagus nerve must act together. CCK has a maximal effect only in the presence of secretin and with the vagus intact. Administration of parasympatholytic substances such as atropine not only inhibits enzyme secretion but also inhibits the liberation of secretin and blocks its action. The only major influence of the sympathetic system on the pancreas seems to lie in regulating blood flow.

The most severe disorder of the pancreas is acute or chronic pancreatitis, in which premature activation of the pancreatic enzymes (especially trypsin, phospholipase A and elastase) causes the organ to digest itself. Removal of the entire pancreas is compatible with life as long as both the exocrine and endocrine substances it produces are supplied from external sources.

Liver and biliary system. The liver is the most important metabolic organ in the body. It has a wide variety of functions in the metabolism of proteins, fats, carbohydrates, hormones, vitamins and exogenous substances. These relationships are treated in textbooks of physiological chemistry. Here we shall consider only the excretory and secretory functions of the liver, as they relate to digestion.

Bile secretion. Bile is secreted by the *liver cells* into the biliary canaliculi, a system of communicating spaces between adjacent liver cells or cell plates. From the canaliculi it flows through intra- or extralobular cholangioles into larger vessels of the periportal fields, which fuse progressively until they finally join in the region of the hepatic portal to form the hepatic duct. From this duct the bile can flow either through the cystic duct into the *gallbladder,* or into the common bile duct. The latter, usually after fusion with the *pancreatic duct,* passes through *Oddi's sphincter* and opens into the duodenum at the *duodenal papilla.*

Bile is secreted **continuously** by the liver, throughout the day, to produce a total volume of 0.5–1.0 liters per day. It has a golden color and a pH of 7.8–8.6, and is nearly isotonic with blood. The bile produced when digestion is not in process accumulates and is concentrated in the gallbladder, Oddi's sphincter being closed. During digestion the sphincter opens and the bile from the **gallbladder** flows into the duodenum. During storage in the gallbladder the composition of the bile changes, as shown in Table 26-2. Its organic components include bile salts, bilirubin, cholesterol, fatty acids and lecithin. It is evident in Table 26-2 that some substances can be concentrated by factors of 5 to 10 in the gallbladder. Because of this concentration, the human gallbladder – with a capacity of only 50–80 ml – can contain the amount of bile secreted by the liver in 12 hours.

Bile secretion is based principally on *active-transport mechanisms.* Bile salts and Na^+ are actively secreted into the canaliculi, and water follows down the osmotic gradient; all the other substances that are actively secreted have a similar choleretic (bile-production-stimulating) action. Production of part of the total volume (ca. 40%), however, is independent of the bile acids; this fraction can be increased by substances such as theophylline and glucagon. K^+ and Cl^- are evidently freely exchanged between plasma and bile. HCO_3^- may be exchanged as in the pancreas, particularly in view of the fact that the release of secretin increases the concentration of bicarbonate in the bile.

The liver cells convert cholesterol into the two primary **bile acids,** *cholic acid* and *chenodeoxycholic acid,* producing the two in a ratio of 2:1. The bile acids, after conjugation with glycine or taurine in the liver, are excreted as glyco- or taurocholic acid (in a ratio of 3:1). These are present in alkaline bile as the Na^+ and K^+ salts, respectively. In the distal ileum ca. 20% of the primary bile acids are metabolized by bacteria to form the secondary bile acids deoxycholic acid and lithocholic acid. In this part of the intestine 90–95% of all the bile acids present are actively reabsorbed, returning to the liver through the portal vessels (enterohepatic circulation). These circulating bile acids constitute a bile-acid pool amounting to 2–4 g, which passes around the enterohepatic circuit 6–10 times per 24 hours. About 0.6 g is excreted in the feces per 24 hours, and it is replaced by new synthesis of the same amount of bile acids.

The **bile pigments** comprise chiefly *bilirubin* and *biliverdin,* with smaller amounts of *urobilinogen.* The bile pigments are products of hemoglobin breakdown. Bilirubin, being insoluble in water, is bound to albumin during transport in the blood. In the liver cell it is primarily in conjugated form, most of it with *glucuronic acid* but a small amount with *sulfate.* These water-soluble conjugates are secreted into the canaliculi by the liver cells. Of the amount of bilirubin entering the duodenum daily in the bile (200–300 mg), ca. 10–20% is reabsorbed as urobilinogen and thus enters the enterohepatic circulation; the rest is excreted. Many pharmaceuticals are conjugated and excreted in the same way as bilirubin.

Regulation of the secretion and release of bile. Although secretion of bile is a continuous process, the rate of secretion can double during digestion. This increased secretion, associated with an increase in bicarbonate concentration, is mediated primarily by *secretin.* The bile stored and concentrated during the interdigestive phase is expelled from the gallbladder when cholecystokinin is released; CCK causes simultaneous *contraction of the gallbladder* and *relaxation of Oddi's sphincter,* so that the bile can pass into the duodenum. Evacuation of the gallbladder under the influence of CCK can also be elicited by introducing

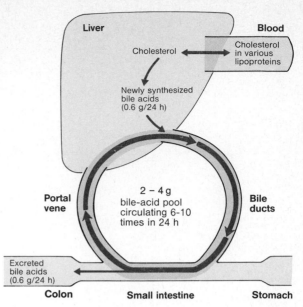

Fig. 26-13. Enterohepatic circulation of the bile acids. After [16]

oil, egg yolk or magnesium sulfate into the duodenum. This action is utilized clinically to study contractility of the gallbladder. In such tests the gallbladder is observed by *roentgenography* after administration of a radiation-opaque substance that is secreted into the bile (e.g., tetraiodophenolphthalein).

Gallstones. The most common disorders of the biliary tract result from the formation of gallstones. Ca. 90% of all gallstones consist chiefly of cholesterol, whereas the main component of the remaining 10% is calcium bilirubinate. Gallbladder bile is a supersaturated solution and thus tends to form precipitates. Normally the cholesterol is present in micellar solution, owing to the relative concentrations of bile salts, lecithin and cholesterol (Fig. 26-14). In patients with gallstones the bile is supersaturated with cholesterol, and the cholesterol precipitates in the form of crystals. The detailed causes of the relative change in concentration of the bile components are not known. The regular consumption of chenodeoxycholic acid alters the proportions of the gallbladder-bile components in such a way as to prevent the formation of cholesterol stones; when it is continued for long periods, even preexisting stones can be dissolved [25]. Concretions containing calcium bilirubinate are formed when insoluble Ca-bilirubinate is released from the water-soluble bilirubin glucuronide – as can happen, for example, by the action of a bacterial β-glucuronidase.

Intestinal secretion. The duodenal wall contains *Brunner's glands,* which secrete an extremely viscous fluid (owing to its mucin content) containing sufficient bicarbonate to have a pH of 8.3–9.3. Its content of Na^+ and Cl^- is nearly the same as that of the blood plasma. The enzymes found in earlier studies of intestinal juice were derived from the brush borders of dead epithelial cells. Such enzymes as may be contained in the pure secretion of the Brunner's glands

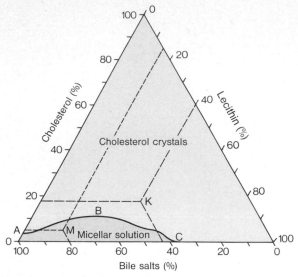

Fig. 26-14. Solubility of cholesterol in the bile as a function of the concentration ratios of bile salts, lecithin and cholesterol. In the area below the curve ABC cholesterol is in micellar solution (Point M). When the concentrations of bile salts and lecithin decrease (above Curve ABC) cholesterol precipitates in crystalline form (Point K). After [23]

are of no practical significance in digestion. Nothing certain is known about the regulation of intestinal secretion.

Large Intestine and Rectum

Production of feces. The mass that passes from the small intestine through the ileocecal valve into the cecum (ca. 200–500 ml per day) is concentrated in the colon by the *reabsorption of water*. At the same time, *electrolytes and water-soluble vitamins* are reabsorbed. The total quantities of water, electrolytes and vitamins reabsorbed in the large intestine are quite small in comparison to the small intestine. Any fats that enter the large intestine are excreted in the stool (steatorrhea).

Whereas the duodenum of a healthy person is almost always sterile, there are usually a few bacteria in the jejunum, appreciably more in the ileum and a permanent population in the colon *(Escherichia coli, Aerobacter aerogenes,* and several species of nonpathogenic cocci). The colon is sterile in the newborn, but is colonized by this **intestinal flora** during the first months of life. *Carbohydrates* are further broken down by bacterial *fermentation* and *proteins* by *putrefactive* bacteria. Carbohydrate fermentation produces acid end products (lactic acid, acetic acid) as well as alcohol, CO_2 and H_2O. During the putrefaction of protein poisonous amines (indole, skatole), amines with marked biological effects (histamine, tyramine) and hydrogen, hydrogen sulfide and me-

thane are formed. With a balanced diet the processes of fermentation and putrefaction are in equilibrium; for example, the acid pH produced by fermentation inhibits putrefaction. If this balance is upset, stools typical of one or the other process are passed (fermentative or putrefactive dyspepsia). The intestinal bacteria also contribute to the breakdown of bile pigments.

The color of feces results from the decomposed bile pigments, its pH of 5–7 from the products of fermentation, and its smell from H_2S, organic acids, indole and skatole. The 100–200 g feces eliminated daily, given a balanced diet, consists of 75–80% water and 20–25% solids. The solids contain variable amounts of cellulose and other indigestible components, ca. 10–30% bacteria, ca. 10–15% inorganic material (insoluble calcium and iron salts), and ca. 5% fat from enterocytes, with small amounts of shed epithelium and mucus.

Motility of the large intestine. A special feature of colonic structure is the arrangement of the external longitudinal musculature to form superficial bands (teniae). The tone of the teniae and local contractions of the circular musculature produce the folds (plicae) and sacculations (haustra) of the colon. When the colon is observed by roentgenography or with the abdomen opened, it exhibits a slow migration of circular-muscle contraction, previously relaxed regions contracting while initially contracted regions relax. This "haustral progression" corresponds to a slow, nonpropulsive peristalsis. But rhythmic segmentation (cf. pp. 587 f.) also occurs in the large intestine. The effect of these forms of contraction is to mix or knead the content of the colon. Propulsive peristalsis here takes the form of *"peristaltic rushes"* which occur two or three times a day. These mass contractions start in the region of the cecum and sweep over the entire colon to the sigmoid, pushing the colonic contents into the sigmoid or rectum. Because this form of movement frequently occurs after eating, it is called a *gastrocolic reflex*. Peristaltic rushes can also be elicited by local stretching. In general the food residues remain in the large intestine for at least 12 hours. Some remnants of a meal are retained in the sigmoid colon for as long as 3 days before transfer to the rectum.

The rhythmic segmentation and the propulsive peristalsis of the large intestine are regulated by the myenteric and submucosal plexuses. Although facilitatory influence is ascribed to the parasympathetic innervation and inhibitory influence to the sympathetic innervation, transection of these nerves does not cause deterioration of function [4, 8].

The congenital absence of the myenteric plexus in a certain region of the large intestine causes constriction of that region, owing to the lack of neurally induced (purinergic?) relaxation. Above this region the large intestine is greatly distended *(congenital megacolon, Hirschsprung's disease).*

Defecation. The stimulus for defecation is filling of the rectum by the mass movement of the colon. The urge to defecate is mediated by stretch receptors in the rectum; their activity is conducted to the reflex center in the sacral cord (anospinal center) by way of the pudendal and pelvic nerves. From about the age of 2 on, this center is under cerebral control. The efferent impulses are carried by parasympathetic fibers to the smooth muscle of the *internal anal sphincter,* which is responsible for continence, and reduce its tone. During evacuation the *external sphincter,* composed of striated muscle, is voluntarily relaxed and the abdominal musculature is contracted to increase intraabdominal pressure. The *defecation reflex* can be voluntarily suppressed to a certain extent; this effect is reinforced by contraction of the striated external sphincter. If such suppression is frequently repeated the threshold for the reflex is raised, so that greater filling of the rectum is necessary to trigger it. For this reason, neglect of the urge to defecate can result in constipation.

26.2 Digestion and Absorption

Digestion. The *macromolecular components* of food are hydrolyzed by the enzymes in the digestive juices and in the epithelial cells of the small intestine, and thus are reduced to absorbable molecules. This splitting produces *amino acids* from *proteins, monosaccharides* from *carbohydrates,* and mainly *glycerin* and *fatty acids* from *fats.* The subsequent absorption of these decomposition products enables the organism to use them for the construction of the substances necessary to the body, or as a substrate for the energy-supplying reactions. When foodstuffs are broken down, the characteristics of the original substances are lost. One result is that digestion protects the body from foreign protein.

Digestive-absorptive surface. Enzymes involved in the breakdown of oligosaccharides and oligopeptides are located on the surfaces of the epithelial cells (enterocytes) in the small intestine. As shown in Fig. 26-15, the enterocyte surface toward the lumen is much enlarged by fingerlike processes (microvilli). Together, the **microvilli** constitute the **brush border** of the cells. Electron-microscopic examination of this region indicates that the structure of the microvilli is as shown schematically in Fig. 26-15 (above); a spe-

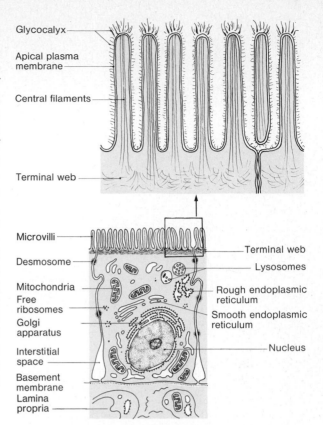

Fig. 26-15. Schematic drawing of an intestinal epithelial cell; above it is an enlarged section of the apical cytoplasmic membrane

cial feature is the filamentous layer **(glycocalyx)** covering them. The brush border can be separated from the enterocytes by ultracentrifugation for chemical analysis. The glycocalyx has been found to consist of mucopolysaccharides in which the enzymes of the *intestinal epithelial cells* (summarized in Tables 26-3 and 26-4) are embedded [1].

The structure of this membrane surface is thought to be as diagrammed in Fig. 26-16. Evidently the *enzymes of the pancreatic juice,* after *adsorptive binding to the glycocalyx,* can become embedded in it. The glycocalyx also contains **membrane-bound enzymes** at its base, which are released only when the membrane is destroyed. According to the concept of **membrane digestion,** hydrolysis by the adsorptively incorporated enzymes produces oligomeres, and hydrolysis by the membrane-bound enzymes produces monomeres. Immediately adjacent to the membrane-bound enzymes, within the cell membrane, *active-transport systems* **(carriers)** are assumed to be responsible for absorption. The term *digestive-absorptive enterocyte surface* reflects this complex function. The cells of the intestinal epithelium have a high turnover rate; they migrate from the crypts of the intestinal mucosa to the

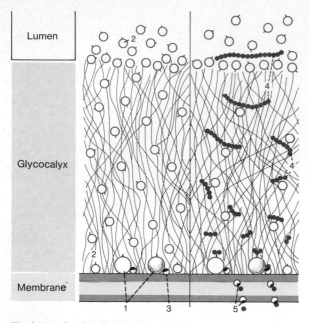

Fig. 26-16. Spatial distribution within the brush border of the membrane-bound enzymes (1), the enzymes of the digestive juices (2), and the hypothetical carriers (3); their interactions with substrate molecules of varying sizes (4) and the mechanism of transport across the membrane (5) are diagrammed on the right

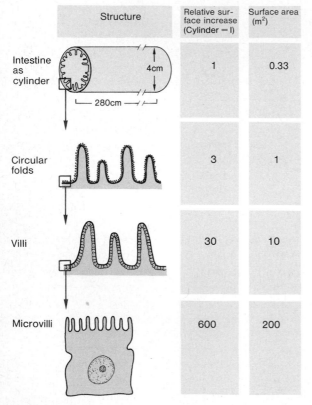

Fig. 26-17. Schematic illustration of the surface-area enlargements produced by structures in the small intestine. After [37]

tips of the villi in the course of ca. 24–36 hours, and after 3 days there they are shed into the lumen of the intestine. Each day ca. 250 g enterocytes – which corresponds to ca. 25 g protein – enters the lumen. The protein of the enterocytes and the proteins secreted daily in the digestive juices (ca. 150 g) are broken down, and most of the products are reabsorbed.

Absorption. Absorption is the process by which substances from the surface of the body (lumen of the gastrointestinal tract) are taken into the interior (intestinal epithelium, interstitial space, lymph and blood). *Absorption occurs principally in the small intestine,* which is specially adapted for the purpose (Figs. 26-17, 26-18). Its length in man, in vivo, is ca. 2.8 m, of which the duodenum accounts for 30 cm, the jejunum for 120 cm, and the ileum for 130 cm. Its total *surface area* in man is ca. 200 m^2, owing chiefly to the circular folds (of Kerckring), the villi and the microvilli (Fig. 26-17). The rhythmic *contractions of the villi* improve their contact with the chyme and press out the contents of the closed ends of the lymph vessels (Fig. 26-12).

The rate of *blood flow* through the intestine – through the *intestinal mucosa* in particular – is a factor of special significance. Mesenteric blood flow in man is ca. 400 ml/min during food consumption, and ca. 750 ml/min in the actual digestion phase. Studies on dogs have shown that the mucosa at rest receives ca. 50–60% of the mesenteric blood flow, and during digestion 60–80%.

Mechanisms of absorption. The definition of absorption given above is concerned only with the aspect of most interest, the *net transport* from the lumen side to the blood side of the intestinal epithelial cell. Many such cells, however, transport materials in both directions at each membrane. The net transport is the difference between the unidirectional flow through the cell toward the serosa and the flow in the opposite direction, into the lumen. When the former predominates the overall process is absorption; otherwise it is excretion (the terms *insorption* and *exsorption,* respectively, are also used). One factor that complicates the analysis of these relationships is that the substances taken into the enterocytes can appear on the serosal side in a different form – for example, fatty acids and glycerin as triglycerides. Note also that for a *quantitative analysis of the transport processes* in the intestine measurement of concentrations by no means suffices; the actual amounts transported on both sides must be determined [1, 17, 37].

For example, a decrease in concentration of a particular substance in the intestinal lumen can be evaluated only if the simul-

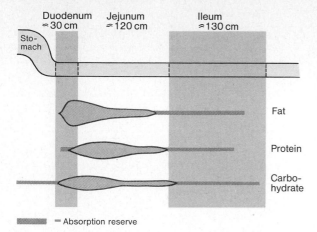

Duodenum
≈ 30 cm

Jejunum
≈ 120 cm

Ileum
≈ 130 cm

Sto-
mach

Fat

Protein

Carbo-
hydrate

▬▬ = Absorption reserve

Fig. 26-18. Relative absorption of fats, proteins and carbohydrates along the small intestine (the length data for the different sections refer to the situation in situ)

taneous movement of fluid is known. In absorption studies the movement of water is measured by introducing a non-absorbable marker substance to the solution in the lumen. To study absorption in man, a double-barrelled probe is passed through the esophagus and stomach, into the small intestine; through one channel a solution containing both the substance of interest and a marker substance is infused, and through the second, which opens further down the intestine (e. g., 40 cm away), samples are taken for measurement of substrate and marker. From these data and the known infusion velocity, the amount of substrate absorbed per unit time and unit intestinal length can be calculated.

Transport processes. The analysis of transport in the intestinal epithelium has been greatly assisted by application of the laws of thermodynamics. These principles allow qualitative description of many mechanisms operating in the intestinal wall, and even quantitative descriptions of some. The basic events in absorption include both **passive** *(diffusion, osmosis)* and **active, energy-consuming transport processes.** The fundamentals of diffusion and osmosis are discussed elsewhere (cf. pp. 649 ff.). In the context of the gastrointestinal translocation of substances we need note only that the large surface area of the intestine and the continuous effect of blood flow through the mucosa on the concentration gradients between lumen and blood are of particular importance. Chief among the substances that move through the intestinal mucosa by diffusion and osmosis are water, Cl^- and molecules such as ascorbic acid, pyridoxine and riboflavin. Because of the high lipid content of the cell membranes, a degree of *fat-solubility* is required for substances to move by diffusion. The main substances that diffuse in this way are the salts of weak acids or weak bases in the undissociated state (theory of **nonionic diffusion**). This consideration is important in the case of drugs, most of which are absorbed by diffusion. According to the Henderson-Hasselbalch equa-

tion (cf. p. 501), the pH in the intestinal lumen and the pK of the substance of interest are particularly significant [1, 37].

There is no entirely satisfactory definition of **active transport** in the intestinal mucosa. However, the transfer of substances by this means has certain special characteristics, as follows: (i) It requires energy (is inhibited by O_2 deficiency, reduced temperature and metabolic inhibitors); (ii) it can run "uphill," against an electrochemical gradient; (iii) the transport rate is relatively high but (iv) cannot be driven beyond a certain saturation level, and (v) can be reduced in the presence of certain substances by competitive inhibition. Most of the components of food are absorbed by active-transport mechanisms (amino acids, monosaccharides, vitamin B_{12}, calcium). In the simplest case such transport can involve **hypothetical carrier systems** located in the outer cell membrane. Presumably these comprise enzymes to which the substrate is bound, so that it moves into the cell as a carrier-substrate complex. On the other side of the membrane the substrate is released and the unloaded carrier can diffuse back. In another form of active transport, the substances are *enclosed in vesicles* (pinocytosis). Small particles at the cell surface are enveloped by infolding of the membrane, after which the invagination constricts off and moves through the interior of the cell.

Two special cases also deserve mention. *Solvent drag* occurs when transport of a solvent sweeps dissolved substances along with it. *Facilitated diffusion* is a transport mechanism which transfers substances rapidly, saturates and can be competitively inhibited, but occurs without the consumption of energy and is not effective against a concentration gradient (cf. pp. 655 f.).

The absorbed substances are **carried away** from the intestinal region in the blood and lymph vessels. Substances carried in the bloodstream from the stomach and small and large intestines travel through the portal veins into the liver before reaching the general circulation. Substances that enter the blood from the oral mucosa and the rectum join the general circulation directly. The intestinal lymph flows from the intestinal vessels into the cisterna chyli, eventually passing through the thoracic duct into the superior vena cava.

Digestion and Absorption of Protein

Digestion. As summarized in Table 26-3, proteins and polypeptides are split into fragments of various sizes (poly- and oligopeptides) by pepsins, trypsin and chymotrypsin. These enzymes are *endopeptidases;*

Table 26-3. The main events in protein digestion

Site of production	Enzyme (proenzyme)	Mechanism of action	Substrate	End products
Gastric glands, chief cells	Pepsin (pepsinogen)	Endopeptidases; split mainly peptide bonds between NH_2 groups of tyrosine or phenylalanine and COOH groups of other amino acids; pH optimum 1.5–3.5	Proteins	Polypeptides
Exocrine pancreas	Trypsin (trypsinogen)	Endopeptidase; splits mainly between COOH groups of lysine or arginine and NH_2 groups of other amino acids; pH optimum 7.5–8.5	Proteins	Polypeptides
	Chymotrypsin (chymotrypsinogen)	Endopeptidase; splits mainly between COOH groups of aromatic amino acids and NH_2 groups of other amino acids except glutamic acid and asparagine; pH optimum 7.5–8.5	Proteins, polypeptides	Polypeptides, oligopeptides
	Carboxypeptidase A, B (procarboxypeptidase)	Exopeptidases; Type A splits off aromatic, nonpolar amino acids at the C-terminal end; Type B splits off basic amino acids in the same position	Polypeptides, oligopeptides	C-terminal amino acids and peptide residues
Duodenal mucosa (?)	Enterokinase	Endopeptidase; splits between isoleucine (pos. 7) and lysine (pos. 6)	Trypsinogen	Trypsin and hexapeptides
Brush border of enterocytes (membrane-bound)	Tripeptidase	Exopeptidase; splits off N-terminal or C-terminal amino acids	Proteins, poly- and oligopeptides	N- or C-terminal amino acids and poly- or oligopeptides
	Aminopolypeptidase	Exopeptidase	Tri-, dipeptides	Amino acids
	Aminopeptidase	Exopeptidase; splits amino bonds	Tri-, dipeptides	Amino acids
	Many dipeptidases, some specific			

that is, they hydrolyze peptide bonds, particularly within the molecule. *Exopeptidases* split off single amino acids at the N- or C-terminal end. The carboxypeptidases of the pancreatic juice and the peptidases of the brush border continue the breakdown of poly- and oligopeptides, to amino acids (Table 26-3, Fig. 26-19 [1, 37]).

Absorption. In the adult intestine there is no appreciable absorption of whole proteins taken in orally. But in the intestine of the newborn proteins in the colostrum are absorbed during the first days of life, as shown by the appearance of maternal globulins in the infant's plasma; these offer some protection against infection.

Once the proteins have been hydrolyzed in the lumen or in the brush border, the fragments (amino acids, oligopeptides) are taken into the enterocytes. The absorption of amino acids is accomplished by **stereospecific Na^+-dependent active-transport systems** in the luminal enterocyte membrane; L amino acids are preferred. Four such systems have been identified so far: 1. a system for *neutral amino acids* (valine, phenylalanine, alanine), 2. a system for *basic amino acids* (argi-

nine, cysteine, lysine, ornithine), 3. a system for imino acids (proline, hydroxyproline) and glycine, and 4. a system for amino dicarbonic acids (glutamic acid, asparagine). Interactions between certain amino acids have been found, by which transport is reciprocally inhibited (competitive antagonism – e.g., glycine and methionine) or facilitated (competitive stimulation – e.g., lysine and leucine).

Oligopeptides are also transported actively, by systems in some cases more efficient than those for amino acids. Certain dipeptides are absorbed more rapidly than their component amino acids. The peptide hydrolases of the brush border split a relatively large proportion (ca. 40–60%) of the short-chain peptides only into di- and tripeptides. The final stages of breakdown, to single amino acids, are accomplished by peptide hydrolases in the cytosol.

The amino acids leave the cytosol at the lateral and basal cell membrane of the enterocytes, by several mechanisms – diffusion, facilitated diffusion and an active, non-Na^+-dependent transport. They are carried by the blood to the liver, by way of the portal vessels.

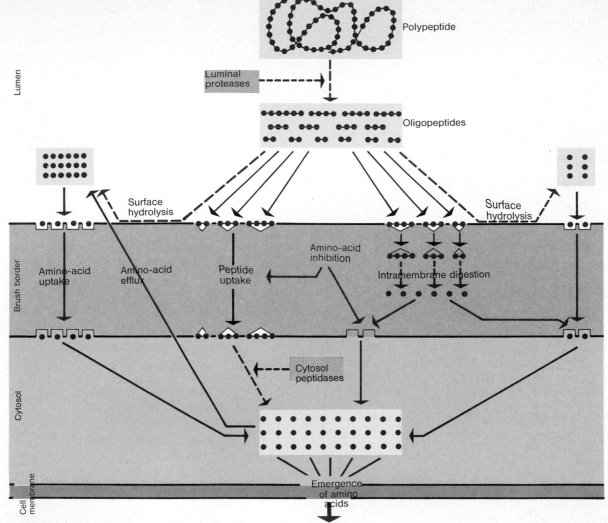

Fig. 26-19. Diagram of the process of protein digestion and absorption

Digestion and Absorption of Carbohydrates

Digestion. Table 26-4 summarizes the most important events in carbohydrate digestion. Food starch contains glucose primarily in the form of long chains linked by α-1,4-glycosidic bonds (amylose), with a certain proportion of 1,6-linked branched chains (amylopectin). The amylose is split by the α-amylase in saliva and pancreatic juice, to form hexasaccharides and smaller amounts of tri- and disaccharides and glucose. The glucose bound by 1,6-linkage to the branch of amylopectin or to glycogen is split off by the oligo-α-1,6-glucosidase of the brush border, and the remaining amylose molecule is broken down as described above. The disaccharides are split in the brush border by the fairly specific disaccharidases located there; in this way monosaccharides are produced from sugars such as sucrose, maltose and lactose.

Absorption. Polysaccharides and disaccharides are not absorbed to any appreciable extent. In certain cases specially designed experiments have revealed starch granules within and on the other side of the intestinal mucosa after the feeding of quite large quantities of starch; these were presumably "massaged in" by the movements of the intestine. The monosaccharides galactose and glucose are absorbed by active transport in two steps. First saccharidases in the brush border split the oligosaccharides to monosaccharides; then, in the presence of Na^+ ions, they attach to a *carrier* (Na^+-dependent carrier transport, Fig. 26-20). The carrier, laden with Na^+ and glucose, diffuses along the electrochemical gradient for Na^+ to the intracellular side of the membrane, where it releases the Na^+ and glucose into the cytosol and returns to the luminal side by diffusion. The relatively low Na^+ concentration in the cytosol is maintained by an energy-consuming Na^+ pump, an indirect ef-

Table 26-4. The most important events in carbohydrate digestion

Site of production	Enzyme (proenzyme)	Mechanism of action	Substrate	End products
Salivary glands	α-amylase (ptyalin)	Endoenzyme, α-amylase; splits α-1,4-bonds (amylose fraction of starch); pH optimum 6.7	Starches	Oligosaccharides and amylopectin (1,6-linked chains)
Exocrine pancreas	Pancreatic amylase	Endoenzyme, α-amylase; cf. ptyalin; pH optimum 7.1	Starches	Oligosaccharides
Brush border of enterocytes (membrane-bound)	Amylase	Glucoamylase	Starches, oligosaccharides	Maltose and glucose
	Oligo-α-1,6-glucosidase	splits α-1,6-bonds (amylopectin fraction of starch)	Glycogen, amylopectin	Oligosaccharides, maltose and glucose
	Many disaccharidases, some specific:			
	Sucrase	β-fructosidase	Cane sugar (saccharose, sucrose)	Fructose and glucose
	Maltase	α-glucosidase; splits α-1,4-bonds	Maltose	Glucose
	Isomaltase	Corresponds to oligo-α-1,6-glucosidase		
	Lactase	β-galactosidase	Lactose	Galactose and glucose

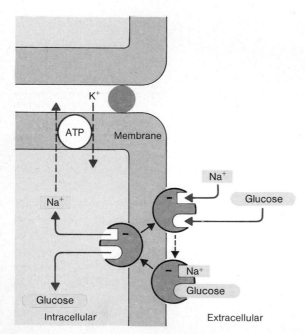

Fig. 26-20. Model of a movable carrier with a specific receptor for the substrate glucose and another for Na$^+$

fect of which is the continual influx of the sodium-bound carrier. Many sugars in addition to glucose and galactose are taken into the enterocytes by this mechanism. By contrast, mannose and pentoses diffuse in and fructose is taken in by facilitated diffu-sion. As far as is known at present, the expulsion of sugars at the lateral and basal cell membrane is not Na$^+$-dependent. The monosaccharides are transported away by way of the portal vein.

Digestion and Absorption of Fats

Digestion. After the chyme has passed from the stomach into the duodenum, the fats (triglycerides, cholesterol, phospholipids) are broken down primarily by the lipid-splitting enzymes in the pancreatic juice (Fig. 26-21). Lipases in the gastric or intestinal juices are of subordinate importance. In the high pH of the small intestine the existing fat emulsion is improved and stabilized by free fatty acids and monoglycerides that are already present; the bile acids, according to recent results, contribute relatively little to emulsification.

The lipid-splitting enzymes attack the lipids at the oil-water interface; first, the fatty acids in positions 1 and 3 are removed from the triglycerides. This step proceeds most rapidly at a lower pH (the pH optimum of pancreatic lipase is 6.5), which is produced by the bile acids. The remaining monoglyceride can be converted into glycerin and fatty acids only by shifting the ester bond, for the lipase splits off only fatty acids in terminal positions; the chain length of the fatty acids,

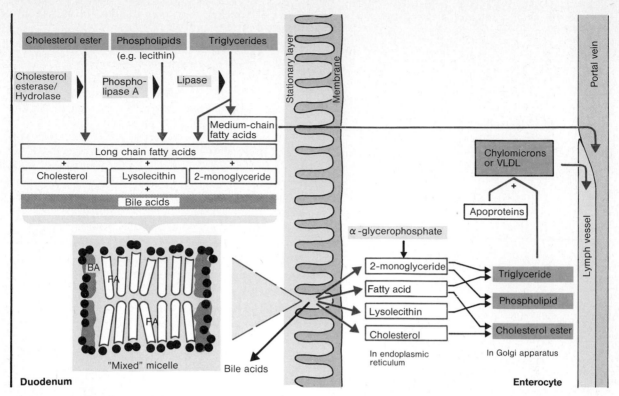

Fig. 26-21. Diagram of fat digestion and absorption. Components of the "mixed" micelle: BA = bile acid, FA = fatty acid, monoglycerides, lecithin, cholesterol. Hydrophilic groups are indicated by ●

however, is of no importance. As the triglycerides are being split, cholesterol esterase cleaves cholesterol ester into cholesterol and free fatty acids. The pH optimum of cholesterol esterase lies between 6.6 and 8; it acts chiefly on unsaturated fatty acids. The phospholipids (predominantly lecithin) are broken down by phospolipases A and B. Phospholipase A is secreted from the pancreas as zymogen and activated by trypsin; it specifically splits the ester bonds of the fatty acid in position 2 of the lecithin, producing lysolecithin and fatty acids.

Absorption. The *short- and intermediate-chain fatty acids* diffuse directly from the lumen into the enterocytes and thence into the blood. The *long-chain fatty acids and cholesterol* must form *micelles* before reaching the enterocyte membrane. At the pH (6–6.5) within the small intestine, the bile acids are polar molecules, one end being lipophilic and the other hydrophilic. At concentrations above 2–5 mmol/l, the so-called critical micellar concentration, micelles are formed – cylindrical aggregations of molecules 3–6 nm in diameter with the hydrophilic ends of the molecules pointing outward. The bile-acid micelles can take up long-chain fatty acids, cholesterol and lecithin, forming larger mixed micelles. The mixed micelles are still small enough to enter the spaces be-

tween the microvilli (50–100 nm wide) and here diffuse to the enterocyte surface. Their contents are transferred into the enterocyte membrane without energy consumption; the micelles apparently make "contact" with the enterocyte membrane in such a way that the enclosed fatty acids diffuse into the membrane. It is not yet known how the bile acids move into the enterocyte. At the inside of the enterocyte membrane the fatty acids are taken up by a transport protein *(fatty-acid-binding protein)*.

Intracellular processing. The fat fragments taken into the enterocytes are put together intracellularly to form triglycerides, cholesterol and phospholipids. The resynthesis of triglycerides and phospholipids occurs in the endoplasmic reticulum and employs acetyl-CoA, activated fatty acids and ATP. The basic building block for the triglycerides and phospholipids is the 2-monoglyceride. That used for triglyceride synthesis appears to come chiefly from the intraintestinal lipolysis, and that for the phospholipids from α-glycerophosphate conversion during carbohydrate metabolism. Cholesterol is re-esterified with long-chain fatty acids by cholesterol esterase.

In the region of the Golgi apparatus of the enterocyte, the intracellularly synthesized fats are converted to *lipoproteins* by coupling to various apoproteins, in particular apoproteins A1 and B. These are the *chy-*

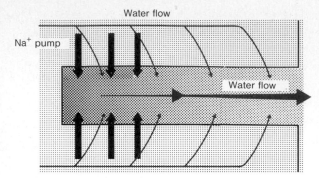

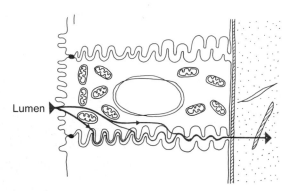

Fig. 26-22. Schematic illustration of the mechanism of Na$^+$ and water absorption. The *arrows* indicate net transport

lomicrons and *very-low-density lipoproteins* (VLDL). Low-density lipoproteins (LDL) and high-density lipoproteins (HDL) are produced in the liver and released into the blood. The differences in density (size and molecular weight) of the lipoproteins result from their varying composition. Chylomicrons, for example, contain ca. 85–90% triglycerides, 6–8% phospholipids, 2–4% cholesterol ester and 2% protein; the VLDL contain a distinctly smaller amount of triglycerides but more protein. These lipoproteins are released from the enterocytes into the lymph vessels, and reach the blood by way of the thoracic duct. After a fatty meal they are present in the blood plasma in such large amounts that it has a milky, turbid appearance (digestive hyperlipemia).

Lipids are absorbed so efficiently that over 95% of the triglycerides and 20–50% of the cholesterol are taken up. With an average fat intake, ca. 6 g fat are passed out in the stool daily. This amount is reduced to about 3 g/24 h with a fat-free diet, in which case the excreted fat comes from shed epithelial cells and bile.

Absorption of Vitamins, Water and Minerals

Vitamins. The absorption of the fat-soluble vitamins (A, D, E and K) is linked to that of fats, and is inhibited when fat absorption is impaired. For example, it

has been shown that vitamin A is esterified with fatty acids and appears in the lymph with the chylomicrons. Of the water-soluble vitamins, vitamin C and riboflavin are taken up by diffusion. Folic acid is presumably absorbed in the jejunum, in conjugated form. Vitamin B$_{12}$ (cyanocobalamine) is absorbed by active transport in the ileum, as a complex with the intrinsic factor of the gastric juice.

Water and sodium. Water and electrolytes move in both directions in the small and large intestines, and to a lesser extent in the stomach. These shifts act to keep the *intestinal contents isotonic with the plasma*. When chyme rapidly enters the duodenum the duodenal contents can become temporarily hypertonic; under such conditions water flows into the intestine. Similarly, when osmotically active particles are absorbed during digestion water follows them, down the osmotic gradient. The *main site* of water and salt absorption is the *upper small intestine*. Most of the water taken orally and secreted with the digestive juices (ca. 8–10 l/d) is absorbed here, only ca. 200–500 ml reaching the large intestine per day. The sodium concentration in duodenum and jejunum corresponds to that of plasma, 150 mmol/l. In the ileum, however, it falls to 100–120 mmol/l – an indication of active transport (Fig. 26-22). The contents of the small intestine are kept isotonic with plasma by the exchange of equimolar amounts of potassium. The absorption of water and electrolytes is also very closely related to that of HCO$_3^-$, sugar and amino acids. The concentration of sodium falls further in the large intestine, but because less fluid is present a smaller amount of Na$^+$ is absorbed here; only ca. 5–6 mmol NaCl is excreted per day in the feces.

Calcium. A small fraction of the calcium consumed in food is absorbed passively in the duodenum and ileum, but most is *transported actively*. The amount absorbed is regulated according to the current needs of the body, with the participation of *vitamin D, parathormone* and *calcitonin*. Normal calcium absorption requires the presence of vitamin D, a Ca-binding protein and amino acids (lysine and L-arginine). The rate of absorption is reduced when the Ca^{++} is converted to insoluble salts (oxalate, phosphate) and in states of vitamin-D and protein deficiency.

Magnesium. The mechanisms of magnesium absorption are like those for calcium. The observation that magnesium competitively inhibits calcium absorption could indicate the use of a common transport system.

Iron. The iron in food is absorbed preferentially in the divalent form. Trivalent iron can be converted to divalent by reducing food components. Iron is absorbed in the upper small intestine and the adjacent jejunum, by *active transport*. In the enterocytes iron combines with the protein *apoferritin* to form *ferritin*, in which it is trivalent. The iron incorporated in this protein complex is the main *iron store* in the body. It can be removed from storage as needed – for example, for the synthesis of iron-containing enzymes or hemoglobin. These and other factors interact to provide an extremely fine regulation of iron balance in the body and to adjust iron absorption to the prevailing demands.

26.3   References

Textbooks and Handbooks

1. BURLAND, W.L., SAMUEL, P.D.: Transport Across the Intestine. A Glaxo Symposium. Edinburgh–London: Churchill Livingstone 1972
2. BROOKS, F.P.: Control of Gastrointestinal Function. London: Macmillan 1970
3. CODE, CH.F., SCHLEGEL, J.F.: Motor action of the esophagus and its sphincters. In: CODE, CH.F.: Handbook of Physiology, Section 6, Alimentary Canal, Vol. IV. Motility, Chapter 90, American Physiological Society. Baltimore; Williams and Wilkins 1968
4. DEMLING, L., OTTENJANN, R.: Gastrointestinal Motility. International Symposium on Motility of the G.I. Tract, Erlangen, July 1969. Stuttgart: Thieme 1971
5. EMMELIN, N., ZOTTERMAN, B.: Oral Physiology. New York: Pergamon Press 1973
6. GREGORY, R.A.: Secretory Mechanism of the Gastrointestinal Glands. London: Arnold 1961
7. JORPES, J.E., MUTT, V.: Secretion, Cholecystokinin, Pancreazymin und Gastrin. Handbuch der experimentellen Pharmakologie, Vol. XXXIV. Berlin–Heidelberg–New York: Springer 1973
8. KRAMER, K.: Physiologie der Verdauung. In: GAUER, O.H., KRAMER, K., JUNG, R.: Physiologie des Menschen, Band 8: Ernährung, Verdauung, Intermediär-Stoffwechsel. München–Berlin–Wien: Urban und Schwarzenberg 1972
9. SIEWERT, R., BLUM, A., WALDECK, F.: Funktionelle Erkrankungen der Speiseröhre. Berlin–Heidelberg–New York: Springer 1976
10. SLEISENGER, M.H., FORDTRAN, J.S.: Gastrointestinal Disease. Pathophysiology, Diagnosis, Management. Philadelphia–London–Toronto: Saunders 1973

Research Reports and Reviews

11. BIANCHI, L., GEROK, W., SICKINGER, K.: Liver and Bile. Proceedings of the IV. Int. Congr. Liver Dis. 1976. MTP, Lancaster 1977
12. BLACK, J.W., DUNCAN, W.A.M., DURANT, C.J., GANELLIN, C.R., PARSONS, E.M.: Definition and antagonism of histamin H_2-receptors. Nature 236, 385 (1972)
13. BONFILS, S.: Clinics in Gastroenterology. Endocrine Secreting Tumors of the G.I. Tract, Vol. 3. London–Philadelphia–Toronto: Saunders 1974
14. BRO-RASMUSSEN, F., KILLMAN, S., THAYSER, J.H.: The composition of pancreatic juice as compared to sweat, parotid saliva and tears. Acta physiol. scand. 37, 97 (1956)
15. CRANE, R.K.: Structural and functional organization of an epithelial cell brush border. In: DANIELLI, J.F.: Symp. Intern. Soc. Cell Biol. V. Intracellular Transport, p.71. New York: Academic Press 1967
16. DIETSCHY, J.M.: The biology of bile acids. Arch. Intern. Med. 130, 473–474 (1972)
17. ELLIOT, K., O'CONNOR, M.: Peptide Transport and Hydrolysis. Ciba Foundation Symp. 50. Elsevier-Excerpta Medica-North Holland (1977)
18. EWE, K.: Die intestinale Calcium-Resorption und ihre Störungen. I.Teil: Physiologie der intestinalen Calcium-Resorption. II.Teil: Klinische Manifestation gestörter Calcium-Resorption. Klin. Wschr. 52, 57 (1974)
19. FORTE, T.M., MACHEN, T.E., FORTE, J.G.: Ultrastructural and physiological changes in piglet oxyntic cells during histamine stimulation and metabolic inhibition. Gastroenterology 69, 1208–1222 (1975)
20. FREEMAN, H.J., KIM, Y.S.: Digestion and absorption of protein. Ann. Rev. Med. 29, 99–116 (1978)
21. GROSSMAN, M.I.: Candidate hormones of the gut. Gastroenterology 67, 730–755 (1974)
22. GREGORY, R.A., TRACY, H.J.: The constitution and properties of two gastrins extracted from hog antral mucosa. Part I: The isolation of two gastrins from hog antral mucosa. Part II: The properties of two gastrins isolated from hog antral mucosa. Gut 5, 103 (1964)
23. GREGORY, R.A.: Recent advances in the physiology of gastrin. Proc. roy. Soc. B 170, 81 (1968)
24. GUTH, P.H., CODE, C.F.: Histamine release and gastric mucosal damage. Gastroenterology 74, 622–623 (1978)
25. HOFMANN, A.F., PAUMGARTNER, G.: Chenodesoxycholic Acid Therapy of Gallstones. Workshop held in Freiburg, Oct. 1973. Stuttgart–New York: Schattauer 1974
26. JOHNSON, R.: Gastrointestinal hormones and their functions. Ann. Rev. Physiol. 39, 135–158 (1977)
27. KOKAS, E., JOHNSTON, C.L. Influence of refined villikinin on motility of intestinal villi. Amer. J. Physiol. 208, 1196 (1965)
28. KRAMER, M., LAUTERBACH, F. Intestinal Permeation. Proceedings of the IV. Workshop Conference Hoechst 1975. Excerpta Medica
29. McCOLL, I., SLADEN, G.E.: Intestinal Absorption in Man. London: Academic Press 1975
30. OCKNER, R.K., ISSELBACHER, K.J.: Recent concepts of intestinal fat absorption. Rev. Physiol. Biochem. Pharmacol. 71, 107–146 (1974)
31. PEARSE, A.G.E.: Cell migration and the alimentary system: Endocrine contributions of the neural crest to the gut and its derivatives. Digestion 8, 372 (1973)
32. SACHS, G., SPENNEY, J.G., REHMS, W.S.: Gastric secretion. In: International Review of Physiology. Gastrointestinal Physiology II, Vol. 12. Ed. R.K.CRANE. University Park Press 1977, pp. 127–171
33. SAMLOFF, J.M., LIEBMANN, W.A.: Radioimmunoassay of Group I pepsinogens in serum. Gastroenterology 66, 494 (1970)
34. SAMLOFF, J.M., TOWNES, P.L.: Electrophoretic heterogeneity and relationships of pepsinogens in human urine, serum and gastric mucosa. Gastroenterology 58, 462 (1970)
35. SCHULZ, I.: Pancreatic bicarbonate transport. In: SACHS, G., HEINZ, E., ULLRICH, K.J.: Gastric Secretion, p.363. New York–London: Academic Press 1974
36. WANG, S.C.: Emetic and antiemetic drugs. In: ROOT, W.S., HOFFMANN, F.G.: Physiological Pharmacology, Vol.II, Part B, 255–328. London–New York: Academic Press 1965
37. WISEMANN, G.: Absorption from the Intestine. London–New York: Academic Press 1964

27 The Function of the Kidneys

O. HARTH

27.1 Fundamentals of Renal Physiology

Outline of Kidney Anatomy

Morphological subdivisions. The renal parenchyma consists of two main regions, externally the *cortex* and internally the *medulla*. The lobate structure of the organ in man is still detectable in the 8 to 12 or more renal pyramids. These are formed by the conical masses of medullary substance. The apex of each pyramid is directed toward the renal pelvis and bears the openings of the papillary ducts; the base is embedded in the outer cortex (cortex corticis), from which descend the renal columns. Blood vessels and uriniferous tubules are arranged in a characteristic way in the cortical and medullary regions, as diagrammed in Fig. 27-1. The arrangement of the structures directly involved in urine formation is quite uniform; these are the **nephrons,** the *morphological and functional units* of the kidney. A human kidney weighing 150 g contains 1 to 1.2 million nephrons.

Structure of the nephron. The nephron consists of the **glomerulus** (renal corpuscle) and the **renal tubule.** Several tubules within the cortex open into each **collecting tubule.** Despite its connection with several tubules and its different embryological origin, physiologically the collecting tubule (or collecting duct) is considered as part of the nephron, for in addition to its collecting function it plays an important role in determining the composition of the *urine* that is ultimately excreted.

The **glomerulus** is composed of a **tuft of capillaries** originating in the afferent arteriole, the *vas afferens,* and converging into the vas efferens; the capillaries are connected with the inner layer of the double-walled **Bowman's capsule** formed by the tubular epithelium. There is a capsular space between the two layers that communicates with the lumen of the attached tubule. All the glomeruli are situated in the cortical substance, but the term *cortical glomerulus is* applied specifically to those in the cortex corticis, those in deeper regions of the renal columns being called *juxtamedullary glomeruli.* The nephrons are designated correspondingly, depending on position of the glomeruli (Fig. 27-1), as cortical or juxtamedullary nephrons.

The **tubule** begins with a tortuously winding section (the pars convoluta) followed by a short straight section (pars recta) that extends into the outer zone of the medulla. The two together constitute the **proximal tubule.** Between the proximal and distal tubule is the **thin segment.** The **distal tubule** begins with the pars recta and ends with the relatively short pars convoluta. Three segments form the **loop of Henle,** curved like a hairpin: the pars recta of the proximal tubule, the thin segment, and the pars recta of the distal tubule. The proximal and distal convolutions always lie within the renal cortex. Remarkably, the distal convolution is in contact with the afferent arteriole of its glomerulus; this junctional region is called the **juxtaglomerular apparatus** (cf. p. 635). The total length of the renal tubule in man varies widely (proximal tubule about 12–24 mm, distal tubule 5–8 mm).

Within the cortex the distal convolution joins a branch of a **collecting tubule.** The collecting tubules form a branching system in the cortex and inner medulla, eventually opening at the tip of the papilla into the calyx of the renal pelvis. The average length of the collecting structures is 22 mm.

The **blood supply** of the renal and collecting tubules is basically a portal system; that is, the peritubular capillary network receives blood from the glomerular capillaries, and therefore between the two networks the vas efferens is a portal vein. In the renal cortex, and even in the outer zone of the medulla, there is a dense capillary network, but the elongated capillary loops within the inner medulla branch relatively rarely. The parts of a superficial nephron accessible to intravital microscopy and micropuncture have been shown to be supplied predominantly by capillaries originating in the vas efferens of the associated glomerulus [49].

Features of Kidney Function

The role of the kidney. The kidneys act to *clear the blood plasma* of certain substances by concentrating them in the urine. A large fraction of these substances are **end products of metabolism** (e.g., urea, uric acid and creatinine), which cannot be put to any further use. These substances *must be excreted in the urine* because they are produced in amounts too great to be eliminated in any other way, and if they were to accumulate in the body a gradual poisoning would result. Many foreign substances also belong in this category – for example, medications of plant or synthetic origin, which are often not completely broken down and can be removed from the body only by the kidneys. In all these cases the only concern is to eliminate the substances in sufficient quantities.

Other components of the urine are **physiologically essential substances** such as sodium ions, calcium, inorganic phosphate and water. In these cases it is important that the amounts excreted, if possible, be such as to keep the plasma concentration of the substances fairly constant despite major changes in daily intake. The rate of renal excretion of such substances is adjusted by hormones that act on the kidney. Thus the kidneys regulate both the *water and electrolyte balance* of the body and the *acid-base status* of the body fluids, and serve to maintain a regular **ionic composition, osmotic concentration and pH**. *The principal task of the kidneys is the differential excretion of substances such that the chemical composition of the blood plasma and the extracellular fluid in general is kept constant.*

The kidneys are also the sites of production of two substances that are released into the blood and act as enzymes. **Renin** participates indirectly in maintaining **arterial blood pressure** and the **volume of the circulating blood** (cf. renin-angiotensin-aldosterone system, p. 634). **Erythropoietin**, the second substance, indirectly stimulates **formation of the red blood cells** (cf. p. 339).

Life without kidneys. The kidneys are vital organs. If both are removed experimentally *(nephrectomy)* or cease to function *(acute kidney failure)* death ensues within one to two weeks. In the absence of renal excretion the extracellular fluid undergoes progressive changes; the concentrations of potentially toxic substances build up **(uremia)**, as do those of sodium, potassium, sulfate and phosphate ions, and the *volume of the extracellular fluid increases*. A progressive *uremic acidosis* develops. Death usually occurs when the blood pH reaches about 7.0. The clearing function of the kidneys can be taken over either by transplanted kidneys or by extracorporeal hemodialysis with an *"artificial kidney"*. The artifical kidney operates on blood flowing through an "extracorporeal circuit" from the radial artery to one of the cubital veins, in which the blood passes through a system of membranes permeable to small dissolved molecules (a dialyzing membrane). By *dialysis* (the exchange of substances through a membrane owing to concentration gradients) between the blood and an isotonic saline solution, the concentrations of the toxic substances and ions in the blood plasma can be normalized – an effective substitute for renal plasma clearance.

The formation of urine. All parts of the nephron participate in the formation of urine. The process begins in

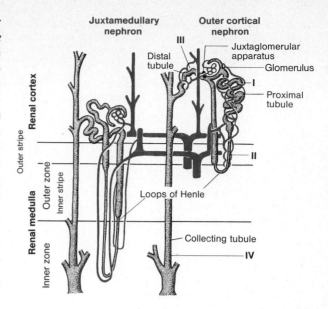

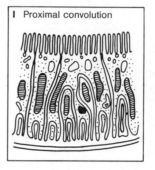

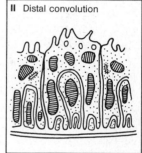

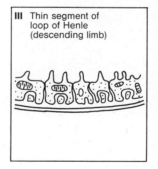

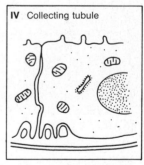

Fig. 27-1. Scheme of cortical and juxtamedullary nephrons with vascular supply. The inserts (below) represent some histological differences among four sections of the nephron (as indicated in the figure on top). Modified from [5, 51]

the glomerulus, where **glomerular filtration** separates the "primary urine" at a high rate from the blood as it flows past. The glomerular filtrate then moves through the tubules and collecting ducts; during this passage its composition can be changed considerably by the *transtubular transport* of water and solutes. Tubular transport occurs in both directions as *tubular reabsorption* or *tubular secretion*.

Table 27-1. Comparison of the renal excretion of certain substances, showing that in principle the rate of excretion ($U \cdot \dot{V}$) depends more on the mode of excretion of the substance than on its concentration in the blood plasma. The concentration of a substance in the urine depends very much on the volume flow rate of the urine. If this is constant (here it is 1 ml/min in all cases) the concentration ratio U/P of a substance is proportional to its clearance

Substance	Concentration in		Urine flow rate $\dot{V}$ ml/min	Rate of excretion $U \cdot \dot{V}$ µmol/min	Concentration ratio U/P	Mode of excretion		
	Plasma (P) mmol/l	Urine (U) mmol/l				Filtration	Reabsorption	Secretion
Na$^+$	142	128	1	128	0.9	+	+	
K$^+$	4.5	54	1	54	12	+	+	+
Cl$^-$	103	134	1	134	1.3	+	+	
Glucose	5	traces	1	0	0	+	+	
Urea	4.5	292	1	292	65	+	+	+
Uric acid	0.27	3.2	1	3.2	12	+	+	+
Creatinine	0.075	12	1	12	160	+		+
Inulin	0.05	6.25	1	6.25	125	+		
p-aminohippuric acid	0.1	65	1	65	650	+		+

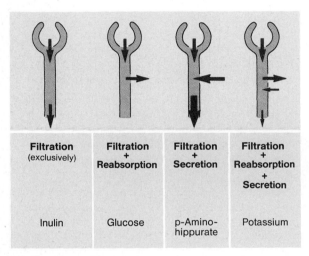

Fig. 27-2. According to the filtration-reabsorption-secretion theory of urine formation, the renal excretion of a substance in the blood plasma is given by the amounts filtered through the glomerulus and secreted in the tubule minus the amount reabsorbed in the tubule. Four modes of handling the excretion are possible: filtration alone (example: inulin), filtration with reabsorption (example of complete reabsorption of the amount filtered: glucose), filtration with secretion (example of massive secretion: p-aminohippuric acid) and all three together (example: potassium ions)

Tubular reabsorption returns the greater part of the filtrate (in particular, water and most of the physiologically required substances) into the blood of the peritubular capillaries (cf. Table 27-4, p. 620). By **tubular secretion** the tubular fluid is enriched with material derived from the peritubular capillary blood (e.g., certain organic acids) or from the tubule cells where they are produced (e.g., hydrogen ions and ammonia).

The *composition of the urine* that finally enters the ureter is thus determined by these three processes –

glomerular filtration, tubular reabsorption and tubular secretion. In general, *the substances in the ureteral urine are those filtered through the glomeruli and secreted by the tubules minus the amounts reabsorbed in the tubules* (Fig. 27-2).

All three processes are involved in the excretion of certain substances, such as potassium ions. A few are excreted entirely by filtration, and many are filtered and subsequently either reabsorbed or secreted in additional amounts. It is understandable, then, that the relative concentrations of substances in urine and plasma differ conspicuously (cf. Table 27-1). Intrarenal handling of a particular substance can be indicated in whole kidneys by the *quantitative clearance procedure* (cf. p. 613).

Driving forces and specificity of urine-formation processes. Various forces underlie the processes of urine formation. **Glomerular filtration,** like all typical filtration, is based on purely **physical forces** (cf. filtration pressure, p. 618). The work involved in this process is performed by the heart. The composition of the glomerular filtrate depends on the physical characteristics of the filter; the transfer of plasma solutes into the filtrate is **not substance-specific.** This is an important feature, for this nonspecific process in principle offers an opportunity for the excretion of all the different filterable solutes in the blood plasma into the urine; because nonphysiological foreign substances such as synthetic drugs are filterable, they can in principle be excreted by the kidneys.

The transport of materials by tubular reabsorption and secretion also depends on general molecular properties such as molecular weight, lipid-solubility and charge. These unspecific properties determine whether or to what extent a substance can pass through biological membranes (cf. p. 655). If any transtubular concentration differences develop as a result of tubular water reabsorption then there exists a driving force for transtubular permeation of the material in question.

Such transport takes place *down the concentration gradient,* and depending on the direction of the gradient, is called *passive tubular reabsorption* or *secretion.* Translocation of this kind is *not substance-specific.*

Substance-specific tubular transport requires the existence of *specific transport systems* (carriers) in the membranes of the tubule cells. In principle such substance-specific transport can be either **passive** or **active.** Passive transport of this kind is based on facilitated diffusion (cf. p. 655); here, again, the direction of transport is always **down the concentration gradient.**

Active transtubular transport is independent of the existence of a concentration gradient; it can take place even **against** the gradient ("uphill transport"). Active transport is always **unidirectional** and highly **substance-specific.** Energy must be specially provided for the purpose, from the **metabolism of the tubule cells.** Today a distinction is made between *primary active transtubular ion transport* (e.g., the reabsorption of sodium or potassium) and *secondary (coupled) active transport* (e.g., the reabsorption of glucose; cf. Fig. 27-15 and p. 622).

Renal Excretion and the Clearance Concept

Systematic study of the renal excretion of a substance in many cases shows that its rate of excretion (amount excreted per unit time) changes in parallel with its concentration in the blood plasma. Comparison of the rates of excretion of different substances nevertheless reveals large differences, which persist even when the results are adjusted to uniform plasma concentrations and identical rates of urine production (cf. Table 27-1). These differences are the result of the different renal handling to which excreted substances can be submitted. For example, it is obvious that the rate of excretion of a substance, both filtered in the glomerulus and secreted in the tubule will be greater than that of a substance reabsorbed in the tubule after its glomerular filtration (cf. Fig. 27-2). Even substances excreted in the same mode can be eliminated at different rates if their tubular transport mechanisms are not potent in the same degree (e.g., simple as compared with facilitated diffusion; cf. pp. 655 and 656). Such differences in renal excretion could not be interpreted until the amounts of substances filtered in the glomeruli and the rates of tubular transport could be measured quantitatively. These measurements became possible with the development of the clearance concept and the filtration-reabsorption-secretion hypothesis.

Definition of the renal clearance of a substance. The renal clearance of a substance S is the ratio of the renal excretion rate of the substance in the urine to its concentration in the blood plasma:

$$C_S = \frac{U_S \cdot \dot{V}}{P_S} \ (\text{ml/min}) \tag{1}$$

(C_S = clearance of S, U_S and P_S = concentrations of S in urine and plasma, respectively; $\dot{V}$ = volume output of urine per minute).

Simple rearrangement of Eq. (1),

$$C_S \cdot P_S = U_S \cdot \dot{V} \,(\text{quantity/time}) \tag{2}$$

shows that the clearance formula is basically a comparison of the amount of a substance removed from the plasma per unit time ($C_S \cdot P_S$) with that excreted in the urine in the same time ($U_S \cdot \dot{V}$). In other words, **renal clearance** is the efficiency with which the **plasma is cleared** of the substance in question; having the unit ml/min, it can be interpreted as a substance-dependent "volume clearing rate." *The clearance of a substance is a measure of the volume of plasma completely freed of the substance per minute by the kidneys.*

It is useful to view the defining equation (1) in this way, but the situation as described, apart from two exceptions, is not actually realized. In general it is not a matter of completely clearing a fraction of the renal plasma flow; rather, the entire flow is partially cleared. In two cases, however, specific volumes of plasma are completely cleared of a substance; these cases are of particular importance with respect to the urine-formation hypothesis, and are the basis of a general test of renal function. They are
1. the *inulin clearance,* which corresponds to the *glomerular filtration rate* – that is, the part of the renal plasma flow separated into the uriniferous tubules (cf. p. 619), and
2. the *p-aminohippuric-acid clearance,* which nearly reaches the theoretical maximum – that is, almost the *entire renal plasma flow* (see below).

Clearance tests of renal function. For clinical evaluation of renal function it is not necessary to measure the clearance of all the many substances the kidneys excrete. In general it suffices to know the **renal plasma flow,** which may be determined from the *p-aminohippuric-acid clearance* (see below), and the **glomerular filtration rate,** which is equivalent to the *inulin clearance.* If both these parameters are distinctly lowered, then likewise the clearances of the substances ordinarily excreted are reduced. Retention of the latter is evident in their increased concentration in the blood plasma. An *increased concentration of nonprotein nitrogen* (i.e., nitrogen-containing substances other than proteins) in the blood plasma is an indication of renal failure (cf. p. 641).

Knowledge of the inulin clearance also permits *determination of the quantity of a substance filtered in the glomeruli* (p. 620, Eq. 11) and of its *tubular transport rate in the kidney as a whole* (p. 621).

Renal clearance and mode of the excretion process. Glomerular filtration and tubular secretion are processes effecting the excretion of substances in the urine, whereas the tubular reabsorption of a filtered or secreted substance reduces the amount excreted. Under the simplified assumption – which may be justified for a number of substances with low molecular weight – that a substance is filtered without restriction and in the tubule is only reabsorbed, only secreted or neither reabsorbed nor secreted, its clearance (C_S) indicates which of these processes are operating (cf. Fig. 27-2 and Table 27-1). By comparison with the inulin clearance one can draw the following conclusions:

1. $C_S < C_{Inulin}$: Excretion is determined by **filtration** and **reabsorption**
2. $C_S = C_{Inulin}$: Excretion by **filtration** alone
3. $C_S > C_{Inulin}$: Excretion by **filtration** and **secretion**.

The validity of these conclusions depends on the appropriateness of the initial assumptions. To test these assumptions, extensive additional study is necessary (e.g., of the molecular weight of the substance and its adsorption to plasma proteins, the dependence of its excretion and tubular transport rates on its plasma concentration, etc.). When dealing with an entirely unknown exogenous substance, inference from the simple clearance comparison is reliable only in case 3 ($C_S > C_{Inulin}$) – the substance must be secreted in the tubule.

27.2   Renal Circulation

Blood Flow through the Kidneys

The overall rate of flow. In the adult (70 kg body weight) the two kidneys are perfused with blood at a rate of ca. **1300 ml/min.** This amount corresponds to about 25% of the *cardiac output* at rest. Given a total kidney weight of 300 g, the specific perfusion rate is over $4 \ ml \cdot min^{-1} \cdot g^{-1}$ – considerably higher than those of other large organs such as the brain, liver and myocardium (cf. Table 21-1, p. 510).

The *high rate of renal perfusion* is not necessary for the metabolism of the organ but primarily to ensure a high rate of *glomerular filtration* (cf. pp. 619, 641). Only a well-perfused kidney with a high filtration rate is functioning as it should. The rate of renal blood flow in man is determined by the clearance procedure.

Determination of renal plasma flow (RPF) and renal blood flow (RBF). In order to use the clearance method for measurement of renal plasma flow or blood flow, a substance must be available that is removed completely from the plasma as the blood passes through the kidney, and transferred to the urine (see

above). The blood plasma in the renal veins must be free of the substance in question; that is, the renal extraction of this substance (E_S) is 1 (cf. Eq. 4).

There is no substance for which renal extraction equals precisely 1. The highest renal extractions are those of **p-aminohippuric acid = PAH** (0.92), **iodine-containing roentgen contrast media** such as *Diodrast* (0.90) and certain **penicillins** (0.92). The clearances of these substances are within 8% of the true RPF. When the clearance of PAH (C_{PAH}) is used as the measure of renal plasma flow it is called the **effective renal plasma flow (ERPF)**:

$$C_{PAH} = ERPF = \frac{U_{PAH} \cdot \dot{V}}{P_{PAH}} \ (ml/min) \qquad (3)$$

Because the renal extraction of PAH is constant at 0.92 under many conditions, C_{PAH} is a reliable criterion of RPF. In case of doubt, or when it is necessary to know the *true RPF* more exactly, a blood sample must be drawn from the renal vein so that the real extraction of PAH (E_{PAH}) can be determined.

The extraction of a substance, in this case PAH, is obtained from its concentrations in the arterial plasma (P_{PAH}) and in the venous plasma leaving the kidney (P_{vPAH}):

$$E_{PAH} = \frac{P_{PAH} - P_{vPAH}}{P_{PAH}} \qquad (4)$$

the true RPF is then

$$RPF = \frac{C_{PAH}}{E_{PAH}} = \frac{U_{PAH} \cdot \dot{V}}{P_{PAH} - P_{vPAH}} \ (ml/min)$$

$$= \frac{amount \ excreted \ per \ unit \ time}{arteriovenous \ concentration \ difference} \qquad (5)$$

Eq. (5) corresponds to **Fick's principle for volume flow** through the lungs (p. 453).

Norms for ERPF = C_{PAH} in man, for an intermediate body surface area (1.73 m²), are 650 ml/min (man) and 600 ml/min (woman).

The **renal blood flow** (RBF) can be computed from the ERPF or RPF and the hematocrit (HCT) of the blood as follows:

$$RBF = \frac{RPF}{1 - HCT} \ (ml/min) \qquad (6)$$

Regional blood flow through the renal cortex and medulla. The intrarenal blood flow is not uniformly distributed between the tissues of cortex and medulla. The **specific perfusion rate** decreases in the sequence cortex-outer medulla-inner medulla, in the approximate proportions 1 : 0.25 : 0.06 (cf. Table 27-2). The reason for the low rate of flow through the inner medulla lies in the long capillary loops (*vasa recta;* Fig. 27-1), which present a high resistance to flow. This resistance is distinctly greater in a kidney producing a small volume of concentrated urine than in one producing large volumes of urine [52], for the following reason. As the blood in the descending limb of a capillary traverses regions of progressively higher interstitial osmotic concentration, water diffuses out and it becomes more viscous; on the other side of this countercurrent diffusion system (cf. p.631) water is taken up by the blood of the ascending capillary limb.

Autoregulation of renal blood flow. Except in extreme situations, blood flow through the kidneys is hardly affected by the general circulation-control processes, mediated chiefly by the sympathetic system. For example, if the mean arterial pressure rises from 100 to 150 mm Hg (13.3 to 20 kPa), renal blood flow usually remains constant. The pressure-flow curves (Fig. 27-3) show that the rate of flow increases linearly with perfusion pressure in the low-pressure range. In the range between 80 and 180 mm Hg, however, there is practically no change; renal blood flow does not begin to rise again until the pressure exceeds 200 mm Hg.

Pressure-flow curves with this *typical "plateau"* have been found under various experimental conditions – in the kidney in situ, the denervated kidney, the isolated perfused kidney and the transplanted kidney. In the isolated, perfused kidney this characteristic is retained (at least for a certain time) even when unphysiological perfusates are used, such as cell-free plasma substitutes and even mineral oil. All these observations indicate that the blood flow in the kidney is regulated by an intrinsic mechanism.

The only plausible interpretation of this constant flow in the pressure range 80–180 mm Hg is that the resistance to flow in the renal resistance vessels can be adjusted appropriately. Because vasomotor nerves are obviously not necessary for this, the effect must be due to a **direct response of the smooth musculature in the renal resistance vessels.** Foremost among these are the **vasa afferentia,** which respond adequately to an elevation in blood pressure with vasoconstriction. This myogenic response to change in the transmural pressure gradients (pressure loading of the vessel wall) is called the *Bayliss effect* (cf. p.404). It permits **autoregulation of the renal circulation** in the pressure range between 80 and 180 mm Hg, in which renal blood flow may be held nearly constant. This is the *myogenic hypothesis* of the autoregulation of renal blood flow.

In vivo measurements have shown that renal blood flow is not as uniform as this autoregulatory capacity suggests [3, 4, 7]. Both neural and hormonal influences not uncommonly decrease the rate of flow (e.g., during exercise, by the release of hormones from the adrenal medulla or angiotensin), and increase is also possible (e.g., by fever-producing substances). Renal-nerve stimulation is known to reduce renal blood flow. Blockage of alpha adrenergic receptors inhibits this response to sympathetic nerve activation as well as to circulating catecholamines.

It is obvious that extrinsic regulation of renal blood flow may overlap the intrinsic autoregulation, though

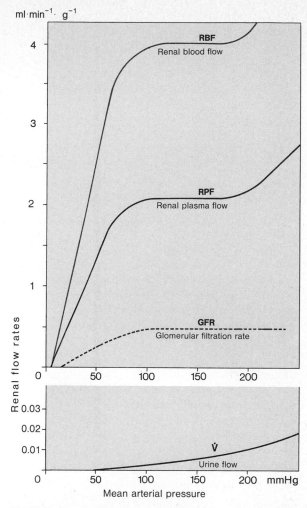

Fig. 27-3. Autoregulation of renal blood flow and glomerular filtration rate. Modified from [46]. Influence of arterial blood pressure on renal blood flow (RBF), renal plasma flow (RPF), glomerular filtration rate (GFR) and volume flow of urine ($\dot{V}$)

Table 27-2. Regional blood flow through the kidney tissue in the dog. From [18]

	Percentage of total kidney weight	Blood flow (ml · min^{-1} · g^{-1})	Percentage of total blood flow
Cortex	70%	4.5	92.5%
Outer zone of medulla	20%	1.1	6.5%
Inner zone of medulla	10%	0.3	1 %

species differences clearly exist. In man renal vascular resistance rises and renal blood flow drops during exercise and emotional stress and especially following hemorrhage.

However, *constancy of glomerular filtration* is certainly of greater functional importance than the main-

$\mu mol \cdot min^{-1} \cdot g^{-1}$

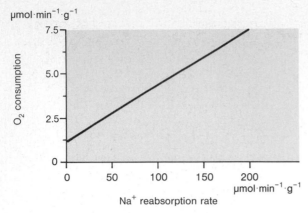

Fig. 27-4. O_2 consumption and Na^+ reabsorption in the kidney. After[19]

tenance of constant renal blood flow by autoregulation. Because the pressure-induced adjustment of resistance actually occurs in the preglomerular vessels, over the autoregulatory range, the pressure in the glomerular capillaries stays constant. This constancy is the basic prerequisite for maintenance of a constant glomerular filtration rate. In effect, then, autoregulation of blood flow is necessary for **autoregulation of the glomerular filtration rate** (Fig. 27-3).
Studies of regional blood flow have shown that when the arterial pressure changes within the autoregulatory range, it is only in the renal cortex that flow remains constant; the rate of flow in the medulla follows the pressure changes. The flow of blood through the medullary tissue is consequently not autoregulated (cf. [18]).

Studies of the overall blood flow of the kidney do not establish that medullary blood flow is pressure-dependent; this is because the medullary blood flow accounts for only 10% of the total renal blood flow (cf. Table 27-2). But the pressure-induced increase in medullary blood flow causes a so-called **pressure diuresis,** because the water-conserving urine-concentrating mechanism in the medulla (p.632) is impaired. Pressure diuresis increases the excretion of Na^+ and water. Thus *hypertensive patients (with intact renal vasculature) excrete more urine, and the ability of their kidneys to concentrate it is reduced.*

Oxygen Consumption and Metabolism of the Kidney

Oxygen consumption. Renal O_2 consumption is quite large in comparison with that of other organs, ca. 55 $\mu l\ O_2 \cdot min^{-1} \cdot g^{-1}$ kidney tissue. The arteriovenous O_2 concentration difference (avD_{O_2}) in the kidney, however, is conspicuously low (1.5 ml/dl as compared with 4–5 ml/dl in the overall circulation). This combination of high consumption and low avD_{O_2} results from the high rate of renal blood flow, which is adjusted not for efficient oxygen extraction

but for filtrate production (see above). The oxygen consumption of the kidney has been shown to decrease when blood flow is slowed by experimental constriction of the renal artery, and to increase when the flow rate exceeds the autoregulatory plateau (owing to paralysis of the vessel musculature by drugs such as *papaverin* [19]). In both cases there is an observable effect on glomerular filtration rate, but this does not indicate direct dependence of glomerular filtration on O_2 consumption; the energy required for the glomerular filtering process is provided by the work of the heart. On the other hand, there is probably a causal relation between the **O_2 consumption** of the kidney and the **Na^+-reabsorption rate** (Fig. 27-4). The correlation with filtration rate arises from the fact that the amount of Na^+ presented to the tubular apparatus for reabsorption **(the "tubular load" or filtered load)** depends on the rate of filtration, and if more Na^+ is filtered its reabsorption rate increases.
Oxygen partial pressures in the renal medulla. The O_2 partial pressure within the renal medulla falls off sharply toward the tip of the papilla. This gradient is not due entirely to the O_2 consumption of the cells in the inner zone of the medulla; it results from the **transport of oxygen** toward the outer zone. This is an effect of the **countercurrent system** in the renal medulla (cf. p.632). From the descending limbs of the capillary loops (and the loops of Henle as well) O_2 diffuses into the ascending limbs and is transported away by convection [33].

Substrates of cellular metabolism. The metabolism of the cells in cortex and medulla differs considerably, in both qualitative and quantitative respects [1,55]. In the **cortex,** with its abundant capillaries and massive blood flow, by far the greater part of the *energy* required for tubular cell function is obtained by oxidative metabolism; the chief substrates are *free fatty acids,* but *lactate, pyruvate,* ketone bodies and *intermediates* in the *citric acid cycle* are also used. The cells of the inner medulla, by contrast, meet their energy requirements primarily by **anaerobic glycolysis.**

The glucose consumption of the renal medulla cannot be determined by the usual balance considerations (RBF · $avD_{glucose}$). The blood flowing away in the renal veins often contains more glucose than that arriving in the arteries. This means that **gluconeogenesis** occurs in the kidney (cortex), from glucoplastic amino acids such as glutamate and aspartate, as well as from lactate and intermediates of the citric acid cycle. Gluconeogenesis probably serves to supply the medullary tissue, and also provides a way to dispose of the lactate derived from glycolysis and the α-ketoglutarate from the synthesis of ammonia.

27.3   The Glomerular Filtration Process

Morphological and Biophysical Fundamentals

Anatomy of the glomerular filter. The glomerular filter comprises 20–40 capillary loops, ensheathed by the inner layer of Bowman's capsule (Fig. 27-5 A). The **glomerular membrane** consists of three layers: the **endothelial layer** of the capillaries, the **basement membrane** and the **inner layer of Bowman's capsule.** Electron micrographs reveal that the capillary endothelium is of the fenestrated type, the interfaced ectoplasmatic basement membrane is very dense (lamina densa) and the specialized epithelial cells of the inner capsule layer (podocytes) cover the basement membrane with interdigitating processes separated by broad slits (slit membrane).

This microstructure indicates that only the middle layer, the basement membrane, can determine the permeability of the glomerular membrane. The basement membrane is a reticular structure formed of fine, (probably) collagenous filaments. The distance between the filaments is ca. 3 to 7.5 nm; these spaces in the network could represent the pores of the filter.

Permeability of the glomerular membrane. Knowing the molecular weights of the various substances that are excreted, one can make certain inferences as to the filter properties of the glomerular membrane and the size of its pores. Free or **unrestricted filterability** is characteristic only of *small molecules,* up to about the size of the inulin molecule (m. w. 5500). These substances are present in the filtrate in the same concentrations as in the blood plasma. As molecular weight increases, passage of the dissolved particles through the pores is progressively impeded (Table 27-3); a kind of **molecular sieving** occurs [40]. The filterability of hemoglobin molecules (m. w. 64,500) is only 3%, and that of the plasma albumins (m. w. 69,000) is far below 1%. The *absolute limit* for the passage of particles through the pores is probably a molecular weight of ca. 80,000. Larger proteins (plasma globulins) cannot permeate the glomerular membrane by filtration. Glomerular filtration is thus an **ultrafiltration,** producing a filtrate nearly free of colloidal macromolecules. Calculations based on these findings indicate that the mean pore radius of the glomerular filter is 3.5–4 nm. This result is in good agreement with the fine structure of the basement membrane, as revealed in electron micrographs.

The permeability of the glomerular membrane to various molecules is not only of theoretical interest. It is of clinical importance to use blood plasma substitutes with colloid-osmotically effective constituents.

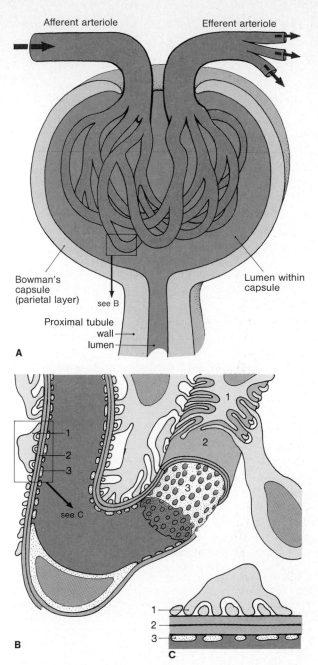

Fig. 27-5 A, B. Scheme of a glomerulus and the glomerular filter membrane. Modified from [2, 42] **A** The vas afferens (= afferent arteriole) gives rise to a tuft of capillaries by ramification. The 20 to 40 capillaries rejoin into the vas efferens (= efferent arteriole). The capillaries are totally covered by the inner layer of the Bowman's capsule. **B** The glomerular filter has three layers (from inside to outside): the capillary endothelium (lamina fenestrae) (3), the basement membrane (lamina densa) (2) and the slit membrane (epithelial podocytes) (1)

Such solutions remain much longer in the bloodstream than a common saline solution. However, the macromolecules have to be eliminated eventually – preferably by way of the kidneys. Thus if the organ-

Table 27-3. The glomerular filterability of molecules with different dimensions. After [4]

Substance	Molecular weight	Molecular dimensions		Filterability* Concentration ratio filtrate/plasma
		Radius found from the diffusion coefficients (nm)	Diameter found from X-ray diffraction (nm)	
Water	18	0.10		1.0
Urea	60	0.16		1.0
Glucose	180	0.36		1.0
Sucrose	342	0.44		1.0
Inulin	5,500	1.48		0.98
Myoglobin	16,000	1.95	5,4 / 0,8	0.75
Egg albumin	43,500	2.85	8,8 / 2,2	0.22
Hemoglobin	64,500	3.25	5,4 / 3,2	0.03
Serum albumin	69,000	3.55	15,0 / 3,6	< 0.01

*"Filterability" used here is otherwise called "permeability"

ism cannot break such substances down into smaller molecules, their molecular weight should not be much above 70,000.

Effective filtration pressure and filtration coefficient.
Whereas the composition of the filtrate is determined by the size of the pores in the glomerular membrane, the rate of filtration depends on the *effective filtration pressure* and the *filtration coefficient*.
The **effective filtration pressure** is the *net "driving force"* for the filtration process. It is the difference in hydrostatic pressure between the capillary lumen and the lumen of Bowman's capsule ($P_{Cap} - P_{Bow}$), minus the mean colloid osmotic pressure of the capillary blood ($P_{C.O.}$):

$$FP_{eff} = P_{Cap} - P_{Bow} - P_{C.O.} \qquad (7)$$

The concept of effective filtration pressure is based on Starling's model of fluid exchange between blood capillaries and the surrounding tissue (pp. 419 f.). Here the glomerular capillary as a whole can be compared with the arterial end of an ordinary capillary, where a low-protein-containing fluid is filtered out of the blood plasma into the interstitial space. (Eq. 22 on p. 419 contains a term representing the oncotic pressure of the interstitial fluid; because the glomerular filtrate contains so little protein, its oncotic pressure is neglected in the above Eq. 7, a simplification not allowed in the case of defective glomerular membrane.)

The second quantity required to find the glomerular filtration rate (GFR) is the **filtration coefficient** (K_f) of the glomerular membrane:

$$GFR = FP_{eff} \cdot K_f \, (volume/time) \qquad (8)$$

The filtration coefficient corresponds to the *conductance of the entire glomerular membrane to the flow of water* (hydraulic conductance). It depends principally on the geometry and density of the pores and the overall area of the membrane.

Unfortunately, the simple relation given by Eq. (8) is of limited value, because the terms on the right can only be estimated roughly for the human kidney, or at best calculated from indirect measurements. At present **two filtration models** are under discussion. Both are based on the premises that (i) resistance to flow is low in the set of parallel capillaries within a glomerulus, so that blood pressure is nearly uniform over the entire length of the capillary (cf. Fig. 27-6), and (ii) filtration is continuous and uniform, so that the pressure in the lumen of Bowman's capsule is constant in time. The essential difference between the two models is that in the older, simpler one the filtration process occurs uniformly at all points on the glomerular membrane; the formation of filtrate from a unit volume of blood ceases only when this blood leaves the glomerular capillary. In this view the glomerular capillary corresponds to a relatively short segment of the arterial end of a capillary in Starling's model. In this case the effective filtration pressure in the human kidney would be ca. 20–30 mm Hg, taking the capillary pressure as ca. 65 mm Hg and that in Bowman's capsule as ca. 15 mm Hg, and the arithmetic mean of the oncotic pressure in the capillary blood as ca. 26 mm Hg.
According to the second, more recent model of the filtration process, the hydraulic conductance of the glomerular membrane is several times greater [12, 17]. The result would be that filtrate is formed more rapidly from a unit volume of blood and the oncotic pressure would rise more sharply (Fig. 27-7 A), equalling the hydrostatic pressure difference ($P_{Cap} - P_{Bow}$) = ΔP while the blood volume in question is still in the glomerular capillary. Therefore no filtration would occur in the last part of the capillary, for *"filtration equilibrium"* would prevail ($FP_{eff} = 0$). A linear increase in oncotic pressure is inconsistent with this model, because the use of the arithmetic mean would give too low a hydraulic permeability. This so-called dynamic model is

based chiefly on the results of experiments on the superficially located glomeruli of mutant rats. Whereas the dynamic model is preferable for certain small animals, the older model is likely to be more applicable to the dog – and probably the human – kidney, for which the long prevailing assumption that filtration equilibration is *not* reached is clearly still valid [5].

The two filtration models differ distinctly with respect to the relation between filtration rate and glomerular plasma flow (for the single nephron abbreviated SNGFR and SNPF; cf. Fig. 27-7). As plasma flow increases, the filtration rate rises linearly as long as filtration equilibrium has not been reached (because filtration always ends when the same concentration of plasma protein has been reached; i.e., the same amount of water is always removed from the blood plasma). The filtration fraction SNFF therefore remains constant. If filtration equilibrium is not reached, the filtration rate increases less with plasma flow; that is, the filtration fraction decreases. These considerations apply only if the other parameters that affect filtration are constant.

Glomerular Filtration Rate and Glomerular Filtrate

Glomerular filtration rate and filtration fraction. The glomerular filtration rate is the volume of filtrate formed by the kidneys per unit time. In the *man* it is ca. **125 ml/min** and in the *woman* **110 ml/min** (assuming 1.73 m² body surface area in each case) [5]. This amounts to about **180 l/d**. Thus the total plasma volume, ca. 3 liters, is filtered in 25 min, so that it is cleared 60 times a day by the kidneys. By the same token, the entire extracellular fluid (14 l) undergoes renal control about 12 times daily.

The glomerular filtration rate (GFR) remains quite constant despite pressure changes in the arterial system **(autoregulation of GFR).** This constancy is provided by the *myogenic response of the smooth musculature* of the afferent vessels, which also mediates the *autoregulation of renal blood flow* and is thus responsible for the *constancy of the glomerular capillary pressure* and of the *effective filtration pressure* (see above). Because a single mechanism is responsible for the constancy of both renal plasma flow and glomerular filtration rate, **constancy of the filtration fraction (FF)** must result. The filtration fraction, the fraction of the renal plasma flow that becomes filtrate (FF = GFR/ RPF), is nearly 0.2 in man; that is, about a fifth of the plasma flowing through the kidneys passes through the filter.

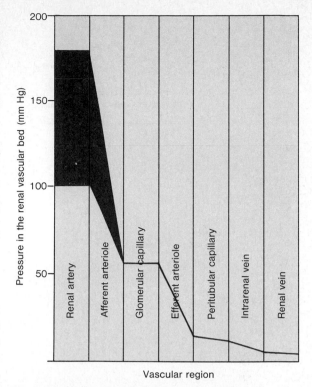

Fig. 27-6. The drop of blood pressure from renal artery to renal vein [54]. Despite variations in the mean systemic arterial pressure (ranging from 100 to 180 mm Hg) the glomerular capillary pressure remains constant due to an intrinsic adjustment of the diameters of the vasa afferentia. This myogenic response is the basic mechanism common to the autoregulation both of renal blood flow and of glomerular filtration rate

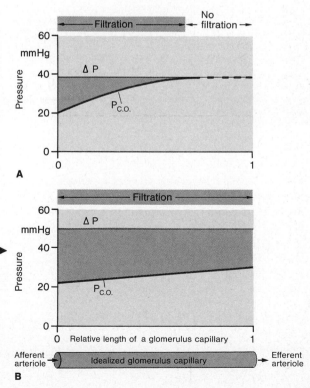

Fig. 27-7 A, B. The two models of filtration in an idealized glomerular capillary. **A** The colloid osmotic pressure of the blood ($P_{C.O.}$) rises rapidly along the capillary, so that filtration-pressure equilibrium is reached. Beyond this point $P_{Cap}-P_{Bow} = \Delta P = P_{C.O.}$ or $\Delta P-P_{C.O.} = 0$; that is, here filtration no longer occurs. **B** $P_{C.O.}$ rises less rapidly along the capillary than in **A**, and the rise is approximately linear. The filtration pressures are unequal along the entire capillary ($\Delta P-P_{C.O.} > 0$), so that filtration occurs throughout its length. Model **B** fulfills the conditions of Eq. (7). For further discussion see text

Table 27-4. Calculations of the filtered and reabsorbed quantities of some substances in the kidneys

	Concentrations in				Urine flow rate ($\dot V$)	Renal clearance[b] ($C = \dfrac{U \cdot \dot V}{P}$)	Amount filtered[c] ($F \cdot$ GFR)	Amount excreted ($U \cdot \dot V$)	Fraction reabsorbed[d] $\dfrac{(F \cdot \text{GFR} - U \cdot \dot V) \cdot 100}{F \cdot \text{GFR}}$
	Blood plasma (P)	Plasma water[a] (W)	Glomerular filtrate (F)	Ureteral urine (U)					
	mmol/l	mmol/l	mmol/l	mmol/l	ml/min	ml/min	mmol/min	mmol/min	%
Na^+	142	150.5	143[e]	140	1	1	17.875	0.14	99.2
K^+	5	5.3	5[e]	60	1	12	0.625	0.06	90.4
Cl^-	103	109	115[e]	150	1	1.5	14.375	0.15	98.9
HCO_3^-	25	26.5	28[e]	1.4	1	0.05	3.5	0.0014	99.96
	mg/l	mg/l	mg/l	mg/l	ml/min	ml/min	mg/min	mg/min	%
Urea	250	265	265	17,000	1	68	33.125	17	48.7
Glucose	900	954	954	traces	1	0	119.25	—	100
Proteins	70,000	74,000	ca. 70	traces	1	0	8.75	— ·	100

[a] Plasma proteins in solution take up a volume of ca. 0.75 ml per gram. Thus 1 l of plasma in which 70 g protein is dissolved contains 0.9425 l plasma water. The correction factor for the concentration of substances dissolved in the water is then 1.06.

[b] cf. p. 613, Eq. (1).

[c] The calculations are based on a glomerular filtration rate GFR of 125 ml/min.

[d] cf. p. 621, Eq. (12).

[e] The concentration difference between W and F results from the Donnan distribution (pp. 653 f.).

In some respects, however, the GFR can vary despite autoregulation (cf. [1, 3]). For example, it exhibits a *day-night rhythm* (ca. 25% smaller at night) uncorrelated with changes in blood pressure. Under certain conditions (e.g., during psychological excitation or after intravenous injection of small doses of adrenalin, noradrenalin or angiotensin) the RPF decreases with no change in GFR, causing an increase in filtration fraction. This result cannot be explained by vasomotion of the afferent arterioles alone; *constriction of the efferent arterioles* must also have occurred. A resistance increase in the vasa efferentia raises the pressure in the glomerular capillaries and thus the effective filtration pressure. In this way the entire resistance of the kidney can be increased, which decreases blood flow (and hence RPF). However, the effective filtration pressure and the glomerular filtration rate can stay constant in this situation. With larger doses of these vasoconstrictor agents, the resistance increase in the vasa afferentia predominates, and RPF and GFR decrease in about the same proportions.

Determination of glomerular filtration rate by inulin clearance. It is impossible to measure GFR directly. But it can be found from the clearance of a substance that reaches the urine **exclusively by glomerular filtration** and is **not reabsorbed, secreted or metabolized in the tubules.** The substance must also meet the following requirements: it must be *filtered without restriction* and must *not be adsorbed to proteins.* These additional properties are necessary in order that the concentration of the test substance in the filtrate be equal to its concentration in the plasma.

All these conditions are best fulfilled by the fructose polysaccharide **inulin** [5]. Thus it holds that the amount filtered per unit time is equal to that excreted in the urine (cf. Eq. 2, p. 613):

$$C_{\text{inulin}} = \text{GFR} = \frac{U_{\text{inulin}} \cdot \dot V}{P_{\text{inulin}}} \; (\text{ml} \cdot \text{min}^{-1}) \qquad (9)$$

C_{inulin} = clearance of inulin, (U = concentration in urine, P = concentration in plasma, $\dot V$ = volume of urine per minute)

If the inulin and PAH clearances (p. 614) are known, the filtration fraction (FF) can be calculated:

$$\text{FF} = \frac{C_{\text{inulin}}}{C_{\text{PAH}}} \qquad (10)$$

Composition of the filtrate. The composition of the filtrate depends primarily on the permeability of the glomerular membrane; the filtrate contains the dissolved components of the blood plasma to the extent that they are filterable (cf. Table 27-3). To a first approximation, therefore, the concentrations of small molecules in plasma and filtrate are the same [59]. The plasma albumins, by contrast, are present in the filtrate only in trace concentrations (between 10 and $100 \text{ mg} \cdot \text{l}^{-1}$).

Measurement of the amounts of solutes filtered. The clearance of inulin can be used to calculate the filtered amounts of other substances that pass the filter without restriction. One need only know, in addition, the concentration of the substance in the blood plasma (P_S):

$$\dot Q_S = C_{\text{inulin}} \cdot P_S \, (\text{quantity/time}) \qquad (11)$$

The quantity of substance filtered per unit time $\dot Q_S$ is also called the *tubular load.*

In order to describe the filtrate composition more exactly, one must keep in mind the following. Unrestrictedly filterable substances that can be *adsorbed to plasma proteins* are present in the filtrate in a concentration corresponding to the amount *freely diffusible* in the **"plasma water."**

Many organic substances are so adsorbed, as are complex-forming inorganic ions such as Ca^{++} or Mg^{++}. In the case of permeant ions, a further correction is required by the presence of impermeant anions (proteinate) in the blood plasma. That is, as a consequence of the *Donnan equilibrium* (Chapter 28, p. 653) the concentrations of the univalent anions in the filtrate are ca. 5% higher than in the plasma water, and those of univalent cations are 5% lower (cf. Table 27-4).

27.4   Tubular Transport Processes

The transport of substances in the tubules, which converts the glomerular filtrate into urine, can be considered and described in terms of the whole kidney or the nephron. To determine the tubular transport rates of the whole kidney one uses the clearance procedure (p. 613).

This procedure is of course not sufficiently refined to give reliable information as to the participation of the individual segments of a nephron. For a more detailed description of tubular transport it is necessary to analyze the original tubular fluid, obtained by micropuncture of specific sections of a single nephron.

It is becoming increasingly apparent that the nephrons in a kidney are *not* a uniform population. The anatomical distinction between cortical and juxtamedullary nephrons was noted above; in the human kidney only the latter have long loops of Henle extending into the inner zone of the medulla (Fig. 27-1), which are the determining factor in concentrating the urine. These two types of nephrons also appear to differ in the process of filtration and in tubular ion permeability and transport. Even within a segment of a nephron, however, transport rates have been found to differ. The reabsorption power for sodium ions and glucose decreases along the proximal tubule, whereas the secretion of organic acids of the type of p-aminohippuric acid (PAH) increases. Local differences in the transport of substances have also been found in other parts of the nephron. But the problem of *heterogeneity of nephrons and nephron segments* is beyond the scope of the present discussion [34].

Fig. 27-8 illustrates, in simplified form, the most important transport processes in the various parts of a nephron. Most of the active reabsorption and secretion occurs in the proximal tubule. The subsequent parts of the nephron then make the fine adjustments of strong electrolytes, water and hydrogen ions necessary to insure homeostasis.

Tubular Reabsorption and Secretion of Organic Substances

Filtered substances are more or less preserved from excretion by tubular reabsorption, or excreted in greater amounts by tubular secretion. These tubular

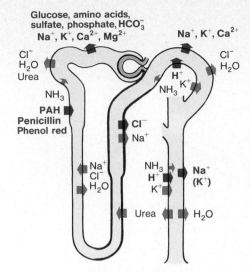

▶ Active tubular reabsorption or secretion

▷ Passive tubular reabsorption or secretion

Fig. 27-8. Sites of the most important transport processes in the nephron

transport processes can be either active or passive; the two categories will be discussed separately here.

Determination of tubular transport rates for the kidney as a whole. The tubular transport rate of a substance is the amount transported through the wall of the tubular apparatus per unit time. It can be computed from the difference between the rates of filtration and excretion of the substance. For a substance S that is filtered and reabsorbed, the transport rate of the reabsorbed fraction Tr_s is

$$Tr_s = GFR \cdot P_S - U_S \cdot \dot{V} \quad (mg \cdot min^{-1} \text{ or } mmol \cdot min^{-1}) \qquad (12)$$

(GFR = glomerular filtration rate, P_S and U_S = concentration of substance in plasma and urine, respectively, $\dot{V}$ = volume of urine per minute)

The transport rate of the secreted fraction T_s of a substance S is found similarly:

$$Ts_s = U_S \cdot \dot{V} - GFR \cdot P_S \quad (mg \cdot min^{-1} \text{ or } mmol \cdot min^{-1}) \qquad (13)$$

The inulin clearance is used for the term GFR. The product $GFR \cdot P_S$ is the rate of filtration of the substance if it is filtered without restriction and not adsorbed to plasma proteins. If these conditions are not fulfilled the appropriate corrections must be made.

Equations (12) and (13) give the actual rates of reabsorption and secretion only if the substance in question is either only reabsorbed or only secreted, once it has been filtered. But if it is transported through the tubule wall in both directions – as certain substances are – comparison of the rates of filtration and excretion gives the net transport in the predominant direction (the difference between the two transport rates).

Determination of the **"tubular transport maxima"** of glucose or phosphate, for example (see below), is based on the same principle. The rate of tubular transport of such a substance reaches a maximum as the amount available is increased (e. g., by raising its concentration in the blood; cf. Figs. 27-9 and 27-10).

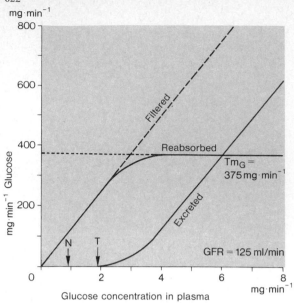

mg · min⁻¹

Fig. 27-9. Reabsorption and excretion of glucose, as a function of its concentration in the plasma [4]. Glucose excretion begins at a threshold concentration T. The rate of glucose reabsorption is limited by a tubular transport maximum (Tm_G). The amounts of filtered glucose in excess of Tm_G are excreted in the urine. Thus the kidneys contribute to adjustment of the glucose concentration in the plasma only at unphysiologically high levels (in diabetes mellitus) and not when the blood glucose level is normal (N)

First we shall consider the **active processes of reabsorption and secretion.**

Reabsorption of glucose. Normally the urine is free of all but slight traces of glucose, although glucose is filtered through the glomerulus without restriction. *Therefore glucose must be completely reabsorbed in the tubule.* It appears in the urine **(glucosuria)** only when the *threshold concentration* of ca. 1.8 g per liter plasma (= 10 mmol/l) is exceeded. At higher concentrations (> 3.5 g · l^{-1}) there is a linear relation between the plasma concentration of glucose and its rate of excretion in the urine (Fig. 27-9). The excretion curve reflects the existence of a **maximal transport rate** (Tm_G) for glucose, which the transport system cannot exceed despite increased concentrations of glucose in the filtrate. In the man the tubular transport maximum averages 375 mg/min, and in the woman 300 mg/min.

If the "tubular load" of glucose is increased not by raising the plasma concentration with a constant GFR, but rather by increase in the GFR with a constant plasma concentration, the maximal transport rate is higher [18]. Under this condition the *glomerulotubular balance* (p. 628) causes enhanced Na⁺ reabsorption in the proximal tubule. A plausible explanation of this finding is that glucose transport is boosted because it is coupled with the Na⁺ transport (cf. Fig. 27-15, p. 627). The active glucose reabsorption is a case of *secondary active transport* (p. 656).

Localization of glucose transport. Glucose is reabsorbed primarily in the *first part of the proximal convolution.* By the end of the first half of the convolution 98% of the filtered amount of glucose has been reabsorbed [18]. The straight part of the proximal tubule is capable of considerably less reabsorption than the convoluted part. The distal parts of the nephron can probably not reabsorb glucose at all.

The coupling of the glucose transport with that of sodium occurs at the luminal cell membranes of the proximal tubule as a coupled cotransport comparable to that of amino acids (Fig. 27-15, p. 627; cf. [56]).

Glucosuria in diabetics. Glucosuria is one of the characteristic symptoms of *diabetes mellitus.* It results from the high concentration of glucose in the plasma of such patients *(hyperglycemia),* which exceeds the renal threshold. In uncomplicated diabetes mellitus the renal threshold and Tm_G are in the normal range, so that the glucosuria is not ascribable to abnormal kidney function. Three other characteristic symptoms are combined with the glucosuria: intense *sensation of thirst,* augmented drinking *(polydipsia)* and increased urine excretion *(polyuria).* The primary effect is the polyuria owing to osmotic diuresis (cf. p. 629); this secondarily results in the sensation of thirst, which motivates increased drinking.

A less common form of glucosuria, resulting from a *genetic defect,* is found in the so-called *diabetes mellitus renalis.* Here the glucose transport system in the proximal tubule is disturbed; the concentration of glucose in the plasma is normal. Renal diabetes can be induced experimentally by *phlorhizin,* an agent derived from the roots of apple trees which inhibits active glucose transport in the kidney. The molecular mechanism of this action is not yet known.

Reabsorption of amino acids. In principle the renal handling of amino acids is similar to that of glucose. Amino acids are filtered without restriction, and the filtered load is reabsorbed nearly completely, so that the urine contains only traces. The renal plasma threshold for their excretion is so high that the kidneys are not involved in regulating their plasma concentrations. The reabsorption of amino acids in the proximal tubule, like that of glucose, is based on cotransport with Na⁺ (cf. [45]). There are different transport systems for the various groups of amino acids, as revealed by the competitive inhibition observable when several amino acids are present simultaneously [4]. A transport system is recognized for each of the following amino-acid categories: basic (arginine, lysine, ornithine), acidic (glutamic acid, asparagine), neutral (glycine, proline and hydroxyproline), and the remainder. However, in some cases the various groups overlap and competitive inhibition is detectable.

Aminoacidurias can result from defects in the transport systems. The most common genetically based disorder of this kind is *cystinuria.* Two different forms are observed. One is rare and occurs in isolation; the classical form is associated with the increased excretion of basic amino acids. Because of the low solubility of cystine, the affected individual begins to develop kidney stones at an early age.

A severe syndrome of multiple proximal tubular transport defects is the *Fanconi syndrome,* with aminoaciduria, glucosuria, phosphaturia, and disturbances of hydrogen-ion and urate excretion.

Reabsorption of proteins (proteinuria). The glomerular membrane allows a small fraction of the plasma albumins to pass into the filtrate (p. 617). The amounts involved are normally in the range 10–100 mg per liter filtrate. Ureteral urine, however, is practically protein-free. The mechanism of protein reabsorption differs from that for smaller molecules. Following intravenous injection of proteins – *albumin* or *hemoglobin* – histological preparation reveals them in the *cells of the proximal tubule,* which have taken them up by **pinocytosis.** After **lysosomal breakdown** the traces of these proteins disappear from the cells [38].

It has been estimated that at most ca. 30 mg protein per min can be reabsorbed in this way. If greater amounts of filtered protein are produced owing to *glomerular defects,* **proteinuria** results.

Active secretion of organic acids and bases. At present we know of three transport systems, located in the proximal tubule, that actively secrete substances (predominantly of foreign origin). One secretes chiefly *organic acids* (**p-aminohippuric acid, iodated roentgen contrast media** such as Diodrast, **penicillin, phenol red** etc.), the second secretes the stronger organic bases (tetraethylammonium, N'-methylnicotinamide etc.), and the third secretes ethylenediaminotetraacetic acid (EDTA).

The three systems operate independently; competitive inhibition occurs only between substances handled by the same system. Because the excretion curves for substances in all three systems differ only quantitatively, it suffices to discuss that for PAH secretion.

PAH transport exhibits a well-defined *tubular transport maximum* (Tm_{PAH}), as shown in Fig. 27-10. When the plasma concentration of PAH is low it is secreted at nearly the theoretically maximal rate; its *renal extraction* is 92%, and its clearance corresponds to the *effective renal plasma flow* (p. 614).

Substances with such a high renal extraction are present in the collecting-tubule urine at concentrations 500–1000 times that in the plasma. It is thus unlikely that such substances are reabsorbed distally. These substances with high extraction are polar and hardly soluble in lipids (p. 655).

Let us now turn to the **passive processes of reabsorption and secretion.**

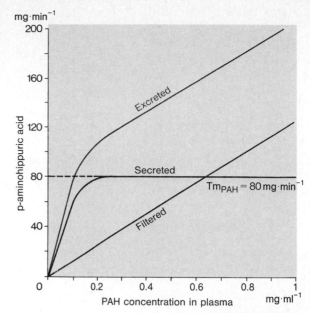

Fig. 27-10. Secretion and excretion of p-aminohippuric acid (PAH) as a function of its concentration in the plasma water [4]. The rate of excretion of PAH is the sum of the filtered and secreted components. The rate of PAH secretion is limited by a tubular transport maximum (Tm_{PAH})

Reabsorption of urea. Urea is a nonpolar substance of very low molecular weight, which therefore crosses cell membranes relatively well. It is filtered through the glomerulus without restriction and concentrated in the proximal tubule due to the reabsorption of water. The transtubular concentration gradient so produced causes diffusion of urea into the blood. The reabsorption of urea thus occurs by *passive transport.*

Urea does not diffuse rapidly enough that its concentration in the flowing tubular fluid comes to equilibrium with that in the plasma. The higher the velocity of intratubular urine flow, the less time is available for diffusion. Thus the rate of reabsorption is reduced, and correspondingly more of the filtered amount of urea is excreted; that is, the **urea clearance is diuresis-dependent** (Fig. 27-11). In the normal state of antidiuresis the clearance of urea is about 50% of the inulin clearance. There is a distinct increase if the urine flow rate is enhanced.

Urea is most concentrated in the collecting-tubule urine. Some of it diffuses into the interstitial spaces of the renal medulla, keeping the concentration there higher than in the fluid in the loop of Henle. Therefore urea diffuses into the loop urine and again is carried through the distal convolution to the collecting tubule *(intrarenal recycling of urea)* [57]. In this case, diffusion in a countercurrent system tends to retain the substance in the system (cf. p. 632).

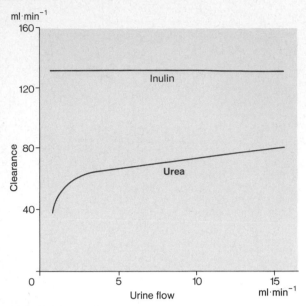

Fig. 27-11. Dependence of urea clearance on diuresis, as compared with the diuresis-independent clearance of inulin. After [14]

Reabsorption and secretion of weak organic acids and bases. A considerable number of weak organic acids and bases excreted by the kidneys can fluctuate widely in rate of excretion or clearance [4, 59]. Some of them have been found in the urine in such high concentrations, under certain circumstances, that active secretion might be inferred. But we now know that the transtubular transport of such substances is brought about by *non-ionic diffusion* and the nonuniform excretion may be caused by variations in urine pH.

Non-ionic diffusion is a special kind of passive mechanism for the tubular transport of a number of weak organic acids and bases. Characteristically, the compounds in question show a relatively high **lipid-solubility** in the undissociated state. In this non-ionized state such molecules can penetrate the lipid phase of the tubule-cell membranes. The tubule cells, however, are less permeable to these substances in the dissociated form. For this reason the ionic form of a weak acid or base may be fixed in the tubular fluid and thus favored for excretion. Nevertheless, transport by *"non-ionic" diffusion requires a transtubular concentration gradient of the undissociated molecules.* Such a concentration gradient typically arises by the *tubular reabsorption of fluid,* because the filtered (and secreted) substances in the remaining tubular fluid are of course more concentrated. The direction of this concentration gradient is therefore such as to promote *reabsorption.*

A transtubular concentration gradient of the neutral molecules can also be produced by a *change in the pH*

of the tubular urine, which alters the *degree of dissociation of the* weak acids and bases. At a relatively low urine pH a weak acid is mainly undissociated, whereas a base is more dissociated. *Accordingly, in acid urine the rate of reabsorption of weak acids is increased and their rate of excretion reduced, whereas the rate of reabsorption of weak bases is reduced and their rate of excretion increased; in alkaline urine the opposite situation prevails.*

The mechanism of non-ionic diffusion can be employed therapeutically in some cases of poisoning with certain drugs, by adjusting the urine pH so as to accelerate the renal excretion of the toxicant. Poisoning by phenobarbital or acetylsalicylic-acid is treated by alkalization (infusion of $NaHCO_3^-$ solution); if anuria has already been incurred by circulatory failure, a sufficient diuresis must be restored, if necessary by inducing osmotic diuresis (cf. p. 629). In case of poisoning by amphetamine, used for doping perhaps, the excretion of the basic drug is accelerated by acidifying the urine (infusion of an arginine-hydrochloride solution).

Tubular Reabsorption of Water and Electrolytes

Site of tubular water reabsorption. Since it has become possible to measure the rate of glomerular filtration by inulin clearance, the urine flow rate (diuresis) has been found to be only a small fraction of the GFR. When barely adequate amounts of water are ingested antidiuresis is normally in operation (cf. p. 629), so that 1% or less of the amount filtered is excreted in a given time. Thus 99% or more of the filtered water is reabsorbed in the tubule. On the other hand, excessive water intake results in water diuresis, in which urine is excreted at about 15% of the filtration rate. In this case the rate of tubular water reabsorption is ca. 85% of the glomerular filtration rate.

A measure of the relative water-reabsorption rate of the whole kidney is given by the ratio of the inulin concentrations in urine and blood plasma, $(U/P)_{inulin}$. According to Eq. (9),

$$\frac{GFR}{\dot{V}} = \frac{U_{inulin}}{P_{inulin}} = (U/P)_{inulin} \gg 1 \qquad (14)$$

Because the quantity of inulin excreted in the urine is identical with that in the glomerular filtrate (reabsorption and secretion of inulin can be ruled out), its high concentration in the urine can result only from a reduction in volume of the filtrate by tubular water reabsorption. For a given plasma concentration of inulin and a constant GFR, the inulin concentration is inversely proportional to the rate of urine flow:

$$\frac{\dot{V}}{GFR} = \frac{1}{(U/P)_{inulin}} \qquad (15)$$

$1/(U/P)_{inulin}$ thus gives the *relative rate of urine excretion* (i. e., the rate of water excretion as a fraction of the filtration rate); accordingly, $1 - 1/(U/P)_{inulin}$ gives the tubular *reabsorption rate of water* as a fraction of the filtration rate.

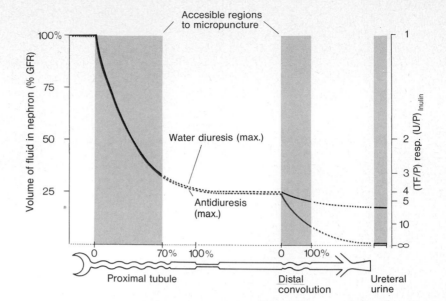

Fig. 27-12. Schematic illustration of intratubular urine flow, in terms of the relative volume of fluid at different points along the tubule; calculated from the measured values of (TF/P)$_{inulin}$ or (U/P)$_{inulin}$ in the rat kidney. Modified from [18]. The shaded regions correspond to the tubular segments accessible to micropuncture in situ because they lie directly below the renal capsule

A (U/P)$_{inulin}$ = 10 signifies that the volume of water excreted is 1/10 the filtered volume, 9/10 being reabsorbed. If the rate of urine excretion is 1 ml/min and the glomerular filtration rate is 125 ml/min, the inulin is 125 times as concentrated in the urine as in the plasma; the fraction of water excreted is thus 0.008 or 0.8% of the filtration rate, and the reabsorbed fraction is 0.992 or 99.2%.

By an analogous calculation, the ratio of the inulin concentrations in tubule fluid and plasma can be used to find the amount of filtered water still present in a particular part of the single nephron. This is done by micropuncture of the part in question; a microsample of the tubule fluid flowing freely past this site is withdrawn and its inulin concentration (TF_{inulin}) is determined. Then 1/(TF/P)$_{inulin}$ is the fraction of the filtrate still present at that site, and 1–1/(TF/P)$_{inulin}$ is the fraction reabsorbed by that point. The results of such experiments on the exposed rat kidney are shown in Fig. 27-12. Accurate micropuncture from the kidney surface is limited to the first two-thirds of the proximal tubule and to the distal convolution, because the deeper parts of the nephron are obscured. In each case (U/P)$_{inulin}$ was determined by analysis of the ureter urine.

The tubular **transit time of lissamine green,** a vital stain filterable through the glomerulus, provides information about the timing of the stages of urine formation [50]. After the rapid injection of the dye into the aorta of the rat, it first appears in the peritubular capillaries and only after ca. 2.5 s becomes detectable in the lumen of the first visible proximal tubule loop. The transit times in the proximal tubule average 8.3 s, whereas those for the very much shorter distal convolution average 40 s. Depending on the degree of diuresis, 1–3 min or more are likely to elapse from filtration to the arrival of the ureteral urine in the calyx of the kidney. These figures are also approximately valid for the dog kidney.

Fig. 27-12 illustrates the *location and extent* of **water reabsorption** along the nephron. In the proximal convolution of the rat (TF/P)$_{inulin}$ rises from 1 to 3; that is, 2/3 of the filtrate is reabsorbed here. *It is irrelevant whether a state of antidiuresis or pronounced water diuresis prevails; in either case the proximal water-reabsorption rate* (and the GFR) *is the same*. In man the proximal water-reabsorption rate (including the pars recta) is probably about 80% of the glomerular filtration rate (cf. Fig. 27-17, p. 631).

In the **distal convolution** of the rat (TF/P)$_{inulin}$ rises from 6 to 18 during *antidiuresis;* the continued reabsorption of water during passage through the collecting ducts finally brings the (U/P)$_{inulin}$ to 100–200. That is, the overall rate of reabsorption of water amounts to 99–99.5% of the filtration rate. During pronounced *water diuresis* (TF/P)$_{inulin}$ in the distal parts of the nephron *rises very slightly*. The inference is that under these conditions *hardly any water is reabsorbed in the distal nephron*.

As Fig. 27-12 shows, in antidiuresis and in water diuresis the essential differences in the reduction of the intratubular flow rates do not appear before the distal convolution is reached. In maximum water diuresis the decrease of the urine flow rate in the more distal parts is negligible, while in maximal antidiuresis it falls from the initial ca. 15% to less than 1%, depending on the glomerular filtration rate.

These studies show that the homeostatic *adjustment of water excretion* depends on variation in the amount of water reabsorbed *in the distal nephron*. This is the site of action of the antidiuretic hormone in the nephron (cf. p. 629).

Another important difference between the proximal and the distal reabsorption of water is evident in the ratio of the **osmotic concentrations** of the tubular fluid and the plasma (Fig. 27-13). Throughout the *proximal convolution* (TF/P)$_{osmol}$ = 1; that is, here there is no transtubular osmotic pressure difference. The *distal convolution* receives *hypotonic urine* ((TF/P)$_{osmol}$ ≪ 1) emerging from the loop of Henle; therefore the transtubular osmotic pressure difference in the distal convolution acts as a driving force for the reabsorption of water. During antidiuresis the value of (TF/P)$_{osmol}$ equals 1 along the distal convolution

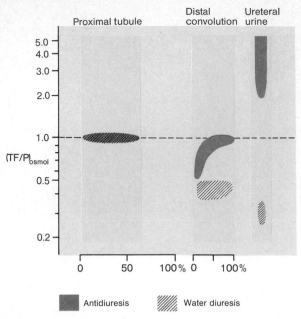

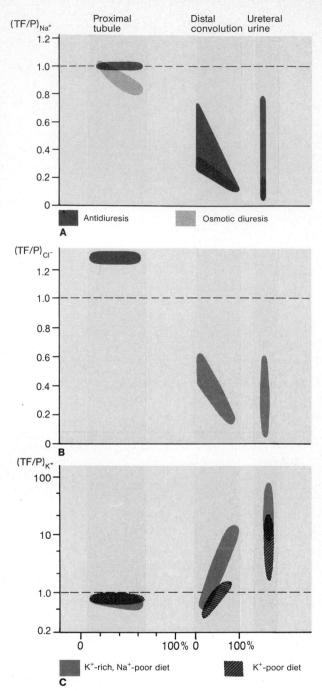

Fig. 27-13. Osmotic concentration ratios between tubular fluid or ureteral urine and blood plasma (($TF/P)_{osmol}$ or ($U/P)_{osmol}$). From [29, 61]. The areas on the graph represent the envelopes of groups of data points. For discussion see text

and the cortical collecting tubules. The urine does not actually become more concentrated – i. e., *hypertonic* to the plasma – until it is traversing the *collecting duct*. During water diuresis the osmotically driven reabsorption of water is almost entirely prevented, in both the distal convolution and the collecting-tubule system, because in the absence of ADH the entire distal nephron is practically impermeable to water (cf. pp. 629, 632).

These studies have shown that the *proximal reabsorption of water is invariant and involves no change in osmotic pressure, whereas distal reabsorption occurs only during antidiuresis (in the presence of antidiuretic hormone) and is based on osmosis.*

Proximal and distal ion transports ((TF/P) values). The concentrations of Na^+, K^+, Ca^{++}, Mg^{++}, Cl^-, and HCO_3^- in the glomerular filtrate are similar to those in the plasma. The ureteral urine contains only small fractions of the filtered quantities of all these ions (Table 27-1, p. 612). The remainder is reabsorbed – the greater part in the proximal convolution, as in the case of water reabsorption.

Fig. 27-14 indicates graphically the (TF/P) values for Na^+, K^+ and Cl^- in the easily accessible parts of the nephron, and the (U/P) values of the ureteral urine. These measures reveal conspicuous differences in electrolyte transport in the proximal and distal convolutions. In interpreting the diagram one must take into account the ($TF/P)_{inulin}$ corresponding to each location (i. e., the degree to which the volume of the tubular fluid has been reduced by water reabsorption).

Fig. 27-14 A–C. (TF/P) and (U/P) concentration ratios for different ions. **A** Na^+, modified from [28, 36]. **B** Cl^-, modified from [37, 59]. **C** K^+, modified from [28, 35]. For discussion see text

In the whole proximal convolution the (TF/P) of Na^+ is found to be 1. Thus Na^+ is reabsorbed together with water, in an amount corresponding to its concentration in the filtrate. Because 2/3 of the filtrate volume is reabsorbed in the proximal convolution (cf. Fig. 27-12), it follows that 2/3 of the filtered Na^+ is reabsorbed here as well. The reabsorption of K^+ is not quite the same; ($TF/P)_{K^+}$ is slightly less than 1, indicating a

Fig. 27-15. Model of the isotonic reabsorption of fluid in the proximal tubule. From [15, 20]. At the luminal membrane of the brush border the transport of Na^+ is passive, in part coupled with the transport of glucose or amino acids and in part in exchange with H^+. The active transport of sodium bicarbonate occurs in the lateral spaces between the cells and in the cisternae of the basal labyrinth. Local osmosis brings about the intense reabsorption of water, which induces solute transport by solvent drag. The numbers on the left edge give the Na^+ concentrations in mmol/liter

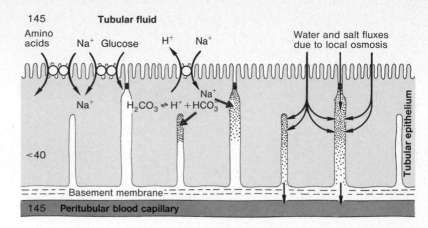

slight preferential proximal reabsorption of K^+ as compared with Na^+.

$(TF/P)_{Cl^-}$ is about 1.2 in the region of the proximal convolution. That is, a smaller fraction of Cl^- is reabsorbed. This difference results from the preferential proximal reabsorption of HCO_3^- (Fig. 27-15).

In the **distal convolution** and during transit through the **collecting tubule** the (TF/P) values for Na^+ and Cl^- are distinctly below 1 (Fig. 27-14), and can become extremely low. At the beginning of the distal convolution $(TF/P)_{K^+}$ is also less than 1, but further on it rises above 1 and in state of K^+ excess can exceed 10. This increase can only be due to K^+ secretion in the distal nephron. Thus K^+ can be reabsorbed and, particularly if present in excess, secreted distally.

The transport of Ca^{++} is very much like that of Na^+, although the distal transport rates of the two ions do not change exactly in parallel.

Mechanisms of tubular electrolyte transport and water reabsorption. The **proximal tubule** is the part of the nephron with the greatest transport rates. As far as the reabsorption of sodium and water is concerned, it exhibits neither transtubular osmotic pressure differences (which could serve as a driving force for water reabsorption) nor sodium concentration gradients indicative of active sodium transport (Figs. 27-13 and 27-14). Nevertheless proximal reabsorption of sodium is active. This may be indicated when the filtrate contains greater amounts of substances that are reabsorbed to a very limited extent (e.g., in osmotic mannitol diuresis; cf. p. 629). In this case the Na^+ concentration in the tubular fluid falls $((TF/P)_{Na^+} < 1)$ although the fluid remains isotonic (cf. Figs. 27-13, 27-14 A). With the *split-oil-drop method* [47] it is possible to show that sodium is actively reabsorbed even under normal conditions, and that the proximal reabsorption of water is passive, a secondary result of this active process.

In this method a double-barrelled microcannula is used to introduce a small column of oil into the proximal tubule. While the oil column remains in position there it is split in two by the injection of an isotonic solution of mannitol and NaCl through the second barrel of the cannula. If the solution contains more

than ca. 110 mmol/l Na, some of this is reabsorbed and the two oil droplets move closer together; if it contains less NaCl and correspondingly more mannitol, the volume of solution between the oil droplets increases by an influx of fluid. In the presence of mannitol, practically none of which is reabsorbed, the sodium concentration in the tubular fluid between the droplets is always adjusted to ca. 110 mmol/l as opposed to 145 mmol/l in the extratubular fluid. In this way there is locally a stationary equilibrium between the rate of Na^+ reabsorption (against the transtubular concentration gradient) and the passive influx (down the gradient). It may be mentioned that in the proximal tubule transtubular electrical potential differences are negligible.

This experiment shows the following: 1. The **sodium reabsorption** *in the proximal tubule is based on* **active transport.** 2. The **rate of sodium reabsorption** *is the resultant of* **outward sodium transport** *and (passive)* **sodium influx.** 3. **Water reabsorption is passive,** *a consequence of the sodium transport.*

The way in which sodium reabsorption causes the reabsorption of water in the proximal tubule can be illustrated by a **model of isosmotic fluid reabsorption.** The model requires (i) the *active transport* of a substance and (ii) an *additional compartment* within the epithelium, in direct communication with the fluid space in which the isotonic reabsorbed fluid is transported. The reabsorption of fluid is based on **local osmosis.** The model also applies to isotonic reabsorption in the intestine and in the gallbladder (cf. p. 608).

As shown in Fig. 27-15, in the proximal tubule the active transport into the additional compartment is an **active transport of sodium bicarbonate into the intercellular spaces and the basal infoldings** of the epithelial cells (*"basal labyrinth"*). These spaces contain extracellular fluid, which is made hypertonic by uptake of the actively transported salt; the result is an osmotically driven influx of water by the shortest path (local osmosis), out of the cell and through the tight junctions at the luminal edges of adjacent cells. By "solvent drag" (p. 653) this water pulls with it many of the particles dissolved in the tubular fluid (chiefly Na^+ and Cl^-, but also urea). As the fluid in the intercellular spaces is diluted to isosmolarity, it flows into the general interstitial compartment and thence joins the blood in the peritubular capillaries. Calculations have shown that in the proximal tubule ca. 50% of the sodium reabsorption is based on active transport across cell membranes, the remaining sodium being reabsorbed passively by solvent drag.

The active transtubular transport of sodium occurs in two steps. Sodium first enters the tubule cell through the luminal membrane of the brush border passively, by facilitated diffusion (p.655) down the concentration gradient – partly in cotransport with glucose and amino acids (cf. [45]) and partly in exchange with hydrogen ions (Fig.27-15). The outward transport of sodium through the membrane of the basal labyrinth and the intercellular spaces is an active process. It keeps the intracellular sodium concentration low, a prerequisite for the continued entry of sodium. Potassium is probably transported actively through the luminal cell membrane, whereas chloride moves through the proximal tubule wall passively to maintain charge balance.

The loop of Henle. The length of the thin limb is quite different in the cortical and juxtamedullary nephrons (Fig.27-1). The further the loop dips into the inner zone of the medulla the greater the increase of the osmolarity in the descending limb fluid, as in the interstitial space. The ascending part of the thin limb of a long loop, in contrast to the descending part, is barely permeable to water and appears capable of active salt transport. It has been suggested that this outward transport dilutes the loop fluid. This is certainly the case in the **thick ascending limb,** for which reason it is also called the **"diluting segment."** The outward transport of substances in this segment in most species consists of an *active Cl^- transport.* Certain diuresis-enhancing drugs act by inhibiting this transport mechanism.

Distal convolution and collecting tubule. The properties of the distal convolution are initially like those of the thick ascending limb of the loop of Henle, and further along like those of the collecting tubule. This more distal part is the site of action of the *antidiuretic hormone,* which controls the renal excretion of water, and the sodium-conserving *mineralocorticoids.* The "passive" permeability of the epithelia of the distal nephron is considerably lower than that of the proximal convolution. Here, therefore, Na^+ can be actively reabsorbed against a considerable concentration gradient. The resulting transtubular potential difference (lumen negative) can be an effective driving force for the influx of cations into the tubular fluid. In this way distal potassium secretion (Fig.27-14C) can occur passively [4, 28]. Because the electrical potential difference is correlated with the rate of sodium

transport, it is understandable that aldosterone increases the rate of potassium secretion. However, the hormonal effects on potassium transport are doubtless extremely diverse. Aldosterone also promotes potassium secretion by increasing the potassium permeability of the tubule-cell membrane. However, the excretion of potassium competes with the excretion of H^+ in exchange with sodium. To the extent that this situation amounts to coupled Na^+–K^+ exchange transfer, this aspect of K^+ secretion could be regarded as secondary active transport, but this interpretation is questionable. On the other hand, it is accepted that the reabsorption of potassium in the distal nephron (e.g. in K^+ deficiency) is an active process. The uptake of potassium at the basal end of the tubule cell is active, just as it is in other cells.

In the distal nephron the reabsorption of water is largely independent of ion transport. Here the driving force is the transtubular osmotic gradient (cf. osmotic concentration in renal medulla, p.631). However, the distal water-reabsorption rate depends in addition on the water permeability of the tubular wall, which is controlled by antidiuretic hormone. Separate hormonal control processes govern the distal transport of ions.

Glomerulotubular balance. It has been noted that by the end of the proximal convolution ⅔ of the filtrate volume has been reabsorbed even if the glomerular filtration rate departs considerably from normal. The rate of fluid reabsorption is adjusted to match the rate of glomerular filtration; that is, the **relative fluid reabsorption rate** is constant. Because of this *glomerulotubular balance,* to a first approximation, the fluid leaving the proximal tubule has about the same ionic composition under most conditions. In absolute terms, of course, the quantities of substances presented to the more distal parts increase with increasing GFR, but the distal transport mechanisms can be impaired by such variation [27].

The glomerulotubular balance is maintained in abnormal conditions, such as in hypertrophied nephrons (following contralateral nephrectomy) and in adrenalectomized animals, with impaired Na^+ reabsorption (see below). Two factors seem to be particularly important in maintaining glomerulotubular balance. 1. The inner diameter of the proximal tubules increases with filtration rate. Reabsorption could thus be enhanced because the absorbing area is enlarged, while the duration of contact with the tubular fluid stays about the same. 2. The increased oncotic pressure in the peritubular capillary blood (because the filtration fraction increases; cf. p.619) with increased GFR could accelerate the transport of the reabsorbed fluid from the interstitial space into the blood, and thus reduce the "backward diffusion" of substances [22].

Hormonal Influences on Tubular Ion Transport and Water Reabsorption

Actions of the adrenocortical hormones. Both the mineralocorticoids and the glucocorticoids affect renal function. **Aldosterone** (cf. pp.683 f.), the most effective mineralocorticoid, increases both the tubular reabsorption of sodium and the tubular secretion of potassium and hydrogen ions.

After a single injection of aldosterone, 30–60 min elapse before a response can be detected (action by enzyme induction). Repeated injections rapidly become less effective (escape phenomenon), and even though injections are continued the balances of Na$^+$ and water are soon restored, though the low-grade retention caused initially still persists. After functional breakdown **of adrenocortical activity** (cf. p. 684) the rate of sodium excretion rises, while that of potassium is relatively low. As a result, the body loses an appreciable fraction of its sodium (and water). The concentration of sodium in the blood plasma sometimes falls below 120 mmol/l, and that of potassium can rise to more than 8 mmol/l. The glomerular filtration rate is also greatly reduced, though this effect is also ascribable to the absence of glucocorticoids. Injection of *aldosterone* renormalizes electrolyte balance. To restore the normal glomerular filtration rate, the required *glucocorticoids* must be replaced. The lack of glucocorticoids in adrenocortical insufficiency also causes a retardation of water excretion after water load.

When the split-oil-drop experiment (cf. p. 627) is performed after adrenalectomy, the reabsorption of Na$^+$ from the embedded solution occurs at only half the normal rate, in both the proximal and the distal tubule [31]. Because of the reduced glomerular filtration rate and the maintenance of glomerulotubular balance, the consequences of the proximal disturbance of reabsorption are not particularly severe. The critical Na$^+$ losses result from the inadequate distal Na$^+$-reabsorption rate.

Nevertheless, the changes that tend to counteract sodium excretion (reduction of filtration rate, prolongation of contact time) are so effective that the sodium losses following adrenalectomy amount to not 50% but only 2–3% of the filtered sodium. It is just barely possible to replace this amount dietetically. Theoretically, a loss of 50% of the filtered sodium mass should be fatal within minutes.

Actions of antidiuretic hormone; types of diuresis. *Antidiuretic hormone* (**ADH** or vasopressin) economizes water by reducing the flow rate of the excreted urine and increasing the urine concentration. Ideally, under the influence of ADH the kidneys excrete all materials to be eliminated with much less water. ADH *increases the distal reabsorption of water,* by making the epithelia of distal convolution and collecting tubule permeable to water for reabsorption. This effect is mediated by cyclic AMP, which is excreted in the urine in parallel with the ADH activity in the kidney. Thus the target of ADH is adenylcyclase, the enzyme that catalyzes the conversion of ATP to cyclic AMP.

In the *presence of ADH* the distal water reabsorption occurs in two steps. First, in the cortical region the hy-potonic fluid delivered from the ascending limb of the loop to the distal convolution is brought up to an isotonic concentration (cf. p. 626). Then the actual concentrating of the urine to hypertonic values occurs by further water reabsorption in the collecting ducts in the renal medulla (cf. pp. 626 and 632). Under these conditions the excretion rate of urine is retarded and amounts to ca. 1 ml/min or less. This type of *retarded diuresis* is called **antidiuresis**; the urine is **hypertonic.**

In the *absence of ADH* the distal nephron is nearly impermeable to water, and only a negligibly small fraction of the normal osmotically driven distal reabsorption of water persists (Fig. 27-12). Diuresis is enhanced and the urine is **hypotonic.** This type of diuresis is called **water diuresis.** The maximal rate of urine excretion may then be ca. 15% of the glomerular filtration rate – i. e., 25 l/day or 18 ml/min (as compared with ca. 0.4 l/d or 0.28 ml/min in maximal antidiuresis).

Thus 15% of water reabsorption is under hormonal (ADH) control *(facultative water reabsorption),* whereas 85% of the filtered water is reabsorbed even without ADH *(obligatory water reabsorption).* A patient with the *ADH-deficiency disease* (**diabetes insipidus**) is in a permanent state of water diuresis, which can be alleviated by parenteral administration of ADH.

A second type of enhanced urine flow, distinct from water diuresis, is **osmotic diuresis.** It results when the filtrate contains abnormally large amounts of material difficult to reabsorb (e. g., after infusion of hypertonic solutions of salt or mannitol). Despite a high ADH activity in the blood the urine is produced so abundantly that the water-conserving action of this hormone can be entirely obscured. Water conservation parallels the urine concentration. However, the higher the rate of urine flow in osmotic diuresis the more the urine approaches isotonic concentration.

With respect to intrarenal mechanisms in osmotic diuresis two facts are of special interest: (i) the proximal tubular fluid remains isotonic as in water and antidiuresis, but in contrast to these a transtubular concentration gradient of sodium may be built up (cf. Fig. 27-14); (ii) the excess of material hard to reabsorb retains water in the proximal tubular fluid, so that the loop of Henle is inundated and the urinary concentrating mechanism, localized in the renal medulla, is overloaded and its effectiveness is diminished.

In maximal osmotic diuresis the rate of urine excretion can reach 40% of the glomerular filtration rate. In the process the organism can lose large quantities of water and also salt, so that pronounced osmotic diuresis is not without danger. This should be taken into account in all osmotic therapeutic treatment.

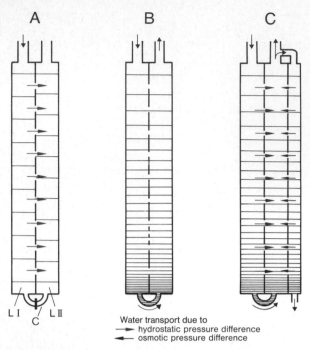

Water transport due to
→ hydrostatic pressure difference
← osmotic pressure difference

Fig. 27-16 A–C. Countercurrent concentration in a two-limb and a three-limb model. The fluid compartments in the individual limbs are separated by semipermeable membranes. The driving force for the concentrating "single effect" is the hydrostatic pressure difference between LI and LII. **A** "single effect" without flow; **B** longitudinal osmotic gradient developed during flow of solution; **C** production and gain of a concentrated solution in the third limb owing to the removal of water by osmotic forces

In cases of *circulatory failure* it is not uncommon for urine production to stop altogether **(anuria).** The drop in arterial blood pressure reduces the glomerular filtration rate so sharply that the entire filtrate is reabsorbed in the tubules. In such cases permanent kidney damage can develop. To prevent this result, moderate osmotic diuresis can be produced (e.g., by infusion of a mannitol solution). – Patients with diabetes mellitus exhibit slight osmotic diuresis owing to the glucose excess in the glomerular filtrate – the glucose not reabsorbed in the proximal tubule.

Actions of parathyroid hormone and calcitonin. Both these hormones control the renal excretion of inorganic phosphate and calcium. **Parathyroid hormone** (PTH) inhibits the tubular reabsorption of phosphate and thus increases its rate of excretion, whereas the rate of calcium excretion is lowered. In addition, PTH inhibits the proximal reabsorption of Na^+ and HCO_3^- and the secretion of H^+.

Calcitonin also increases the excretion of phosphate by inhibition of its tubular reabsorption, but, in contrast to PTH, it increases the rate of calcium excretion as well. It has a saluretic effect – that is, it increases the excretion of sodium chloride.

The characteristic curve for phosphate excretion is like that for glucose (p. 622). Phosphate, like glucose, is a threshold sub-

stance; that is, it is excreted only if its plasma concentration is above a certain level, and its tubular reabsorption is characterized by a transport maximum. Whereas the threshold concentration for glucose is so far above the physiological blood concentrations that the kidney does not usually participate in maintaining a constant blood glucose concentration, the threshold concentration for phosphate is in the lower part of the physiological range of concentrations. Moreover, the tubular transport maximum is in the upper range of the amounts of phosphate normally filtered, so that the kidney makes a very effective contribution to constancy of the concentration of phosphate in the blood plasma in putting an upper limit on its concentration.

27.5 The Concentrating of Urine in the Countercurrent System of the Renal Medulla

According to a theory of KUHN, the urine-concentrating mechanism in the kidney is based on the existence of a *countercurrent system* with the hairpin-shaped loops of Henle as the functional core. In such a system a *small particular concentrating effect (Einzeleffekt,* "single effect") on one side at the expense of the other is amplified owing to the **opposed directions of flow** in the two limbs of the loop. The net result is an increase in the concentration along the first part of the loop, to several times that produced by the "single effect" alone (without countercurrent) – there is **"countercurrent multiplication"** of the concentrating action [62]. These relationships will first be examined by reference to a simplified model.

Concentrating effect in the countercurrent model. The model (Fig. 27-16) consists of a tube divided into two limbs of equal size (LI and LII) by a **semipermeable membrane.** LI and LII are connected by the narrow capillary tube C. The whole system is filled with a solution at a given osmotic concentration.

Initially, the connecting capillary is closed. Now if the solution in LI is placed under **increased hydrostatic pressure** water moves through the membrane to LII. The solution in LI becomes more concentrated and that in LII is diluted. In the equilibrium state the *osmotic pressure difference corresponds to the "single effect."* It is equal to the hydrostatic pressure difference.

If the capillary is now opened, the fluid slowly begins to flow in the two limbs, in opposite directions. The hydrostatic pressure difference between the two is kept the same. The current carries the somewhat more concentrated solution in LI over to the other side, so that the solution in the region near the linking capillary is equal in concentration on both sides. In this region the hydrostatic pressure difference can again act as a driving force to push water from LI to LII; that is, here the "single effect" is exerted again, and the fluid approaching the capillary becomes correspondingly more concentrated. The sequence of events is repeated in the next period of time (third "single effect"), and the affected region extends progressively further away from the capillary. Eventually a state of equilibrium is reached in which there is a **longitudinal osmotic gradient** with **maximal concentration** in the region of the connecting capillary (or the bend in the loop). In the steady state the solution flowing out of the countercurrent system has the same osmotic concentration as that flowing in. In this case the concentrating action of the system is put to no use.

In an expanded system with three limbs, however, the countercurrent concentrating effect is put to use (Fig. 27-16 C). Here a second semipermeable membrane separates LII and the third limb. The volume flow rate through the third limb must be only a fraction of that through LII, so that there is no appreciable change in the concentrating system LI–LII. As the solution flows through the third limb its concentration is matched to that in LII, as the osmotic pressure difference progressively drives water into LII; that is, it gradually becomes more concentrated. The solution flowing out of the third limb has the maximal concentration, that at the "tip of the loop." (The solution leaving LII is somewhat more dilute than that entering the system, because it contains the water that was osmotically displaced from the third limb.)

In summary: The countercurrent system has a concentrating action by virtue of a **combination of "single effect" and flow of solution.** The concentration factor **(countercurrent multiplication)** achieved in a countercurrent system with a given "single effect" increases exponentially with the length of the system and the contact time in a segment. It is therefore reduced as flow velocity increases.

The countercurrent system in the renal medulla. The countercurrent system that concentrates the urine in the kidney consists of the loops of Henle and the collecting tubules. The analogy with the three-limb model just described is obvious. The presence of interstitial spaces between the uriniferous tubules does not constitute a fundamental difference from the model because the interstitial fluid is passively involved and mediates the transport of materials in the concentrating process.

The *most important "single effect"* in the medullary countercurrent system is the *active transport of NaCl from the ascending-limb urine into the interstitial fluid.*

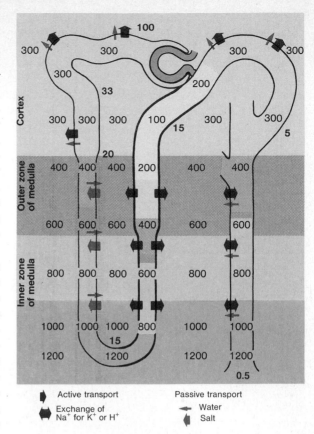

Active transport

Exchange of Na⁺ for K⁺ or H⁺

Passive transport

Water

Salt

Fig. 27-17. Countercurrent system of the renal medulla during antidiuresis. From [4]. The *black* numbers indicate the osmotic concentration of the tubular or peritubular fluid; the *red* numbers show the percentage of the glomerular filtrate still present at successive points in the nephron

A crucial feature is that the *ascending limb is practically impermeable to water* over its whole length. Owing to the outward transport of NaCl, the *ascending-loop urine becomes hypotonic* and the *interstitial fluid, hypertonic* (Fig. 27-17).

The interstitial hypertonicity causes an osmotically driven flow of water from the descending-loop fluid and also from the blood in the vasa recta. Solutes may enter into these structures. The gradually increasing concentration along the descending limb is due to the *combination of "single effect" and flow.* At equilibrium there is a longitudinal osmotic gradient throughout the renal medulla, with the highest osmotic concentration in the region of the papilla. The **final adjustment of the osmotic concentration** of the urine occurs during passage through the **collecting tubule.** When the kidney is producing concentrated urine the collecting duct receives an isotonic fluid from the distal convolution, at a volume flow rate that is much reduced by the osmotically driven removal of water in the distal convolution (cf. p. 625, Fig. 27-12). Therefore the urine flows slowly through the collecting ducts, and has an opportunity to achieve osmotic equilibrium with the hypertonic interstitial fluid. *At a given level in the renal medulla the osmotic concentration is almost the same in all fluid spaces* [63], *except for the ascending limb of the loop of Henle, in which the fluid is hypotonic to the surroundings* [32, 61]. The ureteral urine has the same osmotic concentration as the fluid at the tip of the papilla. However, not only water leaves the urine in the collecting tubules; salts are reabsorbed actively here (p. 626) and urea passively (p. 623). NaCl and urea are the chief contributors to the hypertonicity of the interstitial fluid in the medulla [55]. Antidiuretic hormone plays a role in this effect, by raising the permeability to urea in the deep segments of the collecting ducts (not in the distal convolutions and the cortical collecting tubules) [39].

The **vasa recta** form a **second countercurrent system** in the renal medulla, but without any concentrating "single effect." The blood in the descending capillaries undergoes passive osmotic adjustment in the medullar environment. As the osmotic concentration of the tissue rises, toward the papilla, the blood acquires NaCl and urea and loses water to the tissue. The consequence is an increase in the viscosity and resistance to flow of the blood (cf. p. 614). The blood ascending in the opposed capillary passes through zones of gradually decreasing osmotic concentration, in which it loses salt and urea to the interstitial fluid and takes in water. The countercurrent in the vasa recta amounts to a "short circuit" for water, and creates special conditions for the diffusion of dissolved substances. **Diffusion in a countercurrent system** in particular affects the *time the diffusing substances spend* in the system. Substances such as O_2, which are delivered to the renal medulla by the descending bloodstream and are consumed there, reach the depths in only minimal amounts, for they tend to diffuse across to the ascending blood and be carried away (p. 616). In this way the O_2 partial pressures in the tissue of the tip of papilla and in the ureteral urine are extremely low. On the other hand, substances produced deep in the system (e. g., CO_2, lactic acid) or concentrated there (NaCl and urea) diffuse back and forth between the capillary limbs and are thus retained in the system at relatively high concentrations for long times [55].

The higher the medullar blood flow rate, the more convective transport dominates over diffusion; the removal of the substances is accelerated and the longitudinal osmotic gradient becomes less steep [52]. *Any change that reduces the longitudinal osmotic gradient causes a reduction of the attainable concentration of the urine and an increase in diuresis* (e.g., pressure diuresis, p. 616; osmotic diuresis, p. 629).

Countercurrent concentration during water diuresis. In a state of water diuresis the distal convolution and the collecting duct are nearly impermeable to water because ADH is reduced or absent (p. 629). Therefore, the hypotonicity of the ascending loop urine is not eliminated in the distal convolution, and it is impossible for the solution to achieve osmotic equilibrium with the interstitial fluid during passage through the collecting ducts. The prevention of water reabsorption in all parts of the distal nephrons causes flow rate to rise. The concentrating mechanism in the loop of Henle proceeds normally, but the interstitial fluid is brought to a concentration of only ca. 500–600 mosmol/l (as compared with 1 200–1 400 mosmol/l during antidiuresis).

27.6   Regulatory Function of the Kidneys

The kidneys' regulatory function is to maintain **constancy of the ionic composition and of the volume of the extracellular fluid.** In so doing, the kidneys play the role of an effector organ in various control circuits. Some of their excretory functions are adjusted by the activities of hormones (e. g., aldosterone or parathyroid hormone). The kidneys are part of a closely interlinked set of regulatory processes that serve to maintain the osmolarity and volume of the extracellular fluid, and the acid-base balance of the body.

Regulation of the Osmotic Concentration of the Extracellular Fluid

Transient changes in the direction of both hypertonicity and hypotonicity take place in the normal daily cycle of bodily activities. A **rise in osmolarity** occurs if water is not drunk often enough, because during the intervals the body loses relatively more water through kidneys, lungs, intestines and skin than it excretes osmotically effective solutes. In this case the hypertonicity results from **water deficiency.**

The organism deals with a state of *water deficiency* in two ways: by increasing the rate of **release of antidiuretic hormone** (ADH) from the neurohypophysis and by generating a **sensation of thirst.** The result is that (i) the ADH-induced *antidiuresis* reduces further renal *water loss to a minimum,* and (ii) *water balance is restored by thirst-motivated drinking.* When sufficient water has been drunk, the isotonicity of the body fluids is reestablished.

A **decrease in osmolarity** based on a **surplus of water** (e.g., after excessive drinking) causes inhibition of

ADH release and of the feeling of thirst and eventually, after the ADH still in circulation has been broken down by the liver, results in *water diuresis* (Fig. 27-18). The water diuresis rapidly eliminates the excess water. That this mechanism is activated by water surplus accompanied by hypotonicity is shown by an experiment in which an equal amount of an isotonic solution of NaCl is drunk; a considerably longer time is required to eliminate the water in this case. The excretion of an ingested saline solution is not an osmoregulatory effect but a means of regulating volume.

Osmoreceptor concept. If small volumes of hypertonic solutions of various substances are injected into the internal carotid artery of a waking animal, both antidiuresis and drinking behavior are observed after a brief latency. Injection of the same solutions in equal quantities into the general circulation have no such effect. These experiments implied the existence of *"osmoreceptors"* in the region supplied by this artery, the stimulation of which resulted in the release of antidiuretic hormone and the production of antidiuresis [58].

The critical region has proved to be the hypothalamus. Microinjection into the anteromedian hypothalamus and injection into ventricles I to III have shown that the osmoreceptors thus stimulated respond *specifically* to an *increase in the sodium concentration* in their immediate vicinity. The release of ADH and drinking behavior were observed only if the increase in osmotic concentration of brain tissue or cerebrospinal fluid involved an increase in the Na^+ concentration [10].

The control system for maintenance of isotonicity thus acts by way of the adjustment of water content, by controlling renal water excretion and water intake. But the effective stimulus, which triggers the response of the osmoreceptors, is change in the Na^+ concentration in their surroundings (CSF or interstitial fluid). In a state of primary negative water balance the osmotic concentration always rises together with the Na^+ concentration, for sodium salts account for well over 90% of the osmotically effective material in the extracellular fluid.

A pure osmoreceptor would be expected to respond to changes in osmolarity regardless of the nature of the solutes involved. However, in the case of this hypothalamic system sodium concentration obviously plays a decisive role. In this sense it is not entirely appropriate to refer to the hypothalamic mechanism as osmoregulation. Physiologically, however, the contradiction is not unbridgeable because the sodium concentration in the extracellular fluid is for the most part its osmotic concentration. In the last analysis, all the regulatory functions of the kidneys treated in this section, which serve to maintain physiological osmolarity, ion composition and volume of the extracellular fluid, are so closely interlinked that the various relationships overlap. As long as this aspect is not ignored, the term "osmoregulation"

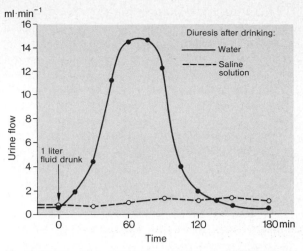

Fig. 27-18. The effect of drinking on urine flow. After [5]. Excessive drinking of water induces water diuresis, which eliminates the surplus water within 2–3 hours. Drinking the same amount of NaCl solution (0.9 g/dl) causes only a slight increase in urine flow

can continue in use. Examples of the connections among the various homeostatic tasks of the kidneys are described in the following paragraphs.

The hypothalamic control system that activates the release of ADH and the sensation of thirst also responds to *other than osmotic stimuli* [9] (cf. Fig. 27-20). The octapeptide **angiotensin** is particularly effective; it acts to maintain extracellular-fluid volume as part of the renin-angiotensin-aldosterone system (pp. 634 ff.). Animal experiments have shown that angiotensin in the cerebrospinal fluid enhances the action of Na^+ on the osmoreceptors or the related periventricular structures [8]. It remains in debate, however, whether angiotensin can pass the blood-CSF or blood-brain barrier in sufficient amounts. But recently several animal species have been found to have an independent cerebral renin-angiotensin system with a very similar action, so that there can hardly be any further doubt that the hypothalamic control system is activated by angiotensin [23, 25].

Afferent nerve activity can also affect the hypothalamic control system; for example, the occurrence of *pain* elicits increased release of ADH. *Changes in the volume and distribution of the blood* also participate in setting the activity level of the control system. For example, an acute increase in the central blood volume (e.g., during negative-pressure respiration or immersion of the body up to the neck in water) causes water diuresis by inhibiting the release of ADH (cf. *Gauer-Henry diuresis reflex,* p. 434). However, in some circumstances an increase of the excretion of NaCl (natriuresis) can also occur. This effect could be due in part to participation of the cardiovascular and cardiopulmonary afferent pathways which are involved in the control circuits for tubular sodium reabsorption via efferent renal nerves reaching the juxtaglomerular apparatus or other renal structures [13]. On the other hand, acute reduction of the central blood volume increases the rate of ADH release and causes thirst. This is one of the mechanisms that makes one thirsty after donating at least 10% of one's total volume of blood. Probably the action of the afferents from the low-pressure system is supplemented here by other, hormonal mechanisms [21, 26].

Regulation of the Extracellular Fluid Volume

Extracellular fluid volume and sodium balance. The volume of the extracellular fluid (ECF) is determined primarily by its total content of sodium. Evidence for this relationship is obtained quite simply, by changing the amount of NaCl in the diet.

If one changes to a **high-salt diet** the excretion of NaCl at first lags behind the intake; that is, initially sodium is retained *(positive sodium balance)*. As a consequence of the increased salt intake a thirst sensation arises and there is a noticeable increase in the amount drunk, and in addition water is retained *(positive water balance)*. The result is an **increase in the extracellular fluid volume with preservation of isotonicity,** whereby the sodium concentration of the ECF remains in the normal range. On the other hand, with a **low-salt diet** the first result is a reduction in body sodium by *negative sodium balance* (more is excreted than taken in), accompanied by increased water excretion *(negative water balance)*. The resulting **decrease in extracellular fluid volume** is again achieved without loss of isotonicity.

In both cases sodium and water balance is reestablished within one or two weeks, but at a *new level;* for the duration of the diet the change in sodium content of the body persists, so that the extracellular fluid volume remains higher or lower than before.

This shift in the equilibrium point is ascribed principally to altered renal excretion, under the controlling influence of *aldosterone* and *antidiuretic hormone.*

Extracellular fluid volume and blood circulation. Blood plasma and interstitial fluid are the two compartments of the extracellular fluid. Therefore, at present it is clear that the volume of the blood usually changes in parallel with changes in ECF volume. But in some conditions an increase in ECF volume is based entirely on increase in the volume of interstitial fluid. In such a case the plasma volume may be unchanged or even reduced – as, for example, in chronic hypoproteinemia. If the blood volume is changed mechanisms regulating the cardiovascular system are

activated, and these then interact with other homeostatic mechanisms.

In **hypervolemia,** an increase in the volume of the blood, the venous return to the heart is usually enhanced. This results in an *increase in the cardiac output* (cf. pp. 387 and 429). In the absence of a compensatory decline in peripheral vascular resistance the *arterial blood pressure rises* and so does the rate of *urine excretion* (cf. pressure-dependence of diuresis, p. 616; Fig. 27-3, p. 615). In this way a portion of the extracellular fluid can be eliminated by way of the kidneys. Other cases of hypervolemia, in which the arterial blood pressure is not elevated, are counteracted by water diuresis, which could be elicited by volume receptors (see above). Finally, one hypothesis proposes a hormonal factor (the so-called Factor III) that raises the rates of excretion of NaCl and water (natriuresis) when the volume of extracellular fluid is increased [48].

In **hypovolemia** venous return is reduced, and as a consequence the cardiac output and the arterial blood pressure fall. If this occurs the regulatory mechanisms that then come into play are not limited to the circulatory system. The effectors (i.e., vessel musculature and kidneys) are activated by the autonomic nerves and in addition by hormones; *antidiuretic hormone* is released and the *juxtaglomerular apparatus (renin-angiotensin-aldosterone mechanism)* is activated. These hormonal mechanisms counteract the drop in blood pressure and increase the volume of the extracellular fluid.

Renin-angiotensin-aldosterone system. Renin is produced in the epithelioid cells of the juxtaglomerular apparatus (Fig. 27-19), the juxtaglomerular cells; it enters the blood, partly by way of the renal lymph. **Renin** is a protease, which splits off the decapeptide *angiotensin I* (AI) from *angiotensinogen,* an α_2-globulin. A **converting enzyme,** highly active in the blood and in the lungs, converts AI into **angiotensin II** (AII), the active form. Proteolytic enzymes ("angiotensinases") break it down, forming first the heptapeptide *angiotensin III* and finally inactive fragments.

Enzymes with the character of renin are also found in other organs (e.g., uterus and placenta), but their significance remains a matter of debate. The cerebral renin-angiotensin system and its function was mentioned above (p. 633). It was discovered only recently that renin is carried in the blood in an active and an inactive form, so that it is very difficult to determine the actual renin activity of a blood sample in vitro. The physiological actions of angiotensins I and III are also debatable. When not otherwise specified, *angiotensin* is always understood to mean *angiotensin II.* In renal physiology the term renin-angiotensin-aldosterone system is used; in other contexts the more general term renin-angiotensin system is preferred.

Angiotensin II is one of the most powerful **vasoconstrictors** known. It produces a conspicuous, prolonged increase in peripheral resistance and thus a marked *rise in arterial blood pressure*. Moreover, it causes the **release of aldosterone** in the adrenal cortex. This hormone very effectively increases the absorption of sodium in the renal tubules (p. 629). The conditions under which the renin-angiotensin-aldosterone system is activated are **falling arterial blood pressure, loss of salt** and **hypovolemia**. These conditions are interrelated, and there is a broad spectrum of transitional states (see above). The activation of the renin-angiotensin-aldosterone system begins with the release of renin.

Various mechanisms serve to **control the release of renin** from the juxtaglomerular cells, as follows:

1. When the blood pressure changes the **intrarenal baroreceptor mechanism** goes into action. It increases the rate of renin release when the blood pressure falls and inhibits it when pressure rises. The actual receptor is probably a pressure- or stretch-sensitive region in the vas afferens.

Because it is the pressure in the vas afferens that affects this intrarenal mechanism, the renin-angiotensin-aldosterone system is also activated with all the aforesaid consequences when the blood pressure is reduced only in the renal arterioles (e. g., when the renal arteries are pathologically narrowed). In this case **renal hypertension** can develop. In animal experiments this sort of hypertension can be produced by artificial stenosis (partial clamping) of the renal arteries (Goldblatt hypertension). However, the enhanced renin release is not maintained, although the experimental hypertension persists.

2. In cases of reduced plasma volume an increase in renin release is observed. It is suggested that this release is mediated by a *chemosensitive mechanism* localized in the **macula densa** of the juxtaglomerular apparatus (Fig. 27-19). These cells are adjacent to the renin-containing granular cells. The macula densa cell as a part of the distal tubular wall may perform the control of the Na^+ or Cl^- load in the early distal tubular fluid. The details of this control mechanism are not yet quite clear. If the delivery of NaCl to the distal tubule is diminished (e. g., because of a reduction of the glomerular filtration rate), the rate of renin release increases. This may occur in clinical or experimental congestive states. The chemosensitive mechanism can cooperate with the baroreceptor mechanism, but it is difficult to estimate their respective contributions.

A local control function of the macula densa at the level of the single nephron is described below.

3. When the **renal nerves** are stimulated there is also an increased liberation of renin, and the same effect is produced by intraarterial injection of noradrenalin or adrenalin. The juxtaglomerular cells receive sym-

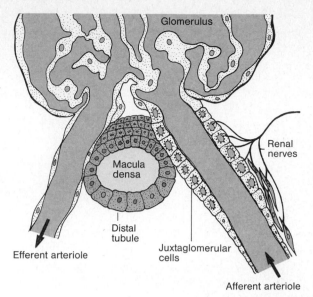

Fig. 27-19. Diagram of the juxtaglomerular apparatus. After [16]

pathetic innervation (Fig. 27-19), and most authors infer that the renin release is mediated by β-receptors (p. 115). Neurally mediated renin release can result, for example, as a consequence of blood loss, as an orthostatic response (p. 441), or from stimulation of the hypothalamus. Denervation of the kidneys, however, does not eliminate the two other intrarenal releasing mechanisms. It should be mentioned here that efferent renal nerves can influence the reabsorption of sodium in another way, independent of the renin-releasing mechanisms [13, 64].

4. Finally, the synthesis and release of renin are subject to **humoral influences**; that is, the function of the juxtaglomerular apparatus is also affected by substances in the blood flowing through it. The amount of renin released in response to the other control mechanisms depends on the momentary Na^+ and K^+ concentrations in the blood plasma or in the macula densa cells. A feature of particular interest is the **negative feedback effect** of *angiotensin II* as well as *ADH* on the further release of renin (Fig. 27-20).

The main effects of the renin-angiotensin-aldosterone system on the organism as a whole are to raise the arterial blood pressure, conserve or retain Na^+, and thus increase the extracellular fluid volume – all of which tend to counteract the eliciting conditions listed above. These multiple homeostatic tasks of the renin-angiotensin-aldosterone system are functionally related to a high degree.

At the level of the single nephron, the macula densa is thought to have the additional task of lowering the glomerular filtration rate by a local mechanism whenever an elevated Na^+ concentration in the fluid of the early distal tubule indicates that the nephron is

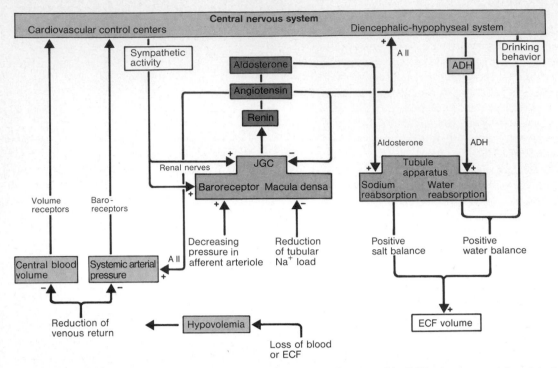

Fig. 27-20. Diagram of the functional pathways controlling the extracellular fluid volume. Initially, the physiological balance is disturbed by a reduction of the ECF volume (or hypovolemia). This activates the homeostatic control circuits, resulting in an increase of the ECF volume toward the original value. (ECF = extracellular fluid, JGC = juxtaglomerular cells, AII = Angiotensin II, ADH = antidiuretic hormone). For discussion see text

losing too much salt [53]. This mechanism, restricted to the individual nephron, could be based on a local renin-angiotensin action on the associated vas afferens. If this mechanism were to operate permanently and simultaneously in many nephrons of a healthy kidney under physiological conditions, it would be of considerable significance in controlling the glomerular filtration rate and the blood flow through the kidney as a whole. This possibility still remains open.

Regulatory mechanisms during hypovolemia. Fig. 27-20 summarizes renal function and the influences acting on the juxtaglomerular apparatus in this situation. To avoid unnecessary complication, more wideranging effects such as circulatory reflexes and the release of ACTH are ignored entirely. Here it is the onset of acute hypovolemia that activates the renin-angiotensin-aldosterone system.

Acute hypovolemia resulting from the loss of blood or plasma reduces the venous return and thus the central blood volume. If at any point the systemic arterial pressure decreases, the *baroreceptors* in the kidney are stimulated. Even if the arterial blood pressure should not fall, other regulatory effects increase the activity in the **renal nerves.** In any case the result is an increased release of **renin** from the juxtaglomerular cells (JGC), and the drop in glomerular filtration rate

enhances this effect. If the general *sympathetic activation* is more pronounced, then the secretion rate of *adrenal-medulla hormones* (**adrenalin and noradrenalin**) rises. In this case the renin release is accelerated more directly by stimulation of the intrarenal adrenergic receptors of the juxtaglomerular cells and indirectly via baroreceptors by constriction of the vascular smooth muscles in preglomerular arteries. In the blood the released renin promotes enzymatically the formation of angiotensin. It is mentioned above that an exhaustive release of renin may be avoided in the first instance by the negative-feedback effect of angiotensin on the juxtaglomerular cells.

The **angiotensin** produced by these events increases the **secretion of aldosterone** in the adrenal cortex. The enhancement of tubular Na^+ reabsorption caused by this hormone results in *NaCl retention*. Both angiotensin and the activation of afferent systems from the circulatory organs cause more **antidiuretic hormone** to be released from the neurohypophysis, and at the same time the threshold for the *sensation of thirst* is lowered. The ADH-induced increase in tubular water reabsorption and the reinforced drinking behavior bring about *water retention*. Salt and water retention togeher lead to an **increase in the volume of extracellular fluid** ad hence, with more or less success, in the volume of blood.

The result of *NaCl and water retention is comparable to that of long-term intravenous instillation of physiological saline*. Such a soution does not remain in the bloodstream, but rather becomes distributed throughout the extracellular compartments. Although the retained salt solution replaces the extracellular fluid with respect to te ionic content and osmotic effect, it does not provide effective correction of the hypovolemia. To replace the lost blood or plasma permanently an increase in the rate of albumin synthesis would also be required, to bring the *oncotic pressure of the plasma* back to normal (p. 334). Even though this does not occur the renin-Angiotensin-aldosterone system remains active, so that a **secondary aldosteronism** gradually develops, with the result that the extracellular fluid volume (predominantly the interstitial fluid) continues to increase. After some time visible **edema** can appear, as an expression of the excessive increase in interstitial fluid.

Regulation of Acid-Base Balance by the Kidneys

The acid-base balance in the various fluid spaces of the organism is adjusted by way of the blood pH, which is kept constant by the combined action of the various extra- and intracellular buffer systems, the lungs and the kidneys (c. pp. 501 ff.). The kidneys are responsible for excreting the nonvolatile acids and bases that are either consumed in excess or produced by metabolism. Nonvolatile (fixed) acids include the sulfate and phosphate anions resulting from the breakdown of proteins and nucleic acids; chief among the nonvolatile bases are the alkali ions consumed in food, accompanied by anions that can be endogenously metabolized. Carbonic acid is in equilibrium with its anhydride CO_2, which is volatile.

Metabolism and acid-base balance. Adults engaged in moderate physical activity and on a *normal diet* produce about 15 mol CO_2 per day. Added to this is a *surplus of anions of strong acids* derived from the breakdown of protein, etc., with about 40 to 88 mmol/d H^+ ions. The surplus CO_2 is blown off in the lungs, and the surplus acid ions are excreted by the kidneys. Variations in the metabolic state disturb the existent acid-base balance. The compensation of the metabolically induced imbalance to the acidic side occurs in two steps: first by respiration and then by the excretion of fixed anions and acidification of the urine.

The respiratory compensation of metabolic disturbance of the acid-base balance by fixed acids (HA) can be described by the following system of reactions:

$$HA + Na^+ + HCO_3^- \rightleftarrows A^- + Na^+ + H_2CO_3$$
$$\rightleftarrows A^- + Na^+ + H_2O + CO_2 \tag{16}$$

It may be noted that the fixed acids that dissociate into H^+ and A^- are neutralized $(A^- + Na^+)$ at cost of the blood buffer anion HCO_3^-, which is changed into CO_2. This CO_2 is released to the exterior by respiration.

The second step of compensation performed by the kidneys is surprisingly economic because the tubular mechanisms abandon A^- for excretion and gain back HCO_3^- for the restitution of the buffer capacity of the blood. Moreover, the strong anion A^- is not excreted together with filtered Na^+; this would strain the economy of the sodium balance. Instead of sodium, H^+ is excreted by way of the tubular Na^+-H^+-exchange mechanism. This mechanism performs the excretion of H^+, the conservation of Na^+, and the recovery of HCO_3^-.

A *vegetarian diet* leads to a *surplus of fixed bases* (see above). Breakdown of the accompanying anions causes an "alkalotic metabolic state"; again the initial response is respiratory compensation, which results in an elevation of the HCO_3^- in the body fluids. The kidneys "clean up" in this case by *excreting the surplus cations together with bicarbonate* – that is, forming **alkaline urine.**

The metabolic disturbances of acid-base balance most frequently encountered physiologically are loads to the acidic side, and pathologically, metabolic acidosis. That nature is prepared to deal with this situation is evident in the difference between the theoretical pK'value of 6.1 and the physiological blood pH of 7.4 (cf. the Henderson-Hasselbalch equation, p. 501). If the blood pH were 6.1 its buffering power on the acid and alkaline sides would be equal. The natural shift of the blood pH to the alkaline side makes a greater buffering capacity available for acidotic than for alkalotic disturbances. The mechanisms for renal compensation of acidosis also function more reliably than those for alkalosis. In any case of acid-base imbalance, renal regulation requires a mutual adjustment of the excretion of hydrogen ions and of bicarbonate.

Renal excretion of hydrogen ions. The lowest urine pH that can be achieved in man is ca. 4.5. This corresponds to a H^+ concentration of ca. 30 µmol/l urine. Accordingly, with a daily excretion of 1.5 l urine at most ca. 50 µmol/d *free H^+ ions* are eliminated by the kidneys. This is an insignificant fraction (about 1/1000) of the acid valences normally produced by the metabolism (about 50 mmol/d hydrogen ions; see above). In fact, the rate of excretion of free H^+ ions is negligibly small as compared with the amount of renally eliminated *hydrogen ions bound to buffer substances in the urine* (ca. 60 mmol/d). These buffer substances include the buffer anions contained in the glomerular filtrate (HPO_4^{--} and anions of weak organic acids) and the ammonia produced by the kidneys (see below).

Investigation of the rate of urinary H^+ excretion. The amount of H^+ eliminated by the kidneys in a certain time can not be deter-

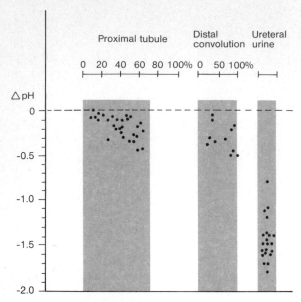

Fig. 27-21. Differences in pH of tubular fluid and ureteral urine from that of arterial blood plasma [30]

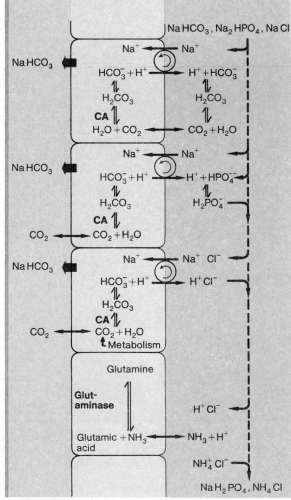

CA = Carbonic anhydrase

mined by titration of the urine alone because the titratable acid represents only a fraction of the total. The *titratable acid* is given by the amount of NaOH that must be added to the urine to bring it to pH 7.4. This amount is equivalent to the amount of H^+ in the urine free or bound to filtered buffer that is not reabsorbed in the tubule. To find the total quantity of H^+ excreted one must add the fraction of urinary H^+ masked as *ammonium*. This substance has to be separately determined. The molar quantity of ammonium is equivalent to the amount of H^+ in this fraction.

Hydrogen ions are secreted both in the proximal tubule and in the distal parts of the nephron. Micropuncture studies have shown that the resulting reduction in pH in the proximal tubule fluid is relatively slight (Fig. 27-21). The final pH of the urine (normally ca. pH 6) is established in the late distal segments.

The H^+ secretion rate is actually greatest in the proximal tubule, but it fails to produce a marked fall in pH for two reasons (cf. Fig. 27-22): (i) the filtrate has a certain buffer capacity, which has a H^+-masking effect, and (ii) the secreted amounts of H^+ are necessary to reabsorb the filtered HCO_3^- in the proximal tubule. It is noteworthy that these quantities of H^+ are not excreted; they are involved in the chemical reaction given by Eq. (17). The H^+ secretion occurs by exchange with Na^+ at the luminal side of the tubule cells (cf. Figs. 27-15 and 27-22).

In the distal tubular fluid most of the buffer materials that have not been removed by reabsorption are saturated, so that H^+ ions secreted here lower the pH sharply.

It is evident in Fig. 27-22 that the source of the secreted H^+ ions is the intracellular hydration of CO_2. The CO_2 can derive from cellular metabolism or from the blood or the tubular urine. The secreted H^+ ions are either used for the reabsorption of bicarbonate or excreted in bound (to buffer anions or NH_3) or free form. It should be noted that the rate of H^+ excretion is only a small fraction of the rate of secretion.

Na^+-H^+ exchange mechanism and bicarbonate reabsorption. The Na^+-H^+ exchange transport is facilitated. It takes place through the luminal cell membrane. The high rate of H^+ secretion into the proximal tubular fluid guarantees a rapid shift of the equilibrium of the reaction sequence

$$H^+ + HCO_3^- \rightleftarrows H_2CO_3 \rightleftarrows CO_2 + H_2O \qquad (17)$$

Fig. 27-22. Schematic illustration of the reabsorption of bicarbonate (1), acidification of the urine (2) and (3), and production of ammonium (4). Modified from [4].
(1) The H^+ ions secreted for HCO_3^- reabsorption are not excreted but rather used up as soon as they appear.
(2) and (3) The secreted H^+ ions that are excreted as free ions or bound to buffer anions constitute the titratable acid.
(4) NH_3 secretion increases the rate of H^+ excretion when the urine pH is low, by the formation of NH_4^+. Further explanation in text

to the right. Thus the filtered bicarbonate in the tubular fluid is rapidly converted to CO_2, in amounts depending on the H^+ secretion rate. The CO_2 molecules, readily diffuse into the tubule cells, where the same reaction sequence proceeds from right to left, accelerated by the presence of **carbonic anhydrase**. The HCO_3^- ion so produced in the cells is actively transferred or reabsorbed together with Na^+, and the simultaneously formed H^+ ion becomes available within the cell for exchange with filtered Na^+ (Fig. 27-22, top).

That most of the secreted H^+ ions are used for the reabsorption of bicarbonate is indicated by the following considerations. With a plasma HCO_3^- concentration of 25 mmol/l and a filtrate volume of 180 l/d, 4500 mmol HCO_3^- enter the proximal tubule per day. Practically all of this is reabsorbed, with the aid of an equivalent amount of secreted H^+ ions. Therefore the total H^+-secretion rate of the kidneys is 4500 mmol/d for HCO_3^- reabsorption plus the relatively slight 60 mmol/d normally excreted (see above). Because about 90% of the filtered bicarbonate is reabsorbed in the proximal tubule, the rate of H^+ secretion must also be greatest here.

In the *distal nephron* K^+ ions compete with the H^+ ions in the Na^+-exchange process; that is, here **Na^+-K^+ exchange** occurs as well. The amounts of H^+ and K^+ secreted and excreted in exchange with Na^+ depend on their relative availability within the cells. Therefore the rates of excretion of K^+ and H^+ sometimes *vary inversely*. When H^+ predominates (in general acidosis or K^+ deficiency) the distal rate of H^+ secretion rises while that of K^+ falls; accordingly, more H^+ ions are excreted and fewer K^+ ions. The situation is reversed when the K^+ ions are more readily available.

On the other hand, the secretion of both ions changes in *parallel* with the distal rate of Na^+ reabsorption. If the latter rises, so do the rates of H^+ and K^+ excretion; this occurs, for example, in hyperaldosteronism, so that hypokalemia with slight alkalosis develops. If the rate of distal sodium reabsorption falls – as happens when its concentration in the tubule fluid is low owing to diminished filtration or in a state of hypoaldosteronism – the reduced excretion of K^+ and H^+ causes hyperkalemia and acidosis.

The Na^+-H^+ exchange mechanism is a very helpful model. Under special experimental conditions at the level of the nephron it is obvious that the coupling of the exchange transport is neither stoichiometrically determinable nor mandatory for H^+ secretion in any conditions. That applies also to the reabsorption mechanism of HCO_3^-, which is much more complicated in its membranal transport mechanisms than described below.

Excretion curve of HCO_3^-. HCO_3^- is designated as a threshold substance; it appears in the urine only if the

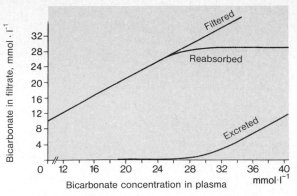

Fig. 27-23. Reabsorption and excretion of bicarbonate as a function of its concentration in the blood plasma [43]

threshold concentration in the blood plasma, about 28 mmol/l, is exceeded (Fig. 27-23). The renal threshold is thus only slightly above the physiological HCO_3^- concentration when the acid-base status (cf. p. 504) tends to become alkalotic. In a metabolic alkalosis the alkaline urine can reach a pH as high as 8 due to the excreted alkali bicarbonate.

The shape of the excretion curve appears to indicate a transport process with a maximal transport capacity similar to that of glucose. However, the absolute maximal reabsorption rate changes in proportion to the glomerular filtration rate (GFR); that is, the maximal amount of HCO_3^- reabsorbed per filtrate is constant. This glomerulotubular equilibrium of the whole kidney (28 mmol/l filtrate) indicates that the renal mechanism for adjustment of HCO_3^- concentration functions properly despite change in the GFR. If it had an invariant transport maximum an increased GFR would be accompanied by the loss of considerable amounts of HCO_3^-, and acidosis would be unavoidable.

Excretion of ammonium ions. H^+ ions can be excreted only until the pH of the urine has fallen to 4.5. The rate of H^+ excretion at the time when the urine has reached this pH depends primarily on the amounts of buffer anions filtered and not reabsorbed (see above). By **producing ammonia** (NH_3) the kidney itself can add a H^+ acceptor to the tubular fluid, thus considerably increasing the rate of H^+ excretion.

NH_3 is formed in all the tubule cells, mainly from *glutamine*. In aqueous solution it is in equilibrium with ammonium ion:

$$NH_3 + H^+ \rightleftarrows NH_4^+ \tag{18}$$

The two compounds differ considerably in their lipid-solubility and thus in their ability to pass through cell membranes (cf. pp. 624, 655). NH_3 is readily soluble in lipids and therefore can easily leave the tubule

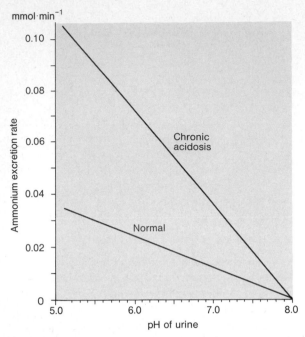

Fig. 27-24. Excretion of ammonium as a function of urine pH, in conditions of normal acid-base balance and chronic acidosis (dog)[4]

cells and diffuse into the tubular urine *(non-ionic diffusion)*. NH_4^+ is hardly lipid-soluble, and cell membranes are only slightly permeable to it. In accordance with Eq. (18), the NH_3 that diffuses into the urine has a greater tendency to be converted to NH_4^+ the lower the urine pH. NH_4^+ is thus "fixed" especially well, and excreted, in acid collecting-tubule urine. The NH_3 in the collecting-tubule urine is derived not only from the epithelium of the collecting tubule, but also from that of cortical tubule cells; it reaches the renal medulla mainly by way of convective transport and accumulates there by countercurrent diffusion.

The rate of NH_4^+ excretion rises with increasing urine acidity (Fig. 27-24). Because each excreted NH_4^+ ion contains a secreted H^+ ion, for a given urine acidity more H^+ ions are eliminated as the amount of NH_4^+ in the urine increases. In chronic acidoses the rate of NH_3 formation increases, in some cases sufficiently to raise the rate of NH_4^+ excretion by a factor of 10. Even in extreme chronic acidosis the pH of the urine cannot fall below 4.5.

The role of the kidneys in the various pathological disturbances of acid-base balance (cf. pp. 504 f.) can be summarized as follows:
In **respiratory acidosis** initially there is an elevation of arterial CO_2 partial pressure, resulting in a fall of plasma pH. Because of the acidosis, more H^+ ions are available for tubular secretion and hence the reabsorption of HCO_3^- is favored. Associated with the enhanced HCO_3^- reabsorption is a reduction of the

Cl^- reabsorption. The consequence is an increase in the HCO_3^- concentration in the plasma, a change in the same direction as that in CO_2 partial pressure. In this process the plasma pH must rise according to the Henderson-Hasselbalch equation (cf. p. 501). The second part of the compensatory mechanism is the more effective excretion of H^+. This is favored by the increased excretion of Cl^-, which results in a more pronounced fall in tubular urine pH combined with an enhanced formation and excretion of NH_4^+.
In **respiratory alkalosis** initially there is a reduction of arterial CO_2 pressure, resulting in a rise in plasma pH. Accordingly, the availability of H^+ for tubular secretion is reduced. Therefore the reabsorption of HCO_3^- decreases and its excretion rate increases. The consequence is a reduction of the HCO_3^- concentration in the plasma, a compensatory lowering of plasma pH. Simultaneously there is a rise in Cl^- reabsorption and K^+ excretion.
In **metabolic acidosis** fixed acids are present in excess, lowering the blood pH and with it the buffer base concentration (i.e., the HCO_3^- concentration) in the plasma. Respiratory compensation reduces the CO_2 pressure in the arterial blood, so that fewer H^+ ions are available; however, because the tubular HCO_3^- load is reduced at the same time, after its complete reabsorption sufficient H^+ ions remain from the Na^+-H^+ exchange process for excretion in the urine. The net result is an increase in the rate of H^+ excretion, evident in the increased titration acidity and NH_4 excretion.
In **metabolic alkalosis** the blood pH and plasma HCO_3^- are elevated, and respiratory compensation brings about a rise in arterial CO_2 partial pressure. The kidneys respond by excreting an alkaline urine, but not without complications. Under the greater tubular HCO_3^- load the secreted H^+ ions are consumed for HCO_3^- reabsorption (Fig. 27-22). The reabsorption of HCO_3^- remains incomplete, and together with Na^+ (and K^+) it is excreted. Gradually, the Na^+ loss may become so great that a Na^+ deficiency state can develop. In this case the Na^+-conserving mechanisms are activated, but the resulting increase in Na^+ reabsorption is accompanied by increased K^+ excretion. If this additional K^+ loss is not replaced, K^+ deficiency develops. As a result, the Na^+-K^+ exchange decreases in favor of Na^+-H^+ exchange. The consequence is an increased renal H^+ excretion, which exacerbates the existent metabolic alkalosis. This is an example of a positive feedback mechanism arising in disease, a "vicious circle". The kidneys are not well prepared to compensate a metabolic alkalosis because of the facility of cation loss under this condition.

Because the mechanisms of H^+ secretion and HCO_3^- reabsorption are so intimately involved with the tubular transport of sodium, potassium and chloride, they also interact with other renal functions associated with electrolyte transport. For example, the reabsorption of HCO_3^- decreases following administration of parathormone and during phosphate deficiency (cf. p. 630), and increases under a glucose load. Moreover, the renal acid-base excretion has also been found to depend on the effective blood volume or the extracellular fluid volume. As yet, however, no explanation of the mechanisms has been generally accepted (cf. [11]).

27.7 Renal Pathophysiology

The renal excretion system has a built-in functional safety factor, in that a person can manage with only one kidney, or with half the normal number of intact nephrons. As a rule, under these conditions, there is a *compensatory hypertrophy* of the remaining glomeruli as well as tubules. For example, after unilateral nephrectomy the weight of the remaining kidney increases by about 50%, with a corresponding increase in the rates of glomerular filtration and renal plasma flow. **Renal insufficiency** does not appear until the number of nephrons falls below 30% of normal or (as can be determined by tests of renal function) when the filtration rate is ca. 50 ml/min or less. At this point retention of the nitrogenous substances normally excreted begins to be significant. These nitrogenous materials are classified as **non-protein nitrogen.** It contains mainly urea, uric acid, creatin, and creatinin. The retention of the **nonprotein nitrogen** in the plasma is called **azotemia,** and the overall syndrome is called **uremia.** Uremic patients generally exhibit *hyperkalemia* and *metabolic acidosis* owing to the inadequate excretion of acids (reduced H^+ secretion and NH_4^+ excretion). In renal insufficiency the ability to concentrate the urine is diminished (hyposthenuria) or abolished (isosthenuria), and the ability to dilute it deteriorates to an equal extent. Therefore in isosthenuria the urine is always isotonic with the plasma. In treating renal insufficiency, the physician must bear in mind that medication normally excreted by the kidneys may be retained. Otherwise there is a risk of iatrogenic (induced by the physician's treatment) poisoning.

Acute renal failure with anuria not uncommonly accompanies severe **states of shock** *(circulatory shock, traumatic shock).* This serious disruption of function leads to progressive uremia and chronic renal insufficiency. At the outset, the disturbance is reversible. In view of the possibility of kidney damage, therefore, it is important to provide early support of the circulatory system when shock threatens (by infusion therapy). When acute renal failure does develop, the diminished renal blood flow plays an important role. As a consequence of local tissue hypoxia (ischemic hypoxia) the tubules are damaged and the reabsorption of Na^+ is impaired. Recovery of this function occurs gradually during the process of healing. The fact that Na^+ reabsorption is not yet fully recovered is reflected in the polyuria that persists for weeks during recuperation.

Diuretics are agents that increase the production of urine. They are usually employed therapeutically to enhance the excretion of salt and water (e.g., in cases of edema or hypertension) or to alleviate acute anuria or oliguria (see above). Diuretics with an osmotic action, such as mannitol, can be given in cases of acute anuria at best for short periods. The so-called saluretics or natriuretics, which primarily inhibit tubular electrolyte reabsorption (and only secondarily that of water), are useful long-term medications. But because the excretion of K^+ and H^+ is also affected (in some cases that of Cl^- and Ca^{++} as well), one must be prepared for disturbances of electrolyte and acid-base balance.

As a rule, diuretics that act directly on the tubules do so in all segments of the nephron, though their effects are more pronounced in a particular section. Acetazolamide is a carbonic-anhydrase inhibitor, which causes increased excretion of $NaHCO_3$ and $KHCO_3$ (resulting in metabolic acidosis with slight K^+ deficit). Thiazides, like the two diuretics to be mentioned next, are secreted proximally; because this inhibits the secretion of uric acid, thiazides are contraindicated by gout. Their chief action is to inhibit the distal reabsorption of Na^+ and Cl^-; during their use the plasma potassium concentration should be checked periodically. Two more powerful diuretics, ethacrynic acid and furosemide, act primarily to inhibit the reabsorption of salt in the ascending limb of the loop of Henle. The resulting chloride losses not uncommonly lead to metabolic alkalosis, exacerbated by the accompanying negative potassium balance. These can be used in combination with potassium-retaining diuretics such as triamterene and amiloride, to reduce the potassium loss.

27.8 References

Textbooks and Handbooks

1. Handbook of Physiology (ORLOFF, J., BERLINER, R. W., Eds.) Section 8: Renal Physiology. Washington D.C.: Amer. Physiol. Soc. 1973
2. Handbuch der mikroskopischen Anatomie des Menschen. Begun by W. VON MÖLLENDORFF, continued by W. BARGMANN. Vol VII/5: BARGMANN, W.: Niere und ableitende Harnwege. Berlin–Heidelberg–New York: Springer 1978
3. Physiology and Biophysics (RUCH, T.C., PATTON, H.D., Eds.) Vol. II: Circulation, Respiration and Fluid Balance. Philadelphia–London–Toronto: Saunders 1974
4. PITTS, R.F.: Physiology of the Kidney and Body Fluids. (3rd ed.) Chicago: Year Book 1974
5. SARRE, H.: Nierenkrankheiten. Physiologie, Pathophysiologie, Untersuchungsmethoden. Klinik und Therapie. Stuttgart: Thieme 1976
6. SMITH, H.W.: The Kidney. Structure and Function in Health and Disease. New York: Oxford Univ. Press 1951
7. VALTIN, H.: Renal Function. Mechanisms Preserving Fluid and Solute Balance in Health. Boston: Little Brown and Company 1973

Research Reports and Reviews

8. ANDERSSON, B.: Regulation of body fluids. Ann. Rev. Physiol. *39,* 185 (1977)
9. ANDERSSON, B.: Regulation of water intake. Physiol. Rev. *58,* 582 (1978)
10. ANDERSSON, B., OLSSON, K.: On central control of body fluid homeostasis. Cond. Reflex *8,* 147 (1973)

11. ARRUDA, J.A.L., KURTZMANN, N.A.: Relationship of renal sodium and water transport to hydrogen ion secretion. Ann. Rev. Physiol. *40*, 43 (1978)

12. BAYLIS, H., BRENNER, B.M.: The physiologic determinants of glomerular ultrafiltration. Rev. Physiol. Biochem. Pharmacol. *80*, 1 (1978)

13. DI BONA, G.F.: Neural control of renal tubular sodium reabsorption in the dog. Fed. Proc. *37*, 1214 (1978)

14. CHASIS, H., SMITH, H.W.: The excretion of urea in man and in subjects with glomerulonephritis. J. clin. Invest. *17*, 347 (1938)

15. CURREN, P.F., MACINTOSH, J.R.: A model system of biological water transport. Nature (Lond.) *193*, 347 (1962)

16. DAVIS, J.O.: What signals the kidney to release renin? Circulation Res. *28*, 301 (1971)

17. DEEN, W.M., ROBERTSON, C.R., BRENNER, B.M.: Glomerular ultrafiltration. Fed. Proc. *32*, 14 (1974)

18. DEETJEN, P.: Nierenphysiologie. In: GAUER, O.H., KRAMER, K., JUNG, R.: Physiologie des Menschen. Vol.7: Niere und Wasserhaushalt. München–Berlin–Wien: Urban & Schwarzenberg 1970

19. DEETJEN, P., KRAMER, K.: Die Abhängigkeit des O_2-Verbrauchs der Niere von der Na-Rückresorption. Pflügers Arch. ges. Physiol. *273*, 636 (1961)

20. DIAMOND, J.M., BOSSERT, W.H.: Standing-gradient osmotic flow. A mechanism for coupling of water and solute transport in epithelia. J. gen. Physiol. *50*, 2061 (1967)

21. EPPSTEIN, M.: Renal effects of head-out water immersion in man: Implications for an understanding of volume homeostasis. Physiol. Rev. *58*, 529 (1978)

22. FALCHUK, K.H., BRENNER, B.M., TADOKORO, M., BERLINER, R.W.: Oncotic and hydrostatic pressures in peritubular capillaries and fluid reabsorption by proximal tubule. Amer. J. Physiol. *220*, 1427 (1971)

23. FISCHER-FERRARO, C., NAHMOD, V.E., GOLDSTEIN, D.J., FINKIELMAN, S.: Angiotensin and renin in rat and dog brain. J. Exp. Med. *133*, 353 (1971)

24. FITZSIMONS, J.T.: Thirst. Physiol. Rev. *52*, 468 (1972)

25. GANTEN, D., MINNICH, J.L., GRANGER, P., HAYDUK, K., BRECHT, H.M., BARBEAU, A., BOUCHER, R., GENEST, J.: Angiotensin-forming enzyme in brain tissue. Science *173*, 64 (1971)

26. GAUER, O.H., HENRY, J.P.: Circulatory basis of fluid control. Physiol. Rev. *43*, 423 (1964)

27. GERTZ, K.H., BOYLAN, J.W.: Glomerular-tubular balance. In: Handbook of Physiology, Sect.8: Renal Physiology, Chap.23, p.763. Washington: Amer. Physiol. Soc. 1973

28. GIEBISCH, G., WINDHAGER, E.E.: Renal tubular transfer of sodium, chloride and potassium. Amer. J. Med. *36*, 643 (1964)

29. GOTTSCHALK, C.W.: Micropuncture studies of tubular function in the mammalian kidney. Physiologist *4*, 35 (1961)

30. GOTTSCHALK, C.W., LASSITER, W.E., MYLLE, M.: Localization of urine acidification in the mammalian kidney. Amer. J. Physiol. *198*, 581 (1960)

31. HIERHOLZER, K., WIEDERHOLT, M., STOLTE, H.: Hemmung der Natriumresorption im proximalen und distalen Konvolut adrenalektomierter Ratten. Pflügers Arch. ges. Physiol. *291*, 43 (1966)

32. JAMISON, R.L., BENNET, C.M., BERLINER, R.W.: Countercurrent multiplication by the thin loops of Henle. Amer. J. Physiol. *212*, 357 (1967)

33. KRAMER, K., DEETJEN, P., BRECHTELSBAUER, H.: Gegenstromdiffusion des Sauerstoffs im Nierenmark. Pflügers Arch. ges. Physiol. *274*, 63 (1961)

34. LAMEIRE, N.H., LIFSCHITZ, M.D., STEIN, H.H.: Heterogeneity of nephron function. Ann. Rev. Physiol. *39*, 159 (1977)

35. MALNIC, G., KLOSE, R.M., GIEBISCH, G.: Micropuncture study of renal potassium excretion in the rat. Amer. J. Physiol. *206*, 674 (1964)

36. MALNIC, G., KLOSE, R.M., GIEBISCH, G.: Micropuncture study of distal tubular potassium and sodium transport in rat nephron. Amer. J. Physiol. *211*, 529 (1966)

37. MALNIC, G., DE MELLO AIRES, M., LACAZ VIEIRA, F.: Chloride excretion in nephrons of rat kidney during alterations of acid-base equilibrium. Amer. J. Physiol. *218*, 20 (1970)

38. MAUNSBACH, A.B.: Ultrastructure of the proximal tubule. In: Handbook of Physiology, Sect.8: Renal Physiology, Chapter 2, p.31. Washington: Amer. Physiol. Soc. 1973

39. MORGAN, T., SAKAI, F., BERLINER, R.W.: In vitro permeability of medullary collecting ducts to water and urea. Amer. J. Physiol. *214*, 574 (1968)

40. PAPPENHEIMER, J.R.: Über die Permeabilität der Glomerulummembran in der Niere. Klin. Wschr. *33*, 362 (1955)

41. PEACH, M.H.: Renin-angiotensin-system: biochemistry and mechanisms of action. Physiol. Rev. *57*, 313 (1977)

42. PEASE, D.C.: Fine structure of the kidney seen by electron microscopy. J. Histochem. Cytochem. *3*, 295 (1955)

43. PITTS, R.F., AYER, L.H., SCHIESS, W.A.: The renal regulation of acid balance in man: III. The reabsorption and excretion of bicarbonate. J. clin. Invest. *28*, 35 (1949)

44. REID, I.A., MORRIS, B.J., GANONG, W.F.: The renin-angiotensin system. Ann. Rev. Physiol. *40*, 377 (1978)

45. SCHULTZ, S.G., CURRAN, P.F.: Coupled transport of sodium and organic solutes. Physiol. Rev. *50*, 637 (1970)

46. SHIPLEY, R.E., STUDY, R.S.: Changes in renal blood flow, extraction of inulin, glomerular filtration rate, tissue pressure and urine flow with acute alterations of renal arterial blood pressure. Amer. J. Physiol. *167*, 676 (1951)

47. SHIPP, J.C., HANENSON, I.B., WINDHAGER, E.E., SCHATZMANN, H.J., WHITTEMBURY, G., YOSHIMURA, H., SOLOMON, A.K.: Single proximal tubules of the Necturus kidney. Method for micropuncture and microperfusion. Amer. J. Physiol. *195*, 563 (1958)

48. STEIN, J.H., REINECK, J.H.: Effect of alterations in extracellular fluid volume on segmental sodium transport. Physiol. Rev. *55*, 127 (1975)

49. STEINHAUSEN, M., EISENBACH, G.M., GALASKE, R.: A countercurrent system in the renal cortex of rats. Science *167*, 1631 (1970)

50. STEINHAUSEN, M., TANNER, G.A.: Microcirculation and tubular urine flow in the mammalian kidney cortex (in vivo microscopy). S.-B. Akad. Wiss. Heidelberg, Math.-nat. Kl., 3.Abtlg. Berlin–Heidelberg–New York: Springer 1976

51. THOENES, W., LANGER, K.H.: Relationship between cell structures of renal tubules and transport mechanisms. In: THURAU, K., JAHRMÄRKER, H.: Renaler Transport und Diuretica. Berlin–Heidelberg–New York: Springer 1969

52. THURAU, K., DEETJEN, P., KRAMER, K.: Hämodynamik des Nierenmarkes. II. Wechselbeziehung zwischen vaskulärem und tubulärem Gegenstromsystem bei arteriellen Drucksteigerungen, Wasserdiurese und osmotische Diurese. Pflügers Arch. ges. Physiol. *270*, 270 (1960)

53. THURAU, K., SCHNERMANN, J.: Die Natriumkonzentration an den Macula-densa-Zellen als regulierender Faktor für das Glomerulumfiltrat. Klin. Wschr. *43*, 410 (1965)

54. THURAU, K., WOBER, E.: Zur Lokalisation der autoregulativen Widerstandsänderung in der Niere. Pflügers Arch. ges. Physiol. *274*, 553 (1962)

55. ULRICH, K.H.: Das Nierenmark – Struktur, Stoffwechsel und Funktion. Ergebn. Physiol. *50*, 434 (1959)

56. ULLRICH, K.H.: Sugar, amino acid and Na^+ cotransport in the proximal tubule. Ann. Rev. Physiol. *41*, 181 (1979)

57. ULLRICH, K.H., KRAMER, K., BOYLAN, J.W.: Present knowledge of the countercurrent system in the mammalian kidney. Progr. cardiovasc. Dis. *3*, 395 (1961)

58. VERNEY, E.B.: The antidiuretic hormone and factors which determine its release. Proc. roy. Soc. B *135*, 25 (1947)

59. WALKER, A.M., BOTT, P.A., OLIVER, J., MACDOWELL, M.C.: The collection and analysis of fluid from single nephrons of the mammalian kidney. Amer. J. Physiol. *134*, 580 (1941)

60. WEINER, I.M., MUDGE, G.H.: Renal tubular mechanism for excretion of organic acids and bases. Amer. J. Med. *36*, 743 (1964)

61. WIRZ, H.: Der osmotische Druck in den kortikalen Tubuli der Rattenniere. Helv. physiol. pharmacol. Acta *14*, 353 (1956)

62. WIRZ, H., DIRIX, R.: Urinary concentration and dilution. In: Handbook of Physiology, Sect. 8: Renal Physiology, Chap.13, p.415. Washington: Amer. Physiol. Soc. 1973

63. WIRZ, H., HARGITAY, B., KUHN, W.: Lokalisation des Konzentrierungsprozesses in der Niere durch direkte Kryoskopie. Helv. physiol. pharmacol. Acta *9*, 196 (1951)

64. ZAMBRASKI, E.J., DIBONA, G.F., KALDYANIDES, G.J.: Specificity of neural effect on renal tubular soldium reabsorption. Proc. Soc. Exp. Biol. Med. *151*, 543 (1976)

28   Water Balance; Transport of Fluids and Solutes

O. HARTH

28.1   Water Balance

Body Water and Water Turnover

Total body water and body weight [6, 8]. Of the chemical compounds that make up an organism, water accounts for by far the largest fraction. About 75% of the weight of a human newborn is water; as the child develops the relative water content of the body decreases, to an average of 63% in the young man and 52% in the young woman. The percentage of water continues to decline with advancing age, reaching averages of 52% and 46%, respectively.

As is evident in Table 28-1, the tissues of the various organs differ in water content. Because the water content of adipose tissue is especially small, the relative water content of the body as a whole depends heavily on the contribution of adipose tissue to the total weight. Women in general have relatively more adipose tissue than men; correspondingly, the relative water content of women is ca. 6–10% lower. Apart from the variable adipose-tissue fraction of the adult human, the water content of the lean body mass is 73.2 ± 3%, and independent of sex. The same percentage and sex-independence are found in most mammals.

The value 73.2% for the relative water content of the lean body mass is so constant that if the water content of the body is known, it can be used to determine the amount of body fat:

$$\% \, \text{fat} = 100 - \frac{\text{water content in \% of body weight}}{0.732} \quad (1)$$

The specific gravity (density relative to water) of the adult body is also correlated with the proportion of body fat (adipose tissue has the lowest density of all tissues, 0.94 g/ml). Once the density of the body has been determined, by weighing in air and under water and taking into account the volume of air in the respiratory tract, both its fat content and its water content can be found with the help of the diagram Fig. 28-1. The specific gravity of extremely lean people is about 1.1. For a 10% increase in the amount of

Table 28-1. Relative water content of the tissues of various organs, with their contribution to the total body weight of an adult. From [17]

Water content (%)	Tissue	Percentage of body weight
72	Skin	18
75.6	Muscle	41.7
22	Skeleton	15.9
74.8	Brain	2.0
68.3	Liver	2.3
79.2	Heart	0.5
79	Lungs	0.7
82.7	Kidneys	0.4
75.8	Spleen	0.2
83.0	Blood	8.0
74.5	Intestine	1.8
10.0	Adipose tissue	10.0

adipose tissue the specific gravity decreases by about 0.02 units and the water content by about 7.3% of the body weight. However, these relations hold only for healthy adults. The water content of children and of patients with disturbed water balance must be determined with the reliable indicator-dilution method (p. 646). This method is more convenient in application than the physical method.

Water balance of the organism [7]. Under normal conditions the water intake and water loss of the organism are in equilibrium. People in a temperate climate, with ordinary eating and drinking habits, have an average **water intake** of ca 2.5 l per day. About half of this is *drunk;* the other half is made up of the *water content of solid food* and the so-called *oxidation water* formed in the breakdown of the organic nutrients (cf. Table 28-2). On the other side of the balance sheet are the water losses through the kidneys, the intestine, the lungs and the skin. On the average ca. 1.4 l water is excreted as urine per day, and 100 ml with the feces; an additional 900 ml water per day is lost by evaporation in the respired air and through the skin. The losses by evaporation are strongly affected by the ambient temperature and the relative humidity of the environment. Water is given off continuously by skin in amounts too small to be noticed *(perspiratio insensibi-*

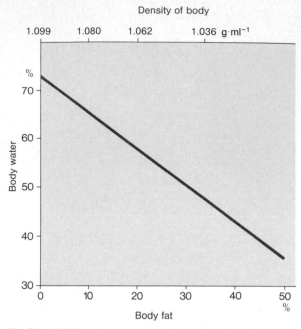

Fig. 28-1. Relation between water, fat, and density of the body. After [12] and [8]

Table 28-2. Daily water balance of adults. From [7]

Water intake	ml/day	Water loss	ml/day
Drinking	1200	Urine	1400
In solid food	900	Lungs and skin	900
Oxidation water[a]	300	Feces	100
Totals	2400		2400

[a] Oxidative decomposition produces the following amounts of water:

per g carbohydrate	0.6 ml
per g fat	1.09 ml
per g protein	0.44 ml

lis); and in a perceptible way by sweat glands (together with salt) under heat load (cf. Chapter 23).

The daily water turnover of an adult thus averages ca. 3–4% of the body weight. In an infant the relative water turnover is considerably greater (ca. 10% of the body weight).

The water balance of people accustomed to drinking large quantities may depart considerably from the above averages. When excessive drinking becomes habitual the hormonal regulatory systems soon adjust to the new situation; less or even no antidiuretic hormone is secreted to conserve water before excretion. In time its production is restricted. The control mechanism for water balance is now deficient and cannot prevent excessive water loss. Therefore, the subject soon returns to a state of water deficiency and suffers thirst. If the individual resumes normal water consumption, some time is required for hormone production to readjust so that the kidneys may again conserve water by normal antidiuresis. In order to achieve this condition, one must exert considerable will power to limit one's drinking. It is a familiar empirical observation that habit can become addiction; in this case some underlying mechanisms are known.

The increase in water turnover during *exposure to heat* (owing to weather or working conditions) results chiefly from the *production of sweat* (cf. Chapter 23). Although sweat is hypotonic it contains sufficient NaCl that heavy sweating causes an appreciable salt loss. Significantly more salt is lost during the early stages of exposure to heat than after acclimation is complete; initially, the losses must be compensated by water as well as by increased salt intake. Workers in hot surroundings can lose as much as 1.6 liters of water per hour, and their drinking requirement rises accordingly. The NaCl content of the sweat of such workers is ca. 0.03% when they are acclimatized, as compared with an initial 0.3%.

The **minimal water requirement of the adult** is ca. 1.5 l/day. To excrete the waste materials produced in the body, the kidneys require at least 500 ml water per day, and there is unavoidable loss of an additional 900 ml/d owing to the physical process of evaporation. If this requirement is not met the result is *hypertonic dehydration* (p. 648).

In *infants,* with their relatively high water turnover, the water balance can rapidly be severely disturbed; the resulting *hydropenia* (loss of water from all fluid compartments, resulting in increased salt concentration and osmolarity) is associated with "salt fever." Therefore when the infant is *weaned* from milk to soft foods it should be given additional water.

Water requirement and nutrition. The organism's water requirement can be lowered or raised by suitable diets. On a **pure carbohydrate** or **carbohydrate-fat diet** *less water is required* because of the greater yield of water during breakdown of these foods (cf. Table 28-2). The extra carbon dioxide produced in the process is blown off through the lungs without difficulty. **Protein-rich foods** give rise not only to water and carbon dioxide but to *metabolic end products* (mainly urea) which must be excreted by the kidneys. The more waste materials are produced by metabolism the more water is required to form the necessary urine. If one's energy requirement is supplied predominantly by, for example, 500 g of food protein (providing 2000 kcal or 8380 kJ), then only 220 ml oxidation water is produced (Table 28-2). On the other hand, the obligatory renal excretion of these end products requires at least 500 ml water; moreover, no allowance has yet been made for the increased salt intake that usually accompanies the eating of meat. For these reasons, the water requirement of the organism increases when the diet consists largely of protein.

These considerations are particularly important to patients with impaired kidney function, especially those with *oliguria* (daily excretion of 400 ml urine or less) or hyposthenuria (decreased urinary concentration capacity). The rate of excretion of osmotically active substances by the kidneys is limited by the **maximum urinary concentrating** they can achieve. The maximum concentration is about 1200 to 1400 mosmol/l. The more osmotically active material there is to excrete, the greater the obligatory volume of urine, and the higher the water requirement.

Normally about 30 g (= 500 mmol) urea is produced and excreted by the kidneys per day. To this is added ca. 12 g NaCl (= 205 mmol) consumed in food. The osmotic activity of the two together corresponds to 500 + 410 = 910 mosmol. To eliminate this amount alone, if the kidneys were achieving maximal concentration (1300 mosmol/l), urine would have to be produced at a rate of 700 ml/day. But other substances must also be excreted, so that a realistic estimate of urine production would be higher. And if the renal concentrating mechanism is impaired, the volume of urine required to excrete this amount of osmotic material is still greater. Fig. 28-2 is a graph of the 24-h urine volume as a function of the concentrating ability of the kidneys, the osmolarity, and of the correlated measure, the specific gravity of the urine. The parameter distinguishing the individual curves is the amount of osmotically active material that must be excreted by the kidneys, in mosmol/d. It is clear that both impairment of the urine-concentrating mechanism and increase in the production of osmotic materials raise the water requirement.

A *low-protein diet* can reduce the osmotic load to 200 mosmol/d. In states of oliguria such a diet is advisable under all conditions. Complete withdrawal of food is contraindicated, for the organism would then need to draw upon its own protein for energy. Note also that the "osmotic material" (osmol/l) in Fig. 28-2 includes all the osmotically active substances excreted, some of which can be concentrated only up to a certain limit, far below the overall maximal osmotic concentration. This is the reason for the inability of humans to excrete NaCl in the urine in a concentration equivalent to that in sea water, so that they cannot use sea water as drinking water (see below).

Water deficiency. A negative water balance causes an increase in the osmotic concentration of the body fluids. Usually such an imbalance results from inadequate water intake. If the balance is not restored a state of *dehydration* ensues, and the associated increase in concentration of the blood has serious effects on the circulation (pp. 399f.). Severe dehydration or hydropenia exists when the water deficit amounts to ca. 10% of the body weight. A water deficit of 20% is lethal.

Dehydration can also be brought about if the kidneys excrete water in excess. This may occur in diabetes insipidus (p. 629), if these patients are prohibited from drinking because the nature of the disease has not been understood. Therapeutically induced osmotic diuresis also causes increased water excretion. If these water losses are not compensated, the consequence is dehydration. For similar reasons shipwrecked people who try to quench their thirst by drinking seawater (ca. 900 mosmol/l) develop an ad-

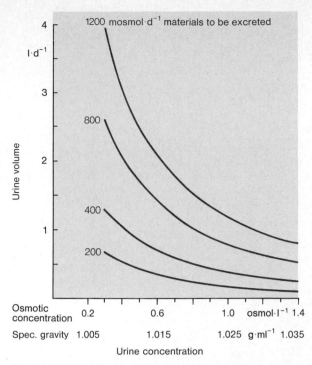

Fig. 28-2. Urine volume as a function of the urine concentration for the excretion of given quantities of osmotic materials. After [6]. 1200 mosmol/d is an average quantity with a normal diet; 800 mosmol/d are produced by the metabolism in fasting; an intake including only 100 g glucose reduces the osmotic production to 400 mosmol/d; 200 mosmol/d are produced with a carbohydrate diet low in protein and salt. To excrete those quantities the kidney needs a quantity of water depending on the actual or the attainable (in a case of hyposthenuria) urine concentration

ditional water deficit. They excrete the excess salt in water provided from their own body fluids (an intake of 500 ml sea water necessitates the production of 800 ml urine).

Water intoxication [7]. This term denotes the occurrence of convulsions (centrally elicited muscle cramps) following water consumption. The positive water balance, which the kidneys cannot prevent by appropriate water diuresis, markedly lowers the osmotic concentration of the extracellular fluid. As a result the cells take in water and swell. The nerve cells are particularly sensitive to hypotonic surroundings.

When renal water excretion is diminished (e.g., in oliguria or owing to the inadequate release of antidiuretic hormone (Chapter 27)), the rate of water intake should not be increased unless appropriate precautions are taken. In such cases, it would be a mistake on the part of the physician to try to promote diuresis by increasing water consumption (p. 633), for water intoxication could result instead.

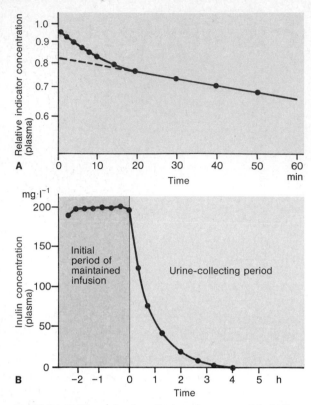

Fig. 28-3 A, B. Determination of volume by means of the indicator-dilution method. After [8]. The concentration of indicator in the plasma is plotted as a function of time, **A** for a low rate of indicator removal following a single injection (example: Evans blue for measuring plasma volume), and **B** for a high rate of indicator removal with maintained infusion until the concentration has equilibrated (example: inulin for measuring the extracellular fluid volume)

Fluid Compartments in the Body

Subdivisions of body fluid [6]. The composition of the aqueous solutions in the various kinds of cells, the interstitial spaces, the blood and lymph vessels, the ducts of the glands and the gastrointestinal tract differs considerably. Despite these differences it is useful to group the diverse body fluids according to certain common functional features. The basic subdivision is that between the **intracellular** and the **extracellular spaces** (cf. Chapter 16, Fig. 16-2). The extracellular compartment in turn has three subdivisions, the *interstitial fluid space* (extracellular spaces in the tissue), the *blood-plasma volume* (blood cells are included in the intracellular space) and the volume of the *transcellular fluids* (cerebrospinal fluid, aqueous humor, peri- and endolymph and the fluids in the body cavities and intestine). In this chapter we are concerned not with the differences among the fluids included in any one of these compartments, but rather with the differences that characterize the differ-

ent compartments – especially those crucial to the distribution of the body water among them. To evaluate these we must describe the distribution equilibria and the driving forces for fluid exchange within the body (cf. pp. 647 ff.).

Measurement of the volume of the systemic fluid compartments [8]. The volumes of the different compartments can be determined by indirect procedures based on the principle of **indicator dilution.** For each compartment to be measured a suitable substance or indicator must be chosen. The applied indicator in question must become uniformly distributed throughout its compartment, at a concentration equal to its concentration in the plasma. Other more general requirements are that the concentration of the substance be easy to measure, that it be nontoxic, and that it have no osmotic or pharmacological side effects that disturb the system. Because quantitative analysis is involved, the indicator must be foreign to the body.

In the indicator-dilution method a certain quantity of indicator (Q_I) dissolved in a negligibly small volume of fluid is injected, and when it has become uniformly distributed its plasma concentration (C_I) is measured. The "distribution volume" V is then calculated by

$$V = \frac{Q_I}{C_I} \quad \text{(ml or l)} \tag{2}$$

If some of the injected indicator is lost during the experiment (e.g., by storage, metabolic alteration or excretion), the slope of its concentration must be determined so that its theoretical concentration at time zero can be found by extrapolation (Fig. 28-3 A).

A variant of this procedure is the application of the indicator substance with a constant rate of infusion until its concentration is uniform throughout its volume of distribution (see below, Fig. 28-3 B).

Determination of total body water (TBW). Indicators suitable for this purpose include *antipyrine, heavy water* (D_2O) and water labelled with tritium or with ^{18}O (THO or $H_2^{18}O$). These substances diffuse through cell membranes, becoming uniformly distributed intra- and extracellularly within two hours. At this time the concentration of the water isotope in the plasma water is measured. The losses incurred meanwhile owing to excretion of the water isotopes (with the urine or by respiration) are negligible, but allowance must be made for the excretion of antipyrine to improve the accuracy of the measurement. As mentioned above, the total body water varies with the mass of body fat, and in an adult amounts to 50–70% of the body weight (p. 643).

Determination of extracellular fluid volume. A particularly useful indicator for the measurement of extracellular fluid volume (ECF) is *inulin.* Because inulin is excreted exclusively and rapidly by the kidneys, it is administered at a constant rate by slow maintained intravenous infusion until equilibration (uniform

distribution) is achieved. Then a blood sample is drawn for analysis, the urinary bladder is emptied and the infusion is
stopped (Fig. 28-3 B). During the following hours all excreted
urine is collected and the inulin it contains is measured. This
quantity and the estimated equilibration concentration of inulin in the plasma at the time the infusion is stopped are entered
in Eq. (2) to determine the ECF.

Other substances that can be used are thiosulfate, thiocyanate
and labelled sulfate. The results obtained with the different indicators, however, are not consistent. It is therefore preferable
to designate the volumes so obtained as "inulin volume," "sulfate volume" etc. The inulin volume is about 20% of the body
weight.

Determination of the volumes of plasma and interstitial fluid. The
measurement of **plasma volume** (PV) is treated on p. 454. Given
the plasma volume and the inulin volume, one can calculate the
interstitial-fluid volume (ISF) as follows:

$$ISF = ECF - PV \qquad (3)$$

The plasma volume averages 4.5%, and the interstitial volume
about 16%, of the body weight.

Determination of the intracellular fluid volume. The intracellular
fluid volume (ICF) cannot be determined directly by means of
an indicator, for no substance becomes distributed uniformly
and exclusively within the cells. The intracellular volume (ICF)
is found by subtracting the *extracellular fluid volume* (ECF)
from the *total body water* (TBW):

$$ICF = TBW - ECF \qquad (4)$$

The intracellular fluid accounts for 30–40% of the body weight.

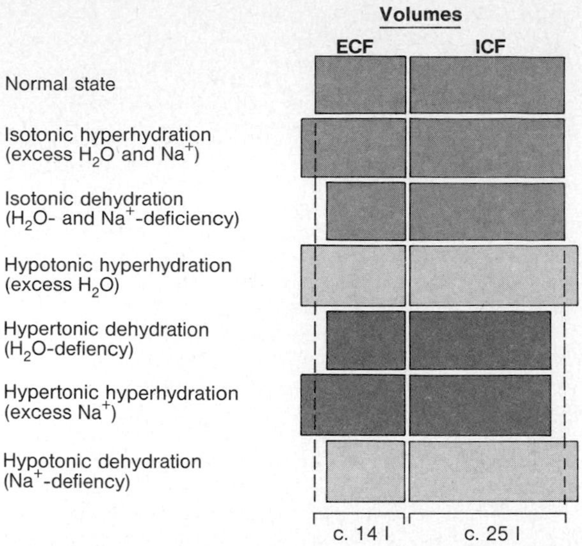

Extra- and intracellular volume changes[6, 13]. The extracellular fluid remains constant in volume and osmotic concentration as long as overall water and solute (chiefly Na^+) balance remains constant (p. 634).
*The distribution of body water between the extra- and
intracellular compartments is that dictated by osmotic
forces.* Should the osmotic concentrations in either
compartment be altered, water immediately shifts
from one to the other until a new osmotic equilibrium
is reached. The corresponding changes in volume
have to be corrected subsequently by the homeostatic
mechanisms so that the normal physiological state is
reastablished.

Changes in the relative extra- and intracellular volumes are of considerable clinical significance. They
can result from a great variety of disorders (e. g., heart,
kidney or liver or in diseases involving chronic vomiting or diarrhea). They can also be caused by inadequate infusion therapy.

The general clinical terms for volume abnormalities
of this kind are **hyperhydration** and **dehydration**
(Fig. 28-4). These two contrasting volume changes
may be classified according to the osmotic conditions
involved.

The volume changes resulting from gain or loss of water and sodium are restricted to the extracellular

Fig. 28-4. Changes in the volume of the extracellular and intracellular compartments, owing to osmotic forces created by disturbances in the water and sodium balances. After [9]. For further discussion see text

space only if the variation does not jeopardize isotonicity. **Isotonic hyperhydration,** with an *enlarged extracellular fluid volume,* appears spontaneously in
edematous diseases (cf. secondary hyperaldosteronism, pp. 637 and 684); the kidneys retain both NaCl
and water. An acute effect on volume of the same
kind is produced by infusion of large amounts of
physiological saline solution. In the opposite condition, **isotonic dehydration,** the *extracellular fluid volume only is reduced.* This deficit is caused by the loss
of isotonic body fluid (e. g., as the result of chronic
vomiting or diarrhea, or of the exudation accompanying extensive burns).

In cases of *primary imbalance of either water or sodium alone, isotonicity is lost* and therefore the resulting
volume changes involve the extra- and *intracellular
fluid.* Such cases are classified as *hypotonic or hypertonic hyperhydration or dehydration.* Under these conditions of osmotic disequilibrium the water always
shifts into the compartment with the higher osmotic
concentration.

Hypotonic hyperhydration resulting from a *positive
water balance* may occur for example, in cases of water accumulation resulting from water retention. Under these conditions the volume of the extracellular
fluid increases while its osmotic concentration decreases. In this way the extra-/intracellular osmotic
equilibrium is disturbed and water is shifted into the
cells; that is, the *intracelluar fluid volume is enlarged.*
Normally such aberrations are corrected by water diuresis. But if the ability of the kidneys to excrete water

is reduced (e.g., in cases of renal insufficiency or overproduction of ADH) drinking can induce a persistent *hypotonic expansion of both fluid compartments*. This condition presents the danger of water intoxication (p.645).

Changes analogous to those in hypotonic hyperhydration sometimes also occur with isotonic solutions, in a roundabout way. The infusion of an isotonic glucose solution acts at least as a strongly hypotonic infusion, because glucose is taken up by the liver and musculature and stored in an osmotically less active form as glycogen. In this way a surplus of osmotically free water remains in the extracellular fluid. Such apparently paradoxical behavior of isotonic solutions must always be considered in infusion solutions mainly containing substances to which the cell membranes are permeable; otherwise an unforeseen swelling of cells and even water intoxication (p.645) may be induced.

Water deficiency produces **hypertonic dehydration.** The water deficit initially causes an increase in extracellular osmolarity, which draws water out of the intracellular space. Then both the *extracellular and intracellular volumes are reduced* (Fig.28–4) and the overall osmolarity is increased. Because of the osmotic displacement of water from the larger, intracellular into the smaller, extracellular space, the loss of extracellular fluid is alleviated – a feature of considerable significance with regard to the maintenance of blood circulation in severe water deficiency.

Hypertonic hyperhydration results from a (selective) *positive sodium balance* (e.g., after infusion of a hypertonic NaCl solution). The initial increase in extracellular osmolarity is followed by movement of water out of the cells. It is characteristic of this state that the *extracellular fluid volume is enlarged while the intracellular volume is reduced.*

A *negative sodium balance* is associated, as a rule, with reduction of the extracellular fluid volume (p.634). In cases of adrenal insufficiency and other impairments of tubular sodium reabsorption, the loss of sodium is disproportionately large as compared with that of water, and **hypotonic dehydration** results. The *extracellular fluid volume is diminished,* as water moves into the more concentrated intracellular compartment; in the process, of course, the *intracellular fluid volume is enlarged correspondingly.*

The terms "hyperhydration" and "dehydration" refer to the extracellular fluid compartment. As we have seen, the intracellular fluid volume can change in the same direction as the extracellular (water imbalance), in the opposite direction (sodium imbalance) or not at all (isotonic imbalances). If one wants to denote the state of the cells, one can speak of *cellular hyperhydration or dehydration* – bearing in mind that this alone gives no reliable information about the state of the extracellular fluid compartment. For example, sodium imbalance produces hypertonic hyperhydration (Fig.28-4) with cellular dehydration.

28.2 Biophysical Bases of the Transport of Fluids and Solutes in the Body

Transport processes are treated in several other chapters, in the context of special problems of cell and organ function. Here we present a systematic outline of the physical laws and physiological mechanisms underlying all these forms of transport.

The various fluid compartments in the body are always separated by membranes through which substances are exchanged. The fluids separated by such a membrane may differ considerably in composition. This state of unequal distribution of materials is maintained by continuous fluxes of fluid or solutes through the membrane, which can be considered constant in time at a macroscopic level. A **dynamic equilibrium** of this sort requires an external supply of materials and/or energy. Should the energy supply fail, the previous state of equilibrium can no longer be maintained. The transport of substances changes spontaneously in such a way as to *equalize their concentrations* on the two sides of the membrane. Eventually, a **uniform distribution** of water and solutes characterizes the system without any directional transport. Under these conditions all functions of a living system cease.

Dynamic equilibria among different fluid compartments are numerous. Ultimately, they are based on the energy gained by the metabolic breakdown of nutrients. Fluids and the materials dissolved in them are transported through membranes under the action of certain driving forces; this transport can be either *active* or *passive.*

The **active transport** of a substance occurs only at cell membranes, and is *unidirectional*. The **energy** it requires is obtained from the splitting of energy-rich phosphates. The substances can be transported *"uphill"* (that is, against their concentration gradients), so that they accumulate at a relatively high concentration on one side of a membrane.

Passive transport, of either fluids or solutes, is based on transmembrane differences in concentration or osmotic or hydrostatic pressure. The processes in this category are *diffusion, osmosis* and *filtration.*

Diffusion, Osmosis and Filtration

Diffusion [1, 10]. The particles in a solution are constantly in random motion. These translational movements *(Brownian motion)* are continually interrupted by collisions. Brownian motion is dependent primarily on the temperature *(thermokinetic motion)*. In a homogeneous solution there is no preferred direction of particle movement; that is, in a macroscopic unit of volume the number of particles is constant in time. Macroscopically, then, there is no transport of substances in a particular direction, which would cause a change in concentration.

If there is a **concentration difference** between two adjacent volume units in a solution, the solute tends to move from the unit with the higher concentration to that with the lower concentration, until the concentrations have equalized. This form of transport is called **diffusion** (cf. p.476).

The driving force for diffusion of a dissolved substance is its concentration gradient. This is understandable in view of the fact that the chemical energy content of a solution depends strongly on its concentration. Therefore, the particle transport by diffusion always occurs in the direction of the slope of energy (i.e., slope of concentration). It ends when a homogeneous distribution of the material is reached. Diffusion occurs at the expense of the internal energy of the system. A modification of solute transport by diffusion is solvent transport by osmosis (see below).

According to Fick's law of diffusion, the particle flux $\dot{Q}_s$ of a substance is directly proportional to the concentration difference ΔC_s and the exchange area A, and inversely proportional to the distance travelled Δx (cf. Fig. 19-21, p.476):

$$\dot{Q}_s = D_s \cdot A \frac{|\Delta C_s|}{|\Delta x|} \quad \text{(quantity/time)} \qquad (5)$$

($\dot{Q}_s$ = particle flux (mol $\cdot$ s^{-1}), D_s = diffusion coefficient of particle species s (cm$^2 \cdot$ s^{-1}), A = area crossed (cm^2), $|\Delta C_s|$ = difference between the concentrations (mol $\cdot$ cm^{-3}) in the regions separated by the distance Δx (cm)).
The direction of particle flux is from the region with higher concentration to that with lower concentration – that is, down the concentration gradient.

The **diffusion coefficient** depends on the properties of the solute (molecular weight) and the solvent. The diffusion coefficients of substances in aqueous solution are very small (orders of magnitude 10^{-5} to 10^{-8} cm$^2 \cdot$ s^{-1}), reflecting the fact that the transport of substances by diffusion over macroscopic distances is relatively slow.

The mathematical treatment of dynamic (time-dependent) transport by diffusion requires partial differential equations,

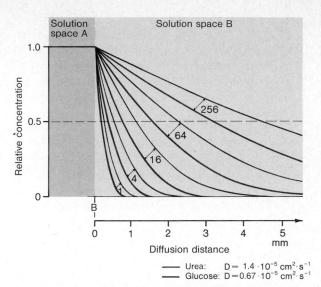

Fig. 28-5. The transport of substances by diffusion. The concentration profile of the "advancing front" of diffusing urea *(black)* and glucose *(red)* as it moves from the boundary (B) of solution space A into solution space B (at 1, 4, 16, 64 and 256 seconds). For further discussion see text

because the driving force – the concentration gradient – changes continually in space and time. The calculated time course of the equalization of concentration between the two solution spaces A and B in Fig. 28-5 is based on the simplest boundary conditions, as follows:

1. Solution space A is of infinite extent; that is, it contains so much glucose and urea that the loss of the amounts diffusing into space B is negligibly small.
2. The solution in A is stirred vigorously, so that the concentration at the boundary (B) with space B is always the initial 1.0.
3. The boundary (B) is infinitely thin, so that no time is required for the substances to cross it. Its purpose is to prevent convection from A to B.
4. In the homogenous solution space B, no convection or other movement of the solvent is permitted; glucose and urea may diffuse only in a direction perpendicular to the boundary.

Under these conditions glucose and urea diffuse like an advancing front into the space B, as shown by the calculated concentration-vs.-position curves for the times 1, 4, 16, 64 and 256 s after the beginning of diffusion. It can be seen that the time required for a certain concentration (cf. the dashed line for concentration 0.5) to be reached at any point in space B is proportional to the square of the distance of that point from the boundary. This relation reflects the fact that diffusion time increases as the square of the diffusion distance. The diffusion time also changes as the reciprocal of the diffusion coefficient; this relation is particularly easily discernible here because the diffusion coefficients of glucose and urea differ by about a factor of ½; glucose needs about twice as much time as urea to reach a certain concentration at a certain place.

Because the diffusion coefficient D is so small for substances dissolved in water, and in view of the quadratic relationship between diffusion time and diffusion distance, the diffusive transport of substances over a macroscopic distance (of the order of

1 mm or more) is very ineffective and inferior to convective transport (by bulk flow of fluid). Cells must be supplied with materials within some seconds, whereas the diffusion time of a solute from the periphery of a spherical organism with a radius of 1 cm to its center would amount to more than a day. A reliable delivery of nutrients by diffusion is possible only within volumes of microscopic dimensions (e. g., the distances between a capillary and the tissue cells supplied).

If two solutions of different concentrations are separated by a **membrane permeable to the solute,** equilibration of the two solutions occurs by way of diffusion. The movement of the solute under these conditions can be described in close anology to the continuous-solution-space situation, provided that the membrane is homogeneous and both its thickness and the diffusion coefficient for the solute in the membrane medium are known. Often, however, the properties of the membrane are not known. In this case the unknown membrane characteristic ($D_s/\Delta x$) is described by a permeability constant P_s, which is introduced in Eq. (5) as a proportionality constant:

$$\dot{Q}_s = -P_s \cdot A \cdot \Delta C_s \tag{6}$$

($\dot{Q}_s$ = particle flux (mol · s^{-1}), A = membrane area (cm^2), ΔC_s = difference between the concentrations of the solutions on the two sides of the membrane (mol · cm^{-3})). The unit of the permeability constant P_s is cm · s^{-1}.

The **supply of substrate to the tissue cells** is based on *convection* and *diffusion*. Particles and fluid are transported along the blood vessels by convection. Here diffusion serves mainly for transport across the thin adjacent resting layer of fluid (at the capillary wall). In the narrow interstitial fluid spaces, where convection is severely restricted, diffusion is the dominant transport process. A critical factor in the provision of an adequate supply of substrate to a tissue is the density of the capillary distribution within it and the width of the interstices (i. e., fluid-filled spaces) in the tissue; with dense capillarization and narrow interstices little time is required for transport. The driving forces for diffusive transport are the concentration gradients generated by consumption of the substances in the cells – or, for transport in the opposite direction, the reverse gradients generated by intracellular production of substances to be delivered to the blood.

Osmosis [3]. Osmosis is defined as the **transport of solvent through a semipermeable membrane** separating *two solutions of different concentrations*. Solvent molecules pass through the membrane, which is impermeable to the solute, into the compartment with higher solute concentration until the concentrations have equalized.

Osmosis is thus a diffusion of solvent particles through a membrane that prevents the diffusion of dissolved particles. When dissolved particles diffuse in a free solution space, solvent particles diffuse in the opposite direction to take their place. The change of place between the two particles proceeds imperceptibly because no volume displacement occurs. Therefore, the "opposed diffusion" of the solvent molecules can be neglected in considering ordinary solute diffusion. But when an interposed semipermeable membrane prevents diffusion of the dissolved particles the only molecular redistribution is the osmotic displacement of the water through the membrane.

If the compartment containing the more concentrated solution cannot accommodate the greater volume caused by the influx of water (e. g., if the walls are rigid and the membrane has high mechanical stability), a small influx of water causes a considerable increase in the hydrostatic **pressure** within the compartment. In this way a hydrostatic pressure difference between the two compartments is established, which acts as a driving force for water efflux. The higher the hydrostatic pressure, the less the influx rate for a given concentration difference. Eventually, no more water is shifted between the solutions because the hydrostatic pressure difference equalizes the oppositely directed driving force caused by the osmotic concentration difference. This **hydrostatic equilibrium pressure** corresponds to the **osmotic pressure difference** between the solutions:

$$\Delta\pi = RT \cdot \Delta C \tag{7}$$

($\Delta\pi$ = osmotic pressure difference, R = universal gas constant, T = absolute temperature, ΔC = concentration difference between the dissolved particles in the two compartments)

In medicine, the osmotic pressure is given either in mm Hg or in atm. Theoretically, a molar aqueous solution of a non-dissociating substance (e. g., glucose) has an osmotic pressure of **22.4 atm** (2262 kPa) as compared with pure water. The osmotic pressure of a many-component solution is proportional to the total concentration of all the particles. For this reason, in a state of complete dissociation a 0.5-molar solution of NaCl has an osmotic pressure of 22.4 atm. Because biological fluids always contain many components, their *osmotically active concentration* (osmolarity) is expressed by the unit osmol/l. The physiological osmolarity of the blood is ca. 300 mosmol/l.

Natural cell membranes are relatively highly permeable to water. Their permeability to dissolved particles is lower in general and varies widely with the molecular characteristics of the substance concerned (p. 655). Because of membrane potentials and ion pumps (pp. 9f.), significant transmembrane concentration differences of certain salts, especially those of sodium and potassium, are maintained. The volume of blood cells introduced to an isotonic saline solution remains practically unchanged although the cell membranes are permeable to sodium. In this case sodium shifts are counteracted by the sodium pump mechanism, which even in vitro still stabilizes the intracellular sodium concentration. Therefore, the cell membrane appears to be sodium-impermeable.

Other components of the extracellular fluid and intracellular fluids pass the membrane more or less quickly and are adjusted to a thermodynamic equilib-

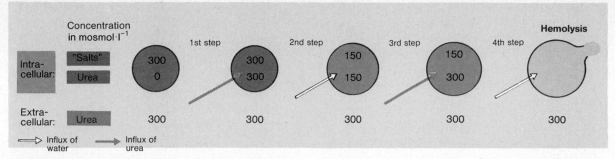

Fig. 28-6. Hemolysis in an isotonic urea solution. The erythrocyte membrane is permeable to water and urea, but in the short term practically impermeable to the intracellular components (here lumped as "salts"). The continuous effects of diffusion and osmosis following introduction of erythrocytes into an isotonic urea solution are shown here in steps. Step 1: the concentration gradient of urea causes urea to diffuse into the cell until the concentrations equalize. Step 2: the total intracellular osmolarity has risen from 300 to 600 mosmol/l. This causes an influx of water until the osmotic concentrations equalize; the cell swells and the intracellular concentrations fall until isotonicity is reestablished. Step 3: again there is an outside-to-inside concentration gradient for urea, which again diffuses inward until equalization. Step 4: like Step 2, and so on until hemolysis occurs by cell rupture

rium. In all these cases the cell membrane behaves as a **non-ideal semipermeable membrane.** The result is that when living cells are placed in a bathing fluid differing in composition from the extracellular fluid, material may enter or leave the cells, the processes of diffusion and osmosis being superimposed (cf. Fig. 28-6).

However, when a drop of blood is introduced into a relatively large volume of *isotonic urea solution,* the blood cells swell. Eventually they burst and *hemolysis* occurs. This effect is due to the fact that the erythrocyte membrane is permeable to the extracellular urea, but not to the intracellular salt and macromolecules. Because of the concentration difference across the membrane, urea diffuses into the blood cells, and the resulting osmotic disequilibrium causes water to follow it in. Although these events overlap in time, for clarity they are presented as successive steps in Fig. 28-6.
It is also easy to visualize the processes leading to hemolysis when the drop of blood is introduced into a hypertonic urea solution. Here the first event is an osmotic flow of water out of the cells, until the osmotic concentrations are equalized; during this stage the erythrocytes shrink. From then on, however, matters proceed as in Fig. 28-6, from the first step to hemolysis.

It is apparent from these considerations that transmembrane water displacement can occur even with no change in tonicity of the extracellular fluid. Therefore to alleviate cellular hyperhydration (p. 648) by osmotherapy one may not use hypertonic solutions of substances to which the cell membrane is permeable.
The **capillary membranes** are so permeable to the small molecules dissolved in the plasma that they present no obstacle to these substances. They act as semipermeable membranes only with regard to particles of high molecular weight (proteins). The **colloid osmotic (oncotic) pressure of the plasma proteins** affects the distribution of fluid between the blood and interstitial fluid, but it is also affected by transcapillary **hydrostatic pressure differences** (cf. the Starling model, pp. 418 f.).

Filtration and ultrafiltration [1, 10]. Filtration is the passage of a solution through a membrane under the driving force of a hydrostatic pressure difference in the fluids on the two sides of the membrane. The filters in common use are pore membranes, the properties of which depend on the dimensions (radius, length) and number of the pores. If these values are known, the fluid flow through the filter membrane can be described by the Hagen-Poiseuille law (p. 401):

$$\dot{V} = \frac{r^4 \cdot \pi \cdot n}{8 \cdot l \cdot \eta} \cdot \Delta p \quad \text{(volume/time)} \tag{8}$$

($\dot{V}$ = volume flow or filtration rate, r = mean or effective pore radius, Δp = hydrostatic pressure difference or filtration pressure, n = number of pores, π = ratio of circumference to diameter of circle, l = length of the pores, which in the geometrically simplest case corresponds to the thickness of the membrane, η = viscosity)

The pore numbers and dimensions in **biological membranes,** to which the pore-membrane model can be applied, are usually not known. Here the following empirical equation is used to describe flow:

$$\frac{\dot{V}}{A_m} = \frac{k \cdot \Delta p}{\eta \cdot \Delta x} \quad (\text{ml} \cdot \text{s}^{-1} \cdot \text{cm}^{-2}) \tag{9}$$

(k = specific filtration constant, A_m = membrane area, Δx = membrane thickness)

Because the uncertainty in measurement of the thickness of biological membranes is relatively large, the

Table 28-3. Filtration coefficient K_f for various membranes. From [1, 10]

Membrane	K_f $ml \cdot s^{-1} \cdot cm^{-2} \cdot (cm\ H_2O)^{-1} \cdot 10^{-8}$
Cell membranes	
Leukocyte	0.2
Erythrocyte	0.9
Capillary membranes	
Muscle	2.5
Glomerulus	500
Peritubular capillary	90
Artificial membrane	
Dialysis membrane	150
(thickness = 0.5 μm	
pore radius = 2 nm)	

specific filtration constant is replaced by the *filtration coefficient* K_f:

$$K_f = \frac{k}{\eta \cdot \Delta x} \quad (ml \cdot s^{-1} \cdot cm^{-2} \cdot (cm\ H_2O)^{-1}) \qquad (10)$$

The filtration coefficient thus corresponds to the volume flow through the membrane per unit pressure and area.

The equation

$$\frac{\dot{V}}{A_m} = K_f \cdot \Delta p \quad (ml \cdot s^{-1} \cdot cm^{-2}), \qquad (11)$$

which uses the filtration coefficient to estimate volume flow rate per unit area, is independent of any particular membrane model. For this reason the equation can be employed to characterize different kinds of biological membranes (cell membranes, epithelial membranes).

Ultrafiltration. A filtration process that not only separates out large suspended particles, but also selectively retains dissolved molecules of a certain size, is called ultrafiltration. The model of a pore membrane can be used to find the relation between the mean or effective radius of the membrane pores and the sieving effect based on molecule radius (cf. Chapter 27, p. 618).

To describe volume flow through the membrane during ultrafiltration, one must add to Eq. (11) a term reflecting osmotic pressure:

$$\frac{\dot{V}}{A_m} = K_f \cdot (\Delta p_{1,2} + \Delta \pi_{2,1}) \qquad (12)$$

($\dot{V}$ = volume flow rate, A_m = membrane area, K_f = filtration coefficient, $\Delta p_{1,2}$ = hydrostatic pressure difference between the

fluids 1 and 2 on the two sides of the membrane, $\Delta \pi_{2,1}$ = osmotic pressure difference between the fluids 2 and 1).

If a solution used for ultrafiltration contains particles to which the membrane is not quite impermeable – that is, the particles are filtered with some restriction – it is erroneous to use π in Eq. (12). The error can be corrected by use of the **reflection coefficient** σ.

By definition, the magnitude of an osmotic pressure difference between two solutions is equal to the magnitude of the opposed hydrostatic pressure difference that just prevents flow of water through the semipermeable membrane. In the case of a non-ideal semipermeable membrane, which allows a limited diffusion of particles, the hydrostatic counterpressure that prevents water flow falls steadily as the osmotic pressure falls. The reflection coefficient can be obtained by extrapolating the hydrostatic pressure to time zero, as follows:

$$\sigma_s = \frac{\Delta p_{t=0}}{\Delta \pi_{ideal}} \qquad (13)$$

(σ_s = reflection coefficient of the substance s, $\Delta p_{t=0}$ = hydrostatic pressure difference at the time t = 0, $\Delta \pi_{ideal}$ = theoretical osmotic pressure difference across an ideal semipermeable membrane)

The reflection coefficient of a substance can lie between $\sigma_s = 1$ and $\sigma_s = 0$. In the case of an ideal semipermeable membrane $\sigma_s = 1$ for all solutes; that is, the dissolved particles are "totally reflected" by the membrane. Under this condition a filtrate would consist of pure water. For particles that are entirely unimpeded by the membrane and thus pass as readily as water, $\sigma_s = 0$. The filtrate now contains all the solutes in an unchanged concentration.

Equation (12) is therefore modified for non-ideal semipermeable membranes by replacing $\Delta \pi_{2,1}$ by $\sigma_s \Delta \pi_{ideal}$.

Combined passive membrane transport of water and solutes [1, 10]. In general, various kinds of transport occur simultaneously at biological membranes. Even if the transport mechanisms of the different substances are mutually independent in themselves, it is quite likely that transport of one substance will have some effect on that of the others. Consider, for example, the alteration of the rate of transport of a substance by the flow of water across the membrane. The transport rate of a substance diffusing through a membrane down a concentration gradient can be raised or lowered by a superimposed water current, depending on the directions of the two transport processes and on the degree to which the shift or flow of water changes the concentration gradient. Analysis of such superimposed transport processes requires differential equations.

The following discussion will be limited to the transport of particles and water together, in the absence of a transmembrane concentration difference – that is, in absence of diffusion. Here, again, the reflection coefficient σ is required.

Solvent drag. This term is used to describe the situation in which the bulk flow (of water) through a membrane affects the transport of dissolved substances – the particles are "dragged" along in the current. Particles not impeded by the membrane ($\sigma = 0$) appear on the downstream side in the original concentration. This is the case, for example, when small molecules such as glucose, dissolved in the blood plasma water, filter through the arterial end of a capillary.

If there is no transmembrane difference in concentration of a substance at the outset, subsequent bulk flow causes a particle flow rate of

$$\dot{Q}_s = (1 - \sigma_s) \cdot \overline{C}_s \cdot \dot{Q}_w \tag{14}$$

($\dot{Q}_s$ = flux of the particles due to solvent drag, σ_s = reflection coefficient of s, $\dot{Q}_w$ = volume flow rate of water, $\overline{C}_s$ = mean concentration of substance in the fluids at the boundaries of the membrane.

In the chapter on the kidney (27) it was pointed out that a considerable fraction of the tubular reabsorption of solutes occurs by solvent drag (pp. 626f. and Fig. 27-15).

Equilibrium Distribution of Ions

Gibbs-Donnan equilibrium [1, 3]. The concentrations of the ions in the blood plasma and the interstitial fluid are not the same, even though the capillary membrane is readily permeable to the small ions present in both fluids. The ionic compositions of the plasma and the glomerular filtrate also differ (cf. Table 27-4). The cause of this nonuniformity is the higher concentration of **impermeant anions** (proteinates) on the blood side of the capillary membrane. The unequal distribution of the small ions on the two sides of the membrane can be simulated with a simple experimental device.

If in a closed system with constant volume a homogeneous saline solution is separated into two compartments by a rigid permeable membrane, and a certain amount of proteinate to which the membrane is impermeable is added to one of the compartments, salt passes through the membrane until a thermodynamic equilibrium – the **Gibbs-Donnan equilibrium** – is reached. In this condition the concentrations of the permeant ions in the two compartments are no longer identical.

The **equilibrium distribution** of the ions, which is maintained with no further transmembrane shifts of ions or water, is governed by two factors: 1. The transmembrane potential difference corresponds to the *equilibrium potential* of the permeant ions, which is expressed by the Nernst equation (Eq. 15). 2. In each of the two solutions the condition of *electrical neutrality* must be fulfilled; that is, the equivalent concentrations of the cations and anions in a solution is the same. Thus the equilibrium distribution of the permeant ions (here we consider, apart from the protein ions, only the monovalent ions Na^+ and Cl^-) is described as follows:

$$\varepsilon_e = \frac{R \cdot T}{F} \ln \frac{[Na^+]_i}{[Na^+]_o} = \frac{R \cdot T}{F} \ln \frac{[Cl^-]_o}{[Cl^-]_i} \tag{15}$$

(ε_e = electrical equilibrium potential, R = universal gas constant, T = absolute temperature, F = Faraday constant, $[Na^+]_{i,o}$ and $[Cl^-]_{i,o}$ = concentrations of the two ions – i, in the proteinate-containing fluid, e.g. plasma, and o, in the proteinate-free or -poor fluid, e.g. interstitial fluid).

Transforming Eq. (15) it follows that

$$\frac{[Na^+]_i}{[Na^+]_o} = \frac{[Cl^-]_o}{[Cl^-]_i} \tag{16}$$

or

$$[Na^+]_i \cdot [Cl^-]_i = [Na^+]_o \cdot [Cl^-]_o \tag{17}$$

Eq. (17) is called the *Donnan rule*. It states that the product of the concentrations of the permeant ions on one side equals that on the other.

The condition of electroneutrality within each solution requires that

$$[Na^+]_o = [Cl^-]_o \tag{18}$$

Therefore, Eq. (17) can be written:

$$[Na^+]_i \cdot [Cl^-]_i = [Cl^-]_o^2 \tag{19}$$

$[Na^+]_i$ equals $[Cl^-]_i + [Pr^-]_i$ (where $[Pr^-]_i$ signifies the equivalent concentration of the impermeant anion), and it is clear that $[Na^+]_i$ is greater than $[Cl^-]_i$. Geometrically the product of the unequal factors of Eq. (19) corresponds to a rectangle, and $[Cl^-]_o^2$ to a square of the same area. In this case, the sum of the unequal sides of the rectangle is greater than the sum of the sides of the square. Therefore, it follows that

$$[Na^+]_i + [Cl^-]_i > 2[Cl^-]_o \tag{20}$$

$$[Na^+]_i + [Cl^-]_i > [Na^+]_o + [Cl^-]_o \tag{21}$$

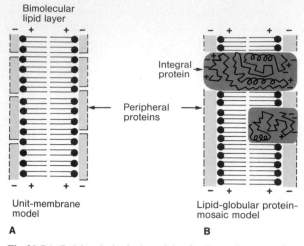

Bimolecular lipid layer

Integral protein

Peripheral proteins

Unit-membrane model

Lipid-globular protein-mosaic model

A   **B**

Fig. 28-7 A, B. Morphological models of cell membranes. After [4, 16]. **A** Model of the unit membrane, according to DANIELLI and DAVSON. **B** The model of LENARD and SINGER ("fluid mosaic model")

The sum of the permeant ions on the side with the impermeant proteinate is greater than on the other side. Because of the higher osmotic (and colloid osmotic) pressure, water would be shifted into this solution if conditions permit.

Gibbs-Donnan equilibria at living cell membranes. Because the cytoplasm contains anions (primarily proteinate ions) that cannot pass the membrane, ions that can move through it passively become distributed according to the Donnan relationships. In the living cell an influx of water due to osmotic forces is not counteracted by hydrostatic pressure as in the capillary, but rather is limited by the **Na⁺ pump.** The pump transports Na^+ outward, thus lowering the effective intracellular osmotic concentration. If the active outward transport of Na^+ is inhibited, the intracellular osmotic pressure increases as a result of the prevailing influx of Na^+. Now water enters the cells osmotically, and the cells swell; this swelling is evident in cells post mortem. One of the tasks of the Na^+ pump is thus to control cell volume. It is evident, then, that **actively transported ions are not governed by the Donnan distribution.**

The concentration ratios of permeant ions that follow passively the Donnan distribution is given by the Donnan factor r:

$$r = \frac{[Cl^-]_i}{[Cl^-]_o} = \frac{[H^+]_o}{[H^+]_i} < 1 \qquad (22)$$

Here H^+ was selected as the cation, because in most cases this ion (unlike Na^+ or K^+) is also in Donnan equilibrium at cell membranes. It follows from Eq. (22) that the intracellular pH is lower than that of the

extracellular fluid (because $r < 1$, $[H^+]_i > [H^+]_o$ and thus $pH_i < pH_o$). Because the Donnan distribution is a thermodynamic equilibrium of all passively distributed ions, the *Donnan factor in a system is identical for all such univalent ions.* If it is known for one ion, the concentrations of which in the two solution compartments have been determined, one need know only one of the concentrations of another ion in the system (e.g., that in the extracellular fluid) to calculate the other (the intracellular concentration) by the Donnan factor. (For multivalent ions, with valency = n, the Donnan factor corresponds to the nth root of the concentration ratio.)

The Donnan factor at the capillary membrane between blood plasma and interstitial fluid is about 0.95; the ratio of the Na^+ concentrations in the interstitial fluid (142 mmol/l) and in the plasma water (150 mmol/l) amounts to 0.947. This supports the argument that Na^+ follows a (passive) Donnan distribution in the region of the capillary membranes. The cerebrospinal fluid has a Na^+ concentration of 155 mmol/l, giving a Donnan factor of 1.033 relative to blood plasma. This value reflects the fact that the Na^+ distribution between blood plasma and CSF (which contains less proteinate) is not passive; the formation of the CSF in the chorioid plexus cannot be based on filtration alone. The filtration process must be supplemented by an active transport of Na^+ into the CSF.

Special Features of Transport through Biological Membranes

Structure of the cell membrane and membrane models

[3, 15]. *Electron micrographs* of cell membranes reveal a three-layered structure; two dense bands are separated by a light band. The overall thickness of the three layers is ca. 7.5 nm. *Biochemically,* the cell membrane consists of proteins and lipids. Most abundant among the lipids are phospholipids ($> 60\%$), followed by cholesterol and cerebrosides. The two current membrane models – the unit membrane model and the lipid-globular protein mosaic model – differ in the proposed arrangement of the various proteins and lipids (Fig. 28-7).

The **unit membrane** is assumed to be a regular assemblage of units such that a **bimolecular lipid layer** in the middle is covered by an inner and outer protein layer. The polar groups of the lipids are oriented toward the protein layers and are adjacent to protein groups of the opposite charge.

The **lipid-globular protein mosaic model** also postulates a membrane with a bimolecular lipid layer. Again, some proteins are associated with the polar lipid groups – these can easily become detached. Other proteins, however, adhere much more firmly to the lipids, so that when they are removed lipids are usually removed from the membrane with them. That is, these proteins appear to be integral components of the membrane *(integral proteins)*.

The integral proteins probably have an asymmetrical configuration. The ionic groups of their amino acids are oriented outward, whereas neutral and lipophilic components of the amino-acid sequences are anchored in the hydrophobic inner layer of the lipids. The integral proteins – and this is the decisive difference from the unit-membrane model – extend well into the lipid layer, and in some cases all the way through it (Fig. 28-7 B). Integral proteins are incorporated into the membrane like tiles in a mosaic.

The integral molecules represent the membrane-bound enzymes and carriers (see below) as well as sites considered to be the basis of "membrane pores".

Diffusion of substances through the cell membrane [2, 3]. The diffusion coefficient of small molecules (m.w. < 1 000) in aqueous solution is inversely proportional to the square root of the molecular weight (MW):

$$D = \frac{\text{const.}}{\sqrt{MW}} \qquad (23)$$

Because this relationship is the same in oily fluids, it could apply to the diffusion of substances through the lipid-containing cell membrane. In that case, if D were replaced by the permeability constant P (cf. Eq. 6), which is independent of membrane thickness, it should hold that

$$P \cdot \sqrt{MW} = \text{const.} \qquad (24)$$

However, experiments have shown that the **passive permeability** of the cell membrane to solutes is determined by other factors as well. The **lipid-solubility** of a molecule has an especially strong influence (it can be found from the substance's **partition coefficient** between an aqueous and an oily phase), as does the number of **hydrogen bonds** between the substance and its water of hydration. These hydrogen bonds must be broken when the molecule crosses the boundary from the aqueous to the lipid phase, and reestablished when it emerges into the aqueous phase again. The permeability of the membrane to a substance rises with increasing lipophilicity, and falls with the number of hydrogen bonds that must be broken. Lipophilic substances therefore pass the membrane more readily than hydrophilic substances of comparable molecular weight, because they penetrate the lipid

phase of the membrane more easily and usually they also form fewer hydrogen bonds with the water. Eq. (24) does not reflect such effects. In a homologous series of molecules the addition of one (lipophilic) CH_2 group increases permeance by a factor of two. On the other hand, each additional hydrogen bond is thought to decrease permeance by about a factor of five.

Many **drugs and toxins** with intracellular sites of action are **lipophilic,** and thus can enter the cells rapidly and act in a short time. The significance of the lipophilic components of the molecules of weak organic acids and bases, and their **non-ionic diffusion** through membranes, are discussed in the chapter on the kidney (p.624).

The relationships are more complicated in the case of passive **membrane permeability to ions** of strong electrolytes such as Na^+, K^+ and Cl^-. The "channels" in the membrane through which the ions enter the cell can bear *fixed charges* that encourage the entry of one ionic species and impede that of oppositely charged ions. The high permeability of the erythrocyte membrane to anions, which makes possible the rapid exchange of Cl^- for HCO_3^- (p.498), is associated with a very low cation permeability. This selectivity is probably ascribable to positive fixed ions (basic amino acids of membrane proteins) in the membrane. By contrast, the permeability of the resting membrane of the nerve fiber is considerably greater to K^+ than to Cl^-. During excitation the passive permeability of the axon membrane to Na^+ becomes many times greater (pp. 13 f.). A specific transport system, briefly activated during excitation, is thought to be responsible for this change.

Facilitated diffusion [2, 3, 10]. Cell membranes are considerably more permeable to certain substances such as D-glucose or L-amino acids than to the L or D (respectively) forms. The permeation properties of molecules discussed so far cannot explain this selectivity. There must be special mechanisms within the membrane that accelerate the passage of substances through the membrane in the presence of a transmembrane concentration difference, so that the concentrations equilibrate more rapidly. This process is denoted by the term **facilitated diffusion** *(facilitated transfer)*.

In Fig. 28-8, the uptake of D-glucose into erythrocytes is taken as an example of facilitated diffusion whereas L-glucose is an example of simple diffusion. The rate of glucose influx into the erythrocytes as a function of the extracellular glucose concentration applies to an initial period of time in which the intracellular concentration is still practically unchanged.

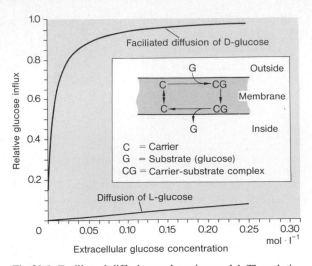

Fig. 28-8. Facilitated diffusion and carrier model. The relative influx into erythrocytes of D-glucose (facilitated diffusion) and L-glucose (simple diffusion) is plotted as a function of the outside concentration; the inside concentration is negligibly small. The facilitated diffusion saturates, a characteristic that can be interpreted in terms of carrier transport (cf. inset)

Transport across membranes by facilitated diffusion exhibits **saturation,** a feature analogous to the kinetics of unidirectional enzyme reactions described by the Michaelis-Menten equation. The influx of glucose into erythrocytes obeys the corresponding equation

$$\dot{Q}_g = \frac{\dot{Q}_{max}C_g}{K_m + C_g} \qquad (25)$$

($\dot{Q}_g$ = glucose influx, C_g = glucose concentration in the external medium, $\dot{Q}_{max}$ = maximal influx, K_m = glucose concentration at $\dot{Q}_{max}/2$, corresponding to the Michaelis constant)

The saturation characteristic of facilitated diffusion is consistent with the assumption of a specific **carrier** in the membrane, which forms a temporary bond with the substrate to be transported. The acceleration of transport can be explained by hypothesizing a movable carrier, which when bound to the substrate moves through the membrane more rapidly than the substrate alone. At the outside of the membrane the carrier binds to the substrate (glucose, in the example); the carrier-substrate complex moves to the opposite side, where the substrate is split off (Fig. 28-8, inset). The saturation of transport would then be due to the limited number of carriers available; as the external substrate concentration increases, a point is reached at which all the carriers are in operation.

The *transport of glucose into erythrocytes* ceases when the external and internal concentrations are equal – that is, the *driving force is the existing concentration gradient.* This, as we have seen, is a distinguishing characteristic of *diffusion* [11].

The glucose carrier can also transport other mono-

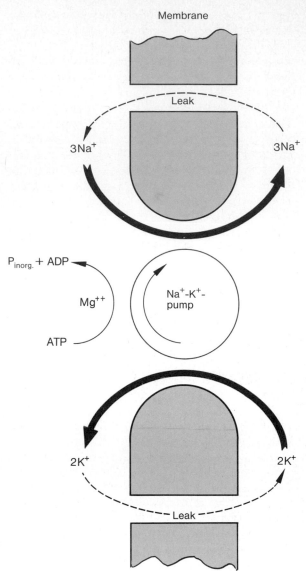

Fig. 28-9. Coupled Na^+-K^+ pump of the erythrocyte membrane. After [14]

saccharides, but as a rule (owing to lower affinity) at a lower rate.

The first step in the active reabsorption of glucose in the kidney (p. 627) is uptake by the tubule cells. It depends on the driving force of a Na^+ concentration gradient between the tubular fluid in the proximal convolution and the interior of the tubule cell. This gradient is maintained by the active outward transport of Na^+ on the opposite side of the cell. The passive luminal influx of Na^+ into the cell is coupled with that of glucose (cotransport). As a result, glucose accumulates in the cell. Because the process as a whole achieves the uphill transport of glucose into the cell, it is called *secondary active transport.* The absorption of glucose and amino acids in the intestine occurs similarly.

Active transport [2, 18]. A typical characteristic of a living cell is the ability to maintain a thermodynamic disequilibrium in ion distribution with respect to the outside medium. If blood is brought to 0 °C, the erythrocytes lose K^+ and take in Na^+ from the plasma, until a thermodynamic equilibrium distribution is reached. As the blood warms up again, the cells eliminate Na^+ and accumulate K^+ again. This ion transport, which concentrates K^+ on the inside and Na^+ on the outside, is called *active transport;* it is fueled by **metabolic energy.**

At 0 °C the rate of cellular metabolism is so low that it can no longer support active transport. Then K^+ and Na^+ move down their respective concentration gradients; that is, the loss of K^+ and acquisition of Na^+ occur passively. These *passive ion fluxes* are also present as **"leakage currents"** at 37 °C, but they are compensated by active transport in the opposite direction under the normal stationary equilibrium conditions.

The **mechanism of the coupled active transport** of Na^+ and K^+, also called the Na^+-K^+ *pump,* is closely associated with an enzyme in the membrane. Because the activity of this enzyme depends on the intracellular Na^+ and extracellular K^+ concentrations, and because ATP is used up during ion transport, the enzyme is called **Na^+-K^+-activated ATPase** (abbreviated Na^+-K^+-ATPase). Activation of the enzyme requires the presence of Mg^{++}.

The Na^+-K^+-ATPase is present in the membrane in different states (conformations), depending on whether or not it is activated. In the presence of Mg^{++} and ATP the enzyme, activated by Na^+, splits off ATP and binds the phosphate. The enzyme-phosphate complex brings about the translocation of Na^+ to the exterior. The K^+ activation causes dephosphorylation of the enzyme and K^+ translocation. The membrane ATPase thus has the property of a double enzyme: phosphotransferase and alcylphosphatase.

The **coupled Na^+-K^+ pump** of the erythrocyte exchanges the ions in about the ratio 3 Na^+ outward to 2 K^+ inward (Fig. 28-9) for each energy-rich phosphate molecule (ATP) split. As mentioned above, this pumping action compensates the opposed leakage currents of the two ions.

The *transepithelial transport* of materials is treated in Chapters 26 (gastrointenstinal tract) and 27 (kidneys). Details are pointed out there.

28.3 References

Textbooks and Handbooks

1. BADER, H.: Morphologische und chemische Grundlagen der Zellmembran. In: GAUER, O.H., KRAMER, K., JUNG, R. (Eds.): Physiologie des Menschen, Vol.1. München–Berlin–Wien: Urban und Schwarzenberg 1972
2. CHRISTENSEN, H.N.: Biological Transport. (2 nd ed.) London: Benjamin 1975
3. DAWSON, H.: A Textbook of General Physiology. Vol.I. (4th. ed.) London: Churchill 1970
4. DAVSON, H., DANIELLI, J.F.: The Permeability of Natural Membranes. Cambridge: University Press 1943
5. DAVSON, H., SEGAL, M.B.: Introduction to Physiology. Vol.1: Basic Mechanisms. Part 1. London–New York–San Francisco: Academic Press 1975
6. GAMBLE, J.L.: Chemical Anatomy, Physiology and Pathology of Extracellular Fluids. (7th ed.) Cambridge/Mass.: Harvard University Press 1958
7. MUNTWYLER, E.: Water and Electrolyte Metabolism and Acid-Base Balance. St. Louis: Mosby 1968
8. PITTS, R.F.: Physiology of the Kidney and Body Fluids. (3 rd ed.) Chicago: Year Book 1974
9. SIEGENTHALER, W. (Ed.): Klinische Pathophysiologie. Stuttgart: Thieme 1964
10. STEIN, W.D.: The Movement of Molecules across the Cell Membrane. New York: Academic Press 1967
11. THEWS, G.: Diffusion und Permeation. In: BARTHELHEIMER, H., HEYDE, W., THORN, W. (Eds.): D-Glucose und verwandte Verbindungen in Medizin und Biologie. Stuttgart: Enke 1966

Research Reports and Reviews

12. BEHNKE, A.R.: Physiologic studies pertaining to deep sea diving and aviation, especially in relation to the fat content and composition of the body. Harvey Lectures 37, 198 (1941/42)
13. DARROW, D.C., YANNET, H.: The changes in the distribution of body water accompanying increase and decrease in extracellular electrolyte. J. clin. Invest. 14, 266 (1935)
14. POST, R.L. (1968), cited by LIN, E.C.C.: The molecular basis of membrane transport systems. In: ROTHFIELD, L.I. (Ed.): Structure and Function of Biological Membranes. New York–London: Academic Press 1971
15. SINGER, S.J.: The molecular organization of biological membranes. In: ROTHFIELD, L.I. (Ed.): Structure and Function of Biological Membranes. New York–London: Academic Press 1971
16. SINGER, S.J., NICHOLSON, G.L.: The fluid mosaic model of the structure of cell membranes. Science 175, 720 (1972)
17. SKELTON, H.: The storage of water by various tissues of the body. Arch. intern. Med. 40, 140 (1937)
18. SKOU, J.C.: The (Na^+ + K^+) activated enzyme and its relationship to transport of sodium and potassium. Q. Rev. Biophys. 7, 401 (1974)

29 Functions of the Endocrine System

K. Brück

29.1 General Endocrinology

Terminology

Endocrine system and hormones. The biological role of the endocrine system is closely linked to that of the nervous system; the two together *coordinate* the functions of the other (in some cases widely separated) organs and organ systems. The distinguishing feature of the endocrine system is that its influence is exerted by way of a number of substances, the **hormones.** Chemically, the hormones are a nonuniform group; the range of compounds represented includes steroids, amino-acid derivatives, peptides and proteins. Their common characteristic is that they are produced in special organs, the **endocrine glands** (glands without secretory ducts) or in circumscribed groups of cells – for example, the islet cells of the pancreas, Leydig's interstitial cells in the testes, and cell groups in the duodenal mucosa (secretin) and the hypothalamus (ADH, oxytocin, etc.) – and are transported *in the blood* to more or less distant organs. They have **specific actions** on these target organs, actions that as a rule cannot be produced by any other substance. The word "specific" also indicates that the action of each hormone is exerted only on its particular functional systems or organs, the **"effector organs."** A further characteristic is that the endocrine glands and cell groups are occupied exclusively with the formation and secretion of their hormones.

Finally, it is characteristic of all hormones that they act only on *complex cell structures* (cell membranes, enzyme systems; for mode of action see p.659). In contrast to enzymes, therefore, their action cannot be demonstrated in *homogenates,* but only *in vivo* or with tissue cultures.

Paracrine cell secretion and transmitter substances. Not all the substances that have recently been counted as hormones meet all these criteria. For example, some are synthesized so near their target organs or structures that they can reach them by diffusion, without entering the bloodstream. The cells producing these are referred to as **paracrine cells** in contrast to the **endocrine cells,** which produce the blood-borne hormones. There is a very ill-defined boundary between the secretory products from paracrine cells (e.g., serotonin, p.685) and the **neurotransmitters** (p.685) produced in neurons; the latter in this context are also called **neurocrine cells,** in order to emphasize their close relationship to *endocrine* and *paracrine* cells. The difficulty in formulating a precise definition of the term "hormone" is particularly well illustrated by the catecholamines noradrenalin and adrenalin. When their production in and release from the adrenal medulla (p.679) is being considered adrenalin and noradrenalin are usually called hormones, but in their role as signal mediators at the sympathetic nerve endings they are called sympathetic "transmitter substances."

The hormone concept has become even more vague since it has been realized that the so-called **regulatory hypothalamic hormones** – a group of peptides that includes the recently discovered *enkephalins* and *endorphins* as well as the *neurohormones* ADH (antidiuretic hormone, or vasopressin) and oxytocin and the *releasing hormones* – act not only as hormones in the strict sense but also have what appears to be a transmitter function or a modulating influence on the function of other transmitter systems [52].
Some of the regulatory hypothalamic peptides are found not only in neurons of the brain but also in special cells of the gut – e.g., substance P, neurotensin, somatostatin (GH, see Table 29-1), cholecystokinin, vasoactive intestinal peptide (VIP); a few of them act, in the gut, as gastrointestinal hormones (p.589), but the function of the others remains to be revealed. The cells producing these peptides constitute, according to a recent concept [46a], the so-called **diffuse neuroendocrine system,** comprised of widely dispersed cells; these have been referred to as the **APUD-system.** The cells of this system are most typically characterized by a high amine content, a capacity for the uptake of amine precursors and the presence of the enzyme decarboxylase (**A**mine **P**recursors **U**ptake and **D**ecarboxylating -system) and the ability to produce, besides the peptides, biogene amines such as 5-hydroxy-tryptamine (serotonin), dopamine, and histamine. The APUD cells are thought to originate from the neuroectoderm and to represent the morphological basis of what has been called the *"brain gut axis".*
The APUD cells are closely related to and partly identical with what have been called "paraneurons" by another group of authors [27a].
The definitions of "endocrine system" and "hormone" given here apply to vertebrates. Invertebrates produce, in addition to endocrine substances, compounds that are released by an individual into the surrounding medium and that elicit reactions of

conspecifics (e.g., sexual attractants). A special term, **phero-mone,** has been proposed for this group of substances [6] to distinguish them more sharply from the hormones of vertebrates.

Functional Significance and Mode of Action of Hormones

The hormones perform three basic functions. (i) Hormones enable and promote **physical, sexual and mental development.** (ii) Hormones enable and promote the **adjustment of performance level;** the ability of organs and organ systems to modify their activity to meet the demands made upon them *(physiological adaptation)* is lost in the absence of certain hormones. (iii) Hormones are necessary to keep certain physiological parameters constant (e.g., osmotic pressure and the blood glucose level). These hormones have a **"homeostatic" function.**

Hormones as information carriers. Hormones are effective in very low concentrations. They do not serve as a substrate for the biochemical processes they **"control."** In some cases (e.g., ADH, adrenalin, aldosterone) the response of the target organ has a more or less strict quantitative relation to the concentration of the hormone in the plasma. In cybernetic terminology these hormones can be called *"information carriers"* – a situation that emphasizes the above-mentioned analogy to the nervous system.

Permissive effects of hormones. Various biochemical reactions can proceed in an orderly manner only in the presence of one or more hormones, although the reaction is not accelerated by increase in the hormone concentration. In these cases the hormone is said to have a **"permissive" action.**

Hormones as elements in regulating systems [56]. When considering hormones as elements in regulating systems (cf. Chapter 15), it is useful to divide them into two classes. In one group, which includes adrenalin, noradrenalin, aldosterone, ADH and others, the rate of secretion and the plasma concentration undergo **wide fluctuations;** the rate of secretion is adjusted to the changing situation. The most typical example of the second group is thyroxin; the plasma concentration of these hormones is normally kept **constant.** This functional difference is illustrated by block diagrams in Fig. 29-1.

Hormones as controlling elements. In the diagram of Fig. 29-1 A, the hormone acts as a **controlling element in the regulating system.** The rate of secretion of the hormone keeps the controlled variable – blood glucose concentration, osmotic pressure of the blood or

some other physiological parameter that is normally kept constant, depending on the hormone concerned – at the desired level. The system is monitored by specific receptors (glucose receptors, osmoreceptors etc.), which send to a "central controller" information (in the form of action potentials) about departures of the controlled variable from the "set point" (cf. p. 543). Deviations from the set point can be caused by disturbances such as change in the rate of oxidation or of water intake, and so on. The controller in turn sends out information – in neural or hormonal form (via an intermediary "glandotropic" hormone; cf. p. 664) – to the endocrine gland, as a result of which its rate of secretion is increased or reduced. In especially demanding situations the set point can be adjusted accordingly (cf. p. 669).

The function of the hormones that act as in Fig. 29-1 A closely resembles that of the nervous system, for in the latter controlling signals are also sent (as impulses in peripheral nerves) to organs so as to modulate their level of activity. A fundamental difference between hormonal and neural control lies in the time factor; neural transmission requires only fractions of a second, whereas hormonal control is considerably more sluggish, with latencies of minutes or hours.

Hormone concentrations as controlled variables. In the second group of hormones (Fig. 29-1 B), the **concentration of the hormone itself** is the **controlled variable.** In these cases temporal constancy of the hormone concentration is required for the orderly performance of various functions (the "permissive" action mentioned above). Under special conditions (e.g., prolonged exposure to cold), however, the rates of secretion and plasma concentrations of even these hormones can be changed (by resetting the set point).

Classification of hormones by function. Three groups of hormones can be distinguished by functional criteria: (i) Hormones that act *directly on the target organ,* such as the sexual hormones; these are called effector hormones. (ii) Hormones, the chief action of which is to control the synthesis and release of the effector hormones; these are called **tropic or glandotropic hormones** (e.g., thyrotropic hormone). (iii) Hormones elaborated by nerve cells in the hypothalamus; these control the synthesis and release of (predominantly tropic) hormones in the adenohypophysis. These hormones are called **releasing hormones** or, if they have the opposite action, **release-inhibiting hormones.** It is chiefly by way of the hormones in group (iii) that the endocrine system is coupled to the CNS.

Mechanism of action. Hormonal action is currently thought to be based on the *enhancement or reduction of the catalytic function of certain enzymes* in the cells of the target organs; this effect can be achieved by (i)

A

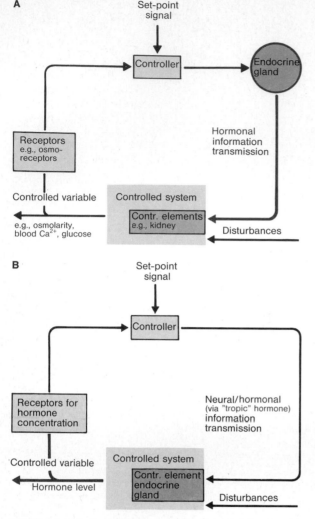

Set-point
signal

Controller

Endocrine
gland

Hormonal
information
transmission

Receptors
e.g., osmo-
receptors

Controlled variable

Controlled system

Contr. elements
e.g., kidney

e.g., osmolarity,
blood Ca²⁺, glucose

Disturbances

B

Set-point
signal

Controller

Neural/hormonal
(via "tropic" hormone)
information
transmission

Receptors for
hormone
concentration

Controlled variable

Controlled system

Contr. element
endocrine
gland

Hormone level

Disturbances

Fig. 29-1 A, B. Basic structure of endocrine control circuits. The two block diagrams illustrate different positions hormones can occupy in biological control systems: **A,** hormones as controlling elements; **B,** hormones as controlled variables

activation (or inhibition) of enzymes already present, an influence transmitted by cyclic adenosine monophosphate (the *"second messenger,"* the hormone being the first messenger), or (ii) increase in the concentration of certain enzymes in the cells of the target organ **("enzyme induction"),** owing to an increase in the rate of enzyme biosynthesis by gene activation. Another basic effect of hormones is to be seen in the alteration of **membrane permeability,** also exerted by way of cyclic AMP. The *specificity* of hormonal action is explained by postulating the existence of *hormone-specific receptors* in the cell membranes. For none of the hormones, however, has the mechanism of action been completely and conclusively explained. The mechanisms thought to underly the actions of particular hormones are discussed in biochemical and specialized texts (for example, [1, 2, 4, 6]).

Inactivation. If the hormones are to function as elements in a control circuit, it is imperative that they not accumulate progressively within the body. Accumulation is prevented both by chemical alteration of the hormone in the effector organ (inactivation) and by excretion in the urine. Some hormones are also inactivated in other organs (the liver, in particular). Moreover, the action of certain hormones can be blocked by the secretion of hormones with an antagonistic action.

Experimental Techniques

Endocrinological methods. The basic approach in experimental endocrinology is to excise or destroy an organ suspected of hormone synthesis and to observe the subsequent changes – the **deficiency symptoms.** The second step is to show that the deficiency symptoms are eliminated by administering extracts from the gland or tissue that produces the supposed hormone – the **replacement experiment.** Not until replacement proves successful has it been shown conclusively that the symptoms that appear after removal of a gland actually are caused by the lack of a substance with a specific action. Removal of the liver or the kidneys, for example, obviously causes severe symptoms which are not relieved by the administration of liver or kidney extracts.

The gland extract used for hormone replacement must be injected parenterally if the active principle is a proteohormone, for if given by mouth it would be destroyed by the proteolytic enzymes in the gastrointestinal tract. It is not necessary to use the glands of conspecifics to obtain the extract, for with only a few exceptions (e.g., growth hormone) the extracts of the glands of other animal species are equally effective. Evidently, then, hormones as a rule are *not species-specific.*

One can learn something more about the function of a hormone by administering gland extracts or the pure hormone to an intact animal **(overdosage experiments).** Such experiments are of special importance in clinical endocrinology, because they allow a more thorough analysis of the functional disturbances found in humans with pathological overactivity of certain endocrine glands.

Measurement of the rate of hormone secretion. In many cases a rough quantitative estimate of the activity level of an endocrine gland can be obtained by *histological examination.* An increase in the rate of secretion is usually associated with enlargement of the hormone-producing cells.

The secretion rate can be determined *precisely* by measuring the concentration of the hormone in the venous blood from the gland concerned, and simultaneously measuring the volume flow of blood (perfusion rate) through the gland. With the recent development of the so-called radioimmunological assays ("RIA"), it became possible to measure, with high specificity, very low concentrations of hormones. Formerly, bioassay techniques had to be used for this purpose, as follows. The sample of blood or plasma to be tested is injected into an animal (usually after the corresponding endocrine gland has been removed) and the resulting change in the relevant biological parameter (e. g., water excretion or blood glucose concentration) is observed. The amount of hormone that alters such a parameter by an arbitrarily established amount is called a *hormone unit* (IU, international unit). "IU" as a quantitative measure of hormone concentration is still being used for some hormones, such as insulin.

Rate of decomposition; half-life. Another important endocrinological measure is the rate of decomposition of individual hormones under normal and special experimental conditions (measurement of **hormone consumption**). In this approach, the gland that produces the hormone is removed and the progressive decline in the concentration of the hormone in the blood is monitored by analysis of repeated blood samples. The concentration decrease is normally quantitatively describable by a negative exponential function. A simple measure of the rate of breakdown, therefore, is the **biological half-life of the hormone.**

Hormone therapy. If an endocrine gland should function inadequately, the hormone can be provided by an external source. This **replacement therapy** must be continued for the rest of the patient's life, unless glandular function recovers.
Ideally, the plasma concentration of the hormone being administered, or the concentration of the substance controlled by the hormone (e. g., glucose), should be monitored continually. Normally this monitoring is done by special receptor organs in the body (cf. Fig. 29-1). Especially in the case of hormones that vary widely in concentration (cf. Fig. 29-1 A), replacement therapy provides only a rough approximation to the normal physiological situation. Devices are now being tested which will allow continous blood-glucose analysis and automatic adjustment of the insulin dosage.

29.2 The Hypothalamic-Hypophyseal System

By morphological and functional criteria, this system can be divided into two parts (Fig. 29-2), as follows:
1. a system consisting of the **supraoptic and paraventricular nuclei** of the hypothalamus plus the **neurohypophysis** (posterior lobe of the pituitary), and

2. a system consisting of the **hypophysiotropic zone of the hypothalamus,** located in the *median eminence,* which is joined to the adenohypophysis (anterior pituitary) by a *neurohemal contact surface.*

The recently discovered group of **neuroregulatory peptides** – enkephalins, endorphins, neurotensin, substance P etc. – constitutes a third hormone system within the framework of the hypothalamic-hypophyseal system; our understanding of its function, however, is still incomplete [52]. A common feature of these substances is their hypophysiotropic activity; they are thus all related to the releasing hormones (see also APUD-system p.685).

Neurohypophysis and Functionally Associated Hypothalamic Nuclei

The hormones of the neurohypophysis and their effects. Two different octapeptides, ADH and oxytocin, can be extracted from both the neurohypophysis and the diencephalon.

ADH (antidiuretic hormone), as its name implies, inhibits diuresis (cf. Chapter 27). In its absence the syndrome known as **diabetes insipidus** develops. In higher concentrations ADH increases the blood pressure; this effect was originally thought to be produced by a separate hormone, which was given the name *vasopressin.* More recent studies have shown that the two are identical.

Oxytocin, in humans and in animal experiments, causes rhythmic contractions of the uterus, but only during estrus (cf. p.677), at the end of pregnancy and after childbirth. In laboratory animals (e. g., rabbits) absence of the hormone interferes with parturition. In humans, however, parturition proceeds normally even without oxytocin. Oxytocin also induces contraction of the myoepithelium of the milk ducts in the mammary gland, which causes **milk ejection** (cf. p.662).

Sites of hormone synthesis. The hormones ADH and oxytocin are produced in the nerve cells of the supraoptic and paraventricular nuclei (Fig.29-2). Bound to a larger polypeptide called **neurophysin,** the hormones are transported as granules from the cell bodies along their axons to the capillaries of the neurohypophysis. (Neurophysin is regarded as a carrier substance, but may also have a hormonal action of its own that has not yet been detected.) The axon terminals of the neurosecretory cells make close contact with the capillaries, into which the hormones are released after the granules have disintegrated. These neurosecretory-cell axons form the **hypothalamo-hypophyseal tract** in the *infundibulum* (Fig. 29-2). The re-

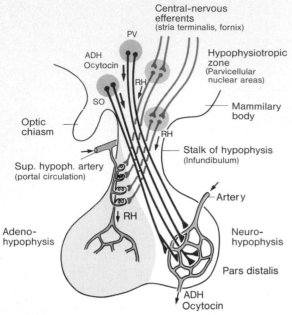

Fig. 29-2. Schematic drawing of the hypothalamic-hypophyseal system. Sites of hormone production, transport routes and release of the hormones in the adenohypophysis or in the venous blood leaving the neurohypophysis are indicated in a sagittal section through hypothalamus and hypophysis. ADH and oxytocin are produced in the large cells of the paraventricular (PV) and supraoptic (SO) nuclei; they travel through axons into the distal part of the neurohypophysis and there enter the bloodstream. The releasing hormones (RH) reach the sites of glandotropic-hormone production by way of the "portal system"

lease of the hormones at the contact sites is triggered when the neurosecretory cell is excited and – like other neurons – generates an action potential which is conducted along the axon. In this regard the release of the neurohormones is an event resembling the release of transmitters from axon terminals (cf. p.658) [20, 31, 32].

Control of ADH secretion. The natural stimulus for ADH control is the excitation of **osmoreceptors.** The existence of such osmoreceptors was first inferred from the classical experiments of Verney [53]. He injected hypertonic NaCl solutions into the carotid arteries of dogs and subsequently observed a decrease in the rate of urine excretion (antidiuresis); this is the same response that occurs after ADH administration (Fig. 29-3). Later the same effect was elicited by microinjection of NaCl solutions into the region of the supraoptic and paraventricular nuclei (cf. Fig. 29-2). When action potentials were recorded from single fibers in this region, an increase in osmolarity by infusion of slightly hypertonic solutions into the carotid artery proved to change the discharge rate of the neurosecretory cells in a characteristic way [32]. It was

thought that the ADH-secreting cells were themselves the osmoreceptors. But in other studies the secretion of ADH could be elicited very effectively by infusion of slightly hypertonic NaCl solutions into the third ventricle of the brain [13]. The conclusion from these results was that processes of *subependymal ganglion cells* projecting into the ventricle *act as osmoreceptors* (for morphology see [45]). In this case one would assume that these osmoreceptors affect ADH secretion by way of synaptic contacts with the neurosecretory cells of the supraoptic nucleus.

ADH secretion can also be affected by injection of hypertonic or hypotonic saline solutions into the hepatic portal veins, which suggests that there is another set of osmoreceptors in the **liver** [30]. These portal osmoreceptors would provide an explanation of the fact that diuresis is enhanced more rapidly after oral water intake than after intravenous injection. But there is still considerable controversy with regard to these findings, and they must await further corroboration (for references see [27]). Modification of ADH secretion by stretch receptors in the low-pressure system is discussed on p.429. The information from these two sets of receptors would presumably be sent to the neurosecretory cells by way of fibers in the vagus nerve.

Given the control processes just described, ADH can be viewed as an **element in a control circuit to ensure constancy of the osmotic pressure** of the body fluids. The block diagram of Fig. 29-1 A would apply to ADH as part of such a system. The secretion of ADH, as of oxytocin, can also be affected by a number of nonspecific stimuli such as pain, sound and light – that is, by stimuli that can lead to a stress-inducing situation. The inference here is that the neurosecretory cells of the supraoptic and paraventricular nuclei receive afference from higher levels of the brain, which have input from sense organs.

Control of oxytocin secretion. The natural stimulus – or at least one of them – for the secretion of oxytocin is suction at the nipple. Presumably mechanosensory afferent pathways from the nipple make connections with the sites of oxytocin formation in the hypothalamus. The resulting **"milk-ejection reflex"** is an example of a mixed **neural-hormonal reflex arc**; the afferent limb is represented by a neural pathway and the efferent, by hormonal transmission. The latency between the stimulus to the nipple and the ejection of milk is of interest in this regard [20]. Experiments on the rabbit indicate that this latency is no greater than 30 s, which is of the same order of magnitude as the circulation time. The latency of this reaction is thus largely determined by the velocity of transport in the blood.

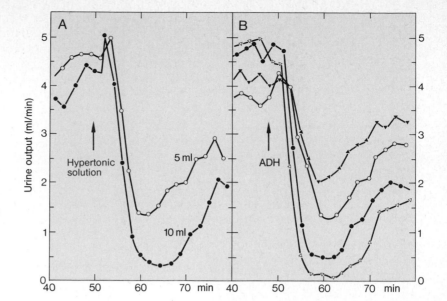

Fig. 29-3 A, B. Antidiuretic responses of different degrees. **A** After injection of 5 or 10 ml of an NaCl solution at 3 × physiological tonicity into the common carotid artery of the dog. **B** After intravenous injection of anti-diuretic hormone in 4 different doses. After [53]

Studies of goats and cows indicate that the oxytocin level in the plasma, almost zero prior to parturition, rises sharply during labor [8]. But it is not yet clear just how oxytocin participates in the natural control mechanisms associated with childbirth (cf. p. 678).

Adenohypophysis and the Hypophysiotropic Zone of the Hypothalamus

Functional relationships between hypothalamus and hypophysis. In addition to the large neurosecretory cells that elaborate ADH and oxytocin, the hypothalamus contains small nerve cells, more recently discovered, that produce the so-called **releasing and release-inhibiting hormones** (Fig. 29-2). This region is called the **hypophysiotropic zone** because it *controls the secretion of the adenohypophyseal hormones.* Because the adenohypophysis in turn controls the secretion of many other hormones, *the hypophysiotropic zone is a nodal point in the communication lines linking the nervous and endocrine systems* (cf. Fig. 6-21, p. 131).

Portal-vessel system of the hypophysis. The hormones from the hypophysiotropic zone reach the adenohypophysis by way of a special arrangement of vessels, the portal veins of the hypophysis (Fig. 29-2). This portal system begins with branches of the superior hypophyseal artery, which split up into fine vascular loops. The recurrent limbs of these loops fuse to form the **portal veins,** which carry the blood to the capillary network of the adenohypophysis. The axons of the secretory neurons in the hypophysiotropic zone end on the walls of these vascular loops **(hemoneural con-**

tact zone). Through these capillaries the hypophysiotropic hormones reach their **target,** the hormone-producing cells of the adenohypophysis.

The hypophysiotropic hormones. In rapid succession during the last few years all the known tropic hormones of the adenohypophysis and the growth hormone have been found to be under the influence of **releasing hormones.** In addition, three **inhibitory hormones** have been found. The names and abbreviations of these hormones are summarized in Table 29-1.

The hypophysiotropic hormones are peptides, some of which comprise few amino acids and thus are of low molecular weight (293 to 28000). TRH, which consists of only three amino acids, has been synthesized artificially, as have LH-RH and somatostatin (SS or GH-IH). This achievement has made it possible to employ these hormones therapeutically on a larger scale.

The biological function of the hypophysiotropic hormones is very probably not limited to controlling the release of the "tropic" hormones of the adenohypophysis. Like the peptides in the group "other regulatory hypothalamic hormones" (see below), they have direct effects on cells within and outside the nervous system. For example, it has been shown that TRH facilitates or inhibits neurons in very different parts of the brain [24, 44, 48]. Clarification of these effects of the neuroregulatory hormones can be expected to expand and at the same time complicate considerably our ideas about the function of the nervous system.

Other regulatory hypothalamic hormones [52]. Only recently a previously unknown group of polypeptides has been isolated from the hypothalamus and hypophysis, the common and most conspicuous

Table 29-1. The hypophysiotropic hormones

Abbreviation*	Name	Acts on (cf. Table 29-2)
A. Releasing hormones		
TRH	Thyrotropin-releasing hormone Chemically: tripeptide	TSH
LH-RH	Luteinizing-hormone-releasing hormone Chemically: decapeptide	LH and FSH
CRH	Corticotropin-releasing hormone	ACTH
GH-RH	Growth-hormone-releasing hormone	GH
PRL-RH	Prolactin-releasing hormone	PRL
MSH-RH	Melanocyte-stimulating-hormone-releasing hormone	MSH
B. Inhibitory hormones		
GH-IH	Growth-hormone inhibitory hormone = somatostatin Chemically: tetradecapeptide	GH
MSH-IH	Melanocyte-stimulating-hormone inhibitory hormone	MSH
PRL-IH	Prolactin inhibitory hormone	PRL

* There is as yet no universally accepted nomenclature. The alternatives CRF (for CRH), PIF (for PRL-IH) etc. derive from the original use of the word "factor" for these hormones. It has recently been proposed that all the releasing hormones be identified by the suffix -*liberin* and the inhibitory hormones by -*statin* (e.g., luliberin for LH-RH and prolactostatin for PRL-IH), but this proposal has also not gained general acceptance. LH-RH = LRH

Table 29-2. The hormones of the adenohypophysis (with abbreviations used internationally)

A. Glandotropic hormones

1. Follicle-stimulating hormone	FSH	Gonadotropic hormones
2. Luteinizing hormone = interstitial-cell-stimulating hormone (ICSH)	LH	
3. Thyrotropin = thyroid-stimulating hormone	TSH	
4. Adrenocorticotropic hormone	ACTH	

B. Effector hormones

5. Growth hormone = somatotropic hormone (STH)	GH
6. Prolactin = luteotropic hormone	PRL
7. Melanocyte-stimulating hormone	MSH

characteristic of which is a morphine-like action. They have been called **enkephalins** and **endorphins.** These polypeptides have been recognized as fractions of the so-called *lipotropic hormone (LPH 91),* a polypeptide composed of 91 amino acids which has been known for some time but not as yet assigned any definite hormonal action. The endorphins and enkephalins evidently bind to the same receptors in neuronal membranes that mediate the effects of *exogenous morphine compounds.* Accordingly, the action of the *"endogenous opiates"* (as the enkephalins and endorphins are also called) can be inhibited by the morphine antagonists used in therapy – for example, naloxone. This new class of substances is thought to play a role in the control of behavior and in autonomic integration processes; it is hoped that once their action is understood considerable progress will have been made toward understanding and influencing the autonomic functions of the CNS.

Still other peptides – substance P, neurotensin, VIP (vasoactive intestinal peptide) and others – have since been found in the hypothalamus. These substances had previously been isolated from the gut (see APUD-system p.685), and originally were regarded as hormones for the regulation of circulation and intestinal activity. Evidently their full biological significance remains to be discovered.

Hormones of the Adenohypophysis

The most striking deficiency symptoms to appear after removal of the hypophysis can be ascribed to the elimination of hormones 1–5 in Table 29-2. Four of these are called **glandotropic hormones,** because their influence is exerted principally or exclusively by way of an action on other, peripheral endocrine glands. The hormones listed as 1 and 2 in Table 29-2 are also called **gonadotropic hormones.** The terms luteinizing hormone (LH) and ICSH are synonyms. The fifth hormone in the list (growth hormone, GH) is an **effector hormone,** with direct effects on the body. Two further hormones, prolactin (PRL) and melanocyte-stimulating hormone (MSH), are also considered effector hormones.

Site of hormone production. The adenohypophyseal hormones listed here are synthesized in histochemically distinct cell types. *Acidophilic, basophilic* and *chromophobic* cells can easily be distinguished by using acid and basic stains, and additional histochemical methods provide criteria for further subdivision. The two subtypes of the acidophilic group synthesize growth hormone and prolactin; the basophilic cells produce the gonadotropins FSH and LH as well as thyrotropin and ACTH. Another basophilic type elaborates MSH (melanocyte-stimulating hormone), which in man plays only a subordinate role; in reptiles MSH is formed in the pars intermedia of the hypophysis, which has regressed in man. The chromophobic cells are thought to be hormonally inactive precursors of the chromophilic cells.

Glandotropic hormones of the adenohypophysis. The glandotropic hormones (cf. Table 29-2) are treated in the sections on their target organs – the *gonads,* the *thyroid* gland and the *adrenal cortex* together with the corresponding effector hormones. Here only a brief description will be given.

Injection of the **gonadotropic hormones** causes development of the gonads and secondary sexual characteristics of experimental animals to resume after it has been halted by removal of the adenohypophysis. The FSH and LH of males are identical to those of females; that is, they are *non-sex-specific hormones*. Both are glycoproteins.

Thyrotropin (thyroid-stimulating hormone, TSH), like the two gonadotropic hormones, is a glycoprotein. It stimulates the growth of the thyroid gland and controls the production and release of thyroid hormone. Thyrotropin is bound to a γ-globulin as it circulates in the plasma, where its concentration is 1–2 µg/l.

Adrenocorticotropic hormone (ACTH) is necessary for the growth and ability to function of two of the three layers (cf. p.667) of the adrenal cortex, the zona fasciculata and the zona reticularis. It controls the production of cortisol, which occurs primarily in the zona fasciculata, as well as its secretion. Stimulation by ACTH is not required for growth and function of the third layer, the zona glomerulosa.

ACTH is a small polypeptide, comprising only 39 amino acids. Its concentration in the plasma varies widely, and is of the order of 5–80 ng/l. Although its structure varies in different mammals, only a sequence of 20 amino acids being identical in all species tested, in its action ACTH exhibits *no species-specificity*.

To a greater extent than the other tropic hormones of the adenohypophysis, ACTH has a so-called *extra-adrenal action;* that is, it acts directly on non-endocrine target organs. A very conspicuous extra-adrenal action, which appears only when there is overproduction of ACTH, is the enhancement of skin pigmentation (cf. Addison's disease, p.670). This effect is elicited in fish and reptiles by a special hormone, MSH (melanocyte-stimulating hormone; see below), and can be explained by the chemical similarity of the two hormones. Another extra-adrenal action of ACTH is to mobilize fat from adipose tissue, an action that also occurs *in vitro*. ACTH also affects the breakdown of cortisol in the liver.

Growth hormone. In contrast to most hormones, growth hormone (GH) is **species-specific.** For example, bovine GH does not cause growth in man or ape; in fact, when GH from another species is administered antibodies against the hormone are produced. Therefore humans in need of therapy must be given human growth hormone (hGH), obtainable from acidophilic tumors of the hypophysis that have been surgically removed. The various growth hormones are all proteins. hGH is composed of 191 amino acids, the sequence of which has been determined. The biological half-life of GH is less than one hour.

GH is classified as an *effector hormone* because at least part of its influence is exerted directly on target functional systems, rather than by way of an intermediary hormone as in the case of the other adenohypophyseal tropic hormones (but cf. "glucagon," p.682 and Fig.29-13).

The **action of GH on growth** is based on promoting endochondral ossification, the basic process by which bones grow longer. In adenohypophysectomized rats, for example, after a few days of treatment with GH there is a distinct broadening of the epiphyseal cartilage. Here there is such a strict quantitative relationship between the increase in epiphyseal width and hormone dosage that the reaction was used as a bioassay for GH before the modern radioimmunological methods became available.

After puberty, when androgens have caused ossification of the cartilaginous epiphyses, GH no longer affects growth of bone length; only apophyseal and periosteal bone growth and the growth of non-osseous tissues can still be promoted. Therefore when overproduction of GH occurs in adults the result is deformation and thickening of the bones and soft tissues; the most striking feature is the enlargement of nose and chin and of the hands and feet. This syndrome is called **acromegaly.** Excessive dosage or endogenous production of GH in juveniles leads to **gigantism.** The extreme case of known human hypophyseal gigantism is a man who became almost 2.5 m tall. When children lack GH their body length under some circumstances can be restricted to 1 m or less. In such **hypophyseal dwarfism** the proportions of the body are normal, in contrast to the so-called *hypothyroid dwarfism* (cf. p.672).

Recent studies have shown that the growth-promoting action of GH is mediated by a substance found in the serum, called **somatomedin.** This substance (which has since been shown to exist in three different forms, somatomedin A, B and C) is produced under the influence of GH, but since its source is evidently not a particular specialized region of tissue it does not meet the criteria (p.658) for classification as a hormone. It is now recognized that one form of hypophyseal dwarfism results from the failure of somatomedin production despite an undiminished GH level [21].

Metabolic effects of GH. GH affects the protein-fat-water proportions in the body, in such a way as to increase the relative amounts of protein and water and decrease that of fat. That is, GH tends to make the composition of the tissues appropriate for a growing organism. The incorporation of protein **(anabolic action)** is accompanied by a reduction in the amount of nitrogen excreted. GH has both a short- and a long-term action on fat and carbohydrate metabolism. A single injection of GH causes a transient fall in the glucose level and the concentration of free fatty acids (FFA) in the plasma; this reaction is called the **"insulin-like effect of GH",** though in more recent studies it is not routinely reproducible [11]. Several hours after the injection there is an increase in the plasma glucose concentration and in that of the free fatty acids. The raised glucose level results from the fact that the entrance of glucose into the cells, ordinarily promoted by insulin, is impeded. In other words, the insulin-induced increase in glucose tolerance is reduced by GH. The rise in glucose concentration is enhanced by an increase in the rate of gluconeogenesis – again under the influence of GH. This long-term influence of GH, possibly exerted in part by stimulation of glucagon, is called its **insulin-antagonizing** or **diabetogenic** effect. In many animal species, an insulin deficiency can be counteracted, and metabolism stabilized to a certain extent, by removal of the adenohypophysis. The long-term metabolic effects of GH described here are correlated with the familiar clinical observation that in hypophyseal dwarfism there is a tendency to *hypoglycemia* and **hypoglycemic shock,** and in gigantism or acromegaly a tendency to *hyperglycemia*.

Control of GH secretion [40]. The concentration of GH in the plasma varies widely in time. During the course of a day there are more or less regular increases in concentration, by a factor of 10 to 20. These are ascribable in part to exogenous factors, such as stress situations. For example, in a young rat an elevated GH level can be induced simply by touching the animal repeatedly or taking it out of its cage. But the fluctuations persist even in fasting animals shielded from almost all external stimuli. There is thus an **endogenous rhythmicity in GH secretion** (cf. *circadian rhythms;* pp. 153 f.). A peak in GH secretion, by which the resting concentration in the plasma ($0.3 \mu g/l$) is exceeded severalfold, occurs in man at night and is associated with the phase of deep sleep (slow-wave sleep; cf. pp. 155 f.).
The rate of GH secretion can be **controlled** by the **releasing hormone GH-RH** and the **inhibitory hormone somatostatin** (GH-IH; cf. Table 29-1). The release of the releasing hormone itself is evidently under the control of higher structures in the brain, in the region of the limbic system.
The GH level is also affected by the *blood chemistry;* reduction of the blood glucose concentration increases the rate of GH secretion, by way of hypotha-

lamic glucose receptors (cf. p. 682). Moreover, the rate of GH secretion depends on the amino-acid concentration of the plasma, as well as the concentration of free fatty acids.
Prolactin. This proteohormone consists of 198 amino acids and it can be revealed in man by radioimmunological methods; its plasma concentration is 2–$15 \mu g/l$, with no difference between the sexes except during pregnancy. The concentration of prolactin in the plasma of a pregnant woman rises to about $300 \mu g/l$. As far as its function is concerned, it is certain that in man it stimulates growth of the mammary glands and milk secretion – hence the now outdated name "mammotropin." In the rat prolactin also has a luteotropic action, so that in this species it can be called a **gonadotropic** hormone; in man it is a purely **effector** hormone.

The melanocyte-stimulating hormone (MSH). This hormone exists in two forms, α-MSH and β-MSH; these are polypeptides with 13 and 22 amino acids, respectively, which are closely related both chemically and functionally to ACTH. The most prominent effect of MSH, especially conspicuous in fish and reptiles, is an increase in skin pigmentation by the dispersion of the melanin within the pigment cells (melanocytes or melanophores). In mammals MSH is involved in the seasonal change of pigmentation of skin and fur; in these cases the pigment can leave the melanocytes and be deposited in epidermal cells. At present MSH is of interest in human biology only because of the **pathological pigmentation** that can result from its overproduction. A number of other actions have been attributed to MSH, but so far they do not seem to have any biological significance.

29.3   The Endocrine Glands and Hormones Controlled by the Adenohypophysis

Four of the seven (Table 29-2) hormones of the adenohypophysis act chiefly by controlling the production of other hormones, the **glucocorticoids** of the adrenal cortex, the **thyroid hormones** and the **sex hormones** of the male and female gonads. The function of these endocrine glands is therefore intimately related to the function of the hypothalamic-hypophyseal system treated in the preceding section. Because of this common characteristic they are discussed here in a single section. The adrenal and thyroid glands also produce other hormones *(aldosterone* and *calcitonin),* the production and release of which is partially or completely independent of the hypothalamic-hypophyseal system. These are discussed elsewhere.

The Adrenal Cortex and the Glucocorticoids

The adrenal gland is composed of two parts that differ in ontogeny, morphology and function – the **cortex** and the **medulla.**

The cortex on each side develops from a fold of the coelomic epithelium, which also forms the gonad. During the fifth fetal week cell elements migrate from the abdominal sympathetic ganglia into the cortex, where they eventually give rise to the hormone-producing cells of the medulla. This ontogenetic history makes understandable both the close relationship between the hormones of adrenal cortex and gonads (both are steroids; see below) and the **synergy of sympathetic nervous system and adreno-medullary hormones** (p. 679).

The human **adrenal cortex** consists of three layers: the **zona glomerulosa** on the outside, the **zona fasciculata** and the **zona reticularis,** adjacent to the medulla. The cortical cells, unlike those of the medulla, have no connection with the sympathetic nervous system.

The adrenal is highly **vascularized.** The blood supply comes from three arteries, whereas venous blood is carried away by a single vessel, the *suprarenal vein.* It is therefore possible to sample the entire amount of blood leaving the gland by inserting a catheter into this vein – an advantage in *determining the rate of hormone secretion.*

The hormones of the adrenal cortex. Many steroid derivatives are found in the adrenal cortex, and about 30 of these are not formed in any other organ; these characteristic cortical hormones are called corticosteroids or **corticoids.** However, only a few of the corticoids can compensate for the deficiency symptoms that appear after removal of the adrenal. In man, only three corticoids are secreted as hormones: **cortisol** (hydrocortisone), **aldosterone** and, to a lesser extent, **corticosterone.** In addition, during certain phases of development corticoids with *androgenic action* play a role. Aldosterone is produced in the zona glomerulosa and cortisol and corticosterone in the zona fasciculata and zona reticularis. The androgenic corticoids derive from the zona reticularis.

Action of the corticoids. The corticoids have a very broad action spectrum with diverse individual actions, but there are two major effects: 1. they influence electrolyte balance (the **mineralocorticoid action**), and 2. they affect carbohydrate metabolism **(glucocorticoid action).** The glucocorticoid and mineralocorticoid properties of the individual corticoids are roughly reciprocal; that is, corticoids with a pronounced glucocorticoid action must be given in very large doses for the mineralocorticoid action to become apparent; conversely, the glucocorticoid action of corticoids with a strong mineralocorticoid action is slight. The glucocorticoid action of aldosterone is essentially zero. The mineralocorticoids are discussed in Section 29.6. The effects of the glucocorticoids are surveyed in the following paragraphs.

Glucocorticoid action. The biological effects of the glucocorticoids can best be studied in adrenalectomized animals injected with aldosterone to avoid the deficiency symptoms that would otherwise result from the lack of mineralocorticoids. For the glucocorticoid cortisol the following picture emerges.

Gluconeogenesis. The depression of the blood glucose level (hypoglycemia) and the associated hypersensivity to insulin are eliminated by cortisol injection. This action of cortisol is mediated by **gluconeogenesis,** the synthesis of glucose from amino acids. Cortisol affects this process in several ways, but chiefly by increasing the activity of some of the enzymes necessary for gluconeogenesis. The glucose produced as a result of cortisol injection refills the glycogen stores in the liver that had been depleted by destruction of the adrenal cortex. The degree of replenishment is quite closely related to the corticoid dosage, so that the amount of liver glycogen in adrenalectomized animals is a measure of the glucocorticoid action of the various corticoids.

Catabolic action. Gluconeogenesis is accompanied by a reduced incorporation of amino acids into the protein of the body and an increased N-excretion rate; thus under certain conditions the glucocorticoids act **catabolically.** This effect is significant, however, only when excessive cortisol is produced under pathological conditions.

Lipolysis. In the absence of glucocorticoids the mobilization and release of fatty acids from adipose tissue – i.e., **lipolysis** – is impaired. But *in vivo* the lipolytic effect is less significant than gluconeogenesis.

Circulation. The **circulatory hypotension** resulting from severe adrenal insufficiency cannot be treated effectively with noradrenalin (cf. p. 680), because in this situation it does not have the usual vasoconstrictor action. After administration of glucocorticoids noradrenalin again elicits vasoconstriction and thus raises the blood pressure. The inference is that corticoids sensitize the vasomotor system to noradrenalin.

Water balance. A characteristic sign of adrenal-cortex insufficiency is diminished water excretion. Water drunk in excess of need cannot be eliminated rapidly enough, and if a great deal is drunk **water intoxication** can result. Cortisol returns the rate of water excretion to normal, in part by increasing glomerular blood flow and thus filtration rate in the course of its circulation-stabilizing action. But cortisol also has a specific action on water excretion, in that it reduces the permeability of the distal tubule to water. As a result, in the absence of cortisol the urine cannot be made sufficiently dilute.

Skeletal musculature. A typical symptom of adrenocortical insufficiency is weakness of the skeletal musculature. Cortisol acts against this form of **asthenia,** by a mechanism that is not understood [3, 47].

Central nervous system and sense organs. Experiments have revealed the presence of many **glucocorticoid receptors in the brain,** concentrated in particular regions. Therefore glucocorticoids can be expected to have a number of actions on central nervous function, although as yet there has been little systematic study of them. Administration of glucocorticoids has long been known to increase **susceptibility to convulsions.**

The glucocorticoids have a considerable influence on the **function of the sense organs.** Discrimination among the various qualities of taste, smell and sound is impaired in adrenocortical insufficiency. For example, "sweet" and "salty" can be discriminated only with sugar and salt solutions of abnormally high concentration. In the case of hearing, the deterioration of quality discrimination is evident in the patient's abnormally frequent misunderstanding of words he hears. The impairment explains the so-called *salt hunger* associated with adrenocortical insufficiency. Normally salted food does not seem salty enough to the patient, so that he constantly adds more [33].

Normal function can be restored by administration of glucocorticoids but not of mineralocorticoids. Surprisingly, while *recognition* acuity is impaired as described the *detection* acuity is increased at the same time.

These changes in sensory function are ascribed to an effect of glucocorticoids on central information processing although their mechanism is ill-understood [33].

Actions on cellular and humoral defense mechanisms. When the adrenal cortex is underactive, the thymus and lymph nodes become enlarged. Cortisol treatment alleviates this situation; aldosterone is ineffective. Higher ("pharmacological") doses of cortisol produce **involution of thymus and lymph nodes** and the spleen is also affected, though to a smaller degree. The involution of these organs begins with a rapid destruction of the lymphocytes in the tissue, in some cases followed by degeneration of the reticular cells;

the number of lymphocytes in the blood also decreases. The breakdown of the lymphatic tissue explains the **inhibition of antibody production** (immunosuppressive action; cf. Chapter 16) by glucocorticoids.

Local inflammation, which consists of vasodilation, diapedesis (the outward movement of leucocytes through the capillary walls) and exudation, is inhibited by cortisol. This **antiphlogistic (inflammation-inhibiting) action** is turned to therapeutic advantage in rheumatic joint diseases, and corticoid suppression of antibody formation is useful in the treatment of so-called allergic reactions (e. g., asthma attacks and anaphylactic shock). But both of these actions require doses of corticoid many times greater than can be produced by the body's own rate of secretion. Moreover, it is remarkable that the number of eosinophilic granulocytes in the blood, which is also related to antigen-antibody reactions, is reduced by glucocorticoids. This effect can be utilized for diagnosis.

Regulation of the glucocorticoid concentration in blood and tissues. The glucocorticoids are in the group of hormones the plasma *concentration* of which is *kept constant by control mechanisms* (cf. Fig. 29-1 B) over more or less long periods. Circadian fluctuation (lower concentrations at night than during the day) can be interpreted as a shift of the set point in the 24-h rhythm (see below). It is not yet known whether the actual "controlled variable" is the concentration in the plasma or that in certain cells. In this regard it should be kept in mind that a large fraction of the plasma cortisol is bound to an α-globulin **(transcortin),** and another fraction is bound to plasma albumins; only a small amount is free in the plasma. But for the following considerations it is immaterial which concentration is controlled, because the relative concentrations of unbound and bound plasma corticoid and cell corticoid are determined entirely by the laws of physics (mass action and diffusion).

Some elements in the **control circuit for cortisol concentration** have been described in previous sections. The situation can be summarized as follows: The releasing hormone CRH, formed in the hypophysiotropic zone of the hypothalamus (p. 663), reaches the adenohypophysis by way of the portal vessels and there causes release of ACTH (Fig. 29-4); ACTH is carried by the blood to the adrenal cortex, where it causes the release of glucocorticoids. This sequence of events has been established by two basic groups of experiments [57]:

1. the demonstration that secretion of ACTH and glucocorticoids is enhanced following electrical stimulation of the median eminence (Fig. 29-2), and
2. the demonstration that the enhancement of ACTH and cortisol secretion normally induced by stressors (cf. p. 669) fails to appear following electrocoagulation of circumscribed regions of the median eminence.

The findings in (2) also showed that the formation of releasing factor in the hypophysiotropic zone is under the control of higher central-nervous structures, which receive and process signals from the periphery of the body (some of them from sense organs). The results also suggest an interpretation of the observation that one's emotional state and behavior are reflected in the secretion of the adrenal cortex [49].

Negative feedback. Microinjection of glucocorticoids into the hypophysiotropic zone brings about a marked reduction in ACTH secretion. Secretion of ACTH is also affected when they are injected into the adenohypophysis [57]. These effects suggest that glucocorticoid receptors that influence ACTH secretion by negative feedback are located both in the hypophysiotropic zone and in the adenohypophysis itself (cf. Fig. 29-4). In the hypophysiotropic zone the corticoids would affect the liberation of CRH, and in the adenohypophysis they would modulate the action of CRH on ACTH release.

It has recently been shown that ACTH can exert a direct inhibitory influence on its own production, by a so-called *short feedback loop;* the site of action is thought to be the neurosecretory cells in the hypophysiotropic zone [57].

When considering the highly simplified control system illustrated in Fig. 29-4, it should be kept in mind that the glucocorticoid receptors have not only **static** but also **dynamic sensitivity,** which allows the rate of secretion to be adjusted to rapid changes in corticoid consumption.

Change of set point under load. In many demanding situations (cf. **stress,** below) the cortisol concentration rises, which in the model control mechanism presented here would amount to a **"set-point shift"** (the term "set point" is discussed in general in the chapter on thermoregulation, p. 543).

This notion has been verified by experiments of the following kind [57]. An animal is exposed to a stimulus (the "stressor"; a loud sound, for example) that triggers an increase in the rate of glucocorticoid secretion and thus raises the glucocorticoid level. In a second experiment glucocorticoids are injected *before* presentation of the same stimulus, so as to bring their concentration to the level reached following stimulation in the first experiment. If the stimulus causes a shift in set point, in Experiment 2 there should be no increase in the rate of glucocorticoid secretion, for the injection has already matched the concentration to the new set point. This was in fact the result. In an "open" system (without negative feedback), by contrast, the stimulus would elicit an increase in the glucocorticoid level regardless of the amount of hormone introduced from an external source.

This control mechanism ensures maintenance of the minimal corticoid level required for the "permissive" action (cf. p.659). The resetting of the corticoid concentration to a higher level enables the **adjustment of system performance** required when the load is increased (cf. "stressors," below).

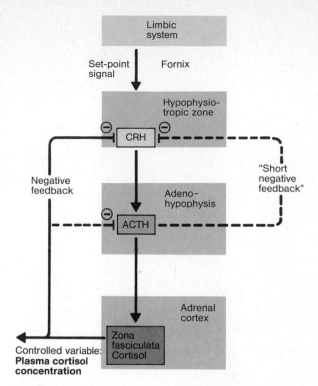

Fig. 29-4. Diagram of the control of glucocorticoid secretion in the adrenal cortex by CRH and ACTH; the negative feedback inhibits primarily the secretion of CRH (ACTH only slightly)

The corticoid concentration, like that of other hormones, undergoes a *diurnal fluctuation*.

Stress and adaptation. A great variety of stimuli – for example, infective substances (antigens), extreme cold or heat, hypoxia, anesthesia, traumata, hypoglycemia, loud sound and all stimuli that cause emotional responses – elicit numerous physiological reactions, all of which are accompanied by an increase in glucocorticoid secretion **("alarm response").** This condition is called **stress,** and the eliciting stimuli are the stressors [10, 49]. In some cases the response to a stressor can be so intense that the entire store of glucocorticoids in the adrenal cortex is exhausted and the cortex tissue itself is damaged (hemorrhage). As would be expected, glucocorticoid therapy ameliorates such conditions.

If the intensity of the stressor is not great enough to cause severe functional disturbance, the rate of glucocorticoid secretion returns to normal even while exposure to the stimulus continues. When the same stressor acts repeatedly, the reaction becomes less and less pronounced [29]. The progressive decline in responsiveness is accompanied by morphological (e. g., increase in red cell count during O_2 deficiency) or functional modifications (cf. the adaptations to

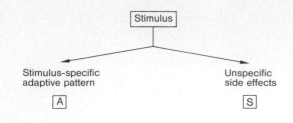

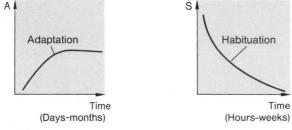

Fig. 29-5. Diagram showing the time courses of adaptation and habituation. Adaptation (A) includes stimulus-specific adaptive modifications (e.g., increased hemoglobin content in O_2 deficiency); the side effects (S) are responses such as increase in the rate of glucocorticoid secretion, sympathetic excitation, and the excretion of adrenomedullary hormones. Boundary condition: when a critical stimulus intensity is exceeded adaptation does not occur

heat, cold and altitude discussed in other chapters) that increase resistance to the stressor. This "physiological adaptation" is strictly stressor-specific – that is, the modifications vary, depending on the stress-inducing situation. By contrast, the alarm response is independent of the nature of the stressor. It seems plausible that the increased rate of glucocorticoid secretion (perhaps in combination with thyroid hormones) is involved in the development of the specific modifications, possibly enabling certain morphological changes (e.g., increased erythropoiesis) by enzyme induction. Once the **specific modifications** have been made the original stimulus is no longer appreciably stressful, for the body has thereby adapted to it.

The extent of the stimulus-specific adaptation pattern (Fig. 29-5) – for example, the amount of additional hemoglobin – can be described quantitatively as a function of stimulus intensity, duration of exposure and frequency of repeated exposures [10].

The nonspecific side effects, which include the increased glucocorticoid secretion described here as well as an increase in sympathetic activity leading to release of hormones from the adrenal **medulla** ("emergency response" [18]; cf. p.680), decrease with repeated exposure (Fig.29-5). This phenomenon is called **habituation.**

Pathophysiology. A syndrome characterized by overproduction of cortisol (**hypercortisolism**) can have various causes:

(i) a tumor (adenoma or carcinoma) in the adrenal cortex produces excessive amounts of cortisol (**"peripheral Cushing's syndrome"**). As is to be expected from the negative feedback, the ACTH level is reduced and hence the contralateral adrenal gland is atrophied.

(ii) there is increased production of ACTH, in some cases resulting from a **basophilic adenoma** in the adenohypophysis; the result is hyperplasia of both adrenal cortices and increased secretion of cortisol (**"central Cushing's syndrome"**).

The most important clinical signs of an elevated cortisol level are adiposity with a characteristic distribution of fat (face, neck and trunk), increased blood glucose content, sugar excretion in the urine, enhanced protein breakdown (catabolic action), retention of water and sodium chloride (edema formation), loss of calcium from the bones (osteoporosis), hypertension, polycythemia (cf. the section on glucocorticoid actions, p.667).

The **decreased cortisol production** underlying the **adrenogenital syndrome** is caused by an enzyme defect such that an adrenocortical androgen is synthesized in place of cortisol. The androgen has a virilizing effect on girls and causes precocious puberty in boys. Because the cortisol receptors are not stimulated by the androgen there is no feedback to limit adrenocortical activity, and the wrong hormone continues to be produced. The vicious circle is broken by the therapeutic administration of cortisol.

Addison's disease is characterized by underproduction of all adrenocortical hormones, though the symptomatology is dominated by the lack of mineralocorticoids (cf. p.683). Another important sign of this disease is increased skin pigmentation, which results from the increased ACTH secretion (feedback interruption; cf. Fig.29-4; cf. also the melatonin-like action of ACTH, p.665).

The Thyroid Gland and the Hormones Thyroxin and Triiodothyronine

In histological sections the thyroid gland exhibits many large cavities, called follicles. The follicle wall is formed by a layer of cuboidal epithelial cells, one cell thick. The follicles are filled with a protein-like substance called colloid, which contains the hormones **thyroxin** and **triiodothyronine.** In the spaces between the follicles are so-called parafollicular cells *(C cells),* which produce calcitonin (or thyrocalcitonin; cf. p.683). The interfollicular spaces also contain a dense network of capillaries, by way of which the components for hormone formation are supplied and the completed hormones are removed.

Production and transport of the thyroid hormones. Thyrotropin (thyrotropic hormone; p.665) controls the production of two hormones in the thyroid gland – tetraiodothyronine (thyroxin, or "T_4") and, in considerably lower concentration, triiodothyronine ("T_3"). The iodine content of the thyroid hormones is their distinguishing characteristic and is crucial to their action. A prerequisite for the production of iodine-containing hormones is that the follicle epithelia be capable of extracting I^- actively from the plasma, against a chemical and electrical gradient, and accumulating it within the cells. As the components are assembled to form T_3 and T_4 they are bound to a glycoprotein, **thyroglobulin.** T_3 and T_4 are still bound to thyroglobulin when they enter the colloid and are stored there. For release into the blood, the hormones must be separated from the thyroglobulin. In the plasma they again bind to proteins, particularly a specific globulin (TBG, thyroxin-binding globulin). Only a very small fraction of the total plasma T_3 and T_4 is in an unbound state. Thus an approximate estimate of the total plasma concentration of thyroid hormones can be obtained by measuring the **protein-bound iodine (PBI).** But the PBI method is subject to error if exogenous iodine or pharmaceuticals containing iodine are consumed, and it has now been largely replaced by more accurate and specific radioimmunological tests; the latter also allow the concentrations of T_3 and T_4 to be assayed selectively. The action of the hormone depends on the amount of T_3 and T_4 in the free state; when the plasma protein level increases (e.g., during pregnancy) the PBI is also increased, but no symptoms of thyroid overactivity result.

Effects of the thyroid hormones. The hormones T_3 and T_4 have basically the same actions, but T_3 is about five times as effective as T_4, and the effects of T_4 appear after a considerably longer latency. T_4 can be converted to T_3 in the peripheral tissues by deiodization. For this reason, and in view of the longer latency of its action, it has been suggested that T_4 might be regarded as the prohormone for the "actual" hormone T_3. This suggestion is still under discussion [50]. Both T_3 and T_4 affect various metabolic processes; they promote growth and physical and mental development. They are also involved in the adaptation of organ performance to special situations.

Metabolic actions. One of the most conspicuous actions of the hormones T_3 and T_4 is their effect on **ener-gy metabolism,** also called the **calorigenic action.** When these hormones are absent the metabolic rate declines – in the extreme case, to half the ordinary basal metabolic rate (cf. pp. 524ff.). When they are present in excess the resting metabolic rate can rise to almost double the basal rate. These effects have a very long latency, up to several days following administration of T_4, and are thus quite different from the short-term calorigenic effects of the catecholamines (p. 680). All the cells in a growing body, but especially those of the nervous system, are affected by the metabolic action of the thyroid hormones. In adults, however, the metabolism of brain, spleen and testes is unaffected [16]. In the current view the hormones act by enzyme induction and the activation of mitochondrial enzymes to enhance the synthesis of protein and the oxidative breakdown of fats and carbohydrates.

It has occasionally been suggested that **decoupling of oxidative phosphorylation** is responsible for the increased metabolic rate. In vitro such decoupling, associated with a reduced P/O ratio, can indeed be achieved by high doses of thyroxin. But even in severe cases of thyroid overactivity *(hyperthyroidism)* there is no sign of decoupling of the respiratory chain. As emphasized at the outset, with regard to these hormones it is necessary to distinguish between the pharmacological and the physiological actions.

According to recent studies [25], thyroxin activates the "sodium pump", which in maintaining the extra-/intracellular electrolyte gradient normally accounts for 30–40% of the basal metabolic rate; under hypothyreotic conditions, primarily the passive sodium inflow seems to be increased and this is opposed by an increased active outward sodium transport.

Another basic action of the hormones T_3 and T_4 is to increase responsiveness to catecholamines (Fig. 29-6). When the plasma level of T_3 and T_4 is high, even small doses of noradrenalin and adrenalin suffice to elicit peripheral vasoconstriction and elevated blood pressure. The glycogenolytic and hyperglycemic actions of the catecholamines (p. 680) are also enhanced by the hormones T_3 and T_4.

Certain other actions of T_3 and T_4 can be regarded as *consequences of the basic actions* just described. Among these are the increase in heart rate (tachycardia), the slight increase in body temperature, and the tendency to secrete sweat in the presence of excess hormone, and the opposite effects (bradycardia, slight hypothermia, dry skin) when there is not enough. Hormone excess is also accompanied by increased physical and mental activity, tremor of the hands and a feeling of restlessness. In addition, the hormones lower the cholesterol level and stimulate the secretion of growth hormone.

Action on growth and development. T_3 and T_4 are indispensable for normal **endochondral ossification at the**

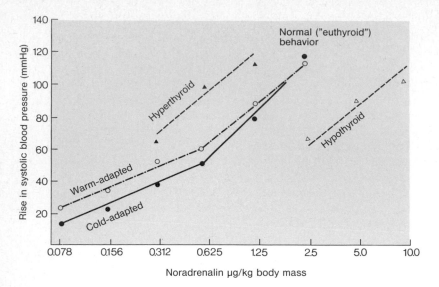

Fig. 29-6. "Noradrenalin sensitivity" as a function of thyroid-gland activity. In a hypothyroid state far higher doses of noradrenalin are required to achieve a particular rise in blood pressure than in the normal (euthyroid) and hyperthyroid states. Between cold- and warm-adapted animals, however, there is practically no difference. After [35]

boundary between diaphysis and epiphysis. Thus when the thyroid fails to function in the young, growth is impeded. Because the subperiostal bone growth continues normally, in **hypothyroid dwarfism** the bones are disproportionately thick.

Mental development is also impaired by hypothyroidism in juveniles; when the hormones are lacking even during embryonic development severe mental deficiency results.

Adaptation. Along with the glucocorticoids, the hormones T_3 and T_4 can affect the development of **adaptive modifications** (p.669). In rats, for example, the daily injection of T_4 for a period of 5 weeks resulted in the formation of brown adipose tissue, making the animals capable of nonshivering thermogenesis (cf. p.532) [38] – a change normally undergone by small animals in the course of cold adaptation (Chapter 23).

Regulation of thyroid-hormone concentration. Like the glucocorticoids, T_3 and T_4 are kept at constant blood (or tissue) concentrations by a control mechanism of the type shown in Fig.29-1 B (Fig.29-7). The plasma level of these hormones normally varies only within a very narrow range. But when the *consumption* of the hormones increases in demanding situations, the rate of secretion is raised accordingly.

Control of hormone secretion. As has been described, secretion is controlled by the **tropic hormone TSH,** which in turn is secreted at a rate depending on the activity of the **releasing hormone TRH.** The latency of an increase in secretion rate is very brief. TSH is currently thought to act on the membrane of the epithelial cells in the thyroid gland, producing the increase in

hormone synthesis and secretion by stimulating adenyl-cyclase activity.

Negative feedback. When the secretion of T_3 and T_4 ceases, the amount of TSH in the plasma rises markedly; conversely, the TSH content of the plasma can be lowered by T_3 and T_4. That is, there is a **negative feedback mechanism.** The results of microinjection experiments suggest that the T_3- and T_4-sensors mediating the negative feedback are located in the adenohypophysis. It is not yet clear whether the release of the releasing hormone (TRH; cf. p.664) in the hypophysiotropic zone of the hypothalamus is also affected by negative feedback involving T_3 and T_4 (dashed line in Fig.29-7).

The rate of T_3 and T_4 secretion is influenced by both **internal** (Fig.29-8) and **external thermoreceptors** (Fig.29-7). Recent studies [28] indicate that this cold-induced enhancement of T_3- and T_4-production is far less pronounced in man and the other primates than in the laboratory animals previously examined. In any case, when exposure to cold is prolonged hormone production gradually returns to the original level (cf. "habituation" and "physiological adaptation", p.670). Thus the state of cold acclimation is not at all equivalent to hyperthyroidism [35]; as Fig.29-6 shows, the noradrenalin sensitivity of the circulation is essentially the same in cold- and warm-adapted animals.

The influence of stressors on secretion rate. Many other stimuli apart from cold (**stressors**; cf. p.669) can **increase the rate of thyroid hormone secretion.** These, however, as in the case of acute cold stress and cold acclimation, leave the plasma concentration of the hormones nearly unchanged. This effect differs from that on the glucocorticoids, in that the **turnover rate** rather than the set point is altered.

Pathophysiology. The experimentally induced conditions hyperthyroidism and hypothyroidism occur in humans as diseases.

Hyperthyroidism. The syndrome called *Graves' disease* has long been known as a **hyperthyroid** condition. It results from the production of a substance **(LATS, long-acting thyroid stimulator)** with an action similar to that of TSH; the release of LATS, however, is not controlled by feedback inhibition, so that it exerts an *unrestricted* stimulatory influence on thyroid-hormone production (cf. Fig. 29-7). Graves' disease is now regarded as an autoimmune disease; LATS is thought to be an antibody against the TSH receptor of the thyreocytes in the adenohypophysis. In addition to the symptoms listed on p.671, some victims of Graves' disease exhibit characteristic changes in the eyes **("endocrine orbitopathy"),** the most striking of which is the protrusion of one or both eyeballs **(exophthalmia).** This orbitopathy involves edema and lymphatic infiltration of the eye muscles and the retrobulbar tissue. The condition is in principle independent of the concentration of thyroid hormone in the plasma, nor has any correlation with the LATS level been demonstrated. The suggestion that a special substance is responsible, the *exophthalmia-producing substance (EPS),* is generally rejected today.

In two other conditions, the rare isolated *autonomic thyroid adenoma* and the more common *toxic nodular goiter,* the elevated plasma concentration of thyroid hormones is brought about by an excessive, uncontrolled secretion in particular hormonally active nodes in the thyroid gland.

Although it is theoretically possible, hyperthyroidism owing to a primary increase in the rate of TSH secretion has been observed only very rarely.

Hypothyroidism. The hypothyroid condition, in which insufficient thyroid hormone is secreted, is usually associated with marked enlargement of the thyroid gland. The development of this form of goiter can easily be understood by reference to Fig. 29-7; because the T_3 and T_4 levels are depressed there is no negative feedback to prevent increased production of TSH in the adenohypophysis, and because of its *trophic* function (p.665) TSH promotes growth of the thyroid. One possible cause of inadequate synthesis of hormone by the thyroid gland is *iodine deficiency* in the food. Mountain water contains little iodine, so that inhabitants of the Alps (for example) are particularly likely to develop goiter *(endemic goiter).* If iodized salt or exogenous thyroxin or triiodothyronine are provided, the enlargement can be reversed –

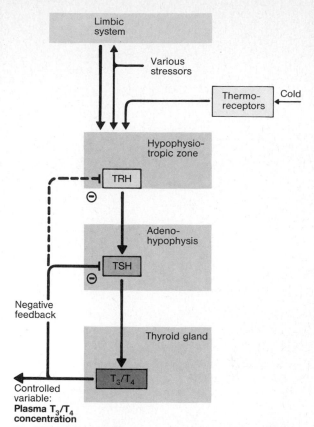

Fig. 29-7. Diagram to illustrate control of thyroid-hormone level. T_3 and T_4 "receptors" in the adenohypophysis mediate negative feedback. The expectation of an increased requirement for thyroid hormone during exposure to cold is signalled by thermoreceptors. T_3, triiodothyronine; T_4, thyroxin

again, as would be expected from the block diagram. Other forms of hypothyroidism arise from genetic abnormalities in thyroid-hormone synthesis or from the autoimmunological destruction of the gland. Hypothyroidism also follows removal of the adenohypophysis; this **"secondary" hypothyroidism** is characterized by a lowered concentration of TSH in the plasma. A so-called **"third form" of hypothyroidism,** which has also been found as a clinical syndrome, is based on inadequate production of the **releasing hormone TRH.**

When the thyroid hormones are absent during the embryonic period mental retardation results. The complete thyroid-deficiency syndrome in infants is called **cretinism.** Thyroid-gland failure in adults causes diminished physical and mental activity. A conspicuous symptom of thyroid deficiency is **myxedema,** a doughy thickening of the skin caused by enlargement of the connective tissue with the retention of water and mucoproteins.

Diagnosis of thyroid function. Modern clinical diagnosis is facilitated by radioimmunological tests of the

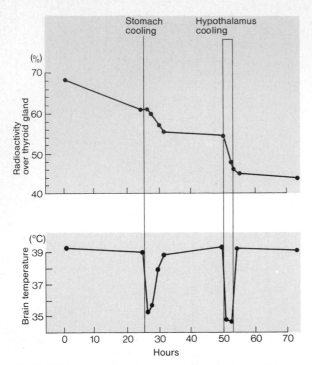

Fig. 29-8. Increase in the rate of secretion of thyroxin by internal cooling; in the first case cooling was produced by introducing ice-water into the stomach, and in the second case by local cooling of the thermosensitive preoptic region of the diencephalon. Negative slope of the curve "radioactivity above thyroid gland" implies increased secretion (cf. methods: "thyroxin release", p.674). After[12]

plasma concentrations of T_3, T_4 and TSH. In the so-called TRH test, the responses of adenohypophysis and thyroid gland to administration of the releasing hormone are tested.

In the morphological diagnostic procedures the radioisotope ^{131}I or, more recently ^{123}I is administered and its uptake into the thyroid gland is monitored by obtaining a map of the emitted radiation (scintiscan).

In the experiment illustrated in Fig. 29-8, the rate of thyroxin release was measured. The radioisotope ^{131}I was injected and enough time was allowed to elapse for the thyroid gland to incorporate it into T_3 and T_4. The radioactivity over the thyroid was observed during the following days. The rate at which radioactivity decreases is a measure of the release of thyroid hormone.

The Gonads and the Sex Hormones

The sex hormones are steroids. They can be divided into three groups on the basis of their actions, as follows: 1. **estrogens**, 2. **gestagens**, and 3. **androgens.**

Groups 1 and 2, the most important members of which are estradiol, estrone and progesterone, are also called the **female sex hormones**; of the **male sex hormones** (Group 3) the most important is testosterone.

Sites of sex-hormone production. The estrogens and gestagens are formed in the female gonad (ovary) and in the placenta, and the androgens in the so-called Leydig cells of the male gonads *(testes)*. Within the *ovary,* the cells of the tunica interna of the follicle capsule produce estrogens, and cells of the corpora lutea produce gestagens. The hormone-producing cells in the placenta have not as yet been definitely identified, but the syncytial structures are thought to be involved.

Small amounts of androgens are also found in the female; they are formed in the ovary and in the adrenal cortex (cf. p.667). Conversely, the testis produces estrogens and gestagens in small quantities.

The actions of the sex hormones. The hormones produced by the gonads bring about *embryonic differentiation* and the development of the *reproductive organs* leading to puberty, as well as the development of the *secondary sexual characteristics*. They trigger the alterations of the uterine *endometrium* that must precede implantation of the egg, and the alterations of the mammary glands required for the *secretion of milk*. They also have a number of so-called *extragenital actions*. Finally, they influence *sexual behavior*.

Embryonic sexual differentiation. In an **early stage of embryonic development** (about at the end of the third month in man) the male gonads become hormonally active; that is, they synthesize the androgens (testosterone in particular), under the influence of which the reproductive organs assume the typical male form. Experiments on animals have shown that a male fetus will develop female genitals **(masculine pseudohermaphroditism)** if testosterone secretion is prevented in the early embryonic stages. If a crystal of testosterone is implanted in a female fetus during those stages, more or less complete male genitalia develop **(feminine pseudohermaphroditism).**

In the rat, testosterone also affects structures in the preoptic region (Fig. 29-10) that in the female control the cyclic production of gonadotropins, which determines the timing of estrus. Implantation of a testosterone crystal in genetically *female rat embryos* suppresses the rhythmic activity of this rhythmogenic zone. In males the rising androgen concentration following puberty affects the corresponding hypothalamic structures in such a way as to elicit male sexual behavior. When rats are castrated early in development, later injection of androgens fails to elicit such behavior. Recent studies [2, 7, 37] have shown that these findings do not apply to other species – in particular not to primates, including man, in which *"masculinization" of the hypothalamus* has not been found.

Puberty. The production of androgens in males comes to a halt after the completion of embryonic development. At the time of **puberty** the endocrine activity of the gonads of boys is revived, and those of girls begin internal secretion for the first time.

Under the influence of the estrogens and gestagens in girls, and of the androgens in boys, the reproductive organs grow and mature. In males testosterone is also involved in spermatogenesis. Estrogen increases the rate of cell division in the germinal epithelium of the ovaries.

The sex hormones also bring about development of the extragenital sexual characteristics – the mammary glands, the typical body structure with the sex-specific distribution of fat, and the sex-based differences in width of hips and shoulders. Pubic hair develops under the influence of androgens even in girls; these hormones are produced in the adrenal cortex (cf. p. 667) and to a lesser extent in the ovary.

Action on the uterus. In females, the sex hormones bring about the changes in the endometrium of the **uterus** that mark the menstrual cycle. Estrogens give rise to the proliferation phase, in which the mucous membrane thickens and endometrial glands develop. Under the additional influence of progesterone, the endometrial glands enter the secretion phase. These changes pave the way for implantation of a fertilized egg (nidation).

Extragenital actions. Progesterone raises the **basal body temperature** (resting temperature before one gets up in the morning). Therefore regular measurements of core temperature (Fig. 29-9) provide information about the changing progesterone level and **time of ovulation.** This effect of progesterone results from an increase in basal metabolic rate, accompanied by an upward shift in the threshold temperatures for sweating and vasodilation (cf. set-point adjustment, p. 543).

The androgens have an anabolic effect – that is, protein synthesis is enhanced (positive nitrogen balance); progesterone has a catabolic action.

The androgens and estrogens interact with other hormones to accelerate epiphyseal and appositional bone growth. Under the influence of the sex hormones growth is eventually halted by *ossification of the epiphyses.* In cases of androgen deficiency the growth hormone continues to act on the unossified

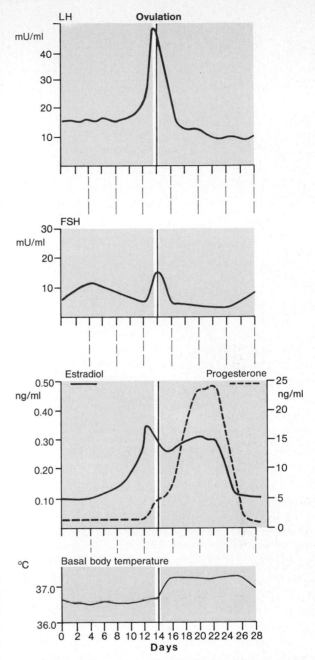

Fig. 29-9. Changes in the plasma concentration of the gonadotropic hormones FSH and LH and the sex hormones estradiol and progesterone during a menstrual cycle (mU = milliunits). The resting body temperature (basal temperature) rises in the middle of the cycle (ovulation). From graphs in [2, 7, 8, 55]

epiphyses, and the result is **eunuchoid** or **hypogonadal gigantism.**

Sexual behavior. The **mating drive** of male animals, like the **libido** and **potency** of men, disappears after castration – not immediately, but over a fairly long period of time. Evidently, therefore, these actions of

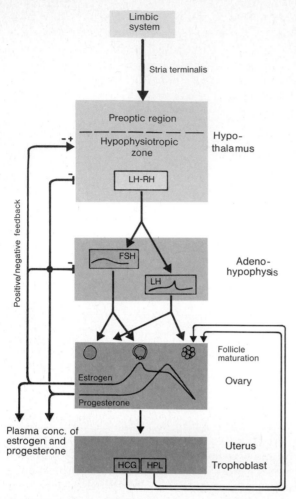

Fig. 29-10. Diagram summarizing follicle maturation and the hormonal control and feedback processes during a menstrual cycle. The placenta hormones HCG and HPL cause the corpus luteum to persist during pregnancy. Lines ending in a cross-bar denote inhibition of hormone secretion, and those with arrowheads denote enhancement

the androgens are mediated by long-lasting influences on nerve cells in the diencephalon. An overabundance of androgens produces hypersexuality.

Female mammals (apart from man and the other primates) are **receptive** of copulation only at certain times, for periods of a few days that coincide with the changes in the uterine and vaginal mucosa elicited by the cyclic elevation of the sex-hormone level **(estrus).** In experiments on spayed females, receptivity is promoted by exogenous estrogen and inhibited by exogenous progesterone. Primate females, which have a menstrual cycle, exhibit increased sexual activity toward the middle of the cycle. Stereotactic implantation experiments have revealed something about the mechanism underlying these hormonal effects. Implantation of a small estrogen crystal in the ventrome-

dial nucleus of the hypothalamus of a spayed female cat elicits estrus, with the appropriate behavior patterns. Suitably located estrogen implants in female rhesus monkeys enhance their tendency to copulate. But the results of such experiments are not always consistent as far as localization is concerned, in part because of species differences. The data available at present do not justify the conclusion that there is a sharply delimited sex center [41].

Sex-hormone level and the menstrual cycle in women. As shown in Fig. 29-9, the plasma concentration of the sex hormones varies considerably during a menstrual cycle. In the second third of the cycle the estrogen level rises sharply, falling again toward the end of the cycle. The progesterone level rises with a few days' delay.

Control of the secretion of estradiol and progesterone. The rate of secretion of the two ovarian hormones is **controlled** by the two **gonadotropic hormones FSH and LH.** Under the influence of the rising FSH level during the first days of the menstrual cycle (Fig. 29-9), a primary follicle matures and the concentration of estradiol rises. The secretion of estradiol is brought about not by FSH alone, but by a particular ratio of FSH to LH. In the middle of the cycle the LH level rises sharply; this **LH peak** [7, 9] is the immediate cause of the rupture of the follicle, **ovulation** and the conversion of the follicle into a **corpus luteum.** *The latency from the LH peak to ovulation is 24 to 36 hours.* The corpus luteum produces progesterone, the concentration of which rises sharply immediately after ovulation. Fig. 29-9 also shows that the rise in progesterone level can be monitored by measuring the *basal body temperature.*

FSH and LH secretion are controlled by the releasing hormone LH-RH (Fig. 29-10). It was first proposed that each gonadotropic hormone had its own releasing hormone, but recent findings indicate that there is no "FSH-RH". The **releasing hormone LH-RH** (or GN-RH, gonadotropin releasing hormone) controls the secretion of both LH and FSH [2, 5, 7, 9]. In this case the different responses of the two, in particular the phase shift of the times of maximal FSH and LH secretion, must be ascribed to modifying factors; the most plausible of these appears to be different operation of the negative-feedback system (see below).

The secretion of LH-RH, as was first shown in monkeys [37], is **episodic**; that is, several-minute phases of enhanced secretion are separated by 60-to-90-minute intervals with a relatively low secretion rate. Under the influence of this pulsatile LH-RH secretion, the rate of FSH secretion is increased in the preovulatory phase, and as the follicle becomes more mature that of estrogen secretion rises in turn (Fig. 29-9).

With regard to the origin of the **LH peak** immediately preceding ovulation (Figs. 29-9, 29-10), the following experimental results are of interest. Estrogen administration in a brief, well-defined phase of the sexual cycle causes a massive increase in the LH level and subsequent ovulation. Moreover, the LH peak does not appear in women whose ovaries have been removed and who thus do not secrete estrogen. In terms of control systems, this action of estrogen amounts to **positive feedback.** The circular process triggered by secretion of LH-RH, FSH, estrogen and LH culminates in **ovulation.** The *second phase* of the cycle is determined by the marked rise in the progesterone level. In this phase the two sex hormones estradiol and progesterone provide a negative feedback that *inhibits* release of FSH and LH and thus prevents further follicle maturation.

The circumstances that bring about a *positive-feedback* effect of the estrogens and gestagens at one time and a *negative feedback* at another are not yet fully clarified. One significant factor is the ratio of the estrogen to the gestagen concentration. The hypophysiotropic zone is regarded as the site of action of the negative or positive feedback. Evidently the responsiveness of the LH- and RH-producing cells is modified by the estrogens and gestagens. In addition, estrogens and gestagens have an inhibitory effect at the level of the adenohypophysis (cf. Fig. 29-10).

The secretion of LH-RH is in turn subject to a **central drive** thought to originate in neural structures of the **preoptic region** of the hypothalamus and other parts of the **limbic system.** Evidence for this localization has been derived from experiments in which electrical stimulation in these areas of animal brains elicited an elevated LH level followed by ovulation. This coupling of the hypophysiotropic zone to the CNS makes it understandable that the menstrual cycle is affected by many exogenous and psychological factors (stress). The changing day length, which influences the reproductive cycle of numerous animals, may also act by way of these central-nervous structures (cf. pineal gland, p. 686). The view that one circumscribed "rhythmogenic zone" in the region of the anterior hypothalamus (suprachiasmatic nucleus) is responsible for the cyclic recurrence of all the reproductive processes is no longer tenable in this general form.

Inhibition of ovulation. Administration of exogenous estrogen and gestagen at the beginning of the cycle inhibits LH-RH secretion by negative feedback; ovulation fails to occur, because the LH peak cannot build up. Some of the **contraceptives** currently in use act in this way. Instead of the natural estrogens and gestagens, derivatives are used that are not broken down in the liver and are effective even when taken orally.

Estrus and the menstrual cycle. In animals other than primates ovulation is accompanied by vaginal bleeding and special sexual behavior; this state of being "in heat" is called **estrus.** Once the egg has been expelled from the follicle it can be fertilized, but only if copulation occurs soon before or after ovulation. In women there is no bleeding at the time of ovulation; menstrual bleeding is associated not with ovulation, but with the shedding of part of the endometrium of the uterus about 2 weeks after ovulation. Ovulation is triggered by the sharp drop in the sex-hormone level at the end of the cycle (Fig. 29-9). Various findings suggest that the uterus of some laboratory animals produces a substance that makes the corpora lutea nonfunctional *(luteolytic principle).*

PRL-IH and maintenance of the corpus-luteum phase. Experiments on the rat have shown that if the corpus-luteum phase is to persist, so that progesterone can be secreted, there must be a high plasma concentration of prolactin during the second half of the cycle. Prolactin is released as soon as the prolactin-inhibiting factor (PRL-IH) is eliminated, which evidently occurs as a result of the action of progesterone on the site of PRL-IH production in the hypophysiotropic zone. *In man* prolactin is not required to maintain the corpus-luteum phase.

Hormonal control of pregnancy, birth and lactation. From an endocrinological point of view, pregnancy and parturition are characterized by the development and sudden loss of an **additional site of hormone production, the placenta.**

Pregnancy. Disintegration of the corpus luteum is prevented when a fertilized egg has become implanted in the endometrium. This effect is brought about by two hormones elaborated by the implanted trophoblast: **chorionic gonadotropin** (in man, human chorionic gonadotropin or HCG), with an action like that of LH, and HPL **(human placental lactogen),** which corresponds to PRL (prolactin) in its effects. Under the influence of these two placental hormones, the corpus luteum increases its rate of progesterone secretion (cf. Fig. 29-10). The maintained high progesterone level prevents breakdown and discharge of the endometrium. Toward the end of the first month of pregnancy the corpus luteum regresses. By this time the **placenta** itself has taken over the **production of progesterone and estrogen** necessary for the pregnancy to continue. At this point the ovary could be removed without interrupting pregnancy.

The diagnosis of pregnancy. The chorionic gonadotropin that begins to be excreted in the urine immedi-

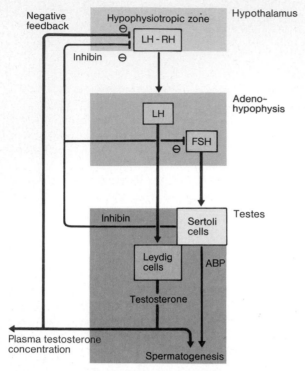

Fig. 29-11. Control of the testosterone level and of spermiogenesis. Lines ending in cross-bars denote inhibition of hormone secretion, and those with arrowheads denote enhancement. ABP, androgen-binding protein

ately after the onset of pregnancy elicits ovulation in rodents and promotes the release of sperm by frogs. Such tests make possible the early **diagnosis of pregnancy.**

Parturition. A woman normally **gives birth** an average of 270 days after conception. This event could be initiated by a number of possible factors – for example, a fall in the progesterone level (which would increase the readiness of the uterus to contract), an increase in the rate of oxytocin secretion (cf. p.661), and a decrease in the concentration of relaxin (another hormone produced by the corpus luteum which, among other things, causes relaxation of the symphysis). Recent studies, especially of the sheep [43], indicate that a decisive factor in triggering parturition is an enhancement of **fetal glucocorticoid secretion** at the end of pregnancy. Glucocorticoids act to increase the rate of production of estrogen from progesterone in the placenta, and as a result the concentration of progesterone falls and that of estrogen rises. The consequence is release of **prostaglandin E** (cf. p.686), which in turn increases the sensitivity of the uterus to oxytocin as a contraction-eliciting stimulus.

Lactation. At puberty the **mammary gland** develops, under the influence of the estrogens. But not until pregnancy occurs do the *increased* estrogen and gestagen levels bring about the formation of the distal alveoli and lobules of the gland. Other substances – prolactin (in man HPL, or human placental lactogen; see above), insulin, thyroxin and cortisol – are also involved in this process. **Milk secretion** begins only after parturition, and only in the presence of prolactin. The *release* of the milk is caused by the suckling stimulus; it is mediated by oxytocin, which elicits contraction of the myoepithelium of the alveolar walls in the mammary gland (**milk-ejection reflex**; cf. p.662). The suckling stimulus also releases prolactin, presumably by way of a decrease in the rate of secretion of PRL-IH (Table 29-1).

Regulation of the sex-hormone level in the man. Except for slight diurnal fluctuations, the plasma level of the male sex hormone is constant. This constancy is attributable to a simple control mechanism of the type shown in Fig. 29-1 B, with testosterone as the controlled variable. A rise in the testosterone level inhibits LH secretion, most probably by way of an inhibition of the corresponding releasing hormone in the hypophysiotropic zone (Fig. 29-11).

In men FSH has no glandotropic action; rather, its targets are special receptors in the Sertoli cells, which bring about formation of an androgen-binding protein (ABP). The ABP-testosterone complex influences **spermatogenesis.** Moreover, the Sertoli cells produce a polypeptide called **inhibin**, which reduces the rate of FSH and LH-RH secretion (Fig. 29-11). It is not clear whether prolactin has a special function in the man.

Pathophysiological aspects. In order to understand certain pathological processes, one must bear in mind that the primordia of the gonads, sexually undifferentiated at first, consist of a cortex and a medulla. In gentically female organisms the ovary develops from the cortex and the medulla regresses, whereas in males the medulla develops into the testis and the cortex disappears.

Malformations of the gonads. In a certain **chromosomal anomaly (X, O)** neither medulla nor cortex develop. In this case the external appearance tends to be female (cf. p.674). Another **chromosomal anomaly (X, X, Y)** leads to inadequate development of the testes; here, again, the appearance is feminine. The simultaneous complete development of male and female gonadal primordia – which would be a case of true hermaphroditism – is rarely observed in humans.

29.4   The Sympathico-Adrenal System

Hormones of the System and Sites of Production

The sympathico-adrenal system functions by way of two hormones, **adrenalin** (epinephrine) and **noradrenalin** (norepinephrine), both of them catecholamines.

Hormone production in the adrenal medulla and the sympathetic nerve endings. Peripheral sites of hormone production are the nerve endings of sympathetic fibers and the adrenal medulla, which in ontogeny is closely related to the sympathetic system (cf. pp. 111 f.). The secretory cells in the adrenal medulla are colored brown by oxidizing stains (e. g., dichromic acid) and therefore are called *chromaffin cells.* Treatment with iodates distinguishes two types of medullary cells; those stained darkly produce noradrenalin, and those that remain light produce adrenalin. The hormone-producing cells are modified sympathetic nerve cells. Accordingly, they are innervated by preganglionic nerve fibers of the sympathetic system.

The **proportions of adrenalin and noradrenalin** in the secretion of the adrenal medulla vary from species to species, as well as with age. In adult humans adrenalin accounts for ca. 70–90% of the medullary secretion. By contrast, the catecholamine released by the nerve endings consists chiefly of noradrenalin.

The precursor of both noradrenalin and adrenalin is the amino acid tyrosine. Both are synthesized from tyrosine in small granules found in the secretory cells of the medulla and the sympathetic nerve endings, which contain the necessary enzyme systems.

Hormone production in the brain. Noradrenalin is also synthesized in very diverse parts of the brain, where it acts as a *transmitter substance.* The blood-brain barrier (p. 4) prevents the adrenalin and noradrenalin released by the sympathetic nerve endings and the adrenal medulla from entering the brain. In this respect the brain – although its internal control is to a great extent effected by catecholamines – is not directly subject to control by the sympathico-adrenal system. Conversely, the noradrenalin formed in the brain is probably not released into the systemic circulation in appreciable amounts due to its reuptake into the nerve terminals. The noradrenalin released by the sympathetic nerve endings enters the bloodstream and can be found in the urine. It thus has the character of a hormone, although it can also be called a transmitter substance (cf. p. 658).

Recent investigations suggest that noradrenalin and adrenalin may possibly – in contradiction to what has been said above – be able to pass the blood-brain barrier at certain places, in the region of the so-called circumventricular organs [45]. If this route should turn out to be quantitatively significant, our concept of the sympathico-adrenal system would have to be extended.

Actions of Noradrenalin and Adrenalin

Adrenalin and noradrenalin act similarly on some target organs and differently on others. These various physiological effects can be ascribed to two basic actions:
1. an influence on the tone and the state of contraction of smooth and striated musculature, and
2. an influence on carbohydrate and fat metabolism.

As in the case of other hormones, the actions of noradrenalin and adrenalin are mediated by hormone-specific attachment sites **(receptors)** in the cell membranes of the target organs. As was discussed in detail in Chapter 6, at least two kinds of adrenergic receptors are recognized, **α-receptors** and **β-receptors.** The β-receptors are further subdivided into β_1- and β_2-receptors. Generally speaking, a contractile action on smooth muscle is mediated by α-receptors and a relaxing action – particularly vasodilation – by β-receptors. Metabolic effects and the excitation of the myocardium are mediated by β_1-receptors [42]. There are inhibitory substances that block selectively the actions of α-, β_1- and β_2-receptors. The opposite actions of a given catecholamine on different target organs – for example, constriction of the cutaneous vessels and dilation of the muscle vessels – can be based on differences in the relative representation of these receptors in the organs.

At various places in this book the actions of noradrenalin and adrenalin are discussed in the context of particular functional systems. Here, therefore, we shall give only a brief survey of these effects.

Peripheral blood flow. In all parts of the **vascular system** (except for the vessels of the brain) noradrenalin causes excitation of the smooth musculature and thus vasoconstriction. Adrenalin causes vasoconstriction in some of the vessels, especially those of the skin, and vasodilation in others, especially those of the skeletal musculature.

Heart. Adrenalin and noradrenalin have *positive chronotropic and inotropic actions* on the isolated **heart.** In the intact organism, however, the two hormones exhibit differences. Here **noradrenalin** administration does not increase the heart rate, but reduces it **(bradycardia),** an effect attributed to reflex vagal excitation because it can be cancelled by atropine injection.

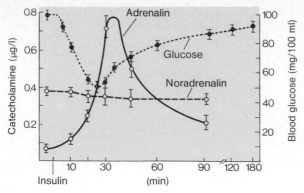

Fig. 29-12. Selective control of adrenalin secretion. The drop in the blood glucose level caused by insulin injection causes a marked rise in the plasma adrenalin level, whereas the noradrenalin level remains unchanged. After[26]

Blood pressure. An elevation of the noradrenalin concentration in the blood is followed by a rise in the systolic and diastolic **blood pressure.** Adrenalin increases the systolic blood pressure while the diastolic pressure remains constant or falls; the result in either case is an increase in blood-pressure amplitude.

Breathing. Noradrenalin and adrenalin increase the depth of breathing; relaxation of the **bronchial musculature** reduces the airway resistance. It is because of this effect that catecholamines and sympathicomimetics are useful in the treatment of bronchial asthma.

Smooth muscle in other organs. In general, adrenalin and noradrenalin exert inhibitory effects on the **smooth musculature** of the **gastrointestinal tract** (for the possible mode of action see p. 48), but the action of both hormones is *excitatory* on the smooth musculature of the capsule of the spleen, the piloerectors of the skin, the nictitating membrane of the cat and the pupil dilators in the iris.

Carbohydrate metabolism. Adrenalin brings about an elevated blood glucose level by the breakdown of liver glycogen; the blood-glucose-elevating action of *noradrenalin* is slight. Its **glycogenolytic action** makes adrenalin the most important antagonist of insulin in the blood-glucose control system (cf. pp. 682 f.).

Fat metabolism. Adrenalin and noradrenalin have a **lipolytic** action, thus causing an increase in the amount of free fatty acids in the plasma. These are utilized, for example, as a substrate for thermogenesis under cold stress.

Energy metabolism. The **metabolic rate** in adult humans is increased by about 30% by the action of adrenalin. Considerably greater increases (up to

300%) are found in the newborn and in cold-adapted organisms that possess brown adipose tissue. This **thermogenetic effect** is produced by both noradrenalin and adrenalin, and is mediated by adrenergic β-receptors[17].

Central nervous system. Adrenalin (but not noradrenalin, or only to a slight extent) stimulates the **ascending reticular system** ("arousal reaction") – an effect evident in the desynchronization of the EEG (cf. pp. 150 ff. and 200). These central nervous phenomena are accompanied by increased attentiveness and in the extreme case by mental agitation and anxiety states.

If one accepts the traditional view that the catecholamines cannot cross the blood-brain barrier, one must assume that the central nervous effects are achieved indirectly. They might, for example, be mediated by afferent activity resulting from the stimulation of pressure, volume or chemosensory receptors. It is also conceivable that the effects are mediated by changes in the blood glucose level or by metabolites that are not excluded by the blood-brain barrier.

Control of the Secretion of Noradrenalin and Adrenalin

The triggering of hormone secretion. The rate of secretion of noradrenalin and adrenalin in the adrenal medulla, and of noradrenalin at the nerve endings, is low under resting conditions and increases only in situations that cause **excitation of the sympathetic nervous system.** Branches of the splanchnic nerve are responsible for secretion in the adrenal medulla. Various kinds of stimuli, acting on different receptors, are effective triggers; for instance, baroreceptors, thermoreceptors and glucose receptors can be involved. Moreover, the rate of noradrenalin/adrenalin secretion can increase together with that of glucocorticoid secretion in a variety of stress-inducing situations (cf. p. 669). For example, parachutists have been found to excrete more noradrenalin/adrenalin metabolites in their urine on jump days than on rest days [26]. Such cases are examples of an **"emergency reaction"** [18] or, expressed less dramatically, an **"ergotropic adjustment"** of the organism.

Selective control of hormone secretion. The secretion of the two hormones can be controlled selectively. Because in the adult adrenalin is secreted chiefly by the adrenal medulla and noradrenalin by the sympathetic nerve endings, "selective" here means that in some cases the sympathetic system is excited without involvement of the adrenal medulla, and in others medullary secretion occurs in the absence of general sympathetic excitation. The **selective control of catecholamine release** is illustrated in the following examples. When the carotid artery is clamped off so as to relieve the pressure on the receptors, there is a selective increase in noradrenalin secretion. Glucose infusion lowers the rate of adrenalin secretion, and when the blood sugar level is depressed by insulin the rate of adrenalin secretion rises while that of noradrenalin remains almost unchanged (Fig. 29-12). Microinjection of small amounts of glucose into the ventromedial nucleus of the hypothalamus (site of the postulated glucose receptors) selectively inhibits adrenalin secretion. By electric stimulation in the hypothalamus and cortex, it has been possible to distinguish central nervous structures responsible for the selective secretion of noradrenalin or adrenalin [39].

29.5 Pancreatic Hormones and the Control of Blood Glucose

Islet-Cell Hormones

The tissue of the pancreas, which in general has a digestive function, includes "islands" of cells (the **islets of Langerhans**) which produce the hormones insulin and glucagon. The cell groups that synthesize the two hormones are distinguishable histologically. The insulin-producing cells are called beta (or B) cells, and those that produce glucagon are called alpha (or A) cells. It has recently been determined that another cell group, the delta cells, secretes somatostatin (cf. Table 29-1).

Insulin is a proteohormone composed of two polypeptide chains arranged in parallel and linked by disulfide bridges; its molecular weight is about 6000. **Glucagon** is a polypeptide in the shape of a single chain, with a molecular weight of ca. 3500. Insulin was the first proteohormone and the first protein to be experimentally synthesized.

Actions of the islet-cell hormones. With regard to their most conspicuous action, **alteration of the blood glucose level,** the two hormones act antagonistically; insulin depresses the level and glucagon raises it. In a quantitative sense, insulin is considerably more effective than glucagon, so that when the pancreas is removed the absence of insulin dominates. A drug called alloxan can be used to destroy the beta cells selectively and thus eliminate the action of insulin alone. Glucagon is produced in glands in the gastric and duodenal mucosa as well as in the pancreatic alpha cells (cf. "APUD-system", p. 685).

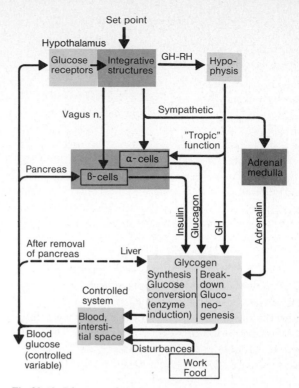

Fig. 29-13. Diagram of the control system governing glucose concentration in blood and body fluids. For details see text

Actions of insulin. The following factors are thought to contribute to the **glucose-level-lowering action** of insulin. (i) The *glucose permeability* of cells, especially those in myocardium, skeletal muscle and adipose tissue (but not brain cells), is increased by insulin so that the rate of glucose influx and of its intracellular metabolism is increased. (ii) In the liver, insulin increases the rate of *glycogen synthesis*. (iii) *Gluconeogenesis* (the formation of glucose from amino acids) is diminished by insulin, which thus has an **anabolic** action (incorporation into the body is promoted; in this respect insulin is a *synergist of the growth hormone*). Insulin also influences fat metabolism, by enhancing the ability of the adipose tissue and liver cells to take up free fatty acids and store them in the form of triglycerides (fat reserves). Thus it acts against the appearance of ketone bodies and tends to prevent acidosis.

Actions of glucagon. Glucagon increases the rate of **glycogenolysis** in the liver and in this regard is a *synergist of adrenalin*. It also promotes *gluconeogenesis*. Its effects on fat metabolism are complex; the oxidation of fatty acids in the liver is accelerated, and more fatty acids are converted to ketone bodies. On the other hand, the storage of fatty acids in the form of triglycerides is enhanced.

Regulation of Blood Glucose Concentration

Islet-cell hormones as elements in a control circuit. The **plasma concentration** of the two pancreatic hormones insulin and glucagon varies, depending on the amount of exogenous glucose taken in and the concentration of several other hormones that affect glucose level (e. g., glucocorticoids). The concentrations of insulin and glucagon in the plasma are not controlled. Rather, these hormones are controlling elements within a control circuit to keep the blood glucose level constant (the type shown in Fig. 29-1 A). Insulin is the only hormone that lowers the blood glucose level; as such, it has a special position among the hormones that affect blood glucose. The role of the two islet-cell hormones in controlling blood sugar goes hand in hand with their role in controlling the metabolic processes taking place at a cellular and subcellular level. But the concentration of glucose in the blood is an easily measurable quantity, which reflects clearly the degree of order or disorder in the metabolic functions of insulin and certain other hormones (Fig. 29-13). For this reason measurement of blood glucose is an important clinical tool.

The *blood glucose concentration is normally kept between 0.8 and 1.0 g/l blood*. This constancy is continually threatened by the changing amounts of carbohydrate consumed in food and by the variable rate of glucose oxidation – which can increase severalfold, for instance, during exercise. The rate of secretion of islet-cell hormones can be adjusted with extreme precision to match these changing requirements. Treatment of diabetes with daily or twice-daily doses of insulin is only a very rough approximation to this fine control. It can be reasonably effective only if potential disturbing factors (food, work) are kept fairly constant.

Control of the rate of islet-hormone secretion. Here we are concerned with the route by which the glucose level affects the rate of secretion of the two hormones.

It was at first thought that **insulin** is controlled by a tropic hormone, although there was no evidence for such control. The vagus nerve has been shown to affect insulin secretion in the dog, but this effect may be of subordinate importance, for denervation of the pancreas did not disrupt blood-glucose regulation in this animal. The most plausible interpretation is that the glucose level is measured in the pancreas itself, and that this information is used directly to control the secretory activity of the beta cells. This inference is supported by the demonstration of increased insulin production by insular tissue in vitro, following the addition of glucose.

Recent studies have shown that insulin release is influenced by a number of polypeptides formed in the gastrointestinal tract (cf. gastrointestinal hormones, Chapter 26). The term *"enteroinsular axis"* reflects this situation. These findings explain why glucose taken orally has a stronger effect on insulin secretion than intravenously injected glucose.

The **control of glucagon secretion** is set in motion by glucose receptors in the anterior hypothalamus, which detect reduction in the blood glucose level. The growth hormone (GH) is thought to act as a tropic hormone in this response (cf. p. 665). It remains an open question whether the entire contrainsular action of GH is mediated by glucagon, or whether GH has a direct action on the target cells. Glucagon secretion can also be influenced by the activity of sympathetic nerve fibers, as well as by way of the somatostatin produced by the delta cells [54].

Interaction of the mechanisms regulating blood glucose. The block diagram of Fig. 29-13 summarizes the mechanisms by which blood glucose is kept constant. This diagram reveals the intermeshing of several control circuits. The fact that the blood glucose level has a diurnal periodicity can be allowed for by regarding the "set point" as variable.

Stress reactions (p. 669) involve not only the release of noradrenalin and adrenalin, but also an increase in the rate of secretion of the glucocorticoids and of thyroxin. These hormones have not been shown to be controlled by glucose receptors, and are therefore not included in Fig. 29-13. Under some circumstances their role in a control circuit tends to be as a disturbing rather than a controlling element. A degree of stabilization of blood glucose can also be achieved in *pancreatectomized dogs receiving exogenous insulin,* presumably by means of a secondary feedback mechanism in which glucose brings about enzyme induction in the liver cells, which results in the increased influx and metabolism of glucose.

Pathophysiology. Departures of the blood glucose level from the norm are called hypoglycemia or hyperglycemia.

Hypoglycemia. When the blood glucose concentration falls sharply to less than 0.5 g/l blood characteristic symptoms appear – sweat secretion, tachycardia, tremor, ravenous hunger and excitation. If the level continues to fall this state soon gives way to so-called **hypoglycemic shock,** which is accompanied by unconsciousness and can rapidly lead to death. The administration of glucose and injection of glucagon are both effective therapeutic measures. In cases of GH deficiency (hypophyseal dwarfism; cf. p. 665) hypoglycemia often appears after even brief fasting. The immediate danger of hypoglycemia lies in an inadequate supply of substrate to the brain cells, which depend on glucose as their only source of energy.

Hyperglycemia. An above-normal blood glucose level (hyperglycemia) is not a direct threat to life unless it has risen so much as to induce *hyperosmolar coma.* It is, however, regarded as a fundamental pathogenic factor in the vascular deterioration that appears in the course of diabetes. With a blood glucose level above 1.8 g/l plasma, glucose is excreted in the urine (glucosuria; cf. p. 622). The widespread disease **diabetes mellitus** is the most common cause of hyperglycemia. When the disease appears in *juveniles* it is associated with a deficiency of insulin resulting from a reduced number of beta cells. In the *adult,* where it is often accompanied by adiposity, the number of beta cells and their insulin content is normal (at least in the initial stages) but secretion is impeded; glucose stimulation causes the release of insulin only after a delay, and the secretion phase is considerably prolonged. The situation is complicated by an *insulin resistance,* reinforced by overeating, which is ascribed to a deficit of insulin receptors in the target systems.

Moderate hyperglycemia accompanies Cushing's syndrome (p. 670), severe hyperthyroidism (p. 673), and hypophyseal gigantism and acromegaly (p. 665).

29.6 The Hormonal Control of Mineral Balance

Several hormones are responsible for the control of homeostatic processes related to mineral balance, and they are produced by various endocrine glands in different parts of the body. They are divisible into two groups:

1. Hormones controlling the plasma concentration and excretion of the **electrolytes Na$^+$ and K$^+$** and of the **H$^+$ ion,** which thus necessarily have a marked influence on **water balance: aldosterone, angiotensin and renin.**
2. Hormones affecting **calcium and phosphate balance: parathormone and calcitonin.**

Na$^+$ and K$^+$ Balance

Mineralocorticoids (aldosterone). The deleterious symptoms following removal of the adrenal cortex are basically ascribable to the absence of the mineralocorticoid aldosterone, formed in the zona glomerulosa. This hormone is essential for homeostasis of the body's electrolyte and water content.

Actions of aldosterone. Aldosterone increases the active transport of Na$^+$ through cell membranes. In the kidney the effect is to increase the reabsorption of Na$^+$ from the tubule system and hence, by osmosis, the reabsorption of water. The transport of K$^+$ and H$^+$ in the opposite direction is facilitated (the physicochemical basis of this electrolyte-exchange transport is discussed on pp. 624ff.). Aldosterone affects the sweat, salivary and intestinal glands correspondingly. The NaCl content of the sweat, normally far less than that of the plasma, rises considerably when there is insufficient aldosterone. In cases of aldosterone deficiency, therefore, the sweating induced by high ambient temperatures can soon cause dangerous loss of NaCl. One factor in heat adaptation is an increase in the rate of aldosterone secretion, as a result of which the NaCl content of the sweat is lower ([34]; cf. also p. 545). The latency of the aldosterone action on the kidney is about 30 min; this time is sufficient for enzyme induction, which is thought to be the basic underlying mechanism.

Control of aldosterone secretion. A great number of studies have shown that there are three fundamental conditions leading to increased aldosterone secretion: 1. **increased potassium intake,** 2. **negative Na balance** (for example, lowered salt content of food or greater loss of NaCl in sweat), and 3. **diminished plasma volume** (for example, by loss of blood or inadequate fluid intake). Increase in the rate of aldosterone secretion by these factors is brought about by various *control mechanisms* [22], as follows.

(i) The hormone-producing cells of the zona glomerulosa respond directly to changes in the Na and K concentration of the plasma, by changing the rate of aldosterone secretion.

(ii) Aldosterone secretion is enhanced by **angiotensin II,** which is carried to the adrenal cortex in the blood and thus serves as a "tropic" hormone for aldosterone secretion. Angiotensin II is an octapeptide formed from angiotensin I, which circulates in the plasma, under the influence of **renin** [23]. In the current view, renin in turn is released owing to the activity of *baroreceptors* in the walls of the afferent vessels to the kidney and the *sodium receptors* in the *macula-densa cells.* These two receptors are elements of the so-called **juxtaglomerular system** (cf. Chapter 27).

(iii) ACTH also influences aldosterone secretion, but the effect is less than that on glucocorticoid secretion. After removal of the adenohypophysis the zona fasciculata and zona reticularis degenerate but not the zona glomerulosa, so that secretion of aldosterone can continue. Therefore hypophysectomy does not produce such severe electrolyte and water imbalance as does removal of the adrenal cortex.

These three control mechanisms suffice for compensation of the disturbances listed under 1–3 above. By virtue of these interlinked functions, **aldosterone** plays a role in **control circuits** to maintain constancy of the **Na/K concentration** in the plasma and, in particular, that of the body's **fluid volume** (cf. volume regulation, Chapter 27). In cybernetic terms, aldosterone represents a controlling element in several meshed biological control circuits.

Pathophysiology. In addition to the abovementioned electrolyte and water imbalance resulting from underactivity of the adrenal cortex **(Addison's disease),** disturbances can be induced by an increased rate of aldosterone secretion. This **hyperaldosteronism** is characterized by hypernatremia, hypokalemia and edema.

Calcium and Phosphate Balance

Hormones of the system and sites of production. In addition to vitamin D_3 two hormones are the main contributors to the processes controlling calcium and phosphate balance – **parathormone** and **calcitonin.** Parathormone is produced in the parathyroid glands, and calcitonin in special cells **(C cells) of the thyroid gland.**
Parathormone is a chain-shaped protein with molecular weight 8500. Calcitonin is also a proteohormone; its molecular weight is about 3600[3, 8].

Actions of the hormones. Both parathormone and calcitonin are controlling elements in a control system to keep the blood calcium (Ca^{2+}) level constant (the type shown in Fig.29-1 A). This function is coupled to maintenance of the balance between the continual buildup and breakdown of bone[51].

Parathormone. This hormone has two fundamental sites of action. 1. It stimulates the activity of osteoclasts, which results in the liberation of calcium and phosphate ions from the mineral substance of which bone is composed (hydroxyapatite). 2. It increases the rate of Ca^{2+} reabsorption in the kidney, thus **raising the plasma calcium level,** which in man is normally very constant at 2.5 mmol/liter (0.1 g/l) plasma. **Parathormone** also promotes absorption of calcium in the intestine if sufficient vitamin D is present. The plasma phosphate level rises little or not at all after parathormone administration, because the hormone increases the rate of excretion of phosphate ions in the renal tubule system (increased phosphate clearance; cf. p.630). But intense parathormone activity raises the plasma phosphate level, because

phosphate excretion cannot keep up. In this case the solubility product for calcium and phosphate is exceeded (normally [calcium·phosphate] = 0.4 g/l blood). In this situation calcium salts are precipitated in various organs, and there is a (usually locally restricted) decalcification of the bones.

Calcitonin. This hormone counteracts parathormone with regard to the blood calcium level; that is, **calcitonin** lowers the calcium level by inhibiting the release of calcium from the bones.

Vitamin D_3-hormone. Vitamin D_3 (cholecalciferol) is converted in the liver into 25-hydroxycholecalciferol which is in turn oxidized in the kidney to 1,25 dihydroxy-cholecalciferol – the biologically active metabolite. This is referred to as **vitamin D_3-hormone** as it is transported *by the blood* to its target organs, the skeletal system and the small intestine. Its main action is to promote intestinal Ca^{2+} absorption and bone calcification.

Control of hormone secretion. No superordinate "tropic" hormone is known to control the secretion of **parathormone.** The results of experiments in which the gland is perfused with solutions at different calcium concentrations imply that the cells of the parathyroid themselves respond to changes in calcium concentration by changing their rate of parathormone secretion. The secretion of **calcitonin** is controlled similarly – an increase in the blood calcium level stimulates directly the secretion of hormone by the C cells of the thyroid.

Pathophysiology. A constant blood calcium level is especially significant with regard to the function of excitable structures.

Tetany. Even a slight reduction in the blood calcium level, to 0.08 g/l plasma, causes increased neuromuscular excitability; slight electrical or mechanical (e.g., tapping on a motor nerve) stimuli, normally subthreshold, elicit tonic contraction of the skeletal musculature. Eventually spasms appear spontaneously, and the tonic contractions of respiratory and pharyngeal muscles can rapidly lead to death. This syndrome is called **tetany.**

The critical factor in the development of tetanic convulsions is the amount of plasma calcium in the *ionized* state. The plasma calcium can be separated into two fractions by ultrafiltration; 40–60% of the total calcium content does not move through the membrane because it is bound to plasma protein. The ultrafiltrable serum calcium is composed of an ionized and a nonionized fraction. According to the law of mass action, the ionized calcium is in equilibrium with the protein-bound calcium:

$$[Ca^{2+}] = \frac{[Ca\text{-proteinate}]}{[protein^{2-}]} \cdot k$$

Here k depends on the pH of the blood; as the blood pH increases (alkalosis) the proportion of ionized calcium decreases. In cases of latent tetany even voluntary hyperventilation, which causes a slight rise in blood pH, can trigger a tetanic attack ("hyperventilation tetany"). If the protein content of the blood increases, as the equilibrium relation shows, the ionized fraction decreases even though the total calcium content of the blood is unchanged. Therefore in evaluating the calcium level the protein content of the blood must also be taken into account. Even in the complete absence of parathormone the blood calcium remains at a concentration in the region of 0.05 g/l plasma – a level sufficient to sustain the electromechanical coupling in cardiac and skeletal musculature (cf. pp. 36 f., 364 f.) and the clotting of the blood (cf. pp. 345 ff.).

Hypoparathyroidism. Tetany is the chief symptom of hypoparathyroidism, a condition brought about, for example, by removal of the parathyroid in the course of thyroidectomy or by the autoimmunological destruction of the cells that produce parathormone.

Hyperparathyroidism. This syndrome results from adenomas (tumors) of the parathyroid gland. The calcium in the blood can increase to as much as 0.17 g/l plasma. A person in this condition can die after eating a calcium-rich meal (e.g., milk), presumably owing to sudden cardiac arrest – for bradycardia is one of the symptoms of **hypercalcemia.** Moreover, because the solubility product is exceeded in **hyperparathyroidism** calcium is deposited in the vessels and in the kidney. In many cases *kidney stones* are the result of parathyroid overactivity, so that removal of the tumors in these glands is an effective treatment.

29.7 Gastrointestinal Hormones

The gastrointestinal tract elaborates a variety of substances that are involved in digestion. Those that are transported in the blood and act at a site different from their site of production – gastrin, secretin, cholecystokinin-pancreozymin and a few others – are to be regarded as hormones. As a class they are treated in Chapter 26.

29.8 Peripheral Topics in Endocrinology

"Tissue Hormones"

Tissue hormone (*Gewebshormon* in the German literature) has recently become a problematic term which is likely to be abandoned completely in the near future. The term was originally meant to identify a number of substances that elicit specific responses of target organs (cf. p. 658), but for which no special endocrine organ had been found (i. e., "formation somewhere in the tissue"). Since then some substances have been given full hormone status even though they are not produced by an endocrine gland in the strict morphological sense – for example, the releasing hormones of the hypophysiotropic zone and most of the gastrointestinal hormones that were previously classified as tissue hormones. Other substances once called tissue hormones are now regarded as neurotransmitters rather than hormones (e.g. acetylcholine). Still others have been included in what has recently been called the APUD-system (see below).

Polypeptides and Amines; the APUD-System

In the following a few secretion products are listed which were formerly embraced by the term "tissue hormone" and which are difficult to classify at present. As peptides and amines they are members of the APUD-system (p. 658).

Serotonin (5-hydroxytryptamine) is released at the nerve endings in certain parts of the brain (hypothalamus, raphé nuclei (p. 67), pineal) and it is produced by the APUD-system of the gastrointestinal tract. Serotonin is also found in blood platelets; in case of injury it is released and helps to stanch the flow of blood by its *vasoconstrictor action* (p. 345).

Histamine is formed from the amino acid histidine in the course of antigen-antibody reactions. It is transported in *mast cells* and elicits the so-called *allergic reactions* – reddening of the skin, rash, itching and contraction of the smooth respiratory musculature (asthma). Histamine has also been found in the hypophysis and the median eminence of the hypothalamus. It is not yet clear whether it also functions as a neurotransmitter. Also it has been suggested that it is involved as a paracrine transmitter in the secretion of gastric acid.

Bradykinin is one of a group of vasoactive polypeptides called **kinins.** It is released during sweating and causes vasodilation in particular vascular beds as a thermoregulatory mechanism (p. 539).

Kallikrein is required for the synthesis of the *kinins* (see above) from their precursors (α_2-globulins).

Vasoactive Intestinal Peptide (VIP) is released from intestinal nerve endings by vagal stimulation and has vasodilatory effects. It is the putative candidate for the long-sought transmitter of the postulated vasodilatory "purinergic nerves".

Erythropoietin, Prostaglandins

These substances do not belong to the classical endocrine system although there is convincing evidence that they serve functions characteristic of hormones. They are thus mentioned briefly here.

Erythropoietin, a glycoprotein produced in the juxtaglomerular apparatus, promotes erythropoiesis (p. 339).

Prostaglandins are a class of substances derived from unsaturated fatty acids with 20 C atoms. They were first discovered in the seminal vesicles, but since have been found in nearly all organs, including the brain. There are three basic groups of prostaglandins, A, E and F. Their diverse actions cannot yet be systematically classified; the following will serve as examples: inhibition of corpus-luteum activity (prostaglandin as a **luteolytic principle;** cf. p. 677), interference with platelet adhesion, and inhibition of gastric-juice secretion. Local hypothalamic injection of prostaglandin E produces **fever.** The action of bacterial fever-producing substances (pyrogens) is therefore presumably mediated by prostaglandin E; *aspirin,* which inhibits prostaglandin synthesis, has long been known to reduce fever.

Organs with Uncertain or Unclear Endocrine Function

Thymus. Since its discovery, the thymus has repeatedly been regarded as an endocrine gland in the absence of any reliable evidence of endocrine function. During the last few years a number of polypeptides have been extracted from the thymus – thymosin, thymopoietin, thymic humoral factor and others; some of them are released into the plasma and seem to play a role in the cell-bound immunoreactions. It remains to be shown whether they meet the criteria for classification as hormones.

Pineal gland. The tendency to accept that the "pineal gland" actually is an endocrine gland has been enhanced by recent findings. This organ, which in the lower vertebrates is a light-sensitive structure with a neurosecretory function (a photo-neuroendocrine transducer), retains its secretory function in the higher vertebrates and mammals [45]. The substances it produces here are **melatonin** and, to a lesser extent, its precursor, 5-hydroxytryptamin **(serotonin)** [36], and certain polypeptides with endocrine actions.

Studies of reptiles have shown that melatonin causes aggregation of the melanin granules in the melanocytes of the skin, thus lightening skin color. It is therefore an antagonist of the MSH (melanocyte-stimulating hormone) produced in the pars intermedia of the hypophysis (p. 666).

More recently, melatonin has also been shown to inhibit the **release of LH-RH** and thus the secretion of gonadotropin and the **activity of the gonads.** This finding is of considerable significance with regard to our understanding of the annual fertility rhythm of many mammalian species, as summarized in the following paragraph.

There is a pronounced *circadian rhythmicity* in melatonin secretion, with a maximum at night; light inhibits melatonin secretion. This process is mediated by the release of noradrenalin [15] at the endings of sympathetic nerve fibers that run to the pineal from the superior cervical ganglion. The sympathetic activity is modulated by tracts descending from the hypothalamus (suprachiasmatic nucleus) to the cells of origin of the peripheral sympathetic fibers in the thorax. The activity of the suprachiasmatic nucleus in turn is modified by exposure of the retina to light, this information being transmitted by way of a retino-hypothalamic pathway [19]. The progressive inhibition of melatonin secretion as the days grow longer increases the total amount of LH-RH (and hence of gonadotropin) secreted each day, thus eliciting **estrus,** growth of testes, and **sexual activity** [36].

Pathophysiology. Destruction (by tumor) of the pineal gland of a young person can cause early sexual maturation (pubertas praecox). The pathophysiological mechanism of this disturbance has not yet been disclosed, but such a mechanism would parallel the inhibitory influence of the pineal on fertility and sexuality described above.

29.9   References

Textbooks and Handbooks

1. GREEP, R.O., ASTWOOD, E.B. (Eds.) Handbook of Physiology. Section 7: Endocrinology, Volumes I–VII. Washington, D.C.: American Physiological Society 1972–76
2. DeGROOT, L.J. (Ed.) Endocrinology, Volumes I–III. New York–San Francisco–London: Grune & Stratton 1979
3. WILLIAMS, R.H. (Ed.) Textbook of Endocrinology. Philadelphia–London–Toronto: Saunders 1974
4. DONOVAN, B.T.: Mammalian Neuroendocrinology. London: McGraw Hill Publ. Co. Ltd. 1970
5. JEFFCOATE, L.S., HUTCHINSON, J.S.M. The Endocrine Hypothalamus. London–New York–San Francisco: Academic Press 1978
6. KARLSON, P.: Mechanisms of Hormone Action. Stuttgart: Thieme 1965

References 687

7. GREEP, R.O. (Ed.) Reproductive Physiology II. In: Int. Rev. Physiol. Vol.13 (GUYTON, A.C. Ed.). Baltimore–London–Tokyo: Univ. Park Press 1977
8. SAWIN, C.T.: The Hormones. Endocrine Physiology. London: Churchill 1969
9. SHEARMAN, R.P. (Ed.) Human Reproductive Physiology. Oxford–London–Edinburgh–Melbourne: Blackwell Scientific Publications 1979

Research Reports and Reviews

10. ADOLPH, E.F.: General and specific characteristics of physiological adaptations. Amer. J. Physiol. *184*, 18 (1956)
11. ALTSZULER, N.: Actions of growth hormone on carbohydrate metabolism. In: Handbook of Physiology, Vol. IV, Part 2 (see Ref. 1)
12. ANDERSSON, B.: Central nervous and hormonal interaction in temperature regulation of the goat. In: Physiological and Behavioral Temperature Regulation (J.D.HARDY, A.P.GAGGE, J.A.J.STOLWIJK, Eds.), p.634. Springfield, Ill.: Ch.C. Thomas 1970
13. ANDERSSON, B.: Receptors subserving hunger and thirst. In: Handbook of Sensory Physiology, Vol. III/1: Enteroceptors (E. NEIL, Ed.), p.187. Berlin–Heidelberg–New York: Springer 1972
14. ARIMURA, A.: Hypothalamic gonadotropin releasing hormone and reproduction. In: see Ref. 7
15. AXELROD, J.: The pineal gland: A neurochemical transducer. Science *184*, 1341 (1974)
16. BARKER, S.B., KLITGAARD, H.M.: Metabolism of tissues excised from thyroxine-injected rats. Amer. J. Physiol. *170*, 81 (1952)
17. BRÜCK, K.: Non-shivering thermogenesis and brown adipose tissue in relation to age, and their integration in the thermoregulatory system. In: Brown Adipose Tissue (O.LINDBERG, Ed.), p.117. New York: Amer. Elsevier Publ. 1970
18. CANNON, W.B.: Die Notfallsfunktionen des sympathicoadrenalen Systems. Ergebn. Physiol *27*, 380 (1928)
19. CONRAD, C.D., STUMPF, W.E.: Endocrine optic pathways to the hypothalamus. In: Anatomical Neuroendocrinolgy (W.E. STUMPF, C.D.GRANT, Eds.). Basel: Karger 1975
20. CROSS, B.A., DYBALL, R.E.J.: Central pathways for neurohypophysial hormone release. In: Handbook of Physiology, Vol. IV, Part 1, The Pituitary Gland (see Ref. 1)
21. DAUGHADAY, H.W., HERINGTON, A.C. PHILLIPS, L.S.: The regulation of growth by endocrines. Ann. Rev. Physiol. *37*, 211 (1975)
22. DAVIS, J.O.: Regulation of aldosteron secretion. In: Handbook of Physiology, Vol. VI, Adrenal Gland (see Ref. 1)
23. DAVIS, J.O., FREEMAN, R.H.: Mechanisms regulating renin release. Physiol. Rev. *56*, 1 (1976)
24. DYER, R.G., DYBALL, R.E.J.: Evidence for a direct effect of LRF and TRF on single unit activity in the rostral hypothalamus. Nature *252*, 486 (1974)
25. EDELMANN, I.S., ISMALL-BEIGI, F.: Thyroid thermogenesis and active sodium transport. In: Recent Progress in Hormone Research (R.O. GREEP, Ed.). New York–London: Academic Press 1974
26. EULER VON, U.S.: Adrenal medullary secretion and its neural control. In: Neuroendocrinology, Vol. II (C. MARTINI, W.F. GANONG, Eds.), p.283. New York–London: Academic Press 1967
27. FITZSIMMONS, J.T.: The Physiology of Thirst and Sodium Appetite. London–New York–Melbourne: Cambridge Univ. Press 1975
27a. FUJITA, T., KOBAYASHI, S., YUI, R., IWANAGA, T.: Evolution of neurons and paraneurons. Hormones, Adaptation and Evolution (S. ISHII et al., eds.), pp. 35–43, Japan Sci. Soc. Press, Tokyo, Berlin: Springer-Verlag 1980
28. GALE, C.C.: Neuroendocrine aspects of thermoregulation. Ann. Rev. Physiol. *35*, 391 (1973)
29. GANONG, W.F., FORSHAM, P.H.: Adenohypophysis and adrenal cortex. Ann. Rev. Physiol. *22*, 579 (1960)
30. HABERICH, F.J., AZIZ, O., NOWACKI, P.E.: Über einen osmoreceptorisch tätigen Mechanismus in der Leber. Pflügers Arch. ges. Physiol. *285*, 73 (1965)
31. HAYWARD, J.N.: Neural control of the posterior pituitary. Ann. Rev. Physiol. *37*, 191 (1975)
32. HAYWARD, J.N., VINCENT, J.D.: Osmosensitive single neurons in the hypothalamus of unanesthetized monkeys. J. Physiol. (Lond.) *210*, 947 (1970)

33. HENKIN, R.I.: The role of adrenal corticosteroids in sensory processes. In: Handbook of Physiology, Vol. VI, Chap. 15 (see Ref. 1)
34. HENSEL, H. BRÜCK, K., RATHS, P.: Homeothermic Organisms. In: Temperature and Life (H. PRECHT, J.CHRISTOPHERSEN, H. HENSEL, W. LARCHER, Eds.), p.505. Berlin–Heidelberg–New York: Springer 1973
35. HSIEH, A.C.C., PUN, C.W., LI, K.M., TI, K.W.: Circulatory and metabolic effects of noradrenaline in cold-adapted rats. Fed. Proc. *25*, 1205 (1966)
36. KLEIN, D.C.: The pineal gland: A model of neuroendocrine regulation. In: The Hypothalamus (S. REICHLIN, R.J. BALDESSARINI, J.B. MARTIN, Eds.), pp.303–327. New York: Raven Press 1978
37. KNOBIL, E.: On the control of gonadotropin secretion in the Rhesus monkey. In: Recent Progress in Hormone Research (R.O. GREEP, Ed.), Vol.30. New York–London: Academic Press 1974
38. LEBLANC, J., VILLEMAIRE, A.: Thyroxine and noradrenaline on noradrenaline sensitivity, cold resistance and brown fat. Amer. J. Physiol. *218*, 1742 (1970)
39. LEWIS, G.P.: Physiological mechanisms controlling secretory activity of adrenal medulla. In: Handbook of Physiology, Vol. VI, Adrenal Gland, pp.309–319 (see Ref. 1)
40. MARTIN, J.B., TANNENBAUM, G., WILLOUGHBY, J.O., RENAUD, L.P., BRAZEAU, P.: Functions of the central nervous system in regulation of pituitary GH secretion. In: Hypothalamic Hormones (M. MOTTA, P.G. CROSIGNANI, L. MARTINI, Eds.). London–New York: Academic Press 1975
41. MICHAEL, R.P.: The effects of hormones on sexual behavior in female cat and Rhesus monkey. In: Handbook of Physiology, Vol. II, Female Reproductive System, Part I, pp.187–222 (see Ref. 1)
42. MORAN, N.C.: Adrenergic receptors. In: Handbook of Physiology, Vol. VI, Adrenal Gland, pp.447–472 (see Ref. 1)
43. NATHANIELS, P.W.: Endocrine mechanisms of parturition. Ann. Rev. Physiol. *40*, 411 (1978)
44. NICOLL, R.A.: Excitatory action of TRH on spinal motoneurons. Nature *265*, 242 (1977)
45. OKSCHE, A.: Circumventricular structures and pituitary functions. Proc. 4th Int. Congr. Endocrinology, Washington. Amsterdam: Excerpta Medica 1972
46. OKSCHE, A., HARTWIG, H.G.: Photoneuroendocrine systems and the third ventricle. In: Brain-endocrine interaction II (K.M. KRIGGE et al., Eds.), pp.40–53. Basel: Karger 1975
46a. PEARSE, A.G.E.: The diffuse neuroendocrine system and the APUD concept: related "endocrine" peptides in brain, intestine, pituitary, placenta, and anuran cutaneous glands. Medical Biology *55*, pp. 115–125 (1978)
47. RAMEY, E.R.: Corticosteroids and skeletal muscle. In: Handbook of Physiology, Vol. VI, Adrenal Gland, Chapter 17 (see Ref. 1)
48. RENAID, L.P., MARTIN, J.P., MARTIN, J.B., BRAZEAU, O.: Depressant action of TRH, LH-RH and somatostatin on activity of central neurons. Nature *255*, 233 (1975)
49. SELYE, H.: The physiology and pathology of exposure to stress. Montreal: Acta Inc. Medical Publ. 1950
50. STERLIN, K., LAZARUS, J.H.: The thyroid and its control. Ann. Rev. Physiol. *39*, 349 (1977)
51. TALMAGE, R.V., MEYER, R.A.: Physiological role of parathyroid hormone. In: Handbook of Physiology, Vol. VII, Parathyroid Gland (see Ref. 1)
52. VALE, W., RIVIER, C., BROWN, M.: Regulatory peptides of the hypothalamus. Ann. Rev. Physiol. *39*, 473 (1977)
53. VERNEY, E.B.: The antidiuretic hormone and factors which determine its release. Proc. roy. Soc. B *135*, 25 (1947)
54. WOODS, S.C., PORTE, D.: Neural control of the endocrine pancreas. Physiol. Rev. *54*, 596 (1974)
55. WUTTKE, W., ARNOLD, P., BECKER, D., CREUTZFELD, O., LANGENSTEIN, S., TIRSCH, W.: Circulating hormones, EEG and performance in psychological tests of women with and without oral contraceptives. Psychoneuroendocrinology *1*, 141 (1975)
56. YAMAMOTO, W.S., BROBECK, J.R., (Eds.): Physiological Controls and Regulations. Philadelphia–London: Saunders 1965
57. YATES, F.E., MARAN, J.W.: Stimulation and inhibition of adrenocorticotropin release. In: Handbook of Physiology, Vol. IV, The Pituitary Gland, Part 2 (see Ref. 1)

G. Thews

International system of units. In recent years various international societies and organizations have recommended that a new system of units be introduced to standardize the physical and chemical quantities used in physiology, as in other branches of the natural sciences. Many countries have followed this recommendation, passing laws that require the use of the new system. This *International System of Units (SI, for Système International d'Unités)* is based on the seven units listed in Table 30-1.

Table 30-1. Names and symbols of the SI base units

Quantity	Name of unit	Symbol
Length	meter	m
Mass	kilogram	kg
Time	second	s
Electric current	ampere	A
Thermodynamic temperature	kelvin	K
Luminous intensity	candela	cd
Amount of substance	mole	mol

These base units are defined as follows:

Meter (m) – The meter is the length equal to 1,650,763.73 wavelengths in vacuum of the radiation corresponding to the transition between the levels $2p_{10}$ and $5d_5$ of the krypton-86 atom.

Kilogram (kg) – The kilogram is the unit of mass; it is equal to the mass of the international prototype of the kilogram.

Second (s) – The second is the duration of 9,192,631,770 periods of the radiation corresponding to the transition between the two hyperfine levels of the ground state of the cesium-133 atom.

Ampere (A) – The ampere is that constant current which, if maintained in two straight parallel conductors of infinite length, of negligible cross section, and placed one meter apart in vacuum, would produce between these conductors a force equal to 2×10^{-7} newton per meter of length.

Kelvin (K) – The kelvin, unit of thermodynamic temperature, is the fraction 1/273.16 of the thermodynamic temperature of the triple point of water.

Candela (cd) – The candela is the luminous intensity, in the perpendicular direction, of a surface of 1/600,000 square meter of a blackbody at the temperature of freezing platinum under a pressure of 101,325 newtons per square meter.

Mole (mol) – The mole is the amount of substance of a system which contains as many elementary entities as there are atoms in 0.012 kilogram of carbon-12.

The units of all the other quantities can be derived from these base units. Some of them are listed in Table 30-2.

The numerical values of the quantities in Tables 30-1 and 30-2 often contain powers of ten as factors. To simplify numerical data, certain commonly used powers of ten have been assigned special prefixes (Table 30-3) which are combined with the names of the units in question.

The conventional units listed in Table 30-4 can continue to be used along with the SI units.

Table 30-2. Names and symbols of some derived SI units

Quantity	Name of unit	Symbol	Definition
Frequency	hertz	Hz	s^{-1}
Force	newton	N	$m \cdot kg \cdot s^{-2}$
Pressure	pascal	Pa	$m^{-1} \cdot kg \cdot s^{-2} (N \cdot m^{-2})$
Energy	joule	J	$m^2 \cdot kg \cdot s^{-2} (N \cdot m)$
Power	watt	W	$m^2 \cdot kg \cdot s^{-3} (J \cdot s^{-1})$
Electric charge	coulomb	C	$s \cdot A$
Electric potential difference	volt	V	$m^2 \cdot kg \cdot s^{-3} \cdot A^{-1} (W \cdot A^{-1})$
Electric resistance	ohm	Ω	$m^2 \cdot kg \cdot s^{-3} \cdot A^{-2} (V \cdot A^{-1})$
Electric conductance	siemens	S	$m^{-2} \cdot kg^{-1} \cdot s^3 \cdot A^2 (\Omega^{-1})$
Electric capacitance	farad	F	$m^{-2} \cdot kg^{-1} \cdot s^4 \cdot A^2 (C \cdot V^{-1})$
Magn. flux	weber	Wb	$m^2 \cdot kg \cdot s^{-2} \cdot A^{-1} (V \cdot s)$
Magn. flux density	tesla	T	$kg \cdot s^{-2} \cdot A^{-1} (Wb \cdot m^{-2})$
Inductance (magn. conductance)	henry	H	$m^2 \cdot kg \cdot s^{-2} \cdot A^{-2} (V \cdot s \cdot A^{-1})$
Luminous flux	lumen	lm	$cd \cdot sr^{a}$
Illuminance	lux	lx	$cd \cdot sr \cdot m^{-2} (lm \cdot m^{-2})$
Activity of a radioactive substance	becquerel	Bq	s^{-1}

[a] sr (steradian) = SI unit of solid angle

Table 30-3. Prefixes and symbols of frequently used power-of-ten factors

Factor	Prefix	Symbol	Factor	Prefix	Symbol
10^{-1}	deci	d	10	deca	da
10^{-2}	centi	c	10^2	hecto	h
10^{-3}	milli	m	10^3	kilo	k
10^{-6}	micro	μ	10^6	mega	M
10^{-9}	nano	n	10^9	giga	G
10^{-12}	pico	p	10^{12}	tera	T
10^{-15}	femto	f	10^{15}	peta	P

Table 30-4. Units not belonging to SI but currently retained

Name of unit	Symbol	SI equivalent
Gram	g	$1\,g = 10^{-3}\,kg$
Liter	l	$1\,l = 1\,dm^3$
Minute	min	$1\,min = 60\,s$
Hour	h	$1\,h = 3.6\,ks$
Day	d	$1\,d = 86.4\,ks$
Degree Celsius	$^\circ C$	$t\,^\circ C = (T - 273.15)\,K$

Conversion among units. Within the provisions of the SI system, concentrations can be given as amount of substance per unit volume (mol/l, mmol/l, μmol/l) or as mass per unit volume (g/l, mg/l). It is recommended that the *substance concentration* always be used for chemically uniform substances of known molecular weight (relative molecular mass). The *mass concentration* is a useful measure in the case of mixtures of dissolved substances – for example, total plasma protein. The conventional concentration units g % (g/dl), mg % (mg/dl) and meq/l can be converted to SI units by reference to the relations summarized in Table 30-5.

The new system will probably not be used consistently in medicine until a fairly long transition period has elapsed. Time is required not only for new equipment to become generally available, but also for the modification of unit-dependent norms to conform to the new system. Not until the most important norms in the new units have become as natural a part of the physician's store of knowledge as the old ones are now will the practicability of the proposed new system have been established. In particular, objections have been raised with regard to the replacement of the traditional unit of pressure, mm Hg, by the less

Table 30-5. Conversion from conventional concentration units (g %, mg %, meq/l) to SI units of mass concentration (g/l) and substance concentration (mmol/l or μmol/l)

	1 g % =	1 g % =
Plasma protein	10 g/l	
Hemoglobin	10 g/l	0.621 mmol/l[a]

	1 mg % =	1 meq/l =
Sodium	0.4350 mmol/l	1.0 mmol/l
Potassium	0.2558 mmol/l	1.0 mmol/l
Calcium	0.2495 mmol/l	0.5 mmol/l
Magnesium	0.4114 mmol/l	0.5 mmol/l
Chloride	0.2821 mmol/l	1.0 mmol/l
Glucose	0.0555 mmol/l	
Cholesterol	0.0259 mmol/l	
Bilirubin	17.10 μmol/l	
Creatinine	88.40 μmol/l	
Uric acid	59.48 μmol/l	

[a] The molar hemoglobin concentration is based on the relative molecular mass of the hemoglobin monomere (cf. p.489)

Table 30-6. Conversion between SI units and conventional units

Quantity	Relationships	
Force	$1\,dyn = 10^{-5}\,N$	$1\,N = 10^5\,dyn$
	$1\,kgf = 9.81\,N$	$1\,N = 0.102\,kgf$
Pressure	$1\,cm\,H_2O = 98.1\,Pa$	$1\,Pa = 0.0102\,cm\,H_2O$
	$1\,mm\,Hg = 133\,Pa$	$1\,Pa = 0.0075\,mm\,Hg$
	$1\,atm = 101\,kPa$	$1\,kPa = 0.0099\,atm$
	$1\,bar = 100\,kPa$	$1\,kPa = 0.01\,bar$
Energy	$1\,erg = 10^{-7}\,J$	$1\,J = 10^7\,erg$
(work)	$1\,m \cdot kgf = 9.81\,J$	$1\,J = 0.102\,m \cdot kgf$
(amount of heat)	$1\,cal = 4.19\,J$	$1\,J = 0.239\,cal$
Power	$1\,m \cdot kgf/s = 9.81\,W$	$1\,W = 0.102\,m \cdot kgf/s$
	$1\,HP = 736\,W$	$1\,W = 0.00136\,HP$
(heat flow)	$1\,kcal/h = 1.16\,W$	$1\,W = 0.860\,kcal/h$
Viscosity	$1\,poise = 0.1\,Pa \cdot s$	$1\,Pa \cdot s = 10\,poise$

easily visualized pascal. On the other hand, the joule is being increasingly accepted as the unit of energy, in place of the conventional calorie. To help the reader become accustomed to the new units, in this book they are usually used together with the conventional units.

Some of the frequently required conversions between SI and earlier units are given in Table 30-6.

The abbreviation f. (ff.) means that the indexed word is also referred to on the following page(s).

Subject Index

Subject Index

Fundamentals of Sensory Physiology

Editor: **R.F. Schmidt**
With contributions by H. Altner, J. Dudel, O.-J. Grüsser, U. Grüsser-Cornehls, R. Klinke, R.F. Schmidt, M. Zimmermann
Translated from the German by M.A. Biedermann-Thorson

2nd corrected edition. 1981. 139 figures. XI, 286 pages
(Springer Study Edition)
ISBN 3-540-10349-X

Contents: General Sensory Physiology, Psychophysics. – Neurophysiology of Sensory Systems. – Somatovisceral Sensibility. – Physiology of Vision. – Physiology of Hearing. – Physiology of the Sense of Equilibrium. – Physiology of Taste. – Physiology of Olfaction. – Thirst and Hunger: General Sensations. – Suggested Reading. – Answer Key. – Subject Index.

Fundamentals of Sensory Physiology is the English translation of a highly successful German original. In this second revised edition, the authors have carefully examined each chapter, improving and expanding the text where necessary.

This text is specifically designed to meet the needs of an introductory course covering sensory physiology. It is ideal for the student with a minimal background in biology and the other natural sciences.

The sense organs, their anatomy and function are examined, together with their association with the central nervous structures. Not only are the physicochemical reactions in these structures presented, but also the conditions under which sensations and perceptions arise and the rules that govern them.

Students and instructors will find this text noteworthy for several reasons:
● emphasis is on clarity
● over 125 problems completing the sections are given, along with their answers found in the key
● excellent diagrams and suggested readings permit the student to learn the subject readily
● coverage of such areas as psychophysics and sensorimotor integration in vision is included

Fundamentals of Sensory Physiology contains a clearly written discussion of the subject. It is of interest to everyone who wishes to, or must, delve into the potentialities and limitations of human sensory experience.

Where other areas of neurophysiology are involved, reference is made to the companion volume, **Fundamentals of Neurophysiology.** Together, these two volumes present an integrated introduction to the field of neurosciences.

Fundamentals of Neurophysiology

Editor: **R.F. Schmidt**
With contributions by J. Dudel; W. Jänig, R.F. Schmidt, M. Zimmermann
Translated from the German by M.A. Biederman-Thorson

2nd revised and enlarged edition. 1978. 137 figures.
IX, 339 pages
(Springer Study Edition)
ISBN 3-540-08188-7

The second edition of this popular book has been extensively revised to present the essential concepts relevant to an introductory understanding of neurophysiology, and to show the most important new results in the field of brain research.

At the suggestion of readers, several new features have been added:
● a chapter on the integrative functions of the nervous system, covering such diverse activities and states of the nervous system as waking, sleeping, dreaming, consciousness, speech, learning and memory
● an introduction to the physiology of the cerebral cortex and the characteristics of the electroencephalogram
● a chapter on ther control system aspects of central nervous activity
● an up-to-date bibliography for further access to the topics of individual chapters

This concise text is readily accessible to students at the undergraduate or graduate level. No prior knowledge of anatomy or physiology is assumed. Each term is defined and explained as it is introduced in the text. To aid the student in checking his or her progress, numerous multiple choice questions at the end of each chapter have been retained and revised. A collection of clearly rendered illustrations enhance the instructional quality of this work. **Fundamentals of Neurophysiology** is essential reading by students of physiology, whatever their majors – medicine, psychology, zoology, biology, pharmacology or other natural sciences.

From the Reviews

"The authors have accurately and knowledgeably expressed current fundamental concepts in neurophysiology based on welldocumented experimental evidence and minimal speculation. They have, morecover, correlated the core material of underlying physical and chemical principles with clinical applications when pertinent. Other outstanding qualities of the book are the clarity of explanations, including timely reiterations of previously introduced concepts, logical organization of material, and excellent use of diagrammatic summaries..."

Springer-Verlag Berlin Heidelberg New York

Basic Physiology

Editor: P.D.Sturkie
With contributions by numerous experts
1981. 286 figures. VIII, 445 pages.
ISBN 3-540-90485-9

J.-P.Ewert
Neuroethology

An Introduction to the Neurophysiological
Fundamentals of Behavior
Translated from the German by Transmantics, Inc.
1980. 171 figures, mostly in color, 9 tables.
VIII, 342 pages. ISBN 3-540-09790-2

W.Fuhrmann, F.Vogel
Genetic Counseling

Translation from the German by S.Kurth
3rd edition. 1982. Approx. 51 figures. Approx. 129
pages. ISBN 3-540-90715-7

Fundamentals of Immunology

By O.G.Bier, W.DiasDaSilva, D.Goetze, I.Mota
1981. 164 figures. VIII, 442 pages
ISBN 3-540-90529-4

M.J.Halhuber, R.Günther, M.Ciresa
ECG – An Introductory Course

A practical introduction to clinical
Electrocardiography
With the assistance of P.Schumacher, W.Newesely
Translated from the 6th German edition by
H.J.Hirsch
1979. 98 figures, 7 tables. X, 155 pages
ISBN 3-540-09326-5

Illustrated Human Embryology

Volume 1:
H.Tuchmann-Duplessis, G.David, P.Haegel
Embryogenesis
Translator: L.S.Hurley
2nd printing. 1980. 226 figures, many in color.
IX, 110 pages. ISBN 3-540-90018-7

Volume 2:
H.Tuchmann-Duplessis, P.Haegel
Organogenesis
Translated from the French by L.S.Hurley
1972. 307 figures, many in color. IX, 153 pages
ISBN 3-540-90019-5

Volume 3:
H.Tuchmann-Duplessis, M.Aroux, P.Haegel
Nervous System and Endocrine Glands
Translator: L.S.Hurley
1974. 255 figures, some in color. VIII, 143 pages
ISBN 3-540-90020-9

I.Lockard
Desk Reference for Neuroanatomy

A Guide to Essential Terms
1977. VII, 157 pages. ISBN 3-540-90278-3

Manual of Clinical Oncology

Edited under the auspices of the International
Union Against Cancer
3rd, fully revised edition. 1982. Approx. 44 figures.
Approx. 370 pages. ISBN 3-540-11746-6

R.Nieuwenhuys, J.Voogd, C.van Huijzen
The Human Central Nervous System

A Synopsis and Atlas
2nd revised edition. 1981. 154 figures.
VIII, 253 pages. ISBN 3-540-10316-3

Pathophysiology

Editors: A.A.Bühlmann, E.R.Froesch
With contributions by numerous experts
Translated from the German by T.C.Telger
1979. 74 figures, 84 tables. XII, 403 pages
ISBN 3-540-90370-4

J.P.Patten
Neurological Differential Diagnosis

An Illustrated Approach
1977. 288 figures. X, 292 pages
ISBN 3-540-90264-3

F.Vogel, A.G.Motulsky
Human Genetics

Problems and Approaches
2nd printing with corrections. 1982. 420 figures,
210 tables. XXVIII, 700 pages. ISBN 3-540-09459-8

Springer-Verlag
Berlin
Heidelberg
New York